INSTRUCTOR'S SOLUTIONS MANUAL

CARRIE GREEN

INTERMEDIATE ALGEBRA
WITH APPLICATIONS
AND VISUALIZATION

THIRD EDITION

Gary K. Rockswold
Minnesota State University, Mankato

Terry A. Krieger
Rochester Community and Technical College

PEARSON
Addison
Wesley

Boston San Francisco New York
London Toronto Sydney Tokyo Singapore Madrid
Mexico City Munich Paris Cape Town Hong Kong Montreal

Reproduced by Pearson Addison-Wesley from electronic files supplied by the author.

ISBN-13: 978-0-321-52345-7
ISBN-10: 0-321-52345-8

1 2 3 4 5 6 OPM 11 10 09 08

PEARSON
Addison
Wesley

Contents

Chapter 1: Real Numbers and Algebra

1.1: Describing Data with Sets of Numbers

Concepts

1.   The natural numbers are the counting numbers and do not include zero. $N = \{1,\ 2,\ 3,\ ...\}$

   The whole numbers are the counting numbers along with zero. $W = \{0,\ 1,\ 2,\ 3,\ ...\}$

2.   The integers are given by the set $I = \{...,\ -3,\ -2,\ -1,\ 0,\ 1,\ 2,\ 3,\ ...\}$. An example is –5. *Answers may vary.*

3.   The rational numbers are numbers which can be written in the form $\dfrac{p}{q}$ where p and $q \neq 0$ are integers. An example is $\dfrac{3}{4}$. *Answers may vary.*

4.   The real numbers are any numbers which can be expressed as a decimal. A number which is real but is not rational is called irrational. An example of an irrational number is $\sqrt{2}$. *Answers may vary.*

5.   An example of the commutative property for addition is $3 + 2 = 2 + 3$. *Answers may vary.*

6.   An example of the commutative property for multiplication is $4 \cdot 3 = 3 \cdot 4$. *Answers may vary.*

7.   The number 1 is called the multiplicative identity since $1 \cdot a = a$ for any number a.

8.   The number 0 is called the additive identity since $0 + a = a$ for any number a.

9.   An example of the associative property for multiplication is $2 \cdot (3 \cdot 4) = (2 \cdot 3) \cdot 4$. *Answers may vary.*

10.   An example of the distributive property is $2(3 + 4) = 2 \cdot 3 + 2 \cdot 4$. *Answers may vary.*

11.   The property illustrated is the commutative property for addition, because the result of adding the amounts in a different order is the same.

12.   The property illustrated is the commutative property for multiplication, because to find the number of people in each marching band the number of rows is multiplied by the number of people in each row, and the results are the same.

Classifying Numbers

13.   The number 26,461 is a natural number, integer, rational number and a real number.

14.   The number 3.8 is a rational number and a real number.

15.   The number $\dfrac{89}{3687}$ is a rational number and a real number.

16.   The number 4 is a natural number, integer, rational number and a real number.

17.   The number 7.5 is a rational number and a real number.

18.   The number 2.57 is a rational number and a real number.

19.   The number $90\sqrt{2}$ is a real number.

20.   The number -71 is an integer, a rational number and a real number.

21.   Natural numbers: 6

Whole numbers: 6

Integers: -5, 6

Rational Numbers: -5, 6, $\frac{1}{7}$, 0.2

Irrational Numbers: $\sqrt{7}$

22.   Natural numbers: $\sqrt{9}$

Whole numbers: $\sqrt{9}$

Integers: -3, $\sqrt{9}$

Rational Numbers: -3, $\sqrt{9}$, $\frac{2}{9}$, -1.37

Irrational Numbers: none

23.   Natural numbers: $\frac{3}{1}$

Whole numbers: $\frac{3}{1}$

Integers: $\frac{3}{1}$

Rational Numbers: $\frac{3}{1}$, $-\frac{5}{8}$, $0.\overline{45}$

Irrational Numbers: $\sqrt{5}$, π

24.   Natural numbers: $\frac{50}{10}$

Whole numbers: 0, $\frac{50}{10}$

Integers: 0, $\frac{50}{10}$

Rational Numbers: 0, $\frac{50}{10}$, $-\frac{23}{27}$, $0.\overline{6}$

Irrational Numbers: $-\sqrt{3}$

25.   Natural numbers: $\sqrt{9} = 3$

Whole numbers: $\sqrt{9} = 3$

Integers: -2, $\sqrt{9} = 3$

Rational numbers: -2, $\frac{1}{2}$, $\sqrt{9} = 3$, $0.\overline{26}$

Irrational numbers: none

26. Natural numbers: $\sqrt{4} = 2$, $\dfrac{4}{2} = 2$

Whole numbers: $\sqrt{4} = 2$, $\dfrac{4}{2} = 2$

Integers: $\sqrt{4} = 2$, $\dfrac{4}{2} = 2$

Rational numbers: $\sqrt{4} = 2$, $\dfrac{4}{2} = 2$, 0.26

Irrational numbers: $\sqrt{6}$

27. Rational numbers. A shoe size could be a fraction such as $8\dfrac{1}{2}$.

28. Natural numbers. A quantity of people must be positive and can not be a fraction.

29. Rational numbers. Gasoline could be measured to any fraction of a gallon.

30. Natural numbers. Speed limits must be positive and are not fractions.

31. Integers. Winter temperatures in Montana could be either positive or negative but are not given as fractions.

32. Natural numbers. A quantity of compact discs must be positive and can not be a fraction.

Properties of Real Numbers

33. Identity

34. Identity

35. Commutative

36. Associative

37. Distributive

38. Distributive

39. Associative

40. Commutative

41. Commutative

42. Commutative

43. Commutative

44. Associative

45. Distributive

46. Distributive

47. $a + 4$

48. ab

49. $\dfrac{1}{3}a$

50. $x + 100$

51. $x+1$

52. $5b$

53. xy

54. $a+b$

55. $(4+5)+b=9+b$

56. $x+(2+3)=x+5$

57. $(5 \cdot 10)x=50x$

58. $a(5 \cdot 4)=a \cdot 20$

59. $x+(y+z)$

60. $(-3 \cdot 4) \cdot x=-12x$

61. $x \cdot (3 \cdot 4)=x \cdot 12$

62. $a+(6+5)=a+11$

63. $4x+4y$

64. $-3a-15$

65. $5x-35$

66. $11a+ba$

67. $-x-1$

68. $-a+2$

69. $a(x-y)$

70. $4(a+b)$

71. $3(4+x)$

72. $2(1-2x)$

73. $(3+7)x=10x$

74. $\left(\dfrac{1}{2}+\dfrac{3}{2}\right)z=2z$

75. $(8-2)t=6t$

76. $\left(1-\dfrac{2}{3}\right)y=\dfrac{1}{3}y$

77. $\left(1-\dfrac{3}{4}\right)x=\dfrac{1}{4}x$

78. $(13-6)r=7r$

79. $3-1+2z=2+2z$

80. $5-1+4y=4+4y$

81. $(3+4+1)z = 8z$

82. $\left(5+4+2\right)z = 11z$

83. $(10-1-4)t = 5t$

84. $(20-2-1)t = 17t$

85. $7(11-3) = 7\cdot8 = 56$ or $7(11-3) = 7\cdot11-7\cdot3 = 77-21 = 56$

86. $(5+9)12 = 14\cdot12 = 168$ or $(5+9)12 = 5\cdot12+9\cdot12 = 60+108 = 168$

87. $13(16+23) = 13\cdot39 = 507$ or $13(16+23) = 13\cdot16+13\cdot23 = 208+299 = 507$

88. $4(12-8) = 4\cdot4 = 16$ or $4(12-8) = 4\cdot12-4\cdot8 = 48-32 = 16$

89. $5(19-7) = 5\cdot12 = 60$ or $5(19-7) = 5\cdot19-5\cdot7 = 95-35 = 60$

90. $(8+12)9 = 20\cdot9 = 180$ or $(8+12)9 = 8\cdot9+12\cdot9 = 72+108 = 180$

91. $(3+4+5+8) \div 4 = 5$; natural number, integer, and rational number

92. $(5+8+10+23+9) \div 5 = 11$; natural number, integer, and rational number

93. $(45+33+52) \div 3 = 43.\overline{3}$; rational number

94. $\left(3.2+7.5+8.1+12.8+13.4\right) \div 5 = 9$; natural number, integer, and rational number

95. $(121.5+45.7+99.3+45.9) \div 4 = 78.1$; rational number

96. $(99.88+39.11+85.67+23.86+19.11) \div 5 = 53.526$; rational number

97. $8+3+2+7 = (8+2)+(3+7) = 10+10 = 20$

98. $52+103+48+97 = (52+48)+(103+97) = 100+200 = 300$

99. $\dfrac{2}{9}\cdot8\cdot9\cdot\dfrac{3}{8} = \left(\dfrac{2}{9}\cdot9\right)\cdot\left(8\cdot\dfrac{3}{8}\right) = 2\cdot3 = 6$

100. $\dfrac{1}{2}\cdot\dfrac{1}{3}\cdot\dfrac{1}{4}\cdot2\cdot3\cdot4 = \left(\dfrac{1}{2}\cdot2\right)\cdot\left(\dfrac{1}{3}\cdot3\right)\cdot\left(\dfrac{1}{4}\cdot4\right) = 1\cdot1\cdot1 = 1$

101. $4\cdot16-4\cdot6 = 4(16-6) = 4\cdot10 = 40$

102. $7\cdot12+7\cdot3+7\cdot5 = 7(12+3+5) = 7\cdot20 = 140$

103. $\dfrac{4}{5}\left(\dfrac{5}{2}+5+\dfrac{15}{4}\right) = \left(\dfrac{4}{5}\cdot\dfrac{5}{2}\right)+\left(\dfrac{4}{5}\cdot5\right)+\left(\dfrac{4}{5}\cdot\dfrac{15}{4}\right)$

$= \dfrac{4}{2}+4+\dfrac{15}{5} = 2+4+3 = 9$

104. $37-19+63-31 = (37+63)-(19+31)$

$= 100-50 = 50$

105. The property used is the identity property of 1, because $\dfrac{a}{a} = 1$ and $1\cdot\dfrac{b}{c} = \dfrac{b}{c}$. *Answers may vary.*

106.   No, consider $\sqrt{2} \cdot \sqrt{2} = \sqrt{2 \cdot 2} = \sqrt{4} = 2$. *Answers may vary.*

Applications

107.   No; $8 \cdot 4 \text{ GB} = 4 \cdot 8 \text{ GB} = 32 \text{ GB}$. The commutative property for multiplication applies.

108. $240(360) = 360(240) = 86,400$; Both images contain 86,400 pixels. This is the commutative property for multiplication.

109.   (a)   From the table, enrollment in 2003 was 16.3 million.

      (b)   The average of the 4 numbers is about 15.7 million. *Answers may vary.*

      (c) $(14.5 + 15.4 + 16.3 + 16.5) \div 4 = 15.675$ million; Yes, the answers nearly agree.

110.   (a)   From the table, the budget in 2003 was $2.2 trillion.

      (b)   The average of the 5 numbers is about $2.2 trillion. *Answers may vary.*

      (c) $(1.9 + 2.0 + 2.2 + 2.3 + 2.5) \div 5 = \$2.18$ trillion; Yes, the answers nearly agree.

111.   (a)   Valid; $2r\pi = 2\pi r$

      (b)   Valid; $2(\pi r) = 2\pi r$

      (c)   Not valid; $2\pi + 2r \neq 2\pi r$

112.   Changing the order of the multiplication illustrates the commutative property for multiplication.

Group Activity Solutions

1.   (a)   From the table, the windchill factor is $-22°F$.

      (b)   No, the amount of the decrease gets smaller as wind speed increases.

      (c)   At a wind speed of 40 miles per hour, each 5-mile-per-hour increase in wind speed accounts for a 1 or 2 degree decrease in windchill. A reasonable estimate might be $-29°F$. *Answers may vary.*

      (d)   The true value of the windchill when the wind speed is 40 miles per hour is $-29°F$.

2.   (a)   From the table, the windchill factor is $-45°F$.

      (b)   No, the amount subtracted varies.

      (c)   It may be reasonable to subtract $13°F$ from the windchill temperature listed for $-30°F$. A reasonable estimate might be $-71°F$. *Answers may vary.*

      (d)   The true value of the windchill when the temperature is $-40°F$ is $-71°F$.

1.2: Operations on Real Numbers

Concepts

1.   right

2.   left

3.   positive

4.   negative

5.   negative

6.   negative

7. $-a$

8. $\dfrac{b}{a}$

9.   positive

10. $-a-b$

The Real Number Line and Absolute Value

11.

12.

13.

14.

15.

16.

17. $\left|-6.1\right| = 6.1$

18. $\left|17\right| = 17$

19. $\left|8-11\right| = \left|-3\right| = 3$

20. $\left|2 \cdot 8 - 23\right| = \left|16 - 23\right| = \left|-7\right| = 7$

21. $\left|x\right| = x$ when $x > 0$

22. $\left|x\right| = -x$ when $x < 0$

23. $\left|x - y\right| = x - y$ when $x > 0$ and $y < 0$

24. $\left|x + y\right| = -\left(x + y\right)$ when $x < 0$ and $y < 0$

25.   Positive. Area can never be negative.

26.   Positive. Distance can never be negative.

27.   Both. Temperature can be both above and below zero.

28.   Both. A person's net worth can be either positive or negative.

29.   Positive. A car's mileage can never be negative.

30.   Both. Elevation can be both above and below sea level.

Arithmetic Operations

31.   The additive inverse of 56 is $-\left(56\right) = -56$.

32.   The additive inverse of $-\dfrac{5}{7}$ is $-\left(-\dfrac{5}{7}\right) = \dfrac{5}{7}$.

33.   The additive inverse of -6.9 is $-\left(-6.9\right) = 6.9$.

34.   The additive inverse of 12.8 is $-\left(12.8\right) = -12.8$.

35.   The additive inverse of $-\pi + 2$ is $-(-\pi + 2) = \pi - 2$.

36.   The additive inverse of $a + b$ is $-(a + b) = -a - b$.

37.   The additive inverse of $a - b$ is $-(a - b) = -a + b$.

38.   The additive inverse of $-x + 3$ is $-(-x + 3) = x - 3$.

39.   The additive inverse of $-(x - y)$ is $-(-(x - y)) = x - y$.

40.   The additive inverse of $-1 - x$ is $-(-1 - x) = 1 + x$.

41.   The additive inverse of $z - (2 - z)$ is $-(z - (2 - z)) = -(2z - 2) = -2z + 2$.

42.   The additive inverse of $2z - (1 + 2z)$ is $-(2z - (1 + 2z)) = -(-1) = 1$.

43. $\dfrac{1}{3}$

44. $\dfrac{8}{3}$

45. $-\dfrac{3}{2}$

46. $\dfrac{2}{3} = 0.\overline{6}$

47. $\dfrac{1}{\pi}$

48. $-\dfrac{y}{x}$

49. $\dfrac{1}{a + 3}$

50. $\dfrac{1}{x - 1}$

51. $-\dfrac{b}{2a}$

52. $-\dfrac{3a}{2b}$

53. $x - 7$

54. $\dfrac{x + y}{3}$

55. $4 + (-6) = -2$

56. $-10 + 14 = 4$

57. $-7.4 + (-9.2) = -16.6$

58. $-8.4 - 10.3 = -18.7$

59. $-\dfrac{3}{4} - \left(-\dfrac{1}{4}\right) = -\dfrac{3}{4} + \dfrac{1}{4} = -\dfrac{2}{4} = -\dfrac{1}{2}$

60. $\dfrac{1}{5} - \left(-\dfrac{3}{10}\right) = \dfrac{2}{10} + \dfrac{3}{10} = \dfrac{5}{10} = \dfrac{1}{2}$

61. $-9 + 1 + (-2) + 5 = -8 + (-2) + 5 = -10 + 5 = -5$

62. $-5 + 7 - (-2) + 3 = 2 - (-2) + 3 = 4 + 3 = 7$

63. $-6 \cdot -12 = 72$

64. $-(8 \cdot -4) = -(-32) = 32$

65. $-\dfrac{1}{2} \cdot \dfrac{5}{7} \cdot \dfrac{1}{3} = -\dfrac{5}{14} \cdot \dfrac{1}{3} = -\dfrac{5}{42}$

66. $-\dfrac{6}{7} \cdot -\dfrac{5}{3} = \dfrac{30}{21} = \dfrac{10}{7}$

67. $-\dfrac{1}{2} \div -\dfrac{3}{4} = -\dfrac{1}{2} \cdot -\dfrac{4}{3} = \dfrac{4}{6} = \dfrac{2}{3}$

68. $-5 \div \dfrac{4}{5} = -\dfrac{5}{1} \cdot \dfrac{5}{4} = -\dfrac{25}{4}$

69. $\dfrac{3}{4} \div (-2) = \dfrac{3}{4} \cdot -\dfrac{1}{2} = -\dfrac{3}{8}$

70. $-\dfrac{4}{5} \div \dfrac{7}{10} = -\dfrac{4}{5} \cdot \dfrac{10}{7} = -\dfrac{40}{35} = -\dfrac{8}{7}$

71. $-\dfrac{8}{2} = -4$

72. $-\dfrac{45}{9} = -5$

73. $-25 \div -5 = 5$

74. $8 \div 0$ is undefined because division by zero is not possible.

75. $\dfrac{1}{0}$ is undefined because division by zero is not possible.

76. $\dfrac{0}{7} = 0$

77. $-4 \cdot 7 \cdot (-5) = -28 \cdot (-5) = 140$

78. $-2 \cdot -6 \cdot 6 \cdot -1 = 12 \cdot 6 \cdot -1 = 72 \cdot -1 = -72$

79. $6 \cdot \dfrac{2}{3} \cdot 3 \cdot \left(-\dfrac{1}{6}\right) = \left[6 \cdot \left(-\dfrac{1}{6}\right)\right] \cdot \left(\dfrac{2}{3} \cdot 3\right) = -1 \cdot 2 = -2$

80. $\left(\dfrac{4}{5}\cdot\dfrac{5}{8}\right)\div\dfrac{1}{2}=\dfrac{20}{40}\cdot\dfrac{2}{1}=\dfrac{40}{40}=1$

81. $4x-9x=(4-9)\,x=-5x$

82. $\dfrac{1}{2}x-\dfrac{3}{4}x=\dfrac{2}{4}x-\dfrac{3}{4}x=\left(\dfrac{2}{4}-\dfrac{3}{4}\right)x=-\dfrac{1}{4}x$

83. $z-4z+2z=(1-4+2)\,z=-z$

84. $5z-3z-6z=(5-3-6)\,z=-4z$

85. Entering $-23.1+45.7-(-34.6)$ into a graphing calculator gives 57.2.

86. Entering $102-(-341)+(-112)$ into a graphing calculator gives 331.

87. Entering $(1/2)+(2/3)-(5/7)$ ▶Frac into a graphing calculator gives $\dfrac{19}{42}$.

88. Entering $(-8/13)+(1/2)-(2/5)$ ▶Frac into a graphing calculator gives $-\dfrac{67}{130}$.

89. Entering $(-3/4)(4/5)/(5/3)$ ▶Frac into a graphing calculator gives $-\dfrac{9}{25}$.

90. Entering $((3/4)/(-11))-(2/5)$ ▶Frac into a graphing calculator gives $-\dfrac{103}{220}$.

91. Entering $(1/2)((4/11)+(2/5))$ ▶Frac into a graphing calculator gives $\dfrac{21}{55}$.

92. Entering $(-5/13)+((3/5)/(2/17))$ ▶Frac into a graphing calculator gives $\dfrac{613}{130}$.

Data and Number Sense

93. $\left[9+5+15+(-9)\right]\div4=5$

94. $\left[12+8+27+(-7)\right]\div4=10$

95. $\left[(-2)+12+7+(-17)\right]\div4=0$

96. $\left[45+55+65+35\right]\div4=50$

97. $\left[101+99+(-42)+82\right]\div4=60$

98. $\left[(-4)+2+5+(-8)+5+24\right]\div6=4$

99. $\left[(a+b)+(a+b)+(a+b)\right]\div6=\dfrac{a+b}{2}$

100. $\left[a+2a+3a+4a+5a\right]\div5=3a$

101. $-2+8+3+2-11=(8+2+3)+\left[(-2)+(-11)\right]=13-13=0$

102. $-22+43-78+7=\left[-22+(-78)\right]+(43+7)=-100+50=-50$

103. $103-44+97-56=(103+97)+\left[(-44)+(-56)\right]=200-100=100$

104. $10+11+12-11-11-11=(10-11)+(11-11)+(12-11)=-1+0+1=0$

105. $\dfrac{1}{5}\cdot\dfrac{2}{3}\cdot\dfrac{1}{7}\cdot\dfrac{1}{9}\cdot5\cdot\dfrac{3}{2}\cdot7\cdot9=\left(\dfrac{1}{5}\cdot5\right)\cdot\left(\dfrac{2}{3}\cdot\dfrac{3}{2}\right)\cdot\left(\dfrac{1}{7}\cdot7\right)\cdot\left(\dfrac{1}{9}\cdot9\right)=1\cdot1\cdot1\cdot1=1$

106. $\dfrac{1}{2}\cdot\dfrac{1}{3}\cdot\dfrac{1}{4}\cdot(-4)\cdot(-3)\cdot(-2)=\left[\dfrac{1}{2}\cdot(-2)\right]\cdot\left[\dfrac{1}{3}\cdot(-3)\right]\cdot\left[\dfrac{1}{4}\cdot(-4)\right]=(-1)\cdot(-1)\cdot(-1)=-1$

107. $\left(\dfrac{1}{2}-\dfrac{1}{3}\right)+\left(\dfrac{1}{3}-\dfrac{1}{4}\right)+\left(\dfrac{1}{4}-\dfrac{1}{5}\right)+\left(\dfrac{1}{5}-\dfrac{1}{6}\right)=\dfrac{1}{2}+\left(\dfrac{1}{3}-\dfrac{1}{3}\right)+\left(\dfrac{1}{4}-\dfrac{1}{4}\right)+\left(\dfrac{1}{5}-\dfrac{1}{5}\right)-\dfrac{1}{6}=\dfrac{1}{2}-\dfrac{1}{6}=\dfrac{1}{3}$

108. $\dfrac{1}{2}\div\dfrac{1}{3}\cdot\dfrac{1}{3}\div\dfrac{1}{4}\cdot\dfrac{1}{4}\div\dfrac{1}{5}\cdot\dfrac{1}{5}=\dfrac{1}{2}\cdot\left(\dfrac{3}{1}\cdot\dfrac{1}{3}\right)\cdot\left(\dfrac{4}{1}\cdot\dfrac{1}{4}\right)\cdot\left(\dfrac{5}{1}\cdot\dfrac{1}{5}\right)=\dfrac{1}{2}\cdot1\cdot1\cdot1=\dfrac{1}{2}$

109. $a\cdot b\cdot c\cdot\frac{1}{a}\cdot\frac{1}{b}\cdot\frac{1}{c}=\left(a\cdot\frac{1}{a}\right)\cdot\left(b\cdot\frac{1}{b}\right)\cdot\left(c\cdot\frac{1}{c}\right)=1\cdot1\cdot1=1$

110. $b-a(b+c)+ab+ac=b-ab-ac+ab+ac$

$$=b+(-ab+ab)+(-ac+ac)$$

$$=b+0+0=b$$

Applications

111. The box contains 1200 cubic inches because if $200=\text{Length}\times\text{Width}\times\text{Height}$ then

$2\cdot3\cdot200=2\cdot\text{Length}\times3\cdot\text{Width}\times\text{Height}$ and $2\cdot3\cdot200=1200$.

112. We estimate the lake contains 87.5 million cubic feet of water because $200\text{ acres}=\dfrac{1}{2}\cdot400\text{ acres}$, and

$10\text{ feet}=\dfrac{1}{2}\cdot20\text{ feet}$, so $\dfrac{1}{2}\cdot\dfrac{1}{2}\cdot350\text{ million}=87.5\text{ million}$.

113. Since $\text{Volume}=\text{Length}\times\text{Width}\times\text{Height}$, the larger pool has a volume $4\cdot2=8$ times greater than the

smaller pool. It will take 8 times longer to fill it, or $8\cdot2\text{ days}=16\text{ days}$.

114. Twice the diameter means twice the radius so if $\pi r^2=A$ then $\pi(2r)^2=\pi(2r)(2r)=\pi\left(4r^2\right)=4\pi r^2=4A$.

If one batch fills the original pan, then 4 batches are needed to fill the larger pan.

115. We may estimate the cost to be \$2600 since $\$200+\$100\cdot24=\$2600$. *Answers may vary.*

The actual cost is $\$202+\$98.99\cdot24=\$2577.76$.

116. We may estimate the cost to be \$10,500 since $\$1500+\$250\cdot36=\$10,500$. *Answers may vary.*

The actual cost is $\$1497+\$249\cdot36=\$10,461$.

117. (a) If we note that the increase from 1998 to 1999 was 6125 and the increase from 2001 to 2002 was 29,436,

we see that the number of hacking incidents has not increased by a fixed amount each year.

(b) $(3734 + 9859 + 21,756 + 52,658 + 82,094) \div 5 = 34,020.2$

(c) One possible estimate is 120,000. Since 2003 lies outside of the given data and the number of hackings does not increase by a fixed amount, it is difficult to make this estimate. *Answers may vary.*

118.   (a) Since 2.2 trillion is the same as 2200 billion, $2200 \div 3 = 733.\overline{3} \approx 733$ cigarettes per person.

(b) Since 5.5 trillion is the same as 5500 billion, $5500 \div 6 = 916.\overline{6} \approx 917$ cigarettes per person.

(c) We may estimate the consumption in 1985 to be 4.9 trillion since the average of the consumption rates for 1980 and 1990 is $(4.4 + 5.4) \div 2 = 4.9$.

(d) If the trend continues, consumption will increase slightly between 2000 and 2010. *Answers may vary.*

119.   (a) The number of cable modem subscribers is increasing.

(b) We may estimate the number of subscribers in 2010 to be about 26.1 million. *Answers may vary.*

120.   (a) DSL use is increasing.

(b) One possible estimate is about 27 to 28 million. The values increase by about 2 million each year. *Answers may vary.*

Checking Basic Concepts for Sections 1.1 & 1.2

1.   (a) The number –9 is an integer, a rational number and a real number.

(b) The number $\dfrac{8}{4}$ is a natural number, integer, rational number and a real number.

(c) The number $\sqrt{5}$ is a real number.

(d) The number 0.5 is a rational number and a real number.

2.   (a) Commutative property; $a + b = b + a$

(b) Associative property; $a \cdot (b \cdot c) = (a \cdot b) \cdot c$

(c) Distributive property; $a(b + c) = ab + ac$

(d) Distributive property; $a(b - c) = ab - ac$ with $a = -1$

3.   (a) $-3 + 4 + (-5) = 1 + (-5) = -4$

(b) $5.1 \cdot (-4) \cdot 2 = -20.4 \cdot 2 = -40.8$

(c) $-\dfrac{2}{3} \cdot \left(\dfrac{1}{4} \div \dfrac{2}{5} \right) = -\dfrac{2}{3} \cdot \left(\dfrac{1}{4} \cdot \dfrac{5}{2} \right) = -\dfrac{2}{3} \cdot \dfrac{5}{8} = -\dfrac{10}{24} = -\dfrac{5}{12}$

4.   Since there are 3 times as many acres and the water is 2 times deeper, we multiply the total gallons by 6. The larger lake has about 12 billion gallons.

1.3: Integer Exponents

Concepts

1.   The base is 8 and the exponent is 3.

2. $97^0 = 1$ and $2^{-1} = \dfrac{1}{2}$

3. 7^3

4. 5^2

5. No. $2^3 = 8$ and $3^2 = 9$

6. No. $-4^2 = -16$ and $(-4)^2 = 16$

7. $\dfrac{1}{7^n}$

8. 6^{m+n}

9. 5^{m-n}

10. $3^k x^k$

11. 2^{mk}

12. $\dfrac{x^m}{y^m}$

13. x^n

14. $\dfrac{b^m}{a^n}$

15. $\left(\dfrac{z}{y}\right)^n$ or $\dfrac{z^n}{y^n}$

16. 500

Properties of Exponents

17. $8 = 2 \times 2 \times 2 = 2^3$

18. $1000 = 10 \times 10 \times 10 = 10^3$

19. $256 = 4 \times 4 \times 4 \times 4 = 4^4$

20. $\dfrac{1}{16} = \dfrac{1}{2 \times 2 \times 2 \times 2} = \dfrac{1}{2^4} = 2^{-4}$

21. $1 = 6^0$

22. $\dfrac{1}{125} = \dfrac{1}{5 \times 5 \times 5} = \dfrac{1}{5^3} = 5^{-3}$

23. (a) $4^3 = 4 \cdot 4 \cdot 4 = 64$

     (b) $3^4 = 3 \cdot 3 \cdot 3 \cdot 3 = 81$

24. (a) $2^{-3} = \dfrac{1}{2^3} = \dfrac{1}{2 \cdot 2 \cdot 2} = \dfrac{1}{8}$

(b) $7^{-2} = \dfrac{1}{7^2} = \dfrac{1}{7 \cdot 7} = \dfrac{1}{49}$

25.   (a) $\dfrac{1}{4^{-2}} = 4^2 = 4 \cdot 4 = 16$

(b) $\dfrac{1}{3^{-3}} = 3^3 = 3 \cdot 3 \cdot 3 = 27$

26.   (a) $5^0 = 1$

(b) $\dfrac{1}{6^0} = \dfrac{1}{1} = 1$

27.   (a) $\left(\dfrac{2}{3}\right)^3 = \dfrac{2}{3} \cdot \dfrac{2}{3} \cdot \dfrac{2}{3} = \dfrac{8}{27}$

(b) $\left(-\dfrac{2}{3}\right)^{-3} = \left(-\dfrac{3}{2}\right)^3 = \left(-\dfrac{3}{2}\right) \cdot \left(-\dfrac{3}{2}\right) \cdot \left(-\dfrac{3}{2}\right) = -\dfrac{27}{8}$

28.   (a) $\left(-\dfrac{1}{2}\right)^4 = \left(-\dfrac{1}{2}\right) \cdot \left(-\dfrac{1}{2}\right) \cdot \left(-\dfrac{1}{2}\right) \cdot \left(-\dfrac{1}{2}\right) = \dfrac{1}{16}$

(b) $\left(-\dfrac{3}{4}\right)^3 = \left(-\dfrac{3}{4}\right) \cdot \left(-\dfrac{3}{4}\right) \cdot \left(-\dfrac{3}{4}\right) = -\dfrac{27}{64}$

29.   (a) $\dfrac{3^{-2}}{2^{-4}} = \dfrac{2^4}{3^2} = \dfrac{2 \cdot 2 \cdot 2 \cdot 2}{3 \cdot 3} = \dfrac{16}{9}$

(b) $\dfrac{4^{-3}}{5^{-2}} = \dfrac{5^2}{4^3} = \dfrac{5 \cdot 5}{4 \cdot 4 \cdot 4} = \dfrac{25}{64}$

30.   (a) $\dfrac{4^{-2}}{2^3} = \dfrac{1}{2^3 \cdot 4^2} = \dfrac{1}{2 \cdot 2 \cdot 2 \cdot 4 \cdot 4} = \dfrac{1}{128}$

(b) $\dfrac{3^3}{5^{-2}} = 3^3 \cdot 5^2 = 3 \cdot 3 \cdot 3 \cdot 5 \cdot 5 = 675$

31.   (a) $\dfrac{1}{2x^{-3}} = \dfrac{x^3}{2}$

(b) $\dfrac{1}{(ab)^{-1}} = ab$

32.   (a) $\dfrac{1}{3b^{-2}} = \dfrac{b^2}{3}$

(b) $\dfrac{2^{-3}}{b^{-1}} = \dfrac{b}{2^3} = \dfrac{b}{2 \cdot 2 \cdot 2} = \dfrac{b}{8}$

33.   (a) $3^5 \cdot 3^{-3} = 3^{5+(-3)} = 3^2 = 9$

(b) $x^2 x^5 = x^{2+5} = x^7$

34. (a) $10^{-5} \cdot 10^2 = 10^{-5+2} = 10^{-3} = \dfrac{1}{10^3} = \dfrac{1}{1000}$

(b) $y^4 y^{-3} = y^{4+(-3)} = y$

35. (a) $\left(-3x^{-2}\right)\left(5x^5\right) = (-3)(5)x^{-2+5} = -15x^3$

(b) $(ab)\left(a^2 b^{-3}\right) = a^{1+2} b^{1+(-3)} = a^3 b^{-2} = \dfrac{a^3}{b^2}$

36. (a) $6z^2 \left(-z^3\right) = -6z^{2+3} = -6z^5$

(b) $\left(a^2 b^{-3}\right)\left(2ab^3\right) = 2a^{2+1} b^{-3+3} = 2a^3 b^0 = 2a^3$

37. (a) $5^{-2} \cdot 5^3 \cdot 2^{-4} \cdot 2^3 = 5^{-2+3} \cdot 2^{-4+3} = 5^1 \cdot 2^{-1} = 5 \cdot \dfrac{1}{2} = \dfrac{5}{2}$

(b) $2a^3 \cdot b^2 \cdot 4a^{-4} \cdot b^{-5} = 2 \cdot 4 \cdot a^{3+(-4)} \cdot b^{2+(-5)} = 8a^{-1} b^{-3} = \dfrac{8}{ab^3}$

38. (a) $2^{-3} \cdot 3^4 \cdot 3^{-2} \cdot 2^5 = 2^{-3+5} \cdot 3^{4+(-2)} = 2^2 \cdot 3^2 = 4 \cdot 9 = 36$

(b) $3x^{-4} \cdot 2x^2 \cdot 5y^4 \cdot y^{-3} = 6x^{-4+2} \cdot 5y^{4+(-3)} = 30x^{-2} y^1 = \dfrac{30y}{x^2}$

39. (a) $\dfrac{4^3}{4^2} = 4^{3-2} = 4^1 = 4$

(b) $\dfrac{10^{-3}}{10^{-5}} = 10^{-3-(-5)} = 10^2 = 100$

40. (a) $\dfrac{5^4}{5^{-7}} = 5^{4-(-7)} = 5^{11} = 48{,}828{,}125$

(b) $\dfrac{6^{-5}}{6} = 6^{-5-1} = 6^{-6} = \dfrac{1}{6^6} = \dfrac{1}{46{,}656}$

41. (a) $\dfrac{b^{-3}}{b^2} = b^{-3-2} = b^{-5} = \dfrac{1}{b^5}$

(b) $\dfrac{24x^3}{6x} = \dfrac{24}{6} x^{3-1} = 4x^2$

42. (a) $\dfrac{x^0}{x^{-5}} = x^{0-(-5)} = x^5$

(b) $\dfrac{10x^5}{5x^{-3}} = \dfrac{10}{5} x^{5-(-3)} = 2x^8$

43. (a) $\dfrac{12a^2 b^3}{18a^4 b^2} = \dfrac{12}{18} a^{2-4} \cdot b^{3-2} = \dfrac{2}{3} a^{-2} b^1 = \dfrac{2b}{3a^2}$

(b) $\dfrac{21x^{-3}y^4}{7x^4y^{-2}} = \dfrac{21}{7}x^{-3-4} \cdot y^{4-(-2)} = 3x^{-7}y^6 = \dfrac{3y^6}{x^7}$

44.   (a) $\dfrac{-6x^7y^3}{3x^2y^{-5}} = -\dfrac{6}{3}x^{7-2} \cdot y^{3-(-5)} = -2x^5y^8$

(b) $\dfrac{32x^3y}{-24x^5y^{-3}} = -\dfrac{32}{24}x^{3-5} \cdot y^{1-(-3)} = -\dfrac{4}{3}x^{-2}y^4 = -\dfrac{4y^4}{3x^2}$

45.   (a) $\left(3^2\right)^4 = 3^{2\cdot4} = 3^8 = 6561$

(b) $\left(x^3\right)^{-2} = x^{3\cdot(-2)} = x^{-6} = \dfrac{1}{x^6}$

46.   (a) $\left(-2^2\right)^3 = -2^{2\cdot3} = -2^6 = -64$

(b) $\left(xy\right)^3 = x^3y^3$

47.   (a) $\left(4y^2\right)^3 = 4^3 \cdot y^{2\cdot3} = 64y^6$

(b) $\left(-2xy^3\right)^{-4} = \dfrac{1}{\left(2xy^3\right)^4} = \dfrac{1}{2^4 \cdot x^4 \cdot y^{3\cdot4}} = \dfrac{1}{16x^4y^{12}}$

48.   (a) $\left(-2a^2\right)^3 = (-2)^3\left(a^2\right)^3 = -8a^{2\cdot3} = -8a^6$

(b) $\left(a^{-1}b^5\right)^{-2} = \left(a^{-1}\right)^{-2}\left(b^5\right)^{-2} = a^{(-1)\cdot(-2)}\,b^{5\cdot(-2)} = a^2b^{-10} = \dfrac{a^2}{b^{10}}$

49.   (a) $\left(\dfrac{4}{x}\right)^3 = \dfrac{4^3}{x^3} = \dfrac{64}{x^3}$

(b) $\left(\dfrac{2x}{z^4}\right)^{-5} = \left(\dfrac{z^4}{2x}\right)^5 = \dfrac{\left(z^4\right)^5}{\left(2x\right)^5} = \dfrac{z^{4\cdot5}}{2^5 \cdot x^5} = \dfrac{z^{20}}{32x^5}$

50.   (a) $\left(\dfrac{-3}{x^3}\right)^2 = \dfrac{(-3)^2}{\left(x^3\right)^2} = \dfrac{9}{x^{3\cdot2}} = \dfrac{9}{x^6}$

(b) $\left(\dfrac{2xy}{3z^5}\right)^{-1} = \left(\dfrac{3z^5}{2xy}\right)^1 = \dfrac{3z^5}{2xy}$

51. $\dfrac{12m^2n^{-5}}{8mn^{-2}} = \dfrac{12}{8}m^{2-1}n^{-5-(-2)} = \dfrac{3}{2}mn^{-3} = \dfrac{3m}{2n^3}$

52. $\dfrac{15m^{-1}n}{5m^{-2}n^3} = \dfrac{15}{5}m^{-1-(-2)}n^{1-3} = 3mn^{-2} = \dfrac{3m}{n^2}$

53. $\left(2x^3y^{-2}\right)^{-2} = 2^{-2}\left(x^3\right)^{-2}\left(y^{-2}\right)^{-2} = \dfrac{1}{2^2}\,x^{3\cdot(-2)}y^{(-2)\cdot(-2)} = \dfrac{1}{4}x^{-6}y^4 = \dfrac{y^4}{4x^6}$

54. $\left(4x^{-4}y\right)^2 = 4^2\left(x^{-4}\right)^2 y^2 = 16x^{-8}y^2 = \dfrac{16y^2}{x^8}$

55. $\dfrac{\left(b^2\right)^3}{\left(b^{-1}\right)^2} = \dfrac{b^{2\cdot3}}{b^{-1\cdot2}} = \dfrac{b^6}{b^{-2}} = b^{6-(-2)} = b^8$

56. $\dfrac{\left(a^3\right)^{-1}}{\left(a^{-3}\right)^{-2}} = \dfrac{a^{3\cdot(-1)}}{a^{(-3)\cdot(-2)}} = \dfrac{a^{-3}}{a^6} = a^{-3-6} = a^{-9} = \dfrac{1}{a^9}$

57. $\dfrac{\left(-3ab^2\right)^3}{\left(a^2b\right)^2} = \dfrac{(-3)^3\,a^3\left(b^2\right)^3}{\left(a^2\right)^2 b^2} = \dfrac{-27a^3b^{2\cdot3}}{a^{2\cdot2}b^2} = \dfrac{-27a^3b^6}{a^4b^2} = -27a^{3-4}b^{6-2} = -27a^{-1}b^4 = -\dfrac{27b^4}{a}$

58. $\dfrac{(-2ab)^3}{(ab)^2} = \dfrac{(-2)^3\,a^3b^3}{a^2b^2} = -8a^{3-2}b^{3-2} = -8ab$

59. $\dfrac{\left(-m^2n^{-1}\right)^{-2}}{(mn)^{-1}} = \dfrac{(mn)^1}{\left(-m^2n^{-1}\right)^2} = \dfrac{mn}{\left(-m^2\right)^2\left(n^{-1}\right)^2} = \dfrac{mn}{m^{2\cdot2}n^{-1\cdot2}} = \dfrac{mn}{m^4n^{-2}} = m^{1-4}n^{1-(-2)} = m^{-3}n^3 = \dfrac{n^3}{m^3}$

60. $\dfrac{\left(-mn^4\right)^{-1}}{\left(m^2n\right)^{-3}} = \dfrac{\left(m^2n\right)^3}{\left(-mn^4\right)^1} = \dfrac{\left(m^2\right)^3 n^3}{-mn^4} = \dfrac{m^{2\cdot3}n^3}{-mn^4} = \dfrac{m^6n^3}{-mn^4} = -m^{6-1}n^{3-4} = -m^5n^{-1} = -\dfrac{m^5}{n}$

61. $\left(\dfrac{2a^3}{6b}\right)^4 = \left(\dfrac{a^3}{3b}\right)^4 = \dfrac{\left(a^3\right)^4}{3^4b^4} = \dfrac{a^{3\cdot4}}{81b^4} = \dfrac{a^{12}}{81b^4}$

62. $\left(\dfrac{-3a^2}{9b^3}\right)^4 = \left(\dfrac{-a^2}{3b^3}\right)^4 = \dfrac{\left(-a^2\right)^4}{3^4\left(b^3\right)^4} = \dfrac{a^{2\cdot4}}{81b^{3\cdot4}} = \dfrac{a^8}{81b^{12}}$

63. $\left(\dfrac{t^{-3}}{t^{-4}}\right)^2 = \left(t^{-3-(-4)}\right)^2 = \left(t^1\right)^2 = t^2$

64. $\left(\dfrac{r^{-2}}{2r^{-1}}\right)^{-4} = \left(\dfrac{1}{2}r^{-2-(-1)}\right)^{-4} = \left(\dfrac{1}{2}r^{-1}\right)^{-4} = \left(\dfrac{1}{2}\right)^{-4}r^{-1\cdot(-4)} = 2^4r^4 = 16r^4$

65. $\dfrac{8x^{-3}y^{-2}}{4x^{-2}y^{-4}} = \dfrac{8}{4}x^{-3-(-2)}y^{-2-(-4)} = 2x^{-1}y^2 = \dfrac{2y^2}{x}$

66. $\dfrac{6x^{-1}y^{-1}}{9x^{-2}y^3} = \dfrac{6}{9}x^{-1-(-2)}y^{-1-3} = \dfrac{2}{3}x^1y^{-4} = \dfrac{2x}{3y^4}$

67. $\left(\dfrac{2t}{-r^2}\right)^{-3} = \left(\dfrac{-r^2}{2t}\right)^3 = \dfrac{\left(-r^2\right)^3}{2^3 t^3} = \dfrac{-r^{2 \cdot 3}}{8t^3} = -\dfrac{r^6}{8t^3}$

68. $\left(\dfrac{t^2}{3r}\right)^{-1} = \dfrac{3r}{t^2}$

69. $\dfrac{\left(r^2 t^2\right)^{-2}}{\left(r^3 t\right)^{-1}} = \dfrac{r^3 t}{\left(r^2 t^2\right)^2} = \dfrac{r^3 t}{\left(r^2\right)^2 \left(t^2\right)^2} = \dfrac{r^3 t}{r^{2 \cdot 2} t^{2 \cdot 2}} = \dfrac{r^3 t}{r^4 t^4} = r^{3-4} t^{1-4} = r^{-1} t^{-3} = \dfrac{1}{rt^3}$

70. $\dfrac{\left(2rt\right)^2}{\left(rt^4\right)^{-2}} = \dfrac{2^2 r^2 t^2}{r^{-2} \left(t^4\right)^{-2}} = \dfrac{4r^2 t^2}{r^{-2} t^{4 \cdot (-2)}} = \dfrac{4r^2 t^2}{r^{-2} t^{-8}} = 4r^{2-(-2)} t^{2-(-8)} = 4r^4 t^{10}$

71. $\dfrac{4x^{-2} y^3}{\left(2x^{-1} y\right)^2} = \dfrac{4x^{-2} y^3}{2^2 \left(x^{-1}\right)^2 y^2} = \dfrac{4x^{-2} y^3}{4x^{-1 \cdot 2} y^2} = \dfrac{4x^{-2} y^3}{4x^{-2} y^2} = \left(\dfrac{4x^{-2}}{4x^{-2}}\right) y^{3-2} = 1y = y$

72. $\dfrac{\left(ab\right)^3}{a^4 b^{-4}} = \dfrac{a^3 b^3}{a^4 b^{-4}} = a^{3-4} b^{3-(-4)} = a^{-1} b^7 = \dfrac{b^7}{a}$

73. $\left(\dfrac{-15r^2 t}{3r^{-3} t^4}\right)^3 = \left(\dfrac{-15}{3} r^{2-(-3)} t^{1-4}\right)^3 = \left(-5r^5 t^{-3}\right)^3 = (-5)^3 \left(r^5\right)^3 \left(t^{-3}\right)^3 = -125 r^{5 \cdot 3} t^{-3 \cdot 3} = -125 r^{15} t^{-9} = -\dfrac{125 r^{15}}{t^9}$

74. $\left(\dfrac{4\left(xy\right)^2}{\left(2xy^{-2}\right)^3}\right)^{-2} = \left(\dfrac{\left(2xy^{-2}\right)^3}{4\left(xy\right)^2}\right)^2 = \left(\dfrac{2^3 x^3 \left(y^{-2}\right)^3}{4x^2 y^2}\right)^2 = \left(\dfrac{8}{4} x^{3-2} y^{-6-2}\right)^2 = \left(2xy^{-8}\right)^2 = 2^2 x^2 \left(y^{-8}\right)^2 = \dfrac{4x^2}{y^{16}}$

Order of Operations

75. $4 + 5 \cdot 6 = 4 + 30 = 34$

76. $4 - 5 - 9 = -1 - 9 = -10$

77. $2\left(4 + (-8)\right) = 2 \cdot (-4) = -8$

78. $500 - 10^3 = 500 - 1000 = -500$

79. $5 \cdot 2^3 = 5 \cdot 8 = 40$

80. $\dfrac{4+8}{2} - \dfrac{6+1}{3} = \dfrac{12}{2} - \dfrac{7}{3} = \dfrac{36}{6} - \dfrac{14}{6} = \dfrac{22}{6} = \dfrac{11}{3}$

81. $\dfrac{-2^4 - 3^2}{4} + \dfrac{1+2}{4} = \dfrac{-16-9}{4} + \dfrac{3}{4} = \dfrac{-25}{4} + \dfrac{3}{4} = \dfrac{-22}{4} = -\dfrac{11}{2}$

82. $\dfrac{\left(-4^2 + 1\right)}{\frac{2}{3}} = \dfrac{-16+1}{\frac{2}{3}} = \dfrac{-15}{\frac{2}{3}} = \dfrac{-15}{\frac{2}{3}} \cdot \dfrac{3}{1} \cdot \dfrac{}{2} = -\dfrac{45}{2}$

83. $\dfrac{1 - 2 \cdot 4^2}{5^{-1}} = \dfrac{1 - 2 \cdot 16}{\frac{1}{5}} = \dfrac{1 - 32}{\frac{1}{5}} = \dfrac{-31}{\frac{1}{5}} = \dfrac{-31}{1} \cdot \dfrac{5}{1} = -155$

84. $6 \div 4 \div 2 = \dfrac{6}{4} \div 2 = \dfrac{3}{2} \cdot \dfrac{1}{2} = \dfrac{3}{4}$

85. $4 + 6 - 3 \cdot 5 \div 3 = 4 + 6 - 15 \div 3 = 4 + 6 - 5 = 10 - 5 = 5$

86. $-3\left(25 - 2 \cdot 5^2\right) \div 5 = -3\left(25 - 2 \cdot 25\right) \div 5 = -3\left(25 - 50\right) \div 5 = -3\left(-25\right) \div 5 = 75 \div 5 = 15$

87. $\dfrac{-3^2 + 3}{3} = \dfrac{-9 + 3}{3} = \dfrac{-6}{3} = -2$

88. $\dfrac{2 \cdot 4 - 7}{7} = \dfrac{8 - 7}{7} = \dfrac{1}{7}$

89. $-4^2 + \dfrac{15 + 2}{8 - 7} = -16 + \dfrac{17}{1} = 1$

90. $1 - 3 \cdot 4^3 = 1 - 3 \cdot 64 = 1 - 192 = -191$

91. $\left| 7 - 2^2 \cdot 3 \right| = \left| 7 - 4 \cdot 3 \right| = \left| 7 - 12 \right| = \left| -5 \right| = 5$

92. $\dfrac{4^2 - \left| 5 - (-6) \right|}{-2^2} = \dfrac{16 - \left| 5 - (-6) \right|}{-4} = \dfrac{16 - \left| 11 \right|}{-4} = \dfrac{16 - 11}{-4} = \dfrac{5}{-4} = -\dfrac{5}{4}$

93. $\sqrt{4^2 + 3^2} = \sqrt{16 + 9} = \sqrt{25} = 5$

94. $\sqrt{13^2 - 12^2} = \sqrt{169 - 144} = \sqrt{25} = 5$

Scientific Notation

95. 2.447×10^6

96. 1.32×10^5

97. 2.69×10^{10}

98. 1.7×10^{12}

99. 5.1×10^{-2}

100. 1.56×10^{-1}

101. 1.0×10^{-6}

102. 2.44×10^{-3}

103. 500,000

104. −7850

105. 9,300,000

106. 296.1

107. −0.006

108. 0.041

109. 0.00005876

110. 0.99

111. $\left(2\times10^4\right)\left(3\times10^2\right)=(2\cdot3)\times10^{4+2}=6\times10^6=6,000,000$

112. $\left(5\times10^{-4}\right)\left(4\times10^6\right)=(5\cdot4)\times10^{-4+6}=20\times10^2=2\times10^3=2000$

113. $\left(4\times10^{-4}\right)\left(2\times10^{-2}\right)=(4\cdot2)\times10^{-4+(-2)}=8\times10^{-6}=0.000008$

114. $\dfrac{6\times10^4}{2\times10^2}=\dfrac{6}{2}\times10^{4-2}=3\times10^2=300$

115. $\dfrac{6.2\times10^3}{3.1\times10^{-2}}=\dfrac{6.2}{3.1}\times10^{3-(-2)}=2\times10^5=200,000$

116. $\dfrac{2\times10^{-2}}{8\times10^{-5}}=\dfrac{2}{8}\times10^{-2-(-5)}=0.25\times10^3=2.5\times10^2=250$

Applications

117. (a) By trial and error $k=10$

  (b) $\dfrac{1024}{52}\approx20$ years

118. (a) $\dfrac{1.86\times10^5\text{ miles}}{1\text{ sec.}}\cdot\dfrac{60\text{ sec.}}{1\text{ min.}}\cdot\dfrac{60\text{ min.}}{1\text{ hr}}\cdot\dfrac{24\text{ hr}}{1\text{ day}}\cdot\dfrac{365\text{ days}}{1\text{ yr}}\approx5.866\times10^{12}$ miles in one light-year

  (b) 5,866,000,000,000 miles

  (c) $4.27\cdot\left(5.866\times10^{12}\right)\approx2.5\times10^{13}$ miles

  (d) First calculate the rocket's speed in miles per year: $\dfrac{50,000\text{ miles}}{1\text{ hr}}\cdot\dfrac{24\text{ hr}}{1\text{ day}}\cdot\dfrac{365\text{ days}}{1\text{ yr}}=4.38\times10^8\text{ mi/yr}$

  The number of years needed to travel to Alpha Centauri is $\dfrac{2.5\times10^{13}\text{ mi}}{4.38\times10^8\text{ mi/yr}}\approx57,078\approx57,000$ yr

119. $V=\left(2a\right)^3=2^3a^3=8a^3$

120. $A=\left(3a\right)^2=3^2a^2=9a^2$

121. $A=\left(3ab\right)^2=3^2a^2b^2=9a^2b^2$

122. $V=\left(4xy\right)^3=4^3x^3y^3=64x^3y^3$

123. (a) $A=500\left(1.05\right)^2=\$551.25$

  (b) $A=1000\left(1.05\right)^4\approx\$1215.51$

124. (a) $A=200\left(1+0.1\right)^7=200\left(1.1\right)^7\approx\$389.74$

  (b) $A=1500\left(1+0.08\right)^{15}=1500\left(1.08\right)^{15}\approx\$4758.25$

125. $\left(2.19\times10^{12}\right)\div\left(2.49\times10^{8}\right)\approx\$8795$ per person

126. $\left(7.1\times10^{11}\right)\div3127=227,054,685\approx227$ million

127. $256\times2^{20}=268,435,456$ bytes

128. 1,073,741,824 bytes

129. See Figure 129.

Country	1996	2025
China	1.2551×10^{9}	1.48×10^{9}
Germany	8.24×10^{7}	8.09×10^{7}
India	9.758×10^{8}	1.3302×10^{9}
Mexico	9.58×10^{7}	1.302×10^{8}
U.S.	2.65×10^{8}	3.325×10^{8}

Figure 129

130. This model estimates the world population in 2010 to be $P=6\left(1.014\right)^{10}\approx6.9$ billion.

The model estimates the world population in 2025 to be $P=6\left(1.014\right)^{25}\approx8.5$ billion.

Group Activity Solutions

1. $\left(2.37\times10^{5}\right)\div4\approx59,250$ hr; that is $59,250$ hr $\cdot\dfrac{1\text{ day}}{24\text{ hr}}\cdot\dfrac{1\text{ yr}}{365\text{ days}}\approx6.76$ yr

2.   (a) This is an extremely good deal.

(b) The person would make $2^{52-1}=2^{51}\approx2.25\times10^{15}$ cents or about $22.5 trillion.

1.4: Variables, Equations, and Formulas

Concepts

1.   variable

2.   equation

3.   equals

4.   formula

5. x and y

6. $3+7=10$ *Answers may vary.*

7. $3x=15$ *Answers may vary.*

8. $3y+x=5$ *Answers may vary.*

9.   3

10. -2

11.   *b*

12.   *b*

13. $y=2x=2\left(3\right)=6$

14. $A = s^2 = (-2)^2 = 4$

Writing Formulas

15. $y = 5280x$

16. $y = \dfrac{x}{4}$

17. $A = s^2$

18. $A = 6s^2$

19. $y = 3600x$

20. $G = \dfrac{m}{g}$

21. $A = \dfrac{1}{2}bh$

22. $P = 4s$

23. $r = \dfrac{1}{2}d$ and $A = \pi r^2$, so

$$A = \pi\left(\tfrac{1}{2}d\right)^2 = \pi\left(\tfrac{1}{4}d^2\right) = \tfrac{1}{4}\pi d^2.$$

24. $C = \pi d$

Using Data, Variables, and Formulas

25. $y = 5(6) = 30$

26. $y = \dfrac{30}{10} = 3$

27. $y = -3.1 + 5 = 1.9$

28. $d = 5 - 4(-1.5) = 5 + 6 = 11$

29. $d = (-3)^2 + 1 = 9 + 1 = 10$

30. $z = 3\left(\dfrac{1}{4}\right)^2 - \dfrac{3}{4} = 3\left(\dfrac{1}{16}\right) - \dfrac{3}{4} = \dfrac{3}{16} - \dfrac{12}{16} = -\dfrac{9}{16}$

31. $z = \sqrt{2(18)} = \sqrt{36} = 6$

32. $y = \sqrt{5-1} = \sqrt{4} = 2$

33. $y = -\dfrac{1}{2}\sqrt[3]{\dfrac{1}{8}} = -\dfrac{1}{2} \cdot \dfrac{1}{2} = -\dfrac{1}{4}$

34. $M = \sqrt[3]{1-65} = \sqrt[3]{-64} = -4$

35. $N = 3\left(\dfrac{1}{3}\right)^3 - 1 = 3\left(\dfrac{1}{27}\right) - 1 = \dfrac{1}{9} - 1 = \dfrac{1}{9} - \dfrac{9}{9} = -\dfrac{8}{9}$

36. $S = 1 - \dfrac{1}{2}(-2)^3 = 1 - \dfrac{1}{2}(-8) = 1 + 4 = 5$

37. $P = |5 - 4.7| = |0.3| = 0.3$

38. $D = |2(2.5) - 5| = |5 - 5| = |0| = 0$

39. $A = \dfrac{1}{2}(3)(6) = \dfrac{1}{2}(18) = 9$

40. $P = 2(9) + 2(7) = 18 + 14 = 32$

41. $V = \pi\left(\dfrac{1}{2}\right)^2 (5) = \pi\left(\dfrac{1}{4}\right)(5) = \dfrac{5}{4}\pi$

42. $S = 2\pi(2)(2 + 8) = 4\pi(10) = 40\pi$

43. (ii)

44. (i)

45. (iii)

46. (i)

47. $a = -3$

48. $a = 1.5$

49. $a = 2$

50. $a = -1$

51. See Figure 51.

52. See Figure 52.

x	0	2	4	6	8
y	−0.5	4.5	9.5	14.5	19.5

Figure 51

x	0	2	4	6	8
y	0	2	8	18	32

Figure 52

53. See Figure 53.

x	−3	−1	1	3
y	15	5	5	15

Figure 53

x	−2	−1	2	7
y	0	1	2	3

Figure 54

54. See Figure 54.

55. See Figure 55.

x	−1	0	1	8
y	−3	−2	−1	0

Figure 55

x	−2	0	1	2
y	0	0	−3	0

Figure 56

56. See Figure 56.

57. See Figure 57.

58. See Figure 58.

x	a	$a-1$	a^2-1
y	$\sqrt{a}+1$	$\sqrt{a}$	a

x	a	$\frac{3}{2}a$	$\frac{1}{2}a-\frac{1}{2}$
y	$2a+1$	$3a+1$	a

Figure 57   Figure 58

59.

X	Y₁
1	2
2	3.2599
3	4.4422
4	5.5874
5	6.71
6	7.8171
7	8.9129

$Y_1 \equiv X + \sqrt[3]{(X)}$

60.

X	Y₁
1	1
2	.70711
3	.57735
4	.5
5	.44721
6	.40825
7	.37796

$Y_1 \equiv 1/\sqrt{(X)}$

61.

X	Y₁
1	2.4495
2	2.2361
3	2
4	1.7321
5	1.4142
6	1
7	0

$Y_1 \equiv \sqrt{(7-X)}$

62.

X	Y₁
1	-.3333
2	1.3333
3	7
4	18.667
5	38.333
6	68
7	109.67

$Y_1 \equiv (X^3 - 2X)/3$

Applications

63. $y = 60t$

64.   (a) $P = 0.445(400) = 178$ psi

(b) $P = 0.445(7000) = 3115$ psi

65.   (a)   See Figure 65.

(b) $d = \dfrac{40^2}{12} = \dfrac{1600}{12} = 133.\overline{3}$ ft

(c)   It quadruples.

(d) $\dfrac{60^2}{9} - \dfrac{60^2}{12} = 400 - 300 = 100$ ft

Speed (mph)	10	20	30	40	50	60	70
Braking Distance (ft)	8.3	33.3	75	133.3	208.3	300	408.3

Figure 65

66.   (a) $\dfrac{1000 \text{ songs}}{4 \text{ GB}} = 250$ songs per GB and $\dfrac{15,000 \text{ songs}}{60 \text{ GB}} =$

250 songs per GB, so $S = 250x$.

(b) $S = 250(30) = 7500$ songs

67. $M = \dfrac{15}{22} \cdot 223.3 = 152.25$ mph

68. (a) $H = \dfrac{x}{340}$

    (b) $H = \dfrac{850}{340} = 2.5$ hours

69. (a) $W = 1.1(0.75)^3 \approx 0.464$ kg

    (b) $W = 1.1(1.5)^3 = 3.7125$ kg

    (c) It increases 8 times.

70. (a) $L = \sqrt[3]{16(5)} = \sqrt[3]{80} \approx 4.3$ feet

    (a) No, the wing span increases by a factor of $\sqrt[3]{2}$.

71. If the shorter animal has a shoulder height of h, then its stepping frequency is $F_1 = \dfrac{0.87}{\sqrt{h}}$.

    For the taller animal with shoulder height $4h$, $F_2 = \dfrac{0.87}{\sqrt{4h}} = \dfrac{0.87}{2\sqrt{h}} = \dfrac{1}{2}F_1$.

    The stepping frequency of the taller animal is half the stepping frequency of the shorter animal.

72. (a) $S = 0.11\sqrt[3]{0.5^2} \approx 0.069$ m^2

    (b) No. For example, when $W = 1$, $S = 0.11$ but when $W = 2$, $S \approx 0.175$. The value of S does not double.

73. Venus: $E = \sqrt{2} \cdot 16,260 \approx 22,995$ mph; Earth: $C = \dfrac{25,040}{\sqrt{2}} \approx 17,706$ mph

    Moon: $C = \dfrac{5360}{\sqrt{2}} \approx 3790$ mph; Mars: $E = \sqrt{2} \cdot 8050 \approx 11,384$ mph

74. $C = \dfrac{136,000}{\sqrt{2}} \approx 96,167$ mph

75. $E = \sqrt{2} \cdot 57,000 \approx 80,610$ mph

76. (a) $F = \dfrac{1.84}{\sqrt{1.5}} \approx 1.5$ steps per second

    (b) It will decrease.

77. (a) $N = \dfrac{885}{\sqrt{25}} = 177$ bpm

    (b) $N = \dfrac{885}{\sqrt{1600}} \approx 22$ bpm

78. If the smaller animal has a pulse rate of $N = \dfrac{885}{\sqrt{W}}$, then the larger animal would have a pulse rate given by

    $\dfrac{N}{2} = \dfrac{885}{2\sqrt{W}} = \dfrac{885}{\sqrt{4W}}$. That is, the larger animal weighs 4 times as much as the smaller animal.

79.   (a) $A = \dfrac{\sqrt{3}}{4}(2)^2 = \dfrac{\sqrt{3}}{4} \cdot 4 = \sqrt{3} \approx 1.73 \text{ ft}^2$

(b) $A = \dfrac{\sqrt{3}}{4}(4)^2 = \dfrac{\sqrt{3}}{4} \cdot 16 = 4\sqrt{3} \approx 6.93 \text{ m}^2$

80.   If the length of the side triples the area is given by $A = \dfrac{\sqrt{3}}{4}(3s)^2 = 9 \cdot \dfrac{\sqrt{3}}{4} s^2$.

That is, the area increases by a factor of 9.

81.   (a) $C = 2\pi(14) = 28\pi \approx 88 \text{ inches}$

(b) $C = 2\pi(1.3) = 2.6\pi \approx 8.2 \text{ miles}$

82.   (a) $A = \pi(12)^2 = 144\pi \approx 452 \text{ in}^2$

(b) $A = \pi(6)^2 = 36\pi \approx 113 \text{ ft}^2$

83.   If $s^2 = 81,$ then $s = 9$ inches.

84.   If $s^2 = 121,$ then $s = 11$ meters.

85.   If $s^3 = 27,$ then $s = 3$ meters.

86.   If $s^3 = 64,$ then $s = 4$ feet.

87.   (a) $C = 336x$

(b) $C = 336 \cdot 30 = 10,080$ calories

88. $P = \dfrac{336}{3500}x$

In 100 days a person could lose $P = \dfrac{336}{3500} \cdot 100 = 9.6$ lb.

Checking Basic Concepts for Sections 1.3 & 1.4

1.   (a) $2^4 = 2 \cdot 2 \cdot 2 \cdot 2 = 16$

(b) $3^{-2} \cdot 2^0 = \dfrac{1}{3^2} \cdot 1 = \dfrac{1}{9}$

(c) $\dfrac{2^4}{2^2 \cdot 2^{-3}} = \dfrac{2^4}{2^{2+(-3)}} = \dfrac{2^4}{2^{-1}} = 2^{4-(-1)} = 2^5 = 32$

(d) $x^3 x^{-4} x^2 = x^{3+(-4)+2} = x^1 = x$

(e) $\left(\dfrac{2x^3}{y^{-4}}\right)^2 = \dfrac{2^2 \cdot x^{3 \cdot 2}}{y^{-4 \cdot 2}} = \dfrac{4x^6}{y^{-8}} = 4x^6 y^8$

2.   (a) $4 + 5 \cdot (-2) = 4 + (-10) = -6$

(b) $\dfrac{1+3}{-4+3} = \dfrac{4}{-1} = -4$

   (c) $2^3 - 5(2 - 3 \cdot 4) = 8 - 5(2 - 12) = 8 - 5(-10) = 8 + 50 = 58$

3. (a) 1.03×10^5

    (b) 5.23×10^{-4}

    (c) 6.7×10^0

4. (a) 5,430,000

    (b) 0.0098

5. See Figure 5. Each person requires 900 ft^3 of ventilation per hour.

People	10	20	30	40
Ventilation (ft³/hr)	9000	18,000	27,000	36,000

Figure 5

1.5: Introduction to Graphing

Concepts

1. A relation is a set of ordered pairs (x, y).

2. The domain is the set of all x-values for the relation and the range is the set of all y-values for the relation.

3. See Figure 3.

Figure 3   Figure 4a   Figure 4b

4. A example of a scatterplot is shown in Figure 4a. An example of a line graph is shown in Figure 4b.

5. No

6. Quadrant III

Relations and the Rectangular Coordinate System

7. $D = \{1, 3, 5\}; R = \{-4, 2, 6\}$

8. $D = \{0, 3, 4\}; R = \{-1, 0, 4, 6\}$

9. $D = \{-2, -1, 0, 1, 2\}; R = \{0, 1, 2, 3\}$

10. $D = \left\{-\dfrac{5}{8}, \dfrac{1}{2}, \dfrac{8}{7}\right\}; R = \left\{-\dfrac{3}{4}, \dfrac{4}{7}, \dfrac{3}{4}\right\}$

11. $D = \{41, 87, 96\}; R = \{24, 53, 67, 88\}$

12. $D = \{-1.2, 0.8, 1.5\}; R = \{-1.1, -0.6, 2.5\}$

13. $S = \{(1, 3), (3, 7), (5, 11), (7, 15), (9, 19)\}; D = \{1, 3, 5, 7, 9\}; R = \{3, 7, 11, 15, 19\}$

14. $S = \{(-2.1,\ 9.6),\ (-1.5,\ 7.4),\ (0.7,\ 3.3),\ (1.3,\ -2.0),\ (2.9,\ -8.8)\}$

   $D = \{-2.1,\ -1.5,\ 0.7,\ 1.3,\ 2.9\};\ R = \{-8.8,\ -2.0,\ 3.3,\ 7.4,\ 9.6\}$

15. $S = \{(2000,\ 4.0),\ (2001,\ 4.2),\ (2002,\ 5.8),\ (2003,\ 6.0),\ (2004,\ 5.5)\};$

   $D = \{2000,\ 2001,\ 2002,\ 2003,\ 2004\};\ R = \{4.0,\ 4.2,\ 5.5,\ 5.8,\ 6.0\}$

16. $S = \{(1800,\ 5),\ (1840,\ 17),\ (1880,\ 50),\ (1920,\ 106),\ (1960,\ 179),\ (2000,\ 281)\}$

   $D = \{1800,\ 1840,\ 1880,\ 1920,\ 1960,\ 2000\}\ ;\ R = \{5,\ 17,\ 50,\ 106,\ 179,\ 281\}$

17.   See Figure 17. (1, 2) is in QI, (–3, 0) is on the *x*-axis, (0, –2) is on the *y*-axis, (–1, 3) is in QII.

    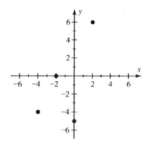

Figure 17   Figure 18

18.   See Figure 18. (2, 6) is in QI, (–4, –4) is in QIII, (–2, 0) is on the *x*-axis, (0, –5) is on the *y*-axis.

19.   See Figure 19. (10, 50) is in QI, (–30, 20) is in QII, (50, –25) is in QIV, (–20, –35) is in QIII.

Figure 19   Figure 20

20.   See Figure 20. (0.2, 3) is in QI, (0.4, 1) is in QI, (0.6, –1) is in QIV, (0.8, –3) is in QIV.

21.   Substituting 0, 1, 2, 3 for *x* gives the ordered pairs $(0,\ 0)$, $(1,\ 4)$, $(2,\ 8)$, $(3,\ 12)$. *Answers may vary.*

22.   Substituting 0, 1, 2, 3 for *x* gives the ordered pairs $(0,\ 5)$, $(1,\ 8)$, $(2,\ 11)$, $(3,\ 14)$. *Answers may vary.*

23.   Substituting 0, 1, 2, 3 for *t* gives the ordered pairs $(0,\ 4)$, $(1,\ 3)$, $(2,\ 0)$, $(3,\ -5)$. *Answers may vary.*

24.   Substituting 0, 1, 2, 3 for *t* gives the ordered pairs $(0,\ 0)$, $(1,\ 3)$, $(2,\ 12)$, $(3,\ 27)$. *Answers may vary.*

25.   Substituting 0, 1, 2, 3 for *r* gives the ordered pairs $(0,\ 1)$, $\left(1,\ \frac{1}{2}\right)$, $\left(2,\ \frac{1}{5}\right)$, $\left(3,\ \frac{1}{10}\right)$. *Answers may vary.*

26.   Substituting 0, 1, 2, 3 for *r* gives the ordered pairs $\left(0,\ \frac{2}{5}\right)$, $\left(1,\ \frac{1}{2}\right)$, $\left(2,\ \frac{2}{3}\right)$, $(3,\ 1)$. *Answers may vary.*

27. $S = \{(-3,\ 2),\ (-2,\ 1),\ (2,\ -3),\ (3,\ 3)\};\ D = \{-3,\ -2,\ 2,\ 3\}\ ;\ R = \{-3,\ 1,\ 2,\ 3\}$

28. $S = \{(-3, -3), (-2, 1), (0, 2), (3, 0)\}; \ D = \{-3, -2, 0, 3\}; \ R = \{-3, 0, 1, 2\}$

29. $S = \{(-4, 4), (-3, 2), (-2, 0), (0, -3), (2, 4), (4, 4)\};$

      $D = \{-4, -3, -2, 0, 2, 4\}; \ R = \{-3, 0, 2, 4\}$

30. $S = \{(-8, -8), (-8, 4), (-4, 8), (4, -4), (4, 4), (8, 8)\};$

      $D = \{-8, -4, 4, 8\}; \ R = \{-8, -4, 4, 8\}$

31. $S = \{(1970, 29), (1980, 41), (1990, 79), (2000, 64)\}$

      $D = \{1970, 1980, 1990, 2000\}; \ R = \{29, 41, 64, 79\}.$ *Answers may vary.*

32. $S = \{(1950, 485), (1960, 375), (1970, 150), (1980, 95), (1990, 70), (2000, 50)\}$

      $D = \{1950, 1960, 1970, 1980, 1990, 2000\}; \ R = \{50, 70, 95, 150, 375, 485\}.$ *Answers may vary.*

33. $a = b$

34.   If b is negative, then $-b$ is positive so $(-b, b)$ lies in Quadrant IV.

Scatterplots and Line Graphs

35.   (a) $D = \{-3, -2, 0, 1\}; \ R = \{-4, -3, 0, 2, 4\}$

      (b) x-min: -3, x-max: 1; y-min: -4, y-max: 4

      (c)   & (d) See Figure 35.

36.   (a) $D = \{-4, 0, 1, 3, 5\}; \ R = \{-4, -2, 0, 1, 3\}$

      (b) x-min: -4, x-max: 5; y-min: -4, y-max: 3

      (c)   & (d) See Figure 36.

Figure 35   Figure 36   Figure 37

37.   (a) $D = \{-30, 10, 20, 30\}; \ R = \{-50, 20, 40, 50\}$

      (b) x-min: -30, x-max: 30; y-min: -50, y-max: 50

      (c)   & (d) See Figure 37.

38.   (a) $D = \{-20, -10, 5, 10, 25\}; \ R = \{-10, 10, 15, 20, 30\}$

      (b) x-min: -20, x-max: 25; y-min: -10, y-max: 30

      (c)   & (d) See Figure 38.

39.   See Figure 39.

Figure 38

Figure 39

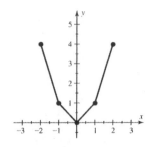

Figure 40

40.   See Figure 40.

41.   See Figure 41.

42.   See Figure 42.

Figure 41

Figure 42

Figure 43

43.   See Figure 43.

44.   See Figure 44.

45.   See Figure 45.

Figure 44

Figure 45

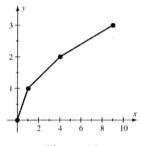

Figure 46

46.   See Figure 46.

47. $(-2, -6)$, $(-1, -3)$, $(0, 0)$, $(1, 3)$, $(2, 6)$. See Figure 47.

48. $(-2, 4)$, $(-1, 2)$, $(0, 0)$, $(1, -2)$, $(2, -4)$. See Figure 48.

Figure 47

Figure 48

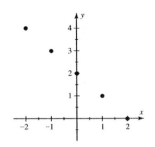

Figure 49

49. $(-2, 4)$, $(-1, 3)$, $(0, 2)$, $(1, 1)$, $(2, 0)$. See Figure 49.

50. $(-2, 0)$, $(-1, 2)$, $(0, 4)$, $(1, 6)$, $(2, 8)$. See Figure 50.

51. $(-2, 1)$, $\left(-1, \frac{1}{2}\right)$, $(0, 0)$, $\left(1, -\frac{1}{2}\right)$, $(2, -1)$. See Figure 51.

52. $(-2, 0)$, $\left(-1, \frac{1}{2}\right)$, $(0, 1)$, $\left(1, \frac{3}{2}\right)$, $(2, 2)$. See Figure 52.

53. $(-2, 3)$, $(-1, 0)$, $(0, -1)$, $(1, 0)$, $(2, 3)$. See Figure 53.

Figure 50

Figure 51

Figure 52

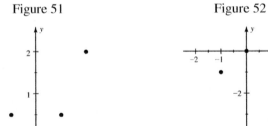

Figure 53

Figure 54

Figure 55

54. $(-2, 2)$, $(-1, 0.5)$, $(0, 0)$, $(1, 0.5)$, $(2, 2)$. See Figure 54.

55. $(-2, -4)$, $(-1, -1)$, $(0, 0)$, $(1, -1)$, $(2, -4)$. See Figure 55.

56. $(-2, 8)$, $(-1, 2)$, $(0, 0)$, $(1, 2)$, $(2, 8)$. See Figure 56.

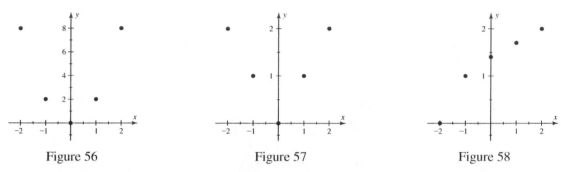

Figure 56   Figure 57   Figure 58

57. $(-2, 2)$, $(-1, 1)$, $(0, 0)$, $(1, 1)$, $(2, 2)$. See Figure 57.

58. $(-2, 0)$, $(-1, 1)$, $\left(0, \sqrt{2}\right)$, $\left(1, \sqrt{3}\right)$, $(2, 2)$. See Figure 58.

Graphing Calculators

59.   See Figure 59. There are 10 tick marks on the positive *x*-axis and 10 tick marks on the positive *y*-axis.

60.   See Figure 60. There are 6 tick marks on the positive *x*-axis and 4 tick marks on the positive *y*-axis.

[–10, 10, 1] by [–10, 10, 1]   [–12, 12, 2] by [–8, 8, 2]

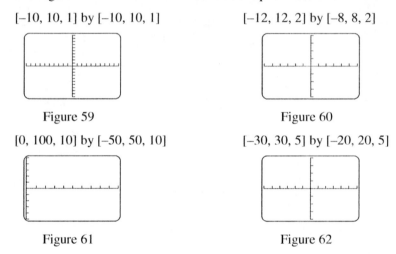

Figure 59   Figure 60

[0, 100, 10] by [–50, 50, 10]   [–30, 30, 5] by [–20, 20, 5]

Figure 61   Figure 62

61.   See Figure 61. There are 10 tick marks on the positive *x*-axis and 5 tick marks on the positive *y*-axis.

62.   See Figure 62. There are 16 tick marks on the positive *x*-axis and 4 tick marks on the positive *y*-axis.

63.   See Figure 63. There are 16 tick marks on the positive *x*-axis and 5 tick marks on the positive *y*-axis.

64.   See Figure 64. There are 10 tick marks on the positive *x*-axis and 12 tick marks on the positive *y*-axis.

[1980, 1995, 1] by [12,000, 16,000, 1000]   [1900, 1990, 10] by [1700, 2800, 100]

Figure 63   Figure 64

[-6, 6, 1] by [-6, 6, 1]   [-6, 6, 1] by [-10, 10, 1]

Figure 69   Figure 70

65. $S = \{(-2, 1), (-1, 0), (1, -1), (2, 1)\}$

66. $S = \{(-5, 1), (-3, 2), (-1, 3), (1, -2), (4, -3)\}$

67. $S = \{(-4, -2), (-2, -2), (0, 2), (2, 1), (4, -1)\}$

68. $S = \{(1920, 100), (1940, 200), (1960, 300), (1980, 400)\}$

69.   See Figure 69.

70.   See Figure 70.

71.   See Figure 71.

72.   See Figure 72.

[-30, 30, 5] by [-50, 50, 5]   [-20, 20, 2] by [-20, 20, 2]

Figure 71   Figure 72

[-200, 200, 50] by [-250, 250, 50]   [-200, 200, 50] by [-100, 100, 25]

Figure 73   Figure 74

73.   See Figure 73.

74.   See Figure 74.

Applications

75.   (a) See Figure 75.

       (b) Participation in Head Start first decreased and then increased.

76.   (a) See Figure 76.

       (b) CD sales increased then decreased.

Figure 75

Figure 76

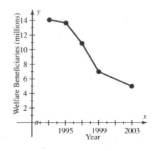

Figure 77

77.   (a) See Figure 77.

       (b) The number of welfare beneficiaries first increased and then decreased.

78.   (a) See Figure 78.

       (b) The number of Medicaid recipients first decreased, then increased.

79.   (a) See Figure 79.

       (b) The Asian-American population is increasing steadily.

Figure 78

Figure 79

Figure 80

80.   (a) See Figure 80.

       (b) Internet use is increasing quite rapidly.

Checking Basic Concepts for Section 1.5

1. $D = \{-5,\ 1,\ 2\};\ R = \{-1,\ 3,\ 4\}$

2.   See Figure 2. (1, 4) is in QI, (0, –3) is on the *y*-axis, (2, –2) is in QIV, (–2, 3) is in QII.

Figure 2

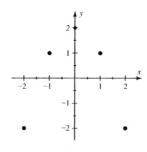

Figure 3

Figure 4

3. $(-2,\ -2),\ (-1,\ 1),\ (0,\ 2),\ (1,\ 1),\ (2,\ -2).$ See Figure 3.

4.   See Figure 4. The number of people below the poverty level decreased, then began to increase. then

       decreased.

Chapter 1 Review Exercises

Section 1.1

1. Natural numbers: 9

    Whole numbers: 9

    Integers: –2, 9

    Rational Numbers: $-2, 9, \dfrac{2}{5}, 2.68$

    Irrational Numbers: $\sqrt{11}, \pi$

2. Natural numbers: $\dfrac{6}{2}$

    Whole numbers: $\dfrac{6}{2}, \dfrac{0}{4}$

    Integers: $\dfrac{6}{2}, \dfrac{0}{4}$

    Rational Numbers: $\dfrac{6}{2}, -\dfrac{2}{7}, 0.\overline{3}, \dfrac{0}{4}$

    Irrational Numbers: $\sqrt{6}$

3. Identity

4. Commutative property

5. Associative property

6. Distributive property

7. Distributive property

8. Distributive property

9. $1 \cdot (a + 0) = 1 \cdot a = a$

10. $x \cdot \dfrac{1}{4} = \dfrac{1}{4}x$

11. $8(10x) = (8 \cdot 10)x = 80x$

12. $5z - 3z = (5 - 3)z = 2z$

13. $5(8 + 11) = 5 \cdot 19 = 95$ or $5(8 + 11) = 5 \cdot 8 + 5 \cdot 11 = 40 + 55 = 95$

14. $3(9 - 5) = 3 \cdot 4 = 12$ or $3(9 - 5) = 3 \cdot 9 - 3 \cdot 5 = 27 - 15 = 12$

15. $(6 + 9 + 3 + 11 + 5 + 20) \div 6 = 9$

16. $(3.2 + 6.8 + 6.1 + 10.8 + 1.7) \div 5 = 5.72$

17. $12 + 23 + (-2) + 7 = \big(12 + (-2)\big) + (23 + 7) = 10 + 30 = 40$

18. $\dfrac{3}{2}\cdot\dfrac{2}{5}\cdot\dfrac{5}{7}\cdot\dfrac{7}{3}=\left(\dfrac{3}{2}\cdot\dfrac{2}{5}\right)\cdot\left(\dfrac{5}{7}\cdot\dfrac{7}{3}\right)=\dfrac{3}{5}\cdot\dfrac{5}{3}=\dfrac{3\cdot5}{5\cdot3}=\dfrac{15}{15}=1$

19. $5\cdot23+5\cdot7=5(23+7)=5\cdot30=150$

20. $45-34+55-66=(45+55)+(-34-66)=100-100=0$

Section 1.2

21.

22. $|-7.2+4|=|-3.2|=3.2$

23. $\dfrac{2}{3}$

24. $\dfrac{5}{4}$

25.   The opposite of $-2x+3$ is $-(-2x+3)=2x-3$.

26.   The reciprocal of $-\dfrac{1}{a+b}$ is $-\dfrac{a+b}{1}=-(a+b)=-a-b$.

27. $-5+(-7)+8=-12+8=-4$

28. $-9+11=2$

29. $-12-(-8)=-4$

30. $\dfrac{1}{2}+(-2)+\dfrac{3}{4}=\dfrac{2}{4}+\left(-\dfrac{8}{4}\right)+\dfrac{3}{4}=-\dfrac{6}{4}+\dfrac{3}{4}=-\dfrac{3}{4}$

31. $\dfrac{2}{3}\div(-4)-\dfrac{1}{3}=\dfrac{2}{3}\cdot\left(-\dfrac{1}{4}\right)-\dfrac{1}{3}=-\dfrac{2}{12}-\dfrac{4}{12}=-\dfrac{6}{12}=-\dfrac{1}{2}$

32. $-\dfrac{7}{11}+\dfrac{\frac{1}{5}}{\frac{2}{9}}=-\dfrac{7}{11}+\dfrac{1}{5}\cdot\dfrac{9}{2}=-\dfrac{7}{11}+\dfrac{9}{10}=-\dfrac{70}{110}+\dfrac{99}{110}=\dfrac{29}{110}$

33. $-7\cdot4\cdot-\dfrac{1}{7}=-7\cdot-\dfrac{1}{7}\cdot4=1\cdot4=4$

34. $\dfrac{3}{4}\cdot\dfrac{4}{7}+1=\dfrac{3}{7}+1=\dfrac{3}{7}+\dfrac{7}{7}=\dfrac{10}{7}$

35. $4x+5x=(4+5)x=9x$

36. $2z-3z+8z=(2-3+8)z=7z$

37.   Entering $1/5-3/7+(2/13)/(4/5)$ ►Frac into a graphing calculator gives $-\dfrac{33}{910}$.

38. $-4+9+4+11-6+16=30$; the average is $30\div6=5$.

Section 1.3

39.   Base: 4; exponent: −2

40.   They are not equal since $3^\pi \approx 31.54$ but $\pi^3 \approx 31.01$.

41. $-2^4 = -(2 \cdot 2 \cdot 2 \cdot 2) = -16$

42. $(-2)^4 = (-2) \cdot (-2) \cdot (-2) \cdot (-2) = 16$

43. $9^0 = 1$

44. $\left(\dfrac{2}{3}\right)^{-3} = \left(\dfrac{3}{2}\right)^3 = \dfrac{3^3}{2^3} = \dfrac{3 \cdot 3 \cdot 3}{2 \cdot 2 \cdot 2} = \dfrac{27}{8}$

45. $4^{-3} = \dfrac{1}{4^3} = \dfrac{1}{4 \cdot 4 \cdot 4} = \dfrac{1}{64}$

46. $\dfrac{1}{5^{-2}} = 5^2 = 5 \cdot 5 = 25$

47. $\dfrac{5^{-3}}{3^{-2}} = \dfrac{3^2}{5^3} = \dfrac{3 \cdot 3}{5 \cdot 5 \cdot 5} = \dfrac{9}{125}$

48. $\dfrac{1}{2 \cdot 4^{-2}} = \dfrac{4^2}{2} = \dfrac{4 \cdot 4}{2} = \dfrac{16}{2} = 8$

49. $4^3 \cdot 4^{-5} = 4^{3+(-5)} = 4^{-2} = \dfrac{1}{4^2} = \dfrac{1}{16}$

50. $10^4 \cdot 10^{-2} = 10^{4+(-2)} = 10^2 = 100$

51. $x^7 \cdot x^{-2} = x^{7+(-2)} = x^5$

52. $\dfrac{3^4}{3^{-7}} = 3^{4-(-7)} = 3^{11} = 177{,}147$

53. $\dfrac{5a^{-4}}{10a^2} = \left(\dfrac{5}{10}\right) \cdot a^{-4-2} = \left(\dfrac{1}{2}\right) \cdot a^{-6} = \left(\dfrac{1}{2}\right) \cdot \left(\dfrac{1}{a^6}\right) = \dfrac{1}{2a^6}$

54. $\dfrac{15a^4b^3}{3a^2b^6} = \left(\dfrac{15}{3}\right) \cdot a^{4-2} \cdot b^{3-6} = 5a^2b^{-3} = \dfrac{5a^2}{b^3}$

55. $\left(2^2\right)^4 = 2^{2\cdot 4} = 2^8 = 256$

56. $\left(x^{-3}\right)^5 = x^{-3\cdot 5} = x^{-15} = \dfrac{1}{x^{15}}$

57. $\left(4x^{-2}y^3\right)^2 = 4^2 \cdot x^{-2\cdot 2} \cdot y^{3\cdot 2} = 16x^{-4}y^6 = \dfrac{16y^6}{x^4}$

58. $(4a)^5 = 4^5 \cdot a^5 = 1024a^5$

59. $\left(\dfrac{5x^3}{3z^4}\right)^3 = \dfrac{5^3 \cdot x^{3 \cdot 3}}{3^3 \cdot z^{4 \cdot 3}} = \dfrac{125x^9}{27z^{12}}$

60. $\left(\dfrac{-3x^4y^3}{z}\right)^{-2} = \left(\dfrac{z}{-3x^4y^3}\right)^2 = \dfrac{z^2}{(-3)^2 \cdot x^{4 \cdot 2} \cdot y^{3 \cdot 2}} = \dfrac{z^2}{9x^8y^6}$

61. $\left(\dfrac{3a^{-4}}{4b^{-7}}\right)^2 = \dfrac{3^2\left(a^{-4}\right)^2}{4^2\left(b^{-7}\right)^2} = \dfrac{9a^{-4 \cdot 2}}{16b^{-7 \cdot 2}} = \dfrac{9a^{-8}}{16b^{-14}} = \dfrac{9b^{14}}{16a^8}$

62. $\left(\dfrac{3m^2n^{-4}}{9m^3n}\right)^{-1} = \dfrac{9m^3n}{3m^2n^{-4}} = \dfrac{9}{3}m^{3-2}n^{1-(-4)} = 3mn^5$

63. $\left(\dfrac{rt}{2r^3t^{-1}}\right)^{-3} = \left(\dfrac{2r^3t^{-1}}{rt}\right)^3 = \dfrac{2^3\left(r^3\right)^3\left(t^{-1}\right)^3}{r^3t^3} = \dfrac{8r^{3 \cdot 3}t^{-1 \cdot 3}}{r^3t^3} = \dfrac{8r^9t^{-3}}{r^3t^3} = 8r^{9-3}t^{-3-3} = 8r^6t^{-6} = \dfrac{8r^6}{t^6}$

64. $\left(\dfrac{3r^2}{4t^{-3}}\right)^2 = \dfrac{3^2\left(r^2\right)^2}{4^2\left(t^{-3}\right)^2} = \dfrac{9r^{2 \cdot 2}}{16t^{-3 \cdot 2}} = \dfrac{9r^4}{16t^{-6}} = \dfrac{9r^4t^6}{16}$

65. $2 + 3 \cdot 9 = 2 + 27 = 29$

66. $4 - 1 - 6 = 3 - 6 = -3$

67. $5 \cdot 2^3 = 5 \cdot 8 = 40$

68. $\dfrac{2+4}{2} + \dfrac{3-1}{3} = \dfrac{6}{2} + \dfrac{2}{3} = 3 + \dfrac{2}{3} = \dfrac{9}{3} + \dfrac{2}{3} = \dfrac{11}{3}$

69. $20 \div 4 \div 2 = 5 \div 2 = \dfrac{5}{2}$

70. $\dfrac{3^3 - 2^4}{4 - 3} = \dfrac{27 - 16}{1} = \dfrac{11}{1} = 11$

71. 1.86×10^5

72. 3.4×10^{-4}

73. $45{,}000$

74. 0.00923

Section 1.4

75. Because there are 12 inches in one foot, the formula is $y = 12x$.

76. Because the area formula for one circle is $A = \pi r^2$, the formula for the area of six circles is $A = 6\pi r^2$.

77. $y = 12(3) = 36$

78. $d = \sqrt{67 - 3} = \sqrt{64} = 8$

79. $N = \left(\dfrac{3}{2}\right)^2 - \dfrac{3}{4} = \dfrac{9}{4} - \dfrac{3}{4} = \dfrac{6}{4} = \dfrac{3}{2}$

80. $P = (-2)^3 - 2 = -8 - 2 = -10$

81. $A = \dfrac{1}{2}(4)(5) = 2(5) = 10$

82. $V = (3)^2(3) = 9(3) = 27$

83.   (iii)

84. $a = \dfrac{3}{2}$

85.   See Figure 85.

x	-2	-1	0	1	2
y	-7	0	1	2	9

Figure 85

86.   See Figure 86.

Figure 86

Section 1.5

87. $D = \{-1,\ 2,\ 3\}$; $R = \{-6,\ 1,\ 3,\ 7\}$

88. $S = \{(-8,\ 4),\ (-4,\ -4),\ (4,\ 0),\ (8,\ 4)\}$; $D = \{-8,\ -4,\ 4,\ 8\}$; $R = \{-4,\ 0,\ 4\}$

89. $(-2,\ 6),\ (-1,\ 3),\ (0,\ 0),\ (1,\ -3),\ (2,\ -6)$. See Figure 89.

90. $(-2,\ -2),\ (-1,\ -1.5),\ (0,\ -1),\ (1,\ -0.5),\ (2,\ 0)$. See Figure 90.

Figure 89

Figure 90

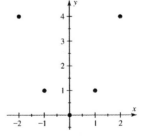

Figure 91

91. $(-2,\ 4),\ (-1,\ 1),\ (0,\ 0),\ (1,\ 1),\ (2,\ 4)$. See Figure 91.

92. $(-2,\ 1),\ (-1,\ 2.5),\ (0,\ 5),\ (1,\ 2.5),\ (2,\ 1)$. See Figure 92.

93.   See Figure 93. $(-2,\ 2)$ is in QII, $(-1,\ -3)$ is in QIII, $(0,\ 1)$ is on the y-axis, $(2,\ -1)$ is in QIV.

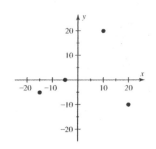

| Figure 92 | Figure 93 | Figure 94 |

94. See Figure 94. $(-15, -5)$ is in QIII, $(-5, 0)$ is on the x-axis, $(10, 20)$ is in QI, $(20, -10)$ is in QIV.

95. See Figure 95. There are 9 tick marks on the positive x-axis and 2 tick marks on the positive y-axis.

$[-9, 9, 1]$ by $[-6, 6, 3]$ $[-20, 20, 5]$ by $[-12, 12, 4]$

| Figure 95 | Figure 96 |

96. See Figure 96. There are 4 tick marks on the positive x-axis and 3 tick marks on the positive y-axis.

97. See Figure 97. $D = \{-1, 0, 2, 3, 4\}$; $R = \{-1, 0, 2, 3, 4\}$.

98. See Figure 98. $D = \{-20, -10, 45, 50\}$; $R = \{-30, -25, 10, 20\}$.

| Figure 97 | Figure 98 | Figure 104 |

Applications

99. (a) The best estimate is $163,200.

    (b) $(170,000 + 165,000 + 160,500 + 157,300) \div 4 = \$163,200$

100. (a) $A = 2500(1.01)^1 = \$2525$

    (b) $A = 800(1.01)^2 = 800(1.01)(1.01) = \$816.08$

101. (a) $C = 2\pi \cdot \left(9.3 \times 10^7\right) \approx 5.8 \times 10^8$ miles

    (b) $\dfrac{5.84 \times 10^8 \text{ mi}}{1 \text{ year}} \cdot \dfrac{1 \text{ year}}{365 \text{ days}} \cdot \dfrac{1 \text{ day}}{24 \text{ hr}} \approx 66,700$ mph

102. $d = 40t$

103.   For a 16-pound cat the pulse rate is $N = \dfrac{885}{\sqrt{16}} = \dfrac{885}{4} \approx 221$ bpm.

For a 144-pound person the pulse rate is $N = \dfrac{885}{\sqrt{144}} = \dfrac{885}{12} \approx 74$ bpm.

104.   See Figure 104. The poverty threshold has increased during this time period.

105. $A = (4ab)^2 = 4^2 a^2 b^2 = 16a^2 b^2$

106. $V = (5z)^3 = 5^3 z^3 = 125z^3$

Chapter 1 Test

1.   Natural numbers: $\sqrt{9}$

Whole numbers: $\sqrt{9}$

Integers: $-5,\ \sqrt{9}$

Rational Numbers: $-5,\ \dfrac{2}{3},\ \sqrt{9},\ -1.83$

Irrational Numbers: $-\dfrac{1}{\sqrt{5}},\ \pi$

2.   (a) Identity

(b) Associative property

(c) Commutative property

(d) Distributive property

3.   (a) $0 + (a \cdot 1) \cdot 1 = 0 + a \cdot 1 = 0 + a = a$

(b) $2x - 5x + 4x = (2 - 5 + 4)x = 1x = x$

(c) $2(x \cdot 3) + 2x = 2(3 \cdot x) + 2x = (2 \cdot 3)x + 2x = 6x + 2x = (6 + 2)x = 8x$

(d) $(a + b)a - ab = a \cdot a + ab - ab = a^2 + 0 = a^2$

4. $(34 + 15 + 96 + 11 + 0) \div 5 = 31.2$

5.

6.   (a) $\left| \dfrac{1}{2} + \dfrac{2}{3} - \dfrac{8}{3} \right| = \left| \dfrac{3}{6} + \dfrac{4}{6} - \dfrac{16}{6} \right| = \left| -\dfrac{9}{6} \right| = \left| -\dfrac{3}{2} \right| = \dfrac{3}{2}$

(b) $12 + (-3) + 18 + (-7) = 9 + 18 + (-7) = 27 + (-7) = 20$

(c) $\dfrac{1}{2} \cdot \dfrac{2}{3} \cdot \dfrac{3}{4} \cdot \dfrac{3}{2} \cdot 2 = \dfrac{3}{4}$

(d) $\dfrac{1}{2} + \dfrac{2}{3} - \dfrac{3}{2} + \dfrac{1}{3} = \dfrac{3}{6} + \dfrac{4}{6} - \dfrac{9}{6} + \dfrac{2}{6} = 0$

7.   (a) $-\dfrac{4}{5}$ (b) $\dfrac{b+1}{2}$

8.   (a) $-\dfrac{1}{2}+\dfrac{2}{3}\div 3 = -\dfrac{1}{2}+\dfrac{2}{3}\cdot\dfrac{1}{3} = -\dfrac{1}{2}+\dfrac{2}{9} = -\dfrac{9}{18}+\dfrac{4}{18} = -\dfrac{5}{18}$

    (b) $-4+\dfrac{\frac{2}{3}}{-\frac{1}{4}} = -4+\dfrac{2}{3}\cdot\left(-\dfrac{4}{1}\right) = -4-\dfrac{8}{3} = -\dfrac{12}{3}-\dfrac{8}{3} = -\dfrac{20}{3}$

    (c) $5-2\cdot 5^2 \div 5 = 5-2\cdot 25 \div 5 = 5-50\div 5 = 5-10 = -5$

    (d) $(6-4\cdot 5)\div(-7) = (6-20)\div(-7) = (-14)\div(-7) = 2$

9.   (a) $5^{-2} = \dfrac{1}{5^2} = \dfrac{1}{25}$

    (b) $\pi^0 = 1$

    (c) $\left(-\dfrac{2}{5}\right)^4 = \left(-\dfrac{2}{5}\right)\cdot\left(-\dfrac{2}{5}\right)\cdot\left(-\dfrac{2}{5}\right)\cdot\left(-\dfrac{2}{5}\right) = \dfrac{16}{625}$

    (d) $\dfrac{6^{-2}}{2^{-4}} = \dfrac{2^4}{6^2} = \dfrac{2\cdot 2\cdot 2\cdot 2}{6\cdot 6} = \dfrac{16}{36} = \dfrac{4}{9}$

    (e) $\dfrac{1}{5^{-3}} = 5^3 = 5\cdot 5\cdot 5 = 125$

    (f) $2^2\cdot 2^{-4} = 2^{\left[2+(-4)\right]} = 2^{-2} = \dfrac{1}{2^2} = \dfrac{1}{4}$

10.   (a) $x^6\cdot x^{-4}\cdot y^3 = x^{6+(-4)}\cdot y^3 = x^2 y^3$

    (b) $\dfrac{16x^{-2}y^8}{6xy^{-7}} = \left(\dfrac{16}{6}\right)\cdot x^{-2-1}\cdot y^{8-(-7)} = \dfrac{8}{3}x^{-3}y^{15} = \dfrac{8y^{15}}{3x^3}$

    (c) $\left(2yz^{-2}\right)^3 = 2^3\cdot y^3\cdot z^{-2\cdot 3} = 8y^3 z^{-6} = \dfrac{8y^3}{z^6}$

    (d) $\left(\dfrac{15x^4}{10xy^{-2}}\right)^{-2} = \left(\dfrac{10xy^{-2}}{15x^4}\right)^2 = \dfrac{10^2\cdot x^2\cdot y^{-2\cdot 2}}{15^2\cdot x^{4\cdot 2}} = \dfrac{100}{225}\cdot x^{2-8}\cdot y^{-4} = \dfrac{4}{9}x^{-6}y^{-4} = \dfrac{4}{9x^6 y^4}$

11.   0.00052

12. 3.4×10^6

13. $H = \dfrac{x}{60}$

14. $y = \sqrt{3+1}+3 = \sqrt{4}+3 = 2+3 = 5;$

    $y = \sqrt{-1+1}+(-1) = \sqrt{0}+(-1) = 0+(-1) = -1$

15. $D = \{-3,\ -1,\ 2\},\ R = \{-4,\ 2,\ 3\}$

16. $(-2, 3)$: QII; $(-1, -2)$: QIII; $(0, 2)$: y-axis;

$(1, -1)$: QIV; $(2, 1)$: QI

See Figure 16.

Figure 16

17. $S = \{(-30, 20), (-20, 20), (-10, 10), (10, 30), (20, 10), (30, -20)\}$

$D = \{-30, -20, -10, 10, 20, 30\}$; $R = \{-20, 10, 20, 30\}$

18.   See Figure 18. The equation $y = 1.25x$ models these data.

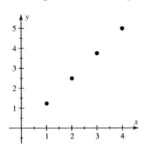

Figure 18

19.   See Figure 19.

$[-20, 20, 5]$ by $[-5, 40, 5]$

Figure 19

20. $C = \dfrac{5}{9}(5 - 32) = \dfrac{5}{9}(-27) = -15°C$

21. $(2.11 \times 10^8) \cdot 2.21 = 4.6631 \times 10^8$ gal

22. $r = \sqrt{\dfrac{25}{\pi}} \approx 2.82$ ft

23. $M = 61t$, because $244 \div 4 = 366 \div 6 = 610 \div 10 = 61$.

Chapter 1 Extended and Discovery Exercises

1. (a) The surface area of the earth is $A = 4\pi \cdot 3960^2 \approx 1.97 \times 10^8$ mi^2.

    (b) The surface area of the oceans is $A = \left(1.97 \times 10^8 \text{ mi}^2\right) \cdot 0.71 \approx 1.40 \times 10^8$ mi^2.

    (c) If the Arctic ice cap were to melt, the rise in sea level would be $\dfrac{6.8 \times 10^5 \text{ mi}^3}{1.40 \times 10^8 \text{ mi}^2} \approx 0.00486$ mi.

        That is $0.00486 \text{ mi} \cdot \dfrac{5280 \text{ ft}}{1 \text{ mi}} \approx 25.7$ ft.

    (d) If the Arctic ice cap melted, cities such as Boston, New Orleans and San Diego would be flooded.

    (e) If the Antarctic ice cap were to melt, the rise in sea level would be $\dfrac{6.3 \times 10^6 \text{ mi}^3}{1.40 \times 10^8 \text{ mi}^2} = 0.045$ mi.

        That is $0.045 \text{ mi} \cdot \dfrac{5280 \text{ ft}}{1 \text{ mi}} \approx 238$ ft.

2. (a) See Figure 2. The injury rate has decreased over this period of time.

    (b) The values in the table decrease by about 1 for each 3-year period, so a reasonable estimate might be about 9.3.

    (c) The values in the table decrease by about 1 for each 3-year period, so a reasonable estimate might be about 4.4.

    (d) It is not valid to try to estimate when the injury rate might reach 0 because the apparent trend cannot continue. There will always be injuries of this type.

Figure 2

3. $y = \dfrac{0.455W}{\left(0.0254H\right)^2} \approx \dfrac{705W}{H^2}$

4. Noting that 5 feet 9 inches = 69 inches, Steffi Graf's BMI is $y = \dfrac{0.455(119)}{\left(0.0254(69)\right)^2} \approx 17.6$

5. Noting that 6 feet 1 inch = 73 inches, Venus Williams' BMI is $y = \dfrac{0.455(160)}{\left(0.0254(73)\right)^2} \approx 21.2.$

6. Noting that 7 feet 1 inch = 85 inches, Shaquille O'Neal's BMI is $y = \dfrac{0.455(300)}{\left(0.0254(85)\right)^2} \approx 29.3.$

7.   When x increases by 2, y decreases by 3, so $a = -\dfrac{3}{2}$. By using substitution and trial-and-error, $b = \dfrac{1}{2}$.

8.   By using substitution we find that $a + b = 1$ and $2a + b = -1$. By trial-and-error, $a = -2$ and $b = 3$.

9.   By using substitution we find that $a + b = 1$ and $4a + 2b = 3$. By trial-and-error, $a = \dfrac{1}{2}$ and $b = \dfrac{1}{2}$.

10.   Substituting $x = 0$ and $y = 3$ gives $b = 3$. Then by substituting $x = 1$ and $y = 6$ we find that $a = 2$.

Critical Thinking Solutions for Chapter 1

Section 1.1

• Yes, for example $-\sqrt{2} + \sqrt{2} = 0$.

Section 1.3

• Each value in the *value* row can be obtained by dividing the value to the left of it by 10 or by multiplying the value to the right of it by 10. Hence $10^0 = 10 \div 10 = 1$ and $10^0 = 10^{-1} \cdot 10 = 1$.

• A student who is 19 years, 4 months and 3 days old is 19 years 123 days old or about 7058 days old.

That is $7058 \text{ days} \cdot \dfrac{24 \text{ hr}}{1 \text{ day}} \cdot \dfrac{60 \text{ min}}{1 \text{ hr}} \cdot \dfrac{60 \text{ sec}}{1 \text{ min}} \approx 610{,}000{,}000$ seconds.

A student who is exactly 18 years old has been alive for about 568,000,000 seconds. *Answers may vary.*

Section 1.4

• The formula is $T = \dfrac{100}{x}$.

Section 1.5

• Quadrant III, because both coordinates are negative.

Chapter 2: Linear Functions and Models

2.1: Functions and Their Representations

Concepts

1. function

2. *y* equals *f* of *x*

3. symbolic

4. numerical

5. domain

6. range

7. one

8. We use the vertical line test to identify graphs of functions.

9. The four types of representations for a function are verbal, numerical, symbolic and graphical or diagrammatic.

10. $(3, 4)$; 3; 6

11. (a, b)

12. *d*

13. 1

14. equal

15. Yes, there is only one output for each input.

16. Yes, there is only one age for each person.

17. No, one exam can have many students who pass.

18. No, the parent may have more than one child.

Representing and Evaluating Functions

19. $f(-1) = 4(-1) - 2 = -6$; $f(0) = 4(0) - 2 = -2$

20. $f(-4) = 5 - 3(-4) = 17$; $f(2) = 5 - 3(2) = -1$

21. $f(0) = \sqrt{0} = 0$; $f\left(\frac{9}{4}\right) = \sqrt{\frac{9}{4}} = \frac{3}{2}$

22. $f(-1) = \sqrt[3]{(-1)} = -1$; $f(27) = \sqrt[3]{27} = 3$

23. $f(-5) = (-5)^2 = 25$; $f\left(\frac{3}{2}\right) = \left(\frac{3}{2}\right)^2 = \frac{9}{4}$

24. $f(-2) = (-2)^3 = -8$; $f(0.1) = (0.1)^3 = 0.001$

25. $f(-8) = 3$; $f\left(\frac{7}{3}\right) = 3$

26. $f(-\pi) = 100;\ f\left(\tfrac{1}{3}\right) = 100$

27. $f(-2) = 5 - (-2)^3 = 5 - (-8) = 13;$

   $f(3) = 5 - 3^3 = 5 - 27 = -22$

28. $f\left(-\dfrac{1}{2}\right) = \left(-\dfrac{1}{2}\right)^2 + 5 = \dfrac{1}{4} + 5 = \dfrac{1}{4} + \dfrac{20}{4} = \dfrac{21}{4};\ f(6) = 6^2 + 5 = 36 + 5 = 41$

29. $f(-5) = \dfrac{2}{-5+1} = \dfrac{2}{-4} = -\dfrac{1}{2};\ f(4) = \dfrac{2}{4+1} = \dfrac{2}{5}$

30. $f(-3) = \dfrac{-3}{-3-4} = \dfrac{-3}{-7} = \dfrac{3}{7};\ f(1) = \dfrac{1}{1-4} = \dfrac{1}{-3} = -\dfrac{1}{3}$

31. (a) Because there are 36 inches in 1 yard, the formula is $I(x) = 36x$.

   (b) $I(10) = 36(10) = 360.$ There are 360 inches in 10 yards.

32. (a) Because there are 5280 feet in 1 mile, the formula is $M(x) = \dfrac{x}{5280}$.

   (b) $M(10) = \dfrac{10}{5280} \approx 0.0019.$ Ten feet is equivalent to about 0.0019 mile.

33. (a) The area formula for a circle is $A(r) = \pi r^2$.

   (b) $A(10) = \pi(10)^2 = 100\pi \approx 314.2.$ The area of a circle with radius 10 is about 314.2.

34. (a) The formula for the circumference of a circle is $C(r) = 2\pi r$.

   (b) $C(10) = 2\pi(10) = 20\pi \approx 62.8.$ The circumference of a circle with radius 10 is about 62.8.

35. (a) Because there are 43,560 square feet in 1 acre, the formula is $A(x) = 43,560x$.

   (b) $A(10) = 43,560(10) = 435,600.$ There are 435,600 square feet in 10 acres.

36. (a) Because there are about 2.2 pounds in 1 kilogram, the formula is $K(x) = \dfrac{x}{2.2}$.

   (b) $K(10) = \dfrac{10}{2.2} = 4.\overline{54}.$ Ten pounds is equivalent to about $4.\overline{54}$ kilograms.

37. $f = \{(1,3),(2,-4),(3,0)\};\ D = \{1,2,3\},\ R = \{-4,0,3\}$

38. $f = \{(-1,4),(0,6),(1,4)\};\ D = \{-1,0,1\},\ R = \{4,6\}$

39. $f = \{(a,b),(c,d),(e,a),(d,b)\};\ D = \{a,c,d,e\},\ R = \{a,b,d\}$

40. $f = \{(a,7),(b,7),(c,7),(d,7)\};\ D = \{a,b,c,d\},\ R = \{7\}$

41. See Figure 41.

42. See Figure 42.

Figure 41

Figure 42

Figure 43

43.   See Figure 43.

44.   See Figure 44.

45.   See Figure 45.

Figure 44

Figure 45

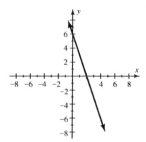

Figure 46

46.   See Figure 46.

47.   See Figure 47.

48.   See Figure 48.

Figure 47

Figure 48

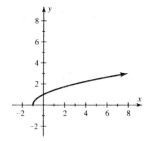

Figure 49

49.   See Figure 49.

50.   See Figure 50.

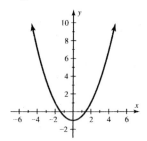

Figure 50

51. $f(0) = 3; f(2) = -1$

52. $f(-2) = -2; f(2) = 0$

53. $f(-2) = 0; f(1) = 2$

54. $f(-1) = 1; f(0) = 0$

55. $f(1) = -4; f(2) = -3$

56. $f(-1) = 3; f(4) = 2$

57. $f(0) = 5.5; f(2) = 3.7$

58. $f(-10) = 23; f(5) = -33$

59. $f(1990) = 26.9$ mpg ; In 1990 average fuel efficiency was 26.9 mpg.

60. $f(1990) = \$1809$; In 1990 average cost of tuition was $1809.

61.   Symbolic: $y = x + 5$. Numerical: See the table in Figure 61a. Graphical: See the graph in Figure 61b.

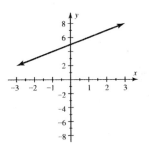

x	-3	-2	-1	0	1	2	3
$y = f(x)$	2	3	4	5	6	7	8

Figure 61a   Figure 61b

62.   Symbolic: $y = x^2$. Numerical: See the table in Figure 62a. Graphical: See the graph in Figure 62b.

x	-3	-2	-1	0	1	2	3
$y = f(x)$	9	4	1	0	1	4	9

Figure 62a   Figure 62b

63.   Symbolic: $y = 5x - 2$. Numerical: See the table in Figure 63a. Graphical: See the graph in Figure 63b.

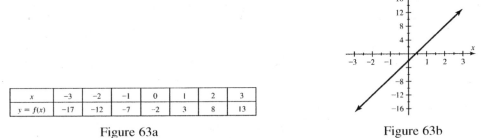

x	-3	-2	-1	0	1	2	3
$y = f(x)$	-17	-12	-7	-2	3	8	13

Figure 63a   Figure 63b

64.   Symbolic: $y = \dfrac{x}{2} + 3$. Numerical: See the table in Figure 64a. Graphical: See the graph in Figure 64b.

x	-3	-2	-1	0	1	2	3
$y = f(x)$	1.5	2	2.5	3	3.5	4	4.5

Figure 64a   Figure 64b

65.   Numerical   Graphical

[−10, 10, 1] by [−10, 10 1]

66.   Numerical   Graphical

[−10, 10, 1] by [−10, 10, 1]

67.   Numerical   Graphical (Dot Mode)

[−10, 10, 1] by [−10, 10, 1]

68.   Numerical   Graphical

[−10, 10, 1] by [−10, 10, 1]

69.   Subtract $\dfrac{1}{2}$ from the input x to obtain the output y.

70.   Multiply the input x by $\dfrac{3}{4}$ to obtain the output y.

71.   Divide the input x by 3 to obtain the output y.

72.   Square the input x and then add 1 to obtain the output y.

73.   Subtract 1 from x and then take the square root to obtain the output y.

74.   Subtract 3 times x from 1 to obtain the output y.

75.   Symbolic: $f(x) = 0.50x$. Graphical: See the graph in Figure 75a. Numerical: See the table in Figure 75b.

Figure 75a

Miles	10	20	30	40	50	60	70
Cost	$5	$10	$15	$20	$25	$30	$35

Figure 75b

76.   Symbolic: $f(x) = 0.15x$. Graphical: See the graph in Figure 76a. Numerical: See the table in Figure 76b.

Figure 76a

Income	$1000	$2000	$3000	$4000	$5000	$6000	$7000
Tax	$150	$300	$450	$600	$750	$900	$1050

Figure 76b

77. $P(1995) = 5.7(1995 - 1990) + 150 = 5.7(5) + 150 = 28.5 + 150$

$$= 178.5$$

     In 1995 the average price was $178,500.

78. $I(2003) = 1.4(2003 - 2000) + 51 = 1.4(3) + 51 = 4.2 + 51 = 55.2$

     In 2003, the median income was $55,200.

Identifying Domains and Ranges

79. $D: -2 \le x \le 2; \; R: 0 \le y \le 2$

80. $D: -2 \le x \le 2; \; R: -3 \le y \le 3$

81. $D: -2 \le x \le 4; \; R: -2 \le y \le 2$

82. D: all real numbers; R: all real numbers

83. D: all real numbers; $R: \; y \ge -1$

84. $D: -1 \le x \le 3; \; R: -3 \le y \le -1$

85. $D: -3 \le x \le 3; \; R: -3 \le y \le 2$

86. $D = \{-6, -4, -2, 2, 4, 6\} \; ; \; R = \{-4, -2, 2, 4, 6\}$

87. $D = \{1, 2, 3, 4\}; R = \{5, 6, 7\}$

88. $D = \{12, 13, 15\}; R = \{9, 26, 32\}$

89.   Any real number is a valid input for this function. D: all real numbers.

90.   Any real number is a valid input for this function. D : all real numbers.

91.   Any real number is a valid input for this function. D : all real numbers.

92.   Any real number is a valid input for this function. D : all real numbers.

93.   The denominator of this function cannot equal zero. $D : x \neq 5$.

94.   The denominator of this function cannot equal zero. $D : x \neq -1$.

95.   The denominator of this function will never equal zero because the variable is squared. D : all real numbers.

96.   The denominator of this function cannot equal zero. $D : x \neq 1$.

97.   The radicand must be greater than or equal to zero. $D : x \geq 1$.

98.   Any real number is a valid input for this function. D : all real numbers.

99.   Any real number is a valid input for this function.

       D: all real numbers.

100.   The radicand must be greater than or equal to zero.

       D: $x \leq 2$.

101.   The denominator of this function cannot equal zero.

       D: $x \neq 0$.

102.   Any real number is a valid input for this function.

       D: all real numbers.

103.   (a) $f(1950) = 60.3$; In 1950 there were 60.3 accidental deaths per 100,000 people.

       (b) $D = \{1910, 1930, 1950, 1970, 1990, 2000\}$; $R = \{35.5, \ 36.9, \ 56.2, \ 60.3, \ 80.5, \ 84.4\}$

       (c)   The number of accidental deaths per 100,000 people decreased over this time period.

104.   (a) $f(1940) = 32$; In 1940 there were 32 million motor vehicles registered in the United States.

       (b) $D = \{1920, 1940, 1960, 1980, 2000\}$; $R = \{9, \ 32, \ 74, \ 156, \ 216\}$

       (c)   See Figure 104.

Figure 104

Identifying a Function

105.   No. The value 1 in the domain corresponds to more than one value in the range.

106.   Yes. Each value in the domain corresponds to exactly one value in the range.

107.   Yes. Each value in the domain corresponds to exactly one value in the range.

108.   No. The value 5 in the domain corresponds to more than one value in the range.

109.   (a)   May is month number 5. The corresponding value for P is 0.2.

(b) Yes. Each month has exactly one average precipitation.

(c) Months 2, 3, 7 and 11.

110. (a) Month number 2, February.

(b) Yes. Each month has exactly one average wind speed.

(c) Months 7, 8 and 9.

111. Yes. The graph passes the vertical line test.; D : all real numbers; R : all real numbers

112. Yes. The graph passes the vertical line test.; $D: -2 \le x \le 2$; $R: -4 \le y \le 4$

113. No. The graph does not pass the vertical line test.

114. Yes. The graph passes the vertical line test.; D : all real numbers; $R: -2 \le y \le 2$

115. Yes. The graph passes the vertical line test.; $D: -4 \le x \le 4$; $R: 0 \le y \le 4$

116. No. The graph does not pass the vertical line test.

117. Yes. The graph passes the vertical line test.; D : all real numbers; $R: y = 3$

118. Yes. The graph passes the vertical line test.; $D: -4 \le x \le 4$; $R: -4 \le y \le 4$

119. No. The graph does not pass the vertical line test when $x = -2$.

120. Yes. The graph passes the vertical line test.; $D = \{-6, -4, -2, 0, 2, 4, 6\}$; $R = \{-6, -4, -2, 2, 4, 6\}$

121. Yes. Each value in the domain corresponds to exactly one value in the range.

122. No. The value 4 in the domain corresponds to more than one value in the range.

123. No. The value 5 in the domain corresponds to more than one value in the range.

124. Yes. Each value in the domain corresponds to exactly one value in the range.

125. Walks away from home, then turns around and walks back a little slower.

126. Walks towards home, stops for a while, then continues home.

2.2: Linear Functions

Concepts

1. $ax + b$

2. b

3. line

4. horizontal line

5. 7

6. 0

7. Carpet costs $2 per square foot. Ten square feet of carpet costs $20.

8. The rate at which water is leaving the tank is 4 gallons per minute. After 5 minutes the tank contains 80 gallons of water.

Identifying Linear Functions

9.   Yes; $a = \dfrac{1}{2}$, $b = -6$

10.   Yes; $a = 1$, $b = 0$

11.   No

12.   No

13.   Yes; $a = 0$, $b = -9$

14.   Yes; $a = -7.3$, $b = 1.5$

15.   Yes; $a = -9$, $b = 0$

16.   No

17.   Yes. The graph is a straight line.

18.   No. The graph is not a straight line.

19.   No. The graph is not a straight line.

20.   Yes. The graph is a straight line.

21.   Yes. For each unit increase in x, the values of $f(x)$ increase by 3 units, so $a = \dfrac{3}{1} = 3$.

    Because $f(x) = -6$ when $x = 0$, the y-intercept is $b = -6$. The function can be written $f(x) = 3x - 6$.

22.   Yes. For each 2-unit increase in x, the values of $f(x)$ increase by 4 units, so $a = \dfrac{4}{2} = 2$.

    Because $f(x) = -2$ when $x = 0$, the y-intercept is $b = -2$. The function can be written $f(x) = 2x - 2$.

23.   Yes. For each 2-unit increase in x, the values of $f(x)$ decrease by 3 units, so $a = -\dfrac{3}{2}$.

    Because $f(x) = 3$ when $x = 0$, the y-intercept is $b = 3$. The function can be written $f(x) = -\dfrac{3}{2}x + 3$.

24.   No. For each 3-unit increase in x, the values of $f(x)$ do not decrease by a constant amount.

25.   No. For each unit increase in x, the values of $f(x)$ do not increase by a constant amount.

26.   Yes. For each unit increase in x, the values of $f(x)$ decrease by 3 units, so $a = \dfrac{-3}{1} = -3$.

    Because $f(x) = 0$ when $x = 0$, the y-intercept is $b = 0$. The function can be written $f(x) = -3x$.

27.   Yes. For each unit increase in x, the values of $f(x)$ increase by 2 units, so $a = \dfrac{2}{1} = 2$.

    Because $f(x) = -2$ when $x = 0$, the y-intercept is $b = -2$. The function can be written $f(x) = 2x - 2$.

28.   No. For each unit increase in x, the values of $f(x)$ do not increase by a constant amount.

Evaluating Linear Functions

29. $f(-4) = 4(-4) = -16$; $f(5) = 4(5) = 20$

30. $f(-2) = -2(-2) + 1 = 5$; $f(3) = -2(3) + 1 = -5$

31. $f\left(-\dfrac{2}{3}\right) = 5 - \left(-\dfrac{2}{3}\right) = \dfrac{15}{3} + \dfrac{2}{3} = \dfrac{17}{3}$; $f(3) = 5 - 3 = 2$

32. $f(0) = \dfrac{1}{2}(0) - \dfrac{1}{4} = -\dfrac{1}{4}$; $f\left(\dfrac{1}{2}\right) = \dfrac{1}{2}\left(\dfrac{1}{2}\right) - \dfrac{1}{4} = \dfrac{1}{4} - \dfrac{1}{4} = 0$

33. $f\left(-\dfrac{3}{4}\right) = -22$; $f(13) = -22$

34. $f(-1.2) = 9(-1.2) - 7 = -17.8$; $f(2.8) = 9(2.8) - 7 = 18.2$

35. $f(-1) = -2$; $f(0) = 0$

36. $f(-2) = 4$; $f(2) = 0$

37. $f(-2) = -1$; $f(4) = -4$

38. $f(0) = -1$; $f(3) = 1$

39. $f(-3) = 1$; $f(1) = 1$

40. $f(1.5) = -2$; $f(0.5\pi) = -2$

41. $f(x) = 6x$; $f(3) = 6(3) = 18$

42. $f(x) = -3x + 7$; $f(3) = -3(3) + 7 = -9 + 7 = -2$

43. $f(x) = \dfrac{x}{6} - \dfrac{1}{2}$; $f(3) = \dfrac{(3)}{6} - \dfrac{1}{2} = \dfrac{1}{2} - \dfrac{1}{2} = 0$

44. $f(x) = 8.7$; $f(3) = 8.7$

Representing Linear Functions

45.   The graph should have a positive slope and pass through (0, 0). d

46.   The graph should have a negative slope and pass through (0, 0). c

47.   The graph should have a positive slope and pass through (0, –2). b

48.   The graph should have a positive slope and pass through (0, 1). a

49.   See Figure 49.

50.   See Figure 50.

Figure 49

Figure 50

Figure 51

51.   See Figure 51.

52.   See Figure 52.

Figure 52

Figure 53

53.   See Figure 53.

54.   See Figure 54.

55.   See Figure 55.

56.   See Figure 56.

Figure 54

Figure 55

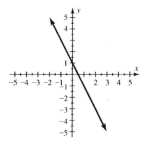

Figure 56

57.   See Figure 57.

58.   See Figure 58.

Figure 57

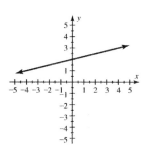

Figure 58

59.   Since each pound is divided into 16 ounces: $f(x) = \dfrac{1}{16}x$

60.   Since there are 10 dimes in each dollar: $f(x) = 10x$

61.   Since the car travels 65 miles each hour: $f(t) = 65t$

62.   Since the cost is 10¢ for each minute plus a fixed fee of $4.95: $f(t) = 0.10t + 4.95$

63.   Since every day has 24 hours: $f(x) = 24$

64.   Since a season pass allows a person to ski as much or as little as desired: $f(x) = 500$

65. a

66. $-\dfrac{1}{c}$

67.   (a) f multiplies the input x by -2 and then adds 1 to obtain the output y.

      (b)

x	-2	0	2
$y = f(x)$	5	1	-3

      (c)

68.   (a) f subtracts the input x from 1 to obtain the output y.

      (b)

x	-2	0	2
$y = f(x)$	3	1	-1

      (c)

69.   (a) f multiplies the input x by $\frac{1}{2}$ and then subtracts 1 to obtain the output y.

      (b)

x	-2	0	2
$y = f(x)$	-2	-1	0

(c)

70.   (a) f multiplies the input x by $\frac{3}{4}$ to obtain the output y.

(b)

x	-2	0	2
$y = f(x)$	$-\frac{3}{2}$	0	$\frac{3}{2}$

(c)

71.   (a)   (b)

                                 $[-6, 6, 1]$ by $[-4, 4, 1]$

72.   (a)   (b)

                                 $[-6, 6\ 1[$ by $[-4, 4, 1]$

73.   (a)   (b)

                                 $[-6, 6, 1]$ by $[-4, 4, 1]$

74.   (a)   (b)

[–6, 6, 1] by [–4, 4, 1]

Modeling

75.   The graph should increase since the cost of tuition has been rising but it should not start at zero. b

76.   The graph should be decreasing since the cost of computer memory has decreased over the past 5 years. d

77.   The graph should be a horizontal line since this distance has not changed over the past 10 years. c

78.   The graph should increase and start at $(0, 0)$. a

Applications

79.   (a) Symbolic: $f(x) = 70$

       Graphical: A graph of the function is shown in Figure 79a.

      (b) A table of the function is shown in Figure 79b.

      (c) The function f is a constant function.

Figure 79a

Hours	0	4	8	12	16	20	24
Temp. (°F)	70	70	70	70	70	70	70

Figure 79b

80.   (a) Symbolic: $f(x) = 60$

       Graphical: A graph of the function is shown in Figure 80a.

      (b) A table of the function is shown in Figure 80b.

      (c) The function f is a constant function.

Figure 80a

Minutes (x)	0	1	2	3	4	5	6
Speed (f)	60	60	60	60	60	60	60

Figure 80b

81.   For each 2-hour increase in t, the distance increases by 120 miles, so $a = \dfrac{120}{2} = 60$.

      Because $D = 50$ when $t = 0$, the y-intercept is $b = 50$. The function can be written $D(t) = 60t + 50$.

82.   (a) The line graph is shown in Figure 82.

(b) No, the data could not be modeled with a linear function because the graph does not form a straight line.

Figure 82

83.   (a) Because the average person disposed of 2.7 pounds of garbage each day, the function is $f(x) = 2.7x$.

$f(60) = 2.7(60) = 162$; In 1960 the average person disposed of 162 pounds of garbage in 60 days.

(b) Because the average person disposed of 4.3 pounds of garbage each day, the function is $g(x) = 4.3x$.

$g(60) = 4.3(60) = 258$; In 2003 the average person disposed of 258 pounds of garbage in 60 days.

84.   (a) Because the world loses 49 million acres of rain forest each year, the function is $f(x) = -49x$.

(b) $f(7) = -49(7) = -343$; In 7 years the world loses 343 million acres of rain forest.

85.   (a) See Figure 85a.

[1, 7, 1] by [0, 300, 100]

Figure 85a

(b) Malware increased.

(c) $N(3) = 16(3) + 136 = 48 + 136 = 184$;

In March there were 184 malware viruses.

(d) The number of malware viruses is increasing at a rate of 16 per month.

86.   (a) $V(0) = 0.147(0) + 40 = 40$; The volume of the gas is 40 cubic inches when the temperature is 0°C.

(b) Because each 1°C increase in temperature results in a 0.147 cubic inch increase in volume, a 10°C increase in temperature will result in a 1.47 cubic inch increase in volume.

(c) At 100°C the volume of the gas is $V(100) = 0.147(100) + 40 = 14.7 + 40 = 54.7$ cubic inches.

87.   (a) Because each 1°C increase in temperature results in a 0.5 cubic centimeter increase in volume, $a = 0.5$. Because the volume is 137 cubic centimeters when the temperature is 0°C, the y-intercept is $b = 137$.

The formula is $V(T) = 0.5T + 137$.

(b) $V(50) = 0.5(50) + 137 = 25 + 137 = 162$ cubic centimeters.

88.   (a) Because each copy of the video costs \$5 to produce, $a = 5$. Because there is a fixed cost of \$750,

           $b = 750$. The formula is $C(x) = 5x + 750$.

      (b) $C(2500) = 5(2500) + 750 = 12,500 + 750 = \$13,250$

89. $f(x) = 40x$

      In 30 days each additional pound of muscle will burn $40(30) = 1200$ calories. Then the amount of muscle

      necessary to lose 1 pound of fat is $3500 \div 1200 \approx 2.92$ lb.

90.   (a) $N(0) = 15,260(0) + 333,200 = 333,200$; In 1970 there were 333,200 doctors in the private sector.

           $N(30) = 15,260(30) + 333,200 = 791,000$; In 2000 there were 791,000 doctors in the private sector.

      (b) The number 15,260 represents the increase in the number of private sector doctors each year.

           The number 333,200 represents the initial number of private sector doctors in 1970.

91.   (a) From the table, the average length of a baseball game in 2000 was 180 minutes.

      (b) Each year the average length of a game decreased by 4 minutes.

      (c) Because the constant change is a decrease of 4 minutes, $a = -4$. Because the initial length is 180,

           $b = 180$. The formula is $f(x) = -4x + 180$.

      (d) The year 2004 corresponds to $x = 4$. $f(4) = -4(4) + 180 = -16 + 180 = 164$ minutes.

92.   (a) From the table, Wal-Mart's share of the market in 1998 was 6%.

      (b) Each year Wal-Mart's share of the market increased by 0.5%.

      (c) Because the constant change is an increase of 0.5%, $a = 0.5$. Because the initial market share is 6%,

           $b = 6$. The formula is $f(x) = 0.5x + 6$.

      (d) The year 2005 corresponds to $x = 7$. $f(7) = 0.5(7) + 6 = 3.5 + 6 = 9.5\%$.

Checking Basic Concepts for Sections 2.1 & 2.2

1.   Symbolic: $f(x) = x^2 - 1$

      Graphical: The graph is shown in Figure 1.

                 Figure 1   Figure 4

2.   (a) $D: -3 \le x \le 3$; $R: -4 \le y \le 4$

      (b) $f(0) = 0$; $f(2) = 4$

(c) No. The graph is not a straight line.

3.   (a) Yes. The function is of the form $f(x) = ax + b$.

(b) No. The function can not be written in the form $f(x) = ax + b$.

(c) Yes. The function could be written $f(x) = 0x - 7$ which is of the form $f(x) = ax + b$.

(d) Yes. The function could be written $f(x) = 3x + 9$ which is of the form $f(x) = ax + b$.

4.   The graph is shown in Figure 4. $f(-2) = 4 - 3(-2) = 4 + 6 = 10$.

5.   For each 2-unit increase in x, the values of $f(x)$ increase by 1 unit, so $a = \dfrac{1}{2}$.

Because $f(x) = -1$ when $x = 0$, the y-intercept is $b = -1$. The function can be written $f(x) = \dfrac{1}{2}x - 1$.

6.   (a) $f(20) = 0.264(20) + 27.7 = 5.28 + 27.7 = 32.98$; In 1990 the median age was about 33 years.

(b) The number 0.264 means that the median age increased by 0.264 year each year. The number 27.7 means that the initial median age in 1970 was 27.7 years.

2.3: The Slope of a Line

Concepts

1. $y; x$

2.   0

3.   rises

4.   horizontal

5.   vertical

6.   slope-intercept

Slope

7.   2. The y-value increases 2 units for every 1 unit increase in the x-value.

8.   −1. The y-value decreases 1 unit for every 1 unit increase in the x-value.

9. $-\dfrac{2}{3}$. The y-value decreases 2 units for every 3 units of increase in the x-value.

10.   Undefined. This is a vertical line.

11.   0. This is a horizontal line.

12. $\dfrac{1}{2}$. The y-value increases 1 unit for every 2 units of increase in the x-value.

13. $m = \dfrac{4 - 2}{2 - 1} = \dfrac{2}{1} = 2$

14. $m = \dfrac{-3 - 2}{2 - (-3)} = \dfrac{-5}{5} = -1$

15. $m = \dfrac{3-1}{-1-2} = \dfrac{2}{-3} = -\dfrac{2}{3}$

16. $m = \dfrac{\frac{3}{5} - \left(-\frac{4}{5}\right)}{\frac{4}{5} - \left(-\frac{3}{5}\right)} = \dfrac{\frac{7}{5}}{\frac{7}{5}} = 1$

17. $m = \dfrac{6-6}{4-(-3)} = \dfrac{0}{7} = 0$

18. $m = \dfrac{5-5}{-5-(-3)} = \dfrac{0}{-2} = 0$

19. $m = \dfrac{\frac{13}{17} - \left(-\frac{2}{7}\right)}{\frac{1}{2} - \frac{1}{2}} = \dfrac{\frac{125}{119}}{0} \Rightarrow$ Undefined

20. $m = \dfrac{-4-6}{-1-(-1)} = \dfrac{-10}{0} \Rightarrow$ Undefined

21. $m = \dfrac{\frac{1}{3} - \left(-\frac{4}{3}\right)}{\frac{1}{6} - \frac{1}{3}} = \dfrac{\frac{1}{3} + \frac{4}{3}}{\frac{1}{6} - \frac{2}{6}} = \dfrac{\frac{5}{3}}{-\frac{1}{6}} = \dfrac{5}{3} \cdot \left(-\dfrac{6}{1}\right) = -\dfrac{30}{3} = -10$

22. $m = \dfrac{\frac{1}{2} - \frac{3}{2}}{2 - \left(-\frac{1}{2}\right)} = \dfrac{-\frac{2}{2}}{\frac{4}{2} + \frac{1}{2}} = \dfrac{-1}{\frac{5}{2}} = -1 \cdot \dfrac{2}{5} = -\dfrac{2}{5}$

23. $m = \dfrac{16-10}{1999-1989} = \dfrac{6}{10} = \dfrac{3}{5}$

24. $m = \dfrac{10.6 - 6.1}{2000 - 1950} = \dfrac{4.5}{50} = 0.09$

25. $m = \dfrac{4.3 - 3.6}{-1.2 - 2.1} = \dfrac{0.7}{-3.3} = -0.\overline{21}$

26. $m = \dfrac{64 - (-34)}{14 - 12} = \dfrac{98}{2} = 49$

27. $m = \dfrac{4b - b}{3a - 2a} = \dfrac{3b}{a}$

28. $m = \dfrac{a - (-b)}{b - (-a)} = \dfrac{a + b}{b + a} = 1$

29. $m = \dfrac{b - 0}{a - (a + b)} = \dfrac{b}{-b} = -1$

30. $m = \dfrac{a - b}{b - a} = -1$

31. (a) $m = \dfrac{-1 - 2}{3 - (-1)} = \dfrac{-3}{4}$

    (b) See Figure 31b.

Figure 31b

Figure 32b

(c) The graph falls 3 units for every 4-unit increase in x.

32.   (a) $m = \dfrac{3-(-2)}{1-(-2)} = \dfrac{5}{3}$

(b) See Figure 32b.

(c) The graph rises 5 units for every 3-unit increase in x.

33.   (a) $m = \dfrac{0-2}{-3-0} = \dfrac{2}{3}$

(b) See Figure 33b.

Figure 33b

Figure 34b

(c) The graph rises 2 units for every 3-unit increase in x.

34.   (a) $m = \dfrac{2-2}{1-(-1)} = \dfrac{0}{2} = 0$

(b) Figure 34b.

(c) The graph neither rises nor falls; it is horizontal.

35.   See Figure 35.

36.   See Figure 36.

Figure 35

Figure 36

Figure 37

37.   See Figure 37.

38. See Figure 38.

39. See Figure 39.

Figure 38

Figure 39

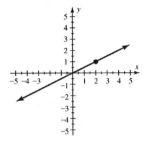

Figure 40

40. See Figure 40.

41. See Figure 41.

42. See Figure 42.

Figure 41

Figure 42

Slope-Intercept Form

43. (a) $m = 1$; $b = 2$

     (b) See Figure 43.

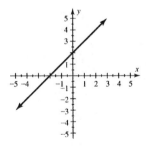

Figure 43

44. (a) $m = 1$; $b = -2$

     (b) See Figure 44.

45. (a) $m = -3$; $b = 2$

     (b) See Figure 45.

Figure 44

Figure 45

Figure 46

46.   (a) $m = \dfrac{1}{2}; \; b = -1$

    (b) See Figure 46.

47.   (a) $m = \dfrac{1}{3}; \; b = 0$

    (b) See Figure 47.

48.   (a) $m = -2; \; b = 0$

    (b) See Figure 48.

Figure 47

Figure 48

Figure 49

49.   (a) $m = 0; \; b = 2$

    (b) See Figure 49.

50.   (a) $m = 0; \; b = -3$

    (b) See Figure 50.

51.   (a) $m = -1; \; b = 3$

    (b) See Figure 51.

Figure 50

Figure 51

Figure 52

52.   (a) $m = \dfrac{2}{3}; \; b = -2$

(b) See Figure 52.

53.   The slope is –1 since the *y*-value decreases 1 unit for every 1–unit increase in the *x*-value.

The *y*-intercept is 4 since the graph crosses the *y*-axis at (0, 4). The equation is $y = -x + 4$.

54.   The slope is –2 since the *y*-value decreases 2 units for every 1–unit increase in the *x*-value.

The *y*-intercept is 2 since the graph crosses the *y*-axis at (0, 2). The equation is $y = -2x + 2$.

55.   The slope is 0 since this is a horizontal line.

The *y*-intercept is 2 since the graph crosses the *y*-axis at (0, 2). The equation is $y = 2$.

56.   The slope is $\dfrac{1}{2}$ since the *y*-value increases 1 unit for every 2 units of increase in the *x*-value.

The *y*-intercept is –1 since the graph crosses the *y*-axis at (0, –1). The equation is $y = \dfrac{1}{2}x - 1$.

57.   The slope is 1 since the *y*-value increases 1 unit for every 1–unit increase in the *x*-value.

The *y*-intercept is –2 since the graph passes through (0, –2). The equation is $y = x - 2$.

58.   The slope is $-\dfrac{2}{3}$ since the *y*-value decreases 2 units for every 3 units of increase in the *x*-value.

The *y*-intercept is 1 since the graph passes through (0, 1). The equation is $y = -\dfrac{2}{3}x + 1$.

59. $y = 3x - 5$

60. $y = -\dfrac{2}{3}x + 7$

61.   The slope is $m = \dfrac{-\frac{3}{2} - 0}{0 - 1} = \dfrac{-\frac{3}{2}}{-1} = \dfrac{3}{2}$. The *y*-intercept is $-\dfrac{3}{2}$ since the graph crosses the *y*-axis at $\left(0, -\dfrac{3}{2}\right)$.

The equation is $y = \dfrac{3}{2}x - \dfrac{3}{2}$.

62.   The slope is $m = \dfrac{0 - 4}{-2 - 0} = \dfrac{-4}{-2} = 2$. The *y*-intercept is 4 since the graph crosses the *y*-axis at (0, 4).

The equation is $y = 2x + 4$.

63. $m = \dfrac{0 - (-2)}{1 - 0} = \dfrac{2}{1} = 2;\ b = -2$

64. $m = \dfrac{15 - 10}{1 - 0} = \dfrac{5}{1} = 5;\ b = 10$

65. $m = \dfrac{-10 - (-3)}{2 - 1} = \dfrac{-7}{1} = -7$; By substituting $x = 1$ and $y = -3$ into $y = -7x + b$, we find that $b = 4$.

66. $m = \dfrac{-6 - (-3)}{4 - 2} = \dfrac{-3}{2} = -\dfrac{3}{2}$; By substituting $x = 2$ and $y = -3$ into $y = -\dfrac{3}{2}x + b$, we find that $b = 0$.

67.   (a) The missing value is 3 since the y-value increases 2 units for every 1–unit increase in the x-value $(m = 2)$.

(b) The y-intercept is –1 since the graph passes through $(0, -1)$. The equation is $f(x) = 2x - 1$.

68.   (a) The missing value is 4 since the y-value decreases 4 units for every 1–unit increase in the x-value $(m = -4)$.

(b) The y-intercept is 16 since the graph must pass through $(0, 16)$. The equation is $f(x) = -4x + 16$.

69.   (a) The missing number is 5 since the y-value increases 9 units for every 6 units of increase in the x-value $\left(m = \dfrac{3}{2} \right)$.

(b) The y-intercept is 5 since the graph passes through $(0, 5)$. The equation is $f(x) = \dfrac{3}{2}x + 5$.

70.   (a) The missing number is 0 since the y-value increases 30 units for every 15 units of increase in the x-value $(m = 2)$.

(b) The y-intercept is 0 since the graph passes through $(0, 0)$. The equation is $f(x) = 2x$.

Interpreting Slope

71.   The graph should be increasing since a person's pay increases with time and it should start at $(0, 0)$. c

72.   The graph should be decreasing since the total acres of rain forest in the world is decreasing. d

73.   The graph should be increasing since the world's population is increasing but it should not start at $(0, 0)$. b

74.   The graph should be a horizontal line since the area of Nevada has not changed over this time period. a

75.   (a) $m_1 = 50$, $m_2 = 0$, $m_3 = 150$ $\left(\text{i.e. } m_1 = \dfrac{300 - 100}{4 - 0} = \dfrac{200}{4} = 50 \right)$

(b) m_1: the pump is adding water at the rate of 50 gallons per hour.

m_2: the pump is turned off

m_3: the pump is adding water at the rate of 150 gallons per hour.

(c) Initially the pool contained 100 gallons of water. The pump added 200 gallons of water over the first 4 hours. Then the pump was turned off for 2 hours. Finally, the pump added 300 gallons of water over the last 2 hours.

76.   (a) $m_1 = 125$, $m_2 = 0$, $m_3 = -125$ $\left(\text{i.e. } m_1 = \dfrac{500 - 0}{4 - 0} = \dfrac{500}{4} = 125 \right)$

(b) m_1: the pump is adding water at the rate of 125 gallons per hour.

m_2: the pump is turned off

m_3: the pump is removing water at the rate of 125 gallons per hour.

(c) Initially the pool was empty. The pump added 500 gallons of water over the first 4 hours. Then the pump was turned off for 4 hours. Finally, the pump removed all 500 gallons of water over the last 4 hours.

77.   (a) $m_1 = 100$, $m_2 = 25$, $m_3 = -100$ $\left(\text{i.e. } m_1 = \dfrac{300-100}{2-0} = \dfrac{200}{2} = 100\right)$

(b) m_1: the pump is adding water at the rate of 100 gallons per hour.

m_2: the pump is adding water at the rate of 25 gallons per hour.

m_3: the pump is removing water at the rate of 100 gallons per hour.

(c) Initially the pool contained 100 gallons of water. The pump added 200 gallons of water over the first 2 hours. Then the pump added 100 gallons of water over the next 4 hours. Finally, the pump removed 200 gallons of water over the last 2 hours.

78.   (a) $m_1 = -100$, $m_2 = -50$, $m_3 = -25$ $\left(\text{i.e. } m_1 = \dfrac{300-500}{2-0} = \dfrac{-200}{2} = -100\right)$

(b) m_1: the pump is removing water at the rate of 100 gallons per hour.

m_2: the pump is removing water at the rate of 50 gallons per hour.

m_3: the pump is removing water at the rate of 25 gallons per hour.

(c) Initially the pool contained 500 gallons of water. The pump removed 200 gallons of water over the first 2 hours. Then the pump removed 100 gallons of water over the next 2 hours. Finally, the pump removed 50 gallons of water over the last 2 hours.

79.   (a) $m_1 = 50$, $m_2 = 0$, $m_3 = -20$, $m_4 = 0$ $\left(\text{i.e. } m_1 = \dfrac{50-0}{1-0} = \dfrac{50}{1} = 50\right)$

(b) m_1: the car is moving away from home at a rate of 50 miles per hour.

m_2: the car is not moving.

m_3: the car is moving toward home at a rate of 20 miles per hour.

m_4: the car is not moving.

(c) The car started at home and moved away from home at 50 mph for 1 hour to a location 50 miles from home.

The car was then parked for 1 hour. Next the car moved toward home at 20 mph for 2 hours to a location 10 miles from home. Finally, the car was parked for 1 hour.

80.   (a) $m_1 = 50$, $m_2 = -50$, $m_3 = 50$ $\left(\text{i.e. } m_1 = \dfrac{50-0}{1-0} = \dfrac{50}{1} = 50\right)$

(b) m_1: the car is moving away from home at a rate of 50 miles per hour.

m_2: the car is moving toward home at a rate of 50 miles per hour.

m_3: the car is moving away from home at a rate of 50 miles per hour.

(c) The car started at home and moved away from home at 50 mph for 1 hour to a location 50 miles from home.

The car then returned home in 1 hour at 50 mph. Finally, the car moved away from home at 50 mph for 2 hours to a location 100 miles from home.

81. See Figure 81.

82. See Figure 82.

Figure 81

Figure 82

Figure 83

83. See Figure 83.

84. See Figure 84.

Figure 84

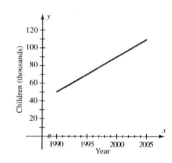
Figure 85

Applications

85. (a) $f(1993) = 4(1993) - 7910 = 62$ thousand

(b) See Figure 85. The graph is increasing.

(c) $m = 4$

(d) The number of children born to older mothers is increasing by about 4000 each year.

86. (a) $f(1980) = 201.7(1980) - 390,477 = 8889$

(b) $m = 201.7$

(c) The number of radio stations increased by about 202 stations per year over this time period.

87. (a) The year 2002 corresponds to $t = 15$. $N(15) = -358.4(15) + 13,723 = 8347$ banks.

(b) The slope is -358.4. The number of federally insured banks decreased by 358.4 banks per year on average.

(c) The y-intercept is 13,723. Initially there were 13,723 federally insured banks in 1987.

88. (a) The year 1900 corresponds to $t = 0$. $D(0) = 0.581(0) + 21.5 = 21.5$ people per square mile.

The year 2000 corresponds to $t = 100$. $D(100) = 0.581(100) + 21.5 = 79.6$ people per square mile.

(b) The slope is 0.581. Each year the population density increased by 0.581 people per square mile on average.

(c) The y-intercept is 21.5. Initially, in 1900, the population density was 21.5 people per square mile.

89. Since the graph passes through the points (0, 0) and (1, 10), the slope is $m = \dfrac{10-0}{1-0} = \dfrac{10}{1} = 10$.

The carpet costs $10 per square yard.

90. Since the graph passes through the points (0, 0) and (4, 100), the slope is $m = \dfrac{100-0}{4-0} = \dfrac{100}{4} = 25$.

Snow removal costs $25 per ton.

91. At the beginning of the 5-hour period, the pool contained $\dfrac{1}{4} \cdot 20,000 = 5000$ gallons of water. At the end of

the 5-hour period, the pool contained $\dfrac{5}{8} \cdot 20,000 = 12,500$ gallons of water. That is, the amount of water in

the pool increased by $12,500 - 5000 = 7500$ gallons in 5 hours. The rate is $\dfrac{7500}{5} = 1500$ gallons per hour.

92. (a) The year 1987 corresponds to $x = 0$ and the year 2004 corresponds to $x = 17$.

$$\text{slope} = \frac{24-46}{17-0} = -\frac{22}{17}, \quad \text{so} \quad a = -\frac{22}{17}.$$

The graph of the line $y = -\dfrac{22}{17}x + b$ goes through (0, 46), so $b = 46$.

(b) The year 1995 corresponds to $x = 8$. $f(8) = -\dfrac{22}{17}(8) + 46 \approx 36$

Using the model, the percentage for 1995 is about 36%. This estimate is 2% too high.

93. (a) The year 1987 corresponds to $x = 0$ and the year 2004 corresponds to $x = 17$.

$$\text{slope} = \frac{12.1-3.8}{17-0} = \frac{8.3}{17} = \frac{83}{170}, \quad \text{so} \quad a = \frac{83}{170}.$$

The graph of the line $y = \dfrac{83}{170}x + b$ goes through (0, 3.8), so $b = 3.8$.

(b) The year 2000 corresponds to $x = 13$.

$$f(13) = \frac{83}{170}(13) + 3.8 \approx 10.1$$

Using the model, the percentage for 2000 is about 10.1%.

This estimate is 0.4% too high.

94.   At the beginning of the 2-hour period, the plane had already traveled $\frac{1}{3} \cdot 1200 = 400$ miles. At the end of the

2-hour period, the plane had traveled $\frac{7}{8} \cdot 1200 = 1050$ miles. That is, the distance traveled by the plane over

the 2-hour period was $1050 - 400 = 650$ miles. The rate is $\frac{650}{2} = 325$ miles per hour.

95.   (a) The value of a is equal to the slope of the line passing through the points (0, 37,000) and (15, 60,000).

$a = \dfrac{60,000 - 37,000}{15} = \dfrac{23,000}{15} \approx 1533.3$. The value of b is the initial value in 1990, $b = 37,000$.

       (b) The year 2000 corresponds to $x = 10$. $f(10) = 1533.3(10) + 37,000 = 15,333 + 37,000 = \$52,333$

96.   (a) From the information given, the graph must pass through the points (0, 3.10) and (25, 5.15).

The slope is $a = \dfrac{5.15 - 3.10}{25 - 0} = \dfrac{2.05}{25} = 0.082$. The y-intercept is $b = 3.10$.

       (b) $f(40) = 0.082(40) + 3.10 = \$6.38$

Group Activity Solutions

1.   (a) See Figure 1. SUV sales increased during this time period.

Figure 1

      (b) $m = \dfrac{3.2 - 1.1}{2000 - 1992} = \dfrac{2.1}{8} \approx 0.27$. *Answers may vary.*

      (c) Using the slope $m = 0.27$ and the y-intercept 1.1, $y = 0.27x + 1.1$

      (d) SUV sales increased by about 0.27 million per year over this time period.

      (e) For 1997, $x = 5$, so $y = 0.27(5) + 1.1 = 2.45$ million. For 2001, $x = 9$, so $0.27(9) + 1.1 = 3.53$ million.

2.4: Equations of Lines and Linear Models

Concepts

1.   One

2.   One

3. $y = mx + b$

4. $y = m(x - x_1) + y_1$ or $y - y_1 = m(x - x_1)$

5. $y = b$

6. $x = h$

7. $m_1 = m_2$

8. -1

9.   The line must have slope $-\dfrac{3}{4}$. One example is $y = -\dfrac{3}{4}x - 3$. *Answers may vary.*

10.   The line must have slope $\dfrac{4}{3}$. One example is $y = \dfrac{4}{3}x + 2$. *Answers may vary.*

11.   The line must be vertical and have an equation of the form $x = h$. For example, $x = 1$. *Answers may vary.*

12.   The line must be horizontal and have an equation of the form $y = b$. For example, $y = -5$. *Answers may vary.*

13.   Yes. By substituting for x in the equation we see that when $x = -3$, $y = 4$.

14.   No. By substituting for x in the equation we see that when $x = 4$, $y = 0 \neq 2$.

15.   No. By substituting for x in the equation we see that when $x = -4$, $y = 2 \neq 3$.

16.   Yes. By substituting for x in the equation we see that when $x = 1$, $y = -13$.

17.   Since $m > 0$ the graph must be increasing. d

18.   Since $m < 0$ and $b \neq 0$ the graph must be decreasing but does not pass through the origin. b

19.   Since $m < 0$ and $b = 0$ the graph must be decreasing and it must pass through the origin. a

20.   This is the equation of a horizontal line. c

21.   Since $m > 0$ and $b = 0$ the graph must be increasing and it must pass through the origin. f

22.   This is the equation of a vertical line. e

Equations of Lines

23.   From the given point, count 3 units down and 4 units to the right to return to the line. Thus $m = \dfrac{-3}{4} = -\dfrac{3}{4}$.

       Using the given point in the point-slope form gives $y = -\dfrac{3}{4}\left(x - (-3)\right) + 2$ or $y = -\dfrac{3}{4}x - \dfrac{1}{4}$.

24.   From the given point, count 1 unit down and 4 units to the left to return to the line. Thus $m = \dfrac{-1}{-4} = \dfrac{1}{4}$.

       Using the given point in the point-slope form gives $y = \dfrac{1}{4}(x - 3) - 2$ or $y = \dfrac{1}{4}x - \dfrac{11}{4}$.

25.   From the given point, count 1 unit down and 3 units to the left to return to the line. Thus $m = \dfrac{-1}{-3} = \dfrac{1}{3}$.

       Using the given point in the point-slope form gives $y = \dfrac{1}{3}(x - 1) + 3$ or $y = \dfrac{1}{3}x + \dfrac{8}{3}$.

26.   From the given point, count 1 unit down and 4 units to the right to return to the line. Thus $m = \dfrac{-1}{4} = -\dfrac{1}{4}$.

Using the given point in the point-slope form gives $y = -\frac{1}{4}\left(x - (-3)\right) - 2$ or $y = -\frac{1}{4}x - \frac{11}{4}$.

27.　Here $m = -2$, $x_1 = 2$ and $y_1 = -3$. The equation is $y = -2(x-2) - 3$.

28.　Here $m = \frac{1}{2}$, $x_1 = -4$ and $y_1 = 1$. The equation is $y = \frac{1}{2}(x+4) + 1$.

29.　Here $m = 1.3$, $x_1 = 1990$ and $y_1 = 25$. The equation is $y = 1.3(x - 1990) + 25$.

30.　Here $m = 45$, $x_1 = 1999$ and $y_1 = 103$. The equation is $y = 45(x - 1999) + 103$.

31.　Here $m = \frac{-1-3}{-5-1} = \frac{-4}{-6} = \frac{2}{3}$. Then either $x_1 = 1$ and $y_1 = 3$ or $x_1 = -5$ and $y_1 = -1$.

　　The equation can be written as either $y = \frac{2}{3}(x-1) + 3$ or $y = \frac{2}{3}(x+5) - 1$.

32.　Here $m = \frac{-1-4}{3-(-2)} = \frac{-5}{5} = -1$. Then either $x_1 = -2$ and $y_1 = 4$ or $x_1 = 3$ and $y_1 = -1$.

　　The equation can be written as either $y = -(x+2) + 4$ or $y = -(x-3) - 1$.

33.　Here $m = \frac{45-5}{2000-1980} = \frac{40}{20} = 2$. Then either $x_1 = 1980$ and $y_1 = 5$ or $x_1 = 2000$ and $y_1 = 45$.

　　The equation can be written as either $y = 2(x-1980) + 5$ or $y = 2(x-2000) + 45$.

34.　Here $m = \frac{-10-50}{2000-1990} = \frac{-60}{10} = -6$. Then either $x_1 = 1990$ and $y_1 = 50$ or $x_1 = 2000$ and $y_1 = -10$.

　　The equation can be written as either $y = -6(x-1990) + 50$ or $y = -6(x-2000) - 10$.

35.　Here $m = \frac{4-0}{0-6} = \frac{4}{-6} = -\frac{2}{3}$. Then either $x_1 = 6$ and $y_1 = 0$ or $x_1 = 0$ and $y_1 = 4$.

　　The equation can be written as either $y = -\frac{2}{3}(x-6) + 0$ or $y = -\frac{2}{3}(x-0) + 4$.

36.　Here $m = \frac{66-16}{2000-1980} = \frac{50}{20} = \frac{5}{2}$. Then either $x_1 = 1980$ and $y_1 = 16$ or $x_1 = 2000$ and $y_1 = 66$.

　　The equation can be written as either $y = \frac{5}{2}(x-1980) + 16$ or $y = \frac{5}{2}(x-2000) + 66$.

37.　$y = 2(x-1) - 2 \Rightarrow y = 2x - 2 - 2 \Rightarrow y = 2x - 4$

38.　$y = -3(x+2) + 5 \Rightarrow y = -3x - 6 + 5 \Rightarrow y = -3x - 1$

39.　$y = \frac{1}{2}(x+4) + 1 \Rightarrow y = \frac{1}{2}x + 2 + 1 \Rightarrow y = \frac{1}{2}x + 3$

40.　$y = -\frac{2}{3}(x-3) - 6 \Rightarrow y = -\frac{2}{3}x + 2 - 6 \Rightarrow y = -\frac{2}{3}x - 4$

41.　$y = 22(x-1.5) - 10 \Rightarrow y = 22x - 33 - 10 \Rightarrow y = 22x - 43$

42. $y = -30(x+3) + 106 \Rightarrow y = -30x - 90 + 106 \Rightarrow y = -30x + 16$

43. $m = \dfrac{-8-7}{2-(-3)} = \dfrac{-15}{5} = -3$

$y = mx + b$

$7 = -3(-3) + b$

$7 = 9 + b$

$-2 = b$

$\Rightarrow y = -3x - 2$

44. $m = \dfrac{3-(-3)}{3-(-6)} = \dfrac{6}{9} = \dfrac{2}{3}$

$y = mx + b$

$-3 = \dfrac{2}{3}(-6) + b$

$-3 = -4 + b$

$1 = b$

$\Rightarrow y = \dfrac{2}{3}x + 1$

45. $m = \dfrac{-5-1}{4-(-4)} = \dfrac{-6}{8} = -\dfrac{3}{4}$

$y = mx + b$

$1 = -\dfrac{3}{4}(-4) + b$

$1 = 3 + b$

$-2 = b$

$\Rightarrow y = -\dfrac{3}{4}x - 2$

46. $m = \dfrac{-6-14}{4-(-1)} = \dfrac{-20}{5} = -4$

$y = mx + b$

$14 = -4(-1) + b$

$14 = 4 + b$

$10 = b$

$\Rightarrow y = -4x + 10$

47. $y = -\dfrac{1}{3}(x-0)-5 \Rightarrow y = -\dfrac{1}{3}x+0-5 \Rightarrow y = -\dfrac{1}{3}x-5$

48. $y = 5(x+1)+4 \Rightarrow y = 5x+5+4 \Rightarrow y = 5x+9$

49. $m = \dfrac{-1-(-2)}{2-3} = \dfrac{1}{-1} = -1 \Rightarrow y = -(x-3)-2 \Rightarrow y = -x+3-2 \Rightarrow y = -x+1$

50. $m = \dfrac{3-3}{-7-8} = \dfrac{0}{-15} = 0 \Rightarrow y = 0(x-8)+3 \Rightarrow y = 0x-0+3 \Rightarrow y = 3$

51.   The y-intercept is given. The point-slope form is not needed. $m = \dfrac{-\frac{2}{3}-0}{0-2} = \dfrac{-\frac{2}{3}}{-2} = \dfrac{1}{3} \Rightarrow y = \dfrac{1}{3}x-\dfrac{2}{3}$

52.   The y-intercept is given. The point-slope form is not needed. $m = \dfrac{4-0}{0-(-3)} = \dfrac{4}{3} \Rightarrow y = \dfrac{4}{3}x+4$

53.   The y-intercept is given. The point-slope form is not needed. $m = \dfrac{3-0}{0-1} = \dfrac{3}{-1} = -3 \Rightarrow y = -3x+3$

54.   The y-intercept is given. The point-slope form is not needed. $m = \dfrac{-5-0}{0-(-4)} = -\dfrac{5}{4} \Rightarrow y = -\dfrac{5}{4}x-5$

55.   Parallel lines have the same slope. $m = 4 \Rightarrow y = 4(x-1)+3 \Rightarrow y = 4x-4+3 \Rightarrow y = 4x-1$

56.   Parallel lines have the same slope. The y-intercept is given. $m = -\dfrac{2}{3} \Rightarrow y = -\dfrac{2}{3}x-10$

57.   Parallel lines have the same slope. $m = \dfrac{-2-3}{1-(-2)} = -\dfrac{5}{3}$

$y = mx+b$

$2 = -\dfrac{5}{3}(-3)+b$

$2 = 5+b$

$-3 = b$

$\Rightarrow y = -\dfrac{5}{3}x-3$

58.   Parallel lines have the same slope. $m = \dfrac{1-(-4)}{-3-1} = -\dfrac{5}{4}$

$y = mx+b$

$-1 = -\dfrac{5}{4}\left(\dfrac{1}{2}\right)+b$

$-1 = -\dfrac{5}{8}+b$

$-\dfrac{3}{8} = b$

$$\Rightarrow y = -\frac{5}{4}x - \frac{3}{8}$$

59.   The product of the slopes of two perpendicular lines is –1.

$$m = 3 \Rightarrow y = 3(x+3)+5 \Rightarrow y = 3x+9+5 \Rightarrow y = 3x+14$$

60.   The product of the slopes of two perpendicular lines is –1.

$$m = -\frac{4}{3} \Rightarrow y = -\frac{4}{3}(x+2)-3 \Rightarrow y = -\frac{4}{3}x - \frac{8}{3} - \frac{9}{3} \Rightarrow y = -\frac{4}{3}x - \frac{17}{3}$$

61.   The line passing through (–1, 6) and (8, –4) has slope $\dfrac{-4-6}{8-(-1)} = -\dfrac{10}{9}$. The product of the slopes of two

perpendicular lines is –1.

$$m = \frac{9}{10} \Rightarrow y = \frac{9}{10}\left(x+\frac{1}{2}\right)-2 \Rightarrow y = \frac{9}{10}x + \frac{9}{20} - \frac{40}{20} \Rightarrow y = \frac{9}{10}x - \frac{31}{20}$$

62.   The line passing through (–4, –1) and (2, 7) has slope $\dfrac{7-(-1)}{2-(-4)} = \dfrac{8}{6} = \dfrac{4}{3}$.

The product of the slopes of two perpendicular lines is –1.

$$m = -\frac{3}{4} \Rightarrow y = -\frac{3}{4}(x-4)-3 \Rightarrow y = -\frac{3}{4}x + 3 - 3 \Rightarrow y = -\frac{3}{4}x$$

63.   The product of the slopes of two perpendicular lines is –1.

$$m = -\frac{1}{c} \Rightarrow y = -\frac{1}{c}x + b$$

64.   The product of the slopes of two perpendicular lines is –1.

$$\text{slope} = \frac{1}{m} \Rightarrow y = \frac{1}{m}(x-a) \Rightarrow y = \frac{1}{m}x - \frac{a}{m}$$

65.   (a)   The slope of the perpendicular line must be the negative reciprocal of $\dfrac{1}{2}$. That is $m = -2$.

        Here $x_1 = 0$ and $y_1 = 2$. The equation is $y = -2(x-0)+2$ or $y = -2x+2$.

     (b)   See Figure 65.

66.   (a)   The slope of the perpendicular line must be the negative reciprocal of -3. That is $m = \dfrac{1}{3}$.

        Here $x_1 = 0$ and $y_1 = -3$. The equation is $y = \dfrac{1}{3}(x-0)-3$ or $y = \dfrac{1}{3}x - 3$.

     (b)   See Figure 66.

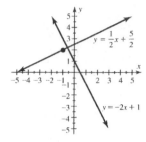

| Figure 65 | Figure 66 | Figure 67 |

67. (a) The slope of the perpendicular line must be the negative reciprocal of -2. That is $m = \dfrac{1}{2}$.

Here $x_1 = -1$ and $y_1 = 2$. The equation is $y = \dfrac{1}{2}(x+1) + 2$ or $y = \dfrac{1}{2}x + \dfrac{5}{2}$.

(b) See Figure 67.

68. (a) The slope of the perpendicular line must be the negative reciprocal of $\dfrac{2}{3}$. That is $m = -\dfrac{3}{2}$.

Here $x_1 = -1$ and $y_1 = 0$. The equation is $y = -\dfrac{3}{2}(x+1) + 0$ or $y = -\dfrac{3}{2}x - \dfrac{3}{2}$.

(b) See Figure 68.

69. (a) The slope of the perpendicular line must be the negative reciprocal of $-\dfrac{1}{3}$. That is $m = 3$.

Here $x_1 = 1$ and $y_1 = 1$. The equation is $y = 3(x-1) + 1$ or $y = 3x - 2$.

(b) See Figure 69.

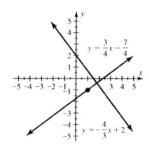

| Figure 68 | Figure 69 | Figure 70 |

70. (a) The slope of the perpendicular line must be the negative reciprocal of $-\dfrac{4}{3}$. That is $m = \dfrac{3}{4}$.

Here $x_1 = 1$ and $y_1 = -1$. The equation is $y = \dfrac{3}{4}(x-1) - 1$ or $y = \dfrac{3}{4}x - \dfrac{7}{4}$.

(b) See Figure 70.

71. (a) The slope of y_1 is $m_1 = \dfrac{2-0}{1-0} = \dfrac{2}{1} = 2$ and the y-intercept is $b = 0$. The equation is $y_1 = 2x$.

The slope of y_2 is $m_2 = \dfrac{1-0}{-2-0} = \dfrac{1}{-2} = -\dfrac{1}{2}$ and the y-intercept is $b = 0$. The equation is $y_2 = -\dfrac{1}{2}x$.

(b) The two lines are perpendicular since $m_1 m_2 = 2\left(-\dfrac{1}{2}\right) = -1$.

72. (a) The slope of y_1 is $m_1 = \dfrac{2-1}{3-0} = \dfrac{1}{3}$ and the y-intercept is $b = 1$. The equation is $y_1 = \dfrac{1}{3}x + 1$.

   The slope of y_2 is $m_2 = \dfrac{4-1}{-1-0} = \dfrac{3}{-1} = -3$ and the y-intercept is $b = 1$. The equation is $y_2 = -3x + 1$.

   (b) The two lines are perpendicular since $m_1 m_2 = \dfrac{1}{3}(-3) = -1$.

73. (a) The slope of y_1 is $m_1 = \dfrac{2-(-1)}{-2-0} = \dfrac{3}{-2} = -\dfrac{3}{2}$ and the y-intercept is $b = -1$. The equation is

   $y_1 = -\dfrac{3}{2}x - 1$.

   The slope of y_2 is $m_2 = \dfrac{1-(-1)}{3-0} = \dfrac{2}{3}$ and the y-intercept is $b = -1$. The equation is $y_2 = \dfrac{2}{3}x - 1$.

   (b) The two lines are perpendicular since $m_1 m_2 = -\dfrac{3}{2}\left(\dfrac{2}{3}\right) = -1$.

74. (a) The slope of y_1 is $m_1 = \dfrac{3-0}{0-(-1)} = \dfrac{3}{1} = 3$ and the y-intercept is $b = 3$. The equation is $y_1 = 3x + 3$.

   The slope of y_2 is $m_2 = \dfrac{0-(-1)}{-1-2} = \dfrac{1}{-3} = -\dfrac{1}{3}$ and the y-intercept is $b = -\dfrac{1}{3}$. The equation is

   $y_2 = -\dfrac{1}{3}x - \dfrac{1}{3}$.

   (b) The two lines are perpendicular since $m_1 m_2 = 3\left(-\dfrac{1}{3}\right) = -1$.

75. The equation of a vertical line is $x = h$. The equation is $x = -1$.

76. The equation of a vertical line is $x = h$. The equation is $x = 2$.

77. The equation of a horizontal line is $y = k$. The equation is $y = -\dfrac{5}{6}$.

78. The equation of a horizontal line is $y = k$. The equation is $y = 6.2$.

79. A line which is perpendicular to a horizontal line is vertical and has equation $x = h$. The equation is $x = 4$.

80. A line which is perpendicular to a vertical line is horizontal and has equation $y = k$. The equation is $y = 4$.

81. A line which is parallel to a vertical line is vertical and has equation $x = h$. The equation is $x = -\dfrac{2}{3}$.

82. A line which is parallel to a horizontal line is horizontal and has equation $y = k$. The equation is $y = 3.5$.

83. Yes. $m = \dfrac{0-(-4)}{2-1} = \dfrac{4}{1} = 4 \Rightarrow y = 4(x-2) + 0 \Rightarrow y = 4x - 8$

84.   No. The change in the y-values does not remain constant as the x-values increase.

85.   No. The change in the y-values does not remain constant as the x-values increase.

86.   Yes. $m = \dfrac{0-(-6)}{2-(-2)} = \dfrac{6}{4} = \dfrac{3}{2} \Rightarrow y = \dfrac{3}{2}(x-2)+0 \Rightarrow y = \dfrac{3}{2}x - 3$

Graphical Interpretation

87.   (a) Since the graph is increasing, the person is traveling away from home.

    (b) (1, 35): After 1 hour the person is 35 miles from home.

        (3, 95): After 3 hours the person is 95 miles from home.

    (c) $m = \dfrac{95-35}{3-1} = \dfrac{60}{2} = 30 \Rightarrow y = 30(x-1)+35$

        A slope of 30 means that the person is traveling 30 miles per hour.

88.   (a) Since the graph is decreasing, water is leaving the tank. There are 50 gallons in the tank after 3 minutes.

    (b) The x-intercept is 8: After 8 minutes the tank is empty.

        The y-intercept is 80: Initially the tank contains 80 gallons of water.

    (c) $m = \dfrac{80-0}{0-8} = \dfrac{80}{-8} = -10 \Rightarrow y = -10x + 80$

        The water is leaving the tank at a rate of 10 gallons per minute.

    (d) $D: 0 \le x \le 8; R: 0 \le y \le 80$

89.   (a) Two acres of land have 100 people and 4 acres of land have 200 people, on average.

    (b) A zero-acre parcel has no people.

    (c) The slope is $m = \dfrac{200-100}{4-2} = \dfrac{100}{2} = 50$, and the y-intercept is $b = 0$. The equation is $y = 50x$.

    (d) The land had 50 people per acre, on average.

    (e) $P(x) = 50x$

90.   (a) Two tons of rock cost \$48 and five tons of rock cost \$120.

    (b) Zero tons of rock would have no cost.

    (c) The slope is $m = \dfrac{120-48}{5-2} = \dfrac{72}{3} = 24$, and the y-intercept is $b = 0$. The equation is $y = 24x$.

    (d) The cost of the rock is \$24 per ton.

    (e) $C(x) = 24x$

Applications

91.   (a) The slope is $m = \dfrac{37,000-25,000}{2007-2003} = \dfrac{12,000}{4} = 3000$. Using the point (2003, 25000) the equation is

        $y = 3000(x-2003)+25,000$ or $y = 3000x - 5,984,000$.

    (b) The cost is increasing by \$3000 per year, on average.

    (c) In 2005 the cost is estimated to be $y = 3000(2005) - 5,984,000 = \$31,000$.

92. (a) The slope is $m = \dfrac{63-20}{2000-1950} = \dfrac{43}{50} = 0.86$. Using the point (1950, 20) the equation is

$$f(x) = 0.86(x-1950)+20 \text{ or } f(x) = 0.86x-1657.$$

(b) $f(1960) = 0.86(1960)-1657 = 28.6$ million. $f(2010) = 0.86(2010)-1657 = 71.6$ million.

(c) $f(1900) = 0.86(1900)-1657 = -23$ million. The model is not valid for 1900. The answer has no

meaning.

93. First find a linear function that can be used to model these data. Then use the function to find the value in

2008.

The slope is $m = \dfrac{60-57}{2010-2005} = \dfrac{3}{5} = 0.6$. Using the point (2005, 57) the equation is

$$f(x) = 0.6(x-2005)+57 \text{ or } f(x) = 0.6x-1146.$$

The estimated chicken consumption in 2008 is $f(2008) = 0.6(2008)-1146 = 58.8$ pounds.

94. First find a linear function that can be used to model these data. Then use the function to find the value in

2005.

The slope is $m = \dfrac{11-9}{2002-2000} = \dfrac{2}{2} = 1$. Using the point (2000, 9) the equation is

$$f(x) = 1(x-2000)+9 \text{ or } f(x) = x-1991.$$

The estimated time spent on the Internet in 2005 is $f(2005) = (2005)-1991 = 14$ hours per week.

95. First find a linear function that can be used to model these data. Then use the function to find the value in

1970.

The slope is $m = \dfrac{77-48}{2000-1900} = \dfrac{29}{100} = 0.29$. Using the point (1900, 48) the equation is

$$f(x) = 0.29(x-1900)+48 \text{ or } f(x) = 0.29x-503.$$

The estimated life expectancy of a baby born in 1970 is $f(1970) = 0.29(1970) - 503 = 68.3$ years.

96. First find a linear function that can be used to model these data. Then use the function to find the value in

1996.

The slope is $m = \dfrac{15,000-22,000}{1999-1994} = \dfrac{-7000}{5} = -1400$. Using the point (1994, 22000) the equation is

$$f(x) = -1400(x-1994)+22,000 \text{ or } f(x) = -1400x+2,813,600.$$

The estimated number of AIDS infections in 1996 is $f(1996) = -1400(1996)+2,813,600 = 19,200$

infections.

97. Using the points (1, 1) and (4, 13) the slope is $m = \dfrac{13-1}{4-1} = \dfrac{12}{3} = 4$.

Then using the point (1, 1) the equation is $y = 4(x-1)+1$ or $y = 4x-3$.

98.   Using the points (1, 3) and (5, –5) the slope is $m = \dfrac{-5-3}{5-1} = \dfrac{-8}{4} = -2$.

Then using the point (1, 3) the equation is $y = -2(x-1)+3$ or $y = -2x+5$.

99.   Using the points (1, 8) and (5, –6) the slope is $m = \dfrac{-6-8}{5-1} = \dfrac{-14}{4} = -3.5$.

Then using the point (1, 8) the equation is $y = -3.5(x-1)+8$ or $y = -3.5x+11.5$.

100.   Using the points (10, 5) and (50, 60) the slope is $m = \dfrac{60-5}{50-10} = \dfrac{55}{40} = 1.375$.

Then using the point (10, 5) the equation is $y = 1.375(x-10)+5$ or $y = 1.375x-8.75$.

101.   Using the points (1998, 1.4) and (2002, 1.8) the slope is $m = \dfrac{1.8-1.4}{2002-1998} = \dfrac{0.4}{4} = 0.1$.

Then using the point (1998, 1.4) the equation is $y = 0.1(x-1998)+1.4$ or $y = 0.1x-198.4$.

102.   Using the points (2001, 9.25) and (2006, 14.25) the slope is $m = \dfrac{14.25-9.25}{2006-2001} = \dfrac{5}{5} = 1$.

Then using the point (2001, 9.25) the equation is $y = 1(x-2001)+9.25$ or $y = x-1991.75$.

103.   Using the points (1950, 1.7) and (1980, 4.4) the slope is $m = \dfrac{4.4-1.7}{1980-1950} = \dfrac{2.7}{30} = 0.09$.

Then using the point (1950, 1.7) the equation is $y = 0.09(x-1950)+1.7$ or $y = 0.09x-173.8$.

104.   Using the points (2002, 4.0) and (2006, 12.6) the slope is $m = \dfrac{12.6-4.0}{2006-2002} = \dfrac{8.6}{4} = 2.15$.

Then using the point (2002, 4.0) the equation is $y = 2.15(x-2002)+4$ or $y = 2.15x-4300.3$.

105.   (a) The cost per mile is $a = 0.30$. The fixed cost is $b = 189.20$.

(b) The y-intercept represents the fixed cost of owning the car for one month.

106.   (a) Because the rate of change is 5.4 million cases per year, $m = 5.4$. Here $x_1 = 1999$ and $y_1 = 24$.

(b) $f(2007) = 5.4(2007-1999)+24 = 67.2$ million cases per year.

107.   (a) $m = \dfrac{7-5}{5.4-4.9} = \dfrac{2}{0.5} = 4$

$\Rightarrow R(c) = 4(c-4.9)+5 \Rightarrow R(c) = 4c-19.6+5 \Rightarrow R(c) = 4c-14.6$

(b) $R(6.16) = 4(6.16)-14.6 = 10.04$; the ring size is about 10.

108.   (a) $m = \dfrac{8-7}{25-21\frac{7}{8}} = \dfrac{1}{3\frac{1}{8}} = \dfrac{1}{\frac{25}{8}} = \dfrac{8}{25} = 0.32$

$\Rightarrow H(c) = 0.32(c-25)+8 \Rightarrow H(c) = 0.32c-8+8$

$\Rightarrow H(c) = 0.32c$

(b) $H(23) = 0.32(23) = 7.36 \approx 7\dfrac{3}{8}$

109. (a) See Figure 109.

(b) Using the points (1970, 203) and (2000, 281) the slope is $m = \dfrac{281 - 203}{2000 - 1970} = \dfrac{78}{30} = 2.6$.

Then using the point (1970, 203), $x_1 = 1970$ and $y_1 = 203$. *Answers may vary.*

(c) The population in 2010 is estimated to be $f(2010) = 2.6(2010 - 1970) + 203 = 307$ million.

Figure 109

110. (a) Using the points (1991, 18.3) and (1995, 20.7) the slope is $m = \dfrac{20.7 - 18.3}{1995 - 1991} = \dfrac{2.4}{4} = 0.6$.

Then using the point (1991, 18.3), $x_1 = 1991$ and $y_1 = 18.3$. *Answers may vary.*

(b) The percentage of women in the state legislatures in 2005 is $f(2005) = 0.6(2005 - 1991) + 18.3 = 26.7$.

Checking Basic Concepts for Sections 2.3 & 2.4

1. (a) The equation is in point-slope form, $m = -3$. One point on this line is (5, 7). *Answers may vary.*

(b) This is a horizontal line, $m = 0$. One point on this line is (1, 10). *Answers may vary.*

(c) This is a vertical line, m is undefined. One point on this line is (–5, 0). *Answers may vary.*

(d) The equation is in slope-intercept form, $m = 5$. One point on this line is (0, 3). *Answers may vary.*

2. (a) $m = \dfrac{2 - (-4)}{5 - 2} = \dfrac{6}{3} = 2$

(b) For the point-slope form of the equation either $y = 2(x - 2) - 4$ or $y = 2(x - 5) + 2$.

The slope-intercept form is $y = 2(x - 2) - 4 \Rightarrow y = 2x - 4 - 4 \Rightarrow y = 2x - 8$.

(c) x-intercept: $0 = 2x - 8 \Rightarrow 8 = 2x \Rightarrow x = 4$; y-intercept: $y = 2(0) - 8 \Rightarrow y = -8$

3. A vertical line has an equation of the form $x = h$. The equation is $x = -2$.

A horizontal line has an equation of the form $y = k$. The equation is $y = 5$.

4. The given line has slope $m = -\dfrac{1}{2}$; thus a parallel line has slope $m = -\dfrac{1}{2}$ and a perpendicular line has slope

$m = 2$.

Perpendicular: $y = 2(x - 2) + (-4) \Rightarrow y = 2x - 4 - 4 \Rightarrow y = 2x - 8$

Parallel: $y = -\dfrac{1}{2}(x-2)+(-4) \;\Rightarrow\; y = -\dfrac{1}{2}x+1-4 \;\Rightarrow\; y = -\dfrac{1}{2}x-3$

5.   (a) Since the line is decreasing, the distance from home is decreasing. The car is moving toward home.

(b) $m = -50$ since the y-value decreases 50 units for every unit increase in the x-value. The car is moving toward home at 50 mph.

(c) x-intercept: 5; after 5 hours the car is home. y-intercept: 250; The car is initially 250 miles from home.

(d) The slope is $a = -50$ and the y-intercept is $b = 250$.

(e) $D: 0 \le x \le 5$; $R: 0 \le y \le 250$

Chapter 2 Review Exercises

Section 2.1

1. $f(-2) = 3(-2)-1 = -7$; $f\left(\dfrac{1}{3}\right) = 3\left(\dfrac{1}{3}\right)-1 = 0$

2. $f(-3) = 5-3(-3)^2 = 5-27 = -22$; $f(1) = 5-3(1)^2 = 5-3 = 2$

3. $f(0) = \sqrt{0}-2 = -2$; $f(9) = \sqrt{9}-2 = 3-2 = 1$

4. $f(-5) = 5$; $f\left(\dfrac{7}{5}\right) = 5$

5.   (a) Since there are 2 pints in a quart, $P(q) = 2q$.

(b) $P(5) = 2(5) = 10$. There are 10 pints in 5 quarts.

6.   (a) Three less than four times a number is written $f(x) = 4x-3$.

(b) $f(5) = 4(5)-3 = 17$. Three less than four times five is 17.

7. $(3, -2)$

8. $f(4) = -6$; the answers are 4 and –6.

9.   See Figure 9.

10.   See Figure 10.

Figure 9

Figure 10

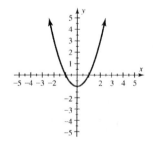

Figure 11

11.   See Figure 11.

12.   See Figure 12.

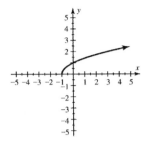

Figure 12

13. $f(0) = 1;\ f(-3) = 4$

14. $f(-2) = 1;\ f(1) = -2$

15. $f(-1) = 7;\ f(3) = -1$

16.   Numerical: The table is shown in Figure 16a.

Symbolic: $f(x) = 3x - 2$

Graphical: The graph is shown in Figure 16b.

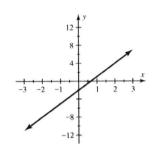

x	-3	-2	-1	0	1	2	3
$y = f(x)$	-11	-8	-5	-2	1	4	7

Figure 16a   Figure 16b

17. D: all real numbers; R: $y \le 4$

18. D: $-4 \le x \le 4$; R: $-4 \le y \le 0$

19.   Yes. The graph passes the vertical line test.

20.   No. The graph does not pass the vertical line test.

21. $D = \{-3, -1, 2, 4\}$; $R = \{-1, 3, 4\}$; Yes, S is a function since each input has exactly one output.

22. $D = \{-1, 0, 1, 2\}$; $R = \{-2, 2, 3, 4, 5\}$; No, S is not a function because the input -1 has more than one output.

23.   Any real number is a valid input for this function. D: all real numbers.

24.   The radicand must be greater than or equal to zero. D: $x \ge 0$.

25.   The denominator of this function cannot equal zero. D: $x \ne 0$.

26.   Any real number is a valid input for this function because the variable is squared. D: all real numbers.

27.   The radicand must be greater than or equal to zero. D: $x \le 5$

28.   The denominator of this function cannot equal zero. D: $x \ne -2$

29.   Any real number is a valid input for this function. D: all real numbers

30.   Any real number is a valid input for this function. D: all real numbers

Section 2.2

31.   No. The graph is not a straight line.

32.   Yes. The graph is a straight line.

33.   This function is linear because it is in the form $f(x) = ax + b$ with $a = -4$ and $b = 5$.

34.   This function is linear because it can be written in the form $f(x) = ax + b$ with $a = -1$ and $b = 7$.

35.   This function is not linear because it contains a square root.

36.   This function is linear because it can be written in the form $f(x) = ax + b$ with $a = 0$ and $b = 6$.

37.   Yes. For each 2-unit increase in x, the values of $f(x)$ increase by 3 units, so $a = \dfrac{3}{2}$.

Because $f(x) = -3$ when $x = 0$, the y-intercept is $b = -3$. The function can be written $f(x) = \dfrac{3}{2}x - 3$.

38.   No. For each unit increase in x, the values of $f(x)$ do not increase by a constant amount.

39. $f(-4) = \dfrac{1}{2}(-4) + 3 = -2 + 3 = 1$

40. $f(-2) = -3$ and $f(1) = 0$

41.   See Figure 41.

42.   See Figure 42.

Figure 41

Figure 42

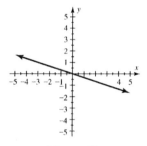

Figure 43

43.   See Figure 43.

44.   See Figure 44.

Figure 44

Figure 55

Figure 56

45.   There are 24 hours in each day, so $H(x) = 24x$.

$H(2) = 24(2) = 48$; there are 48 hours in 2 days.

46.   (a) See Figure 46a.   (b) See Figure 46b. Domain: $x \geq -2$

$[-10, 10, 1]$ by $[-10, 10, 1]$

Figure 46a

Figure 46b

Section 2.3

47.   –2. The *y*-value decreases 2 units for every 1–unit increase in the *x*-value.

48.   0. This is a horizontal line.

49. $\dfrac{1}{3}$. The *y*-value increases 1 unit for every 3 units of increase in the *x*-value.

50.   Undefined. This is a vertical line.

51. $m = \dfrac{8-2}{3-(-1)} = \dfrac{6}{4} = \dfrac{3}{2}$

52. $m = \dfrac{-\frac{1}{2}-\frac{5}{2}}{1-(-3)} = \dfrac{-\frac{6}{2}}{4} = \dfrac{-3}{4} = -\dfrac{3}{4}$

53. $m = \dfrac{-4-(-4)}{5-3} = \dfrac{0}{2} = 0$

54. $m = \dfrac{8-6}{-2-(-2)} = \dfrac{2}{0} \Rightarrow$ undefined

55.   See Figure 55.

56.   By writing the equation in the form $y = -\dfrac{2}{3}x + 0$, the slope is $-\dfrac{2}{3}$ and the *y*-intercept is 0. See Figure 56.

57.   The slope is –3 since the *y*-value decreases 3 units for every 1–unit increase in the *x*-value.

The *y*-intercept is 1 since the graph crosses the *y*-axis at (0, 1). The equation is $y = -3x + 1$.

58.   The slope is $m = \dfrac{2-0}{0-(-1)} = \dfrac{2}{1} = 2$. The *y*-intercept is 2. The equation is $y = 2x + 2$.

59.   The slope is –1 since the *y*-value decreases 1 unit for every 1–unit increase in the *x*-value.

The *y*-intercept is 1 since the graph crosses the *y*-axis at (0, 1).

60.   (a) $m_1 = \dfrac{1000-500}{2-0} = \dfrac{500}{2} = 250$; Similarly, $m_2 = 500$, $m_3 = 0$, $m_4 = -750$

(b) m_1: Water is being added to the pool at a rate of 250 gallons per hour. m_2: Water is being added to the pool at a rate of 500 gallons per hour. m_3: No water is being added or removed. m_4: Water is being removed from the pool at a rate of 750 gallons per hour.

(c) Initially the pool contains 500 gallons of water. For the first two hours water is added to the pool at a rate of 250 gallons per hour until there are 1000 gallons in the pool. Then water is added at a rate of 500 gallons per hour for 1 hour until there are 1500 gallons in the pool. For the next hour, no water is added or removed. Finally, water is removed from the pool at a rate of 750 gallons per hour for 1 hour until it contains 750 gallons.

61.   See Figure 61.

Figure 61   Figure 62

62.   (a) The equation is in the form $f(x) = mx + b$. The slope is $\frac{1}{2}$ and the y-intercept is -2.

(b) See Figure 62.

Section 2.4

63.   Yes, the point (2, 1) lies on the graph because when $x = 2$, $y = \frac{3}{2}(2) - 2 = 3 - 2 = 1$.

64.   The slope is $m = \frac{4-6}{0-(-1)} = \frac{-2}{1} = -2$. From the table, the x-intercept is 2 and the y-intercept is 4.

65. $y = -3(x-2) + 1 \Rightarrow y = -3x + 6 + 1 \Rightarrow y = -3x + 7$

66. $y = -3(x+2) + 3; \ y = -3x - 6 + 3 \Rightarrow y = -3x - 3$

67.   Here $m = \frac{-3-0}{0-2} = \frac{-3}{-2} = \frac{3}{2}$. Use $x_1 = 2$ and $y_1 = 0$ in the point-slope form to get the slope-intercept form.

The slope-intercept equation is $y = \frac{3}{2}(x-2) + 0 \Rightarrow y = \frac{3}{2}x - 3$.

68.   Here $m = \frac{-2-4}{2-(-1)} = \frac{-6}{3} = -2$. Use $x_1 = -1$ and $y_1 = 4$ in the point-slope form to get the slope-intercept form.

The slope-intercept equation is $y = -2(x+1) + 4 \Rightarrow y = -2x + 2$.

69.   Parallel lines have the same slope, thus $m = 4$. Use $x_1 = -\frac{3}{5}$ and $y_1 = \frac{1}{5}$ in the point-slope form to get the slope-intercept form. The slope-intercept equation is $y = 4\left(x + \frac{3}{5}\right) + \frac{1}{5} \Rightarrow y = 4x + \frac{12}{5} + \frac{1}{5} \Rightarrow y = 4x + \frac{13}{5}$.

70.   The product of the slopes of two perpendicular lines is -1 thus $m = -2$. Then $x_1 = -1$ and $y_1 = 1$.

The slope-intercept equation is $y = -2(x+1)+1 \Rightarrow y = -2x-2+1 \Rightarrow y = -2x-1$.

71.   By inspection we see that the slope is $m = -1$. The y-intercept is 2. The equation is $y = -x+2$.

72.   By inspection we see that the slope is $m = 2$. The y-intercept is –3. The equation is $y = 2x-3$.

73.   No. By substituting for x in the equation we see that when $x = 2$, $y = 1 \neq -1$.

74.   Yes. By substituting for x in the equation we see that when $x = 4$, $y = -\dfrac{5}{2}$.

75.   The equation of a vertical line is $x = h$. The equation is $x = -4$.

76.   The equation of a horizontal line is $y = k$. The equation is $y = -\dfrac{7}{13}$.

77.   The line $x = -3$ is vertical, so a line perpendicular to it is horizontal. The horizontal line through $(-2, 1)$ is

$y = 1$.

78.   The line $y = 5$ is horizontal, so a line parallel to it is also horizontal. The horizontal line through $(4, -8)$ is

$y = -8$.

79.   No. The change in the y-values does not remain constant as the x-values increase.

80.   Yes. $m = \dfrac{5-1}{0-(-2)} = \dfrac{4}{2} = 2 \Rightarrow y = 2(x-0)+5 \Rightarrow y = 2x+5$

Applications

81.   (a) $m_1 = 1.3, m_2 = 2.35, m_3 = 2.4, m_4 = 2.7$ $\left(\text{i.e. } m_1 = \dfrac{132-106}{1940-1920} = \dfrac{26}{20} = 1.3\right)$

(b) m_1 : from 1920 to 1940 the population increased on average by 1.3 million per year.

m_2 : from 1940 to 1960 the population increased on average by 2.35 million per year.

m_3 : from 1960 to 1980 the population increased on average by 2.4 million per year.

m_4 : from 1980 to 2000 the population increased on average by 2.7 million per year.

82.   For the first 2 minutes the inlet pipe is open. For the next 3 minutes both pipes are open. For the next 2 minutes only the outlet pipe is open. Finally, for the last 3 minutes both pipes are closed.

83.   (a) $f(1910) = -0.0492(1910)+119.1 \approx 25.1$ years

(b)   Graph $Y_1 = -0.0492X +119.1$ in [1885, 1965, 10] by [22, 26, 1]. See Figure 83.

The median age at first marriage for males has decreased over this time period.

(c)   The slope is –0.0492. The median age decreased by about 0.0492 year per year.

[1885, 1965, 10] by [22, 26, 1]

Figure 83

84.   (a) $f(1991) = 2.4$ million

(b) The number of marriages each year did not change over this time period.

85.   (a) $f(x) = 8x$

(b) The slope of the graph of f is 8.

(c) The total fat changes at a rate of 8 grams per cup of milk.

86.   (a) See Figure 86.

(b) Using the first and last data points to find the linear function results in $f(x) = -0.31x + 633.6$.

(c) $f(2000) = -0.31(2000 - 1990) + 16.7 = -0.31(10) + 16.7 = -3.1 + 16.7 = 13.6$

The birth rate is about 13.6 per 1000 people. *Answers may vary.*

Figure 86

87.   (a) From the table $f(1995) = 113$. In 1995 there were 113 unhealthy days.

(b) $D = \{1995, 1997, 1999, 2000, 2003\}$; $R = \{56, 60, 87, 88, 113\}$

(c) The number of unhealthy days decreased and then increased over this time period.

88.   (a) See Figure 88. There is a linear relationship.

(b) Using the points (0, 32) and (100, 212) the slope is $m = \dfrac{212 - 32}{100 - 0} = \dfrac{180}{100} = \dfrac{9}{5}$. The y-intercept is 32.

The function is given by $f(x) = \dfrac{9}{5}x + 32$. The slope of $\dfrac{9}{5}$ means that

a 1°C change equals a $\dfrac{9}{5}$°F change.

(c) $f(20) = \dfrac{9}{5}(20) + 32 = 36 + 32 = 68°$ F.

Figure 88

Figure 89

89.   See Figure 89.

90.   (a) Because the rate of change is 25,000 cases per year, $m = 25,000$. Here $x_1 = 2000$ and $y_1 = 875,000$.

The equation is $f(x) = 25,000(x - 2000) + 875,000$.

(b) $f(2007) = 25,000(2007 - 2000) + 875,000 = 1,050,000$ cases. This is the total (cumulative) number of

U.S. AIDS cases reported in 2007.

91.   The graph should be increasing and should initially be a positive amount. b

92.   The graph should be a horizontal line above the *x*-axis since this distance is a positive constant. e

93.   The graph should be increasing and should start at zero. a

94.   The graph should be decreasing since this film format is nearly extinct. d

95.   The graph should be a horizontal line below the *x*-axis since this temperature is a negative constant. f

96.   The graph should start below the *x*-axis and then increase to a value above the *x*-axis. c

Chapter 2 Test

1. $f(4) = 3(4)^2 - \sqrt{4} = 3(16) - 2 = 48 - 2 = 46; (4, 46)$

2. $C(x) = 4x;\ C(5) = 4(5) = 20;\ $ 5 pounds of candy costs \$20.

3.   (a) See Figure 3a.

(b) See Figure 3b.

(c) See Figure 3c.

(d) See Figure 3d.

Figure 3a

Figure 3b

Figure 3c

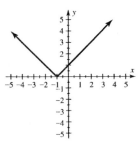

Figure 3d

4. $f(-3) = 0;\ f(0) = -3;\ D:\{x | -3 \le x \le 3\}$ and $R:\{x | -3 \le y \le 0\}$

5.   Symbolic: $f(x) = x^2 - 5$

Numerical: The table is shown in Figure 5a.

Graphical: The graph is shown in Figure 5b.

x	−3	−2	−1	0	1	2	3
$y = f(x)$	4	−1	−4	−5	−4	−1	4

Figure 5a   Figure 5b

6.   No. It does not pass the vertical line test.

7.   (a) $D = \{-2, -1, 0, 5\}$, $R = \{3, 5, 7\}$

(b) Any real number is a valid input for this function.

D: all real numbers

(c) The radicand must be greater than or equal to zero.

$D: x \geq -4$

(d) Any real number is a valid input for this function.

D: all real numbers

(e) The denominator of this function cannot equal zero.

$D: x \neq 5$

8.   It is; $f(x) = -8x + 6$

9. $m = \dfrac{-2 - 7}{6 - (-3)} = \dfrac{-9}{9} = -1$

10. $-\dfrac{1}{2}$. The y-value decreases 1 unit for every 2 units of increase in the x-value.

11.   (a) The line passes through $(-2, 0)$ and $(0, -4)$.

$$m = \frac{-4 - 0}{0 - (-2)} = \frac{-4}{2} = -2 \Rightarrow y = -2x - 4$$

(b) The line passing through $(-2, 5)$ and $(-1, 3)$ is $\dfrac{3 - 5}{-1 - (-2)} = \dfrac{-2}{1} = -2$. The product of the slopes of

perpendicular lines is -1. $m = \dfrac{1}{2} \Rightarrow y = \dfrac{1}{2}(x + 5) + 2 \Rightarrow y = \dfrac{1}{2}x + \dfrac{5}{2} + 2 \Rightarrow y = \dfrac{1}{2}x + \dfrac{9}{2}$

(c) $m = \dfrac{\frac{3}{2} - (-2)}{-5 - 1} = \dfrac{\frac{3}{2} + \frac{4}{2}}{-6} = \dfrac{\frac{7}{2}}{-6} = \dfrac{7}{2} \cdot \left(-\dfrac{1}{6}\right) = -\dfrac{7}{12}$

$\Rightarrow y = -\dfrac{7}{12}(x - 1) - 2 \Rightarrow y = -\dfrac{7}{12}x - \dfrac{17}{12}$

12. The slope is $m = \dfrac{0-4}{2-0} = \dfrac{-4}{2} = -2$. From the table, the x-intercept is 2 and the y-intercept is 4.

13. A line parallel to the given line has slope $m = -3$.

    The slope-intercept equation is $y = -3\left(x - \dfrac{1}{3}\right) + 2 \;\Rightarrow\; y = -3x + 1 + 2 \;\Rightarrow\; y = -3x + 3$.

14. By inspection the line has slope $m = \dfrac{2}{3}$. The y-intercept is -2. The slope-intercept equation is $y = \dfrac{2}{3}x - 2$.

    A line perpendicular to this line that passes through the origin would have slope $m = -\dfrac{3}{2}$ and y-intercept

    0. The equation of the perpendicular line is $y = -\dfrac{3}{2}x$.

15. A vertical line has equation $x = h$. The equation is $x = \dfrac{2}{3}$. A horizontal line has equation $y = k$. The

    equation is $y = -\dfrac{1}{7}$.

16. (a) $m_1 = \dfrac{11-7}{1980-1970} = \dfrac{4}{10} = 0.4$; Similarly, $m_2 = 0$, $m_3 = -0.4$

    (b) m_1: From 1970 to 1980 the number of welfare beneficiaries increased by 0.4 million per year on

    average.

    m_1: From 1980 to 1990 there was no change in the number of welfare beneficiaries.

    m_1: From 1990 to 2000 the number of welfare beneficiaries decreased by 0.4 million per year on

    average.

17. See Figure 17.

Figure 17

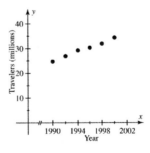

Figure 18

18. (a) See Figure 18.

    (b) Using the points (1990, 24.8) and (2000, 34.4): $m = \dfrac{34.4 - 24.8}{2000 - 1990} = \dfrac{9.6}{10} = 0.96$, $x_1 = 1990$, $y_1 = 24.8$

    Answers may vary.

    (c) $f(2002) = 0.96(2002 - 1990) + 24.8 = 0.96(12) + 24.8 = 11.52 + 24.8 \approx 36.3$

    In 2002 the number of travelers was about 36.3 million. *Answers may vary.*

Chapter 2 Extended and Discovery Exercises

1. (a) The graph for tank A is linear. See Figures 1a. The graph for tank B is nonlinear. See Figure 1b.

   (b) Tank B flows faster at first so it is the first to be half empty.

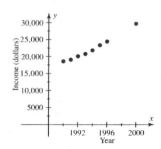

Figure 1a   Figure 1b   Figure 2

2. (a) See Figure 2.

   (b) Since the data appears to be nearly linear with an annual increase of about $1100 per year we may find a point-slope form of a linear equation using the point (1990, 18,666) and slope $m = 1100$.

   The equation is $f(x) = 1100(x - 1990) + 18,666$. *Answers may vary.*

   (c) $f(1998) = 1100(1998 - 1990) + 18,666 = 8800 + 18,666 = \$27,466$

3. The line that passes through (0, 0) and (5, 3) has slope $m = \dfrac{3-0}{5-0} = \dfrac{3}{5}$ and y-intercept 0.

   The equation for this line is $y = \dfrac{3}{5}x$. The line parallel to this line has the same slope and y-intercept 5.

   The equation for this parallel line is $y = \dfrac{3}{5}x + 5$. The perpendicular line which passes through (0, 0) has

   slope $m = -\dfrac{5}{3}$ and y-intercept 0. Its equation is $y = -\dfrac{5}{3}x$. Finally, the fourth side of the rectangle passes

   through (5, 3) and has slope $m = -\dfrac{5}{3}$. Its equation is $y = -\dfrac{5}{3}(x - 5) + 3 \Rightarrow y = -\dfrac{5}{3}x + \dfrac{34}{3}$.

4. The line that passes through (0, 0) and (2, 2) has slope $m = \dfrac{2-0}{2-0} = \dfrac{2}{2} = 1$ and y-intercept 0.

   The equation for this line is $y = x$. The line parallel to this line has the same slope and passes through (1, 3).

   The equation for this parallel line is $y = 1(x - 1) + 3 \Rightarrow y = x + 2$. The perpendicular line which passes

   through (0, 0) has slope $m = -1$ and y-intercept 0. Its equation is $y = -x$. Finally, the fourth side of the

   rectangle passes through (1, 3) and has slope $m = -1$. Its equation is $y = -1(x - 1) + 3 \Rightarrow y = -x + 4$.

   See Figure 4.

Figure 4

Figure 5

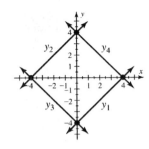

Figure 6

5. The line that passes through (1, 1) and (5, 1) is horizontal and has equation $y = 1$. The line parallel to this line is also horizontal and passes through (5, 5). Its equation is $y = 5$. The perpendicular line which passes through the point (1, 1) is vertical and has equation $x = 1$. Finally, the other vertical line passes through (5, 1) and has equation $x = 5$. See Figure 5.

6. The line that passes through (4, 0) and (0, 4) has slope $m = \dfrac{4 - 0}{0 - 4} = \dfrac{4}{-4} = -1$ and y-intercept 4.

    The equation for this line is $y = -x + 4$. The line parallel to this line has the same slope and y-intercept -4. The equation for this parallel line is $y = -x - 4$. The perpendicular line which passes through (0, 4) has slope $m = 1$ and y-intercept 4. Its equation is $y = x + 4$. Finally, the fourth side of the rectangle has slope $m = 1$ and y-intercept -4. Its equation is $y = x - 4$. See Figure 6.

7. (a) See Figure 7.

    (b) $m_1 = -0.24$, $m_2 = -0.98$, $m_3 = -0.97$, $m_4 = -0.95$, $m_5 = -0.93$, $m_6 = -0.85$, $m_7 = -0.76$, $m_8 = -0.63$ ie. we may calculate the slope of the first line segment as follows: $m_1 = \dfrac{69.9 - 72.3}{10 - 0} = \dfrac{-2.4}{10} = -0.24$ m_1: from age 0 to age 10 the remaining life expectancy decreases at the rate of 0.24 years per year The remaining slopes may be interpreted in a similar way.

    (c) A 20-year-old woman is expected to live 60.1 more years making her total life expectancy 80.1 years. A 70-year-old woman is expected to live 15.5 more years making her total life expectancy 85.5 years. The 70-year-old woman has already lived through much of the risk that a 20-year-old must still face.

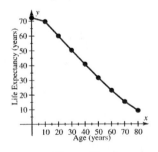

Figure 7

8. (a) When the fish hatches it weighs about 7 mg. It weighs about 105 mg at 6 weeks of age and about 158 mg at 12 weeks of age. *Answers may vary.*

(b) From hatching to 6 weeks: $\dfrac{105-7}{6-0}=\dfrac{98}{6}\approx 16.3$ mg/week.

From 6 weeks to 12 weeks: $\dfrac{158-105}{12-6}=\dfrac{53}{6}\approx 8.8$ mg/week.

(c) On average the fish gains about 16.3 mg per week during the first 6 weeks of its life and about 8.8 mg per week during the second 6 weeks of its life.

(d) The fish gains weight the fastest during the first 6 weeks of its life.

9.   (a) The carbon dioxide levels are increasing.

(b) The carbon dioxide levels oscillate each year.

(c) Seasonal changes in plant growth affect the carbon dioxide levels on a small scale. This can be attributed to the use of carbon dioxide by many plants during the process of photosynthesis.

10.   (a) The graph shows a general increasing trend which is similar to the graph for Hawaii but the yearly oscillations are larger.

(b) The climate in Alaska is more extreme so the seasonal changes in plant growth are more dramatic. Both graphs show an overall increasing trend due to the use of fossil fuels and other factors.

Chapters 1–2 Cumulative Review Exercises

1.   Natural number: $\sqrt[3]{8}$

Whole number: $\sqrt[3]{8}$

Integer: $-3,\sqrt[3]{8}$

Rational number: $-3,\frac{3}{4},-5.8,\sqrt[3]{8}$

Irrational number: $\sqrt{7}$

2.   Natural number: $\frac{50}{10}$

Whole number: $0,\frac{50}{10}$

Integer: $0,-5,-\sqrt{9},\frac{50}{10}$

Rational number: $0,-5,\frac{1}{2},-\sqrt{9},\frac{50}{10}$

Irrational number: $\sqrt{8}$

3.   Distributive property; $6x+8x=(6+8)x=14x$

4.   Commutative property for addition

5. $-5^2+3+4\cdot 5=-25+3+4\cdot 5=-25+3+20=-2$

6. $(x+1)x+(x+1)5=(x+1)(x+5)$

7. $-(a-b)=-a-(-b)=-a+b$

8. $\dfrac{c}{a+b}$

9. Entering $(1/3) \div ((3/4)(7/8)) + (5/6)$ ▶ Frac into a graphing calculator gives $\dfrac{169}{126}$.

10. (a) $\left(\dfrac{2^{-3}}{3^{-2}}\right)^2 = \left(\dfrac{3^2}{2^3}\right)^2 = \left(\dfrac{9}{8}\right)^2 = \dfrac{81}{64}$

    (b) $\dfrac{\left(3x^2 y^{-3}\right)^4}{x^3 \left(y^4\right)^{-2}} = \dfrac{3^4 x^8 y^{-12}}{x^3 y^{-8}} = 81 x^{8-3} y^{-12-(-8)} = 81 x^5 y^{-4}$

    $$= \dfrac{81 x^5}{y^4}$$

    (c) $\left(\dfrac{ab^{-2}}{a^{-3} b^4}\right)^{-2} = \left(\dfrac{a^{-3} b^4}{ab^{-2}}\right)^2 = \dfrac{\left(a^{-3} b^4\right)^2}{\left(ab^{-2}\right)^2} = \dfrac{a^{-6} b^8}{a^2 b^{-4}}$

    $$= a^{-6-2} b^{8-(-4)} = a^{-8} b^{12} = \dfrac{b^{12}}{a^8}$$

11. 9.54×10^3

12. $f(4) = 2(4)^2 + \sqrt{4} = 2(16) + 2 = 32 + 2 = 34$

13. $B = \dfrac{1}{2}(4)(3)^2 = \dfrac{1}{2}(4)(9) = 18$

14. (a) $D = \{-3, 0, 2\}$

    (b) The denominator of the function cannot equal zero. $D: x \ne -6$

    (c) The radicand of the function must be greater than or equal to zero. $D: x \ge -4$

15.   16.

Figure 15

Figure 16

17.   18.

Figure 17

Figure 18

19.   20.

Figure 19

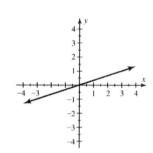

Figure 20

21.   (a) Yes, the graph passes the vertical line test so it represents a function.

(b) D: all real numbers; R: all real numbers

(c) From the graph, $f(-1) = 1.5$ and $f(0) = 1$.

(d) x-intercept:$(2, 0)$; y-intercept:$(0, 1)$

(e) For each 2-unit increase in x, the values of $f(x)$ decrease by 1 unit, so $m = -\dfrac{1}{2}$.

(f) $f(x) = -\dfrac{1}{2}x + 1$

22. $m = \dfrac{-4-5}{2-(-4)} = \dfrac{-9}{6} = -\dfrac{3}{2} \Rightarrow y = -\dfrac{3}{2}(x+4)+5$

$\Rightarrow y = -\dfrac{3}{2}x - 6 + 5 \Rightarrow y = -\dfrac{3}{2}x - 1$

23.   The slope of the line passing through $(1, -3)$ and $(2, 0)$ is $\dfrac{0-(-3)}{2-1} = \dfrac{3}{1} = 3$. The slope of the perpendicular

line must be the negative reciprocal of 3, thus $m = -\dfrac{1}{3} \Rightarrow y = -\dfrac{1}{3}(x+1)+2 \Rightarrow y = -\dfrac{1}{3}x - \dfrac{1}{3} + \dfrac{6}{3}$

$\Rightarrow y = -\dfrac{1}{3}x + \dfrac{5}{3}$.

24.   A line perpendicular to the x-axis must be vertical. The vertical line passing through $(-2, 4)$ is $x = -2$.

25. $m = \dfrac{-3-0}{2-1} = \dfrac{-3}{1} = -3$; the *x*-intercept is given in the table: 1; By substituting $x = 1$ and $y = 0$ into

   $y = -3x + b$, we find that $b = 3$.

26.   For each 2-unit increase in *x*, the *y*- values decrease by 3 units, so $m = -\dfrac{3}{2}$. The *y*-intercept is $\dfrac{3}{2}$, so

   $y = -\dfrac{3}{2}x + \dfrac{3}{2}$.

Applications

27.   Commutative property for addition; $120 + 80 = 200 = 80 + 120$

28.   Since Volume $= \text{Length} \times \text{Width} \times \text{Height}$, $2(\text{Length}) \times \text{Width} \times 2(\text{Height}) = 4(\text{Volume})$ so

   $4(400 \text{ cubic inches}) = 1600$ cubic inches.

29.   (a) We can estimate the 1995 injury rate by finding the average of the 1992 and 1998

      rates. $(8.3 + 6.7) \div 2 = 15 \div 2 = 7.5$

      We can estimate the 2000 injury rate by finding the average of the 1999 and 2001

      rates. $(6.3 + 5.4) \div 2 = (11.7) \div 2 = 5.85$

   (b) 5.85; *Answers may vary.*

30.   The person earns \$9 per hour.

31.   See Figure 31.

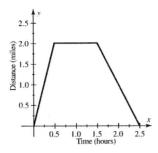

   Figure 31

32.   (a) See Figure 32a. Median age is increasing.

      [1820, 1995, 20] by [0, 40, 10]

      Figure 32a

   (b)

Year (x)	1820	1840	1860	1880	1900	1920	1940
Median Age	16.7	18.5	20.3	22.1	23.9	25.7	27.5

      $f(1900) = 23.9$; In 1900 the median age was 23.9.

   (c) Each year the median age increased by 0.09 year, on average.

33.   (a) $f(x) = 10x$

(b) See Figure 33b.

(c) 10

(d) Total fat increases at a rate of 10 g of fat per slice of pizza.

Figure 33b

Figure 34b

34.   (a) $f(6) = \dfrac{4}{25}(6) = \dfrac{24}{25} = 0.96$ pint

(b) See Figure 34b.

(c) $\dfrac{4}{25} = 0.16$

(d) 0.16 pint of oil should be added per gallon of gasoline.

35.   (a) $f(1960) = 3.4(1960 - 1960) + 87.8 = 3.4(0) + 87.8 = 87.8$. In 1960, there were 87.8 million tons of waste.

(b) See Figure 35b.

Figure 35b

(c) 3.4; solid waste increased by 3.4 million tons per year.

36.   (a) $m_1 = \dfrac{200 - 300}{2 - 0} = \dfrac{-100}{2} = -50$

$m_2 = 0$

$m_3 = \dfrac{0 - 200}{7 - 3} = \dfrac{-200}{4} = -50$

(b) m_1: The driver is traveling toward home at a rate of 50 miles per hour.

m_2: The car is not moving.

m_3: The driver is traveling toward home at a rate of 50 miles per hour.

(c) The car started 300 miles from home and moved toward home at 50 mph for 2 hours to a location 200 miles from home. The car was then parked for 1 hour. Finally, the car moved toward home at 50 mph for 4 hours, at which point it was home.

Critical Thinking Solutions for Chapter 2

Section 2.1

•   The graph is shown in Figure 2.1. Here the domain and range are given by $D: 0 \le x \le 5$ and $R: 0 \le y \le 250$.

Figure 2.1

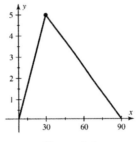

Figure 2.3

Section 2.2

•   A third point will verify that the first two points are plotted correctly.

Section 2.3

•   The graph is shown in Figure 2.3.

Section 2.4

•   A graph of a function cannot have more than one y-intercept since it would not pass the vertical line test.

A graph of a function can have more than one x-intercept since it could still pass the vertical line test.

Chapter 3: Linear Equations and Inequalities

3.1: Linear Equations

Concepts

1. $ax + b = 0$, where $a \neq 0$

2.   One

3.   Yes, since $4(1) - 1 = 3$ and $3(1) = 3$.

4.   Yes, we obtain the equation $x = 2$ if we divide both sides of the equation $3x = 6$ by 3.

5.   4

6. -2

7.   An equals sign (=)

8.   Three methods for solving linear equations are numerical, graphical and symbolic.

9.   The solution is the x-coordinate of the intersection point. That is, the solution is 3.

10.   The standard form of the equation of a line is $ax + by = c$, where a and b cannot both be 0.

11. $a + c = b + c$

12. $ac = bc$, for $c \neq 0$

13.   No, since $5 - 6 = -1 \neq -2$.

14.   Yes, since $-\frac{1}{2}(2) + 1 = 0$ and $\frac{1}{3}(2) - \frac{2}{3} = 0$.

15.   Yes, since $3\left[2\left(-\frac{2}{3}\right) + 3\right] = 6\left(-\frac{2}{3}\right) + 9 = -4 + 9 = 5$ and $\frac{13}{3} - \left(-\frac{2}{3}\right) = \frac{15}{3} = 5$.

16.   No, since $2 - 1 = 1$ but $2 - (2 + 1) = 2 - 3 = -1$.

17.   Yes, since $-(2(-2) - 3) + 2(-2) = 3$ and $1 - (-2) = 3$.

18.   Yes, since $-\frac{1}{3}(4 - 1) + \frac{2}{5}(1 + 1) = -\frac{1}{3}(3) + \frac{2}{5}(2) = -1 + \frac{4}{5} = -\frac{1}{5}$.

Symbolic Solutions

19. $x - 4 = 10 \Rightarrow x = 14$; Check: $14 - 4 = 10 \Rightarrow 10 = 10$, so $x = 14$

20. $x - \frac{1}{2} = \frac{3}{2} \Rightarrow x = \frac{4}{2} \Rightarrow x = 2$; Check: $2 - \frac{1}{2} = \frac{3}{2} \Rightarrow \frac{4}{2} - \frac{1}{2} = \frac{3}{2}$

        $\Rightarrow \frac{3}{2} = \frac{3}{2}$, so $x = 2$

21. $5 + x = 3 \Rightarrow x = -2$; Check: $5 + (-2) = 3 \Rightarrow 3 = 3$, so $x = -2$

22. $8 + x = -5 \Rightarrow x = -13$; Check: $8 + (-13) = -5 \Rightarrow -5 = -5$, so $x = -13$

23. $\frac{1}{2}-x=2 \Rightarrow \frac{1}{2}-x=\frac{4}{2} \Rightarrow -x=\frac{3}{2} \Rightarrow x=-\frac{3}{2}$; Check: $\frac{1}{2}-\left(-\frac{3}{2}\right)=2$

$\Rightarrow \frac{4}{2}=2 \Rightarrow 2=2$, so $x=-\frac{3}{2}$

24. $10-x=-5 \Rightarrow -x=-15 \Rightarrow x=15$; Check: $10-15=-5 \Rightarrow -5=-5$, so $x=15$

25. $-6x=-18 \Rightarrow x=3$; Check: $-6(3)=-18 \Rightarrow -18=-18$, so $x=3$

26. $-5x=15 \Rightarrow x=-3$; Check: $-5(-3)=15 \Rightarrow 15=15$, so $x=-3$

27. $-\frac{1}{3}x=4 \Rightarrow x=-12$; Check: $-\frac{1}{3}(-12)=4 \Rightarrow 4=4$, so $x=-12$

28. $\frac{3}{4}x=9 \Rightarrow x=\frac{4}{3}(9) \Rightarrow x=12$; Check: $\frac{3}{4}(12)=9 \Rightarrow 9=9$, so $x=12$

29. $2x+3=13 \Rightarrow 2x=10 \Rightarrow x=5$; Check: $2(5)+3=13 \Rightarrow 10+3=13 \Rightarrow 13=13$, so $x=5$

30. $6x-4=-10 \Rightarrow 6x=-6 \Rightarrow x=-1$; Check: $6(-1)-4=-10 \Rightarrow -6-4=-10 \Rightarrow -10=-10$, so $x=-1$

31. $3x-7=8 \Rightarrow 3x=15 \Rightarrow x=5$; Check: $3(5)-7=8 \Rightarrow 15-7=8 \Rightarrow 8=8$, so $x=5$

32. $5-2x=-2 \Rightarrow -2x=-7 \Rightarrow x=\frac{-7}{-2} \Rightarrow x=\frac{7}{2}$; Check: $5-2\left(\frac{7}{2}\right)=-2 \Rightarrow 5-7=-2 \Rightarrow -2=-2$, so $x=\frac{7}{2}$

33. $2x=8-\frac{1}{2}x \Rightarrow 2x+\frac{1}{2}x=8 \Rightarrow \frac{5}{2}x=8 \Rightarrow x=8\left(\frac{2}{5}\right) \Rightarrow x=\frac{16}{5}$; Check:

$2\left(\frac{16}{5}\right)=8-\frac{1}{2}\left(\frac{16}{5}\right) \Rightarrow \frac{32}{5}=8-\frac{8}{5} \Rightarrow \frac{32}{5}=\frac{40}{5}-\frac{8}{5} \Rightarrow \frac{32}{5}=\frac{32}{5}$, so $x=\frac{16}{5}$

34. $-7=3.5x \Rightarrow \frac{-7}{3.5}=x \Rightarrow x=-2$; Check: $-7=3.5(-2) \Rightarrow -7=-7$, so $x=-2$

35. $3x-1=11(1-x) \Rightarrow 3x-1=11-11x \Rightarrow 14x=12 \Rightarrow x=\frac{12}{14} \Rightarrow x=\frac{6}{7}$; Check:

$3\left(\frac{6}{7}\right)-1=11\left(1-\frac{6}{7}\right) \Rightarrow \frac{18}{7}-\frac{7}{7}=11\left(\frac{7}{7}-\frac{6}{7}\right) \Rightarrow \frac{11}{7}=11\left(\frac{1}{7}\right) \Rightarrow \frac{11}{7}=\frac{11}{7}$, so $x=\frac{6}{7}$

36. $4-3x=-5(1+2x) \Rightarrow 4-3x=-5-10x \Rightarrow 7x=-9 \Rightarrow x=-\frac{9}{7}$; Check:

$4-3\left(-\frac{9}{7}\right)=-5\left(1+2\left(-\frac{9}{7}\right)\right) \Rightarrow \frac{28}{7}+\frac{27}{7}=-5\left(\frac{7}{7}-\frac{18}{7}\right) \Rightarrow \frac{55}{7}=-5\left(-\frac{11}{7}\right) \Rightarrow \frac{55}{7}=\frac{55}{7}$, so $x=-\frac{9}{7}$

37. $x+4=2-\frac{1}{3}x \Rightarrow x+\frac{1}{3}x=-2 \Rightarrow \frac{4}{3}x=-2 \Rightarrow x=-2\left(\frac{3}{4}\right) \Rightarrow x=-\frac{3}{2}$; Check:

$-\frac{3}{2}+4=2-\frac{1}{3}\left(-\frac{3}{2}\right) \Rightarrow -\frac{3}{2}+\frac{8}{2}=\frac{4}{2}+\frac{1}{2} \Rightarrow \frac{5}{2}=\frac{5}{2}$, so $x=-\frac{3}{2}$

38. $2x-5=6-\dfrac{5}{2}x \Rightarrow 2x+\dfrac{5}{2}x=11 \Rightarrow \dfrac{9}{2}x=11 \Rightarrow x=11\left(\dfrac{2}{9}\right) \Rightarrow x=\dfrac{22}{9}$; Check:

$2\left(\dfrac{22}{9}\right)-5=6-\dfrac{5}{2}\left(\dfrac{22}{9}\right) \Rightarrow \dfrac{44}{9}-\dfrac{45}{9}=\dfrac{54}{9}-\dfrac{55}{9} \Rightarrow -\dfrac{1}{9}=-\dfrac{1}{9},$ so $x=-\dfrac{3}{2}$

39. $2(x-1)=5-2x \Rightarrow 2x-2=5-2x \Rightarrow 4x=7 \Rightarrow x=\dfrac{7}{4}$; Check:

$2\left(\dfrac{7}{4}-1\right)=5-2\left(\dfrac{7}{4}\right) \Rightarrow 2\left(\dfrac{7}{4}-\dfrac{4}{4}\right)=\dfrac{20}{4}-\dfrac{14}{4} \Rightarrow 2\left(\dfrac{3}{4}\right)=\dfrac{6}{4} \Rightarrow \dfrac{6}{4}=\dfrac{6}{4},$ so $x=\dfrac{7}{4}$

40. $-(x-4)=4(x+1)+3(x-2) \Rightarrow -x+4=4x+4+3x-6 \Rightarrow 6=8x \Rightarrow \dfrac{6}{8}=x \Rightarrow x=\dfrac{3}{4}$; Check:

$-\left(\dfrac{3}{4}-4\right)=4\left(\dfrac{3}{4}+1\right)+3\left(\dfrac{3}{4}-2\right) \Rightarrow -\left(\dfrac{3}{4}-\dfrac{16}{4}\right)=4\left(\dfrac{3}{4}+\dfrac{4}{4}\right)+3\left(\dfrac{3}{4}-\dfrac{8}{4}\right)$

$\Rightarrow -\left(-\dfrac{13}{4}\right)=4\left(\dfrac{7}{4}\right)+3\left(-\dfrac{5}{4}\right) \Rightarrow \dfrac{13}{4}=\dfrac{28}{4}-\dfrac{15}{4} \Rightarrow \dfrac{13}{4}=\dfrac{13}{4},$ so $x=\dfrac{3}{4}$

41. $\dfrac{2x+1}{3}=\dfrac{2x-1}{2} \Rightarrow 2(2x+1)=3(2x-1) \Rightarrow 4x+2=6x-3 \Rightarrow 5=2x \Rightarrow x=\dfrac{5}{2}$; Check:

$\dfrac{2\left(\frac{5}{2}\right)+1}{3}=\dfrac{2\left(\frac{5}{2}\right)-1}{2} \Rightarrow \dfrac{5+1}{3}=\dfrac{5-1}{2} \Rightarrow \dfrac{6}{3}=\dfrac{4}{2} \Rightarrow 2=2,$ so $x=\dfrac{5}{2}$

42. $\dfrac{3-4x}{5}=\dfrac{3x-1}{2} \Rightarrow 2(3-4x)=5(3x-1) \Rightarrow 6-8x=15x-5 \Rightarrow 11=23x \Rightarrow x=\dfrac{11}{23}$; Check:

$\dfrac{3-4\left(\frac{11}{23}\right)}{5}=\dfrac{3\left(\frac{11}{23}\right)-1}{2} \Rightarrow \dfrac{1}{5}\left(\dfrac{69}{23}-\dfrac{44}{23}\right)=\dfrac{1}{2}\left(\dfrac{33}{23}-\dfrac{23}{23}\right) \Rightarrow \dfrac{1}{5}\left(\dfrac{25}{23}\right)=\dfrac{1}{2}\left(\dfrac{10}{23}\right) \Rightarrow \dfrac{5}{23}=\dfrac{5}{23},$ so $x=\dfrac{11}{23}$

43. $4.2x-6.2=1-1.1x \Rightarrow 5.3x=7.2 \Rightarrow x=\dfrac{7.2}{5.3} \Rightarrow x=\dfrac{72}{53} \approx 1.36$; Check:

$4.2\left(\dfrac{72}{53}\right)-6.2=1-1.1\left(\dfrac{72}{53}\right) \Rightarrow \dfrac{302.4}{53}-\dfrac{328.6}{53}=\dfrac{53}{53}-\dfrac{79.2}{53} \Rightarrow -\dfrac{26.2}{53}=-\dfrac{26.2}{53},$ so $x=\dfrac{72}{53}$

44. $8.4-2.1x=1.4x \Rightarrow 8.4=3.5x \Rightarrow x=\dfrac{8.4}{3.5} \Rightarrow x=2.4$; Check:

$8.4-2.1(2.4)=1.4(2.4) \Rightarrow 8.4-5.04=3.36 \Rightarrow 3.36=3.36,$ so $x=2.4$

45. $\dfrac{1}{2}x-\dfrac{3}{2}=4 \Rightarrow \dfrac{1}{2}x=4+\dfrac{3}{2} \Rightarrow \dfrac{1}{2}x=\dfrac{11}{2} \Rightarrow x=\dfrac{11}{2}\left(\dfrac{2}{1}\right) \Rightarrow x=11$; Check:

$\dfrac{1}{2}(11)-\dfrac{3}{2}=4 \Rightarrow \dfrac{11}{2}-\dfrac{3}{2}=4 \Rightarrow \dfrac{8}{2}=4 \Rightarrow 4=4,$ so $x=11$

46. $5-\dfrac{1}{3}x=x-3 \Rightarrow 8=x+\dfrac{1}{3}x \Rightarrow 8=\dfrac{4}{3}x \Rightarrow 8\left(\dfrac{3}{4}\right)=x \Rightarrow x=6$; Check: $5-\dfrac{1}{3}(6)=6-3 \Rightarrow 5-2=3 \Rightarrow 3=3,$ so

$x=6$

47. $4(x-1980)+6=18 \Rightarrow 4x-7920+6=18 \Rightarrow 4x=7932 \Rightarrow x=\dfrac{7932}{4} \Rightarrow x=1983$; Check:

$4(1983-1980)+6=18 \Rightarrow 4(3)+6=18 \Rightarrow 12+6=18 \Rightarrow 18=18,$ so $x=1983$

48. $-5(x-1900)-55=145 \Rightarrow -5x+9500-55=145 \Rightarrow -5x=-9300 \Rightarrow x=\dfrac{-9300}{-5} \Rightarrow x=1860$; Check:

$-5(1860-1900)-55=145 \Rightarrow -5(-40)-55=145 \Rightarrow 200-55=145 \Rightarrow 145=145,$ so $x=1860$

49. $2(y-3)+5(1-2y)=4y+1 \Rightarrow 2y-6+5-10y=4y+1 \Rightarrow -12y=2 \Rightarrow y=-\dfrac{1}{6}$; Check:

$2\left(-\dfrac{1}{6}-3\right)+5\left(1-2\left(-\dfrac{1}{6}\right)\right)=4\left(-\dfrac{1}{6}\right)+1 \Rightarrow 2\left(-\dfrac{1}{6}-\dfrac{18}{6}\right)+5\left(\dfrac{6}{6}+\dfrac{2}{6}\right)=-\dfrac{4}{6}+\dfrac{6}{6}$

$\Rightarrow 2\left(-\dfrac{19}{6}\right)+5\left(\dfrac{8}{6}\right)=\dfrac{2}{6} \Rightarrow -\dfrac{38}{6}+\dfrac{40}{6}=\dfrac{2}{6} \Rightarrow \dfrac{2}{6}=\dfrac{2}{6},$ so $y=-\dfrac{1}{6}$

50. $4(y+1)-(3-5y)=-2(y-2) \Rightarrow 4y+4-3+5y=-2y+4 \Rightarrow 11y=3 \Rightarrow y=\dfrac{3}{11}$; Check:

$4\left(\dfrac{3}{11}+1\right)-\left(3-5\left(\dfrac{3}{11}\right)\right)=-2\left(\dfrac{3}{11}-2\right) \Rightarrow 4\left(\dfrac{3}{11}+\dfrac{11}{11}\right)-\left(\dfrac{33}{11}-\dfrac{15}{11}\right)=-2\left(\dfrac{3}{11}-\dfrac{22}{11}\right)$

$\Rightarrow 4\left(\dfrac{14}{11}\right)-\dfrac{18}{11}=-2\left(-\dfrac{19}{11}\right) \Rightarrow \dfrac{56}{11}-\dfrac{18}{11}=\dfrac{38}{11} \Rightarrow \dfrac{38}{11}=\dfrac{38}{11},$ so $y=\dfrac{3}{11}$

51. $-3(2-3z)+2z=1-3z \Rightarrow -6+9z+2z=1-3z \Rightarrow 14z=7 \Rightarrow z=\dfrac{1}{2}$; Check:

$-3\left(2-3\left(\dfrac{1}{2}\right)\right)+2\left(\dfrac{1}{2}\right)=1-3\left(\dfrac{1}{2}\right) \Rightarrow -3\left(\dfrac{4}{2}-\dfrac{3}{2}\right)+\dfrac{2}{2}=\dfrac{2}{2}-\dfrac{3}{2}$

$\Rightarrow -3\left(\dfrac{1}{2}\right)+\dfrac{2}{2}=-\dfrac{1}{2} \Rightarrow -\dfrac{3}{2}+\dfrac{2}{2}=-\dfrac{1}{2} \Rightarrow -\dfrac{1}{2}=-\dfrac{1}{2},$ so $z=\dfrac{1}{2}$

52. $-(5-(z+1))=9-(5-(2z-3)) \Rightarrow -(5-z-1)=9-(5-2z+3) \Rightarrow$

$-5+z+1=9-5+2z-3 \Rightarrow z-4=2z+1 \Rightarrow -z=5 \Rightarrow z=-5$; Check:

$-(5-(-5+1))=9-(5-(2(-5)-3)) \Rightarrow -(5-(-4))=9-(5-(-10-3))$

$\Rightarrow -9=9-(5-(-13)) \Rightarrow -9=9-18 \Rightarrow -9=-9,$ so $z=-5$

53. Clear fractions by multiplying each side of the equation by 6.

$\dfrac{2}{3}(t-3)+\dfrac{1}{2}t=5 \Rightarrow 4(t-3)+3t=30 \Rightarrow 4t-12+3t=30 \Rightarrow 7t=42 \Rightarrow t=6$; Check:

$\dfrac{2}{3}(6-3)+\dfrac{1}{2}(6)=5 \Rightarrow \dfrac{2}{3}(3)+3=5 \Rightarrow 2+3=5 \Rightarrow 5=5,$ so $t=6$

54. Clear fractions by multiplying each side of the equation by 10.

$$\frac{1}{5}t+\frac{3}{10}=2-\frac{1}{2}t \Rightarrow 2t+3=20-5t \Rightarrow 7t=17 \Rightarrow t=\frac{17}{7}; \text{Check:}$$

$$\frac{1}{5}\left(\frac{17}{7}\right)+\frac{3}{10}=2-\frac{1}{2}\left(\frac{17}{7}\right) \Rightarrow \frac{17}{35}+\frac{3}{10}=2-\frac{17}{14} \Rightarrow \frac{34}{70}+\frac{21}{70}=\frac{28}{14}-\frac{17}{14} \Rightarrow \frac{55}{70}=\frac{11}{14} \Rightarrow \frac{11}{14}=\frac{11}{14}, \text{ so } t=\frac{17}{7}$$

55. Clear fractions by multiplying each side of the equation by 12.

$$\frac{3k}{4}-\frac{2k}{3}=\frac{1}{6} \Rightarrow 9k-8k=2 \Rightarrow k=2; \text{Check: } \frac{3(2)}{4}-\frac{2(2)}{3}=\frac{1}{6} \Rightarrow \frac{6}{4}-\frac{4}{3}=\frac{1}{6} \Rightarrow \frac{18}{12}-\frac{16}{12}=\frac{2}{12} \Rightarrow \frac{2}{12}=\frac{2}{12}, \text{ so}$$

$$k=2$$

56. Clear fractions by multiplying each side of the equation by 6.

$$\frac{k+1}{3}-\frac{1}{2}=\frac{3k-3}{6} \Rightarrow 2k+2-3=3k-3 \Rightarrow 2k-1=3k-3 \Rightarrow -k=-2 \Rightarrow k=2; \text{Check:}$$

$$\frac{2+1}{3}-\frac{1}{2}=\frac{3(2)-3}{6} \Rightarrow \frac{3}{3}-\frac{1}{2}=\frac{6-3}{6} \Rightarrow 1-\frac{1}{2}=\frac{3}{6} \Rightarrow \frac{1}{2}=\frac{1}{2}, \text{ so } k=2$$

57. $0.2(n-2)+0.4n=0.05 \Rightarrow 0.2n-0.4+0.4n=0.05 \Rightarrow 0.6n=0.45 \Rightarrow n=\frac{0.45}{0.6} \Rightarrow n=0.75; \text{Check:}$

$0.2(0.75-2)+0.4(0.75)=0.05 \Rightarrow 0.2(-1.25)+0.3=0.05 \Rightarrow -0.25+0.3=0.05 \Rightarrow 0.05=0.05, \text{ so}$

$n=0.75$

58. $0.15(n+1)=0.1n+1 \Rightarrow 0.15n+0.15=0.1n+1 \Rightarrow 0.05n=0.85 \Rightarrow n=\frac{0.85}{0.05} \Rightarrow n=17; \text{Check:}$

$0.15(17+1)=0.1(17)+1 \Rightarrow 0.15(18)=1.7+1 \Rightarrow 2.7=2.7, \text{ so } n=17$

59. $0.7y-0.8(y-1)=2 \Rightarrow 0.7y-0.8y+0.8=2 \Rightarrow -0.1y=1.2 \Rightarrow y=\frac{1.2}{-0.1} \Rightarrow y=-12; \text{Check:}$

$0.7(-12)-0.8(-12-1)=2 \Rightarrow -8.4-0.8(-13)=2 \Rightarrow -8.4+10.4=2 \Rightarrow 2=2, \text{ so } y=-12$

60. $0.2y+0.3(5-2y)=-0.2y \Rightarrow 0.2y+1.5-0.6y=-0.2y \Rightarrow -0.2y=-1.5 \Rightarrow y=\frac{-1.5}{-0.2} \Rightarrow y=7.5; \text{Check:}$

$0.2(7.5)+0.3(5-2(7.5))=-0.2(7.5) \Rightarrow 1.5+0.3(5-15)=-1.5$

$\Rightarrow 1.5+0.3(-10)=-1.5 \Rightarrow 1.5+(-3)=-1.5 \Rightarrow -1.5=-1.5, \text{ so } y=7.5$

61. $ax+b=0 \Rightarrow ax=-b \Rightarrow x=-\frac{b}{a}, a\neq 0$

62. $ax-b=cx \Rightarrow ax-cx=b \Rightarrow (a-c)x=b$

$\Rightarrow x=\frac{b}{a-c}, a\neq c$

Numerical Solutions

63.   The completed table is shown in Figure 63. From the table we see that $-4x + 8 = 0$ when $x = 2$.

x	1	2	3	4	5
$-4x + 8$	4	0	-4	-8	-12

x	-2	-1	0	1	2
$3x + 2$	-4	-1	2	5	8

Figure 63   Figure 64

64.   The completed table is shown in Figure 64. From the table we see that $3x + 2 = 5$ when $x = 1$.

65.   The completed table is shown in Figure 65. From the table we see that $4 - 2x = x + 7$ when $x = -1$.

x	-2	-1	0	1	2
$4 - 2x$	8	6	4	2	0
$x + 7$	5	6	7	8	9

x	-2	-1	0	1	2
$3(x - 1)$	-9	-6	-3	0	3
$-2(1 - x)$	-6	-4	-2	0	2

Figure 65   Figure 66

66.   The completed table is shown in Figure 66. From the table we see that $3(x-1) = -2(1-x)$ when $x = 1$.

67.   From a table of values (not shown) we find that $x - 3 = 7$ when $x = 10$.

68.   From a table of values (not shown) we find that $2x + 1 = 11$ when $x = 5$.

69.   From a table of values (not shown) we find that $2y - \dfrac{1}{2} = \dfrac{3}{2}$ when $y = 1$.

70.   From a table of values (not shown) we find that $7 - 4y = -5$ when $y = 3$.

71.   From a table of values (not shown) we find that $3(z - 1) + 1.5 = 2z$ when $z = 1.5$.

72.   From a table of values (not shown) we find that $-3z - 6 = z + 2$ when $z = -2$.

Graphical Solutions

73.   The graphs intersect when $x = -2$.

74.   The graphs intersect when $x = 1$.

75.   The graphs intersect when $x = -1$.

76.   The graphs intersect when $x = -2$.

77.   Graph $Y_1 = 5 - 2X$ and $Y_2 = 7$ in [–10, 10, 1] by [–10, 10, 1]. See Figure 77. The solution is $x = -1$.

78.   Graph $Y_1 = -2X + 3$ and $Y_2 = -7$ in [–10, 10, 1] by [–10, 10, 1]. See Figure 78. The solution is $x = 5$.

[–10, 10, 1] by [–10, 10, 1]   [–10, 10, 1] by [–10, 10, 1]

Figure 77   Figure 78

79.   Graph $Y_1 = 2X - (X + 2)$ and $Y_2 = -2$ in [–10, 10, 1] by [–10, 10, 1]. See Figure 79. The solution is $x = 0$.

[−10, 10, 1] by [−10, 10, 1]   [−10, 10, 1] by [−10, 10, 1]

Figure 79   Figure 80

80.   Graph $Y_1 = X + 1$ and $Y_2 = 3 - X$ in [−10, 10, 1] by [−10, 10, 1]. See Figure 80. The solution is $x = 1$.

81.   Graph $Y_1 = 3(X + 2) + 1$ and $Y_2 = X + 1$ in [−10, 10, 1] by [−10, 10, 1]. See Figure 81. The solution is

$x = -3$.

82.   Graph $Y_1 = X + 5$ and $Y_2 = 2X + 2$ in [−10, 10, 1] by [−10, 10, 1]. See Figure 82. The solution is $x = 3$.

[−10, 10, 1] by [−10, 10, 1]   [−10, 10, 1] by [−10, 10, 1]

Figure 81   Figure 82

[1980, 2020, 10] by [0, 150, 10]   [1980, 2000, 5] by [0, 100, 10]

Figure 83   Figure 84

83.   Graph $Y_1 = 5(X - 1990) + 15$ and $Y_2 = 100$ in [1980, 2020, 10] by [0, 150, 10]. See Figure 83. Here

$x = 2007$.

84.   Graph $Y_1 = 10(X - 1985) - 20$ and $Y_2 = 55$ in [1980, 2000, 5] by [0, 100, 10]. See Figure 84. Here

$x = 1992.5$.

85.   Graph $Y_1 = \sqrt{2} + 4(X - \pi)$ and $Y_2 = 1/7 X$ in [−2, 8, 1] by [−5, 5, 1]. The solution is $x \approx 2.89$.

Figure 85

86.   Graph $Y_1 = \pi(X - \sqrt{5})$ and $Y_2 = (7X + 5)/3$ in [0, 20, 1] by [15, 35, 1]. The solution is $x \approx 10.75$.

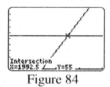

Figure 86

Solving Linear Equations by More Than One Method

87. (a) Table $Y_1 = 2X - 1$ and $Y_2 = 13$ with TblStart = 1 and ΔTbl = 1. See Figure 87a. $x = 7$

(b) Graph $Y_1 = 2X - 1$ and $Y_2 = 13$ in [0, 10, 1] by [0, 20, 2]. See Figure 87b. $x = 7$

(c) $2x - 1 = 13 \Rightarrow 2x = 14 \Rightarrow x = \dfrac{14}{2} \Rightarrow x = 7$

[0, 10, 1] by [0, 20, 2]

[0, 10, 1] by [0, 10, 1]

| Figure 87a | Figure 87b | Figure 88a | Figure 88b |

88. (a) Table $Y_1 = 9 - X$ and $Y_2 = 3X + 1$ with TblStart = 0 and ΔTbl = 1. See Figure 88a. $x = 2$

(b) Graph $Y_1 = 9 - X$ and $Y_2 = 3X + 1$ in [0, 10, 1] by [0, 10, 1]. See Figure 88b. $x = 2$

(c) $9 - x = 3x + 1 \Rightarrow 8 = 4x \Rightarrow \dfrac{8}{4} = x \Rightarrow x = 2$

89. (a) Table $Y_1 = 3X - 5 - (X + 1)$ and $Y_2 = 0$ with TblStart = 0 and ΔTbl = 1. See Figure 89a. $x = 3$

(b) Graph $Y_1 = 3X - 5 - (X + 1)$ and $Y_2 = 0$ in [−10, 10, 1] by [−10, 10, 1]. See Figure 89b. $x = 3$

(c) $3x - 5 - (x + 1) = 0 \Rightarrow 3x - 5 - x - 1 = 0 \Rightarrow 2x = 6 \Rightarrow x = \dfrac{6}{2} \Rightarrow x = 3$

[−10, 10, 1] by [−10, 10, 1]   [−10, 10, 1] by [−10, 10, 1]

| Figure 89a | Figure 89b | Figure 90a | Figure 90b |

90. (a) Table $Y_1 = (1/2)X - 1$ and $Y_2 = (5 - X)/2$ with TblStart = 1 and ΔTbl = 0.5. See Figure 90a. $x = 3.5$

(b) Graph $Y_1 = (1/2)X - 1$ and $Y_2 = (5 - X)/2$ in [−10, 10, 1] by [−10, 10, 1]. See Figure 90b. $x = 3.5$

(c) $\dfrac{1}{2}x - 1 = \dfrac{5 - x}{2} \Rightarrow x - 2 = 5 - x \Rightarrow 2x = 7 \Rightarrow x = \dfrac{7}{2} \Rightarrow x = 3.5$

91. $2x + 3 = 2x \Rightarrow 3 = 0$, false; contradiction

92. $x + 5 = x - 4 \Rightarrow 5 = -4$, false; contradiction

93. $2x + 3x = 5x \Rightarrow (2 + 3)x = 5x \Rightarrow 5x = 5x$; identity

94. $-3x = 4x - 7x \Rightarrow -3x = (4 - 7)x \Rightarrow -3x = -3x$; identity

95. $2(x - 1) = 2x - 2 \Rightarrow 2x - 2 = 2x - 2 \Rightarrow -2 = -2$; identity

96. $3x - 10 = 2(x - 5) + x \Rightarrow 3x - 10 = 2x - 10 + x \Rightarrow 3x - 10 = 3x - 10$

$\Rightarrow -10 = -10$; identity

97. $5 - 7(4 - 3x) = x - 4(2 - 4x) \Rightarrow 5 - 28 + 21x = x - 8 + 16x$

$\Rightarrow -23 + 21x = 17x - 8 \Rightarrow -23 + 4x = -8 \Rightarrow 4x = 15$

$x = \dfrac{15}{4}$; conditional

98. $7 - 2(x + 3) - x = -4(x - 5) - 22 \Rightarrow 7 - 2x - 6 - x = -4x + 20 - 22$

$\Rightarrow 1 - 3x = -4x - 2 \Rightarrow 1 + x = -2 \Rightarrow x = -3$; conditional

99.   Graph of f: $m = \dfrac{-1 - 9}{1 - (-4)} = \dfrac{-10}{5} = -2$; $y - 9 = -2(x - (-4))$

$\Rightarrow y - 9 = -2x - 8 \Rightarrow y = -2x + 1$

Graph of g: $m = \dfrac{13 - 1}{0 - (-3)} = \dfrac{12}{3} = 4$; $y - 13 = 4(x - 0) \Rightarrow$

$y - 13 = 4x \Rightarrow y = 4x + 13$

$-2x + 1 = 4x + 13 \Rightarrow -6x + 1 = 13 \Rightarrow -6x = 12 \Rightarrow x = -2$;

$y = -2(-2) + 1 \Rightarrow y = 4 + 1 \Rightarrow y = 5; (-2, 5)$

100.   Graph of f: $m = \dfrac{-7 - (-2)}{8 - (-2)} = \dfrac{-5}{10} = -\dfrac{1}{2}$; $y - (-2) = -\dfrac{1}{2}(x - (-2))$

$\Rightarrow y + 2 = -\dfrac{1}{2}x - 1 \Rightarrow y = -\dfrac{1}{2}x - 3$

Graph of g: $m = \dfrac{1 - (-11)}{12 - (-4)} = \dfrac{12}{16} = \dfrac{3}{4}$; $y - (-11) = \dfrac{3}{4}(x - (-4))$

$\Rightarrow y + 11 = \dfrac{3}{4}x + 3 \Rightarrow y = \dfrac{3}{4}x - 8$

$-\dfrac{1}{2}x - 3 = \dfrac{3}{4}x - 8 \Rightarrow -\dfrac{5}{4}x - 3 = -8 \Rightarrow -\dfrac{5}{4}x = -5$

$\Rightarrow x = 4; \ y = -\dfrac{1}{2}(4) - 3 \Rightarrow y = -2 - 3 \Rightarrow y = -5; (4, -5)$

Finding Intercepts

101.   (a) To find the x-intercept, let $y = 0$ and solve for x: $x + 0 = 4 \Rightarrow x = 4$; to find the y-intercept, let $x = 0$ and

solve for y: $0 + y = 4 \Rightarrow y = 4$

(b) See Figure 101b.

Figure 101b

Figure 102b

Figure 103b

(c) $x + y = 4 \Rightarrow y = -x + 4$

102. (a) To find the *x*-intercept, let $y = 0$ and solve for x: $x - 0 = -2 \Rightarrow x = -2$; to find the *y*-intercept, let $x = 0$

and solve for y: $0 - y = -2 \Rightarrow y = 2$

(b) See Figure 102b.

(c) $x - y = -2 \Rightarrow -y = -x - 2 \Rightarrow y = x + 2$

103. (a) To find the *x*-intercept, let $y = 0$ and solve for x: $2x + 5(0) = 10$

$\Rightarrow 2x = 10 \Rightarrow x = 5$; to find the *y*-intercept, let $x = 0$ and solve for y: $2(0) + 5y = 10 \Rightarrow 5y = 10 \Rightarrow y = 2$

(b) See Figure 103b.

(c) $2x + 5y = 10 \Rightarrow 5y = -2x + 10 \Rightarrow y = -\dfrac{2}{5}x + 2$

104. (a) To find the *x*-intercept, let $y = 0$ and solve for x: $-3x + 4(0) = -6 \Rightarrow -3x = -6 \Rightarrow x = 2$; to find the *y*-

intercept, let $x = 0$ and solve for y: $-3(0) + 4y = -6 \Rightarrow 4y = -6 \Rightarrow y = -\dfrac{6}{4} \Rightarrow y = -\dfrac{3}{2}$

(b) See Figure 104b.

Figure 104b

Figure 105b

Figure 106b

(c) $-3x + 4y = -6 \Rightarrow 4y = 3x - 6 \Rightarrow y = \dfrac{3}{4}x - \dfrac{3}{2}$

105. (a) To find the *x*-intercept, let $y = 0$ and solve for x: $2x - 3(0) = 9 \Rightarrow 2x = 9 \Rightarrow x = \dfrac{9}{2}$; to find the *y*-

intercept, let $x = 0$ and solve for y: $2(0) - 3y = 9 \Rightarrow -3y = 9 \Rightarrow y = -3$

(b) See Figure 105b.

(c) $2x - 3y = 9 \Rightarrow -3y = -2x + 9 \Rightarrow y = \dfrac{2}{3}x - 3$

106. (a) To find the x-intercept, let $y = 0$ and solve for x: $\dfrac{1}{2}x - \dfrac{1}{4}(0) = 1 \Rightarrow \dfrac{1}{2}x = 1 \Rightarrow x = 2$; to find the y-

intercept, let $x = 0$ and solve for y: $\dfrac{1}{2}(0) - \dfrac{1}{4}y = 1 \Rightarrow -\dfrac{1}{4}y = 1 \Rightarrow y = -4$

(b) See Figure 106b.

(c) $\dfrac{1}{2}x - \dfrac{1}{4}y = 1 \Rightarrow -\dfrac{1}{4}y = -\dfrac{1}{2}x + 1 \Rightarrow y = 2x - 4$

107. (a) To find the x-intercept, let $y = 0$ and solve for x: $-\dfrac{2}{3}x - 0 = 2 \Rightarrow -\dfrac{2}{3}x = 2 \Rightarrow x = -3$; to find the y-

intercept, let $x = 0$ and solve for y: $-\dfrac{2}{3}(0) - y = 2 \Rightarrow -y = 2 \Rightarrow y = -2$

(b) See Figure 107b.

Figure 107b

Figure 108b

(c) $-\dfrac{2}{3}x - y = 2 \Rightarrow -y = \dfrac{2}{3}x + 2 \Rightarrow y = -\dfrac{2}{3}x - 2$

108. (a) To find the x-intercept, let $y = 0$ and solve for x: $-x - \dfrac{2}{5}(0) = 2 \Rightarrow -x = 2 \Rightarrow x = -2$; to find the y-

intercept, let $x = 0$ and solve for y: $-(0) - \dfrac{2}{5}y = 2 \Rightarrow -\dfrac{2}{5}y = 2 \Rightarrow y = -5$

(b) See Figure 108b.

(c) $-x - \dfrac{2}{5}y = 2 \Rightarrow -\dfrac{2}{5}y = x + 2 \Rightarrow y = -\dfrac{5}{2}x - 5$

Applications

109. (a) $m = \dfrac{16.6 - 10.3}{2004 - 1960} = \dfrac{6.3}{44} = \dfrac{63}{440}$; $S(x) = \dfrac{63}{440}(x - 1960) + 10.3$

(b) $S(2000) = \dfrac{63}{440}(2000 - 1960) + 10.3 = \dfrac{63}{440}(40) + 10.3 \approx 5.7 + 10.3 = 16$; about 16 pounds

(c) $20 = \dfrac{63}{440}(x - 1960) + 10.3 \Rightarrow 9.7 = \dfrac{63}{440}(x - 1960) \Rightarrow 67.7 \approx x - 1960 \Rightarrow 2027.7 \approx x$; about 2028

110. (a) Since we are given a point and a rate of change, $m = 8260$, $x_1 = 1990$ and $y_1 = 37,306$.

(b) $8260(x-1990)+37,306=450,000 \Rightarrow 8260x-16,437,400=412,694 \Rightarrow 8260x=16,850,094 \Rightarrow$

$x \approx 2040$

111. (a) $70x-138,532=908 \Rightarrow 70x=139,440 \Rightarrow x=\dfrac{139,440}{70} \Rightarrow x=1992$

(b) Table $Y_1=70X-138532$ and $Y_2=908$ with TblStart = 1988 and ΔTbl = 1. See Figure 111b. $x=1992$

(c) Graph $Y_1=70X-138532$ and $Y_2=908$ in [1988, 1995, 1] by [0, 1000, 100]. See Figure

111c. $x=1992$

[1988, 1995, 1] by [0, 1000, 100]   [1960, 1990, 5] by [0, 20, 2]

Figure 111b   Figure 111c   Figure 112b   Figure 112c

112. (a) $0.47x-919.3=6.6 \Rightarrow 0.47x=925.9 \Rightarrow x=\dfrac{925.9}{0.47} \Rightarrow x=1970$

(b) Table $Y_1=0.47X-919.3$ and $Y_2=6.6$ with TblStart = 1960 and ΔTbl = 2. See Figure 112b. $x=1970$

(c) Graph $Y_1=0.47X-919.3$ and $Y_2=6.6$ in [1960, 1990, 5] by [0, 20, 2]. See Figure 112c. $x=1970$

113. (a) The slope is $m=\dfrac{1.8-1.4}{2002-1998}=\dfrac{0.4}{4}=0.1$.

Then using the point (1998, 1.4) we have $y=0.1(x-1998)+1.4$ or $y=0.1x-198.4$.

(b) $0.1x-198.4=1.7 \Rightarrow 0.1x=200.1 \Rightarrow x=2001$

(c) $0.1x-198.4=2 \Rightarrow 0.1x=200.4 \Rightarrow x=2004$

114. (a) The slope is $m=\dfrac{5.4-8.3}{2002-1992}=\dfrac{-2.9}{10}=-0.29$.

Then using the point (1992, 8.3) we have $y=-0.29(x-1992)+8.3$ or $y=-0.29x+585.98$.

(b) $-0.29x+585.98=6 \Rightarrow -0.29x=-579.98 \Rightarrow x \approx 2000$

115. $51.6(x-1985)+9.1=-31.9(x-1985)+167.7 \Rightarrow 51.6x-102,416.9=-31.9x+63,489.2 \Rightarrow$

$83.5x=165,906.1 \Rightarrow x \approx 1986.89$. Sales were about equal in late 1986 or around 1987.

116. (a) The slope is $m=\dfrac{80-22}{2000-1900}=\dfrac{58}{100}=0.58$.

Then using the point (1900, 22) we have $y=0.58(x-1900)+22$ or $y=0.58x-1080$.

(b) $0.58x-1080=51 \Rightarrow 0.58x=1131 \Rightarrow x=1950$

Group Activity Solutions

(a) A scatterplot is shown. The number of fatal private plane crashes is decreasing.

(b) Using the points (1982, 372) and (2004, 191), $m = \dfrac{191 - 372}{2004 - 1982} = \dfrac{-181}{22}$

$\approx -9;\ f(x) = -9(x - 1982) + 372$

(c) Fatal crashes decreased by 9 per year, on average.

(d) $200 = -9(x - 1982) + 372 \Rightarrow -172 = -9(x - 1982)$

$\Rightarrow 19 \approx x - 1982 \Rightarrow x \approx 2001$

(e) $120 = -9(x - 1982) + 372 \Rightarrow -252 = -9(x - 1982)$

$\Rightarrow 28 = x - 1982 \Rightarrow x = 2010$

3.2: Introduction to Problem Solving

Concepts

1.   We divide each side by 2 to obtain $y = \dfrac{x}{2}$.

2. $4x - 7$

3.   The perimeter is $P = 2W + 2L$.

4.   read the problem carefully

5. $43.1\% = 0.431$

6. $0.20 \times 50 = 10$

Solving for a Variable

7. $4x + 3y = 12 \Rightarrow 3y = -4x + 12 \Rightarrow y = \dfrac{-4x + 12}{3} \Rightarrow y = -\dfrac{4}{3}x + 4$

8. $6x - 3y = 6 \Rightarrow 6x - 6 = 3y \Rightarrow \dfrac{6x - 6}{3} = y \Rightarrow 2x - 2 = y \Rightarrow y = 2x - 2$

9. $5(2x - 3y) = 2x \Rightarrow 10x - 15y = 2x \Rightarrow 8x = 15y \Rightarrow x = \dfrac{15}{8}y$

10. $-2(2x + y) = 3y \Rightarrow -4x - 2y = 3y \Rightarrow -4x = 5y \Rightarrow x = -\dfrac{5}{4}y$

11. $S = 6ab \Rightarrow \dfrac{S}{6a} = \dfrac{6ab}{6a} \Rightarrow b = \dfrac{S}{6a}$

12. $S = 2\pi rh \Rightarrow \dfrac{S}{2\pi h} = \dfrac{2\pi rh}{2\pi h} \Rightarrow r = \dfrac{S}{2\pi h}$

13. $\dfrac{r+t}{2} = 7 \Rightarrow r+t = 14 \Rightarrow t = 14 - r$

14. $\dfrac{2+a+b}{3} = 8 \Rightarrow 2+a+b = 24 \Rightarrow a+b = 22 \Rightarrow a = 22 - b$

15. $-3x + y = 8 \Rightarrow y = 3x + 8 \Rightarrow f(x) = 3x + 8$

16. $2x - 5y = 10 \Rightarrow 2x - 10 = 5y \Rightarrow \dfrac{2x-10}{5} = y \Rightarrow y = \dfrac{2}{5}x - 2 \Rightarrow f(x) = \dfrac{2}{5}x - 2$

17. $4x = 2\pi y \Rightarrow \dfrac{4x}{2\pi} = \dfrac{2\pi y}{2\pi} \Rightarrow \dfrac{2x}{\pi} = y \Rightarrow f(x) = \dfrac{2x}{\pi}$

18. $\dfrac{x}{2} = \dfrac{y}{3} \Rightarrow 6 \cdot \dfrac{x}{2} = 6 \cdot \dfrac{y}{3} \Rightarrow 3x = 2y \Rightarrow \dfrac{3x}{2} = y \Rightarrow f(x) = \dfrac{3x}{2}$

19. $\dfrac{3y}{8} = x \Rightarrow 3y = 8x \Rightarrow y = \dfrac{8x}{3} \Rightarrow f(x) = \dfrac{8x}{3}$

20. $\dfrac{3x+2y}{4} = 3 \Rightarrow 3x + 2y = 12 \Rightarrow 2y = -3x + 12 \Rightarrow y = \dfrac{-3x+12}{2} \Rightarrow f(x) = -\dfrac{3}{2}x + 6$

Writing and Solving Equations

21.   (a) $x + 2 = 12$

       (b) $x + 2 = 12 \Rightarrow x = 10$

22.   (a) $2x + 7 = 9$

       (b) $2x + 7 = 9 \Rightarrow 2x = 2 \Rightarrow x = \dfrac{2}{2} \Rightarrow x = 1$

23.   (a) $\dfrac{x}{5} = x + 1$

       (b) $\dfrac{x}{5} = x + 1 \Rightarrow x = 5x + 5 \Rightarrow -4x = 5 \Rightarrow x = -\dfrac{5}{4}$

24.   (a) $25x = 125$

       (b) $25x = 125 \Rightarrow x = \dfrac{125}{25} \Rightarrow x = 5$

25.   (a) $\dfrac{x+5}{2} = 7$

       (b) $\dfrac{x+5}{2} = 7 \Rightarrow x + 5 = 14 \Rightarrow x = 9$

26.   (a) $8 - x = 5$

       (b) $8 - x = 5 \Rightarrow -x = -3 \Rightarrow x = 3$

27. (a) $\dfrac{x}{2} = 17$

(b) $\dfrac{x}{2} = 17 \Rightarrow x = 34$

28. (a) $5x = 95$

(b) $5x = 95 \Rightarrow x = \dfrac{95}{5} \Rightarrow x = 19$

29. (a) $x + (x+1) + (x+2) = 30$

(b) $x + (x+1) + (x+2) = 30 \Rightarrow 3x + 3 = 30 \Rightarrow 3x = 27 \Rightarrow x = \dfrac{27}{3} \Rightarrow x = 9$

30. (a) $2x + 2(x+5) = 60$

(b) $2x + 2(x+5) = 60 \Rightarrow 2x + 2x + 10 = 60 \Rightarrow 4x = 50 \Rightarrow x = \dfrac{50}{4} \Rightarrow x = 12.5$

Applications

31. (a) Solve $P = 2L + 2W$ for L. $P = 2L + 2W \Rightarrow \dfrac{P}{2} = L + W \Rightarrow L = \dfrac{P}{2} - W$

(b) $L = \dfrac{86}{2} - 19 = 43 - 19 = 24$ feet

32. (a) $P = a + b + c \Rightarrow a = P - b - c$

(b) $a = 15 - 5 - 7 = 3$

33. $A = 2\pi r h \Rightarrow \dfrac{A}{2\pi r} = \dfrac{2\pi r h}{2\pi r} \Rightarrow h = \dfrac{A}{2\pi r}$

34. $V = \pi r^2 h \Rightarrow \dfrac{V}{\pi r^2} = \dfrac{\pi r^2 h}{\pi r^2} \Rightarrow h = \dfrac{V}{\pi r^2}$

35. $F = \dfrac{9}{5}C + 32 \Rightarrow F - 32 = \dfrac{9}{5}C \Rightarrow \dfrac{5}{9}(F - 32) = C \Rightarrow C = \dfrac{5}{9}(F - 32)$

36. $A = bh \Rightarrow \dfrac{A}{h} = \dfrac{bh}{h} \Rightarrow b = \dfrac{A}{h}$

37. $A = \dfrac{1}{2}bh \Rightarrow 2A = bh \Rightarrow \dfrac{2A}{b} = \dfrac{bh}{b} \Rightarrow h = \dfrac{2A}{b}$

38. $V = WLH \Rightarrow \dfrac{V}{WH} = \dfrac{WLH}{WH} \Rightarrow L = \dfrac{V}{WH}$

39. Let x represent the smallest integer. Then $x+1$ and $x+2$ represent the next consecutive integers.

$x + (x+1) + (x+2) = 135 \Rightarrow 3x + 3 = 135 \Rightarrow 3x = 132 \Rightarrow x = 44$. The integers are 44, 45, and 46.

40. No. Let x represent the smallest even integer. Then $x+2$ and $x+4$ represent the next consecutive even integers.

$x+(x+2)+(x+4)=82 \Rightarrow 3x+6=82 \Rightarrow 3x=76 \Rightarrow x=25.\overline{3}$, which is not an integer.

41.   Let x represent the smallest odd integer. Then $x+2$ and $x+4$ represent the next consecutive odd integers.

$2[x+(x+2)+(x+4)]=150 \Rightarrow 3x+6=75 \Rightarrow 3x=69 \Rightarrow x=23$. The integers are 23, 25, and 27.

42.   Let x represent the smaller integer. Then $x+1$ represents the next consecutive integer.

$10+2[x+(x+1)]=196 \Rightarrow 2[2x+1]=186 \Rightarrow 2x+1=93 \Rightarrow 2x=92 \Rightarrow x=46$.

The integers are 46 and 47.

43.   Two sides of length x plus two sides of length $x+8$ equals 48.

$2x+2(x+8)=48 \Rightarrow 2x+2x+16=48 \Rightarrow 4x=32 \Rightarrow x=\dfrac{32}{4} \Rightarrow x=8$ feet

44.   The train must travel a total of $100+410=510$ miles at 60 miles per hour. We use the formula $d=rt$.

$510=60t \Rightarrow \dfrac{510}{60}=t \Rightarrow t=8.5$ hours

45.   Let x represent the length of a side of the square (and the diameter of each circle). Then $2\pi x+4x=41$

$\Rightarrow (2\pi+4)x=41 \Rightarrow x=\dfrac{41}{2\pi+4} \Rightarrow x\approx 4$.

The wire should be cut at about $4(4)=16$ inches for the square and $\pi(4)\approx 12.5$ inches for each circle.

46.   The length of each pen is $2x+2$. Six pieces of length x plus four pieces of length $2x+2$ equals 120.

$6x+4(2x+2)=120 \Rightarrow 6x+8x+8=120 \Rightarrow 14x=112 \Rightarrow x=\dfrac{112}{14} \Rightarrow x=8$ feet

The width of each pen is 8 feet and the length of each pen is $2(8)+2=18$ feet. The pens are 8 ft by 18 ft.

47.   Use the formula $d=rt$. Let x represent the speed of one car and $x+6$ the speed of the other

car. $355=x(2.5)+(x+6)(2.5) \Rightarrow 355=2.5x+2.5x+15 \Rightarrow 340=5x \Rightarrow x=68$. One car is traveling at 68

miles per hour, and the other car is traveling at 74 miles per hour.

48.   Using the formula $d=rt$, the athlete ran $6x$ miles at 6 mph and $5(1.3-x)$ at 5 mph. The total must be 7.

$6x+5(1.3-x)=7 \Rightarrow 6x+6.5-5x=7 \Rightarrow x=0.5$ hour.

The athlete jogged for 0.5 hour at 6 miles per hour and for $1.3-0.5=0.8$ hour at 5 miles per hour.

49.   Mixing 3 liters of 30% acid with x liters of 80% acid results in $x+3$ liters of 60% acid.

$0.30(3)+0.80x=0.60(x+3) \Rightarrow 0.9+0.8x=0.6x+1.8 \Rightarrow 0.2x=0.9 \Rightarrow x=4.5$

The chemist used 4.5 liters of 80% sulfuric acid.

50.   Let x represent the amount of antifreeze that is drained and replaced. Then the remaining amount is $4-x$.

So, mixing $4-x$ gallons of 20% solution with x gallons of 70% solution results in 4 gallons of 50% solution.

$0.20(4-x)+0.70x=0.50(4) \Rightarrow 0.8-0.2x+0.7x=2 \Rightarrow 0.5x=1.2 \Rightarrow x=2.4$

The amount of antifreeze to be drained and replaced is 2.4 gallons.

51.   Let x represent the loan amount at 6% interest. Then the remaining amount at 4% interest is $5000 - x$.

$0.06x + 0.04(5000 - x) = 244 \Rightarrow 0.06x + 200 - 0.04x = 244 \Rightarrow 0.02x = 44 \Rightarrow x = 2200$

The loans were for $2200 at 6% and $2800 at 4%.

52.   Let x represent the amount invested at 5% interest. Then the remaining amount at 6% interest is $2400 - x$.

$0.05x + 0.06(2400 - x) = 130.50 \Rightarrow 0.05x + 144 - 0.06x = 130.5 \Rightarrow -0.01x = -13.5 \Rightarrow x = 1350$.   The

investments are $1350 at 5% and $1050 at 6%.

53.   Let x represent the measure of the smallest angle. Then the largest angle has measure $2x$ and the third angle

has measure $2x - 10$. $x + 2x + 2x - 10 = 180 \Rightarrow 5x = 190 \Rightarrow x = 38$. The angle measures are

$38°$, $66°$, and $76°$.

54. $x + 2x + (x - 20) = 180 \Rightarrow 4x - 20 = 180 \Rightarrow 4x = 200 \Rightarrow x = 50°$

55.   (a) $900(40) = 36,000 \text{ ft}^3/\text{hr}$

(b)   There should be no more than 66 people in the room. $900x = 60,000 \Rightarrow x = \dfrac{60,000}{900} \Rightarrow x \approx 66.7$

56.   (a) $36.5x$

(b) $36.5x = 500 \Rightarrow x = \dfrac{500}{36.5} \Rightarrow x \approx 13.7$ years

57.   Let x represent the cost of a gallon of gasoline. $873 = \dfrac{15,000}{50}x \Rightarrow 873 = 300x \Rightarrow x = \$2.91$

58.   Let x represent the average mileage per gallon of gasoline.

$1000 = \dfrac{15,000}{x}(2.60) \Rightarrow 1000 = \dfrac{39,000}{x} \Rightarrow x = \dfrac{39,000}{1000} \Rightarrow x = 39$ miles per gallon

59.   Let x represent the area of Nevada. $0.09x = 9900 \Rightarrow x = 110,000$ square miles

60.   Let x represent the number of months. $0.20(125)x = 275 \Rightarrow 25x = 275 \Rightarrow x = 11$ months

61.   Let x represent the number of Wal-Mart employees in 2002. $x + 0.57x = 2.2 \Rightarrow 1.57x = 2.2 \Rightarrow x \approx 1.401$

There were about 1.4 million Wal-Mart employees in 2002.

62.   Let x represent the average fare paid in 2001. $x - 0.0844x = 282 \Rightarrow 0.9156x = 282 \Rightarrow x \approx 307.99$

The average one-way fare paid by American Express clients in 2001 was about $308.

63.   Let x be the number of people surveyed. Remember to write 32% as 0.32.

$0.32x = 480 \Rightarrow x = \dfrac{480}{0.32} \Rightarrow x = 1500$ people

64.   Let x be the number of government workers. Remember to write 37.5% as 0.375.

$0.375x = 6.9 \Rightarrow x = \dfrac{6.9}{0.375} \Rightarrow x = 18.4$ million government workers

65. Since heart disease accounts for 29.1% more deaths than cancer, the number of deaths that can be attributed to heart disease is $1.291(550,000) = 710,050$. The total number of deaths is

$$550,000 + 710,050 = 1,260,050.$$

That is, about 1,260,000 deaths can be attributed to heart disease *and* cancer.

66. Let x be the percentage score achieved on the final exam. We count the final exam as two 100 point exams.

$$\frac{83+87+94+91+2x}{6} = 90 \Rightarrow 355 + 2x = 540 \Rightarrow 2x = 185 \Rightarrow x = \frac{185}{2} \Rightarrow x = 92.5\% \text{ or } 185 \text{ pts.}$$

Checking Basic Concepts for Sections 3.1 & 3.2

1. A linear equation has one solution.

2. Multiply each side of the equation by 6 to clear fractions.

$$\frac{1}{2}z - (1-2z) = \frac{2}{3}z \Rightarrow 3z - 6(1-2z) = 4z \Rightarrow 3z - 6 + 12z = 4z \Rightarrow 11z = 6 \Rightarrow z = \frac{6}{11}$$

3. (a) $2(3x+4)+3 = -1 \Rightarrow 6x + 8 + 3 = -1 \Rightarrow 6x = -12 \Rightarrow x = \frac{-12}{6} \Rightarrow x = -2$

   (b) Graph $Y_1 = 2(3X+4)+3$ and $Y_2 = -1$ in [−10, 10, 1] by [−10, 10, 1]. See Figure 3b. $x = -2$

   (c) Table $Y_1 = 2(3X+4)+3$ and $Y_2 = -1$ with TblStart = −5 and ΔTbl = 1. See Figure 3c. $x = -2$

   The answers agree.

   [−10, 10, 1] by [−10, 10, 1]

Figure 3b   Figure 3c

4. Let x represent the time the athlete spends jogging at 10 miles per hour. Then $1.2 - x$ represents the time spent jogging at 8 miles per hour. $10x + 8(1.2 - x) = 10.2 \Rightarrow 10x + 9.6 - 8x = 10.2 \Rightarrow 2x = 0.6 \Rightarrow x = 0.3$

   The athlete jogged for 0.3 hour at 10 miles per hour and 0.9 hour at 8 miles per hour.

5. To find the x-intercept, Let $y = 0$ and solve for x: $5x - 4(0) = 20 \Rightarrow 5x = 20 \Rightarrow x = 4$; to find the y-intercept,

   let $x = 0$ and solve for y: $5(0) - 4y = 20 \Rightarrow -4y = 20 \Rightarrow y = -5$.

6. (a) $3(x-2) = 3x - 6 \Rightarrow 3x - 6 = 3x - 6 \Rightarrow -6 = -6$; identity

   (b) $2x + 3x = 5x - 2 \Rightarrow (2+3)x = 5x - 2 \Rightarrow 5x = 5x - 2 \Rightarrow 0 = -2$; contradiction

3.3: Linear Inequalities

Concepts

1. An example of a linear inequality is $3x + 2 < 5$. *Answers may vary.*

2. Yes. For example, any positive number will satisfy the inequality $x + 2 > 2$.

3.   Yes. Subtract 5 from each side.

4.   Yes. Add 7 to each side.

5.   Yes. They have the same solution set.

6.   No, $-4x < 8$ is equivalent to $x > -2$.

7.   An equation has an equals sign while an inequality has an inequality symbol.

8.   Three methods for solving a linear inequality are numerical, graphical and symbolic.

9.   Yes. $2 - 5 \le 3$

10.   No. $\frac{3}{2}(-2) - \frac{1}{2} \ngeq 1 - (-2)$

11.   No. $2(5) - 3 \nless 5(5) - \left[2(5) + 1\right]$

12.   Yes. $2(\pi - 1) < 3(\pi + 1)$

13.   (a) $x - 2 = 0 \Rightarrow x = 2 \Rightarrow \{x \mid x = 2\}$

      (b) $x - 2 < 0 \Rightarrow x < 2 \Rightarrow \{x \mid x < 2\}$

      (c) $x - 2 > 0 \Rightarrow x > 2 \Rightarrow \{x \mid x > 2\}$

14.   (a) $x + 5 = 0 \Rightarrow x = -5 \Rightarrow \{x \mid x = -5\}$

      (b) $x + 5 < 0 \Rightarrow x < -5 \Rightarrow \{x \mid x < -5\}$

      (c) $x + 5 > 0 \Rightarrow x > -5 \Rightarrow \{x \mid x > -5\}$

15.   (a) $-2x + 6 = 0 \Rightarrow -2x = -6 \Rightarrow x = 3 \Rightarrow \{x \mid x = 3\}$

      (b) $-2x + 6 < 0 \Rightarrow -2x < -6 \Rightarrow x > 3 \Rightarrow \{x \mid x > 3\}$

      (c) $-2x + 6 > 0 \Rightarrow -2x > -6 \Rightarrow x < 3 \Rightarrow \{x \mid x < 3\}$

16.   (a) $-6 - 6x = 0 \Rightarrow -6x = 6 \Rightarrow x = -1 \Rightarrow \{x \mid x = -1\}$

      (b) $-6 - 6x < 0 \Rightarrow -6x < 6 \Rightarrow x > -1 \Rightarrow \{x \mid x > -1\}$

      (c) $-6 - 6x > 0 \Rightarrow -6x > 6 \Rightarrow x < -1 \Rightarrow \{x \mid x < -1\}$

Symbolic Solutions

17. $x + 3 \le 5 \Rightarrow x \le 2 \Rightarrow \{x \mid x \le 2\}$

18. $x - 5 \ge -3 \Rightarrow x \ge 2 \Rightarrow \{x \mid x \ge 2\}$

19. $\frac{1}{4}x > 9 \Rightarrow x > 36 \Rightarrow \{x \mid x > 36\}$

20. $14 < -3.5x \Rightarrow \frac{14}{-3.5} > x \Rightarrow x < -4 \Rightarrow \{x \mid x < -4\}$

21. $4 - 3x \leq -\dfrac{2}{3} \Rightarrow -3x \leq -\dfrac{2}{3} - 4 \Rightarrow -3x \leq -\dfrac{14}{3} \Rightarrow x \geq -\dfrac{1}{3}\left(-\dfrac{14}{3}\right) \Rightarrow x \geq \dfrac{14}{9} \Rightarrow \left\{x \,\middle|\, x \geq \dfrac{14}{9}\right\}$

22. $4x - 2 \geq \dfrac{5}{2} \Rightarrow 4x \geq \dfrac{5}{2} + 2 \Rightarrow 4x \geq \dfrac{9}{2} \Rightarrow x \geq \dfrac{1}{4}\left(\dfrac{9}{2}\right) \Rightarrow x \geq \dfrac{9}{8} \Rightarrow \left\{x \,\middle|\, x \geq \dfrac{9}{8}\right\}$

23. $7 - \dfrac{1}{2}x < x - \dfrac{3}{2} \Rightarrow 14 - x < 2x - 3 \Rightarrow -3x < -17 \Rightarrow x > \dfrac{17}{3} \Rightarrow \left\{x \,\middle|\, x > \dfrac{17}{3}\right\}$

24. $4x - 6 > 12 - 10x \Rightarrow 14x > 18 \Rightarrow x > \dfrac{18}{14} \Rightarrow x > \dfrac{9}{7} \Rightarrow \left\{x \,\middle|\, x > \dfrac{9}{7}\right\}$

25. $\dfrac{5}{2}(2x - 3) < 6 - 2x \Rightarrow 5x - \dfrac{15}{2} < 6 - 2x \Rightarrow 7x < \dfrac{27}{2} \Rightarrow x < \dfrac{1}{7}\left(\dfrac{27}{2}\right) \Rightarrow x < \dfrac{27}{14} \Rightarrow \left\{x \,\middle|\, x < \dfrac{27}{14}\right\}$

26. $1 - \left(\dfrac{3}{2}x - 4\right) > \dfrac{1}{2}(x + 1) \Rightarrow 2 - 3x + 8 > x + 1 \Rightarrow 9 > 4x \Rightarrow \dfrac{9}{4} > x \Rightarrow x < \dfrac{9}{4} \Rightarrow \left\{x \,\middle|\, x < \dfrac{9}{4}\right\}$

27. $\dfrac{3x - 2}{-2} \leq \dfrac{x - 4}{-5} \Rightarrow -15x + 10 \leq -2x + 8 \Rightarrow -13x \leq -2 \Rightarrow x \geq \dfrac{2}{13} \Rightarrow \left\{x \,\middle|\, x \geq \dfrac{2}{13}\right\}$

28. $\dfrac{5 - 2x}{2} \geq \dfrac{2x + 1}{4} \Rightarrow 20 - 8x \geq 4x + 2 \Rightarrow 18 \geq 12x \Rightarrow \dfrac{18}{12} \geq x \Rightarrow x \leq \dfrac{3}{2} \Rightarrow \left\{x \,\middle|\, x \leq \dfrac{3}{2}\right\}$

29. $3(x - 2000) + 15 < 45 \Rightarrow 3x < 6030 \Rightarrow x < \dfrac{6030}{3} \Rightarrow x < 2010 \Rightarrow \{x \,|\, x < 2010\}$

30. $-2(x - 1990) + 75 > 25 \Rightarrow -2x > -4030 \Rightarrow x < \dfrac{-4030}{-2} \Rightarrow x < 2015 \Rightarrow \{x \,|\, x < 2015\}$

31. $0.4x - 0.7 < 1.3 \Rightarrow 0.4x < 2 \Rightarrow x < 5 \Rightarrow \{x \,|\, x < 5\}$

32. $-0.3(x - 5) + 0.2 > 2 \Rightarrow -0.3x + 1.5 + 0.2 > 2 \Rightarrow -0.3x > 0.3 \Rightarrow x < -1 \Rightarrow \{x \,|\, x < -1\}$

33. $\dfrac{4}{5}x - \dfrac{1}{5} \geq -5 \Rightarrow 4x - 1 \geq -25 \Rightarrow 4x \geq -24 \Rightarrow x \geq -6 \Rightarrow \{x \,|\, x \geq -6\}$

34. $\dfrac{3x}{4} - \dfrac{1}{2} \leq \dfrac{1}{4}(2x + 1) \Rightarrow 3x - 2 \leq 2x + 1 \Rightarrow x \leq 3 \Rightarrow \{x \,|\, x \leq 3\}$

35. $-\dfrac{1}{3}(z - 3) - \dfrac{1}{4} \geq \dfrac{1}{4}(5 - z) \Rightarrow -4(z - 3) - 3 \geq 3(5 - z) \Rightarrow -4z + 12 - 3 \geq 15 - 3z \Rightarrow$

    $-4z + 9 \geq 15 - 3z \Rightarrow -z \geq 6 \Rightarrow z \leq -6 \Rightarrow \{z \,|\, z \leq -6\}$

36. $2(3 - 2z) - (1 - z) \leq 4z - (1 + z) \Rightarrow 6 - 4z - 1 + z \leq 4z - 1 - z \Rightarrow -3z + 5 \leq 3z - 1 \Rightarrow$

    $-6z \leq -6 \Rightarrow z \geq 1 \Rightarrow \{z \,|\, z \geq 1\}$

37. $\dfrac{3}{4}(2t - 5) \leq \dfrac{1}{2}(4t - 6) + 1 \Rightarrow 3(2t - 5) \leq 2(4t - 6) + 4 \Rightarrow 6t - 15 \leq 8t - 12 + 4 \Rightarrow$

    $6t - 15 \leq 8t - 8 \Rightarrow -2t \leq 7 \Rightarrow t \geq -\dfrac{7}{2} \Rightarrow \left\{t \,\middle|\, t \geq -\dfrac{7}{2}\right\}$

38. $\dfrac{5}{6}x+(3-x)\geq\dfrac{x-3}{3}\Rightarrow 5x+6(3-x)\geq 2(x-3)\Rightarrow 5x+18-6x\geq 2x-6\Rightarrow$

   $-x+18\geq 2x-6\Rightarrow -3x\geq -24\Rightarrow x\leq 8\Rightarrow\left\{x\,\middle|\,x\leq 8\right\}$

39. $\dfrac{1}{2}(4-(x+3))+4>-\dfrac{1}{3}(2x-(1-x))\Rightarrow 3(4-x-3)+24>-2(2x-1+x)\Rightarrow$

   $12-3x-9+24>-4x+2-2x\Rightarrow -3x+27>-6x+2\Rightarrow 3x>-25\Rightarrow x>-\dfrac{25}{3}\Rightarrow\left\{x\,\middle|\,x>-\dfrac{25}{3}\right\}$

40. $\dfrac{x-(2-3x)}{2}<\dfrac{1-(4-5x)}{6}\Rightarrow 3(x-2+3x)<1-4+5x\Rightarrow 3x-6+9x<1-4+5x\Rightarrow$

   $12x-6<-3+5x\Rightarrow 7x<3\Rightarrow x<\dfrac{3}{7}\Rightarrow\left\{x\,\middle|\,x<\dfrac{3}{7}\right\}$

41. $0.05+0.08x<0.01x-0.04(3-4x)\Rightarrow 5+8x<x-4(3-4x)$

   $\Rightarrow 5+8x<x-12+16x\Rightarrow -9x<-17\Rightarrow x>\dfrac{17}{9}\Rightarrow\left\{x\,\middle|\,x>\dfrac{17}{9}\right\}$

42. $-0.2(5x+2)\geq 0.4+1.5x\Rightarrow -2(5x+2)\geq 4+15x\Rightarrow -10x-4\geq 4+15x$

   $\Rightarrow -25x\geq 8\Rightarrow x\leq -\dfrac{8}{25}\Rightarrow\left\{x\,\middle|\,x\leq -\dfrac{8}{25}\right\}$

Numerical Solutions

43.   See Figure 43. $\left\{x\,\middle|\,x\geq 3\right\}$

x	1	2	3	4	5
$-2x+6$	4	2	0	-2	-4

x	0	1	2	3	4
$3x-1$	-1	2	5	8	11

Figure 43   Figure 44

44.   See Figure 44. $\left\{x\,\middle|\,x<3\right\}$

45.   Table $Y_1=X-3$ and $Y_2=0$ with TblStart $=0$ and ΔTbl $=1$. See Figure 45. $\left\{x\,\middle|\,x>3\right\}$

46.   Table $Y_1=2X$ and $Y_2=0$ with TblStart $=-3$ and ΔTbl $=1$. See Figure 46. $\left\{x\,\middle|\,x<0\right\}$

Figure 45   Figure 46   Figure 47   Figure 48

47.   Table $Y_1=2X-1$ and $Y_2=3$ with TblStart $=0$ and ΔTbl $=1$. See Figure 47. $\left\{x\,\middle|\,x\geq 2\right\}$

48.   Table $Y_1=2-3X$ and $Y_2=-4$ with TblStart $=0$ and ΔTbl $=1$. See Figure 48. $\left\{x\,\middle|\,x\geq 2\right\}$

Graphical Solutions

49. (a) The graph crosses the *x*-axis at the point $(-1, 0)$. The solution set is $\{x \mid x = -1\}$.

(b) The graph is below the *x*-axis whenever $x < -1$. The solution set is $\{x \mid x < -1\}$.

(c) The graph is above the *x*-axis whenever $x > -1$. The solution set is $\{x \mid x > -1\}$.

50. (a) The graph crosses the *x*-axis at the point $(2, 0)$. The solution set is $\{x \mid x = 2\}$.

(b) The graph is below the *x*-axis whenever $x < 2$. The solution set is $\{x \mid x < 2\}$.

(c) The graph is above the *x*-axis whenever $x > 2$. The solution set is $\{x \mid x > 2\}$.

51. (a) The graph crosses the *x*-axis at the point $\left(\frac{1}{2}, 0\right)$. The solution set is $\left\{x \mid x = \frac{1}{2}\right\}$.

(b) The graph is below the *x*-axis whenever $x > \frac{1}{2}$. The solution set is $\left\{x \mid x > \frac{1}{2}\right\}$.

(c) The graph is above the *x*-axis whenever $x < \frac{1}{2}$. The solution set is $\left\{x \mid x < \frac{1}{2}\right\}$.

52. (a) The graph crosses the *x*-axis at the point $(0, 0)$. The solution set is $\{x \mid x = 0\}$.

(b) The graph is below the *x*-axis whenever $x > 0$. The solution set is $\{x \mid x > 0\}$.

(c) The graph is above the *x*-axis whenever $x < 0$. The solution set is $\{x \mid x < 0\}$.

53. The graph of y_1 is below the graph of y_2 whenever $x \geq 1$. The solution set is $\{x \mid x \geq 1\}$.

54. The graph of y_2 is above the graph of y_1 whenever $x < 2$. The solution set is $\{x \mid x < 2\}$.

55. The graph of y_1 is above the graph of y_2 whenever $x > 2$. The solution set is $\{x \mid x > 2\}$.

56. The graph of y_1 is below the graph of y_2 whenever $x \geq -2$. The solution set is $\{x \mid x \geq -2\}$.

57. (a) Car 1 is traveling faster. The slope of the line for Car 1 is greater than the slope of the line for Car 2.

(b) They are the same distance from St. Louis when $x = 5$ hours. The distance from St. Louis is 400 miles.

(c) Car 2 is farther from St. Louis than Car 1 for times in the interval $0 \leq x < 5$.

58. (a) $\{x \mid x > 10\}$

(b) $\{x \mid x \leq 10\}$

59. Graph $Y_1 = X - 1$ and $Y_2 = 0$ in $[-10, 10, 1]$ by $[-10, 10, 1]$. See Figure 59. $\{x \mid x < 1\}$

60. Graph $Y_1 = 4 - 2X$ and $Y_2 = 0$ in $[-10, 10, 1]$ by $[-10, 10, 1]$. See Figure 60. $\{x \mid x \geq 2\}$

[−10, 10, 1] by [−10, 10, 1]   [−10, 10, 1] by [−10, 10, 1]

Figure 59   Figure 60

[−10, 10, 1] by [−10, 10, 1]   [−10, 10, 1] by [−10, 10, 1]

Figure 61   Figure 62

61.   Graph $Y_1 = 2X$ and $Y_2 = 0$ in [−10, 10, 1] by [−10, 10, 1]. See Figure 61. $\{x \mid x \geq 0\}$

62.   Graph $Y_1 = 3X + 6$ and $Y_2 = 0$ in [−10, 10, 1] by [−10, 10, 1]. See Figure 62. $\{x \mid x > -2\}$

63.   Graph $Y_1 = 4 - 2X$ and $Y_2 = 8$ in [−10, 10, 1] by [−10, 10, 1]. See Figure 63. $\{x \mid x \geq -2\}$

64.   Graph $Y_1 = -2X + 3$ and $Y_2 = -3$ in [−10, 10, 1] by [−10, 10, 1]. See Figure 64. $\{x \mid x > 3\}$

[−10, 10, 1] by [−10, 10, 1]   [−10, 10, 1] by [−10, 10, 1]

Figure 63   Figure 64

[−10, 10, 1] by [−10, 10, 1]   [0, 10, 1] by [0, 20, 2]

Figure 65   Figure 66

65.   Graph $Y_1 = X - (2X + 4)$ and $Y_2 = 0$ in [−10, 10, 1] by [−10, 10, 1]. See Figure 65. $\{x \mid x < -4\}$

66.   Graph $Y_1 = 2X + 1$ and $Y_2 = 3X - 4$ in [0, 10, 1] by [0, 20, 2]. See Figure 66. $\{x \mid x \leq 5\}$

67.   Graph $Y_1 = 2(X + 2) + 5$ and $Y_2 = -X$ in [−10, 10, 1] by [−10, 10, 1]. See Figure 67. $\{x \mid x < -3\}$

[−10, 10, 1] by [−10, 10, 1]   [−10, 10, 1] by [−10, 10, 1]

Figure 67   Figure 68

[1985, 2000, 5] by [-50, 50, 10]   [1975, 2000, 5] by [0, 100, 10]

Figure 69   Figure 70

68.   Graph $Y_1 = (X+5)/3$ and $Y_2 = (1-X)/2$ in [-10, 10, 1] by [-10, 10, 1]. See Figure 68. $\{x \mid x \ge -1.4\}$

69.   Graph $Y_1 = 25(X-1995)+100$ and $Y_2 = 0$ in [1985, 2000, 5] by [-50, 50, 10]. See Figure

       69. $\{x \mid x \le 1991\}$

70.   Graph $Y_1 = 5(X-1980)-20$ and $Y_2 = 50$ in [1975, 2000, 5] by [0, 100, 10]. See Figure 70. $\{x \mid x > 1994\}$

71.   Graph $Y_1 = \pi\left(\sqrt{(2)}X - 1.2\right) + \sqrt{(3)}X$ and $Y_2 = (\pi+1)/3$ in [-10, 10, 1] by [-10, 10, 1]. $\{x \mid x > 0.834\}$

       Figure 71

72.   Graph $Y_1 = 3.1X - 0.5(\pi - X)$ and $Y_2 = \sqrt{(5)} - 0.4X$ in [-10, 10, 1] by [-10, 10, 1]. $\{x \mid x \le 0.952\}$

       Figure 72

73.   Reverse the inequality symbol: $\{x \mid x < a\}$

74.   Either $\{x \mid x \le a\}$ or $\{x \mid x \ge a\}$

Solving Linear Inequalities by More Than One Method

75.   (a) Table $Y_1 = 5X - 2$ and $Y_2 = 8$ with TblStart = 0 and ΔTbl = 1. See Figure 75a. $\{x \mid x < 2\}$

       (b) Graph $Y_1 = 5X - 2$ and $Y_2 = 8$ in [-10, 10, 1] by [-10, 10, 1]. See Figure 75b. $\{x \mid x < 2\}$

       (c) $5x - 2 < 8 \Rightarrow 5x < 10 \Rightarrow x < \dfrac{10}{5} \Rightarrow x < 2 \Rightarrow \{x \mid x < 2\}$

                           [-10, 10, 1] by [-10, 10, 1]   [-20, 0, 1] by [-10, 10, 1]

       Figure 75a   Figure 75b   Figure 76a   Figure 76b

76.   (a) Table $Y_1 = 2X - 4 - 3(X+3)$ and $Y_2 = 0$ with TblStart $= -15$ and ΔTbl $= 1$. See Figure

   76a. $\{x \mid x \geq -13\}$

   (b) Graph $Y_1 = 2X - 4 - 3(X+3)$ and $Y_2 = 0$ in $[-20, 0, 1]$ by $[-10, 10, 1]$. See Figure 76b. $\{x \mid x \geq -13\}$

   (c) $2x - 4 - 3(x+3) \leq 0 \Rightarrow 2x - 4 - 3x - 9 \leq 0 \Rightarrow -x \leq 13 \Rightarrow x \geq -13 \Rightarrow \{x \mid x \geq -13\}$

77.   (a) Table $Y_1 = 3X - 3$ and $Y_2 = 2X$ with TblStart $= 0$ and ΔTbl $= 1$. See Figure 77a. $\{x \mid x \leq 3\}$

   (b) Graph $Y_1 = 3X - 3$ and $Y_2 = 2X$ in $[-10, 10, 1]$ by $[-10, 10, 1]$. See Figure 77b. $\{x \mid x \leq 3\}$

   (c) $2x \geq 3x - 3 \Rightarrow x \leq 3 \Rightarrow \{x \mid x \leq 3\}$

$[-10, 10, 1]$ by $[-10, 10, 1]$ $[-10, 10, 1]$ by $[-10, 10, 1]$

Figure 77a   Figure 77b   Figure 78a   Figure 78b

78.   (a) Table $Y_1 = X - 1$ and $Y_2 = (4 - X)/2$ with TblStart $= 0$ and ΔTbl $= 1$. See Figure 78a. $\{x \mid x > 2\}$

   (b) Graph $Y_1 = X - 1$ and $Y_2 = (4 - X)/2$ in $[-10, 10, 1]$ by $[-10, 10, 1]$. See Figure 78b. $\{x \mid x > 2\}$

   (c) $x - 1 > \dfrac{4 - x}{2} \Rightarrow 2x - 2 > 4 - x \Rightarrow 3x > 6 \Rightarrow x > \dfrac{6}{3} \Rightarrow x > 2 \Rightarrow \{x \mid x > 2\}$

Inequalities and Functions

79.   (a) $x - 5 = 7 \Rightarrow x = 12 \Rightarrow \{x \mid x = 12\}$

   (b) $x - 5 > 7 \Rightarrow x > 12 \Rightarrow \{x \mid x > 12\}$

80.   (a) $4x = -2 \Rightarrow x = \dfrac{-2}{4} \Rightarrow x = -\dfrac{1}{2} \Rightarrow \left\{x \mid x = -\dfrac{1}{2}\right\}$

   (b) $4x < -2 \Rightarrow x < \dfrac{-2}{4} \Rightarrow x < -\dfrac{1}{2} \Rightarrow \left\{x \mid x < -\dfrac{1}{2}\right\}$

81.   (a) $4 - 3x \geq 11 \Rightarrow -3x \geq 7 \Rightarrow x \leq -\dfrac{7}{3} \Rightarrow \left\{x \mid x \leq -\dfrac{7}{3}\right\}$

   (b) $4 - 3x \leq 11 \Rightarrow -3x \leq 7 \Rightarrow x \geq -\dfrac{7}{3} \Rightarrow \left\{x \mid x \geq -\dfrac{7}{3}\right\}$

82.   (a) $9 - 3x < 0 \Rightarrow -3x < -9 \Rightarrow x > 3 \Rightarrow \{x \mid x > 3\}$

   (b) $9 - 3x > 0 \Rightarrow -3x > -9 \Rightarrow x < 3 \Rightarrow \{x \mid x < 3\}$

83.   (a) $3(x+7) + 1 \leq -5 \Rightarrow 3x + 22 \leq -5 \Rightarrow 3x \leq -27 \Rightarrow x \leq -9 \Rightarrow \{x \mid x \leq -9\}$

(b) $3(x+7)+1 \geq -5 \Rightarrow 3x+22 \geq -5 \Rightarrow 3x \geq -27 \Rightarrow x \geq -9 \Rightarrow \{x \mid x \geq -9\}$

84. (a) $-2(4-3x) > 16 \Rightarrow -8+6x > 16 \Rightarrow 6x > 24 \Rightarrow x > 4 \Rightarrow \{x \mid x > 4\}$

    (b) $-2(4-3x) < 16 \Rightarrow -8+6x < 16 \Rightarrow 6x < 24 \Rightarrow x < 4 \Rightarrow \{x \mid x < 4\}$

Applications

85. From the graph the deficit was less than $1 trillion in 1980 or before.

86. (a) A loan of $1000 will earn $100 interest.

    (b) A loan of more than $1000 will earn more than $100 interest.

    (c) A loan of $1000 or less will earn $100 or less interest.

87. (a) The band paid $200 for the blank CDs because $P = -200$ when $x = 0$.

    (b) The band charged $5 for each recorded CD because the slope of the line is 5.

    (c) Since the slope of the line is 5 and the y-intercept is -200, the equation is $P = 5x - 200$.

    (d) The break-even point occurs when $P = 0$. From the graph, this is $x = 40$ CDs.

    (e) The band will make a profit if it sells more than 40 CDs or when $x > 40$.

88. First, find the slope of the line that passes through the points (1, 21) and (30, 46); $m = \dfrac{46-21}{30-1} = \dfrac{25}{29}$.

    The equation is $y = \dfrac{25}{29}(x-1)+21$ or $y = \dfrac{25}{29}x + \dfrac{584}{29}$. Next solve this as an inequality when $y \leq 31$.

    $\dfrac{25}{29}x + \dfrac{584}{29} \leq 31 \Rightarrow 25x + 584 \leq 899 \Rightarrow 25x \leq 315 \Rightarrow x \leq 12.6$

    The average high temperature is 31°F or less on about March 13 or before.

89. Two widths plus two lengths must be less than 50.

    $2x + 2(x+5) < 50 \Rightarrow 2x + 2x + 10 < 50 \Rightarrow 4x < 40 \Rightarrow x < \dfrac{40}{4} \Rightarrow x < 10$ ft

90. Let x be the width of the rectangle. Then the length is $2x$. The perimeter must be less than 36 inches.

    $2x + 2(2x) \leq 36 \Rightarrow 2x + 4x \leq 36 \Rightarrow 6x \leq 36 \Rightarrow x \leq \dfrac{36}{6} \Rightarrow x \leq 6$ inches

    The width must be 6 inches or less.

91. (a) The first car is traveling 70 mph and the second car is traveling 60 mph.

    (b) They are the same distance away when $70x = 60x + 35 \Rightarrow 10x = 35 \Rightarrow x = \dfrac{35}{10} \Rightarrow x = 3.5$ hr.

    (c) The first car is farther away when time has elapsed past 3.5 hours.

92. (a) Graph $Y_1 = 51.6(X - 1985) + 9.1$ and $Y_2 = -31.9(X - 1985) + 167.7$ in [1984, 1991, 1] by [0, 350, 50].

    See Figure 92.

    (b) CD sales were greater than or equal to LP sales in 1987 and after.

(c) $51.6(x-1985)+9.1 \geq -31.9(x-1985)+167.7 \Rightarrow 51.6x-102,416.9 \geq -31.9x+63,489.2 \Rightarrow$

$83.5x \geq 165,906.1 \Rightarrow x \geq 1986.899$ (approximate).

CD sales were greater than or equal to LP sales about 1987 or after.

[1984, 1991, 1] by [0, 350, 50]

Figure 92

93. $60-19x>0 \Rightarrow 60>19x \Rightarrow \dfrac{60}{19}>x \Rightarrow x<3.16$ (approximate). Below about 3.16 miles.

94.   (a) Since the slope is $-5.8,$ the dew point decreases by $5.8°F$ for each one-mile increase in altitude.

(b) $70-5.8x>30 \Rightarrow -5.8x>-40 \Rightarrow x<\dfrac{-40}{-5.8} \Rightarrow x<6.9$ (approximate). Below about 6.9 miles.

95. $19 \leq \dfrac{705W}{(70)^2} \Rightarrow 19 \leq \dfrac{705W}{4900} \Rightarrow 93,100 \leq 705W$

$\Rightarrow 132 \leq W$

$25 \geq \dfrac{705W}{(70)^2} \Rightarrow 25 \geq \dfrac{705W}{4900} \Rightarrow 122,500 \geq 705W$

$\Rightarrow 174 \geq W$

W is between 132 pounds and 174 pounds.

96. $\dfrac{1}{4}\left(\dfrac{75}{100}+\dfrac{86}{100}+\dfrac{72}{100}+\dfrac{S}{150}\right) \geq 0.80 \Rightarrow \dfrac{1}{4}\left(\dfrac{233}{100}+\dfrac{S}{150}\right) \geq 0.8$

$\Rightarrow 2.33+\dfrac{S}{150} \geq 3.2 \Rightarrow \dfrac{S}{150} \geq 0.87 \Rightarrow S \geq 130.5.$

S is between 131 and 150.

97.   First, find the slope of the line that passes through the points (1994, 1.3) and (2000, 1.8);

$m=\dfrac{1.8-1.3}{2000-1994}=\dfrac{0.5}{6} \approx 0.083.$ The equation is $y=0.083(x-1994)+1.3$ or $y=0.083x-164.202.$

Solve this as an inequality when $y \geq 1.55.$ $0.083x-164.202 \geq 1.55 \Rightarrow 0.083x \geq 165.752 \Rightarrow x \geq 1997.01$

AIDS funding was greater than or equal to \$1.55 billion in 1997 or after.

98. $4.43(x-1994)+7 \leq 20.3 \Rightarrow 4.43x \leq 8846.72 \Rightarrow x \leq \dfrac{8846.72}{4.43} \Rightarrow x \leq 1997$ (approximate)

Funding was less than or equal to \$20.3 million from 1994 to 1997.

99.   (a) $0.96x-14.4=6.7 \Rightarrow 0.96x=21.1 \Rightarrow x=\dfrac{21.1}{0.96} \Rightarrow x \approx 22$

A bass that weighs 6.7 pounds is about 22 inches long.

(b) Bass which are less than 22 inches long weigh less than 6.7 pounds.

100. (a) The farther the galaxy is from Earth, the faster it is receding from Earth.

(b) The galaxy must be more than 800 light-years from Earth. *Answers may vary slightly.*

Group Activity Solutions

1. First, find the slope of the line that passes through the points (1970, 4.7) and (2000, 10.4);

$$m = \frac{10.4 - 4.7}{2000 - 1970} = \frac{5.7}{30} = 0.19.$$ The equation is $y = 0.19(x - 1970) + 4.7$ or $y = 0.19x - 369.6$.

Solve this equation for x when $y = 7$. $0.19x - 369.6 = 7 \Rightarrow 0.19x = 376.6 \Rightarrow x \approx 1982.11$

The percentage of the foreign-born portion of the population was 7% in 1982.

2. Solve the equation for x when $y = 12$. $0.19x - 369.6 = 12 \Rightarrow 0.19x = 381.6 \Rightarrow x \approx 2008.42$

The percentage of the foreign-born portion of the population might be 12% in about 2008 or 2009.

3. When $x = 1940$, $y = 0.19(1940) - 369.6 = -1\%$ and when $x = 2500$, $y = 0.19(2500) - 369.6 = 105.4\%$.

These answers are not reasonable because the model is not accurate for years that are not near 1970 or 2000.

3.4: Compound Inequalities

Concepts

1. An example of a compound inequality containing the word *and* is $x > 1$ and $x \le 7$; *Answers may vary.*

2. An example of a compound inequality containing the word *or* is $x \le 3$ or $x > 5$; *Answers may vary.*

3. No, $1 \not> 3$.

4. Yes, $1 < 3$.

5. Yes. The inequality can be written in either form.

6. Three ways for solving a compound inequality are numerically, graphically and symbolically.

7. Yes, $x = 2$ satisfies both inequalities. No, $x = 6$ does not satisfy $x - 1 < 5$.

8. No, $x = -2$ does not satisfy $2x + 1 \ge 4$. Yes, $x = 3$ satisfies both inequalities.

9. No, $x = 0$ does not satisfy either inequality. Yes, $x = 3$ satisfies $2x \ge 3$.

10. Yes, $x = -5$ satisfies $x + 1 \le -4$. No, $x = 2$ does not satisfy either inequality.

11. No, $x = -3$ does not satisfy $2 - x \le 4$. Yes, $x = 0$ satisfies both inequalities.

12. Yes, $x = -1$ satisfies $3x \le 3$. Yes, $x = 1$ satisfies either inequality.

Interval Notation

13. $[2, 10]$

14. $(-1, 5)$

15. $(5, 8]$

16. $\left[-\frac{1}{2}, \frac{5}{6}\right]$

17. $(-\infty, 4)$

18. $(-\infty, -3]$

19. $(-2, \infty)$

20. $[6, \infty)$

21. $[-2, 5)$

22. $[2, 6]$

23. $(-8, 8]$

24. $[-4, 3)$

25. $(3, \infty)$

26. $(-\infty, -3)$

27. $(-\infty, -2] \cup [4, \infty)$

28. $(-\infty, -1] \cup (6, \infty)$

29. $(-\infty, 1) \cup [5, \infty)$

30. $(-\infty, -3) \cup (3, \infty)$

31. $(-3, 5]$

32. $[2, \infty)$

33. $(-\infty, -2)$

34. $[-4, 4]$

35. $(-\infty, 4)$

36. $[-1, 4)$

37. $(-\infty, 1) \cup (2, \infty)$

38. $(-\infty, \infty)$

Symbolic Solutions

39. $x \le 3$ and $x \ge -1 \Rightarrow -1 \le x \le 3; \{x \mid -1 \le x \le 3\}$; See Figure 39.

Figure 39   Figure 40

40. $x \ge 5$ and $x > 6 \Rightarrow x > 6; \{x \mid x > 6\}$; See Figure 40.

41. $2x < 5$ and $2x > -4 \Rightarrow x < \dfrac{5}{2}$ and $x > -2 \Rightarrow -2 < x < 2.5; \{x| -2 < x < 2.5\}$; See Figure 41.

Figure 41

Figure 42

42. $2x + 1 < 3$ and $x - 1 \geq -5 \Rightarrow x < 1$ and $x \geq -4 \Rightarrow -4 \leq x < 1; \{x| -4 \leq x < 1\}$; See Figure 42.

43. $x \leq -1$ or $x \geq 2; \{x| x \leq -1 \text{ or } x \geq 2\}$; See Figure 43.

Figure 43

Figure 44

44. $2x \leq -6$ or $x \geq 6 \Rightarrow x \leq -3$ or $x \geq 6 \Rightarrow x \leq -3$ or $x \geq 6; \{x| x \leq -3 \text{ or } x \geq 6\}$; See Figure 44.

45. $5 - x > 1$ or $x + 3 \geq -1 \Rightarrow -x > -4$ or $x \geq -4 \Rightarrow x < 4$ or $x \geq -4$; All real numbers; See Figure 45.

Figure 45

Figure 46

46. $1 - 2x > 3$ or $2x - 4 \geq 4 \Rightarrow -2x > 2$ or $2x \geq 8 \Rightarrow x < -1$ or $x \geq 4; \{x| x < -1 \text{ or } x \geq 4\}$; See Figure 46.

47. $x - 3 \leq 4 \Rightarrow x \leq 7$ and $x + 5 \geq -1 \Rightarrow x \geq -6$

The solutions must satisfy both of these inequalities. The interval is $[-6, 7]$.

48. $2z \geq -10 \Rightarrow z \geq -5$ and $z < 8$

The solutions must satisfy both of these inequalities. The interval is $[-5, 8)$.

49. $3t - 1 > -1 \Rightarrow 3t > 0 \Rightarrow t > 0$ and $2t - \dfrac{1}{2} > 6 \Rightarrow 2t > \dfrac{13}{2} \Rightarrow t > \dfrac{13}{4}$

The solutions must satisfy both of these inequalities. The interval is $\left(\dfrac{13}{4}, \infty\right)$.

50. $2(x + 1) < 8 \Rightarrow 2x + 2 < 8 \Rightarrow 2x < 6 \Rightarrow x < 3$ and

$-2(x - 4) > -2 \Rightarrow -2x + 8 > -2 \Rightarrow -2x > -10 \Rightarrow x < 5$

The solutions must satisfy both of these inequalities. The interval is $(-\infty, 3)$.

51. $x - 4 \geq -3 \Rightarrow x \geq 1$ or $x - 4 \leq 3 \Rightarrow x \leq 7$

The solutions may satisfy either one or both of these inequalities. The interval is $(-\infty, \infty)$.

52. $1 - 3n \geq 6 \Rightarrow -3n \geq 5 \Rightarrow n \leq -\dfrac{5}{3}$ or $1 - 3n \leq -4 \Rightarrow -3n \leq -5 \Rightarrow n \geq \dfrac{5}{3}$

The solutions may satisfy either one or both of these inequalities. The interval is $\left(-\infty, -\dfrac{5}{3}\right] \cup \left[\dfrac{5}{3}, \infty\right)$.

53. $-x < 1 \Rightarrow x > -1$ or $5x + 1 < -10 \Rightarrow 5x < -11 \Rightarrow x < -\dfrac{11}{5}$

The solutions may satisfy either one or both of these inequalities. The interval is $\left(-\infty, -\dfrac{11}{5}\right] \cup (-1, \infty)$.

54. $7x - 6 > 0 \Rightarrow 7x > 6 \Rightarrow x > \dfrac{6}{7}$ or $-\dfrac{1}{2}x \le 6 \Rightarrow x \ge -12$

The solutions may satisfy either one or both of these inequalities. The interval is $[-12, \infty)$.

55. $1 - 7x < -48 \Rightarrow -7x < -49 \Rightarrow x > 7$ and $3x + 1 \le -9 \Rightarrow 3x \le -10 \Rightarrow x \le -\dfrac{10}{3}$

The solutions must satisfy both of these inequalities. This is not possible. No solutions.

56. $3x - 4 \le 8 \Rightarrow 3x \le 12 \Rightarrow x \le 4$ or $4x - 1 \le 13 \Rightarrow 4x \le 14 \Rightarrow x \le \dfrac{7}{2}$

The solutions may satisfy either one or both of these inequalities. The interval is $(-\infty, 4]$.

57. $-2 \le t + 4 < 5 \Rightarrow -6 \le t < 1; [-6, 1)$

58. $5 < t - 7 < 10 \Rightarrow 12 < t < 17; (12, 17)$

59. $-\dfrac{5}{8} \le y - \dfrac{3}{8} < 1 \Rightarrow -\dfrac{1}{4} \le y < \dfrac{11}{8}; \left[-\dfrac{1}{4}, \dfrac{11}{8}\right)$

60. $-\dfrac{1}{2} < y - \dfrac{3}{2} < \dfrac{1}{2} \Rightarrow 1 < y < 2; (1, 2)$

61. $-27 \le 3x \le 9 \Rightarrow -9 \le x \le 3; [-9, 3]$

62. $-4 < 2y < 22 \Rightarrow -2 < y < 11; (-2, 11)$

63. $\dfrac{1}{2} < -2y \le 8 \Rightarrow -\dfrac{1}{4} > y \ge -4 \Rightarrow -4 \le y < -\dfrac{1}{4}; \left[-4, -\dfrac{1}{4}\right)$

64. $-16 \le -4x \le 8 \Rightarrow 4 \ge x \ge -2 \Rightarrow -2 \le x \le 4; [-2, 4]$

65. $-4 < 5z + 1 \le 6 \Rightarrow -5 < 5z \le 5 \Rightarrow -1 < z \le 1; (-1, 1]$

66. $-3 \le 3z + 6 < 9 \Rightarrow -9 \le 3z < 3 \Rightarrow -3 \le z < 1; [-3, 1)$

67. $3 \le 4 - n \le 6 \Rightarrow -1 \le -n \le 2 \Rightarrow 1 \ge n \ge -2 \Rightarrow -2 \le n \le 1; [-2, 1]$

68. $-1 < 3 - n \le 1 \Rightarrow -4 < -n \le -2 \Rightarrow 4 > n \ge 2 \Rightarrow 2 \le n < 4; [2, 4)$

69. $-1 < 2z - 1 < 3 \Rightarrow 0 < 2z < 4 \Rightarrow 0 < z < 2; (0, 2)$

70. $2 \le 4z + 5 \le 6 \Rightarrow -3 \le 4z \le 1 \Rightarrow -\dfrac{3}{4} \le z \le \dfrac{1}{4}; \left[-\dfrac{3}{4}, \dfrac{1}{4}\right]$

71. $-2 \le 5 - \dfrac{1}{3}m < 2 \Rightarrow -7 \le -\dfrac{1}{3}m < -3 \Rightarrow 21 \ge m > 9 \Rightarrow 9 < m \le 21; (9, 21]$

72. $-\dfrac{3}{2} < 4 - 2m < \dfrac{7}{2} \Rightarrow -\dfrac{11}{2} < -2m < -\dfrac{1}{2} \Rightarrow \dfrac{11}{4} > m > \dfrac{1}{4} \Rightarrow \dfrac{1}{4} < m < \dfrac{11}{4}; \left(\dfrac{1}{4}, \dfrac{11}{4}\right)$

73. $100 \le 10(5x-2) \le 200 \Rightarrow 10 \le 5x-2 \le 20 \Rightarrow 12 \le 5x \le 22 \Rightarrow \dfrac{12}{5} \le x \le \dfrac{22}{5}; \left[\dfrac{12}{5}, \dfrac{22}{5}\right]$

74. $-15 < 5(x-1990) < 30 \Rightarrow -3 < x-1990 < 6 \Rightarrow 1987 < x < 1996; (1987, 1996)$

75. $-3 < \dfrac{3z+1}{4} < 1 \Rightarrow -12 < 3z+1 < 4 \Rightarrow -13 < 3z < 3 \Rightarrow -\dfrac{13}{3} < z < 1; \left(-\dfrac{13}{3}, 1\right)$

76. $-3 < \dfrac{z-1}{2} < 5 \Rightarrow -6 < z-1 < 10 \Rightarrow -5 < z < 11; (-5, 11)$

77. $-\dfrac{5}{2} \le \dfrac{2-m}{4} \le \dfrac{1}{2} \Rightarrow -10 \le 2-m \le 2 \Rightarrow -12 \le -m \le 0 \Rightarrow 12 \ge m \ge 0 \Rightarrow 0 \le m \le 12; [0, 12]$

78. $\dfrac{4}{5} \le \dfrac{4-2m}{10} \le 2 \Rightarrow 8 \le 4-2m \le 20 \Rightarrow 4 \le -2m \le 16 \Rightarrow -2 \ge m \ge -8 \Rightarrow -8 \le m \le -2; [-8, -2]$

Numerical and Graphical Solutions

79. The values of $3x$ are between -3 and 6 when $-1 \le x \le 2$. The interval is $[-1, 2]$.

80. The values of $2x-1$ are between -5 and 1 when $-2 \le x \le 1$. The interval is $[-2, 1]$.

81. The values of $1-x$ are between -1 and 2 when $-1 < x < 2$. The interval is $(-1, 2)$.

82. The values of $-2x$ are between $-2 < x \le 1$. The interval is $(-2, 1]$.

83. The values of y_1 are between the lines $y = -2$ and $y = 2$ when $-3 \le x \le 1$. The interval is $[-3, 1]$.

84. The values of y_1 are between the lines $y = 1$ and $y = 3$ when $-2 < x \le 0$. The interval is $(-2, 0]$.

85. The values of y_1 are below the line $y = -2$ and above the line $y = 2$ when $x < -2$ or $x > 0$.

    The interval is $(-\infty, -2) \cup (0, \infty)$.

86. The values of y_1 are below the line $y = -2$ and above the line $y = 4$ when $x \le -1$ or $x \ge 1$.

    The interval is $(-\infty, -1] \cup [1, \infty)$.

87. (a) The car is moving toward Omaha since the distance is decreasing.

    (b) The car is 100 miles from Omaha when $x = 4$ hr. The car is 200 miles from Omaha when $x = 2$ hr.

    (c) The car is 100 to 200 miles from Omaha when the elapsed time is between 2 and 4 hours.

    (d) The car's distance from Omaha is greater than or equal to 200 miles during the first 2 hours.

88. (a) $x = 1$

    (b) $x = 3$

    (c) $\{x | 1 \le x \le 3\}$

    (d) $\{x | 0 \le x < 3\}$

89. Numerical: Table $Y_1 = 2X - 4$ with TblStart $= 0$ and ΔTbl $= 1$. See Figure 89a.

Graphical: Graph $Y_1 = -2$, $Y_2 = 2X - 4$ and $Y_3 = 4$ in $[-5, 5, 1]$ by $[-5, 5, 1]$. See Figure 89b.

The solution is $[1, 4]$.

$[-5, 5, 1]$ by $[-5, 5, 1]$ $[-5, 5, 1]$ by $[-5, 5, 1]$

Figure 89a   Figure 89b   Figure 90a   Figure 90b

90.   Numerical: Table $Y_1 = 1 - X$ with TblStart $= -3$ and ΔTbl $= 1$. See Figure 90a.

Graphical: Graph $Y_1 = -1$, $Y_2 = 1 - X$ and $Y_3 = 3$ in $[-5, 5, 1]$ by $[-5, 5, 1]$. See Figure 90b.

The solution is $[-2, 2]$.

91.   Numerical: Table $Y_1 = X + 1$ with TblStart $= -4$ and ΔTbl $= 1$. See Figure 91a.

Graphical: Graph $Y_1 = -1$, $Y_2 = X + 1$ and $Y_3 = 1$ in $[-5, 5, 1]$ by $[-5, 5, 1]$. See Figure 91b.

The solution is $(-\infty, -2) \cup (0, \infty)$.

$[-5, 5, 1]$ by $[-5, 5, 1]$ $[-10, 10, 1]$ by $[-10, 10, 1]$

Figure 91a   Figure 91b   Figure 92a   Figure 92b

92.   Numerical: Table $Y_1 = 2X - 1$ with TblStart $= -2$ and ΔTbl $= 1$. See Figure 92a.

Graphical: Graph $Y_1 = -3$, $Y_2 = 2X - 1$ and $Y_3 = 5$ in $[-10, 10, 1]$ by $[-10, 10, 1]$. See Figure 92b.

The solution is $(-\infty, -1) \cup (3, \infty)$.

93.   Numerical: Table $Y_1 = 25(X - 2000) + 45$ with TblStart $= 2000$ and ΔTbl $= 1$.

Graphical: Graph $Y_1 = 95$, $Y_2 = 25(X - 2000) + 45$ and $Y_3 = 295$ in $[2000, 2020, 1]$ by $[0, 325, 25]$.

The solution is $[2002, 2010]$.

94.   Numerical: Table $Y_1 = -13(X - 2005) + 120$ with TblStart = 2005 and ΔTbl = 1.

Graphical: Graph $Y_1 = 42$, $Y_2 = -13(X - 2005) + 120$ and $Y_3 = 94$ in [2000, 2020, 1] by [0, 100, 10].

The solution is $[2007, 2011]$.

Using More Than One Method

95. $4 \leq 5x - 1 \leq 14 \Rightarrow 5 \leq 5x \leq 15 \Rightarrow 1 \leq x \leq 3; [1, 3]$

Graphical: Graph $Y_1 = 4$, $Y_2 = 5X - 1$ and $Y_3 = 14$ in [0, 10, 1] by [0, 20, 1]. See Figure 95a.

Numerical: Table $Y_1 = 5X - 1$ with TblStart = 0 and ΔTbl = 1. See Figure 95b.

The solution is $[1, 3]$.

[0, 10, 1] by [0, 20, 1]   [–5, 5, 1] by [–5, 5, 1]

Figure 95a   Figure 95b   Figure 96a   Figure 96b

96. $-4 < 2x < 4 \Rightarrow -2 < x < 2; (-2, 2)$

Graphical: Graph $Y_1 = -4$, $Y_2 = 2X$ and $Y_3 = 4$ in [–5, 5, 1] by [–5, 5, 1]. See Figure 96a.

Numerical: Table $Y_1 = 2X$ with TblStart = –3 and ΔTbl = 1. See Figure 96b.

The solution is $(-2, 2)$.

97. $4 - x \geq 1$ or $4 - x < 3 \Rightarrow -x \geq -3$ or $-x < -1 \Rightarrow x \leq 3$ or $x > 1; (-\infty, \infty)$

Graphical: Graph $Y_1 = 1$, $Y_2 = 4 - X$ and $Y_3 = 3$ in [–10, 10, 1] by [–10, 10, 1]. See Figure 97a.

Numerical: Table $Y_1 = 4 - X$ with TblStart = –1 and ΔTbl = 1. See Figure 97b.

The solution is $(-\infty, \infty)$.

[–10, 10, 1] by [–10, 10, 1]   [–10, 10, 1] by [–10, 10, 1]

Figure 97a   Figure 97b   Figure 98a   Figure 98b

98. $x+3 \geq -2$ or $x+3 \leq 1 \Rightarrow x \geq -5$ or $x \leq -2; (-\infty, \infty)$

Graphical: Graph $Y_1 = -2$, $Y_2 = X+3$ and $Y_3 = 1$ in $[-10, 10, 1]$ by $[-10, 10, 1]$. See Figure 98a.

Numerical: Table $Y_1 = X+3$ with TblStart $= -10$ and ΔTbl $= 1$. See Figure 98b.

The solution is $(-\infty, \infty)$.

99. $2x+1 < 3$ or $2x+1 \geq 7 \Rightarrow x < 1$ or $x \geq 3; (-\infty, 1) \cup [3, \infty)$

Graphical: Graph $Y_1 = 3$, $Y_2 = 2X+1$ and $Y_3 = 7$ in $[-10, 10, 1]$ by $[-10, 10, 1]$.

Numerical: Table $Y_1 = 2X+1$ with TblStart $= 0$ and ΔTbl $= 1$.

The solution is $(-\infty, 1) \cup [3, \infty)$.

100. $3 - x \leq 4$ or $3 - x > 8 \Rightarrow x \geq -1$ or $x < -5; (-\infty, -5) \cup [-1, \infty)$

Graphical: Graph $Y_1 = 4$, $Y_2 = 3 - X$ and $Y_3 = 8$ in $[-10, 10, 1]$ by $[-10, 10, 1]$.

Numerical: Table $Y_1 = 3 - X$ with TblStart $= -6$ and ΔTbl $= 1$.

The solution is $(-\infty, -5) \cup [-1, \infty)$.

101. $c < x+b \leq d \Rightarrow c-b < x \leq d-b; (c-b, d-b]$

102. $c \leq ax+b \leq d \Rightarrow c-b \leq ax \leq d-b \Rightarrow \dfrac{c-b}{a} \geq x \geq \dfrac{d-b}{a}; \left[\dfrac{d-b}{a}, \dfrac{c-b}{a} \right]$

Applications

103.   (a) $178.5 \leq 5.7(x-1990) + 150 \leq 207$

$\Rightarrow 28.5 \leq 5.7(x-1990) \leq 57 \Rightarrow 5 \leq x-1990 \leq 10$

$\Rightarrow 1995 \leq x \leq 2000;$ The average price ranged from \$178,500 to \$207,000 from 1995 to 2000.

(b) Table $Y_1 = 5.7(X - 1990) + 150$ with TblStart = 1995 and ΔTbl = 1. The solution is 1995 to 2000.

104. (a) $52.4 \leq 1.4(x - 2000) + 51 \leq 56.6 \Rightarrow 1.4 \leq 1.4(x - 2000) \leq 5.6$

$\Rightarrow 1 \leq x - 2000 \leq 4 \Rightarrow 2001 \leq x \leq 2004$; The median income ranged from \$52,400 to \$56,600 from 2001 to 2004.

(b) Table $Y_1 = 1.4(X - 2000) + 51$ with TblStart = 2000 and ΔTbl = 1. The solution is 2001 to 2004.

105. $51.3 \leq 60 - 5.8x \leq 57.1 \Rightarrow -8.7 \leq -5.8x \leq -2.9$

$\Rightarrow 1.5 \geq x \geq 0.5$; The dew point ranges from 57.1°F to 51.3°F from 0.5 to 1.5 miles high.

106. $250 \leq 18x - 35,750 \leq 340 \Rightarrow 36,000 \leq 18x \leq 36,090 \Rightarrow 2000 \leq x \leq 2005$

Medicare costs will be from 250 to 340 billion dollars from 2000 to 2005.

107. The perimeter of the rectangle is given by $2(x + 3) + 2(2x)$.

$40 \leq 2(x + 3) + 2(2x) \leq 60 \Rightarrow 40 \leq 6x + 6 \leq 60 \Rightarrow 34 \leq 6x \leq 54 \Rightarrow 5.\overline{6} \leq x \leq 9$

108. Let x represent the width of the rectangle. Then the perimeter is given by $2x + 2(3x)$.

$100 \leq 2x + 2(3x) \leq 160 \Rightarrow 100 \leq 8x \leq 160 \Rightarrow 12.5 \leq x \leq 20$

The width can be from 12.5 to 20 inches.

109. $22.5 \leq 70 - 19x \leq 41.5 \Rightarrow -47.5 \leq -19x \leq -28.5 \Rightarrow 2.5 \geq x \geq 1.5 \Rightarrow 1.5 \leq x \leq 2.5$

The air temperature is from 22.5°F to 41.5°F at altitudes from 1.5 to 2.5 miles.

110. (a) Table $Y_1 = 70X + 50$ with TblStart = 4 and ΔTbl = 1. See Figure 110. $[6, 9]$

The car is from 470 to 680 miles from the rest stop for times from 6 to 9 hours.

(b) $470 \leq 70x + 50 \leq 680 \Rightarrow 420 \leq 70x \leq 630 \Rightarrow 6 \leq x \leq 9; [6, 9]$

x	4	5	6	7	8	9	10
$f(x) = 70x + 50$	330	400	470	540	610	680	750

Figure 110

111. $-90 \leq \dfrac{9}{5}C + 32 \leq 98 \Rightarrow -122 \leq \dfrac{9}{5}C \leq 66 \Rightarrow -122\left(\dfrac{5}{9}\right) \leq C \leq 66\left(\dfrac{5}{9}\right) \Rightarrow -67.\overline{7} \leq C \leq 36.\overline{6}$

The temperature range in Celsius is $-67.\overline{7}$°C to $36.\overline{6}$°C.

112. $5 \leq \dfrac{5}{9}(F - 32) \leq 20 \Rightarrow 5\left(\dfrac{9}{5}\right) \leq F - 32 \leq 20\left(\dfrac{9}{5}\right) \Rightarrow 9 \leq F - 32 \leq 36 \Rightarrow 41 \leq F \leq 68$

The temperature range in Fahrenheit is 41°F to 68°F.

Checking Basic Concepts for Sections 3.3 & 3.4

1. $4 - 3x < \dfrac{1}{2}x \Rightarrow 8 - 6x < x \Rightarrow 8 < 7x \Rightarrow \dfrac{8}{7} < x \Rightarrow \left\{ x \mid x > \dfrac{8}{7} \right\}$

2. (a) The two lines intersect at $(2, 0)$. The solution is $\{ x \mid x = 2 \}$.

    (b) The line $y = \dfrac{1}{2}x - 1$ is below the line $y = 2 - x$ when $x < 2$. The solution set is $\{ x \mid x < 2 \}$.

    (c) The line $y = \dfrac{1}{2}x - 1$ intersects and is above the line $y = 2 - x$ when $x \geq 2$. The solution set is $\{ x \mid x \geq 2 \}$.

3. (a) Yes, since $2(3) - 1 = 5 \geq 3$.

    (b) No, since $(3) + 2 = 5 \not< 4$.

4. (a) $-5 \leq 2x + 1 \leq 3 \Rightarrow -6 \leq 2x \leq 2 \Rightarrow -3 \leq x \leq 1; [-3, 1]$

    (b) $1 - x \leq -2 \Rightarrow -x \leq -3 \Rightarrow x \geq 3$ or $1 - x > 2 \Rightarrow -x > 1 \Rightarrow x < -1; (-\infty, -1) \cup [3, \infty)$

    (c) $-2 < \dfrac{4 - 3x}{2} \leq 6 \Rightarrow -4 < 4 - 3x \leq 12 \Rightarrow -8 < -3x \leq 8 \Rightarrow \dfrac{8}{3} > x \geq -\dfrac{8}{3}; \left[-\dfrac{8}{3}, \dfrac{8}{3} \right)$

3.5: Absolute Value Equations and Inequalities

Concepts

1. An example of an absolute value equation is $|3x + 2| = 6$. *Answers may vary.*

2. An example of an absolute value inequality is $|2x - 1| \leq 17$. *Answers may vary.*

3. Yes, since $|-3| = 3$.

4. Yes, since $|-4| = 4 > 3$.

5. Yes

6. No, it is equivalent to $-3 < x < 3$.

7. 2 times

8. 0 times

9. No, $|2(-3) - 5| = |-11| = 11 \neq 1$. Yes, $|2(3) - 5| = |1| = 1$.

10. Yes, $|5 - 6(1)| = |-1| = 1$. No, $|5 - 6(0)| = |5| = 5 \neq 1$.

11. No, $|7 - 4(-2)| = |15| = 15 \not\leq 5$. Yes, $|7 - 4(2)| = |-1| = 1 \leq 1$.

12. No, $|2 + (-4)| = |-2| = 2 \not< 2$. Yes, $|2 + (-1)| = |1| = 1 < 2$.

13. Yes, $\left| 7\left(-\dfrac{4}{7} \right) + 4 \right| = |-4 + 4| = |0| = 0 > -1$. Yes, $|7(2) + 4| = |18| = 18 > -1$.

14. No, $\left|12\left(-\dfrac{1}{4}\right)+3\right| = |-3+3| = |0| = 0 \not\geq 3$. Yes, $|12(2)+3| = |27| = 27 \geq 3$.

15. $x = 0$ or $x = 4$

16. $x = -2$ or $x = 1$

Symbolic Solutions

17. $x = -7$ or $x = 7$

18. $x = -4$ or $x = 4$

19. An absolute value can not be negative. No solution.

20. $x = 0$

21. $4x = 9 \Rightarrow x = \dfrac{9}{4}$ or $4x = -9 \Rightarrow x = -\dfrac{9}{4}$

22. $-3x = 7 \Rightarrow x = -\dfrac{7}{3}$ or $-3x = -7 \Rightarrow x = \dfrac{7}{3}$

23. Since $|-2x| - 6 = 2 \Rightarrow |-2x| = 8$: $-2x = 8 \Rightarrow x = -4$ or $-2x = -8 \Rightarrow x = 4$

24. Since $|5x| + 1 = 5 \Rightarrow |5x| = 4$; $5x = 4 \Rightarrow x = \dfrac{4}{5}$ or $5x = -4 \Rightarrow x = -\dfrac{4}{5}$

25. $2x + 1 = 11 \Rightarrow 2x = 10 \Rightarrow x = 5$ or $2x + 1 = -11 \Rightarrow 2x = -12 \Rightarrow x = -6$

26. $1 - 3x = 4 \Rightarrow -3x = 3 \Rightarrow x = -1$ or $1 - 3x = -4 \Rightarrow -3x = -5 \Rightarrow x = \dfrac{5}{3}$

27. Since $|-2x+3| + 3 = 4 \Rightarrow |-2x+3| = 1$:

    $-2x + 3 = 1 \Rightarrow -2x = -2 \Rightarrow x = 1$ or $-2x + 3 = -1 \Rightarrow -2x = -4 \Rightarrow x = 2$

28. Since $|6x+2| - 2 = 6 \Rightarrow |6x+2| = 8$:

    $6x + 2 = 8 \Rightarrow 6x = 6 \Rightarrow x = 1$ or $6x + 2 = -8 \Rightarrow 6x = -10 \Rightarrow x = -\dfrac{10}{6} \Rightarrow x = -\dfrac{5}{3}$

29. $\dfrac{1}{2}x - 1 = 5 \Rightarrow \dfrac{1}{2}x = 6 \Rightarrow x = 12$ or $\dfrac{1}{2}x - 1 = -5 \Rightarrow \dfrac{1}{2}x = -4 \Rightarrow x = -8$

30. $6 - \dfrac{3}{4}x = 3 \Rightarrow -\dfrac{3}{4}x = -3 \Rightarrow x = 4$ or $6 - \dfrac{3}{4}x = -3 \Rightarrow -\dfrac{3}{4}x = -9 \Rightarrow x = 12$

31. An absolute value can not be negative. No solution.

32. Since $\left|1 - \dfrac{2}{3}x\right| = 0 \Rightarrow 1 - \dfrac{2}{3}x = 0 \Rightarrow 1 = \dfrac{2}{3}x \Rightarrow \dfrac{3}{2} = x$ or $x = \dfrac{3}{2}$.

33. Since $\left|\dfrac{2}{3}z - 1\right| - 3 = 8 \Rightarrow \left|\dfrac{2}{3}z - 1\right| = 11$:

    $\dfrac{2}{3}z - 1 = 11 \Rightarrow \dfrac{2}{3}z = 12 \Rightarrow z = 18$ or $\dfrac{2}{3}z - 1 = -11 \Rightarrow \dfrac{2}{3}z = -10 \Rightarrow z = -15$

34.   Since $|1-2z|+5=10 \Rightarrow |1-2z|=5$:

$1-2z=5 \Rightarrow -2z=4 \Rightarrow z=-2$ or $1-2z=-5 \Rightarrow -2z=-6 \Rightarrow z=3$

35. $z-1=2z \Rightarrow -z=1 \Rightarrow z=-1$ or $z-1=-2z \Rightarrow 3z=1 \Rightarrow z=\dfrac{1}{3}$

36. $2z+3=2-z \Rightarrow 3z=-1 \Rightarrow z=-\dfrac{1}{3}$ or $2z+3=-2+z \Rightarrow z=-5$

37. $3t+1=2t-4 \Rightarrow t=-5$ or $3t+1=-2t+4 \Rightarrow 5t=3 \Rightarrow t=\dfrac{3}{5}$

38. $\dfrac{1}{2}t-1=3-\dfrac{3}{2}t \Rightarrow 2t=4 \Rightarrow t=2$ or $\dfrac{1}{2}t-1=-3+\dfrac{3}{2}t \Rightarrow -t=-2 \Rightarrow t=2$

39. $\dfrac{1}{4}x=3+\dfrac{1}{4}x \Rightarrow 0=3$ (no solution)   or $\dfrac{1}{4}x=-3-\dfrac{1}{4}x \Rightarrow \dfrac{1}{2}x=-3 \Rightarrow x=-6$

40. $2x-1=2x+2 \Rightarrow -1=2$ (no solution)   or $2x-1=-2x-2 \Rightarrow 4x=-1 \Rightarrow x=-\dfrac{1}{4}$

41.   (a) $2x=8 \Rightarrow x=4$ or $2x=-8 \Rightarrow x=-4$

(b) $\{x|-4<x<4\}$

(c) $\{x|x<-4 \text{ or } x>4\}$

42.   (a) $3x-9=6 \Rightarrow 3x=15 \Rightarrow x=5$ or $3x-9=-6 \Rightarrow 3x=3 \Rightarrow x=1$

(b) $\{x|1\le x\le 5\}$

(c) $\{x|x\le 1 \text{ or } x\ge 5\}$

43.   (a) $5-4x=3 \Rightarrow -4x=-2 \Rightarrow x=\dfrac{1}{2}$ or $5-4x=-3 \Rightarrow -4x=-8 \Rightarrow x=2$

(b) $\left\{x|\dfrac{1}{2}\le x\le 2\right\}$

(c) $\left\{x|x\le \dfrac{1}{2} \text{ or } x\ge 2\right\}$

44.   (a) $\dfrac{x-5}{2}=2 \Rightarrow x-5=4 \Rightarrow x=9$ or $\dfrac{x-5}{2}=-2 \Rightarrow x-5=-4 \Rightarrow x=1$

(b) $\{x|1<x<9\}$

(c) $\{x|x<1 \text{ or } x>9\}$

45.   The solutions to $|x|\le 3$ satisfy $c\le x\le d$ where c and d are the solutions to $|x|=3$.

$|x|=3$ is equivalent to $x=-3$ and $x=3$. The interval is $[-3,\ 3]$.

46.   The solutions to $|x|<2$ satisfy $c<x<d$ where c and d are the solutions to $|x|=2$.

$|x|=2$ is equivalent to $x=-2$ and $x=2$. The interval is $(-2,\ 2)$.

47. The solutions to $|k| > 4$ satisfy $k < c$ or $k > d$ where c and d are the solutions to $|k| = 4$.

    $|k| = 4$ is equivalent to $k = -4$ and $k = 4$. The interval is $(-\infty, \, -4) \cup (4, \, \infty)$.

48. The solutions to $|k| \geq 5$ satisfy $k \leq c$ or $k \geq d$ where c and d are the solutions to $|k| = 5$.

    $|k| = 5$ is equivalent to $k = -5$ and $k = 5$. The interval is $(-\infty, \, -5] \cup [5, \, \infty)$.

49. The inequality $|t| \leq -3$ has no solutions because absolute value is never negative.

50. The inequality $|t| < -1$ has no solutions because absolute value is never negative.

51. The inequality $|z| > 0$ is true for any value of z except $z = 0$. The interval is $(-\infty, \, 0) \cup (0, \, \infty)$.

52. The inequality $|2z| \geq 0$ is true for all values of z because absolute value is never negative.

    The interval is $(-\infty, \, \infty)$.

53. The solutions to $|2x| > 7$ satisfy $x < c$ or $x > d$ where c and d are the solutions to $|2x| = 7$.

    $|2x| = 7$ is equivalent to $2x = -7 \Rightarrow x = -\dfrac{7}{2}$ or $2x = 7 \Rightarrow x = \dfrac{7}{2}$.

    The interval is $\left(-\infty, \, -\dfrac{7}{2}\right) \cup \left(\dfrac{7}{2}, \, \infty\right)$.

54. The solutions to $|-12x| < 30$ satisfy $c < x < d$ where c and d are the solutions to $|-12x| = 30$.

    $|-12x| = 30$ is equivalent to $-12x = -30 \Rightarrow x = \dfrac{5}{2}$ or $-12x = 30 \Rightarrow x = -\dfrac{5}{2}$. The interval is $\left(-\dfrac{5}{2}, \, \dfrac{5}{2}\right)$.

55. The solutions to $|-4x + 4| < 16$ satisfy $c < x < d$ where c and d are the solutions to $|-4x + 4| = 16$.

    $|-4x + 4| = 16$ is equivalent to $-4x + 4 = -16 \Rightarrow x = 5$ or $-4x + 4 = 16 \Rightarrow x = -3$.

    The interval is $(-3, \, 5)$.

56. The solutions to $|-5x - 8| > 2$ satisfy $x < c$ or $x > d$ where c and d are the solutions to $|-5x - 8| = 2$.

    $|-5x - 8| = 2$ is equivalent to $-5x - 8 = -2 \Rightarrow x = -\dfrac{6}{5}$ or $-5x - 8 = 2 \Rightarrow x = -2$.

    The interval is $(-\infty, \, -2) \cup \left(-\dfrac{6}{5}, \, \infty\right)$.

57. First divide each side of $2|x + 5| \geq 8$ by 2 to obtain $|x + 5| \geq 4$.

    The solutions to $|x + 5| \geq 4$ satisfy $x \leq c$ or $x \geq d$ where c and d are the solutions to $|x + 5| = 4$.

    $|x + 5| = 4$ is equivalent to $x + 5 = -4 \Rightarrow x = -9$ or $x + 5 = 4 \Rightarrow x = -1$.

    The interval is $(-\infty, \, -9] \cup [-1, \, \infty)$.

58. First divide each side of $-3|x - 1| \geq -9$ by -3 to obtain $|x - 1| \leq 3$.

    The solutions to $|x - 1| \leq 3$ satisfy $c \leq x \leq d$ where c and d are the solutions to $|x - 1| = 3$.

$|x-1| = 3$ is equivalent to $x-1 = -3 \Rightarrow x = -2$ or $x-1 = 3 \Rightarrow x = 4$. The interval is $[-2,\ 4]$.

59.   First add 1 to each side of $|8-6x|-1 \le 2$ to obtain $|8-6x| \le 3$.

The solutions to $|8-6x| \le 3$ satisfy $c \le x \le d$ where c and d are the solutions to $|8-6x| = 3$.

$|8-6x| = 3$ is equivalent to $8-6x = -3 \Rightarrow x = \dfrac{11}{6}$ or $8-6x = 3 \Rightarrow x = \dfrac{5}{6}$. The interval is $\left[\dfrac{5}{6},\ \dfrac{11}{6}\right]$.

60.   First subtract 4 from each side of $4-\left|\dfrac{2x}{3}\right| < -7$ and then multiply each side by -1 to obtain $\left|\dfrac{2x}{3}\right| > 11$.

The solutions to $\left|\dfrac{2x}{3}\right| > 11$ satisfy $x < c$ or $x > d$ where c and d are the solutions to $\left|\dfrac{2x}{3}\right| = 11$.

$\left|\dfrac{2x}{3}\right| = 11$ is equivalent to $\dfrac{2x}{3} = -11 \Rightarrow x = -\dfrac{33}{2}$ or $\dfrac{2x}{3} = 11 \Rightarrow x = \dfrac{33}{2}$.

The interval is $\left(-\infty,\ -\dfrac{33}{2}\right) \cup \left(\dfrac{33}{2},\ \infty\right)$.

61.   First subtract 5 from each side of $5+\left|\dfrac{2-x}{3}\right| \le 9$ to obtain $\left|\dfrac{2-x}{3}\right| \le 4$.

The solutions to $\left|\dfrac{2-x}{3}\right| \le 4$ satisfy $c \le x \le d$ where c and d are the solutions to $\left|\dfrac{2-x}{3}\right| = 4$.

$\left|\dfrac{2-x}{3}\right| = 4$ is equivalent to $\dfrac{2-x}{3} = -4 \Rightarrow x = 14$ or $\dfrac{2-x}{3} = 4 \Rightarrow x = -10$. The interval is $[-10,\ 14]$.

62.   The solutions to $\left|\dfrac{x+3}{5}\right| \le 12$ satisfy $c \le x \le d$ where c and d are the solutions to $\left|\dfrac{x+3}{5}\right| = 12$.

$\left|\dfrac{x+3}{5}\right| = 12$ is equivalent to $\dfrac{x+3}{5} = -12 \Rightarrow x = -63$ or $\dfrac{x+3}{5} = 12 \Rightarrow x = 57$.

The interval is $[-63,\ 57]$.

63.   The inequality $|2x-1| \le -3$ has no solutions because absolute value is never negative.

64.   The inequality $|x+6| \ge -5$ is true for all values of x because absolute value is never negative.

The interval is $(-\infty,\ \infty)$.

65.   First add 1 to each side of $|x+1|-1 > -3$ to obtain $|x+1| > -2$.

The inequality $|x+1| > -2$ is true for all values of x because absolute value is never negative.

The interval is $(-\infty,\ \infty)$.

66.   First divide each side of $-2|1-7x| \ge 2$ by -2 to obtain $|1-7x| \le -1$.

The inequality $|1-7x| \le -1$ has no solutions because absolute value is never negative.

67.   The inequality $|2z-4| \le -1$ has no solutions because absolute value is never negative.

68. Since absolute value can never be negative, $|4-z| \le 0$ is equivalent to $|4-z| = 0$.

   $|4-z| = 0$ is equivalent to $4-z = 0 \Rightarrow z = 4$. The only solution is 4.

69. The inequality $|3z-1| > -3$ is true for all values of z because absolute value is never negative.

   The interval is $(-\infty,\ \infty)$.

70. The inequality $|2z| \ge -2$ is true for all values of z because absolute value is never negative.

   The interval is $(-\infty,\ \infty)$.

71. The solutions to $\left|\dfrac{2-t}{3}\right| \ge 5$ satisfy $t \le c$ or $t \ge d$ where c and d are the solutions to $\left|\dfrac{2-t}{3}\right| = 5$.

   $\left|\dfrac{2-t}{3}\right| = 5$ is equivalent to $\dfrac{2-t}{3} = -5 \Rightarrow t = 17$ or $\dfrac{2-t}{3} = 5 \Rightarrow x = -13$.

   The interval is $(-\infty,\ -13] \cup [17,\ \infty)$.

72. The solutions to $\left|\dfrac{2t+3}{5}\right| \ge 7$ satisfy $t \le c$ or $t \ge d$ where c and d are the solutions to $\left|\dfrac{2t+3}{5}\right| = 7$.

   $\left|\dfrac{2t+3}{5}\right| = 7$ is equivalent to $\dfrac{2t+3}{5} = -7 \Rightarrow t = -19$ or $\dfrac{2t+3}{5} = 7 \Rightarrow x = 16$.

   The interval is $(-\infty,\ -19] \cup [16,\ \infty)$.

73. The solutions to $|t-1| \le 0.1$ satisfy $c \le t \le d$ where c and d are the solutions to $|t-1| = 0.1$.

   $|t-1| = 0.1$ is equivalent to $t-1 = -0.1 \Rightarrow t = 0.9$ or $t-1 = 0.1 \Rightarrow t = 1.1$. The interval is $[0.9,\ 1.1]$.

74. The solutions to $|t-2| \le 0.01$ satisfy $c \le t \le d$ where c and d are the solutions to $|t-2| = 0.01$.

   $|t-2| = 0.01$ is equivalent to $t-2 = -0.01 \Rightarrow t = 1.99$ or $t-2 = 0.01 \Rightarrow t = 2.01$.

   The interval is $[1.99,\ 2.01]$.

75. The solutions to $|b-10| > 0.5$ satisfy $b < c$ or $b > d$ where c and d are the solutions to $|b-10| = 0.5$.

   $|b-10| = 0.5$ is equivalent to $b-10 = -0.5 \Rightarrow b = 9.5$ or $b-10 = 0.5 \Rightarrow b = 10.5$.

   The interval is $(-\infty,\ 9.5) \cup (10.5,\ \infty)$.

76. The solutions to $|b-25| \ge 1$ satisfy $b \le c$ or $b \ge d$ where c and d are the solutions to $|b-25| = 1$.

   $|b-25| = 1$ is equivalent to $b-25 = -1 \Rightarrow b = 24$ or $b-25 = 1 \Rightarrow b = 26$.

   The interval is $(-\infty,\ 24] \cup [26,\ \infty)$.

Numerical and Graphical Solutions

77. (a) From the table, $y = 2$ when $x = -1$ or $x = 3$.

   (b) $y < 2$ when $-1 < x < 3$. The interval is $(-1,\ 3)$.

(c) $y > 2$ when $x < -1$ or $x > 3$. The interval is $(-\infty,\ -1) \cup (3,\ \infty)$.

78. (a) From the table, $y = 6$ when $x = -6$ or $x = 18$.

(b) $y \leq 6$ when $-6 \leq x \leq 18$. The interval is $[-6,\ 18]$.

(c) $y \geq 6$ when $x \leq -6$ or $x \geq 18$. The interval is $(-\infty,\ -6] \cup [18,\ \infty)$.

79. (a) From the graph $y_1 = 1$ when $x = -1$ or $x = 0$.

(b) $y_1 \leq 1$ when $-1 \leq x \leq 0$. The interval is $[-1,\ 0]$.

(c) $y_1 \geq 1$ when $x \leq -1$ or $x \geq 0$. The interval is $(-\infty,\ -1] \cup [0,\ \infty)$.

80. (a) From the graph $y_1 = 3$ when $x = -2$ or $x = 4$.

(b) $y_1 < 3$ when $-2 < x < 4$. The interval is $(-2,\ 4)$.

(c) $y_1 > 3$ when $x < -2$ or $x > 4$. The interval is $(-\infty,\ -2) \cup (4,\ \infty)$.

81. Graph $Y_1 = \text{abs}(X)$ and $Y_2 = 1$ in $[-3, 3, 1]$ by $[-3, 3, 1]$. See Figures 81a and 81b. $(-\infty,\ -1] \cup [1,\ \infty)$

$[-3, 3, 1]$ by $[-3, 3, 1]$ $[-3, 3, 1]$ by $[-3, 3, 1]$

Figure 81a   Figure 81b

82. Graph $Y_1 = \text{abs}(X)$ and $Y_2 = 2$ in $[-3, 3, 1]$ by $[-3, 3, 1]$. See Figures 82a and 82b. $(-2,\ 2)$

$[-3, 3, 1]$ by $[-3, 3, 1]$ $[-3, 3, 1]$ by $[-3, 3, 1]$

Figure 82a   Figure 82b

$[-5, 5, 1]$ by $[-5, 5, 1]$ $[-5, 5, 1]$ by $[-5, 5, 1]$

Figure 83a   Figure 83b

83. Graph $Y_1 = \text{abs}(X-1)$ and $Y_2 = 3$ in $[-5, 5, 1]$ by $[-5, 5, 1]$. See Figures 83a and 83b. $[-2,\ 4]$

84. Graph $Y_1 = \text{abs}(X+5)$ and $Y_2 = 2$ in $[-10, 0, 1]$ by $[0, 5, 1]$. See Figures 84a and 84b. $(-\infty,\ -7] \cup [-3,\ \infty)$

[–10, 0, 1] by [0, 5, 1]   [–10, 0, 1] by [0, 5, 1]

    Figure 84a   Figure 84b

[0, 5, 1] by [0, 5, 1]   [0, 5, 1] by [0, 5, 1]

    Figure 85a   Figure 85b

85.   Graph $Y_1 = abs(4-2X)$ and $Y_2 = 2$ in [0, 5, 1] by [0, 5, 1]. See Figures 85a and 85b. $(-\infty, 1) \cup (3, \infty)$

86.   Graph $Y_1 = abs(1.5X-3)$ and $Y_2 = 6$ in [–8, 8, 1] by [0, 10, 1]. See Figures 86a and 86b.

      $(-\infty, -2] \cup [6, \infty)$

[–8, 8, 1] by [0, 10, 1]   [–8, 8, 1] by [0, 10, 1]

    Figure 86a   Figure 86b

[0, 6, 1] by [0, 6, 1]   [0, 6, 1] by [0, 6, 1]

    Figure 87a   Figure 87b

87.   Graph $Y_1 = abs(10-3X)$ and $Y_2 = 4$ in [0, 6, 1] by [0, 6, 1]. See Figures 87a and 87b. $\left(2, 4.\overline{6}\right)$

88.   Graph $Y_1 = abs(7-4X)$ and $Y_2 = 2.5$ in [0, 4, 1] by [0, 4, 1]. See Figures 88a and 88b. $[1.125, 2.375]$

[0, 4, 1] by [0, 4, 1]   [0, 4, 1] by [0, 4, 1]

    Figure 88a   Figure 88b

89.   Graph $Y_1 = abs(8.1-X)$ and $Y_2 = -2$ in [0, 15, 1] by [–5, 5, 1]. See Figure 89. $(-\infty, \infty)$

[0, 15, 1] by [–5, 5, 1]   [–5, 5, 1] by [–5, 5, 1]

Figure 89   Figure 90

90.   Graph $Y_1 = abs((5X - 9)/2)$ and $Y_2 = -1$ in [–5, 5, 1] by [–5, 5, 1]. See Figure 90. No solutions.

Using More Than One Method

91.   (a) $3x = 9 \Rightarrow x = 3$ or $3x = -9 \Rightarrow x = -3$; $\{x | -3 \le x \le 3\}$

      (b)   Graph $Y_1 = abs(3X)$ and $Y_2 = 9$ in [–5, 5, 1] by [–5, 15, 1]. See Figures 91a and 91b.

      (c)   Table $Y_1 = abs(3X)$ with TblStart = –7 and ΔTbl = 2. See Figure 91c.

      The solution set is $\{x | -3 \le x \le 3\}$.

[–5, 5, 1] by [–5, 15, 1]   [–5, 5, 1] by [–5, 15, 1]

Figure 91a   Figure 91b   Figure 91c

92.   (a) $5 - x = 3 \Rightarrow -x = -2 \Rightarrow x = 2$ or $5 - x = -3 \Rightarrow -x = -8 \Rightarrow x = 8$; $\{x | x \le 2 \text{ or } x \ge 8\}$

      (b)   Graph $Y_1 = abs(5 - X)$ and $Y_2 = 3$ in [0, 10, 1] by [0, 5, 1]. See Figures 92a and 92b.

      (c)   Table $Y_1 = abs(5 - X)$ with TblStart = –2 and ΔTbl = 2. See Figure 92c.

      The solution set is $\{x | x \le 2 \text{ or } x \ge 8\}$.

[0, 10, 1] by [0, 5, 1]   [0, 10, 1] by [0, 5, 1]

Figure 92a   Figure 92b   Figure 92c

93.   (a) $2x - 5 = 1 \Rightarrow 2x = 6 \Rightarrow x = 3$ or $2x - 5 = -1 \Rightarrow 2x = 4 \Rightarrow x = 2$; $\{x | x < 2 \text{ or } x > 3\}$

      (b)   Graph $Y_1 = abs(2X - 5)$ and $Y_2 = 1$ in [0, 5, 1] by [–1, 2, 1]. See Figures 93a and 93b.

      (c)   Table $Y_1 = abs(2X - 5)$ with TblStart = 1 and ΔTbl = 0.5. See Figure 93c.

      The solution set is $\{x | x < 2 \text{ or } x > 3\}$.

[0, 5, 1] by [−1, 2, 1]   [0, 5, 1] by [−1, 2, 1]

Figure 93a   Figure 93b   Figure 93c

94.   (a) $-8-4x = 6 \Rightarrow x = -3.5$ or $-8-4x = -6 \Rightarrow x = -0.5$; $\{x|-3.5 < x < -0.5\}$

(b) Graph $Y_1 = \text{abs}(-8-4X)$ and $Y_2 = 6$ in $[-5, 0, 1]$ by $[0, 10, 1]$. See Figures 94a and 94b.

(c) Table $Y_1 = \text{abs}(-8-4X)$ with TblStart $= -4.5$ and ΔTbl $= 1$. See Figure 94c.

The solution set is $\{x|-3.5 < x < -0.5\}$.

[−5, 0, 1] by [0, 10, 1]   [−5, 0, 1] by [0, 10, 1]

Figure 94a   Figure 94b   Figure 94c

95. $|x| \le 4$

96. $|y| < 0.1$

97. $|y| > 2$

98. $|x| \le 0.1$

99. $|2x+1| \le 0.3$

100. $|4x| > 5$

101. $|\pi x| \ge 7$

102. $\left|x-\sqrt{2}\right| \le 0.9$

103.   two

104. $|ax+b| < k \Rightarrow -k < ax+b < k \Rightarrow -k-b < ax < k-b \Rightarrow$

$\dfrac{-k-b}{a} < x < \dfrac{k-b}{a} \Rightarrow \left(\dfrac{-k-b}{a},\ \dfrac{k-b}{a}\right)$

Applications

105.   (a) $T-43 = 24 \Rightarrow T = 67$ or $T-43 = -24 \Rightarrow T = 19$; $\{T|19 \le T \le 67\}$

(b) The monthly average temperatures in Marquette, Michigan vary from 19°F to 67°F.

106.   (a) $T-62 = 19 \Rightarrow T = 81$ or $T-62 = -19 \Rightarrow T = 43$; $\{T|43 \le T \le 81\}$

(b) The monthly average temperatures in Memphis, Tennessee vary from 43°F to 81°F.

107.   (a) $T-10 = 36 \Rightarrow T = 46$ or $T-10 = -36 \Rightarrow T = -26$; $\{T|-26 \le T \le 46\}$

(b) The monthly average temperatures in Chesterfield, Canada vary from –26°F to 46°F.

108. (a) $T - 61.5 = 12.5 \implies T = 74$ or $T - 61.5 = -12.5 \implies T = 49$; $\{T \mid 49 \le T \le 74\}$

(b) The monthly average temperatures in Buenos Aires, Argentina vary from 49°F to 74°F.

109. (a) $A = (29{,}028 + 22{,}834 + 20{,}320 + 19{,}340 + 18{,}510 + 16{,}066 + 7{,}310) \div 7 \approx 19{,}058$ feet

(b) Africa and Europe have elevations within 1000 feet of A.

(c) South America, North America, Africa, Europe and Antarctica have elevations within 5000 feet of A.

110. (a) See Figure 110.

(b) At 60 mph the distance between the cars is decreasing at 2 miles per minute: $\left|-2x + 4\right| = 2$

(c) $-2x + 4 = 2 \implies -2x = -2 \implies x = 1$ or $-2x + 4 = -2 \implies -2x = -6 \implies x = 3$

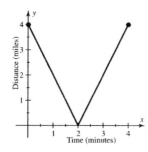

Figure 110

111. $d - 2.5 = 0.002 \implies d = 2.502$ or $d - 2.5 = -0.002 \implies d = 2.498$; $\{d \mid 2.498 \le d \le 2.502\}$

The diameter can vary from 2.498 inches to 2.502 inches.

112. $\left|t - 51.57\right| \le 0.02$.

113. $\left|d - 3.8\right| \le 0.03$

114. $\left|d - 36\right| \le \dfrac{0.1}{\pi}$

115. The solutions to $\left|\dfrac{x - 20}{20}\right| < 0.05$ satisfy $c < x < d$ where c and d are the solutions to $\left|\dfrac{x - 20}{20}\right| = 0.05$.

$\left|\dfrac{x - 20}{20}\right| = 0.05$ is equivalent to $\dfrac{x - 20}{20} = -0.05 \implies x = 19$ or $\dfrac{x - 20}{20} = 0.05 \implies x = 21$.

The interval is $(19,\ 21)$. The values must be between 19 and 21, exclusively.

116. The solutions to $\left|\dfrac{x - 50}{50}\right| < 0.03$ satisfy $c < x < d$ where c and d are the solutions to $\left|\dfrac{x - 50}{50}\right| = 0.03$.

$\left|\dfrac{x - 50}{50}\right| = 0.03$ is equivalent to $\dfrac{x - 50}{50} = -0.03 \implies x = 48.5$ or $\dfrac{x - 50}{50} = 0.03 \implies x = 51.5$.

The interval is $(48.5,\ 51.5)$. The values must be between 48.5 and 51.5 cubic inches.

Checking Basic Concepts for Section 3.5

1. $\left|\dfrac{3}{4}x-1\right|-3=5 \;\Rightarrow\; \left|\dfrac{3}{4}x-1\right|=8$

    $\dfrac{3}{4}x-1=-8 \;\Rightarrow\; \dfrac{3}{4}x=-7 \;\Rightarrow\; x=-\dfrac{28}{3}$ or $\dfrac{3}{4}x-1=8 \;\Rightarrow\; \dfrac{3}{4}x=9 \;\Rightarrow\; x=12$

2. (a) $3x-6=8 \;\Rightarrow\; 3x=14 \;\Rightarrow\; x=\dfrac{14}{3}$ or $3x-6=-8 \;\Rightarrow\; 3x=-2 \;\Rightarrow\; x=-\dfrac{2}{3}$

    (b) The solutions to $|3x-6|<8$ satisfy $c<x<d$ where c and d are the solutions to $|3x-6|=8$.

    From part (a), the interval is $\left(-\dfrac{2}{3},\ \dfrac{14}{3}\right)$.

    (c) The solutions to $|3x-6|>8$ satisfy $x<c$ or $x>d$ where c and d are the solutions to $|3x-6|=8$.

    From part (a), the interval is $\left(-\infty,\ -\dfrac{2}{3}\right)\cup\left(\dfrac{14}{3},\ \infty\right)$.

3. The solutions to $\left|-2(3-x)\right|<6$ satisfy $c<x<d$ where c and d are the solutions to $\left|-2(3-x)\right|=6$.

    $\left|-2(3-x)\right|=6$ is equivalent to $-2(3-x)=-6 \;\Rightarrow\; x=0$ or $-2(3-x)=6 \;\Rightarrow\; x=6$.

    The interval is $(0,\ 6)$. Similarly, the solution to $\left|-2(3-x)\right|\ge 6$ is the interval $(-\infty,\ 0]\cup[6,\ \infty)$.

4. (a) From the graph $y=2$ when $x=1$ or $x=3$.

    (b) $y\le 2$ when $1\le x\le 3$. The interval is $[1,\ 3]$.

    (c) $y\ge 2$ when $x\le 1$ or $x\ge 3$. The interval is $(-\infty,\ 1]\cup[3,\ \infty)$.

Chapter 3 Review Exercises

Section 3.1

1. The completed table is shown in Figure 1. From the table we see that $3x-6=0$ when $x=2$.

x	0	1	2	3	4
$3x-6$	-6	-3	0	3	6

x	-1	0	1	2	3
$5-2x$	7	5	3	1	-1

Figure 1   Figure 2

2. The completed table is shown in Figure 2. From the table we see that $5-2x=3$ when $x=1$.

3. Yes it is a solution since $\dfrac{1}{2}\left(-\dfrac{2}{3}\right)-2\left(2\left(-\dfrac{2}{3}\right)+3\right)=-\dfrac{11}{3}$ and $4\left(-\dfrac{2}{3}\right)-1=-\dfrac{11}{3}$.

4. Since the graphs intersect at the point $(1, 3)$, the solution is $x=1$.

5. Graph $Y_1=5-2X$ and $Y_2=-1+X$ in $[-10, 10, 1]$ by $[-10, 10, 1]$. See Figure 5. $x=2$

$[-10, 10, 1]$ by $[-10, 10, 1]$

Figure 5   Figure 6

6.   Table $Y_1 = 4X - 3$ and $Y_2 = 5 + 2X$ with TblStart $= 0$ and ΔTbl $= 1$. See Figure 6. $x = 4$

7. $2x - 7 = 21 \ \Rightarrow \ 2x = 28 \ \Rightarrow \ x = \dfrac{28}{2} \ \Rightarrow \ x = 14$

8. $1 - 7x = -\dfrac{5}{2} \ \Rightarrow \ -7x = -\dfrac{5}{2} - 1 \ \Rightarrow \ -7x = -\dfrac{7}{2} \ \Rightarrow \ x = -\dfrac{1}{7}\left(-\dfrac{7}{2}\right) \ \Rightarrow \ x = \dfrac{1}{2}$

9. $-2(4x - 1) = 1 - x \ \Rightarrow \ -8x + 2 = 1 - x \ \Rightarrow \ 1 = 7x \ \Rightarrow \ \dfrac{1}{7} = x \ \Rightarrow \ x = \dfrac{1}{7}$

10. $-\dfrac{3}{4}(x - 1) + 5 = 6 \ \Rightarrow \ -\dfrac{3}{4}x + \dfrac{3}{4} + 5 = 6 \ \Rightarrow \ -\dfrac{3}{4}x = \dfrac{1}{4} \ \Rightarrow \ x = -\dfrac{4}{3}\left(\dfrac{1}{4}\right) \ \Rightarrow \ x = -\dfrac{1}{3}$

11. $\dfrac{x - 4}{3} = 2 \ \Rightarrow \ x - 4 = 6 \ \Rightarrow \ x = 10$

12. $\dfrac{2x - 3}{2} = \dfrac{x + 3}{5} \ \Rightarrow \ 5(2x - 3) = 2(x + 3) \ \Rightarrow \ 10x - 15 = 2x + 6 \ \Rightarrow \ 8x = 21 \ \Rightarrow \ x = \dfrac{21}{8}$

13. $-2(z - 1960) + 32 = 8 \ \Rightarrow \ -2(z - 1960) = -24 \ \Rightarrow \ z - 1960 = 12 \ \Rightarrow \ z = 1972$

14. $5 - (3 - 2z) + 4 = 5(2z - 3) - (3z - 2) \ \Rightarrow \ 2z + 6 = 7z - 13 \ \Rightarrow \ -5z = -19 \ \Rightarrow \ z = \dfrac{19}{5}$

15. $\dfrac{2}{3}\left(\dfrac{t - 3}{2}\right) + 4 = \dfrac{1}{3}t - (1 - t) \ \Rightarrow \ \dfrac{t - 3}{3} + 4 = \dfrac{4}{3}t - 1 \ \Rightarrow \ t - 3 + 12 = 4t - 3 \ \Rightarrow$

$t + 9 = 4t - 3 \ \Rightarrow \ -3t = -12 \ \Rightarrow \ t = 4$

16. $0.3r - 0.12(r - 1) = 0.4r + 2.1 \ \Rightarrow \ 0.18r + 0.12 = 0.4r + 2.1 \ \Rightarrow \ -0.22r = 1.98 \ \Rightarrow \ r = -9$

17. $-4(5 - 3x) = 12x - 20 \Rightarrow -20 + 12x = 12x - 20 \Rightarrow -20 = -20;$ identity

18. $4x - (x - 3) = 3x - 3 \Rightarrow 4x - x + 3 = 3x - 3 \Rightarrow 3x + 3 = 3x - 3 \Rightarrow 3 = -3;$ contradiction

19.   To find the x-intercept, let $y = 0$ and solve for $x: 4x - 5(0) = 20 \Rightarrow 4x = 20 \Rightarrow x = 5;$ to find the y-intercept,

let $x = 0$ and solve for $y: 4(0) - 5y = 20 \Rightarrow -5y = 20 \Rightarrow y = -4;$

$4x - 5y = 20 \Rightarrow -5y = -4x + 20 \Rightarrow y = \dfrac{4}{5}x - 4$

20.   To find the x-intercept, let $y = 0$ and solve for $x: 2x + \frac{1}{2}(0) = -6 \Rightarrow 2x = -6 \Rightarrow x = -3$; to find the y-intercept,

let $x = 0$ and solve for $y: 2(0) + \frac{1}{2}y = -6 \Rightarrow \frac{1}{2}y = -6 \Rightarrow y = -12$;

$2x + \frac{1}{2}y = -6 \Rightarrow \frac{1}{2}y = -2x - 6 \Rightarrow y = -4x - 12$

Section 3.2

21. $5x - 4y = 20 \Rightarrow 5x - 20 = 4y \Rightarrow \frac{5x - 20}{4} = y \Rightarrow y = \frac{5}{4}x - 5$

22. $-\frac{1}{3}x + \frac{1}{2}y = 1 \Rightarrow \frac{1}{2}y = \frac{1}{3}x + 1 \Rightarrow y = \frac{2}{3}x + 2$

23. $2a + 3b = a \Rightarrow a = -3b$

24. $4m - 5n = 6m + 2n \Rightarrow -7n = 2m \Rightarrow n = -\frac{2}{7}m$

25. $A = \frac{1}{2}h(a+b) \Rightarrow 2A = h(a+b) \Rightarrow \frac{2A}{h} = a + b \Rightarrow \frac{2A}{h} - a = b \Rightarrow b = \frac{2A}{h} - a$

26. $V = \frac{1}{3}\pi r^2 h \Rightarrow 3V = \pi r^2 h \Rightarrow \frac{3V}{\pi r^2} = h \Rightarrow h = \frac{3V}{\pi r^2}$

27. $\frac{1}{2}x - \frac{3}{4}y = 2 \Rightarrow 2x - 3y = 8 \Rightarrow -3y = -2x + 8 \Rightarrow y = \frac{2}{3}x - \frac{8}{3} \Rightarrow f(x) = \frac{2}{3}x - \frac{8}{3}$

28. $-7(x - 4y) = y + 1 \Rightarrow -7x + 28y = y + 1 \Rightarrow 27y = 7x + 1 \Rightarrow y = \frac{7}{27}x + \frac{1}{27} \Rightarrow f(x) = \frac{7}{27}x + \frac{1}{27}$

29. $3x + 4y = 10 - y \Rightarrow 5y = -3x + 10 \Rightarrow y = -\frac{3}{5}x + 2 \Rightarrow f(x) = -\frac{3}{5}x + 2$

30. $\frac{y}{x} = 3 \Rightarrow y = 3x \Rightarrow f(x) = 3x$

31. $2x + 25 = 19;\ 2x + 25 = 19 \Rightarrow 2x = -6 \Rightarrow x = \frac{-6}{2} \Rightarrow x = -3$

32. $2x - 5 = x + 1;\ 2x - 5 = x + 1 \Rightarrow x = 6$

Section 3.3

33.   From the table $f(x) < 5$ when $x > -1; \{x | x > -1\}$.

34. $2(3 - x) + 4 < 0 \Rightarrow 6 - 2x + 4 < 0 \Rightarrow -2x + 10 < 0 \Rightarrow -2x < -10 \Rightarrow x > 5; \{x | x > 5\}$

35.   From the graph $y_1 \geq y_2$ when $x \geq 2; \{x | x \geq 2\}$.

36.   (a) $5 - 4x = -2 \Rightarrow -4x = -7 \Rightarrow x = \frac{7}{4}$

       (b) $5 - 4x < -2 \Rightarrow -4x < -7 \Rightarrow x > \frac{7}{4} \Rightarrow \{x | x > \frac{7}{4}\}$

(c) $5 - 4x > -2 \Rightarrow -4x > -7 \Rightarrow x < \dfrac{7}{4} \Rightarrow \left\{ x \middle| x < \dfrac{7}{4} \right\}$

37. $-2x + 1 \le 3 \Rightarrow -2x \le 2 \Rightarrow x \ge -1; \left\{ x \middle| x \ge -1 \right\}$

38. $x - 5 \ge 2x + 3 \Rightarrow -x \ge 8 \Rightarrow x \le -8; \left\{ x \middle| x \le -8 \right\}$

39. $\dfrac{3x - 1}{4} > \dfrac{1}{2} \Rightarrow 3x - 1 > 2 \Rightarrow 3x > 3 \Rightarrow x > 1; \left\{ x \middle| x > 1 \right\}$

40. $-3.2 (x - 2) < 1.6x \Rightarrow -3.2x + 6.4 < 1.6x \Rightarrow 6.4 < 4.8x \Rightarrow \dfrac{6.4}{4.8} < x \Rightarrow x > \dfrac{4}{3}; \left\{ x \middle| x > \dfrac{4}{3} \right\}$

41. $\dfrac{2}{5} t - (5 - t) + 3 > 2 \left(\dfrac{3 - t}{5} \right) \Rightarrow 2t - 25 + 5t + 15 > 6 - 2t \Rightarrow 7t - 10 > 6 - 2t \Rightarrow$

$9t > 16 \Rightarrow t > \dfrac{16}{9}; \left\{ t \middle| t > \dfrac{16}{9} \right\}$

42. $\dfrac{2 (3x - 5)}{5} - 3 \ge \dfrac{2 - x}{3} + 2 \Rightarrow 18x - 30 - 45 \ge 10 - 5x + 30 \Rightarrow 18x - 75 \ge -5x + 40 \Rightarrow$

$23x \ge 115 \Rightarrow x \ge 5; \left\{ x \middle| x \ge 5 \right\}$

43. $0.05t - 0.15 \le 0.03 - 0.75 (t - 2) \Rightarrow 0.05t - 0.15 \le -0.75t + 1.53 \Rightarrow$

$0.8t \le 1.68 \Rightarrow t \le 2.1; \{ t \mid t \le 2.1 \}$

44. $0.6z - 1.55 (z + 5) < 1 - 0.35 (2z - 1) \Rightarrow 0.6z - 1.55z - 7.75 < 1 - 0.7z + 0.35 \Rightarrow$

$-0.95z - 7.75 < -0.7z + 1.35 \Rightarrow -0.25z < 9.1 \Rightarrow z > -36.4; \{ z \mid z > -36.4 \}$

45.   Graph $Y_1 = 0.72 (\pi - 1.3x)$ and $Y_2 = 0.54$ in $[-10, 10, 1]$ by $[-10, 10, 1]$. The solution is $\{ x \mid x \le 1.840 \}$.

Figure 45

46.   Graph $Y_1 = \sqrt{(2)} - (4 - \pi x)$ and $Y_2 = \sqrt{(7)}$ in $[-10, 10, 1]$ by $[-10, 10, 1]$. The solution is $\{ x \mid x > 1.665 \}$.

Figure 46

Section 3.4

47. $x + 1 \le 3 \Rightarrow x \le 2$ and $x + 1 \ge -1 \Rightarrow x \ge -2; [-2, 2]$. See Figure 47.

Figure 47   Figure 48

48. $2x+7<5 \Rightarrow 2x<-2 \Rightarrow x<-1$ and $-2x \geq 6 \Rightarrow x \leq -3$; $(-\infty, -3]$. See Figure 48.

49. $5x-1 \leq 3 \Rightarrow 5x \leq 4 \Rightarrow x \leq \dfrac{4}{5}$ or $1-x<-1 \Rightarrow 2<x$; $\left(-\infty, \dfrac{4}{5}\right] \cup (2, \infty)$. See Figure 49.

Figure 49

Figure 50

50. $3x+1>-1 \Rightarrow 3x>-2 \Rightarrow x>-\dfrac{2}{3}$ or $3x+1<10 \Rightarrow 3x<9 \Rightarrow x<3$; $(-\infty, \infty)$. See Figure 50.

51. $2x+2$ is between -2 and 4 when $-2 \leq x \leq 1$; $[-2, 1]$

52. (a) The intersection point of y_1 and y_2 is $(-4, -100)$. The solution is $x = -4$.

(b) The intersection point of y_2 and y_3 is $(2, 50)$. The solution is $x = 2$.

(c) y_2 is between y_1 and y_3 when $-4 \leq x \leq 2$; $[-4, 2]$

(d) y_2 is below y_3 when $x < 2$; $(-\infty, 2)$

53. (a) The intersection point of y_1 and y_2 is $(2, 2)$. The solution is $x = 2$.

(b) y_1 is below y_2 when $x > 2$; $(2, \infty)$

(c) y_1 is above y_2 when $x < 2$; $(-\infty, 2)$

54. (a) The intersection point of $f(x)$ and $g(x)$ is $(4, 20)$. The solution is $x = 4$.

(b) The intersection point of $g(x)$ and $h(x)$ is $(2, 40)$. The solution is $x = 2$.

(c) $g(x)$ is between $f(x)$ and $h(x)$ when $2 < x < 4$; $(2, 4)$

55. $\left[-3, \dfrac{2}{3}\right]$

56. $(-6, 45]$

57. $\left(-\infty, \dfrac{7}{2}\right)$

58. $[1.8, \infty)$

59. $(-3, 4)$

60. $(-\infty, 4) \cup (10, \infty)$

61. $-4 < x+1 < 6 \Rightarrow -5 < x < 5$; The solution set is $(-5, 5)$.

62. $20 \leq 2x+4 \leq 60 \Rightarrow 16 \leq 2x \leq 56 \Rightarrow 8 \leq x \leq 28$; The solution set is $[8, 28]$.

63. $-3 < 4-\dfrac{1}{3}x < 7 \Rightarrow -7 < -\dfrac{1}{3}x < 3 \Rightarrow 21 > x > -9 \Rightarrow -9 < x < 21$; The solution set is $(-9, 21)$.

64. $2 \leq \dfrac{1}{2}x-2 \leq 12 \Rightarrow 4 \leq \dfrac{1}{2}x \leq 14 \Rightarrow 8 \leq x \leq 28$; The solution set is $[8, 28]$.

65. $-3 \leq \dfrac{4-5x}{3} - 2 < 3 \Rightarrow -9 \leq 4 - 5x - 6 < 9 \Rightarrow -9 \leq -5x - 2 < 9 \Rightarrow -7 \leq -5x < 11 \Rightarrow$

 $\dfrac{7}{5} \geq x > -\dfrac{11}{5} \Rightarrow -\dfrac{11}{5} < x \leq \dfrac{7}{5}; \ \left(-\dfrac{11}{5}, \ \dfrac{7}{5}\right]$

66. $30 \leq \dfrac{2x-6}{5} - 4 < 50 \Rightarrow 150 \leq 2x - 6 - 20 < 250 \Rightarrow 150 \leq 2x - 26 < 250 \Rightarrow$

 $176 \leq 2x < 276 \Rightarrow 88 \leq x < 138; \ [88, \ 138)$

Section 3.5

67. No, $\left|12(-3) - 24\right| = \left|-60\right| = 60 \neq 24.$ No, $\left|12(2) - 24\right| = \left|0\right| = 0 \neq 24.$

68. No, $\left|5 - 3\left(\dfrac{4}{3}\right)\right| = \left|1\right| = 1 \not> 3.$ Yes, $\left|5 - 3(0)\right| = \left|5\right| = 5 > 3.$

69. No, $\left|3(-3) - 6\right| = \left|-15\right| = 15 \not\leq 6.$ Yes, $\left|3(4) - 6\right| = \left|6\right| = 6 \leq 6.$

70. No, $\left|2 + 3(-3)\right| + 4 = \left|-7\right| + 4 = 7 + 4 = 11 \not< 11.$ Yes, $\left|2 + 3\left(\dfrac{2}{3}\right)\right| + 4 = \left|4\right| + 4 = 4 + 4 = 8 < 11.$

71. (a) From the table, $y_1 = 2$ when $x = 0$ or $x = 4.$

 (b) From the table, $y_1 < 2$ when $0 < x < 4; \ (0, \ 4).$

 (c) From the table, $y_1 > 2$ when $x < 0$ or $x > 4; \ (-\infty, \ 0) \cup (4, \ \infty).$

72. (a) From the graph, $\left|2x + 2\right| = 4$ when $x = -3$ or $x = 1.$

 (b) From the graph, $\left|2x + 2\right| \leq 4$ when $-3 \leq x \leq 1; \ [-3, \ 1].$

 (c) From the graph, $\left|2x + 2\right| \geq 4$ when $x \leq -3$ or $x \geq 1; \ (-\infty, \ -3] \cup [1, \ \infty).$

73. $x = -22$ or $x = 22$

74. $2x - 9 = 7 \Rightarrow 2x = 16 \Rightarrow x = 8$ or $2x - 9 = -7 \Rightarrow 2x = 2 \Rightarrow x = 1$

75. $4 - \dfrac{1}{2}x = 17 \Rightarrow -\dfrac{1}{2}x = 13 \Rightarrow x = -26$ or $4 - \dfrac{1}{2}x = -17 \Rightarrow -\dfrac{1}{2}x = -21 \Rightarrow x = 42$

76. First note that $\dfrac{1}{3}\left|3x - 1\right| + 1 = 9 \Rightarrow \dfrac{1}{3}\left|3x - 1\right| = 8 \Rightarrow \left|3x - 1\right| = 24.$

 $3x - 1 = 24 \Rightarrow 3x = 25 \Rightarrow x = \dfrac{25}{3}$ or $3x - 1 = -24 \Rightarrow 3x = -23 \Rightarrow x = -\dfrac{23}{3}$

77. $2x - 5 = 5 - 3x \Rightarrow 5x = 10 \Rightarrow x = 2$ or $2x - 5 = -5 + 3x \Rightarrow -x = 0 \Rightarrow x = 0$

78. $-3 + 3x = -2x + 6 \Rightarrow 5x = 9 \Rightarrow x = \dfrac{9}{5}$ or $-3 + 3x = 2x - 6 \Rightarrow x = -3$

79. (a) $x + 1 = 7 \Rightarrow x = 6$ or $x + 1 = -7 \Rightarrow x = -8$

 (b) The solutions to $\left|x + 1\right| \leq 7$ satisfy $c \leq x \leq d$ where c and d are the solutions to $\left|x + 1\right| = 7.$

 From part (a), the interval is $[-8, \ 6].$

(c) The solutions to $|x+1| \geq 7$ satisfy $x \leq c$ or $x \geq d$ where c and d are the solutions to $|x+1| = 7$.

From part (a), the interval is $(-\infty, -8] \cup [6, \infty)$.

80.   (a) $1-2x = 6 \Rightarrow -2x = 5 \Rightarrow x = -\dfrac{5}{2}$ or $1-2x = -6 \Rightarrow -2x = -7 \Rightarrow x = \dfrac{7}{2}$

(b) The solutions to $|1-2x| \leq 6$ satisfy $c \leq x \leq d$ where c and d are the solutions to $|1-2x| = 6$.

From part (a), the interval is $\left[-\dfrac{5}{2}, \dfrac{7}{2}\right]$.

(c) The solutions to $|1-2x| \geq 6$ satisfy $x \leq c$ or $x \geq d$ where c and d are the solutions to $|1-2x| = 6$.

From part (a), the interval is $\left(-\infty, -\dfrac{5}{2}\right] \cup \left[\dfrac{7}{2}, \infty\right)$.

81.   The solutions to $|x| > 3$ satisfy $x < c$ or $x > d$ where c and d are the solutions to $|x| = 3$.

$|x| = 3$ is equivalent to $x = -3$ or $x = 3$. The interval is $(-\infty, -3) \cup (3, \infty)$.

82.   The solutions to $|-5x| < 20$ satisfy $c < x < d$ where c and d are the solutions to $|-5x| = 20$.

$|-5x| = 20$ is equivalent to $-5x = -20 \Rightarrow x = 4$ or $-5x = 20 \Rightarrow x = -4$. The interval is $(-4, 4)$.

83.   The solutions to $|4x-2| \leq 14$ satisfy $c \leq x \leq d$ where c and d are the solutions to $|4x-2| = 14$.

$|4x-2| = 14$ is equivalent to $4x-2 = -14 \Rightarrow x = -3$ or $4x-2 = 14 \Rightarrow x = 4$. The interval is $[-3, 4]$.

84.   The solutions to $\left|1-\dfrac{4}{5}x\right| \geq 3$ satisfy $x \leq c$ or $x \geq d$ where c and d are the solutions to $\left|1-\dfrac{4}{5}x\right| = 3$.

$\left|1-\dfrac{4}{5}x\right| = 3$ is equivalent to $1-\dfrac{4}{5}x = -3 \Rightarrow x = 5$ or $1-\dfrac{4}{5}x = 3 \Rightarrow x = -\dfrac{5}{2}$.

The interval is $\left(-\infty, -\dfrac{5}{2}\right] \cup [5, \infty)$.

85.   The solutions to $|t-4.5| \leq 0.1$ satisfy $c \leq t \leq d$ where c and d are the solutions to $|t-4.5| = 0.1$.

$|t-4.5| = 0.1$ is equivalent to $t-4.5 = -0.1 \Rightarrow t = 4.4$ or $t-4.5 = 0.1 \Rightarrow t = 4.6$.

The interval is $[4.4, 4.6]$.

86.   First divide each side of $-2|13t-5| \geq -4$ by -2 to obtain $|13t-5| \leq 2$.

The solutions to $|13t-5| \leq 2$ satisfy $c \leq t \leq d$ where c and d are the solutions to $|13t-5| = 2$.

$|13t-5| = 2$ is equivalent to $13t-5 = -2 \Rightarrow t = \dfrac{3}{13}$ or $13t-5 = 2 \Rightarrow t = \dfrac{7}{13}$.

The interval is $\left[\dfrac{3}{13}, \dfrac{7}{13}\right]$.

87.   The inequality $|5-4x| > -5$ is true for all values of x because absolute value is never negative.

The interval is $(-\infty, \infty)$.

88.   Since absolute value can never be negative, $|2t-3| \le 0$ is equivalent to $|2t-3| = 0$.

$|2t-3| = 0$ is equivalent to $2t-3 = 0 \Rightarrow t = \dfrac{3}{2}$. The only solution is $\dfrac{3}{2}$.

89.   Graph $Y_1 = \text{abs}(2X)$ and $Y_2 = 3$ in $[-3, 3, 1]$ by $[0, 5, 1]$. See Figures 89a and 89b.

From the graph, $|2x| \ge 3$ in the interval $(-\infty, -1.5] \cup [1.5, \infty)$.

$[-3, 3, 1]$ by $[0, 5, 1]$ $[-3, 3, 1]$ by $[0, 5, 1]$

Figure 89a   Figure 89b

$[-7, 7, 1]$ by $[0, 4, 1]$ $[-7, 7, 1]$ by $[0, 4, 1]$

Figure 90a   Figure 90b

90.   Graph $Y_1 = \text{abs}((1/2)X - 1)$ and $Y_2 = 2$ in $[-7, 7, 1]$ by $[0, 4, 1]$. See Figures 90a and 90b.

From the graph, $\left|\dfrac{1}{2}x - 1\right| \le 2$ in the interval $[-2, 6]$.

91. $|x| \le 0.05$

92. $|5x - 1| > 4$

Applications

93.   Let x represent the loan amount at 5%. Then $7700 - x$ represents the loan amount at 7%.

$0.05x + 0.07(7700 - x) = 469 \Rightarrow 0.05x + 539 - 0.07x = 469 \Rightarrow -0.02x = -70 \Rightarrow x = 3500$

The loan amount at 5% was \$3500 and the loan amount at 7% was $7700 - 3500 = \$4200$.

94.   Let x represent the amount of time spent running at 8 mph. Then $1.4 - x$ represents the time running at 10 mph.

$8x + 10(1.4 - x) = 12.8 \Rightarrow 8x + 14 - 10x = 12.8 \Rightarrow -2x = -1.2 \Rightarrow x = 0.6$

The athlete ran for 0.6 hour at 8 mph and for $1.4 - 0.6 = 0.8$ hour at 10 mph.

95.   Let x represent the cost of the house if it was located in San Francisco.

$0.54x = 415,000 \Rightarrow x = \dfrac{415,000}{0.54} \approx 768,518.5$

The house would cost about $769,000 in San Francisco.

96. (a) $m = \dfrac{498 - 1369}{1999 - 1980} = \dfrac{-871}{19} \approx -45.84$

   $y = -45.84(x - 1980) + 1369 \Rightarrow y = -45.84x + 92{,}136; \; f(x) = -45.84x + 92{,}136 \text{ (approximate)}$

   (b) $f(1988) = -45.84(1988) + 92{,}136 \approx 1006.$ *Answers may vary slightly.*

97. (a) The distance between the riders is zero (they meet) when $x = 3$ hours.

   (b) The distance between the riders is 20 when $x = 2$ hours and $x = 4$ hours.

   (c) The riders are less than 20 miles apart between 2 and 4 hours exclusively.

   (d) The sum of the speeds of the two bicyclists is 20 mph.

98. (a) The annual interest will be $300 for a loan of $2000.

   (b) The annual interest will be more than $300 for loans of more than $2000.

   (c) The annual interest will be less than $300 for loans of less than $2000.

99. (a) Car 1 is traveling faster since its graph has the steeper slope.

   (b) The cars are both 200 miles from Austin at $x = 3$ hours.

   (c) Car 1 is closer to Austin than Car 2 at times before $x = 3$ hours.

100. There were more than 10 deaths in 1989, 1990, 1991, 1993 and 1995.

101. (a) The median age of the U.S. population is increasing at a rate of 0.09 year per year.

   (b) $0.09x - 147.1 = 23 \Rightarrow 0.09x = 170.1 \Rightarrow x = 1890.$ Median age was 23 in 1890.

102. $490 \le 17.7x - 34{,}636 \le 670 \Rightarrow 35{,}126 \le 17.7x \le 35{,}306 \Rightarrow 1984.5 \le x \le 1994.7 \text{ (approximate)}$

   The number of female officers was from 490 to 670 from about 1985 to 1995.

103. (a) $1.11x - 23.3 = 12 \Rightarrow 1.11x = 35.3 \Rightarrow x \approx 31.8$ inches

   (b) Walleyes with lengths less than 31.8 inches would weigh less than 12 pounds.

104. (a) When $x = 0$ (ground level), $T(x) = 60$ so the T-intercept is $b = 60$. Since the temperature decreases by

   $19°$ for each one-mile increase in altitude, the slope is $a = -19$. The formula is $T(x) = -19x + 60.$

   (b) $20 \le -19x + 60 \le 40 \Rightarrow -40 \le -19x \le -20 \Rightarrow 2.11 \ge x \ge 1.05 \Rightarrow 1.05 \le x \le 2.11 \text{ (approximate)}$

   The temperature is from $40°F$ to $20°F$ for altitudes from about 1.05 to 2.11 miles.

105. Note that the car must travel a total of $200 + 395 = 595$ miles. Use the formula $d = rt$.

   $595 = 70t \Rightarrow t = \dfrac{595}{70} \Rightarrow t = 8.5$ hours

106. Let x be the width of the rectangle. Then its length is $2x + 5$ and its perimeter is $2x + 2(2x + 5)$.

   $2x + 2(2x + 5) = 88 \Rightarrow 2x + 4x + 10 = 88 \Rightarrow 6x = 78 \Rightarrow x = 13$

   The width is 13 feet and the length is $2(13) + 5 = 31$ feet. The rectangle is 13 ft by 31 ft.

107. $-48 \le \dfrac{9}{5}C + 32 \le 107 \Rightarrow -80 \le \dfrac{9}{5}C \le 75 \Rightarrow -80\left(\dfrac{5}{9}\right) \le C \le 75\left(\dfrac{5}{9}\right) \Rightarrow -44.\overline{4} \le C \le 41.\overline{6}$

The temperature range in Celsius is $-44.\overline{4}°C$ to $41.\overline{6}°C$.

108. $|L-160| \le 1$; $L-160=1 \Rightarrow L=161$ or $L-160=-1 \Rightarrow L=159$; $\{L|159 \le L \le 161\}$

109.   (a) $|A-3.9| \le 1.7$

(b) $A-3.9=1.7 \Rightarrow A=5.6$ or $A-3.9=-1.7 \Rightarrow A=2.2$; $\{A|2.2 \le A \le 5.6\}$

110.   The solutions to $\left|\dfrac{T-35}{35}\right| < 0.08$ satisfy $c < T < d$ where c and d are the solutions to $\left|\dfrac{T-35}{35}\right| = 0.08$.

$\left|\dfrac{T-35}{35}\right| = 0.08$ is equivalent to $\dfrac{T-35}{35} = -0.08 \Rightarrow x=32.2$ and $\dfrac{T-35}{35} = 0.08 \Rightarrow x=37.8$.

The interval is $(32.2,\ 37.8)$. The values must be between 32.2 and 37.8, exclusively.

Chapter 3 Test

1.   Yes; $3-4\left(1-2 \cdot \dfrac{1}{6}\right) = 3-4\left(1-\dfrac{2}{6}\right) = 3-4\left(\dfrac{4}{6}\right)$

$= 3-\dfrac{16}{6} = \dfrac{18}{6}-\dfrac{16}{6} = \dfrac{2}{6} = \dfrac{1}{3}$ and $2 \cdot \dfrac{1}{6} = \dfrac{2}{6} = \dfrac{1}{3}$

2.

x	-2	-1	0	1	2
$2-3x$	8	5	2	-1	-4

The solution set for $2-3x \le -1$ is $\{x|x \ge 1\}$.

3. $3-5x=18 \Rightarrow -5x=15 \Rightarrow x=-3$. Check: $3-5(-3) = 3-(-15) = 3+15 = 18$

4.   (a) The intersection point of y_1 and y_2 is $(2,\ 1)$. The solution is $x=2$.

(b) y_1 is above y_2 when $x \le 2$; $(-\infty,\ 2]$

(c) y_1 is below y_2 when $x \ge 2$; $[2,\ \infty)$

5.   The graphs of $y_1 = 4-2x$ and $y_2 = 1+x$ (not shown) intersect at the point $(1,\ 2)$. The solution is $x=1$.

6.   (a) $-\dfrac{2}{3}(3x-2)+1 = x \Rightarrow -2x+\dfrac{4}{3}+1 = x$

$\Rightarrow \dfrac{7}{3} = 3x \Rightarrow \dfrac{1}{3}\left(\dfrac{7}{3}\right) = x \Rightarrow x = \dfrac{7}{9}$

(b) $\dfrac{2z+1}{3} = \dfrac{3(1-z)}{2} \Rightarrow 2(2z+1) = 3[3(1-z)]$

$\Rightarrow 4z+2 = 9-9z \Rightarrow 13z=7 \Rightarrow z = \dfrac{7}{13}$

(c) $0.4(2-3x) = 0.5x-0.2 \Rightarrow 4(2-3x) = 5x-2$

$\Rightarrow 8-12x = 5x-2 \Rightarrow 10 = 17x \Rightarrow x = \dfrac{10}{17}$

7. x-intercept: $-6x + 3(0) = 9 \Rightarrow -6x = 9 \Rightarrow x = -\dfrac{3}{2}$

  y-intercept: $-6(0) + 3y = 9 \Rightarrow 3y = 9 \Rightarrow y = 3$

  $-6x + 3y = 9 \Rightarrow 3y = 6x + 9 \Rightarrow y = 2x + 3$

8. $2 + 5x = x - 4$; $2 + 5x = x - 4 \Rightarrow 4x = -6 \Rightarrow x = \dfrac{-6}{4} \Rightarrow x = -\dfrac{3}{2}$

9. $3x - 2y = 6 \Rightarrow -2y = -3x + 6 \Rightarrow y = \dfrac{3}{2}x - 3$;

  $f(x) = \dfrac{3}{2}x - 3$

10. $-\dfrac{5}{2}x + \dfrac{1}{2} \le 2 \Rightarrow -5x + 1 \le 4 \Rightarrow -5x \le 3 \Rightarrow x \ge -\dfrac{3}{5}$; $\left[-\dfrac{3}{5},\ \infty\right)$

11. $3.1(3 - x) < 2.9x \Rightarrow 9.3 - 3.1x < 2.9x \Rightarrow -6x < -9.3 \Rightarrow x > 1.55$; $(1.55,\ \infty)$

12. $2x + 6 < 2$ and $-3x \ge 3 \Rightarrow 2x < -4$ and $x \le -1 \Rightarrow x < -2$ and $x \le -1$; See Figure 12.

                Figure 12

13.   From the table, $-3x < -3$ when $x > 1$ and $-3x > 6$ when $x < -2$. The interval is $(-\infty,\ -2) \cup (1,\ \infty)$.

14.   (a) The intersection point of y_1 and y_2 is $(-5,\ -300)$. The solution is $x = -5$.

  (b) The intersection point of y_2 and y_3 is $(5,\ 100)$. The solution is $x = 5$.

  (c) y_2 is between y_1 and y_3 when $-5 \le x \le 5$. The interval is $[-5,\ 5]$.

  (d) y_2 is below y_3 when $x < 5$. The interval is $(-\infty,\ 5)$.

15. $-2 < 2 + \dfrac{1}{2}x < 2 \Rightarrow -4 < \dfrac{1}{2}x < 0 \Rightarrow -8 < x < 0$; $(-8,\ 0)$

16. $2 - \dfrac{1}{3}x = 6 \Rightarrow -\dfrac{1}{3}x = 4 \Rightarrow x = -12$ or $2 - \dfrac{1}{3}x = -6 \Rightarrow -\dfrac{1}{3}x = -8 \Rightarrow x = 24$

17.   (a) $-5 \le x \le 5$; $[-5,\ 5]$

  (b) The solution set is all real numbers except 0, or $(-\infty,\ 0) \cup (0,\ \infty)$.

  (c) There are no solutions for this inequality. There are no values of x for which $|2x + 7|$ is negative.

  (d) $5x = 10 \Rightarrow x = 2$ or $5x = -10 \Rightarrow x = -2$

    The solution set is $x < -2$ or $x > 2$, or $(-\infty,\ -2) \cup (2,\ \infty)$.

  (e) $-2|2 - 5x| + 1 \le 5 \Rightarrow |2 - 5x| \ge -2$

    This is true for all values of x, or $(-\infty,\ \infty)$.

  (f) $-5 < 3 - x < 5 \Rightarrow -8 < -x < 2 \Rightarrow -2 < x < 8$; $(-2,\ 8)$

18.   (a) $1-5x = 3 \Rightarrow -5x = 2 \Rightarrow x = -\dfrac{2}{5}$ or $1-5x = -3 \Rightarrow -5x = -4 \Rightarrow x = \dfrac{4}{5}$

       (b) The solutions to $|1-5x| \le 3$ satisfy $c \le x \le d$ where c and d are the solutions to $|1-5x| = 3$.

            From part (a), the interval is $\left[-\dfrac{2}{5}, \dfrac{4}{5}\right]$.

       (c) The solutions to $|1-5x| \ge 3$ satisfy $x \le c$ or $x \ge d$ where c and d are the solutions to $|1-5x| = 3$.

            From part (a), the interval is $\left(-\infty, -\dfrac{2}{5}\right] \cup \left[\dfrac{4}{5}, \infty\right)$.

19.   (a) A sports drink with 16 grams of carbohydrates will have 64 calories.

       (b) A sports drink with more than 16 grams of carbohydrates will have more than 64 calories.

       (c) A sports drink with less than 16 grams of carbohydrates will have less than 64 calories.

       (d) Each gram of carbohydrates corresponds to 4 calories.

20.   (a) First divide the weight 150 by 2 to get 75. The function is $f(x) = 0.4x + 75$.

       (b) $0.4x + 75 = 89 \Rightarrow 0.4x = 14 \Rightarrow x = \dfrac{14}{0.4} \Rightarrow x = 35$ minutes

21. $d = \dfrac{1}{2}gt^2 \Rightarrow 2d = gt^2 \Rightarrow \dfrac{2d}{t^2} = g \Rightarrow g = \dfrac{2d}{t^2}$

22.   Let x represent the loan amount at 4%. Then $5000 - x$ represents the loan amount at 6%.

       $0.04x + 0.06(5000 - x) = 230 \Rightarrow 0.04x + 300 - 0.06x = 230 \Rightarrow -0.02x = -70 \Rightarrow x = 3500$

       The loan amount at 4% was \$3500 and the loan amount at 6% was $5000 - 3500 = \$1500$.

23. x: measure of smallest angle

       $2x$: measure of largest angle

       $x + 16$: measure of third angle

       $x + 2x + x + 16 = 180 \Rightarrow 4x + 16 = 180 \Rightarrow 4x = 164$

       $\Rightarrow x = 41, \; 2x = 82, \; x + 16 = 57$

       The measures of the angles are $41°$, $57°$, and $82°$.

24. x: retail price of jacket

       $x - 0.25x$: sale price of jacket

       $x - 0.25x = 81 \Rightarrow 0.75x = 81 \Rightarrow x = 108$

       The retail price was \$108.

Chapter 3 Extended and Discovery Exercises

1.   (a) The temperature at ground level is $T(0) = 90 - 19(0) = 90\,°\text{F}$.

            The dew point at ground level is $D(0) = 70 - 5.8(0) = 70\,°\text{F}$.

(b) $90 - 19x = 70 - 5.8x \Rightarrow 20 = 13.2x \Rightarrow \dfrac{20}{13.2} = x \Rightarrow x \approx 1.52$

The temperature and dew point are equal at an altitude of about 1.52 miles.

(c)   Clouds will not form at altitudes below about 1.52 miles.

(d)   Clouds will form at altitudes above about 1.52 miles.

2.   (a)   At some altitudes it is likely that the air temperature will reach the dew point.

(b)   Clouds will form at much lower altitudes than usual. In this case, it may become foggy.

3.   (a)   The scatterplot is shown in Figure 3a.

(b)   The relationship appears to be linear. This seems reasonable if one considers that when the number of megabytes doubles, the number of seconds should also double.

(c)   Using the points (0.129, 6.010) and (1.260, 60.18) $m = \dfrac{60.18 - 6.010}{1.260 - 0.129} \approx 47.9$, $x_1 = 0.129$ and $y_1 = 6.010$.

The equation is $y \approx 47.9(x - 0.129) + 6.010 \Rightarrow y \approx 47.9x - 0.1691$.

Each additional megabyte of memory can record approximately 47.9 seconds of music.

(d)   The scatterplot and the line are shown in Figure 3d.

(e) $47.9x - 0.1691 = 120$

(f)   Symbolic: $47.9x - 0.1691 = 120 \Rightarrow 47.9x = 120.1691 \Rightarrow x \approx 2.5$ MB

Figure 3a

Figure 3d

4.   (a)   Using (25,000, 12) and (100,000, 96), $m = \dfrac{96 - 12}{100,000 - 25,000} \approx 0.00112$, $x_1 = 25,000$ and $y_1 = 12$.

(b)   A graph of the line and the data points are shown in Figure 4b.

(c) $28.8 \leq 0.00112(x - 25,000) + 12 \leq 51.2$

(d)   Graph $Y_1 = 0.00112(X - 25,000) + 12$, $Y_2 = 28.8$ and $Y_3 = 51.2$ in [0, 110,000, 10,000] by [0, 100, 10].

See Figures 4d and 4e. $\{x \mid 40,000 \leq x \leq 60,000\}$

Symbolic: $28.8 \leq 0.00112(x - 25,000) + 12 \leq 51.2 \Rightarrow 40,000 \leq x \leq 60,000$; $\{x \mid 40,000 \leq x \leq 60,000\}$

Figure 4b

[0, 110,000, 10,000] by [0, 100, 10]   [0, 110,000, 10,000] by [0, 100, 10]

Figure 4d   Figure 4e

Chapters 1-3 Cumulative Review Exercises

1. Natural: $\dfrac{8}{2} = 4$; Whole: 0, $\dfrac{8}{2} = 4$; Integer: -7, 0, $\dfrac{8}{2} = 4$; Rational: -7, $-\dfrac{3}{5}$, 0, $\dfrac{8}{2} = 4$, $5.\overline{12}$;

    Irrational: $\sqrt{5}$

2. Natural: $\sqrt{9} = 3$; Whole: $\dfrac{0}{9}$, $\sqrt{9} = 3$; Integer: $-\dfrac{6}{3}$, $\dfrac{0}{9}$, $\sqrt{9} = 3$;

    Rational: $-\dfrac{6}{3}$, $\dfrac{0}{9}$, $\sqrt{9} = 3$, $4.\overline{6}$; Irrational: π

3. Distributive

4. Associative

5. $11 + 26 + (-1) + 14 = 11 + (-1) + 26 + 14 = 10 + 40 = 50$

6. $7 \cdot 98 = 7(100 - 2) = 700 - 14 = 686$

7.

8. $-(-5y - 4) = 5y + 4$

9. $\dfrac{24x^{-4}y^2}{8xy^{-5}} = \dfrac{24}{8} \cdot x^{-4-1}y^{2-(-5)} = 3x^{-5}y^7 = \dfrac{3y^7}{x^5}$

10. $\left(\dfrac{3a^2}{4b^3}\right)^{-3} = \left(\dfrac{4b^3}{3a^2}\right)^3 = \dfrac{4^3 b^9}{3^3 a^6} = \dfrac{64b^9}{27a^6}$

11. $15 - 2^3 \div 4 = 15 - 8 \div 4 = 15 - 2 = 13$

12. Move the decimal point 5 places to the right: $0.000059 = 5.9 \times 10^{-5}$.

13. $J = \sqrt{38 - (13)} = \sqrt{25} = 5$

14. $r = 3 - (-3)^3 = 3 - (-27) = 3 + 27 = 30$

15. By testing data points in each formula, we find that the best model is (ii).

16. The domain corresponds to the x-coordinates and the range corresponds to the y-coordinates.

    $D = \{-2,\ 0,\ 1,\ 3\};\ R = \{0,\ 2,\ 4\}$

17. When $x = -2$, $y = -2(-2) + 1 = 5$. The other ordered pairs can be found similarly.

    The ordered pairs are $(-2,\ 5)$, $(-1,\ 3)$, $(0,\ 1)$, $(1,\ -1)$, $(2,\ -3)$. See Figure 17.

18. When $x = -2$, $y = \dfrac{(-2)^3 + 4}{2} = \dfrac{-8+4}{2} = \dfrac{-4}{2} = -2$. The other ordered pairs can be found similarly.

    The ordered pairs are $(-2,\ -2)$, $\left(-1,\ \dfrac{3}{2}\right)$, $(0,\ 2)$, $\left(1,\ \dfrac{5}{2}\right)$, $(2,\ 6)$. See Figure 18.

Figure 17

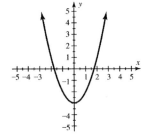

Figure 18

Figure 19

19. See Figure 19.

20. The function is defined for all values of the variable except 0. The domain is $\{x \mid x \neq 0\}$.

21. From the graph, when $x = 0$, $y = 2$. Therefore $f(0) = 2$. Similarly, $f(-2) = -2$.

22. From the table, when $x = 0$, $f(x) = 2$. Therefore $f(0) = 2$. Similarly, $f(-2) = -4$.

23. Yes; $a = -3$, $b = 11$

24. No. A linear function cannot contain a square root.

25. The slope is $m = \dfrac{11-7}{2-1} = 4$. Since $f(x) = 3$ when $x = 0$ the y-intercept is 3. Here $f(x) = 4x + 3$.

26. See Figure 26.

Figure 26

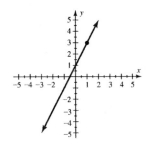

Figure 29

27. The equation is in the form $f(x) = mx + b$. The slope is 5 and the y-intercept is -4.

28. $m = \dfrac{6-(-2)}{-1-3} = \dfrac{8}{-4} = -2$

29.   See Figure 29.

30.   The graph falls 1 unit for each 2 units of run. The slope is $-\dfrac{1}{2}$. The y-intercept is -1. So $y = -\dfrac{1}{2}x - 1$.

31.   Since $f(x)$ increases by 3 for each unit increase in x, the slope is 3. From the point $(-1,\ 0)$, the x-intercept is -1.

      From the point $(0,\ 3)$, the y-intercept is 3.

32.   Vertical lines have equations of the form $x = k$. The equation of the vertical line passing through $(5, 7)$ is $x = 5$.

33.   Since the line is parallel to $y = 3x - 4$, the slope is $m = 3$. Using the point-slope form gives

      $y = 3(x-2)+1 \Rightarrow y = 3x-6+1 \Rightarrow y = 3x-5$

34.   Since the line is perpendicular to $y = -x - 5$, the slope is $m = 1$. Using the point-slope form gives

      $y = 1(x-(-3))+0 \Rightarrow y = x+3$

35.   Yes since $\dfrac{1}{2}\left(\dfrac{8}{5}\right) - 4\left(\dfrac{8}{5}-1\right) = -\dfrac{8}{5}$ and $\dfrac{1}{4}\left(\dfrac{8}{5}\right) - 2 = -\dfrac{8}{5}$.

36.   The graphs intersect at the point $(1,\ -2)$, so $y_1 = y_2$ when $x = 1$.

37. $\dfrac{3}{4}(x-2)+4 = 2 \Rightarrow \dfrac{3}{4}(x-2) = -2 \Rightarrow x-2 = -\dfrac{8}{3} \Rightarrow x = -\dfrac{2}{3}$

38. $\dfrac{2}{3}\left(\dfrac{t-7}{4}\right) - 2 = \dfrac{1}{3}t - (2t+3) \Rightarrow \dfrac{t-7}{6} - 2 = \dfrac{1}{3}t - 2t - 3 \Rightarrow t-7-12 = 2t-12t-18 \Rightarrow$

      $t-19 = -10t-18 \Rightarrow 11t = 1 \Rightarrow t = \dfrac{1}{11}$

39.   To find the x-intercept, let $y = 0$ and solve for x: $x - \dfrac{1}{3}(0) = 2 \Rightarrow x = 2$; to find the y-intercept, let $x = 0$

      and solve for y: $0 - \dfrac{1}{3}y = 2 \Rightarrow -\dfrac{1}{3}y = 2 \Rightarrow y = -6$;

      $x - \dfrac{1}{3}y = 2 \Rightarrow -\dfrac{1}{3}y = -x+2 \Rightarrow y = 3x-6$

40.   To find the x-intercept, let $y = 0$ and solve for x: $5x - 4(0) = -10 \Rightarrow 5x = -10 \Rightarrow x = -2$; to find the

      y-intercept, let $x = 0$ and solve for y: $5(0) - 4y = -10 \Rightarrow -4y = -10 \Rightarrow y = \dfrac{5}{2}$;

      $5x - 4y = -10 \Rightarrow -4y = -5x - 10 \Rightarrow y = \dfrac{5}{4}x + \dfrac{5}{2}$

41.   Here $y < 2$ when $x > 0$. $\{x \mid x > 0\}$

42. Here y_1 is below y_2 when $x \le -3$. The interval is $(-\infty, -3]$.

43. $\dfrac{4x-9}{6} > \dfrac{1}{2} \Rightarrow 4x-9 > 3 \Rightarrow 4x > 12 \Rightarrow x > 3$. The interval is $(3, \infty)$.

44. $\dfrac{2}{3}z - 2 \le \dfrac{1}{4}z - (2z+2) \Rightarrow 8z - 24 \le 3z - 24z - 24 \Rightarrow 8z - 24 \le -21z - 24 \Rightarrow$

    $29z \le 0 \Rightarrow z \le 0$. The interval is $(-\infty, 0]$.

45. $x + 2 > 1 \Rightarrow x > -1$ and $2x - 1 \le 9 \Rightarrow 2x \le 10 \Rightarrow x \le 5$

    The solutions must satisfy both of these inequalities. The interval is $(-1, 5]$. See Figure 45.

    Figure 45

46. $4x + 7 < 1 \Rightarrow 4x < -6 \Rightarrow x < -\dfrac{3}{2}$ or $3x + 2 \ge 11 \Rightarrow 3x \ge 9 \Rightarrow x \ge 3$. The solutions may satisfy only one (or

    both) of these inequalities. The interval is $\left(-\infty, -\dfrac{3}{2}\right) \cup [3, \infty)$. See Figure 46.

    Figure 46

47. $-7 \le 2x - 3 \le 5 \Rightarrow -4 \le 2x \le 8 \Rightarrow -2 \le x \le 4$. The interval is $[-2, 4]$.

48. $-8 \le -\dfrac{1}{2}x - 3 \le 5 \Rightarrow -5 \le -\dfrac{1}{2}x \le 8 \Rightarrow 10 \ge x \ge -16 \Rightarrow -16 \le x \le 10$. The interval is $[-16, 10]$.

49. The solutions to $|3x+5| > 13$ satisfy $x < c$ or $x > d$ where c and d are the solutions to $|3x+5| = 13$.

    $|3x+5| = 13$ is equivalent to $3x+5 = -13 \Rightarrow x = -6$ or $3x+5 = 13 \Rightarrow x = \dfrac{8}{3}$.

    The interval is $(-\infty, -6) \cup \left(\dfrac{8}{3}, \infty\right)$.

50. First divide each side of $-3|2t-11| \ge -9$ by -3 to obtain $|2t-11| \le 3$.

    The solutions to $|2t-11| \le 3$ satisfy $c \le t \le d$ where c and d are the solutions to $|2t-11| = 3$.

    $|2t-11| = 3$ is equivalent to $2t-11 = -3 \Rightarrow t = 4$ or $2t-11 = 3 \Rightarrow t = 7$. The interval is $[4, 7]$.

51. (a) $y_1 = 2$ when $x = -3$ or when $x = 1$.

    (b) $y_1 \le 2$ when $-3 \le x \le 1$. $[-3, 1]$

    (c) $y_1 \ge 2$ when $x \le -3$ or $x \ge 1$. $(-\infty, -3] \cup [1, \infty)$

52. $\dfrac{2}{3}x - 4 = -8 \Rightarrow \dfrac{2}{3}x = -4 \Rightarrow x = -6$ or $\dfrac{2}{3}x - 4 = 8 \Rightarrow \dfrac{2}{3}x = 12 \Rightarrow x = 18$

53. (a) $A = 4300(1.05)^{10} \approx \$7004.25$

(b) $A = 11,000(1.05)^6 \approx \$14,741.05$

54.   For each 2-hour increase in time, the car travels an additional 130 miles. The car's speed is 65 mph. $d = 65t$

55.   (a) There are 120 milligrams of sodium in a 12-ounce can so there are 10 milligrams of sodium per ounce. The formula is $f(x) = 10x$.

(b) The slope of this line is 10.

(c) The soda contains 10 milligrams of sodium per ounce.

56.   See Figure 56.

Figure 56

57.   (a) The bicyclist is traveling away from Euclid because the slope of the line for the bicyclist is positive.

(b) The lines intersect at the point (3, 200). When 3 hours has elapsed, they are both 200 miles from Euclid.

(c) The motorcyclist is farther from Euclid from 0 to 3 hours.

58. $410 \le 17.7(x-1960) + 56 \le 605 \Rightarrow 354 \le 17.7(x-1960) \le 549 \Rightarrow$

$20 \le x - 1960 \le 31.02 \Rightarrow 1980 \le x \le 1991$ (approximate). From 1980 to 1991.

Critical Thinking Solutions for Chapter 3

Section 3.1

•   The answer must satisfy the given equation. A different equation could have an error in it.

Section 3.3

•   We may substitute x-values from the solution set into the inequality and check them.

If they do not check, then our solution set is incorrect.

•   To get the desired solution set, we need only to reverse the inequality symbol. $\{x \mid x \le 2\}$

Section 3.4

•   1.   See Figure 1a. There are no numbers that satisfy *both* inequalities.

2.   See Figure 1b. Every real number is *either* greater than 2 *or* less than 5.

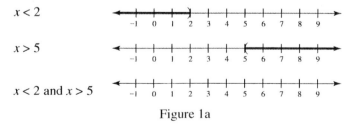

Figure 1a

$x > 2$

$x < 5$

$x > 2$ or $x < 5$

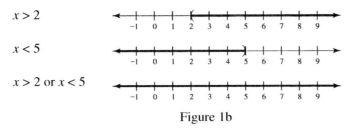

Figure 1b

• Students exhale more carbon dioxide during an exam than they do during a lecture. This increase may be due to anxiety experienced during examinations.

Chapter 4: Systems of Linear Equations

4.1: Systems of Linear Equations in Two Variables

Concepts

1. No, two straight lines cannot have exactly two points of intersection.

2. $3x + 2y = 5$

    $2x - y = 0$ *Answers may vary.*

3. Numerically and graphically.

4. There is one solution.

5. There are no solutions.

6. There are infinitely many solutions. The two lines are identical.

7. $(1, -2)$ since it satisfies both equations. The ordered pair $(4, 4)$ does not satisfy $3x + y = 1$.

8. $(3, 1)$ since it satisfies both equations. The ordered pair $(-3, -1)$ does not satisfy $3x + y = 10$.

9. $\left(-1, \dfrac{13}{3}\right)$ since it satisfies both equations. The ordered pair $(4, 6)$ does not satisfy $4x + 3y = 9$.

10. $(4, 0)$ since it satisfies both equations. The ordered pair $(3, 5)$ does not satisfy $5x - 4y = 20$.

Graphical Solutions

11. See Figure 11. The solution is $(1, 1)$.

Figure 11

Figure 12

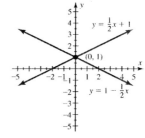
Figure 13

12. See Figure 12. The solution is $(-1, 2)$.

13. See Figure 13. The solution is $(0, 1)$.

14. See Figure 14. The solution is $(-1, 2)$.

Figure 14

Figure 15

Figure 16

15. See Figure 15. The solution is $(3, -2)$.

16. See Figure 16. The solution is $(-1, 1)$.

17. See Figure 17. The solution is $(4, -1)$.

| Figure 17 | Figure 18 |

18. See Figure 18. The solution is $(3, 0)$.

19. The solution is the intersection point $(3, 1)$.

20. The solution is the intersection point $(2, -1)$.

21. The two lines do not intersect. There are no solutions.

22. The two lines are identical. There are infinitely many solutions that satisfy $\{(x, y) | x + y = 2\}$.

23. The system can be solved graphically by solving each equation for y and then graphing.

   $-x + y = 1 \Rightarrow y = x + 1$ and $x + y = 3 \Rightarrow y = 3 - x$

   The graphs (not shown) intersect at the point $(1, 2)$. The system is consistent. The equations are independent.

24. The system can be solved graphically by solving each equation for y and then graphing.

   $x + y = 2 \Rightarrow y = 2 - x$ and $x - y = 2 \Rightarrow y = x - 2$

   The graphs (not shown) intersect at the point $(2, 0)$. The system is consistent. The equations are independent.

25. The system can be solved graphically by solving each equation for y and then graphing.

   $2x + y = 5 \Rightarrow y = 5 - 2x$ and $-2x + y = -3 \Rightarrow y = 2x - 3$

   The graphs (not shown) intersect at the point $(2, 1)$. The system is consistent. The equations are independent.

26. The system can be solved graphically by solving each equation for y and then graphing.

   $x + 2y = 3 \Rightarrow y = \dfrac{3 - x}{2}$ and $2x - y = 1 \Rightarrow y = 2x - 1$

   The graphs (not shown) intersect at the point $(1, 1)$. The system is consistent. The equations are independent.

27. The system can be solved graphically by solving each equation for y and then graphing.

   $x + y = 3 \Rightarrow y = 3 - x$ and $2x + 2y = 6 \Rightarrow y = 3 - x$

   The graphs (not shown) are identical, $\{(x, y) | x + y = 3\}$. The system is consistent. The equations are

   dependent.

28. The system can be solved graphically by solving each equation for y and then graphing.

   $x - y = 1 \Rightarrow y = x - 1$ and $-x + y = 3 \Rightarrow y = x + 3$

   The graphs (not shown) are parallel. There are no solutions. The system is inconsistent.

29.   The system can be solved graphically by solving each equation for y and then graphing.

$3x - y = 0 \Rightarrow y = 3x$ and $2x + y = 5 \Rightarrow y = 5 - 2x$

The graphs (not shown) intersect at the point $(1, 3)$. The system is consistent. The equations are independent.

30.   The system can be solved graphically by solving each equation for y and then graphing.

$-2x - y = -3 \Rightarrow y = 3 - 2x$ and $x + y = 2 \Rightarrow y = 2 - x$

The graphs (not shown) intersect at the point $(1, 1)$. The system is consistent. The equations are independent.

31.   The system can be solved graphically by solving each equation for y and then graphing.

$-2x + y = 3 \Rightarrow y = 2x + 3$ and $4x - 2y = 2 \Rightarrow y = 2x - 1$

The graphs (not shown) are parallel. There are no solutions. The system is inconsistent.

32.   The system can be solved graphically by solving each equation for y and then graphing.

$2x + 4y = 2 \Rightarrow y = \dfrac{1 - x}{2}$ and $-x - 2y = -1 \Rightarrow y = \dfrac{1 - x}{2}$

The graphs (not shown) are identical, $\{(x, y) | x + 2y = 1\}$. The system is consistent. The equations are dependent.

33.   The system can be solved graphically by solving each equation for y and then graphing.

$x + y = 6 \Rightarrow y = 6 - x$ and $x - y = 2 \Rightarrow y = x - 2$

The graphs (not shown) intersect at the point $(4, 2)$. The system is consistent. The equations are independent.

34.   The system can be solved graphically by solving each equation for y and then graphing.

$x + y = 9 \Rightarrow y = 9 - x$ and $x - y = 3 \Rightarrow y = x - 3$

The graphs (not shown) intersect at the point $(6, 3)$. The system is consistent. The equations are independent.

35.   The system can be solved graphically by solving each equation for y and then graphing.

$x - y = 4 \Rightarrow y = x - 4$ and $2x - 2y = 4 \Rightarrow y = x - 2$

The graphs (not shown) are parallel. There are no solutions. The system is inconsistent.

36.   The system can be solved graphically by solving each equation for y and then graphing.

$2x + y = 5 \Rightarrow y = 5 - 2x$ and $4x + 2y = 10 \Rightarrow y = 5 - 2x$

The graphs (not shown) are identical, $\{(x, y) | 2x + y = 5\}$. The system is consistent. The equations are dependent.

37.   The system can be solved graphically by solving each equation for y and then graphing.

$6x - 4y = -2 \Rightarrow y = \dfrac{3x + 1}{2}$ and $-3x + 2y = 1 \Rightarrow y = \dfrac{3x + 1}{2}$

The graphs (not shown) are identical, $\{(x, y) | -3x + 2y = 1\}$. The system is consistent. The equations are dependent.

38.   The system can be solved graphically by solving each equation for y and then graphing.

$4x - 3y = 3 \Rightarrow y = \dfrac{4x - 3}{3}$ and $-8x + 6y = 1 \Rightarrow y = \dfrac{8x + 1}{6}$

The graphs (not shown) are parallel. There are no solutions. The system is inconsistent.

39.   The system can be solved graphically by solving each equation for y and then graphing.

$$4x + 3y = 2 \Rightarrow y = \frac{2-4x}{3} \text{ and } 5x + 2y = 6 \Rightarrow y = \frac{6-5x}{2}$$

The graphs (not shown) intersect at the point $(2, -2)$. The system is consistent. The equations are independent.

40.   The system can be solved graphically by solving each equation for y and then graphing.

$$-3x + 2y = 4 \Rightarrow y = \frac{3x+4}{2} \text{ and } 4x - y = 3 \Rightarrow y = 4x - 3$$

The graphs (not shown) intersect at the point $(2, 5)$. The system is consistent. The equations are independent.

41.   The system can be solved graphically by solving each equation for y and then graphing.

$$2x + 2y = 4 \Rightarrow y = 2 - x \text{ and } x - 3y = -2 \Rightarrow y = \frac{x+2}{3}$$

The graphs (not shown) intersect at the point $(1, 1)$.

42.   The system can be solved graphically by solving each equation for y and then graphing.

$$6x - y = 3 \Rightarrow y = 6x - 3 \text{ and } x - 2y = -5 \Rightarrow y = \frac{x+5}{2}$$

The graphs (not shown) intersect at the point $(1, 3)$.

43.   The system can be solved graphically by solving each equation for y and then graphing.

$$-\frac{1}{2}x - \frac{1}{2}y = \frac{3}{2} \Rightarrow y = -x - 3 \text{ and } x - \frac{1}{2}y = 3 \Rightarrow y = 2x - 6$$

The graphs (not shown) intersect at the point $(1, -4)$.

44.   The system can be solved graphically by solving each equation for y and then graphing.

$$\frac{1}{2}x + \frac{1}{8}y = 1 \Rightarrow y = 8 - 4x \text{ and } -\frac{1}{2}x + \frac{5}{6}y = -1 \Rightarrow y = \frac{3x-6}{5}$$

The graphs (not shown) intersect at the point $(2, 0)$.

45.   (a) $x + y = 4$: To find the x-intercept, let $y = 0$ and solve for x: $x + 0 = 4 \Rightarrow x = 4$; to find the y-intercept, let $x = 0$ and solve for y: $0 + y = 4 \Rightarrow y = 4$.

$x - y = -2$: To find the x-intercept, let $y = 0$ and solve for x: $x - 0 = -2 \Rightarrow x = -2$; to find the y-intercept, let $x = 0$ and solve for y: $0 - y = -2 \Rightarrow -y = -2 \Rightarrow y = 2$.

(b)   See Figure 45b. The solution is $(1, 3)$.

Figure 45b

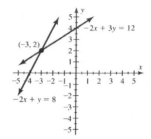

Figure 46b   Figure 47b

46.   (a) $2x + 3y = 12$: To find the x-intercept, let $y = 0$ and solve for x: $2x + 3(0) = 12 \Rightarrow 2x = 12 \Rightarrow x = 6$; to find

the y-intercept, let $x = 0$ and solve for y: $2(0) + 3y = 12 \Rightarrow 3y = 12 \Rightarrow y = 4$.

$2x - y = 4$: To find the x-intercept, let $y = 0$ and solve for x: $2x - 0 = 4 \Rightarrow 2x = 4 \Rightarrow x = 2$; to find the y-

intercept, let $x = 0$ and solve for y: $2(0) - y = 4 \Rightarrow -y = 4 \Rightarrow y = -4$.

(b)   See Figure 46b. The solution is (3, 2).

47.   (a) $-2x + 3y = 12$: To find the x-intercept, let $y = 0$ and solve for x: $-2x + 3(0) = 12 \Rightarrow -2x = 12 \Rightarrow x = -6$;

to find the y-intercept, let $x = 0$ and solve for y: $-2(0) + 3y = 12 \Rightarrow 3y = 12 \Rightarrow y = 4$.

$-2x + y = 8$: To find the x-intercept, let $y = 0$ and solve for x: $-2x + 0 = 8 \Rightarrow -2x = 8 \Rightarrow x = -4$; to find

the y-intercept, let $x = 0$ and solve for y: $-2(0) + y = 8 \Rightarrow y = 8$.

(b)   See Figure 47b. The solution is (–3, 2).

48.   (a) $-x + y = 2$: To find the x-intercept, let $y = 0$ and solve for x: $-x + 0 = 2 \Rightarrow -x = 2 \Rightarrow x = -2$; to find the

y-intercept, let $x = 0$ and solve for y: $-(0) + y = 2 \Rightarrow y = 2$.

$x + y = 4$: To find the x-intercept, let $y = 0$ and solve for x: $x + 0 = 4 \Rightarrow x = 4$; to find the y-intercept, let

$x = 0$ and solve for y: $0 + y = 4 \Rightarrow y = 4$.

(b)   See Figure 48b. The solution is (1, 3).

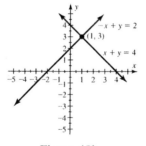

Figure 48b

49.   Note that $\dfrac{1}{4}x + \dfrac{1}{2}y = \dfrac{3}{20} \Rightarrow y = -\dfrac{1}{2}x + \dfrac{3}{10}$ and $\dfrac{1}{8}x - y = -\dfrac{3}{10} \Rightarrow y = \dfrac{1}{8}x + \dfrac{3}{10}$.

Graph $Y_1 = (-1/2)X + (3/10)$ and $Y_2 = (1/8)X + (3/10)$ in [–1, 1, 0.1] by [–1, 1, 0.1]. See Figure 49.

The unique solution is the intersection point (0, 0.3).

50.   Note that $\dfrac{1}{2}x - \dfrac{3}{8}y = \dfrac{1}{8} \Rightarrow y = \dfrac{4}{3}x - \dfrac{1}{3}$ and $\dfrac{1}{3}x - \dfrac{1}{2}y = -\dfrac{1}{12} \Rightarrow y = \dfrac{2}{3}x + \dfrac{1}{6}$.

Graph $Y_1 = (4/3)X - (1/3)$ and $Y_2 = (2/3)X + (1/6)$ in [0, 1, 1] by [0, 1, 1]. See Figure 50.

The unique solution is the intersection point $(0.75, 0.\overline{6})$.

[−1, 1, 0.1] by [−1, 1, 0.1]

[0, 1, 1] by [0, 1, 1]

Figure 49

Figure 50

51.   Note that $0.1x + 0.2y = 0.25 \Rightarrow y = -\frac{1}{2}x + \frac{5}{4}$ and $0.7x - 0.3y = 0.9 \Rightarrow y = \frac{7}{3}x - 3.$

Graph $Y_1 = (-1/2)X + (5/4)$ and $Y_2 = (7/3)X - 3$ in [−4, 4, 1] by [−4, 4, 1]. See Figure 51.

The unique solution is the intersection point $(1.5, 0.5)$.

[−4, 4, 1] by [−4, 4, 1]

[0, 2, 1] by [0, 2, 1]

Figure 51

Figure 52

52.   Note that $2.3x + 4.3y = 5.63 \Rightarrow y = -\frac{23}{43}x + \frac{563}{430}$ and $1.1x - 3.6y = 0.43 \Rightarrow y = \frac{11}{36}x - \frac{43}{360}.$

Graph $Y_1 = (-23/43)X + (563/430)$ and $Y_2 = (11/36)X - (43/360)$ in [0, 2, 1] by [0, 2, 1]. See Figure 52.

The unique solution is the intersection point $(1.7, 0.4)$.

53.   Note that $0.1x + 0.2y = 50 \Rightarrow y = -0.5x + 250$ and $0.3x - 0.1y = 10 \Rightarrow y = 3x - 100.$

Graph $Y_1 = -0.5X + 250$ and $Y_2 = 3X - 100$ in [0, 300, 50] by [0, 300, 50]. See Figure 53.

The unique solution is the intersection point $(100, 200)$.

54.   Note that $0.5x + 0.2y = 14 \Rightarrow y = -2.5x + 70$ and $-0.1x + 0.4y = 6 \Rightarrow y = 0.25x + 15.$

Graph $Y_1 = -2.5X + 70$ and $Y_2 = 0.25X + 15$ in [0, 30, 5] by [0, 30, 5]. See Figure 54.

The unique solution is the intersection point $(20, 20)$.

[0, 300, 50] by [0, 300, 50]

[0, 30, 5] by [0, 30, 5]

Figure 53

Figure 54

[–10, 10, 1] by [–10, 10, 1]   [–10, 10, 1] by [–10, 10, 1]

Figure 55   Figure 56

55.   Note that $x - 2y = 5 \Rightarrow y = \frac{1}{2}x - \frac{5}{2}$ and $-2x + 4y = -2 \Rightarrow y = \frac{1}{2}x - \frac{1}{2}$.

Graph $Y_1 = (1/2)X - (5/2)$ and $Y_2 = (1/2)X - (1/2)$ in [–10, 10, 1] by [–10, 10, 1]. See Figure 55.

Since the lines are parallel, there is no solution.

56.   Note that $3x + 4y = 5 \Rightarrow y = -\frac{3}{4}x + \frac{5}{4}$ and $6x + 8y = 10 \Rightarrow y = -\frac{3}{4}x + \frac{5}{4}$.

Graph $Y_1 = (-3/4)X + (5/4)$ and $Y_2 = (-3/4)X + (5/4)$ in [–10, 10, 1] by [–10, 10, 1]. See Figure 56.

Since the lines coincide, there are infinitely many solutions of the form $\{(x, y) | 3x + 4y = 5\}$.

Numerical Solutions

57.   Since $y_1 = y_2 = 3$ when $x = 2$, the solution is (2, 3).

58.   Since $y_1 = y_2 = 5$ when $x = -2$, the solution is (–2, 5).

59.   Since $y_1 = y_2 = 1$ when $x = 1$, the solution is (1, 1).

60.   Since $y_1 \neq y_2$ for all x, there is no solution.

61.   Note that $x + y = 3 \Rightarrow y = 3 - x$ and $x - y = 7 \Rightarrow y = x - 7$.

Table $Y_1 = 3 - X$ and $Y_2 = X - 7$ with TblStart = 0 and ΔTbl = 1. See Figure 61.

Since $Y_1 = Y_2 = -2$ when $X = 5$, the solution is (5, –2).

62.   Note that $2x + y = 3 \Rightarrow y = 3 - 2x$ and $3x - y = 7 \Rightarrow y = 3x - 7$.

Table $Y_1 = 3 - 2X$ and $Y_2 = 3X - 7$ with TblStart = 0 and ΔTbl = 1. See Figure 62.

Since $Y_1 = Y_2 = -1$ when $X = 2$, the solution is (2, –1).

Figure 61   Figure 62   Figure 63   Figure 64

63.   Note that $3x + 2y = 5 \Rightarrow y = -\frac{3}{2}x + \frac{5}{2}$ and $-x - y = -5 \Rightarrow y = -x + 5$.

Table $Y_1 = (-3/2)X + (5/2)$ and $Y_2 = -X + 5$ with TblStart = –8 and ΔTbl = 1. See Figure 63.

Since $Y_1 = Y_2 = 10$ when $X = -5$, the solution is (–5, 10).

64.   Note that $2x + 3y = 3.5 \Rightarrow y = -\frac{2}{3}x + \frac{7}{6}$ and $3x + 2y = 6.5 \Rightarrow y = -\frac{3}{2}x + \frac{13}{4}$.

Table $Y_1 = (-2/3)X + (7/6)$ and $Y_2 = (-3/2)X + (13/4)$ with TblStart = 0 and ΔTbl = 0.5. See Figure 64.

Since $Y_1 = Y_2 = -0.5$ when X = 2.5, the solution is (2.5, –0.5).

65.   Note that $0.5x - 0.1y = 0.1 \Rightarrow y = 5x - 1$ and $0.1x - 0.3y = -0.4 \Rightarrow y = \frac{1}{3}x + \frac{4}{3}$.

Table $Y_1 = 5X - 1$ and $Y_2 = (1/3)X + (4/3)$ with TblStart = –1 and ΔTbl = 0.5. See Figure 65.

Since $Y_1 = Y_2 = 1.5$ when X = 0.5, the solution is (0.5, 1.5).

66.   Note that $\frac{x}{3} + \frac{y}{6} = -\frac{1}{2} \Rightarrow y = -2x - 3$ and $\frac{x}{6} + \frac{y}{3} = \frac{5}{2} \Rightarrow y = -\frac{1}{2}x + \frac{15}{2}$.

Table $Y_1 = -2X - 3$ and $Y_2 = (-1/2)X + (15/2)$ with TblStart = –10 and ΔTbl = 1. See Figure 66.

Since $Y_1 = Y_2 = 11$ when X = –7, the solution is (–7, 11).

Figure 65   Figure 66

67. $x + ay = 1 \Rightarrow ay = -x + 1 \Rightarrow y = -\frac{1}{a}x + \frac{1}{a}$; $2x + 2ay = 4 \Rightarrow 2ay = -2x + 4 \Rightarrow y = -\frac{1}{a}x + \frac{2}{a}$. So the graphs of

the two lines have the same slope $\left(-\frac{1}{a}\right)$ but different y-intercepts. Therefore, the lines are parallel and do not

intersect, so there are no solutions.

68. $-ax + y = 4 \Rightarrow y = ax + 4$; $ax + y = 4 \Rightarrow y = -ax + 4$. The lines have slopes whose product is –1 so the lines

are perpendicular and intersect at exactly one point. Both lines have y-intercept 4, so the point (0, 4) must be

the point of intersection, and hence the solution of the system.

Writing and Solving Equations

69.   (a) Let x and y represent the two numbers. Then the system needed is $x + y = 18$ and $x - y = 6$.

   (b) Note that $x + y = 18 \Rightarrow y = -x + 18$ and $x - y = 6 \Rightarrow y = x - 6$.

   The graphs of these equations (not shown) intersect at the point (12, 6). The numbers are 12 and 6.

70.   (a) Let x and y represent the two numbers. Then the system needed is $2x - y = 5$ and $x + y = 16$.

   (b) Note that $2x - y = 5 \Rightarrow y = 2x - 5$ and $x + y = 16 \Rightarrow y = -x + 16$.

   The graphs of these equations (not shown) intersect at the point (7, 9). The numbers are 7 and 9.

71.   (a) Let x and y represent the time spent running at 6 mph and 8 mph respectively.

   Then the system needed is $x + y = 1$ and $6x + 8y = 7$.

   (b) Note that $x + y = 1 \Rightarrow y = 1 - x$ and $6x + 8y = 7 \Rightarrow y = \frac{7 - 6x}{8}$.

   The graphs of these equations (not shown) intersect at the point (0.5, 0.5).

   The athlete ran for 0.5 hour at 6 mph and for 0.5 hour at 8 mph.

72.   (a) Let x and y represent the time spent driving 40 mph and 60 mph respectively.

Then the system needed is $x + y = 2$ and $40x + 60y = 90$.

(b) Note that $x + y = 2 \Rightarrow y = -x + 2$ and $40x + 60y = 90 \Rightarrow y = -\frac{2}{3}x + \frac{3}{2}$.

The graphs of these equations (not shown) intersect at the point (1.5, 0.5).

The car was driven for 1.5 hour at 40 mph and for 0.5 hour at 60 mph.

73.   (a) Let x and y represent the length and width of the rectangle respectively.

Then the system needed is $2x + 2y = 76$ and $x - y = 4$.

(b) Note that $2x + 2y = 76 \Rightarrow y = -x + 38$ and $x - y = 4 \Rightarrow y = x - 4$.

The graphs of these equations (not shown) intersect at the point (21, 17).

The length of the rectangle is 21 inches and the width is 17 inches.

74.   (a) Let x represent the length of the longest side and y represent the length of each of the shorter sides.

Then the system needed is $x + 2y = 100$ and $x - y = 10$.

(b) Note that $x + 2y = 100 \Rightarrow y = -\frac{1}{2}x + 50$ and $x - y = 10 \Rightarrow y = x - 10$.

The graphs of these equations (not shown) intersect at the point (40, 30).

The length of the longest side is 40 inches and the length of each of the shorter sides is 30 inches.

75.   (a) Let x and y represent the measure of the largest angle and the measure of one of the equal angles respectively.

Then the system needed is $x + 2y = 180$ and $x - y = 60$.

(b) Note that $x + 2y = 180 \Rightarrow y = -\frac{1}{2}x + 90$ and $x - y = 60 \Rightarrow y = x - 60$.

The graphs of these equations (not shown) intersect at the point (100, 40).

The measure of the largest angle is 100° and the measure of each of the smaller angles is 40°.

76.   (a) Let x and y represent the price of a box of popcorn and the price of a soft drink respectively.

Then the system needed is $2x + 3y = 7$ and $3x + 2y = 8$.

(b) Note that $2x + 3y = 7 \Rightarrow y = -\frac{2}{3}x + \frac{7}{3}$ and $3x + 2y = 8 \Rightarrow y = -\frac{3}{2}x + 4$.

The graphs of these equations (not shown) intersect at the point (2, 1).

Popcorn costs $2 per box and soft drinks cost $1 each.

Applications

77.   Let x and y represent the number of times Kentucky and UCLA have appeared respectively. Then the system needed is $x + y = 80$ and $x - y = 8$. By solving each equation for y and graphing each (figure not shown) we find the intersection point is (44, 36). Kentucky appeared 44 times and UCLA appeared 36 times.

78.   Let x and y represent the amount spent on travel and the amount spent on hardware respectively. Then the system needed is $x + y = 40$ and $y = \dfrac{1}{3}x$. By solving each equation for y and graphing each (figure not shown) we find the intersection point is (30, 10). $30 billion was spent on travel and $10 billion on computer hardware.

79.   Let x and y represent the number of home runs hit by McGwire and Sosa respectively. Then the system needed is $x + y = 136$ and $x - y = 4$. By solving each equation for y and graphing each (figure not shown) we find the intersection point is (70, 66). McGwire hit 70 home runs and Sosa hit 66.

80.   Let x and y represent the amount borrowed at 10% and 5% respectively. Then the system needed is $x + y = 4000$ and $0.1x + 0.05y = 250$. By solving each equation for y and graphing each (figure not shown) we find the intersection point is (1000, 3000). The student borrowed $1000 at 10% and $3000 at 5%.

81.   Let x represent the amount invested at 4% interest, and y represent the amount invested at 5% interest. Then the system needed is $x + y = 600$ and $y = x + 100$. By solving the first equation for y and graphing both equations (figure not shown) we find the intersection point is (250, 350). $250 is invested at 4% and $350 is invested at 5%.

82.   Let x and y represent the length and width, respectively. Then the system needed is $2x + 2y = 14$ and $x = y + 1$. By solving each equation for y and graphing each (figure not shown) we find the intersection point is (4, 3). The building has dimensions 4 yards by 3 yards.

4.2: The Substitution and Elimination Methods

Concepts

1.   Substitution and elimination.

2.   No, all methods will produce the same solution. However, calculator solutions are sometimes rounded.

3.   Elimination yields a contradiction.

4.   Elimination yields an identity.

5.   Solve the first equation for y.

6.   Multiply the second equation by –2.

Substitution Method

7.   Substituting $y = 2x$ into the second equation yields the following:

$3x + (2x) = 5 \Rightarrow 5x = 5 \Rightarrow x = 1$ and so $y = 2(1) \Rightarrow y = 2$. The solution is (1, 2).

8.   Substituting $y = x + 1$ into the second equation yields the following:

$x + 2(x + 1) = 8 \Rightarrow 3x = 6 \Rightarrow x = 2$ and so $y = (2) + 1 \Rightarrow y = 3$. The solution is (2, 3).

9.   Substituting $x = 2y - 1$ into the second equation yields the following:

$(2y - 1) + 5y = 20 \Rightarrow 7y = 21 \Rightarrow y = 3$ and so $x = 2(3) - 1 \Rightarrow x = 5$. The solution is (5, 3).

10.   Substituting $x = 3y$ into the second equation yields the following:

$-(3y)+2y=4 \Rightarrow -y=4 \Rightarrow y=-4$ and so $x=3(-4) \Rightarrow x=-12$. The solution is $(-12,-4)$.

11. Note that $x-2y=0 \Rightarrow x=2y$. Substituting $x=2y$ into the second equation yields the following:

$3(2y)+y=7 \Rightarrow 7y=7 \Rightarrow y=1$ and so $x=2(1) \Rightarrow x=2$. The solution is $(2, 1)$.

This result is supported by the graph's intersection point of $(2, 1)$.

12. Note that $2x+3y=8 \Rightarrow y=\dfrac{8-2x}{3}$. Substituting $y=\dfrac{8-2x}{3}$ into the second equation yields:

$3x-2\left(\dfrac{8-2x}{3}\right)=-14 \Rightarrow 13x=-26 \Rightarrow x=-2$ and so $y=\dfrac{8-2(-2)}{3} \Rightarrow y=4$. The solution is $(-2, 4)$.

This result is supported by the graph's intersection point of $(-2, 4)$.

13. Substituting $y=3x$ into the second equation yields the following:

$x+(3x)=4 \Rightarrow 4x=4 \Rightarrow x=1$ and so $y=3(1)=3$. The solution is $(1, 3)$.

By solving each equation for y and graphing each (figure not shown), the intersection point is $(1, 3)$.

14. Substituting $x=\dfrac{1}{2}y$ into the second equation yields the following:

$2\left(\dfrac{1}{2}y\right)+y=4 \Rightarrow 2y=4 \Rightarrow y=2$ and so $x=\dfrac{1}{2}(2)=1$. The solution is $(1, 2)$.

By solving each equation for y and graphing each (figure not shown), the intersection point is $(1, 2)$.

15. Note that $x+y=2 \Rightarrow y=2-x$. Substituting $y=2-x$ into the second equation yields:

$2x-(2-x)=1 \Rightarrow 3x-2=1 \Rightarrow 3x=3 \Rightarrow x=1$ and so $y=2-(1)=1$. The solution is $(1, 1)$.

By solving each equation for y and graphing each (figure not shown), the intersection point is $(1, 1)$.

16. Note that $x-y=2 \Rightarrow x=y+2$. Substituting $x=y+2$ into the second equation yields:

$(y+2)+2y=-1 \Rightarrow 3y=-3 \Rightarrow y=-1$ and so $x=(-1)+2=1$. The solution is $(1, -1)$.

By solving each equation for y and graphing each (figure not shown), the intersection point is $(1, -1)$.

17. Note that $x-2y=-4 \Rightarrow x=2y-4$. Substituting $x=2y-4$ into the first equation yields:

$2(2y-4)+3y=6 \Rightarrow 7y=14 \Rightarrow y=2$ and so $x=2(2)-4=0$. The solution is $(0, 2)$.

By solving each equation for y and graphing each (figure not shown), the intersection point is $(0, 2)$.

18. Note that $2x-y=2 \Rightarrow y=2x-2$. Substituting $y=2x-2$ into the second equation yields:

$3x+2(2x-2)=10 \Rightarrow 7x=14 \Rightarrow x=2$ and so $y=2(2)-2=2$. The solution is $(2, 2)$.

By solving each equation for y and graphing each (figure not shown), the intersection point is $(2, 2)$.

19. Note that $4x + y = 3 \Rightarrow y = -4x + 3$. Substituting $y = -4x + 3$ into the second equation yields:

$2x - 3(-4x + 3) = -2 \Rightarrow 2x + 12x - 9 = -2 \Rightarrow 14x = 7 \Rightarrow x = \dfrac{1}{2}$ and so $y = -4\left(\dfrac{1}{2}\right) + 3 \Rightarrow y = 1$. The solution is

$\left(\dfrac{1}{2}, 1\right)$.

20. Note that $2x - y = 3 \Rightarrow y = 2x - 3$. Substituting $y = 2x - 3$ into the first equation yields:

$3x + 4(2x - 3) = 32 \Rightarrow 3x + 8x - 12 = 32 \Rightarrow 11x = 44 \Rightarrow x = 4$ and so $y = 2(4) - 3 \Rightarrow y = 5$. The solution is

$(4, 5)$.

21. Note that $x - 2y = 0 \Rightarrow x = 2y$. Substituting $x = 2y$ into the second equation yields:

$-3(2y) + 2y = -1 \Rightarrow -6y + 2y = -1 \Rightarrow -4y = -1 \Rightarrow y = \dfrac{1}{4}$ and so $x = 2\left(\dfrac{1}{4}\right) = \dfrac{1}{2}$. The solution is $\left(\dfrac{1}{2}, \dfrac{1}{4}\right)$.

22. Note that $-x + 3y = 3 \Rightarrow -x = -3y + 3 \Rightarrow x = 3y - 3$. Substituting $x = 3y - 3$ into the second equation yields:

$2(3y - 3) + 5y = -\dfrac{1}{2} \Rightarrow 6y - 6 + 5y = -\dfrac{1}{2} \Rightarrow 11y = \dfrac{11}{2} \Rightarrow y = \dfrac{1}{2}$ and so $x = 3\left(\dfrac{1}{2}\right) - 3 \Rightarrow x = \dfrac{3}{2} - \dfrac{6}{2} \Rightarrow x = -\dfrac{3}{2}$.

The solution is $\left(-\dfrac{3}{2}, \dfrac{1}{2}\right)$.

23. Note that $-x + 3y = 0 \Rightarrow x = 3y$. Substituting $x = 3y$ into the first equation yields:

$2(3y) - 5y = -1 \Rightarrow y = -1$ and so $x = 3(-1) \Rightarrow x = -3$. The solution is $(-3, -1)$.

24. Note that $-10x + 5y = 60 \Rightarrow y = 2x + 12$. Substituting $y = 2x + 12$ into the first equation yields:

$5x + 10(2x + 12) = -5 \Rightarrow 25x = -125 \Rightarrow x = -5$ and so $y = 2(-5) + 12 \Rightarrow y = 2$. The solution is $(-5, 2)$.

25. Note that $x - y = 1 \Rightarrow x = y + 1$. Substituting $x = y + 1$ into the second equation yields:

$2(y + 1) + 6y = -2 \Rightarrow 8y = -4 \Rightarrow y = -\dfrac{1}{2}$ and so $x = \left(-\dfrac{1}{2}\right) + 1 \Rightarrow x = \dfrac{1}{2}$. The solution is $\left(\dfrac{1}{2}, -\dfrac{1}{2}\right)$.

26. Note that $4x - y = -4 \Rightarrow y = 4x + 4$. Substituting $y = 4x + 4$ into the second equation yields:

$-2x + 5(4x + 4) = 29 \Rightarrow 18x = 9 \Rightarrow x = \dfrac{1}{2}$ and so $y = 4\left(\dfrac{1}{2}\right) + 4 \Rightarrow y = 6$. The solution is $\left(\dfrac{1}{2}, 6\right)$.

27. Note that $2x - y = 6 \Rightarrow y = 2x - 6$. Substituting $y = 2x - 6$ into the first equation yields:

$\dfrac{1}{2}x - \dfrac{1}{2}(2x - 6) = 1 \Rightarrow -\dfrac{1}{2}x = -2 \Rightarrow x = 4$ and so $y = 2(4) - 6 = 2$. The solution is $(4, 2)$.

28. Note that $x - 2y = 12 \Rightarrow x = 2y + 12$. Substituting $x = 2y + 12$ into the first equation yields:

$\dfrac{3}{4}(2y + 12) + \dfrac{1}{2}y = 5 \Rightarrow 2y = -4 \Rightarrow y = -2$ and so $x = 2(-2) + 12 = 8$. The solution is $(8, -2)$.

29. Note that $\dfrac{1}{6}x - \dfrac{1}{3}y = -1 \Rightarrow x = 2y - 6$. Substituting $x = 2y - 6$ into the second equation yields:

$\frac{1}{3}(2y-6)+\frac{5}{6}y=7 \Rightarrow \frac{3}{2}y=9 \Rightarrow y=6$ and so $x=2(6)-6=6$. The solution is $(6,\ 6)$.

30. Note that $\frac{3}{5}x-\frac{1}{10}y=4 \Rightarrow \frac{1}{10}y=\frac{3}{5}x-4$. Substituting $\frac{1}{10}y=\frac{3}{5}x-4$ into the second equation yields:

$\frac{2}{5}x+\left(\frac{3}{5}x-4\right)=6 \Rightarrow x=10$ and so $\frac{1}{10}y=\frac{3}{5}(10)-4 \Rightarrow y=20$. The solution is $(10,\ 20)$.

31. Note that $\frac{1}{4}x-\frac{1}{3}y=3 \Rightarrow x=\frac{4}{3}y+12$. Substituting $x=\frac{4}{3}y+12$ into the first equation yields:

$\frac{1}{2}\left(\frac{4}{3}y+12\right)+\frac{2}{3}y=-2 \Rightarrow \frac{4}{3}y=-8 \Rightarrow y=-6$ and so $x=\frac{4}{3}(-6)+12 \Rightarrow x=4$. The solution is $(4,\ -6)$.

32. Note that $\frac{1}{5}x-\frac{1}{10}y=\frac{7}{40} \Rightarrow y=2x-\frac{7}{4}$. Substituting $y=2x-\frac{7}{4}$ into the second equation yields:

$\frac{1}{4}x-\frac{1}{5}\left(2x-\frac{7}{4}\right)=\frac{11}{40} \Rightarrow -\frac{3}{20}x=-\frac{3}{40} \Rightarrow x=\frac{1}{2}$ and so $y=2\left(\frac{1}{2}\right)-\frac{7}{4} \Rightarrow y=-\frac{3}{4}$.

The solution is $\left(\frac{1}{2},\ -\frac{3}{4}\right)$.

33. Note that $0.1x+0.4y=1.3 \Rightarrow x=-4y+13$. Substituting $x=-4y+13$ into the second equation yields:

$0.3(-4y+13)-0.2y=1.1 \Rightarrow -1.4y=-2.8 \Rightarrow y=2$ and so $x=-4(2)+13 \Rightarrow x=5$.

The solution is $(5, 2)$.

34. Note that $2.7x-0.1y=0.76 \Rightarrow y=27x-7.6$. Substituting $y=27x-7.6$ into the first equation yields:

$1.5x-4.1(27x-7.6)=-1.6 \Rightarrow -109.2x=-32.76 \Rightarrow x=0.3$ and so $y=27(0.3)-7.6 \Rightarrow y=0.5$.

The solution is $(0.3, 0.5)$.

35. Note that $x-y=5 \Rightarrow x=y+5$. Substituting $x=y+5$ into the second equation yields:

$2(y+5)-2y=10 \Rightarrow 10=10$ and this result is an identity. The system is dependent.

36. Note that $-x+2y=5 \Rightarrow x=2y-5$. Substituting $x=2y-5$ into the second equation yields:

$2(2y-5)-4y=10 \Rightarrow -10=10$ and this result is a contradiction. The system is inconsistent.

37. Note that $-\frac{5}{3}x-y=2 \Rightarrow y=-\frac{5}{3}x-2$. Substituting $y=-\frac{5}{3}x-2$ into the first equation yields:

$5x+3\left(-\frac{5}{3}x-2\right)=6 \Rightarrow 5x-5x-6=6 \Rightarrow -6=6$, a contradiction. Therefore the system is inconsistent and

there are no solutions.

38. Note that $-x+2y=1 \Rightarrow x=2y-1$. Substituting $x=2y-1$ into the first equation yields:

$2(2y-1)-4y=5 \Rightarrow 4y-2-4y=5 \Rightarrow -2=5$, a contradiction. Therefore the system is inconsistent and

there are no solutions.

39.	Note that $x + 3y = -2 \Rightarrow x = -3y - 2$. Substituting $x = -3y - 2$ into the second equation yields:

$-\dfrac{1}{2}(-3y - 2) - \dfrac{3}{2}y = 1 \Rightarrow \dfrac{3}{2}y + 1 - \dfrac{3}{2}y = 1 \Rightarrow 1 = 1$, an identity. Therefore the system is dependent and the

solution set is $\{(x, y) \mid x + 3y = -2\}$.

40.	Note that $2x - 4y = 4 \Rightarrow 2x = 4y + 4 \Rightarrow x = 2y + 2$. Substituting $x = 2y + 2$ into the second equation yields:

$-3(2y + 2) + 6y = -6 \Rightarrow -6y - 6 + 6y = -6 \Rightarrow -6 = -6$, an identity. Therefore the system is dependent and

the solution set is $\{(x, y) \mid x - 2y = 2\}$.

Elimination Method

41.	Adding the two equations will eliminate the variable y.

$\begin{array}{r} x - y = 5 \\ x + y = 9 \\ \hline 2x = 14 \end{array}$ Thus, $x = 7$. And so $(7) - y = 5 \Rightarrow y = 2$. The solution is (7, 2).

This result is supported by the graph's intersection point of (7, 2).

42.	Adding the two equations will eliminate the variable y.

$\begin{array}{r} 3x - 2y = 9 \\ 5x + 2y = 7 \\ \hline 8x = 16 \end{array}$ Thus, $x = 2$. And so $3(2) - 2y = 9 \Rightarrow -2y = 3 \Rightarrow y = -1.5$. The solution is (2, -1.5).

This result is supported by the graph's intersection point of (2, -1.5).

43.	Adding the two equations will eliminate the variable y.

$\begin{array}{r} x + y = 3 \\ x - y = 1 \\ \hline 2x = 4 \end{array}$ Thus, $x = 2$. And so $(2) + y = 3 \Rightarrow y = 1$. The solution is $(2, 1)$.

By solving each equation for y and graphing each (figure not shown), the intersection point is $(2, 1)$.

44.	Multiplying the first equation by 2 and adding the two equations will eliminate the variable y.

$\begin{array}{r} 4x - 2y = 6 \\ x + 2y = -1 \\ \hline 5x = 5 \end{array}$ Thus, $x = 1$. And so $(1) + 2y = -1 \Rightarrow y = -1$. The solution is $(1, -1)$.

By solving each equation for y and graphing each (figure not shown), the intersection point is $(1, -1)$.

45.	Multiplying the first equation by 2 and adding the two equations will eliminate the variable y.

$\begin{array}{r} 8x - 2y = 8 \\ x + 2y = 1 \\ \hline 9x = 9 \end{array}$ Thus, $x = 1$. And so $(1) + 2y = 1 \Rightarrow y = 0$. The solution is $(1, 0)$.

By solving each equation for y and graphing each (figure not shown), the intersection point is $(1, 0)$.

46.	Multiplying the first equation by -1 and adding the two equations will eliminate the variable x.

$\begin{array}{r} -x + y = -1 \\ x + 4y = 6 \\ \hline 5y = 5 \end{array}$ Thus, $y = 1$. And so $x - (1) = 1 \Rightarrow x = 2$. The solution is $(2, 1)$.

By solving each equation for y and graphing each (figure not shown), the intersection point is $(2, 1)$.

47.   Adding the two equations will eliminate the variable y.

$$x + y = 4$$
$$\underline{x - y = 2}$$
$$2x = 6$$

Thus, $x = 3$. And so $3 + y = 4 \Rightarrow y = 1$. The solution is $(3, 1)$.

48.   Adding the two equations will eliminate the variable x.

$$x - 3y = 5$$
$$\underline{-x + 5y = -7}$$
$$2y = -2$$

Thus, $y = -1$. And so $x - 3(-1) = 5 \Rightarrow x = 2$. The solution is $(2, -1)$.

49.   Multiplying the first equation by -1 and adding the two equations will eliminate the variable x.

$$3x + y = -5$$
$$\underline{-3x + 2y = -1}$$
$$3y = -6$$

Thus $y = -2$. And so $-3x - (-2) = 5 \Rightarrow -3x = 3 \Rightarrow x = -1$. The solution is $(-1, -2)$.

50.   Multiplying the first equation by -1 and adding the two equations will eliminate the variable y.

$$2x - 3y = -13$$
$$\underline{x + 3y = \quad 7}$$
$$3x = -6$$

Thus $x = -2$. And so $-2 + 3y = 7 \Rightarrow 3y = 9 \Rightarrow y = 3$. The solution is $(-2, 3)$.

51.   Adding the two equations will eliminate the variable y.

$$2x + y = \quad 4$$
$$\underline{2x - y = -2}$$
$$4x = 2$$

Thus, $x = \frac{1}{2}$. And so $2\left(\frac{1}{2}\right) + y = 4 \Rightarrow y = 3$. The solution is $\left(\frac{1}{2}, 3\right)$.

52.   Multiplying the first equation by -1 and adding the two equations will eliminate the variable x.

$$-2x - 3y = 6$$
$$\underline{2x - y = 4}$$
$$-4y = 10$$

Thus, $y = -\frac{5}{2}$. And so $2x - \left(-\frac{5}{2}\right) = 4 \Rightarrow 2x = \frac{3}{2} \Rightarrow x = \frac{3}{4}$. The solution is $\left(\frac{3}{4}, -\frac{5}{2}\right)$.

53.   Multiplying the second equation by -2 and adding the two equations will eliminate the variable x.

$$6x - 4y = 12$$
$$\underline{-6x - 10y = 12}$$
$$-14y = 24$$

Thus, $y = -\frac{12}{7}$. And so $6x - 4\left(-\frac{12}{7}\right) = 12 \Rightarrow 6x = \frac{36}{7} \Rightarrow x = \frac{6}{7}$.

The solution is $\left(\frac{6}{7}, -\frac{12}{7}\right)$.

54.   Multiplying the first equation by -1 and adding the two equations will eliminate the variable y.

$$5x + 4y = 8$$
$$\underline{x - 4y = 10}$$
$$6x = 18$$

Thus, $x = 3$. And so $(3) - 4y = 10 \Rightarrow -4y = 7 \Rightarrow y = -\frac{7}{4}$. The solution is $\left(3, -\frac{7}{4}\right)$.

55.   Multiplying the second equation by 2 and adding the two equations will eliminate both variables.

$$2x - 4y = 5$$
$$\underline{-2x + 4y = 18}$$
$$0 = 23 \qquad$$ This is always false and the system is inconsistent. No solutions.

56.   Multiplying the first equation by –2 and adding the two equations will eliminate both variables.

$$-2x + 6y = -10$$
$$\underline{2x - 6y = 1}$$
$$0 = -9 \qquad$$ This is always false and the system is inconsistent. No solutions.

57.   Multiplying the first equation by –2 and adding the two equations will eliminate both variables.

$$-4x - 2y = -4$$
$$\underline{4x + 2y = 4}$$
$$0 = 0 \qquad$$ This is always true and the system is dependent with solutions: $\{(x,\ y)|2x + y = 2\}$.

58.   Multiplying the first equation by –14 and adding the two equations will eliminate both variables.

$$-7x - 2y = -28$$
$$\underline{7x + 2y = 28}$$
$$0 = 0$$

This is always true and the system is dependent with solutions:

$$\{(x,\ y)|7x + 2y = 28\}.$$

59.   Multiply the first equation by $-\dfrac{1}{2}$, the second equation by $\dfrac{2}{15}$ and add the equations to eliminate the variable

y.

$$-x - 2y = 11$$
$$\underline{10x + 2y = -16}$$
$$9x = -5$$

Thus, $x = -\dfrac{5}{9}$. And so $2\left(-\dfrac{5}{9}\right) + 4y = -22 \Rightarrow 4y = -\dfrac{188}{9} \Rightarrow y = -\dfrac{47}{9}$.

The solution is $\left(-\dfrac{5}{9}, -\dfrac{47}{9}\right)$.

60.   Multiplying the second equation by –4 and adding the two equations will eliminate the variable y.

$$-3x + 20y = 67$$
$$\underline{-8x - 20y = -188}$$
$$-11x = -121 \qquad$$ Thus, $x = 11$. And so $2(11) + 5y = 47 \Rightarrow 5y = 25 \Rightarrow y = 5$. The solution is $(11, 5)$.

61.   Multiply the first equation by 30, the second equation by –20 and add the equations to eliminate the variable

y.

$$9x + 6y = 24$$
$$\underline{-8x - 6y = -22}$$
$$x = 2 \qquad$$ Thus, $x = 2$. And so $0.3(2) + 0.2y = 0.8 \Rightarrow 0.2y = 0.2 \Rightarrow y = 1$. The solution is $(2, 1)$.

62.   Multiplying the first equation by –2 and adding the two equations will eliminate the variable x.

$$-2.4x - 8.6y = -3.4$$
$$\underline{2.4x - 1.5y = 1.38}$$
$$-10.1y = -2.02 \qquad$$ Thus, $y = 0.2$. And so $1.2x + 4.3(0.2) = 1.7 \Rightarrow 1.2x = 0.84 \Rightarrow x = 0.7$.

The solution is $(0.7, 0.2)$.

63.   Note that $2x - y = -13 \Rightarrow y = 2x + 13$. Substituting $y = 2x + 13$ into the first equation yields:

$$2x + 3(2x + 13) = 7 \Rightarrow 8x = -32 \Rightarrow x = -4 \text{ and so } x = 2(-4) + 13 = 5. \text{ The solution is } (-4, 5).$$

64. Adding the two equations will eliminate the variable y.

$$2x - 3y = -25$$
$$\underline{x + 3y = 10}$$
$$3x = -15$$

Thus, $x = -5$. And so $(-5) + 3y = 10 \Rightarrow y = 5$. The solution is $(-5, 5)$.

65. Note that $5u + v = 2 \Rightarrow v = 2 - 5u$. Substituting $v = 2 - 5u$ into the first equation yields:

$$3u - 5(2 - 5u) = 4 \Rightarrow 28u = 14 \Rightarrow u = \frac{1}{2} \text{ and so } v = 2 - 5\left(\frac{1}{2}\right) = -\frac{1}{2}. \text{ The solution is } \left(\frac{1}{2}, -\frac{1}{2}\right).$$

66. Multiplying the first equation by 3 and adding the two equations will eliminate the variable v.

$$12u - 9v = -6$$
$$\underline{-8u + 9v = 5}$$
$$4u = -1$$

Thus, $u = -\frac{1}{4}$. And so $4\left(-\frac{1}{4}\right) - 3v = -2 \Rightarrow v = \frac{1}{3}$. The solution is $\left(-\frac{1}{4}, \frac{1}{3}\right)$.

67. Multiplying the first equation by 2 and adding the two equations will eliminate both variables.

$$4r - 6t = 14$$
$$\underline{-4r + 6t = -14}$$
$$0 = 0$$

This is an identity. The system is dependent with solutions of the form $\{(r, t) | 2r - 3t = 7\}$.

68. Multiplying the first equation by 2 and adding the two equations will eliminate both variables.

$$2r - 2t = 20$$
$$\underline{-2r + 2t = -20}$$
$$0 = 0$$

This is an identity. The system is dependent with solutions of the form $\{(r, t) | r - t = 10\}$.

69. Multiplying the first equation by -1 and adding the two equations will eliminate both variables.

$$-m + n = -5$$
$$\underline{m - n = 7}$$
$$0 = 2$$

This is a contradiction. The system is inconsistent and has no solutions.

70. Multiplying the second equation by $\frac{3}{2}$ and adding the two equations will eliminate both variables.

$$6m + 9n = 4$$
$$\underline{-6m - 9n = 3}$$
$$0 = 7$$

This is a contradiction. The system is inconsistent and has no solutions.

71. Note that $2x - 3y = 2 \Rightarrow x = \frac{3}{2}y + 1$. Substituting $x = \frac{3}{2}y + 1$ into the second equation yields:

$$3\left(\frac{3}{2}y + 1\right) - 5y = 4 \Rightarrow -\frac{1}{2}y = 1 \Rightarrow y = -2 \text{ and so } x = \frac{3}{2}(-2) + 1 = -2. \text{ The solution is } (-2, -2).$$

72. Multiplying the first equation by 2 and adding the two equations will eliminate the variable x.

$$2x + 6y = \tfrac{5}{2}$$
$$\underline{-2x - 7y = -\tfrac{11}{4}}$$
$$-y = -\tfrac{1}{4}$$

Thus, $y = \frac{1}{4}$. And so $x + 3\left(\frac{1}{4}\right) = \frac{5}{4} \Rightarrow x = \frac{1}{2}$. The solution is $\left(\frac{1}{2}, \frac{1}{4}\right)$.

73. Note that $0.1x - 0.3y = -5 \Rightarrow x = 3y - 50$. Substituting $x = 3y - 50$ into the second equation yields:

$$0.5(3y - 50) + 1.1y = 27 \Rightarrow 2.6y = 52 \Rightarrow y = 20 \text{ and so } x = 3(20) - 50 = 10. \text{ The solution is } (10, 20).$$

74. Note that $-0.1x - 0.5y = 1.3 \Rightarrow x = -5y - 13$. Substituting $x = -5y - 13$ into the first equation yields:

   $0.6(-5y - 13) - 0.2y = 1.8 \Rightarrow -3.2y = 9.6 \Rightarrow y = -3$ and so $x = -5(-3) - 13 = 2$. The solution is $(2, -3)$.

75. Multiplying the first equation by -4 and the second equation by 4 will eliminate the variable z when adding.

   $$\begin{array}{r} -2y + 2z = 4 \\ 3y - 2z = 4 \\ \hline y = 8 \end{array}$$ Thus, $y = 8$. And so $-2(8) + 2z = 4 \Rightarrow z = 10$. The solution is $(8, \ 10)$.

76. Multiplying the first equation by -4 and the second equation by 4 will eliminate the variable z when adding.

   $$\begin{array}{r} -3y - z = -52 \\ -y + z = -12 \\ \hline -4y = -64 \end{array}$$ Thus, $y = 16$. And so $-(16) + z = -12 \Rightarrow z = 4$. The solution is $(16, \ 4)$.

77. Multiplying the first equation by -5 and adding the two equations will eliminate the variable x.

   $$\begin{array}{r} -x + 2y = 3 \\ x - y = 1 \\ \hline y = 4 \end{array}$$ Thus, $y = 4$. And so $x - (4) = 1 \Rightarrow x = 5$. The solution is $(5, \ 4)$.

78. Multiplying the first equation by 10 and the second equation by 20 will eliminate the variable y when adding.

   $$\begin{array}{r} x - 2y = 20 \\ -4x + 2y = -38 \\ \hline -3x = -18 \end{array}$$ Thus, $x = 6$. And so $(6) - 2y = 20 \Rightarrow y = -7$. The solution is $(6, -7)$.

Using More Than One Method

79. Note that $x - y = 4 \Rightarrow y = x - 4$ and $x + y = 6 \Rightarrow y = -x + 6$.

   Graphical: Graph $Y_1 = X - 4$ and $Y_2 = -X + 6$ in [0, 10, 1] by [0, 2, 1]. See Figure 79a.

   The unique solution is the intersection point $(5, 1)$.

   Numerical: Table $Y_1 = X - 4$ and $Y_2 = -X + 6$ with TblStart $= 0$ and ΔTbl $= 1$. See Figure 79b.

   Since $Y_1 = Y_2 = 1$ when X $= 5$, the solution is $(5, 1)$.

   Symbolic: Adding the two equations will eliminate the variable y.

   $$\begin{array}{r} x - y = 4 \\ x + y = 6 \\ \hline 2x = 10 \end{array}$$ Thus, $x = 5$. And so $(5) - y = 4 \Rightarrow -y = -1 \Rightarrow y = 1$. The solution is $(5, 1)$.

   [0, 10, 1] by [0, 2, 1]   [0, 5, 1] by [–5, 0, 1]

   Figure 79a   Figure 79b   Figure 80a   Figure 80b

80. Note that $2x - y = 7 \Rightarrow y = 2x - 7$ and $3x + y = 3 \Rightarrow y = -3x + 3$.

Graphical: Graph $Y_1 = 2X - 7$ and $Y_2 = -3X + 3$ in [0, 5, 1] by [–5, 0, 1]. See Figure 80a.

The unique solution is the intersection point (2, –3).

Numerical: Table $Y_1 = 2X - 7$ and $Y_2 = -3X + 3$ with TblStart = 0 and ΔTbl = 1. See Figure 80b.

Since $Y_1 = Y_2 = -3$ when X = 2, the solution is (2, –3).

Symbolic: Adding the two equations will eliminate the variable y.

$$2x - y = 7$$
$$\underline{3x + y = 3}$$
$$5x = 10$$

Thus, $x = 2$. And so $2(2) - y = 7 \Rightarrow -y = 3 \Rightarrow y = -3$. The solution is (2, –3).

81.   Note that $5x + 2y = 9 \Rightarrow y = -\dfrac{5}{2}x + \dfrac{9}{2}$ and $3x - y = 1 \Rightarrow y = 3x - 1$.

Graphical: Graph $Y_1 = (-5/2)X + (9/2)$ and $Y_2 = 3X - 1$ in [0, 3, 1] by [0, 3, 1]. See Figure 81a.

The unique solution is the intersection point (1, 2).

Numerical: Table $Y_1 = (-5/2)X + (9/2)$ and $Y_2 = 3X - 1$ with TblStart = 0 and ΔTbl = 1. See Figure 81b.

Since $Y_1 = Y_2 = 2$ when X = 1, the solution is (1, 2).

Symbolic: Multiplying the second equation by 2 and adding the two equations will eliminate the variable y.

$$5x + 2y = 9$$
$$\underline{6x - 2y = 2}$$
$$11x = 11$$

Thus, $x = 1$. And so $5(1) + 2y = 9 \Rightarrow 2y = 4 \Rightarrow y = 2$. The solution is (1, 2).

[0, 3, 1] by [0, 3, 1]   [–5, 0, 1] by [0, 5, 1]

Figure 81a   Figure 81b   Figure 82a   Figure 82b

82.   Note that $-x + 4y = 17 \Rightarrow y = \dfrac{1}{4}x + \dfrac{17}{4}$ and $3x + 6y = 21 \Rightarrow y = -\dfrac{1}{2}x + \dfrac{7}{2}$.

Graphical: Graph $Y_1 = (1/4)X + (17/4)$ and $Y_2 = (-1/2)X + (7/2)$ in [–5, 0, 1] by [0, 5, 1]. See Figure 82a.

The unique solution is the intersection point (–1, 4).

Numerical: Table $Y_1 = (1/4)X + (17/4)$ and $Y_2 = (-1/2)X + (7/2)$ with TblStart = –5 and ΔTbl = 1. See Figure 82b.

Since $Y_1 = Y_2 = 4$ when X = –1, the solution is (–1, 4).

Symbolic: Multiplying the first equation by 3 and adding the two equations will eliminate the variable x.

$$-3x + 12y = 51$$
$$\underline{3x + 6y = 21}$$
$$18y = 72$$

Thus, $y = 4$. And so $-x + 4(4) = 17 \Rightarrow -x = 1 \Rightarrow x = -1$. The solution is (–1, 4).

83. Note that $3x - 2y = 8.5 \Rightarrow y = \dfrac{3x - 8.5}{2}$ and $2x + 4y = 3 \Rightarrow y = \dfrac{-2x + 3}{4}$.

    Graphical: Graph $Y_1 = (3X - 8.5)/2$ and $Y_2 = (-2X + 3)/4$ in $[-5, 5, 1]$ by $[-5, 5, 1]$. See Figure 83a.

    The unique solution is the intersection point $(2.5, -0.5)$.

    Numerical: Table $Y_1 = (3X - 8.5)/2$ and $Y_2 = (-2X + 3)/4$ with TblStart $= 0$ and ΔTbl $= 0.5$. See Figure 83b.

    Since $Y_1 = Y_2 = -0.5$ when $X = 2.5$, the solution is $(2.5, -0.5)$.

    Symbolic: Multiplying the first equation by 2 and adding the two equations will eliminate the variable y.

    $$\begin{array}{r} 6x - 4y = 17 \\ 2x + 4y = \ \ 3 \\ \hline 8x = 20 \end{array}$$
    Thus, $x = 2.5$. And so $2(2.5) + 4y = 3 \Rightarrow y = -0.5$. The solution is $(2.5, -0.5)$.

    $[-5, 5, 1]$ by $[-5, 5, 1]$ $[-5, 5, 1]$ by $[-5, 5, 1]$

           Figure 83a   Figure 83b   Figure 84a   Figure 84b

84. Note that $-x - 3y = 1.8 \Rightarrow y = \dfrac{-x - 1.8}{3}$ and $2x - 5y = 0.8 \Rightarrow y = \dfrac{2x - 0.8}{5}$.

    Graphical: Graph $Y_1 = (-X - 1.8)/3$ and $Y_2 = (2X - 0.8)/5$ in $[-5, 5, 1]$ by $[-5, 5, 1]$. See Figure 84a.

    The unique solution is the intersection point $(-0.6, -0.4)$.

    Numerical: Table $Y_1 = (-X - 1.8)/3$ and $Y_2 = (2X - 0.8)/5$ with TblStart $= -1$ and ΔTbl $= 0.1$. See Figure 84b.

    Since $Y_1 = Y_2 = -0.4$ when $X = -0.6$, the solution is $(-0.6, -0.4)$.

    Symbolic: Multiplying the first equation by 2 and adding the two equations will eliminate the variable x.

    $$\begin{array}{r} -2x - 6y = 3.6 \\ 2x - 5y = 0.8 \\ \hline -11y = 4.4 \end{array}$$
    Thus, $y = -0.4$. And so $2x - 5(-0.4) = 0.8 \Rightarrow x = -0.6$. The solution is $(-0.6, -0.4)$.

85. Multiplying the second equation by -1 and adding the two equations will eliminate the variable y:

    $$\begin{array}{r} ax + y = 4 \\ -x - y = -4 \\ \hline (a - 1)x = 0 \end{array}$$
    Thus $x = 0$ since $a \neq 1$. And so $0 + y = 4 \Rightarrow y = 4$. The solution is $(0, 4)$.

86. Multiplying the first equation by -1 and adding the two equations will eliminate the variable x:

$$-2x - y = -1$$
$$\underline{2x + ay = a}$$
$$(a-1)y = a - 1 \qquad \text{Thus } y = 1 \text{ since } a \neq 1. \text{ And so } 2x + 1 = 1 \Rightarrow x = 0. \text{ The solution is } (0, 1).$$

Applications

87.   Let x and y represent the number fat calories burned by the heavier and lighter athlete respectively. Then the system needed is $x - y = 58$ and $x + y = 290$. Adding the two equations will eliminate the variable y.

$$x - y = 58$$
$$\underline{x + y = 290}$$
$$2x = 348 \qquad \text{Thus, } x = 174. \text{ And so } (174) - y = 58 \Rightarrow y = -116 \Rightarrow y = 116.$$

The heavier athlete burned 174 fat calories or $174 \div 9 = 19.\overline{3}$ fat grams. The lighter athlete burned 116 fat calories or $116 \div 9 = 12.\overline{8}$ fat grams.

88.   Let x and y represent the time spent on the rowing machine and stair climber respectively. Then the system needed is $x + y = 60$ and $10x + 11.5y = 633$. Multiplying the first equation by -10 and adding the two equations will eliminate the variable x.

$$-10x \quad -10y = -600$$
$$\underline{10x + 11.5y = 633}$$
$$1.5y = 33 \qquad \text{Thus, } y = 22. \text{ And so } x + (22) = 60 \Rightarrow x = 38.$$

The athlete spent 38 minutes on the rowing machine and 22 minutes on the stair climber.

89.   Let x and y represent the amount of 10% and 80% solution respectively. Then the system needed is $x + y = 4$ and $0.10x + 0.80y = 0.50(4)$. Multiplying the second equation by -10 and adding the two equations will eliminate the variable x.

$$x + y = 4$$
$$\underline{-x - 8y = -20}$$
$$-7y = -16 \qquad \text{Thus, } y = \frac{16}{7}. \text{ And so } x + \left(\frac{16}{7}\right) = 4 \Rightarrow x = \frac{12}{7}. \text{ Drain and replace } \frac{16}{7} \text{ gallons.}$$

90.   Let x and y represent the amount of 10% and 25% solution respectively. Then the system needed is $x + y = 20$ and $0.10x + 0.25y = 0.18(20)$. Multiplying the second equation by -10 and adding the two equations will eliminate the variable x.

$$x \quad + y = 20$$
$$\underline{-x - 2.5y = -36}$$
$$-1.5y = -16 \qquad \text{Thus, } y = 10.\overline{6}. \text{ And so } x + (10.\overline{6}) = 20 \Rightarrow x = 9.\overline{3}.$$

Mix $9.\overline{3}$ mL of 10% acid with $10.\overline{6}$ mL of 25% acid.

91.   Let x and y represent the number of premium and regular rooms respectively. Then the system needed is $x + y = 50$ and $115x + 80y = 4945$. Multiplying the first equation by -80 and adding will eliminate y.

$$-80x - 80y = -4000$$
$$\underline{115x + 80y = \quad 4945}$$
$$35x = 945 \qquad \text{Thus, } x = 27. \text{ And so } (27) + y = 50 \Rightarrow y = 23.$$

The hotel rented 27 premium rooms and 23 regular rooms.

92. Let x and y represent the number of dimes and quarters respectively. Then the system needed is $x + y = 111$ and $0.10x + 0.25y = 18$. Multiplying the second equation by -10 and adding will eliminate x.

$$\begin{aligned} x + y &= 111 \\ -x - 2.5y &= -180 \\ \hline -1.5y &= -69 \end{aligned}$$

Thus, $y = 46$. And so $x + (46) = 111 \Rightarrow x = 65$. There are 65 dimes and 46 quarters.

93. Let x and y represent the larger and smaller angles respectively. Then the system needed is $x + y = 180$ and $x - 2y = 30$. Multiplying the first equation by 2 and adding will eliminate y.

$$\begin{aligned} 2x + 2y &= 360 \\ x - 2y &= 30 \\ \hline 3x &= 390 \end{aligned}$$

Thus, $x = 130$. And so $(130) + y = 180 \Rightarrow y = 50$. The angles are $50°$ and $130°$.

94. Let x and y represent the measures of the smaller and larger angles, respectively. Then the system needed is $x + y = 90$ and $y = 2x - 6$. Substituting $y = 2x - 6$ into the first equation yields:

$x + 2x - 6 = 90 \Rightarrow 3x = 96 \Rightarrow x = 32$ and so $y = 2(32) - 6 \Rightarrow y = 58$. The angles are $32°$ and $58°$.

95. Let x and y represent the numbers of males and females (in millions) in 2003, respectively. Then the system needed is $x + y = 291$ and $y = x + 5$. Substituting $y = x + 5$ into the first equation yields:

$x + x + 5 = 291 \Rightarrow 2x = 286 \Rightarrow x = 143$ and so $y = 143 + 5 \Rightarrow y = 148$. In 2003, there were 143 million males and 148 million females in the United States.

96. Let x and y represent the per capita incomes of Alaska and Arizona respectively. Then the system needed is $x + y = 56,000$ and $x - y = 4000$. Adding the two equations will eliminate y.

$$\begin{aligned} x + y &= 56,000 \\ x - y &= 4000 \\ \hline 2x &= 60,000 \end{aligned}$$

Thus, $x = 30,000$. And so $(30,000) - y = 4000 \Rightarrow y = 26,000$.

The per capita income for Alaska was \$30,000 and the per capita income for Arizona was \$26,000.

97. Let x and y represent the average speed of the plane and the jet stream respectively. Using the formula $d = rt$ and converting the times to minutes, the system is $2400 = (x - y)(250)$ and $2400 = (x + y)(225)$.

These equations may be written as follows: $5x - 5y = 48$ and $3x + 3y = 32$.

Multiplying the first equation by 3, the second by 5 and adding the equations will eliminate the variable y.

$$\begin{aligned} 15x - 15y &= 144 \\ 15x + 15y &= 160 \\ \hline 30x &= 304 \end{aligned}$$

Thus, $x = \dfrac{152}{15}$. And so $3\left(\dfrac{152}{15}\right) + 3y = 32 \Rightarrow 3y = \dfrac{8}{5} \Rightarrow y = \dfrac{8}{15}$.

Plane: $\dfrac{152}{15}$ miles per minute or 608 mph; jet stream: $\dfrac{8}{15}$ miles per minute or 32 mph.

98. Let x and y represent the speed of the airplane and the speed of the jetstream respectively. Then the system needed is $x + y = 600$ and $x - y = 500$. Adding the two equations will eliminate y.

$x + y = 600$

$\underline{x - y = 500}$

$2x = 1100$

Thus, $x = 550$. And so $(550) + y = 600 \Rightarrow y = 50$.

The speed of the airplane is 550 mph and the speed of the jetstream is 50 mph.

99.   Let x and y represent the speed of the boat and the speed of the current respectively. Then the system needed is $x + y = 30$ and $x - y = 20$. Adding the two equations will eliminate y.

$x + y = 30$

$\underline{x - y = 20}$

$2x = 50$ Thus, $x = 25$. And so $(25) + y = 30 \Rightarrow y = 5$.

The speed of the boat is 25 mph and the speed of the current is 5 mph.

100.   Let x and y represent the speed of the tugboat and the current respectively. Using the formula $d = rt$ the system is $165 = (x - y)(33)$ and $165 = (x + y)(15)$. These equations may be written: $x - y = 5$ and $x + y = 11$.

Adding the equations together will eliminate the variable y.

$x - y = 5$

$\underline{x + y = 11}$

$2x = 16$ Thus, $x = 8$. And so $8 + y = 11 \Rightarrow y = 3$.

The tugboat travels at a rate of 8 mph and the river flows at a rate of 3 mph.

101.   Let x and y represent the amount borrowed at 8% and at 9% respectively. The system needed is $x + y = 3500$ and $0.08x + 0.09y = 294$. Multiplying the first equation by –8, the second by 100 and adding the equations will eliminate the variable x.

$-8x - 8y = -28,000$

$\underline{8x + 9y = 29,400}$

$y = 1400$ Thus, $y = 1400$. And so $x + 1400 = 3500 \Rightarrow x = 2100$.

There was $2100 borrowed at 8% and $1400 borrowed at 9%.

102.   Let x and y represent the amount borrowed at 4% and at 6% respectively. The system needed is $x + y = 5000$ and $0.04x + 0.06y = 254$. Multiplying the second by -25 and adding the equations will eliminate x.

$x \quad + y = 5000$

$\underline{-x - 1.5y = -6350}$

$-0.5y = -1350$ Thus, $y = 2700$. And so $x + (2700) = 5000 \Rightarrow x = 2300$.

There was $2300 borrowed at 84% and $2700 borrowed at 6%.

103.   Let x and y represent the cost of each day credit and each night credit respectively. The system needed is $12x + 6y = 1800$ and $x - y = 30$. Multiplying the second by 6 and adding the equations will eliminate y.

$12x + 6y = 1800$

$\underline{6x - 6y = 180}$

$18x = 1980$ Thus, $x = 110$. And so $(110) - y = 30 \Rightarrow y = 80$.

Day credits cost \$110 each and night credits cost \$80 each.

104. Let x and y represent the number of computers sold in 2000 and 2001 respectively. The system needed is $x + y = 264$ and is $1.129x = y$. By substitution we have $x + 1.129x = 264 \Rightarrow 2.129x = 264 \Rightarrow x \approx 124$.

And so $(124) + y = 264 \Rightarrow y \approx 140$.

About 124 million in 2000 and about 140 million in 2001.

105. Multiplying the second equation by $\dfrac{2}{\sqrt{3}}$ and adding the equations will eliminate W_2.

$$W_1 - W_2 = \quad 0$$
$$\underline{W_1 + W_2 \approx 231}$$
$$2W_1 \approx 231 \qquad \text{Thus, } W_1 \approx 115.5. \text{ And so } (115.5) - W_2 = 0 \Rightarrow W_2 = 115.5.$$

The weight exerted on each rafter is about 115.5 pounds.

106. Adding the equations will eliminate W_2.

$$W_1 + \sqrt{2}W_2 = 300$$
$$\underline{\sqrt{3}W_1 - \sqrt{2}W_2 = \quad 0}$$
$$\left(1 + \sqrt{3}\right)W_1 = 300 \qquad \text{Thus, } W_1 \approx 109.8. \text{ And so } (109.8) + \sqrt{2}W_2 = 300 \Rightarrow W_2 \approx 134.5.$$

The weights exerted on the rafter are $W_1 \approx 109.8$ pounds and $W_2 \approx 134.5$ pounds.

107. Let x and y represent the length and width of the court respectively. The system needed is $2x + 2y = 296$ and is $x - y = 44$. Multiplying the first equation by 0.5 and adding the equations will eliminate the variable y.

(a) $$x + y = 148$$
$$\underline{x - y = 44}$$
$$2x = 192 \qquad \text{Thus, } x = 96. \text{ And so } 2(96) + 2y = 296 \Rightarrow 2y = 104 \Rightarrow y = 52.$$

The court has a length 96 feet and a width 52 feet.

Note that $2x + 2y = 296 \Rightarrow y = -x + 148$ and $x - y = 44 \Rightarrow y = x - 44$.

(b) Graph $Y_1 = -X + 148$ and $Y_2 = X - 44$ in [0, 150, 10] by [0, 100, 10]. See Figure 107b.

The unique solution is the intersection point (96, 52).

(c) Table $Y_1 = -X + 148$ and $Y_2 = X - 44$ with TblStart = 92 and ΔTbl = 1. See Figure 107c.

Since $Y_1 = Y_2 = 52$ when X = 96, the solution is (96, 52).

[0, 150, 10] by [0, 100, 10]   [0, 2000, 100] by [0, 2000, 100]

Figure 107b   Figure 107c   Figure 108b   Figure 108c

108. Let x and y represent the number of \$55 and \$40 tickets sold respectively. The system needed is

$x + y = 2000$ and is $55x + 40y = 90,500$. Multiplying the first equation by –40 and adding the equations will

eliminate the variable y.

(a) $\begin{aligned} -40x - 40y &= -80,000 \\ 55x + 40y &= 90,500 \\ \hline 15x &= 10,500 \end{aligned}$ Thus, $x = 700$. And so $(700) + y = 2000 \Rightarrow y = 1300$.

There were 700 tickets sold at \$55 per ticket and 1300 tickets sold at \$40 per ticket.

Note that $x + y = 2000 \Rightarrow y = -x + 2000$ and $55x + 40y = 90,500 \Rightarrow y = -\dfrac{11}{8}x + \dfrac{4525}{2}$.

(b) Graph $Y_1 = -X + 2000$ and $Y_2 = (-11/8)X + (4525/2)$ in [0, 2000, 100] by [0, 2000, 100]. See Figure

108b.

The unique solution is the intersection point (700, 1300).

(c) Table $Y_1 = -X + 2000$ and $Y_2 = (-11/8)X + (4525/2)$ with TblStart = 650 and ΔTbl = 10. See Figure

108c.

Since $Y_1 = Y_2 = 1300$ when X = 700, the solution is (700, 1300).

Checking Basic Concepts for Sections 4.1 & 4.2

1.   Note that $2x - y = 5 \Rightarrow y = 2x - 5$ and $-x + 3y = 0 \Rightarrow y = \dfrac{1}{3}x$.

(a) Graph $Y_1 = 2X - 5$ and $Y_2 = (1/3)X$ in [0, 5, 1] by [0, 2, 1]. See Figure 1a.

The unique solution is the intersection point (3, 1).

(b) Table $Y_1 = 2X - 5$ and $Y_2 = (1/3)X$ with TblStart = 0 and ΔTbl = 1. See Figure 1b.

Since $Y_1 = Y_2 = 1$ when X = 3, the solution is (3, 1).

Yes, the answers agree.

[0, 5, 1] by [0, 2, 1]

Figure 1a   Figure 1b

2.   Note that $x + 4y = 14 \Rightarrow x = 14 - 4y$. Substituting $x = 14 - 4y$ into the first equation yields the following:

$4(14 - 4y) - 3y = -1 \Rightarrow -19y = -57 \Rightarrow y = 3$ and so $x = 14 - 4(3) \Rightarrow x = 2$. The solution is (2, 3).

3.   Multiply the first equation by 2, the second equation by 3 and add the equations to eliminate the variable y.

$\begin{aligned} 8x - 6y &= -34 \\ -18x + 6y &= 69 \\ \hline -10x &= 35 \end{aligned}$ Thus, $x = -\dfrac{7}{2}$. And so $4\left(-\dfrac{7}{2}\right) - 3y = -17 \Rightarrow -3y = -3 \Rightarrow y = 1$.

The solution is $\left(-\dfrac{7}{2}, 1\right)$. The system is not dependent. The system is not inconsistent.

4.   (a) Let x and y represent the larger and smaller angles respectively. Then the system needed is $x + y = 90$

and $x - y = 40$.

(b) Adding the two equations will eliminate y.

$x + y = 90$

$\underline{x - y = 40}$

$2x = 130$ Thus, $x = 65$. And so $(65) + y = 90 \Rightarrow y = 25$. The angles are $65°$ and $25°$.

4.3: Systems of Linear Inequalities

Concepts

1.   Two

2.   Yes, many points may satisfy a system of inequalities.

3.   Yes, since $5(3) - 2(1) = 13 > 8$. No, since $5(2) - 2(1) = 8 \not> 8$.

4.   No, since $2(3) - 4 = 2 \not< 1$. The second inequality is not satisfied. $(-2, 0)$ is a solution because

$-2 - 2(0) = -2 \geq -8$ and $2(-2) - 0 = -4 < 1$.

5.   solid

6.   dashed

Linear Inequalities

7.   See Figure 7.

8.   See Figure 8.

Figure 7

Figure 8

Figure 9

9.   See Figure 9.

10.   See Figure 10.

11.   See Figure 11.

Figure 10

Figure 11

Figure 12

12.   See Figure 12.

13.   See Figure 13.

14. ˘ See Figure 14.

Figure 13

Figure 14

Figure 15

15.   See Figure 15.

16.   See Figure 16.

17.   See Figure 17.

Figure 16

Figure 17

Figure 18

18.   See Figure 18.

19.   See Figure 19.

20.   See Figure 20.

Figure 19

Figure 20

Figure 21

21.   See Figure 21.

22.   See Figure 22.

23.   See Figure 23.

Figure 22

Figure 23

Figure 24

24.   See Figure 24.

25.   See Figure 25.

26.   See Figure 26.

Figure 25

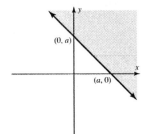

Figure 26

Systems of Inequalities

27.   See Figure 27.

28.   See Figure 28.

Figure 27

Figure 28

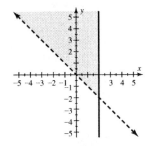

Figure 29

29.   See Figure 29.

30.   See Figure 30.

31.   See Figure 31.

Figure 30

Figure 31

Figure 32

32.   See Figure 32.

33.   See Figure 33.

34.   See Figure 34.

Figure 33

Figure 34

Figure 39

35.   See Figure 35.

36.   See Figure 36.

Figure 35

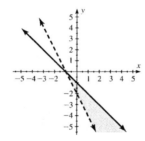

Figure 36

37.   See Figure 37.

38.   See Figure 38.

Figure 37

Figure 38

39.   See Figure 39.

40.   See Figure 40.

41.   See Figure 41.

Figure 40

Figure 41

Figure 42

42.   See Figure 42.

43.   See Figure 43.

44.   See Figure 44.

Figure 43

Figure 44

Figure 45

45.   See Figure 45.

46.   See Figure 46.

47.   See Figure 47.

Figure 46

Figure 47

Figure 48

48.   See Figure 48.

49.   This region can be shaded using the *Shade* feature of the TI-83, found under the DRAW menu.

Shade$(-3, 5)$ in [–10, 10, 1] by [–10, 10, 1]. See Figure 49.

50.   This region can be shaded using the *Shade* feature of the TI-83, found under the DRAW menu.

Shade$(-X, X+1)$ in [–10, 10, 1] by [–10, 10, 1]. See Figure 50.

[–10, 10, 1] by [–10, 10, 1]   [–10, 10, 1] by [–10, 10, 1]   [–10, 10, 1] by [–10, 10, 1]

Figure 49

Figure 50

Figure 51

51.   This region can be shaded using the *Shade* feature of the TI-83, found under the DRAW menu.

Note that $x + 2y \geq 8 \Rightarrow y \geq -\dfrac{1}{2}x + 4$ and $6x - 3y \geq 10 \Rightarrow y \leq 2x - \dfrac{10}{3}$.

Shade$\left((-1/2)X + 4, 2X - (10/3) \right)$ in [–10, 10, 1] by [–10, 10, 1]. See Figure 51.

52.   This region can be shaded using the *Shade* feature of the TI-83, found under the DRAW menu.

Shade$\left(2.1X - 3.5, 2.1X - 1.7 \right)$ in [–10, 10, 1] by [–10, 10, 1]. See Figure 52.

53.   This region can be shaded using the *Shade* feature of the TI-83, found under the DRAW menu.

Note that $0.9x + 1.7y \leq 3.2 \Rightarrow y \leq \dfrac{-0.9}{1.7}x + \dfrac{3.2}{1.7}$ and $1.9x - 0.7y \leq 1.3 \Rightarrow y \geq \dfrac{1.9}{0.7}x - \dfrac{1.3}{0.7}$.

Shade$\left((1.9/0.7)X - (1.3/0.7), (-0.9/1.7)X + (3.2/1.7) \right)$ in [–10, 10, 1] by [–10, 10, 1]. See Figure 53.

[–10, 10, 1] by [–10, 10, 1]   [–10, 10, 1] by [–10, 10, 1]   [–10, 10, 1] by [–10, 10, 1]

Figure 52   Figure 53   Figure 54

54.   This region can be shaded using the *Shade* feature of the TI-83, found under the DRAW menu.

Note that $21x \geq 31y - 51 \Rightarrow y \leq \dfrac{21}{31}x + \dfrac{51}{31}$ and $5x - 17y \leq 18 \Rightarrow y \geq \dfrac{5}{17}x - \dfrac{18}{17}$.

Shade$\left((5/17)X - (18/17), (21/31)X + (51/31) \right)$ in [–10, 10, 1] by [–10, 10, 1]. See Figure 54.

55.   *b*; The point (1, 8) satisfies this inequality. Only graph *b* contains this point.

56.   *d*; The point (0, 0.5) satisfies this system of inequalities. Only graph *d* contains this point.

57.   *a*; The point (1, –7) satisfies this inequality. Only graph *a* contains this point.

58.   *c*; The point (–2, 2) satisfies this system of inequalities. Only graph *c* contains this point.

59.   The equation of a horizontal line through the point (0, 2) is $y = 2$. The inequality is $y \geq 2$.

60.   The equation of a line through the points (0, 4) and (2, 0) is $y = -2x + 4$. The inequality is $y \leq -2x + 4$.

61.   The equation of a vertical line through the point (–2, 0) is $x = -2$. The equation of a line through the points (0, 0) and (1, 1) is $y = x$. The system of inequalities is $y \geq x$ and $x \geq -2$.

62.   The equation of a line through the points (0, 4) and (4, 0) is $y = -x + 4$. The equation of a line through the points (0, 0) and (1, 1) is $y = x$. The system of inequalities is $y > x$ and $y < -x + 4$.

Applications

63.   First note that the amount of candy cannot be negative so $x \geq 0$ and $y \geq 0$. Also, if the cost must be less than

$15, the inequality $3x + 5y < 15$ must be satisfied. See Figure 63.

64.   First note that the number of tickets and bags of popcorn cannot be negative so $x \geq 0$ and $y \geq 0$. Also, if the

cost is not to exceed $32, the inequality $8x + 4y \leq 32$ must be satisfied. See Figure 64.

Figure 63

Figure 64

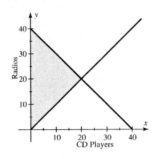

Figure 65

65.   First note that the number of CD players and radios cannot be negative so $x \geq 0$ and $y \geq 0$. Then, if the

business must manufacture at least as many radios as CD players, the inequality $y \geq x$ must be

satisfied. Also, the total number made each day cannot exceed 40 so the inequality $x + y \leq 40$ must be

satisfied. See Figure 65.

66.   First note that the number of large and small crates cannot be negative so $x \geq 0$ and $y \geq 0$. Then, if the

business can manufacture no more than 40 large crates and 30 small crates, the inequalities $x \leq 40$ and $y \leq 30$

must be satisfied. See Figure 66.

Figure 66

67.   (a) The range is approximately 105 to 134 bpm.

(b) The inequalities are $y \leq -0.6(x - 20) + 140$ and $y \geq -0.5(x - 20) + 110$.

68.   (a) The inequalities are $7P - 5T \leq -70$ and $35P - 3T \geq 140$.

(b) The point (40, 15) is located in the region representing grasslands. Yes, these values satisfy the

inequalities.

69.   The person weighs less than recommended.

70.   About 150 to 200 pounds.

71.   The inequalities are $25h - 7w \leq 800$ and $5h - w \geq 170$.

72.   People differ in body build, which makes it more appropriate to use a range of values.

73.   First note that the amounts of candy and peanuts cannot be negative so $x \geq 0$ and $y \geq 0$. Also,

$3x \leq 6 \Rightarrow x \leq 2$ and $2y \leq 8 \Rightarrow y \leq 4$. See Figure 73.

   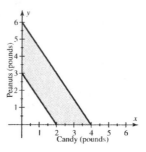

Figure 73   Figure 74.

74.   First note that the amounts of candy and peanuts cannot be negative so $x \geq 0$ and $y \geq 0$. Also, if the total spent must be at least \$6 but not more than \$12 then the inequalities $3x + 2y \geq 6$ and $3x + 2y \leq 12$ must be satisfied. See Figure 74.

Group Activity Solutions

1.   (a) The linear system needed is $1987a + b = 12$ and $1997a + b = 70$.

(b) Multiplying the first equation by -1 and adding the equations together will eliminate the variable b.

$$\begin{array}{r} -1987a - b = -12 \\ 1997a + b = 70 \\ \hline 10a = 58 \end{array}$$ Thus, $a = 5.8$. And so $1987(5.8) + b = 12 \Rightarrow b = -11{,}512.6$.

To solve this system graphically or numerically on a calculator we must rewrite each equation:

$-1987a - b = -12$ becomes $-1987x - y = -12$ and $1997a + b = 70$ becomes $1997x + y = 70$.

Now solve each equation for y and graph or table as needed (not shown). The solutions found graphically or numerically will be $x = 5.8$ and $y = -11{,}512.6$. These answers correspond to the answers above.

2.   (a) The linear system needed is $1987c + d = 63$ and $1997c + d = 18$.

(b) Multiplying the first equation by -1 and adding the equations together will eliminate the variable d.

$$\begin{array}{r} -1987c - d = -63 \\ 1997c + d = 18 \\ \hline 10c = -45 \end{array}$$ Thus, $c = -4.5$. And so $1987(-4.5) + d = 63 \Rightarrow d = 9004.5$.

To solve this system graphically or numerically on a calculator we must rewrite each equation:

$-1987c - d = -63$ becomes $-1987x - y = -63$ and $1997c + d = 18$ becomes $1997x + y = 18$.

Now solve each equation for y and graph or table as needed (not shown). The solutions found graphically or numerically will be $x = -4.5$ and $y = 9004.5$. These answers correspond to the answers above.

3. $5.8x - 11{,}512.6 = -4.5x + 9004.5 \Rightarrow 10.3x = 20{,}517.1 \Rightarrow x \approx 1992$

They shared an equal percentage of the market in 1992. CD sales were greater than cassette sales after 1992.

4.4: Introduction to Linear Programming

Concepts

1.   linear programming

2.   objective

3.   feasible solutions

4.   linear inequalities

5.   vertex

6.   objective

Regions of Feasible Solutions

7.   See Figure 7.

8.   See Figure 8.

Figure 7

Figure 8

Figure 9

9.   See Figure 9.

10.   See Figure 10.

11.   See Figure 11.

Figure 10

Figure 11

Figure 12

12.   See Figure 12.

13.   See Figure 13.

14.   See Figure 14.

Figure 13

Figure 14

Figure 15

15.   See Figure 15.

16.   See Figure 16.

17.   See Figure 17.

Figure 16

Figure 17

Figure 18

18.   See Figure 18.

19.   See Figure 19.

Figure 19

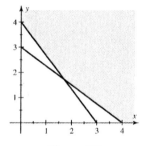

Figure 20

20.   See Figure 20.

Linear Programming

21.   The maximum value of R occurs at one of the vertices.

For $(1, 1)$, $R = 4(1) + 5(1) = 9$.   For $(1, 3)$, $R = 4(1) + 5(3) = 19$.   For $(4, 1)$, $R = 4(4) + 5(1) = 21$.

For $(4, 3)$, $R = 4(4) + 5(3) = 31$. The maximum value is $R = 31$.

22.   The maximum value of R occurs at one of the vertices.

For $(0, 0)$, $R = 2(0) + 3(0) = 0$.   For $(0, 4)$, $R = 2(0) + 3(4) = 12$.   For $(4, 0)$, $R = 2(4) + 3(0) = 8$.

The maximum value is $R = 12$.

23.   The maximum value of R occurs at one of the vertices.

For $(0, 2)$, $R = (0) + 3(2) = 6$.   For $(0, 5)$, $R = (0) + 3(5) = 15$.   For $(3, 3)$, $R = (3) + 3(3) = 12$.

For $(5, 0)$, $R = (5) + 3(0) = 5$. For $(2, 0)$, $R = (2) + 3(0) = 2$. The maximum value is $R = 15$.

24.   The maximum value of R occurs at one of the vertices.

For $(0, 3)$, $R = 12(0) + 9(3) = 27$. For $(0, 5)$, $R = 12(0) + 9(5) = 45$.   For $(5, 0)$, $R = 12(5) + 9(0) = 60$.

For $(3, 0)$, $R = 12(3) + 9(0) = 36$. The maximum value is $R = 60$.

25.   The minimum value of C occurs at one of the vertices.

For $(1, 1)$, $C = 2(1) + 3(1) = 5$. For $(1, 3)$, $C = 2(1) + 3(3) = 11$.   For $(4, 1)$, $C = 2(4) + 3(1) = 11$.

For $(4, 3)$, $C = 2(4) + 3(3) = 17$. The minimum value is $C = 5$.

26.   The minimum value of C occurs at one of the vertices.

For $(0, 0)$, $C = 3(0) + (0) = 0$. For $(0, 4)$, $C = 3(0) + (4) = 4$.   For $(4, 0)$, $C = 3(4) + (0) = 12$.

The minimum value is $C = 0$.

27.   The minimum value of C occurs at one of the vertices.

For $(0, 2)$, $C = 5(0) + (2) = 2$. For $(0, 5)$, $C = 5(0) + (5) = 5$.   For $(3, 3)$, $C = 5(3) + (3) = 18$.

For $(5, 0)$, $C = 5(5) + (0) = 25$. For $(2, 0)$, $C = 5(2) + (0) = 10$. The minimum value is $C = 2$.

28.   The minimum value of C occurs at one of the vertices.

For $(0, 3)$, $C = 2(0) + 7(3) = 21$. For $(0, 5)$, $C = 2(0) + 7(5) = 35$.   For $(5, 0)$, $C = 2(5) + 7(0) = 10$.

For $(3, 0)$, $C = 2(3) + 7(0) = 6$. The minimum value is $C = 6$.

29.   From the graph of the region of feasible solutions (not shown), the vertices are (0, 0), (0, 150), and (150, 0).

The maximum value of R occurs at one of the vertices. For $(0, 0)$, $R = 3(0) + 5(0) = 0$.

For $(0, 150)$, $R = 3(0) + 5(150) = 750$. For $(150, 0)$, $R = 3(150) + 5(0) = 450$.

The maximum value is $R = 750$.

30.   From the graph of the region of feasible solutions (not shown), the vertices are (0, 0), (0, 8), and (8, 0).

The maximum value of R occurs at one of the vertices. For $(0, 0)$, $R = 6(0) + 5(0) = 0$.

For $(0, 8)$, $R = 6(0) + 5(8) = 40$. For $(8, 0)$, $R = 6(8) + 5(0) = 48$. The maximum value is $R = 48$.

31.   From the graph of the region of feasible solutions (not shown), the vertices are (0, 0), (0, 6), and (3, 0).

The maximum value of R occurs at one of the vertices. For $(0, 0)$, $R = 3(0) + 2(0) = 0$.

For $(0, 6)$, $R = 3(0) + 2(6) = 12$. For $(3, 0)$, $R = 3(3) + 2(0) = 9$. The maximum value is $R = 12$.

32.   From the graph of the region of feasible solutions (not shown), the vertices are (0, 0), (0, 2), and (4, 0).

The maximum value of R occurs at one of the vertices. For $(0, 0)$, $R = (0) + 3(0) = 0$.

For $(0, 2)$, $R = (0) + 3(2) = 6$. For $(4, 0)$, $R = (4) + 3(0) = 4$. The maximum value is $R = 6$.

33.   From the graph of the region of feasible solutions (not shown), the vertices are (0, 0), (0, 2), (1.5, 1.5) and (2, 0).

Note: to find the intersection point (1.5, 1.5), solve the system of equations $3x + y = 6$ and $x + 3y = 6$.

The maximum value of R occurs at one of the vertices. For $(0, 0)$, $R = 12(0) + 9(0) = 0$.

For $(0, 2)$, $R = 12(0) + 9(2) = 18$. For $(1.5, 1.5)$, $R = 12(1.5) + 9(1.5) = 31.5$.

For $(2, 0)$, $R = 12(2) + 9(0) = 24$. The maximum value is $R = 31.5$.

34.   From the graph of the region of feasible solutions (not shown), the vertices are (0, 0), (0, 4), (3, 3) and (4, 0).

Note: to find the intersection point (3, 3), solve the system of equations $x + 3y = 12$ and $3x + y = 12$.

The maximum value of R occurs at one of the vertices. For $(0, 0)$, $R = 10(0) + 30(0) = 0$.

For $(0, 4)$, $R = 10(0) + 30(4) = 120$. For $(3, 3)$, $R = 10(3) + 30(3) = 120$.

For $(4, 0)$, $R = 10(4) + 30(0) = 40$. The maximum value is $R = 120$.

35.   From the graph of the region of feasible solutions (not shown), the vertices are (0, 2), (4, 0), and (2, 0).

The maximum value of R occurs at one of the vertices. For $(0, 2)$, $R = 4(0) + 5(2) = 10$.

For $(4, 0)$, $R = 4(4) + 5(0) = 16$. For $(2, 0)$, $R = 4(2) + 5(0) = 8$. The maximum value is $R = 16$.

36.   From the graph of the region of feasible solutions (not shown), the vertices are (0, 1), (0, 3), and (1, 0).

The maximum value of R occurs at one of the vertices. For $(0, 1)$, $R = 3(0) + 7(1) = 7$.

For $(0, 3)$, $R = 3(0) + 7(3) = 21$. For $(1, 0)$, $R = 3(1) + 7(0) = 3$. The maximum value is $R = 21$.

37.   From the graph of the region of feasible solutions (not shown), the vertices are (0, 0), (0, 2), (3, 2) and (3, 0).

The minimum value of C occurs at one of the vertices. For $(0, 0)$, $C = (0) + 2(0) = 0$.

For $(0, 2)$, $C = (0) + 2(2) = 4$. For $(3, 2)$, $C = (3) + 2(2) = 7$. For $(3, 0)$, $C = (3) + 2(0) = 3$.

The minimum value is $C = 0$.

38.   From the graph of the region of feasible solutions (not shown), the vertices are (1, 1), (1, 3), (5, 3) and (5, 1).

The minimum value of C occurs at one of the vertices. For $(1, 1)$, $C = 3(1) + (1) = 4$.

For $(1, 3)$, $C = 3(1) + (3) = 6$. For $(5, 3)$, $C = 3(5) + (3) = 18$. For $(5, 1)$, $C = 3(5) + (1) = 16$.

The minimum value is $C = 4$.

39.   From the graph of the region of feasible solutions (not shown), the vertices are (0, 4), and (4, 0).

Note that this region is unbounded. The minimum value of C occurs at one of the vertices.

For $(0, 4)$, $C = 8(0) + 15(4) = 60$. For $(4, 0)$, $C = 8(4) + 15(0) = 32$. The minimum value is $C = 32$.

40.   From the graph of the region of feasible solutions (not shown), the vertices are (0, 3), and (4, 0).

Note that this region is unbounded. The minimum value of C occurs at one of the vertices.

For $(0, 3)$, $C = (0) + 2(3) = 6$. For $(4, 0)$, $C = (4) + 2(0) = 4$. The minimum value is $C = 4$.

41.   From the graph of the region of feasible solutions (not shown), the vertices are (0, 2), (0, 6), (3, 0) and (2, 0).

The minimum value of C occurs at one of the vertices. For $(0, 2)$, $C = 30(0) + 40(2) = 80$.

For $(0, 6)$, $C = 30(0) + 40(6) = 240$. For $(3, 0)$, $C = 30(3) + 40(0) = 90$.

For $(2, 0)$, $C = 30(2) + 40(0) = 60$. The minimum value is $C = 60$.

42.   From the graph of the region of feasible solutions (not shown), the vertices are (0, 1), (0, 2), (3, 0) and (1, 0).

The minimum value of C occurs at one of the vertices. For $(0, 1)$, $C = 50(0) + 70(1) = 70$.

For $(0, 2)$, $C = 50(0) + 70(2) = 140$. For $(3, 0)$, $C = 50(3) + 70(0) = 150$.

For $(1, 0)$, $C = 50(1) + 70(0) = 50$. The minimum value is $C = 50$.

43.   Let x and y represent the amount of candy and coffee respectively. The business can sell no more than a total
of 100 pounds so $x + y \leq 100$. Also, because at least 20 pounds of candy must be sold each day
$x \geq 20$. Finally, the amount of coffee cannot be negative so $y \geq 0$. Here the revenue function is
$R = 4x + 6y$. From the graph of the region of feasible solutions (not shown), the vertices are (20, 0), (20,
80), and (100, 0). The maximum value of R occurs at one of the vertices. For
$(20, 0)$, $R = 4(20) + 6(0) = 80$.

For $(20, 80)$, $R = 4(20) + 6(80) = 560$. For $(100, 0)$, $R = 4(100) + 6(0) = 400$.

To maximize revenue, the business should sell 20 pounds of candy and 80 pounds of coffee.

44.   Let x and y represent the number of CD players and radios respectively. The business must make a total of at
least 50 CD players and radios so $x + y \geq 50$. Also, because at least as many CD players as radios must be
manufactured $y \leq x$. Finally the quantities cannot be negative so $x \geq 0$ and $y \geq 0$. Here the cost function is
$C = 20x + 10y$. From the graph of the region of feasible solutions (not shown), the vertices are (25, 25), and
(50, 0). Note that this region is unbounded. The minimum value of C occurs at one of the vertices.
For $(25, 25)$, $C = 20(25) + 10(25) = 750$. For $(50, 0)$, $C = 20(50) + 10(0) = 1000$.

To minimize cost, the business should manufacture 25 CD players and 25 radios.

45.   Let x and y represent the amount of Brand X and Brand Y respectively. Since each ounce of Brand X
contains 20 units of vitamin A, each ounce of Brand Y contains 10 units of vitamin A and the total amount of
vitamin A must be at least 40 units, $20x + 10y \geq 40$. Since each ounce of Brand X contains 10 units of
vitamin C, each ounce of Brand Y contains 10 units of vitamin C and the total amount of vitamin C must be at
least 30 units, $10x + 10y \geq 30$. Finally the quantities cannot be negative so $x \geq 0$ and $y \geq 0$. Here the cost
function is $C = 0.90x + 0.60y$. From the graph of the region of feasible solutions (not shown), the vertices
are (0, 4), (1, 2) and (3, 0). Note that this region is unbounded. To find the intersection point (1, 2) solve the
system of equations $20x + 10y = 40$ and $10x + 10y = 30$. The minimum value of C occurs at one of the
vertices.

For $(0, 4)$, $C = 0.90(0) + 0.60(4) = 2.40$. For $(1, 2)$, $C = 0.90(1) + 0.60(2) = 2.10$.

For $(3, 0)$, $C = 0.90(3) + 0.60(0) = 2.70$.

To minimize cost, 1 ounce of Brand X and 2 ounces of Brand Y should be mixed.

46.   Let x and y represent the amount of Brand X and Brand Y respectively. Since each unit of Brand X contains 20 grams of protein, each unit of Brand Y contains 10 grams of protein and the total amount of protein must be at least 60 grams, $20x + 10y \geq 60$. Since each unit of Brand X contains 10 grams of fat, each unit of Brand Y contains 10 grams of fat and the total amount of fat must be at least 40 grams, $10x + 10y \geq 40$. Finally the quantities cannot be negative so $x \geq 0$ and $y \geq 0$. Here the cost function is $C = 0.75x + 0.50y$. From the graph of the region of feasible solutions (not shown), the vertices are (0, 6), (2, 2) and (4, 0). Note that this region is unbounded. To find the point (2, 2) solve the equations $20x + 10y = 60$ and $10x + 10y = 40$.

The minimum value of C occurs at one of the vertices. For $(0, 6)$, $C = 0.75(0) + 0.50(6) = 3.00$.

For $(2, 2)$, $C = 0.75(2) + 0.50(2) = 2.50$. For $(4, 0)$, $C = 0.75(4) + 0.50(0) = 3.00$.

To minimize cost, 2 units of Brand X and 2 units of Brand Y should be mixed.

47.   Let x and y represent the number of hamsters and mice respectively. Since the total number of animals cannot exceed 50, $x + y \leq 50$. Because no more than 20 hamsters can be raised, $x \leq 20$. Here the revenue function is $R = 15x + 10y$. From the graph of the region of feasible solutions (not shown), the vertices are (0, 50), (20, 30) and (20, 0). To find (20, 30) solve the equations $x + y = 50$ and $x = 20$. The maximum value of R occurs at one of the vertices. For $(0, 50)$, $R = 15(0) + 10(50) = 500$. For $(20, 30)$, $R = 15(20) + 10(30) = 600$.

For $(20, 0)$, $R = 15(20) + 10(0) = 300$. The maximum revenue is $600.

48.   Let x and y represent the number of part X and part Y respectively. Since part X requires machine A for 3 hours, part Y requires machine A for 1 hour and machine A is only available for 60 hours, $3x + y \leq 60$. Since part X requires machine B for 1 hour, part Y requires machine B for 2 hours and machine B is only available for 50 hours, $x + 2y \leq 50$. Since the number of parts cannot be negative $x \geq 0$ and $y \geq 0$. Here the profit function is $P = 300x + 250y$. From the graph of the region of feasible solutions (not shown), the vertices are (0, 0), (0, 25), (14, 18) and (20, 0). To find (14, 18) solve the system of equations $3x + y = 60$ and $x + 2y = 50$.

The maximum value of P occurs at one of the vertices.

For $(0, 0)$, $P = 300(0) + 250(0) = 0$. For $(0, 25)$, $P = 300(0) + 250(25) = 6250$.

For $(14, 18)$, $P = 300(14) + 250(18) = 8700$. For $(20, 0)$, $P = 300(20) + 250(0) = 6000$.

The maximum profit is attained when 14 of part X and 18 of part Y are manufactured.

Checking Basic Concepts for Sections 4.3 & 4.4

1. The equation of a line through the points (0, 3) and (1, 1) is $y = -2x + 3$. The inequality is $y \le -2x + 3$.

2. See Figure 2.

Figure 2

3. From the graph of the region of feasible solutions (not shown), the vertices are (0, 0), (0, 5), (2, 3) and (4, 0).

   To find the intersection point (2, 3) solve the system of equations $3x + 2y = 12$ and $4x + 4y = 20$.

   The maximum value of R occurs at one of the vertices. For $(0, 0)$, $R = 3(0) + 2(0) = 0$.

   For $(0, 5)$, $R = 3(0) + 2(5) = 10$. For $(2, 3)$, $R = 3(2) + 2(3) = 12$. For $(4, 0)$, $R = 3(4) + 2(0) = 12$.

   The maximum value is $R = 12$.

4.5: Systems of Linear Equations in Three Variables

Concepts

1. No, three planes cannot intersect at exactly 2 points.

2.

$$x + y + z = 5 \qquad \text{\textit{Answers may vary.}}$$
$$2x - 3y + z = 7$$
$$x + 2y - 4z = 2$$

3. Yes, since $1 + 2 + 3 = 6$.

4. No, a solution must be an ordered triple.

5. Two

6. Three

7. No

8. Infinitely many

Solving Linear Systems

9. (1, 2, 3) satisfies all three inequalities.

10. (0, 4, 4) satisfies all three inequalities.

11. (−1, 1, 2) satisfies all three inequalities.

12. $\left(\dfrac{1}{2}, \dfrac{3}{2}, -\dfrac{1}{2} \right)$ satisfies all three inequalities.

13. Substitute $z = 1$ into the second equation: $2y + (1) = -1 \Rightarrow 2y = -2 \Rightarrow y = -1$

Substitute $z = 1$ and $y = -1$ into the first equation: $x + (-1) - (1) = 1 \Rightarrow x - 2 = 1 \Rightarrow x = 3$

The solution is $(3, -1, 1)$.

14. Substitute $z = -1$ into the second equation: $y + 4(-1) = 0 \Rightarrow y = 4$

Substitute $z = -1$ and $y = 4$ into the first equation: $2x + (4) - 3(-1) = 1 \Rightarrow 2x = -6 \Rightarrow x = -3$

The solution is $(-3, 4, -1)$.

15. Substitute $z = 2$ into the second equation: $2y + 3(2) = 3 \Rightarrow 2y = -3 \Rightarrow y = -\dfrac{3}{2}$

Substitute $z = 2$ and $y = -\dfrac{3}{2}$ into the first equation: $-x - 3\left(-\dfrac{3}{2}\right) + (2) = -2 \Rightarrow -x = -\dfrac{17}{2} \Rightarrow x = \dfrac{17}{2}$

The solution is $\left(\dfrac{17}{2}, -\dfrac{3}{2}, 2\right)$.

16. Substitute $z = 0$ into the second equation: $-y + 2(0) = 4 \Rightarrow -y = 4 \Rightarrow y = -4$

Substitute $z = 0$ and $y = -4$ into the first equation: $3x + 2(-4) - 3(0) = -4 \Rightarrow 3x = 4 \Rightarrow x = \dfrac{4}{3}$

The solution is $\left(\dfrac{4}{3}, -4, 0\right)$.

17. Substitute $c = -2$ into the second equation: $-3b + (-2) = 4 \Rightarrow -3b = 6 \Rightarrow b = -2$

Substitute $c = -2$ and $b = -2$ into the first equation: $a - (-2) + 2(-2) = 3 \Rightarrow a - 2 = 3 \Rightarrow a = 5$

The solution is $(5, -2, -2)$.

18. Substitute $c = 3$ into the second equation: $5b - 2(3) = -4 \Rightarrow 5b = 2 \Rightarrow b = \dfrac{2}{5}$

Substitute $c = 3$ and $b = \dfrac{2}{5}$ into the first equation: $5a + 2\left(\dfrac{2}{5}\right) - 3(3) = 10 \Rightarrow 5a = \dfrac{91}{5} \Rightarrow a = \dfrac{91}{25}$

The solution is $\left(\dfrac{91}{25}, \dfrac{2}{5}, 3\right)$.

19. Add the first two equations together to eliminate the variable x.

$$\begin{array}{r} x + y - z = 11 \\ -x + 2y + 3z = -1 \\ \hline 3y + 2z = 10 \end{array}$$

From the third equation, $2z = 4 \Rightarrow z = 2$. And so $3y + 2(2) = 10 \Rightarrow 3y = 6 \Rightarrow y = 2$.

Substitute $z = 2$ and $y = 2$ into the first equation: $x + (2) - (2) = 11 \Rightarrow x = 11$

The solution is $(11, 2, 2)$.

20. Multiply the first equation by 2 and add the first two equations together to eliminate the variable x.

$$2x + 4y - 6z = -14$$
$$\underline{-2x + y + z = -1}$$
$$5y - 5z = -15$$

From the third equation, $3z = 9 \Rightarrow z = 3$. And so $5y - 5(3) = -15 \Rightarrow 5y = 0 \Rightarrow y = 0$.

Substitute $z = 3$ and $y = 0$ into the first equation: $x + 2(0) - 3(3) = -7 \Rightarrow x = 2$

The solution is (2, 0, 3).

21.   Add the first two equations together to eliminate both of the variables x and z.

$$x + y - z = -2$$
$$\underline{-x + z = 1}$$
$$y = -1$$

Substitute $y = -1$ into the third equation, $(-1) + 2z = 3 \Rightarrow 2z = 4 \Rightarrow z = 2$.

Substitute $z = 2$ and $y = -1$ into the first equation: $x + (-1) - (2) = -2 \Rightarrow x = 1$

The solution is (1, –1, 2).

22.   Multiply the first equation by 2 and add the first two equations together to eliminate the variable x.

$$2x + 2y - 6z = 22$$
$$\underline{-2x + y + 2z = 1}$$
$$3y - 4z = 23$$

Add this new equation and the third equation together to eliminate the variable y.

$$3y - 4z = 23$$
$$\underline{-3y + 3z = -21}$$
$$-z = 2$$

And so $z = -2$. Substitute $z = -2$ into the third equation, $-3y + 3(-2) = -21 \Rightarrow -3y = -15 \Rightarrow y = 5$.

Substitute $z = -2$ and $y = 5$ into the first equation: $x + (5) - 3(-2) = 11 \Rightarrow x = 0$

The solution is (0, 5, –2).

23.   Add the second and third equations together to eliminate the variable y.

$$y + z = -1$$
$$\underline{-y + 3z = 9}$$
$$4z = 8$$

And so $z = 2$. Substitute $z = 2$ into the second equation, $y + (2) = -1 \Rightarrow y = -3$.

Substitute $z = 2$ and $y = -3$ into the first equation: $x + (-3) - 2(2) = -7 \Rightarrow x = 0$

The solution is (0, –3, 2).

24.   Multiply the second equation by 2 and add the second and third equations together to eliminate the variable y.

$$2y + 4z = 8$$
$$\underline{-2y + z = 2}$$
$$5z = 10$$

And so $z = 2$. Substitute $z = 2$ into the second equation, $y + 2(2) = 4 \Rightarrow y = 0$.

Substitute $z = 2$ and $y = 0$ into the first equation: $2x + 3(0) + (2) = 5 \Rightarrow 2x = 3 \Rightarrow x = \dfrac{3}{2}$

The solution is $\left(\dfrac{3}{2}, 0, 2 \right)$.

25.   Multiply the second equation by -2 and add the first and second equations to eliminate the variables y and z.

$$x + 2y + 2z = 1$$
$$\underline{-2x - 2y - 2z = 0}$$
$$-x = 1$$

And so $x = -1$. Add the first and third equations together to eliminate the variables x and y.

$$x + 2y + 2z = 1$$
$$\underline{-x - 2y + 3z = -11}$$
$$5z = -10$$

And so $z = -2$. Substitute $x = -1$ and $z = -2$ into the second equation: $(-1) + y + (-2) = 0 \Rightarrow y = 3$

The solution is $(-1, 3, -2)$.

26.   Multiply the first equation by 3 and add the first and second equations to eliminate the variable y.

$$3x + 3y - 3z = 0$$
$$\underline{x - 3y + z = -2}$$
$$4x - 2z = -2$$

Add the first and third equations together to eliminate the variable y.

$$x + y - z = 0$$
$$\underline{x - y + 3z = 8}$$
$$2x + 2z = 8$$

Add these two *new* equations together to eliminate the variable z.

$$4x - 2z = -2$$
$$\underline{2x + 2z = 8}$$
$$6x = 6$$

And so $x = 1$. Substitute $x = 1$ into the first *new* equation: $4(1) - 2z = -2 \Rightarrow -2z = -6 \Rightarrow z = 3$

Substitute $x = 1$ and $z = 3$ into the *original* first equation: $(1) + y - (3) = 0 \Rightarrow y = 2$

The solution is $(1, 2, 3)$.

27.   Multiply the second equation by -1 and add the first and second equations to eliminate the variables y and z.

$$x + y + z = 5$$
$$\underline{-y - z = -6}$$
$$x = -1$$

And so $x = -1$. Substitute $x = -1$ into the third equation: $(-1) + z = 3 \Rightarrow z = 4$

Substitute $x = -1$ and $z = 4$ into the first equation: $(-1) + y + (4) = 5 \Rightarrow y = 2$

The solution is $(-1, 2, 4)$.

28. Add the first and second equations to eliminate the variables y and z.

$$\begin{array}{l} x+y+y=0 \\ \underline{x-y-z=6} \\ \quad 2x=6 \end{array}$$

And so, $x = 3$. Now add the first and third equations to eliminate the variables x and z.

$$\begin{array}{l} x+y+z=0 \\ \underline{-x+y-z=4} \\ \quad 2y=4 \end{array}$$

And so $y = 2$. Substitute $x = 3$ and $y = 2$ in the first equation: $(3) + (2) + z = 0 \Rightarrow z = -5$

The solution is $(3, 2, -5)$.

29. Add the second and third equations to eliminate the variables x and z.

$$\begin{array}{l} -x+y+2z=1 \\ \underline{x+y-2z=9} \\ \quad 2y=10 \end{array}$$

And so, $y = 5$. Now add the first and second equations to eliminate the variable x.

$$\begin{array}{l} x+2y+3z=24 \\ \underline{-x\ +y+2z=\ 1} \\ \quad 3y+5z=25 \end{array}$$

Now substitute $y = 5$ in this new equation: $3(5) + 5z = 25 \Rightarrow 5z = 10 \Rightarrow z = 2$

Finally substitute $y = 5$ and $z = 2$ in the first equation: $x + 2(5) + 3(2) = 24 \Rightarrow x = 8$

The solution is $(8, 5, 2)$.

30. Multiply the first equation by 2 and add the first and second equations to eliminate the variables x and z.

$$\begin{array}{l} 10x-30y+2z=44 \\ \underline{-10x+12y-2z=-8} \\ \quad -18y=36 \qquad \text{And so, } y=-2. \end{array}$$

Multiply the first equation by 3 and add the first and third equations together to eliminate the variable z.

$$\begin{array}{l} 15x-45y+3z=\ 66 \\ \underline{4x\ -2y-3z=\ 9} \\ \quad 19x-47y=75 \end{array}$$

Now substitute $y = -2$ in this new equation: $19x - 47(-2) = 75 \Rightarrow 19x = -19 \Rightarrow x = -1$

Finally substitute $x = -1$ and $y = -2$ in the third equation: $4(-1) - 2(-2) - 3z = 9 \Rightarrow -3z = 9 \Rightarrow z = -3$

The solution is $(-1, -2, -3)$.

31.   Add the first and second equations to eliminate the variable y.

$$x + y + z = 2$$
$$\underline{x - y + z = 1}$$
$$2x + 2z = 3$$

Multiply the third equation by -2 and add to this new equation to eliminate the variables x and z.

$$2x + 2z\ = 3$$
$$\underline{-2x + -2z = -6}$$
$$0 = -3 \qquad \text{This is a contradiction, so there are no solutions.}$$

32.   Add the first and second equations to eliminate the variable y.

$$4x - y + 3z = 3$$
$$\underline{2x + y + \ z = 2}$$
$$6x \quad + 4z = 5$$

Add the second and third equations to eliminate the variable y.

$$2x + y + z = 2$$
$$\underline{x - y + z = 1}$$
$$3x \quad + 2z = 3$$

Multiply this new equation by -2 and add to the result of the sum of the first two equations to eliminate the variables x and z.

$$6x + 4z = 5$$
$$\underline{-6x - 4z = -6}$$
$$0 = -1 \qquad \text{This is a contradiction, so there are no solutions.}$$

33.   Add the first two equations to eliminate the variable y.

$$x + y + z = 6$$
$$\underline{x - y + z = 2}$$
$$2x \quad + 2z = 8 \quad \Rightarrow x + z = 4 \Rightarrow x = 4 - z$$

Add the second and third equations to eliminate the variables x and z.

$$x - \ y + z = 2$$
$$\underline{-x + 5y - z = 6}$$
$$4y \quad = 8 \qquad \Rightarrow y = 2.$$

The system is dependent, and the solutions are all ordered triples of the form $(4 - z, 2, z)$.

34.   Multiply the first equation by -1 and add to the second equation to eliminate the variables y and z.

$$-x + y - z = -3$$
$$\underline{2x - y + z = \ \ 2}$$
$$x \qquad = -1$$

Add the first and third equations to eliminate the variable x.

$$x - y + z = 3$$
$$\underline{-x - y + z = 5}$$
$$-2y + 2z = 8 \qquad \Rightarrow -y + z = 4 \Rightarrow y = z - 4$$

The system is dependent, and the solutions are all ordered triples of the form $(-1, z - 4, z)$.

35.   Add the first and second equations to eliminate the variables y and z.

$$2x + y + z = 3$$
$$\underline{2x - y - z = 9}$$
$$4x = 12$$

And so, $x = 3$. Add the second and third equations together to eliminate the variable y.

$$2x - y - z = 9$$
$$\underline{x + y - z = 0}$$
$$3x - 2z = 9$$

Now substitute $x = 3$ in this new equation: $3(3) - 2z = 9 \Rightarrow -2z = 0 \Rightarrow z = 0$

Finally substitute $x = 3$ and $z = 0$ in the third equation: $(3) + y - (0) = 0 \Rightarrow y = -3$

The solution is $(3, -3, 0)$.

36.   Add the first and third equations to eliminate the variable z.

$$x + 3y + z = -8$$
$$\underline{2y - z = -16}$$
$$x + 5y = -24$$

Multiply this *new* equation by -1 and add it to the second equation to eliminate the variable x.

$$-x - 5y = 24$$
$$\underline{x - 2y = 11}$$
$$-7y = 35$$

And so $y = -5$. Substitute $y = -5$ into the second equation: $x - 2(-5) = 11 \Rightarrow x = 1$

Finally substitute $y = -5$ in the third equation: $2(-5) - z = -16 \Rightarrow -z = -6 \Rightarrow z = 6$

The solution is $(1, -5, 6)$.

37.   Multiply the first equation by -1 and add the first and second equations to eliminate the variable x.

$$-2x - 6y + 2z = -47$$
$$\underline{2x + y + 3z = -28}$$
$$-5y + 5z = -75$$

Multiply the third equation by 2 and add the first and third equations to eliminate the variables x and z.

$$2x + 6y - 2z = 47$$
$$\underline{-2x + 2y + 2z = -7}$$
$$8y = 40$$

And so $y = 5$. Substitute $y = 5$ into the first *new* equation: $-5(5) + 5z = -75 \Rightarrow 5z = -50 \Rightarrow z = -10$

Substitute $y = 5$ and $z = -10$ into the *original* third equation: $-x + (5) + (-10) = -\dfrac{7}{2} \Rightarrow x = -\dfrac{3}{2}$

The solution is $\left(-\dfrac{3}{2}, 5, -10\right)$.

38.   Multiply the second equation by 2 and add the second and third equations to eliminate the variable y.

$$6x - 2y + 6z = 16$$
$$\underline{2x + 2y\ \ + z = 13}$$
$$8x + 7z = 29$$

Multiply the first equation by -2 and add the first and third equations to eliminate the variables x and y.

$$-2x - 2y - 4z = -46$$
$$\underline{2x + 2y\ \ + z = 13}$$
$$-3z = -33$$

And so $z = 11$. Substitute $z = 11$ into the first *new* equation: $8x + 7(11) = 29 \Rightarrow 8x = -48 \Rightarrow x = -6$

Substitute $x = -6$ and $z = 11$ into the *original* first equation: $(-6) + y + 2(11) = 23 \Rightarrow y = 7$

The solution is $(-6, 7, 11)$.

39.   Multiply the second equation by -1 and add the first and second equations to eliminate the variable y.

$$x + 3y - 4z = \dfrac{13}{2}$$
$$\underline{2x - 3y\ \ + z\ = -\dfrac{1}{2}}$$
$$3x - 3z = 6$$

Multiply this *new* equation by -1 and add it to the third equation to eliminate the variable x.

$$-3x + 3z = -6$$
$$\underline{3x\ \ + z = 4}$$
$$4z = -2$$

And so $z = -\dfrac{1}{2}$. Substitute $z = -\dfrac{1}{2}$ into the first *new* equation: $3x - 3\left(-\dfrac{1}{2}\right) = 6 \Rightarrow 3x = \dfrac{9}{2} \Rightarrow x = \dfrac{3}{2}$

Substitute $x = \dfrac{3}{2}$ and $z = -\dfrac{1}{2}$ into the *original* first equation: $\left(\dfrac{3}{2}\right) + 3y - 4\left(-\dfrac{1}{2}\right) = \dfrac{13}{2} \Rightarrow y = 1$

The solution is $\left(\dfrac{3}{2}, 1, -\dfrac{1}{2}\right)$.

40.   Multiply the first equation by -3 and add the first and second equations to eliminate the variable z.

$$-3x + 6y - 3z = -\dfrac{27}{2}$$
$$\underline{4x\ \ - y + 3z = 9}$$
$$x + 5y = -\dfrac{9}{2}$$

Multiply this *new* equation by -1 and add it to the third equation to eliminate the variable x.

$$-x - 5y = \frac{9}{2}$$

$$\underline{x + 2y = -\frac{3}{2}}$$

$$-3y = 3$$

And so $y = -1$. Substitute $y = -1$ into the first *new* equation: $x + 5(-1) = -\frac{9}{2} \Rightarrow x = \frac{1}{2}$

Substitute $x = \frac{1}{2}$ and $y = -1$ into the *original* first equation: $\left(\frac{1}{2}\right) - 2(-1) + z = \frac{9}{2} \Rightarrow z = 2$

The solution is $\left(\frac{1}{2}, -1, 2\right)$.

41. Multiply the second equation by -1 and add to the third equation to eliminate the variables x, y, and z.

$$-x + y - z = -1$$

$$\underline{x - y + z = 3}$$

$$0 = 2 \qquad \text{This is a contradiction. There are no solutions.}$$

42. Multiply the first equation by -1 and add to the second equation to eliminate the variables x.

$$-x + 2y - 3z = -1$$

$$\underline{x + 3y + \ z = \ 2}$$

$$5y - 2z = \ 1$$

Multiply the second equation by -3 and add to the third equation to eliminate the variable x.

$$-3x - 9y - 3z = -6$$

$$\underline{3x + 4y + 5z = \ 7}$$

$$-5y + 2z = 1$$

Add this new equation to the result of the first sum of equations to eliminate the variables y and z.

$$5y - 2z = 1$$

$$\underline{-5y + 2z = 1}$$

$$0 = 2 \qquad \text{This is a contradiction. There are no solutions.}$$

43. Add the first two equations to eliminate the variable y.

$$x + y + z = 5$$

$$\underline{x - y + z = 3}$$

$$2x \ + 2z = 8 \qquad \Rightarrow x + z = 4 \Rightarrow x = 4 - z$$

Multiply the first equation by -1 and add the second equation to eliminate the variables x and z.

$$-x - y - z = -5$$

$$\underline{x - y + z = 3}$$

$$-2y \quad = -2 \qquad \Rightarrow y = 1$$

The system is dependent, and the solutions are all ordered pairs of the form $(4 - z, 1, z)$.

44. Multiply the third equation by -1 and add the first equation to eliminate the variables y and z.

$$x + y - 2z = 0$$
$$\underline{\quad -y + 2z = 1}$$
$$x \qquad = 1$$

Multiply the first equation by –1 and add the second equation to eliminate the variable x.

$$-x - y + 2z = 0$$
$$\underline{x + 2y - 4z = -1}$$
$$y - 2z = -1 \quad \Rightarrow y = 2z - 1$$

The system is dependent, and the solutions are all ordered pairs of the form $(1, 2z - 1, z)$.

45.   Multiply the first equation by –1 and add the second equation to eliminate the variables x, y, and z.

$$-x - y - z = -a$$
$$\underline{x + y + z = 2a}$$
$$0 = a \qquad \text{But } a \neq 0, \text{ so this is a contradiction.}$$

There are no solutions.

46.   Add the second and third equations to eliminate the variable y.

$$-x - y - z = -a$$
$$\underline{\quad y - z = 0}$$
$$-x \quad -2z = -a \qquad \Rightarrow x + 2z = a \Rightarrow x = a - 2z$$
$$y - z = 0 \Rightarrow y = z$$

The system is dependent. All solutions are ordered triples of the form $(a - 2z, z, z)$.

Applications

47.   (a) $x + 2y + 4z = 10$
$$x + 4y + 6z = 15$$
$$3y + 2z = 6$$

(b)   Using techniques similar to those used in exercises 19-44, the solution is $(2, 1, 1.5)$.

A hamburger costs $2.00, fries cost $1.00 and a soft drink costs $1.50.

48.   (a) $x + y + z = 37$
$$3x + 2y + z = 69$$
$$x + y + 4z = 82$$

(b)   Using techniques similar to those used in exercises 19-44, the solution is $(10, 12, 15)$.

CDs of type A cost $10.00, CDs of type B cost $12.00 and CDs of type C cost $15.00.

49.   (a) $x + y + z = 180$
$$x \quad -z = 55$$
$$x - y - z = -10$$

(b)   Using techniques similar to those used in exercises 19-44, the solution is $(85, 65, 30)$.

The angles are $x = 85°$, $y = 65°$, and $z = 30°$.

(c)   These values check.

50.   (a) $x + y + z = 90$

         $x \quad\; - z = 20$

         $x - y \quad\; = 10$

    (b)   Using techniques similar to those used in exercises 19-44, the solution is (40, 30, 20).

        The sides have lengths $x = 40$ inches, $y = 30$ inches, and $z = 20$ inches.

    (c)   These values check.

51.   Add the first two equations to eliminate the variables y and z.

$$x + y + z = 180$$
$$\underline{x - y - z = 40}$$
$$2x \qquad\;\; = 220 \quad \Rightarrow x = 110$$

$x - z = 90 \Rightarrow z = x - 90 \Rightarrow z = 110 - 90 \Rightarrow z = 20$

Substitute the values for x and z into the first equation and solve for y.

$110 + y + 20 = 180 \Rightarrow y = 50$

The angle measures are 110°, 50°, and 20°.

52.   Let x, y, and z represent the amounts of the subsidized, unsubsidized, and parent loans, respectively. The system needed is

$$x + y + z = 5000$$

$$x = 200 + y + z$$

$$y = 2z$$

Note that $x = 200 + y + z \Rightarrow x - y - z = 200$. Add this equation to the first equation to eliminate the variables y and z.

$$x + y + z = 5000$$
$$\underline{x - y - z = 200}$$
$$\quad 2x \;\; = 5200 \quad \Rightarrow x = 2600$$

Substitute the value $x = 2600$ into the second equation: $2600 = 200 + y + z \Rightarrow 2400 = y + z \Rightarrow y = 2400 - z$.

Then $y = 2z$ and $y = 2400 - z \Rightarrow 2z = 2400 - z \Rightarrow 3z = 2400 \Rightarrow z = 800$ and $y = 2z = 2(800) = 1600$.

The subsidized loan is for \$2600, the unsubsidized loan is for \$1600, and the parent loan is for \$800.

53.   (a) $a + 600b + 4c = 525$

         $a + 400b + 2c = 365$

         $a + 900b + 5c = 805$

    (b)   Using techniques similar to those used in exercises 19-44, the solution is (5, 1, –20).

        That is, $a = 5$, $b = 1$, and $c = -20$ and so the equation is $F = 5 + A - 20W$.

    (c)   When $A = 500$ and $W = 3$, $F = 5 + (500) - 20(3) = 445$ fawns.

54.   (a) $x + y + z = 100$

$x + y \quad = 80$

$x \quad - z = 34$

(b)   Using techniques similar to those used in exercises 19-44, the solution is (54, 26, 20).

The machines make 54, 26 and 20 containers, respectively, per day.

55.   (a) $N + P + K = 80$

$N + P - K = 8$

$9P - K = 0$

(b)   Using techniques similar to those used in exercises 19-44, the solution is (40, 4, 36).

The sample contains 40 pounds of nitrogen, 4 pounds of phosphorus and 36 pounds of potassium.

56.   (a) $a + 20b + 2c = 190$

$a + 5b + 3c = 320$

$a + 40b + c = 50$

(b)   Using techniques similar to those used in exercises 19-44, the solution is (30, –2, 100).

That is, $a = 30$, $b = 2$, and $c = 100$ and so the equation is $P = 30 - 2A + 100S$.

(c)   When $A = 10$ and $S = 2500$, $P = 30 - 2(10) + 100(2500) = \$260,000$.

57.   Let x, y and z represent the amounts invested at 8%, 10% and 15% respectively. The system needed is:

$x \quad + y \quad + z = 30,000$

$0.08x + 0.10y + 0.15z = 3550$

$x \quad + y \quad - z = 2000$

Using techniques similar to those used in exercises 19-44, the solution is (7500, 8500, 14,000).

There was $7500 invested at 8%, $8500 invested at 10% and $14,000 invested at 15%.

58.   Let x, y and z represent the number of child, student and adult tickets sold respectively. The system needed is:

$x + y + z = 2500$

$2x + 3y + 5z = 7250$

$2x - y \quad = 0$

Using techniques similar to those used in exercises 19-44, the solution is (750, 1500, 250).

There were 750 child tickets, 1500 student tickets and 250 adult tickets sold.

Group Activity Solutions

1.   (a) $x + y + z = 44$

$x - y - z = 2$

$x - y \quad = 7$

(b)   Using techniques similar to those used in section 4.5, the solution is (23, 16, 5).

The top CEO made $23,000/hr, the 2nd CEO made $16,000/hr and the 3rd CEO made $5000/hr.

(c) $\dfrac{23,000}{16.23} \approx 1417$ hours

4.6: Matrix Solutions of Linear Systems

Concepts

1.   A rectangular array of numbers

2. $\begin{bmatrix} 2 & 1 & 3 \\ 0 & -4 & 2 \end{bmatrix}$; 2×3;   *Answers may vary.*

3. $\left[\begin{array}{cc|c} 1 & 3 & 10 \\ 2 & -6 & 4 \end{array}\right]$; 2×3; *Answers may vary.*

4. 3×4

5. $\left[\begin{array}{cc|c} 1 & 0 & -3 \\ 0 & 1 & 5 \end{array}\right]$; *Answers may vary.*

6. $4, 2, -3$

Dimensions of Matrices and Augmented Matrices

7. 3×3

8. 2×3

9. 3×2

10. 3×4

11. $\left[\begin{array}{cc|c} 1 & -3 & 1 \\ -1 & 3 & -1 \end{array}\right]$

12. $\left[\begin{array}{cc|c} 4 & 2 & -5 \\ 5 & 8 & 2 \end{array}\right]$

13. $\left[\begin{array}{ccc|c} 2 & -1 & 2 & -4 \\ 1 & -2 & 0 & 2 \\ -1 & 1 & -2 & -6 \end{array}\right]$

14. $\left[\begin{array}{ccc|c} 3 & -2 & 1 & 5 \\ -1 & 0 & 2 & -4 \\ 1 & -2 & 1 & -1 \end{array}\right]$

15. $\begin{aligned} x + 2y &= -6 \\ 5x - y &= 4 \end{aligned}$

16. $\begin{aligned} x - 5y &= 7 \\ -3y &= 6 \end{aligned}$

17. $\begin{aligned} x - y + 2z &= 6 \\ 2x + y - 2z &= 1 \\ -x + 2y - z &= 3 \end{aligned}$

18. $\begin{aligned} 3x - y + 2z &= -1 \\ 2x - 2y + 2z &= 4 \\ x + 7y - 2z &= 2 \end{aligned}$

19. $\begin{aligned} x &= 4 \\ y &= -2 \\ z &= 7 \end{aligned}$

20. $\begin{aligned} x &= 6 \\ y &= -2 \\ z &= 4 \end{aligned}$

Gaussian Elimination

21. $\begin{bmatrix} 1 & 1 & | & 4 \\ 1 & 3 & | & 10 \end{bmatrix} R_2 - R_1 \rightarrow \begin{bmatrix} 1 & 1 & | & 4 \\ 0 & 2 & | & 6 \end{bmatrix} (1/2)R_2 \rightarrow \begin{bmatrix} 1 & 1 & | & 4 \\ 0 & 1 & | & 3 \end{bmatrix} R_1 - R_2 \rightarrow \begin{bmatrix} 1 & 0 & | & 1 \\ 0 & 1 & | & 3 \end{bmatrix}$

The solution is $(1, 3)$.

22. $\begin{bmatrix} 1 & -3 & | & -7 \\ 2 & 1 & | & 0 \end{bmatrix} R_2 - 2R_1 \rightarrow \begin{bmatrix} 1 & -3 & | & -7 \\ 0 & 7 & | & 14 \end{bmatrix} (1/7)R_2 \rightarrow \begin{bmatrix} 1 & -3 & | & -7 \\ 0 & 1 & | & 2 \end{bmatrix} R_1 + 3R_2 \rightarrow \begin{bmatrix} 1 & 0 & | & -1 \\ 0 & 1 & | & 2 \end{bmatrix}$

The solution is $(-1, 2)$.

23. $\begin{bmatrix} 2 & 3 & | & 3 \\ -2 & 2 & | & 7 \end{bmatrix} R_2 + R_1 \rightarrow \begin{bmatrix} 2 & 3 & | & 3 \\ 0 & 5 & | & 10 \end{bmatrix} (1/5)R_2 \rightarrow \begin{bmatrix} 2 & 3 & | & 3 \\ 0 & 1 & | & 2 \end{bmatrix} R_1 - 3R_2 \rightarrow \begin{bmatrix} 2 & 0 & | & -3 \\ 0 & 1 & | & 2 \end{bmatrix} (1/2)R_2 \rightarrow \begin{bmatrix} 1 & 0 & | & -\frac{3}{2} \\ 0 & 1 & | & 2 \end{bmatrix}$

The solution is $\left(-\dfrac{3}{2}, 2\right)$.

24. $\begin{bmatrix} 1 & 3 & | & -14 \\ 2 & 5 & | & -24 \end{bmatrix} R_2 - 2R_1 \rightarrow \begin{bmatrix} 1 & 3 & | & -14 \\ 0 & -1 & | & 4 \end{bmatrix} (-1)R_2 \rightarrow \begin{bmatrix} 1 & 3 & | & -14 \\ 0 & 1 & | & -4 \end{bmatrix} R_1 - 3R_2 \rightarrow \begin{bmatrix} 1 & 0 & | & -2 \\ 0 & 1 & | & -4 \end{bmatrix}$

The solution is $(-2, -4)$.

25. $\begin{bmatrix} 1 & -1 & | & 5 \\ 1 & 3 & | & -1 \end{bmatrix} R_2 - R_1 \rightarrow \begin{bmatrix} 1 & -1 & | & 5 \\ 0 & 4 & | & -6 \end{bmatrix} (1/4)R_2 \rightarrow \begin{bmatrix} 1 & -1 & | & 5 \\ 0 & 1 & | & -\frac{3}{2} \end{bmatrix} R_1 + R_2 \rightarrow \begin{bmatrix} 1 & 0 & | & \frac{7}{2} \\ 0 & 1 & | & -\frac{3}{2} \end{bmatrix}$

The solution is $\left(\dfrac{7}{2}, -\dfrac{3}{2}\right)$.

26. $\begin{bmatrix} 1 & 4 & | & 1 \\ 3 & -2 & | & 10 \end{bmatrix} R_2 - 3R_1 \rightarrow \begin{bmatrix} 1 & 4 & | & 1 \\ 0 & -14 & | & 7 \end{bmatrix} (-1/14)R_2 \rightarrow \begin{bmatrix} 1 & 4 & | & 1 \\ 0 & 1 & | & -\frac{1}{2} \end{bmatrix} R_1 - 4R_2 \rightarrow \begin{bmatrix} 1 & 0 & | & 3 \\ 0 & 1 & | & -\frac{1}{2} \end{bmatrix}$

The solution is $\left(3, -\dfrac{1}{2}\right)$.

27. $\begin{bmatrix} 4 & -8 & | & -10 \\ 1 & 1 & | & 2 \end{bmatrix} \begin{matrix} Exchange \\ R_2 \leftrightarrow R_1 \end{matrix} \begin{bmatrix} 1 & 1 & | & 2 \\ 4 & -8 & | & -10 \end{bmatrix} (-1/2)R_2 \rightarrow \begin{bmatrix} 1 & 1 & | & 2 \\ -2 & 4 & | & 5 \end{bmatrix} R_2 + 2R_1 \rightarrow \begin{bmatrix} 1 & 1 & | & 2 \\ 0 & 6 & | & 9 \end{bmatrix}$

$(1/6)R_2 \rightarrow \begin{bmatrix} 1 & 1 & | & 2 \\ 0 & 1 & | & \frac{3}{2} \end{bmatrix} R_1 - R_2 \rightarrow \begin{bmatrix} 1 & 0 & | & \frac{1}{2} \\ 0 & 1 & | & \frac{3}{2} \end{bmatrix}$

The solution is $\left(\dfrac{1}{2}, \dfrac{3}{2}\right)$.

28. $\begin{bmatrix} 1 & -7 & | & -16 \\ 4 & 10 & | & 50 \end{bmatrix} R_2 - 4R_1 \rightarrow \begin{bmatrix} 1 & -7 & | & -16 \\ 0 & 38 & | & 114 \end{bmatrix} (1/38)R_2 \rightarrow \begin{bmatrix} 1 & -7 & | & -16 \\ 0 & 1 & | & 3 \end{bmatrix} R_1 + 7R_2 \rightarrow \begin{bmatrix} 1 & 0 & | & 5 \\ 0 & 1 & | & 3 \end{bmatrix}$

The solution is $(5, 3)$.

29. $\begin{bmatrix} 1 & 1 & 1 & | & 6 \\ 0 & 2 & -1 & | & 1 \\ 0 & 1 & 1 & | & 5 \end{bmatrix} \begin{matrix} R_1 - R_3 \to \\ R_2 - 2R_3 \to \end{matrix} \begin{bmatrix} 1 & 0 & 0 & | & 1 \\ 0 & 0 & -3 & | & -9 \\ 0 & 1 & 1 & | & 5 \end{bmatrix} \begin{matrix} Exchange \\ R_2 \leftrightarrow R_3 \end{matrix} \begin{bmatrix} 1 & 0 & 0 & | & 1 \\ 0 & 1 & 1 & | & 5 \\ 0 & 0 & -3 & | & -9 \end{bmatrix} (-1/3)R_3 \to \begin{bmatrix} 1 & 0 & 0 & | & 1 \\ 0 & 1 & 1 & | & 5 \\ 0 & 0 & 1 & | & 3 \end{bmatrix}$

$R_2 - R_3 \to \begin{bmatrix} 1 & 0 & 0 & | & 1 \\ 0 & 1 & 0 & | & 2 \\ 0 & 0 & 1 & | & 3 \end{bmatrix}$

The solution is $(1, 2, 3)$.

30. $\begin{bmatrix} 1 & 1 & 1 & | & 3 \\ 1 & 1 & -1 & | & 2 \\ 0 & 1 & 1 & | & 2 \end{bmatrix} \begin{matrix} R_1 - R_3 \to \\ R_2 - R_1 \to \end{matrix} \begin{bmatrix} 1 & 0 & 0 & | & 1 \\ 0 & 0 & -2 & | & -1 \\ 0 & 1 & 1 & | & 2 \end{bmatrix} \begin{matrix} Exchange \\ R_2 \leftrightarrow R_3 \end{matrix} \begin{bmatrix} 1 & 0 & 0 & | & 1 \\ 0 & 1 & 1 & | & 2 \\ 0 & 0 & -2 & | & -1 \end{bmatrix} (-1/2)R_3 \to \begin{bmatrix} 1 & 0 & 0 & | & 1 \\ 0 & 1 & 1 & | & 2 \\ 0 & 0 & 1 & | & \frac{1}{2} \end{bmatrix}$

$R_2 - R_3 \to \begin{bmatrix} 1 & 0 & 0 & | & 1 \\ 0 & 1 & 0 & | & \frac{3}{2} \\ 0 & 0 & 1 & | & \frac{1}{2} \end{bmatrix}$

The solution is $\left(1, \dfrac{3}{2}, \dfrac{1}{2}\right)$.

31. $\begin{bmatrix} 1 & 2 & 3 & | & 6 \\ -1 & 3 & 4 & | & 0 \\ 1 & 1 & -2 & | & -6 \end{bmatrix} \begin{matrix} R_2 + R_1 \to \\ R_3 - R_1 \to \end{matrix} \begin{bmatrix} 1 & 2 & 3 & | & 6 \\ 0 & 5 & 7 & | & 6 \\ 0 & -1 & -5 & | & -12 \end{bmatrix} (-1)R_3 \to \begin{bmatrix} 1 & 2 & 3 & | & 6 \\ 0 & 5 & 7 & | & 6 \\ 0 & 1 & 5 & | & 12 \end{bmatrix}$

$\begin{matrix} R_1 - 2R_3 \to \\ R_2 - 5R_3 \to \end{matrix} \begin{bmatrix} 1 & 0 & -7 & | & -18 \\ 0 & 0 & -18 & | & -54 \\ 0 & 1 & 5 & | & 12 \end{bmatrix} \begin{matrix} Exchange \\ R_2 \leftrightarrow R_3 \end{matrix} \begin{bmatrix} 1 & 0 & -7 & | & -18 \\ 0 & 1 & 5 & | & 12 \\ 0 & 0 & -18 & | & -54 \end{bmatrix} (-1/18)R_3 \to \begin{bmatrix} 1 & 0 & -7 & | & -18 \\ 0 & 1 & 5 & | & 12 \\ 0 & 0 & 1 & | & 3 \end{bmatrix}$

$\begin{matrix} R_1 + 7R_3 \to \\ R_2 - 5R_3 \to \end{matrix} \begin{bmatrix} 1 & 0 & 0 & | & 3 \\ 0 & 1 & 0 & | & -3 \\ 0 & 0 & 1 & | & 3 \end{bmatrix}$

The solution is $(3, -3, 3)$.

32. $\begin{bmatrix} 2 & -4 & 2 & | & 10 \\ -1 & 3 & -4 & | & -19 \\ 2 & -1 & -6 & | & -28 \end{bmatrix} \begin{matrix} (1/2)R_1 \to \\ R_2 + (1/2)R_1 \to \\ R_3 - R_1 \to \end{matrix} \begin{bmatrix} 1 & -2 & 1 & | & 5 \\ 0 & 1 & -3 & | & -14 \\ 0 & 3 & -8 & | & -38 \end{bmatrix} \begin{matrix} R_1 + 2R_2 \to \\ \\ R_3 - 3R_2 \to \end{matrix} \begin{bmatrix} 1 & 0 & -5 & | & -23 \\ 0 & 1 & -3 & | & -14 \\ 0 & 0 & 1 & | & 4 \end{bmatrix}$

$\begin{matrix} R_1 + 5R_3 \to \\ R_2 + 3R_3 \to \end{matrix} \begin{bmatrix} 1 & 0 & 0 & | & -3 \\ 0 & 1 & 0 & | & -2 \\ 0 & 0 & 1 & | & 4 \end{bmatrix}$

The solution is $(-3, -2, 4)$.

33. $\begin{bmatrix} 1 & 1 & 1 & | & 0 \\ 2 & 1 & 2 & | & -1 \\ 1 & 1 & 0 & | & 0 \end{bmatrix} \begin{matrix} R_2 - 2R_1 \to \\ R_3 - R_1 \to \end{matrix} \begin{bmatrix} 1 & 1 & 1 & | & 0 \\ 0 & -1 & 0 & | & -1 \\ 0 & 0 & -1 & | & 0 \end{bmatrix} \begin{matrix} (-1)R_2 \to \\ (-1)R_3 \to \end{matrix} \begin{bmatrix} 1 & 1 & 1 & | & 0 \\ 0 & 1 & 0 & | & 1 \\ 0 & 0 & 1 & | & 0 \end{bmatrix} R_1 - R_2 \to \begin{bmatrix} 1 & 0 & 1 & | & -1 \\ 0 & 1 & 0 & | & 1 \\ 0 & 0 & 1 & | & 0 \end{bmatrix}$

$R_1 - R_3 \to \begin{bmatrix} 1 & 0 & 0 & | & -1 \\ 0 & 1 & 0 & | & 1 \\ 0 & 0 & 1 & | & 0 \end{bmatrix}$

The solution is $(-1, 1, 0)$.

34. $\begin{bmatrix} 1 & 1 & -2 & | & 5 \\ 1 & 2 & -2 & | & 4 \\ -1 & -1 & 1 & | & -4 \end{bmatrix} \begin{matrix} R_2 - R_1 \to \\ R_3 + R_1 \to \end{matrix} \begin{bmatrix} 1 & 1 & -2 & | & 5 \\ 0 & 1 & 0 & | & -1 \\ 0 & 0 & -1 & | & 1 \end{bmatrix} (-1)R_3 \to \begin{bmatrix} 1 & 1 & -2 & | & 5 \\ 0 & 1 & 0 & | & -1 \\ 0 & 0 & 1 & | & -1 \end{bmatrix}$

$$R_1 - R_2 \rightarrow \begin{bmatrix} 1 & 0 & -2 & | & 6 \\ 0 & 1 & 0 & | & -1 \\ 0 & 0 & 1 & | & -1 \end{bmatrix} R_1 + 2R_3 \rightarrow \begin{bmatrix} 1 & 0 & 0 & | & 4 \\ 0 & 1 & 0 & | & -1 \\ 0 & 0 & 1 & | & -1 \end{bmatrix}$$

The solution is $(4, -1, -1)$.

35. $\begin{bmatrix} 1 & 1 & 1 & | & 3 \\ -1 & 0 & -1 & | & -2 \\ 1 & 1 & 2 & | & 4 \end{bmatrix} \begin{matrix} \\ R_2 + R_1 \rightarrow \\ R_3 - R_1 \rightarrow \end{matrix} \begin{bmatrix} 1 & 1 & 1 & | & 3 \\ 0 & 1 & 0 & | & 1 \\ 0 & 0 & 1 & | & 1 \end{bmatrix} \begin{matrix} R_1 - R_2 \rightarrow \\ \\ \end{matrix} \begin{bmatrix} 1 & 0 & 1 & | & 2 \\ 0 & 1 & 0 & | & 1 \\ 0 & 0 & 1 & | & 1 \end{bmatrix} \begin{matrix} R_1 - R_3 \rightarrow \\ \\ \end{matrix} \begin{bmatrix} 1 & 0 & 0 & | & 1 \\ 0 & 1 & 0 & | & 1 \\ 0 & 0 & 1 & | & 1 \end{bmatrix}$

The solution is $(1, 1, 1)$.

36. $\begin{bmatrix} 1 & 2 & -1 & | & 3 \\ -1 & -1 & 1 & | & 0 \\ 1 & 2 & 0 & | & 5 \end{bmatrix} \begin{matrix} \\ R_2 + R_1 \rightarrow \\ R_3 - R_1 \rightarrow \end{matrix} \begin{bmatrix} 1 & 2 & -1 & | & 3 \\ 0 & 1 & 0 & | & 3 \\ 0 & 0 & 1 & | & 2 \end{bmatrix} \begin{matrix} R_1 - 2R_2 \rightarrow \\ \\ \end{matrix} \begin{bmatrix} 1 & 0 & -1 & | & -3 \\ 0 & 1 & 0 & | & 3 \\ 0 & 0 & 1 & | & 2 \end{bmatrix} \begin{matrix} R_1 + R_3 \rightarrow \\ \\ \end{matrix} \begin{bmatrix} 1 & 0 & 0 & | & -1 \\ 0 & 1 & 0 & | & 3 \\ 0 & 0 & 1 & | & 2 \end{bmatrix}$

The solution is $(-1, 3, 2)$.

37. $\begin{bmatrix} 1 & 2 & 1 & | & 3 \\ 2 & 1 & -1 & | & -6 \\ -1 & -1 & 2 & | & 5 \end{bmatrix} \begin{matrix} \\ R_2 - 2R_1 \rightarrow \\ R_3 + R_1 \rightarrow \end{matrix} \begin{bmatrix} 1 & 2 & 1 & | & 3 \\ 0 & -3 & -3 & | & -12 \\ 0 & 1 & 3 & | & 8 \end{bmatrix} \begin{matrix} \\ (-1/3)R_2 \rightarrow \\ \end{matrix} \begin{bmatrix} 1 & 2 & 1 & | & 3 \\ 0 & 1 & 1 & | & 4 \\ 0 & 1 & 3 & | & 8 \end{bmatrix}$

$\begin{matrix} \\ \\ R_3 - R_2 \rightarrow \end{matrix} \begin{bmatrix} 1 & 2 & 1 & | & 3 \\ 0 & 1 & 1 & | & 4 \\ 0 & 0 & 2 & | & 4 \end{bmatrix} \begin{matrix} R_1 - 2R_2 \rightarrow \\ \\ (1/2)R_3 \rightarrow \end{matrix} \begin{bmatrix} 1 & 0 & -1 & | & -5 \\ 0 & 1 & 1 & | & 4 \\ 0 & 0 & 1 & | & 2 \end{bmatrix} \begin{matrix} R_1 + R_3 \rightarrow \\ R_2 - R_3 \rightarrow \\ \end{matrix} \begin{bmatrix} 1 & 0 & 0 & | & -3 \\ 0 & 1 & 0 & | & 2 \\ 0 & 0 & 1 & | & 2 \end{bmatrix}$

The solution is $(-3, 2, 2)$.

38. $\begin{bmatrix} 1 & 1 & 1 & | & -3 \\ 1 & -1 & -1 & | & -1 \\ -2 & 1 & 4 & | & 4 \end{bmatrix} \begin{matrix} \\ R_2 - R_1 \rightarrow \\ R_3 + 2R_1 \rightarrow \end{matrix} \begin{bmatrix} 1 & 1 & 1 & | & -3 \\ 0 & -2 & -2 & | & 2 \\ 0 & 3 & 6 & | & -2 \end{bmatrix} \begin{matrix} \\ (-1/2)R_2 \rightarrow \\ \end{matrix} \begin{bmatrix} 1 & 1 & 1 & | & -3 \\ 0 & 1 & 1 & | & -1 \\ 0 & 3 & 6 & | & -2 \end{bmatrix}$

$\begin{matrix} \\ \\ R_3 - 3R_2 \rightarrow \end{matrix} \begin{bmatrix} 1 & 1 & 1 & | & -3 \\ 0 & 1 & 1 & | & -1 \\ 0 & 0 & 3 & | & 1 \end{bmatrix} \begin{matrix} R_1 - R_2 \rightarrow \\ \\ (1/3)R_3 \rightarrow \end{matrix} \begin{bmatrix} 1 & 0 & 0 & | & -2 \\ 0 & 1 & 1 & | & -1 \\ 0 & 0 & 1 & | & \frac{1}{3} \end{bmatrix} \begin{matrix} \\ R_2 - R_3 \rightarrow \\ \end{matrix} \begin{bmatrix} 1 & 0 & 0 & | & -2 \\ 0 & 1 & 0 & | & -\frac{4}{3} \\ 0 & 0 & 1 & | & \frac{1}{3} \end{bmatrix}$

The solution is $\left(-2, -\frac{4}{3}, \frac{1}{3}\right)$.

39. See example 6 in the text for graphing calculator instructions.

$[A] = \begin{bmatrix} 1 & 4 & | & 13 \\ 5 & -3 & | & -50 \end{bmatrix}$; $\text{rref}([A]) = \begin{bmatrix} 1 & 0 & | & -7 \\ 0 & 1 & | & 5 \end{bmatrix}$; The solution is $(-7, 5)$.

40. See example 6 in the text for graphing calculator instructions.

$[A] = \begin{bmatrix} 9 & -11 & | & 7 \\ 5 & 6 & | & 16 \end{bmatrix}$; $\text{rref}([A]) = \begin{bmatrix} 1 & 0 & | & 2 \\ 0 & 1 & | & 1 \end{bmatrix}$; The solution is $(2, 1)$.

41. See example 6 in the text for graphing calculator instructions.

$[A] = \begin{bmatrix} 2 & -1 & 3 & | & 9 \\ -4 & 5 & 2 & | & 12 \\ 2 & 0 & 7 & | & 23 \end{bmatrix}$; $\text{rref}([A]) = \begin{bmatrix} 1 & 0 & 0 & | & 1 \\ 0 & 1 & 0 & | & 2 \\ 0 & 0 & 1 & | & 3 \end{bmatrix}$; The solution is $(1, 2, 3)$.

42. See example 6 in the text for graphing calculator instructions.

$[A] = \begin{bmatrix} 3 & -2 & 4 & | & 29 \\ 2 & 3 & -7 & | & -14 \\ 5 & -1 & 11 & | & 59 \end{bmatrix}$; $\text{rref}([A]) = \begin{bmatrix} 1 & 0 & 0 & | & 5 \\ 0 & 1 & 0 & | & -1 \\ 0 & 0 & 1 & | & 3 \end{bmatrix}$; The solution is $(5, -1, 3)$.

43. See example 6 in the text for graphing calculator instructions.

$$[A] = \begin{bmatrix} 6 & 2 & 1 & | & 4 \\ -2 & 4 & 1 & | & -3 \\ 2 & -8 & 0 & | & -2 \end{bmatrix}; \text{rref}([A]) = \begin{bmatrix} 1 & 0 & 0 & | & 1 \\ 0 & 1 & 0 & | & 0.5 \\ 0 & 0 & 1 & | & -3 \end{bmatrix}; \quad \text{The solution is } (1, 0.5, -3).$$

44.   See example 6 in the text for graphing calculator instructions.

$$[A] = \begin{bmatrix} -1 & -9 & 2 & | & -28.5 \\ 2 & -1 & 4 & | & -17 \\ 1 & -1 & 8 & | & -9 \end{bmatrix}; \text{rref}([A]) = \begin{bmatrix} 1 & 0 & 0 & | & -7 \\ 0 & 1 & 0 & | & 4 \\ 0 & 0 & 1 & | & 0.25 \end{bmatrix}; \quad \text{The solution is } (-7, 4, 0.25).$$

45.   See example 6 in the text for graphing calculator instructions.

$$[A] = \begin{bmatrix} 4 & 3 & 12 & | & -9.25 \\ -1 & 15 & 8 & | & -4.75 \\ 0 & 6 & 7 & | & -5.5 \end{bmatrix}; \text{rref}([A]) = \begin{bmatrix} 1 & 0 & 0 & | & 0.5 \\ 0 & 1 & 0 & | & 0.25 \\ 0 & 0 & 1 & | & -1 \end{bmatrix}; \quad \text{The solution is } (0.5, 0.25, -1).$$

46.   See example 6 in the text for graphing calculator instructions.

$$[A] = \begin{bmatrix} 5 & 4 & -1 & | & 13.3 \\ 1 & 7 & 9 & | & 16.9 \\ 1 & -3 & 4 & | & -4.1 \end{bmatrix}; \text{rref}([A]) = \begin{bmatrix} 1 & 0 & 0 & | & 1.1 \\ 0 & 1 & 0 & | & 2 \\ 0 & 0 & 1 & | & 0.2 \end{bmatrix}; \quad \text{The solution is } (1.1, 2, 0.2).$$

47.   See example 6 in the text for graphing calculator instructions.

$$[A] = \begin{bmatrix} 1.2 & -0.9 & 2.7 & | & 5.37 \\ 3.1 & -5.1 & 7.2 & | & 14.81 \\ 0.2 & 1.8 & -3.6 & | & -6.38 \end{bmatrix}; \text{rref}([A]) = \begin{bmatrix} 1 & 0 & 0 & | & 0.5 \\ 0 & 1 & 0 & | & -0.2 \\ 0 & 0 & 1 & | & 1.7 \end{bmatrix}; \quad \text{The solution is } (0.5, -0.2, 1.7).$$

48.   See example 6 in the text for graphing calculator instructions.

$$[A] = \begin{bmatrix} 11 & 13 & -17 & | & 380 \\ 5 & -14 & -19 & | & 24 \\ -7 & -21 & 46 & | & -676 \end{bmatrix}; \text{rref}([A]) = \begin{bmatrix} 1 & 0 & 0 & | & 8 \\ 0 & 1 & 0 & | & 12 \\ 0 & 0 & 1 & | & -8 \end{bmatrix}; \quad \text{The solution is } (8, 12, -8).$$

49. $$\begin{bmatrix} 1 & 2 & | & 4 \\ -2 & -4 & | & -8 \end{bmatrix} R_2 + 2R_1 \rightarrow \begin{bmatrix} 1 & 2 & | & 4 \\ 0 & 0 & | & 0 \end{bmatrix}$$

Row 2 represents the equation $0 = 0$. The system is dependent.

50. $$\begin{bmatrix} 1 & -5 & | & 4 \\ -2 & 10 & | & 8 \end{bmatrix} R_2 + 2R_1 \rightarrow \begin{bmatrix} 1 & -5 & | & 4 \\ 0 & 0 & | & 16 \end{bmatrix}$$

Row 2 represents the equation $0 = 16$. The system is inconsistent.

51. $$\begin{bmatrix} 1 & 1 & 1 & | & 3 \\ 1 & 1 & -1 & | & 1 \\ 1 & 1 & 0 & | & 3 \end{bmatrix} \begin{matrix} \\ R_2 - R_1 \rightarrow \\ R_3 - R_1 \rightarrow \end{matrix} \begin{bmatrix} 1 & 1 & 1 & | & 3 \\ 0 & 0 & -2 & | & -2 \\ 0 & 0 & -1 & | & 0 \end{bmatrix} R_2 - 2R_3 \rightarrow \begin{bmatrix} 1 & 1 & 1 & | & 3 \\ 0 & 0 & 0 & | & -2 \\ 0 & 0 & -1 & | & 0 \end{bmatrix}$$

Row 2 represents the equation $0 = -2$. The system is inconsistent.

52. $$\begin{bmatrix} 1 & 1 & 1 & | & 5 \\ 1 & -1 & -1 & | & 8 \\ 2 & 2 & 2 & | & 6 \end{bmatrix} \begin{matrix} \\ R_2 - R_1 \rightarrow \\ R_3 - 2R_1 \rightarrow \end{matrix} \begin{bmatrix} 1 & 1 & 1 & | & 5 \\ 0 & -2 & -2 & | & 3 \\ 0 & 0 & 0 & | & -4 \end{bmatrix}$$

Row 3 represents the equation $0 = -4$. The system is inconsistent.

53. $$\begin{bmatrix} 1 & 2 & 3 & | & 14 \\ 2 & -3 & -2 & | & -10 \\ 3 & -1 & 1 & | & 4 \end{bmatrix} \begin{matrix} \\ R_2 - 2R_1 \rightarrow \\ R_3 - 3R_1 \rightarrow \end{matrix} \begin{bmatrix} 1 & 2 & 3 & | & 14 \\ 0 & -7 & -8 & | & -38 \\ 0 & -7 & -8 & | & -38 \end{bmatrix} R_3 - R_2 \rightarrow \begin{bmatrix} 1 & 2 & 3 & | & 14 \\ 0 & -7 & -8 & | & -38 \\ 0 & 0 & 0 & | & 0 \end{bmatrix}$$

Row 3 represents the equation $0 = 0$. The system is dependent.

54. $\begin{bmatrix} 1 & 2 & 3 & | & 6 \\ -1 & 3 & 4 & | & 6 \\ 0 & 5 & 7 & | & 12 \end{bmatrix} R_2 + R_1 \rightarrow \begin{bmatrix} 1 & 2 & 3 & | & 6 \\ 0 & 5 & 7 & | & 12 \\ 0 & 5 & 7 & | & 12 \end{bmatrix} R_3 - R_2 \rightarrow \begin{bmatrix} 1 & 2 & 3 & | & 6 \\ 0 & 5 & 7 & | & 12 \\ 0 & 0 & 0 & | & 0 \end{bmatrix}$

Row 3 represents the equation $0 = 0$. The system is dependent.

55. $\begin{bmatrix} a & 0 & 0 & | & 1 \\ 0 & b & 0 & | & 1 \\ 0 & 0 & ab & | & 2 \end{bmatrix} \begin{matrix} (1/a)R_1 \rightarrow \\ (1/b)R_2 \rightarrow \\ (1/(ab))R_3 \rightarrow \end{matrix} \begin{bmatrix} 1 & 0 & 0 & | & \frac{1}{a} \\ 0 & 1 & 0 & | & \frac{1}{b} \\ 0 & 0 & 1 & | & \frac{2}{ab} \end{bmatrix}$

The solution is $\left(\frac{1}{a}, \frac{1}{b}, \frac{2}{ab}\right)$.

56. There are no solutions, because $a \neq 0$.

Applications

57. The equation found in example 7 is $W = -374 + 19H + 6L$. When $H = 12$ and $L = 60$,

$W = -374 + 19(12) + 6(60) = 214$ lb.

58. (a) $a + 16b + 26c = 80$
$a + 28b + 45c = 344$
$a + 31b + 54c = 416$

(b) Using the graphing calculator to solve the system, the solution is $a \approx -272.9$, $b \approx 19.8$, $c \approx 1.4$.

So the equation is $W \approx -272.9 + 19.8N + 1.4C$.

(c) When $N = 22$ and $C = 38$, $W \approx -272.9 + 19.8(22) + 1.4(38) \approx 216$ lb.

59. (a) $a + 2b + 1.4c = 3$
$a + 1.5b + 0.65c = 2$
$a + 4b + 3.4c = 6$

(b) Using the graphing calculator to solve the system, the solution is $a = 0.6$, $b = 0.5$, $c = 1$.

So the equation is $H = 0.6 + 0.5M + P$.

(c) When $M = 3$ and $P = 2$, $H \approx 0.6 + 0.5(3) + (2) = 4.1 \approx 4$ people.

60. (a) $a + 276b + 94c = 160$
$a + 203b + 84c = 125$
$a + 245b + 79c = 140$

(b) Using the graphing calculator to solve the system, the solution is $a \approx 0.828$, $b \approx 0.414$, $c \approx 0.478$.

So the equation is $H \approx 0.828 + 0.414D + 0.478T$.

(c) When $D = 220$ and $T = 81$, $H \approx 0.828 + 0.414(220) + 0.478(81) \approx 131$ ft.

61. Let x, y and z represent the time spent running at 5, 6 and 8 mph respectively. The system needed is:

$\begin{matrix} x + y + z = 2 \\ 5x + 6y + 8z = 12.5 \\ x \quad\quad - z = 0 \end{matrix}$ and so $[A] = \begin{bmatrix} 1 & 1 & 1 & | & 2 \\ 5 & 6 & 8 & | & 12.5 \\ 1 & 0 & -1 & | & 0 \end{bmatrix}$; $\operatorname{rref}([A]) = \begin{bmatrix} 1 & 0 & 0 & | & 0.5 \\ 0 & 1 & 0 & | & 1 \\ 0 & 0 & 1 & | & 0.5 \end{bmatrix}$

The solution is $(0.5, 1, 0.5)$. The runner ran 0.5 hr at 5 mph, 1 hr at 6 mph and 0.5 hr at 8 mph.

62. Let x, y and z represent the required pounds of \$2, \$3 and \$4 candy respectively. The system needed is:

$$\begin{aligned} x + y + z &= 5 \\ 2x + 3y + 4z &= 14.50 \\ y - z &= 0 \end{aligned} \quad \text{and so } [A] = \begin{bmatrix} 1 & 1 & 1 & | & 5 \\ 2 & 3 & 4 & | & 14.5 \\ 0 & 1 & -1 & | & 0 \end{bmatrix}; \text{rref}([A]) = \begin{bmatrix} 1 & 0 & 0 & | & 2 \\ 0 & 1 & 0 & | & 1.5 \\ 0 & 0 & 1 & | & 1.5 \end{bmatrix}$$

The solution is $(2, 1.5, 1.5)$. Use 2 pounds of \$2 candy, and 1.5 pounds each of \$3 and \$4 candy.

63.   Let x, y and z represent the amount invested at 5%, 8% and 12% respectively. The system needed is:

$$\begin{aligned} x + y + z &= 3000 \\ 0.05x + 0.08y + 0.12z &= 285 \\ 3x \qquad\quad - z &= 0 \end{aligned} \quad \text{and so } [A] = \begin{bmatrix} 1 & 1 & 1 & | & 3000 \\ 0.05 & 0.08 & 0.12 & | & 285 \\ 3 & 0 & -1 & | & 0 \end{bmatrix}; \text{rref}([A]) = \begin{bmatrix} 1 & 0 & 0 & | & 500 \\ 0 & 1 & 0 & | & 1000 \\ 0 & 0 & 1 & | & 1500 \end{bmatrix}$$

The solution is $(500, 1000, 1500)$. There was \$500 invested at 5%, \$1000 at 8% and \$1500 at 12%.

64.   Let x, y and z represent the measure of the largest, middle and smallest angle respectively. The system needed is:

$$\begin{aligned} x + y + z &= 180 \\ x \qquad - 2z &= 0 \\ x - y \qquad &= 10 \end{aligned} \quad \text{and so } [A] = \begin{bmatrix} 1 & 1 & 1 & | & 180 \\ 1 & 0 & -2 & | & 0 \\ 1 & -1 & 0 & | & 10 \end{bmatrix}; \text{rref}([A]) = \begin{bmatrix} 1 & 0 & 0 & | & 76 \\ 0 & 1 & 0 & | & 66 \\ 0 & 0 & 1 & | & 38 \end{bmatrix}$$

The solution is $(76, 66, 38)$. The angles are $76°$, $66°$, and $38°$.

Checking Basic Concepts for Sections 4.5 & 4.6

1. $(1, 3, -1)$ satisfies all three equations.

2.   Multiply the first equation by -2 and add the first and second equations to eliminate the variable x.

$$\begin{aligned} -2x + 2y - 2z &= -4 \\ \underline{2x - 3y + z} &= \underline{-1} \\ -y - z &= -5 \end{aligned}$$

Add the first and third equations to eliminate the variables x and y.

$$\begin{aligned} x - y + z &= 2 \\ \underline{-x + y + z} &= \underline{4} \\ 2z &= 6 \end{aligned}$$

And so $z = 3$. Substitute $z = 3$ into the first *new* equation: $-y - (3) = -5 \Rightarrow -y = -2 \Rightarrow y = 2$

Substitute $y = 2$ and $z = 3$ into the *original* first equation: $x - (2) + (3) = 2 \Rightarrow x = 1$

The solution is $(1, 2, 3)$.

3.   (a)

$$\begin{bmatrix} 1 & 2 & 1 & | & 1 \\ 1 & 1 & 1 & | & -1 \\ 0 & 1 & 1 & | & 1 \end{bmatrix} R_2 - R_1 \rightarrow \begin{bmatrix} 1 & 2 & 1 & | & 1 \\ 0 & -1 & 0 & | & -2 \\ 1 & 1 & 1 & | & 1 \end{bmatrix} \begin{matrix} R_1 + 2R_2 \rightarrow \\ -1R_2 \rightarrow \\ R_3 + R_2 \rightarrow \end{matrix} \begin{bmatrix} 1 & 0 & 1 & | & -3 \\ 0 & 1 & 0 & | & 2 \\ 0 & 0 & 1 & | & -1 \end{bmatrix}$$

$$R_1 - R_3 \rightarrow \begin{bmatrix} 1 & 0 & 0 & | & -2 \\ 0 & 1 & 0 & | & 2 \\ 0 & 0 & 1 & | & -1 \end{bmatrix}; \text{ The solution is } (-2, 2, -1).$$

(b) $[A] = \begin{bmatrix} 1 & 2 & 1 & | & 1 \\ 1 & 1 & 1 & | & -1 \\ 0 & 1 & 1 & | & 1 \end{bmatrix}; \text{rref}([A]) = \begin{bmatrix} 1 & 0 & 0 & | & -2 \\ 0 & 1 & 0 & | & 2 \\ 0 & 0 & 1 & | & -1 \end{bmatrix}; \text{ The solution is } (-2, 2, -1).$

4.7: Determinants

concepts

1.   square

2.   number

3.   system of linear equations

4.   0

Calculating Determinants

5. $\det A = 1(-8) - 3(-2) = -8 + 6 = -2$

6. $\det A = 5(7) - 3(-1) = 35 + 3 = 38$

7. $\det A = -3(-1) - 8(7) = 3 - 56 = -53$

8. $\det A = 0(1) - (-3)(-7) = 0 - 21 = -21$

9. $\det A = 23(-13) - 6(4) = -299 - 24 = -323$

10. $\det A = 44(32) - (-9)(-51) = 1408 - 459 = 949$

11. $\det A = 1\left[(1)(7) - (-4)(-3)\right] - 0\left[(-1)(7) - (-4)(2)\right] + 0\left[(-1)(-3) - (1)(2)\right] = -5 - 0 + 0 = -5$

12. $\det A = 2\left[(4)(4) - (1)(-2)\right] - (-1)\left[(-1)(4) - (1)(-5)\right] + 0\left[(-1)(-2) - (4)(-5)\right] = 36 + 1 + 0 = 37$

13. $\det A = 2\left[(-2)(8) - (1)(6)\right] - 1\left[(-1)(8) - (1)(0)\right] + 0\left[(-1)(6) - (-2)(0)\right] = -44 + 8 + 0 = -36$

14. $\det A = 0\left[(-6)(7) - (-2)(10)\right] - 3\left[(1)(7) - (-2)(-4)\right] + 4\left[(1)(10) - (-6)(-4)\right] = 0 + 3 - 56 = -53$

15. $\det A = (-1)\left[(-3)(7) - (-3)(5)\right] - 3\left[(3)(7) - (-3)(5)\right] + 2\left[(3)(5) - (-3)(5)\right] = 6 - 108 + 60 = -42$

16. $\det A = 6\left[(0)(-1) - (5)(-3)\right] - 7\left[(-1)(-1) - (5)(9)\right] + 2\left[(-1)(-3) - (0)(9)\right] = 90 + 308 + 6 = 404$

17. $\det A = 5\left[(-2)(5) - (0)(0)\right] - 0\left[(0)(5) - (0)(0)\right] + 0\left[(0)(0) - (-2)(0)\right] = -50 - 0 + 0 = -50$

18. $\det A = 1\left[(4)(9) - (6)(6)\right] - 2\left[(2)(9) - (6)(3)\right] + 3\left[(2)(6) - (4)(3)\right] = 0 + 0 + 0 = 0$

19. $\det A = 0\left[(3)(9) - (5)(-9)\right] - 0\left[(2)(9) - (5)(-3)\right] + 0\left[(2)(-9) - (3)(-3)\right] = 0 - 0 + 0 = 0$

20. $\det A = 3\left[(5)(-1) - (0)(7)\right] - 0\left[(-1)(-1) - (0)(2)\right] + 0\left[(-1)(7) - (5)(2)\right] = -15 - 0 + 0 = -15$

21.   Using the calculator we find $\det\left([A]\right) = -3555$.

22.   Using the calculator we find $\det\left([A]\right) = -7.027$.

23.   Using the calculator we find $\det\left([A]\right) = -7466.5$.

24.   Using the calculator we find $\det\left([A]\right) = 798,584$.

25. $\det A = a\,(bc - 0) - 0\,(0 \cdot c - 0) + 0\,(0 - 0 \cdot b) = abc$

26. $\det A = 0\,(bc-0)-0\,(ac-0)+0(a\cdot 0-0\cdot b)=0$

Calculating Area

27. The triangle has vertices (3, 2), (5, 8) and (9, 5). The matrix needed is $A=\begin{bmatrix}3&5&9\\2&8&5\\1&1&1\end{bmatrix}$.

The area is $D=\left|\dfrac{1}{2}\det([A])\right|=15\text{ ft}^2$.

28. The triangle has vertices (–4, 4), (4, –4) and (6, 6). The matrix needed is $A=\begin{bmatrix}-4&4&6\\4&-4&6\\1&1&1\end{bmatrix}$.

The area is $D=\left|\dfrac{1}{2}\det([A])\right|=48\text{ ft}^2$.

29. The triangle has vertices (–6, –4), (2, 6) and (6, –2). The matrix needed is $A=\begin{bmatrix}-6&2&6\\-4&6&-2\\1&1&1\end{bmatrix}$.

The area is $D=\left|\dfrac{1}{2}\det([A])\right|=52\text{ ft}^2$.

30. The triangle has vertices (–100, 50), (50, –50) and (100, 0). The matrix needed is $A=\begin{bmatrix}-100&50&100\\50&-50&0\\1&1&1\end{bmatrix}$.

The area is $D=\left|\dfrac{1}{2}\det([A])\right|=6250\text{ ft}^2$.

31. Split the figure into two triangles with vertices (2, 1), (3, 6), (9, 3) and vertices (3, 6), (7, 7), (9, 3).

The matrices needed are $A=\begin{bmatrix}2&3&9\\1&6&3\\1&1&1\end{bmatrix}$ and $B=\begin{bmatrix}3&7&9\\6&7&3\\1&1&1\end{bmatrix}$.

The area is $D=\left|\dfrac{1}{2}\det([A])\right|+\left|\dfrac{1}{2}\det([B])\right|=16.5+9=25.5\text{ ft}^2$.

32. Split the figure into two triangles with vertices (–6, –2), (–4, 6), (4, 4) and vertices (–6, –2), (4, 4), (6, –6).

The matrices needed are $A=\begin{bmatrix}-6&-4&4\\-2&6&4\\1&1&1\end{bmatrix}$ and $B=\begin{bmatrix}-6&4&6\\-2&4&-6\\1&1&1\end{bmatrix}$.

The area is $D=\left|\dfrac{1}{2}\det([A])\right|+\left|\dfrac{1}{2}\det([B])\right|=34+56=90\text{ ft}^2$.

Cramer's Rule

33. $E=\det\begin{bmatrix}4&3\\20&-4\end{bmatrix}=-16-60=-76;\quad F=\det\begin{bmatrix}5&4\\6&20\end{bmatrix}=100-24=76$

$D=\det\begin{bmatrix}5&3\\6&-4\end{bmatrix}=-20-18=-38;$ The solution is $x=\dfrac{E}{D}=\dfrac{-76}{-38}=2$ and $y=\dfrac{F}{D}=\dfrac{76}{-38}=-2$.

34. $E = \det \begin{bmatrix} -5 & 4 \\ -32 & 4 \end{bmatrix} = -20 - (-128) = 108; \quad F = \det \begin{bmatrix} -5 & -5 \\ 4 & -32 \end{bmatrix} = 160 - (-20) = 180$

   $D = \det \begin{bmatrix} -5 & 4 \\ 4 & 4 \end{bmatrix} = -20 - 16 = -36; \quad \text{The solution is } x = \frac{E}{D} = \frac{108}{-36} = -3 \text{ and } y = \frac{F}{D} = \frac{180}{-36} = -5.$

35. $E = \det \begin{bmatrix} -3 & -5 \\ -8 & 6 \end{bmatrix} = -18 - 40 = -58; \quad F = \det \begin{bmatrix} 7 & -3 \\ -4 & -8 \end{bmatrix} = -56 - 12 = -68$

   $D = \det \begin{bmatrix} 7 & -5 \\ -4 & 6 \end{bmatrix} = 42 - 20 = 22; \quad \text{The solution is } x = \frac{E}{D} = \frac{-58}{22} = -\frac{29}{11} \text{ and } y = \frac{F}{D} = \frac{-68}{22} = -\frac{34}{11}.$

36. $E = \det \begin{bmatrix} -17 & -9 \\ 9 & 4 \end{bmatrix} = -68 - (-81) = 13; \quad F = \det \begin{bmatrix} -4 & -17 \\ 8 & 9 \end{bmatrix} = -36 - (-136) = 100$

   $D = \det \begin{bmatrix} -4 & -9 \\ 8 & 4 \end{bmatrix} = -16 - (-72) = 56; \quad \text{The solution is } x = \frac{E}{D} = \frac{13}{56} \text{ and } y = \frac{F}{D} = \frac{100}{56} = \frac{25}{14}.$

37. $E = \det \begin{bmatrix} -61 & -3 \\ -23 & -4 \end{bmatrix} = 244 - 69 = 175; \quad F = \det \begin{bmatrix} 8 & -61 \\ -1 & -23 \end{bmatrix} = -184 - 61 = -245$

   $D = \det \begin{bmatrix} 8 & -3 \\ -1 & -4 \end{bmatrix} = -32 - 3 = -35; \quad \text{The solution is } x = \frac{E}{D} = \frac{175}{-35} = -5 \text{ and } y = \frac{F}{D} = \frac{-245}{-35} = 7.$

38. $E = \det \begin{bmatrix} -188 & 15 \\ -173 & 23 \end{bmatrix} = -4324 - (-2595) = -1729; \quad F = \det \begin{bmatrix} 22 & -188 \\ 16 & -173 \end{bmatrix} = -3806 - (-3008) = -798$

   $D = \det \begin{bmatrix} 22 & 15 \\ 16 & 23 \end{bmatrix} = 506 - 240 = 266; \quad \text{The solution is } x = \frac{E}{D} = \frac{-1729}{266} = -\frac{13}{2} \text{ and } y = \frac{F}{D} = \frac{-798}{266} = -3.$

Checking Basic Concepts for Section 4.7

1.   (a) $\det A = -3(3) - (-2)(4) = -9 + 8 = -1$

   (b) $\det A = 1[(1)(-1) - (2)(1)] - 5[(-2)(-1) - (2)(3)] + 0[(-2)(1) - (1)(3)] = -3 + 20 + 0 = 17$

2. $E = \det \begin{bmatrix} -14 & -1 \\ -36 & -4 \end{bmatrix} = 56 - 36 = 20; \quad F = \det \begin{bmatrix} 2 & -14 \\ 3 & -36 \end{bmatrix} = -72 - (-42) = -30$

   $D = \det \begin{bmatrix} 2 & -1 \\ 3 & -4 \end{bmatrix} = -8 - (-3) = -5; \quad \text{The solution is } x = \frac{E}{D} = \frac{20}{-5} = -4 \text{ and } y = \frac{F}{D} = \frac{-30}{-5} = 6.$

3.   The triangle has vertices $(-1, 2)$, $(5, 6)$ and $(2, -3)$. The matrix needed is $A = \begin{bmatrix} -1 & 5 & 2 \\ 2 & 6 & -3 \\ 1 & 1 & 1 \end{bmatrix}$.

   The area is $D = \left| \frac{1}{2} \det([A]) \right| = 21$ square units.

Chapter 4 Review Exercises

Section 4.1

1. $(3, 2)$ is a solution since it satisfies both equations.

2. $(4, -3)$ is a solution since it satisfies both equations.

3.   The unique solution is the intersection point $(-1, -3)$.

4. Since $Y_1 = Y_2 = 8.5$ when $x = 3.5$, the solution is $(3.5, 8.5)$.

5. Note that $x + y = 6 \Rightarrow y = -x + 6$ and $x - y = -4 \Rightarrow y = x + 4$.

    Graph $Y_1 = -X + 6$ and $Y_2 = X + 4$ in $[0, 5, 1]$ by $[0, 8, 1]$. See Figure 5. The intersection point is $(1, 5)$.

    Since there is one unique intersection point, the system is consistent. The equations are independent.

    [0, 5, 1] by [0, 8, 1]   [–10, 10, 1] by [–10, 10, 1]

    Figure 5   Figure 6

6. Note that $x - y = -2 \Rightarrow y = x + 2$ and $-2x + 2y = 4 \Rightarrow y = x + 2$.

    Graph $Y_1 = X + 2$ and $Y_2 = X + 2$ in $[-10, 10, 1]$ by $[-10, 10, 1]$. See Figure 6. The graphs coincide. The solution is $\{(x, y) | x - y = -2\}$. The system is consistent, and the equations are dependent.

7. Note that $4x + 2y = 1 \Rightarrow y = -2x + \dfrac{1}{2}$ and $2x + y = 5 \Rightarrow y = -2x + 5$.

    Graph $Y_1 = -2X + (1/2)$ and $Y_2 = -2X + 5$ in $[-10, 10, 1]$ by $[-10, 10, 1]$. See Figure 7.

    Since the two lines are parallel, the system has no solutions. The system is inconsistent.

8. Note that $x - 3y = 5 \Rightarrow y = \dfrac{1}{3}x - \dfrac{5}{3}$ and $x + 5y = -3 \Rightarrow y = -\dfrac{1}{5}x - \dfrac{3}{5}$.

    Graph $Y_1 = (1/3)X - (5/3)$ and $Y_2 = (-1/5)X - (3/5)$ in $[0, 3, 1]$ by $[-3, 0, 1]$. See Figure 8. The intersection point is $(2, -1)$.

    Since there is one unique intersection point, the system is consistent. The equations are independent.

    [–10, 10, 1] by [–10, 10, 1]   [0, 3, 1] by [–3, 0, 1]

    Figure 7   Figure 8   Figure 9   Figure 10

9. Note that $3x + y = 7 \Rightarrow y = -3x + 7$ and $6x + y = 16 \Rightarrow y = -6x + 16$.

    Table $Y_1 = -3X + 7$ and $Y_2 = -6X + 16$ with TblStart = 0 and ΔTbl = 1. See Figure 9.

    Since $Y_1 = Y_2 = -2$ when $X = 3$, the solution is $(3, -2)$.

10. Note that $4x + 2y = -6 \Rightarrow y = -2x - 3$ and $3x - y = -7 \Rightarrow y = 3x + 7$.

    Table $Y_1 = -2X - 3$ and $Y_2 = 3X + 7$ with TblStart = –5 and ΔTbl = 1. See Figure 10.

    Since $Y_1 = Y_2 = 1$ when $X = -2$, the solution is $(-2, 1)$.

11. (a) Let x and y represent the two numbers. Then the system needed is $x + y = 25$ and $x - y = 10$.

    (b) Note that $x + y = 25 \Rightarrow y = -x + 25$ and $x - y = 10 \Rightarrow y = x - 10$.

The graphs of these equations (not shown) intersect at the point (17.5, 7.5). The numbers are 17.5 and 7.5.

12.   (a) Let x and y represent the two numbers. Then the system needed is $3x - 2y = 19$ and $x + y = 18$.

(b) Note that $3x - 2y = 19 \Rightarrow y = \dfrac{3}{2}x - \dfrac{19}{2}$ and $x + y = 18 \Rightarrow y = -x + 18$.

The graphs of these equations (not shown) intersect at the point (11, 7). The numbers are 11 and 7.

13.   Note that $\pi x - 2.1y = \sqrt{2} \Rightarrow -2.1y = -\pi x + \sqrt{2} \Rightarrow y = -\dfrac{1}{2.1}(-\pi x + \sqrt{2})$ and $\sqrt{3}x + y = \dfrac{5}{6} \Rightarrow y = -\sqrt{3}x + \dfrac{5}{6}$.

Graph $Y_1 = -1/2.1(-\pi X + \sqrt{(2)})$ and $Y_2 = -\sqrt{(3)}X + 5/6$ in $[-10, 10, 1]$ by $[-10, 10, 1]$. The solution is approximately $(0.467, 0.025)$.

14.   Note that $\sqrt{5}x - \pi y = \dfrac{2}{7} \Rightarrow -\pi y = -\sqrt{5}x + \dfrac{2}{7} \Rightarrow y = -\dfrac{1}{\pi}\left(-\sqrt{5}x + \dfrac{2}{7}\right)$ and

$x + 0.3y = \pi \Rightarrow 0.3y = -x + \pi \Rightarrow y = \dfrac{1}{0.3}(-x + \pi)$. Graph $Y_1 = -1/\pi(-\sqrt{(5)}X + 2/7)$

and $Y_2 = 1/0.3(-X + \pi)$ in $[-10, 10, 1]$ by $[-10, 10, 1]$. The solution is approximately $(2.611, 1.768)$.

Section 4.2

15.   Note that $x + 2y = -1 \Rightarrow x = -2y - 1$. Substituting $x = -2y - 1$ into the first equation yields the following:

$2(-2y - 1) + 5y = -1 \Rightarrow y = 1$ and so $x = -2(1) - 1 \Rightarrow x = -3$. The solution is $(-3, 1)$.

16.   Note that $3x + y = 6 \Rightarrow y = -3x + 6$. Substituting $y = -3x + 6$ into the second equation yields the following:

$4x + 5(-3x + 6) = 8 \Rightarrow -11x = -22 \Rightarrow x = 2$ and so $y = -3(2) + 6 \Rightarrow y = 0$. The solution is $(2, 0)$.

17.   Note that $4x + 2y = 0 \Rightarrow y = -2x$. Substituting $y = -2x$ into the first equation yields the following:

$2x - 3(-2x) = -8 \Rightarrow 8x = -8 \Rightarrow x = -1$ and so $y = -2(-1) = 2$. The solution is $(-1, 2)$.

18.   Note that $5x + 3y = -1 \Rightarrow y = \dfrac{-5x - 1}{3}$. Substituting $y = \dfrac{-5x - 1}{3}$ in the second equation yields the following:

$3x - 5\left(\dfrac{-5x - 1}{3}\right) = -21 \Rightarrow 9x + 25x + 5 = -63 \Rightarrow 34x = -68 \Rightarrow x = -2$ and so $y = \dfrac{-5(-2) - 1}{3} = 3$.

The solution is $(-2, 3)$.

19.   Adding the two equations will eliminate the variable y.

$$3x + y = 4$$
$$\underline{2x - y = -2}$$
$$5x = 2$$

Thus, $x = \dfrac{2}{5}$. And so $3\left(\dfrac{2}{5}\right) + y = 4 \Rightarrow y = 4 - \dfrac{6}{5} \Rightarrow y = \dfrac{14}{5}$. The solution is $\left(\dfrac{2}{5}, \dfrac{14}{5}\right)$.

20.   Multiply the first equation by 2, the second equation by 3 and add the equations to eliminate the variable y.

$$4x + 6y = -26$$
$$\underline{9x - 6y = 0}$$
$$13x = -26$$

Thus, $x = -2$. And so $2(-2) + 3y = -13 \Rightarrow 3y = -9 \Rightarrow y = -3$. The solution is $(-2, -3)$.

21.   Multiplying the first equation by 2 and adding the two equations will eliminate both variables.

$$6x - 2y = 10$$
$$\underline{-6x + 2y = -10}$$
$$0 = 0$$

This is always true and the system is dependent with solutions: $\{(x, y)|3x - y = 5\}$.

22.   Multiplying the second equation by 2 and adding the two equations will eliminate both variables.

$$8x - 6y = 7$$
$$\underline{-8x + 6y = 22}$$
$$0 = 29$$

This is always false and the system is inconsistent. No solution.

Section 4.3

23.   See Figure 23.

24.   See Figure 24.

Figure 23   Figure 24   Figure 25

25.   See Figure 25.

26.   See Figure 26.

27.   See Figure 27.

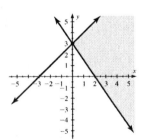

Figure 26   Figure 27   Figure 28

28.   See Figure 28.

29.   See Figure 29.

Figure 29   Figure 30

30.   See Figure 30.

31.   The equation of a vertical line through the point $(1, 0)$ is $x = 1$. The equation of a horizontal line through the point $(0, -1)$ is $y = -1$. The system of inequalities is $y < -1$ and $x > 1$.

32.   The equation of a line through the points $(-1, -1)$ and $(0, 1)$ is $y = 2x + 1$. The equation of a line through the points $(0, 4)$ and $(4, 0)$ is $y = -x + 4$. The system of inequalities is $y \leq -x + 4$ and $y \geq 2x + 1$.

Section 4.4

33.   The maximum value of R occurs at one of the vertices.

For $(1, 1)$, $R = 7(1) + 8(1) = 15$. For $(1, 3)$, $R = 7(1) + 8(3) = 31$. For $(3, 1)$, $R = 7(3) + 8(1) = 29$.

The maximum value is $R = 31$.

34.   The minimum value of R occurs at one of the vertices.

For $(1, 1)$, $C = (1) + 2(1) = 3$. For $(1, 3)$, $C = (1) + 2(3) = 7$. For $(3, 1)$, $C = (3) + 2(1) = 5$.

The minimum value is $C = 3$.

35.   From the graph of the region of feasible solutions (not shown), the vertices are $(0, 1)$, $(0, 3)$, $(3, 0)$, and $(1, 0)$.

The maximum value of R occurs at one of the vertices. For $(0, 1)$, $R = 2(0) + (1) = 1$.

For $(0, 3)$, $R = 2(0) + (3) = 3$. For $(3, 0)$, $R = 2(3) + (0) = 6$. For $(1, 0)$, $R = 2(1) + (0) = 2$.

The maximum value is $R = 6$.

36.   From the graph of the region of feasible solutions (not shown), the vertices are $(0, 0)$, $(0, 4)$, $(3, 3)$, and $(4, 0)$.

Note: to find the intersection point $(3, 3)$, solve the system of equations $3x + y = 12$ and $x + 3y = 12$.

The maximum value of R occurs at one of the vertices. For $(0, 0)$, $R = 6(0) + 9(0) = 0$.

For $(0, 4)$, $R = 6(0) + 9(4) = 36$. For $(3, 3)$, $R = 6(3) + 9(3) = 45$. For $(4, 0)$, $R = 6(4) + 9(0) = 24$.

The maximum value is $R = 45$.

Section 4.5

37.   Yes, since $3 + (-4) + 5 = 4$.

38. $(1, -1, 2)$ is a solution since it satisfies all three of the equations.

39.   Add the first two equations together to eliminate the variable x.

$$x - y - 2z = -11$$
$$-x + 2y + 3z = 16$$
$$\overline{y + z = 5}$$

From the third equation, $3z = 6 \Rightarrow z = 2$. And so $y + (2) = 5 \Rightarrow y = 3$.

Substitute $z = 2$ and $y = 3$ into the first equation: $x - (3) - 2(2) = -11 \Rightarrow x = -4$

The solution is (–4, 3, 2).

40.   Multiply the second equation by –5 and the third equation by 3. Add these equations to eliminate the variable z.

$$10x - 5y - 15z = 10$$
$$3x - 6y + 15z = -78$$
$$\overline{13x - 11y = -68}$$

Multiply the first equation by 11 and add it to this *new* equation to eliminate the variable y.

$$11x + 11y = 44$$
$$13x - 11y = -68$$
$$\overline{24x = -24}$$

And so $x = -1$. Substitute $x = -1$ into the first equation: $(-1) + y = 4 \Rightarrow y = 5$

Substitute $x = -1$ and $y = 5$ into the second equation: $-2(-1) + (5) + 3z = -2 \Rightarrow 3z = -9 \Rightarrow z = -3$

The solution is (–1, 5, –3).

41.   Multiply the second equation by –1 and add it to the third equation to eliminate the variable z.

$$-x - 2y - z = -7$$
$$-2x + y + z = 7$$
$$\overline{-3x - y = 0}$$

Multiply the first equation by –1 and add it to this *new* equation to eliminate the variable y.

$$-2x + y = 5$$
$$-3x - y = 0$$
$$\overline{-5x = 5}$$

And so $x = -1$. Substitute $x = -1$ into the first equation: $2(-1) - y = -5 \Rightarrow y = 3$

Substitute $x = -1$ and $y = 3$ into the second equation: $-2(-1) + (3) + z = 7 \Rightarrow z = 2$

The solution is (–1, 3, 2).

42.   Multiply the second equation by 2 and add the first and second equations to eliminate the variable x.

$$2x + 3y + z = 6$$
$$-2x + 4y + 4z = 6$$
$$\overline{7y + 5z = 12}$$

Add the second and third equations together to eliminate the variable x.

$$-x + 2y + 2z = 3$$
$$\underline{x\ +\ y + 2z = 4}$$
$$3y + 4z = 7$$

Multiply the first *new* equation by 4 and the second *new* equation by –5. Add these to eliminate the variable *z*.

$$28y + 20z = 48$$
$$\underline{-15y - 20z = -35}$$
$$13y = 13$$

And so $y = 1$. Substitute $y = 1$ into the second *new* equation: $3(1) + 4z = 7 \Rightarrow 4z = 4 \Rightarrow z = 1$

Substitute $y = 1$ and $z = 1$ into the *original* third equation: $x + (1) + 2(1) = 4 \Rightarrow x = 1$

The solution is (1, 1, 1).

43.   Add the first two equations to eliminate the variable *y*.

$$x - y + 3z = 2$$
$$\underline{2x + y + 4z = 3}$$
$$3x\qquad + 7z = 5$$

Multiply the second equation by –2 and add to the third equation to eliminate the variable *y*.

$$-4x - 2y - 8z = -6$$
$$\underline{x + 2y + \ z = 5}$$
$$-3x\qquad -7z = -1$$

Add this new equation to the result of the first sum to eliminate the variables *x* and *z*.

$$3x + 7z = 5$$
$$\underline{-3x - 7z = -1}$$
$$0 = 4 \qquad \text{This is a contradiction. There are no solutions.}$$

44.   Solve the third equation for x: $x + z = 2 \Rightarrow x = 2 - z$. Substitute $x = 2 - z$ into the second equation:

$2 - z + y - z = 1 \Rightarrow y - 2z = -1 \Rightarrow y = 2z - 1$. The system is dependent, and all solutions are of the form of the

ordered triple $(2 - z, 2z - 1, z)$

Section 4.6

45. $\begin{bmatrix} 1 & 1 & 1 & | & -6 \\ 1 & 2 & 1 & | & -8 \\ 0 & 1 & 1 & | & -5 \end{bmatrix} R_2 - R_1 \rightarrow \begin{bmatrix} 1 & 1 & 1 & | & -6 \\ 0 & 1 & 0 & | & -2 \\ 0 & 1 & 1 & | & -5 \end{bmatrix} \begin{matrix} R_1 - R_3 \rightarrow \\ \\ R_3 - R_2 \rightarrow \end{matrix} \begin{bmatrix} 1 & 0 & 0 & | & -1 \\ 0 & 1 & 0 & | & -2 \\ 0 & 0 & 1 & | & -3 \end{bmatrix};$ The solution is (–1, –2, –3).

46. $\begin{bmatrix} 1 & 1 & 1 & | & -3 \\ -1 & 1 & 0 & | & 5 \\ 0 & 1 & 1 & | & -1 \end{bmatrix} \begin{matrix} R_1 - R_3 \rightarrow \\ R_2 + R_1 \rightarrow \end{matrix} \begin{bmatrix} 1 & 0 & 0 & | & -2 \\ 0 & 2 & 1 & | & 2 \\ 0 & 1 & 1 & | & -1 \end{bmatrix} R_2 - R_3 \rightarrow \begin{bmatrix} 1 & 0 & 0 & | & -2 \\ 0 & 1 & 0 & | & 3 \\ 0 & 1 & 1 & | & -1 \end{bmatrix} R_3 - R_2 \rightarrow \begin{bmatrix} 1 & 0 & 0 & | & -2 \\ 0 & 1 & 0 & | & 3 \\ 0 & 0 & 1 & | & -4 \end{bmatrix}$

The solution is (–2, 3, –4).

47. $\begin{bmatrix} 1 & 2 & -1 & | & 1 \\ -1 & 1 & -2 & | & 5 \\ 0 & 2 & 1 & | & 10 \end{bmatrix} \begin{matrix} R_1 - R_3 \rightarrow \\ R_2 + R_1 \rightarrow \end{matrix} \begin{bmatrix} 1 & 0 & -2 & | & -9 \\ 0 & 3 & -3 & | & 6 \\ 0 & 2 & 1 & | & 10 \end{bmatrix} (1/3)R_2 \rightarrow \begin{bmatrix} 1 & 0 & -2 & | & -9 \\ 0 & 1 & -1 & | & 2 \\ 0 & 2 & 1 & | & 10 \end{bmatrix}$

$$\begin{array}{c} \\ \\ R_3 - 2R_2 \to \end{array} \begin{bmatrix} 1 & 0 & -2 & | & -9 \\ 0 & 1 & -1 & | & 2 \\ 0 & 0 & 3 & | & 6 \end{bmatrix} (1/3)R_3 \to \begin{bmatrix} 1 & 0 & -2 & | & -9 \\ 0 & 1 & -1 & | & 2 \\ 0 & 0 & 1 & | & 2 \end{bmatrix} \begin{array}{c} R_1 + 2R_3 \to \\ R_2 + R_3 \to \\ \\ \end{array} \begin{bmatrix} 1 & 0 & 0 & | & -5 \\ 0 & 1 & 0 & | & 4 \\ 0 & 0 & 1 & | & 2 \end{bmatrix}$$

The solution is (–5, 4, 2).

48.
$$\begin{bmatrix} 2 & 2 & -2 & | & -14 \\ -2 & -3 & 2 & | & 12 \\ 1 & 1 & -4 & | & -22 \end{bmatrix} \begin{array}{c} (1/2)R_1 \to \\ R_2 + R_1 \to \\ R_3 - (1/2)R_1 \to \end{array} \begin{bmatrix} 1 & 1 & -1 & | & -7 \\ 0 & -1 & 0 & | & -2 \\ 0 & 0 & -3 & | & -15 \end{bmatrix} \begin{array}{c} R_1 + R_2 \to \\ -1R_2 \to \\ (-1/3)R_3 \to \end{array} \begin{bmatrix} 1 & 0 & -1 & | & -9 \\ 0 & 1 & 0 & | & 2 \\ 0 & 0 & 1 & | & 5 \end{bmatrix}$$

$$R_1 + R_3 \to \begin{bmatrix} 1 & 0 & 0 & | & -4 \\ 0 & 1 & 0 & | & 2 \\ 0 & 0 & 1 & | & 5 \end{bmatrix}; \text{ The solution is } (-4, 2, 5).$$

49.   See example 6 in section 4.6 in the text for graphing calculator instructions.

$$[A] = \begin{bmatrix} 3 & -2 & 6 & | & -17 \\ -2 & -1 & 5 & | & 20 \\ 0 & 4 & 7 & | & 30 \end{bmatrix}; \text{rref}([A]) = \begin{bmatrix} 1 & 0 & 0 & | & -7 \\ 0 & 1 & 0 & | & 4 \\ 0 & 0 & 1 & | & 2 \end{bmatrix}; \text{ The solution is } (-7, 4, 2).$$

50.   See example 6 in section 4.6 in the text for graphing calculator instructions.

$$[A] = \begin{bmatrix} 19 & -13 & -7 & | & 7.4 \\ 22 & 33 & -8 & | & 110.5 \\ 10 & -56 & 9 & | & 23.7 \end{bmatrix}; \text{rref}([A]) = \begin{bmatrix} 1 & 0 & 0 & | & 5.4 \\ 0 & 1 & 0 & | & 2.1 \\ 0 & 0 & 1 & | & 9.7 \end{bmatrix}; \text{ The solution is } (5.4, 2.1, 9.7)$$

Section 4.7

51. $\det A = 6(2) - (-4)(-5) = 12 - 20 = -8$

52. $\det A = 0(9) - 5(-6) = 0 + 30 = 30$

53. $\det A = 3\left[(4)(1) - (-3)(7)\right] - 1\left[(-5)(1) - (-3)(-3)\right] + 0\left[(-5)(7) - (4)(-3)\right] = 75 - (-14) + 0 = 89$

54. $\det A = -2\left[(1)(8) - (-5)(-3)\right] - 2\left[(-1)(8) - (-5)(-7)\right] + 3\left[(-1)(-3) - (1)(-7)\right] = 14 - (-86) + 30 = 130$

55.   Using the calculator we find $\det([A]) = 181,845$

56.   Using the calculator we find $\det([A]) = 67.688$

57.   The triangle has vertices (–4, 6), (–2, –4) and (6, 2). The matrix needed is $A = \begin{bmatrix} -4 & -2 & 6 \\ 6 & -4 & 2 \\ 1 & 1 & 1 \end{bmatrix}$.

The area is $D = \left| \dfrac{1}{2}\det([A]) \right| = 46 \text{ ft}^2$.

58.   The triangle has vertices (–12, –8), (4, 8) and (8, –4). The matrix needed is $A = \begin{bmatrix} -12 & 4 & 8 \\ -8 & 8 & -4 \\ 1 & 1 & 1 \end{bmatrix}$.

The area is $D = \left| \dfrac{1}{2}\det([A]) \right| = 128 \text{ ft}^2$.

59. $E = \det \begin{bmatrix} 8 & 6 \\ 18 & -8 \end{bmatrix} = -64 - 108 = -172; \quad F = \det \begin{bmatrix} 7 & 8 \\ 5 & 18 \end{bmatrix} = 126 - 40 = 86$

$D = \det \begin{bmatrix} 7 & 6 \\ 5 & -8 \end{bmatrix} = -56 - 30 = -86; \text{ The solution is } x = \dfrac{E}{D} = \dfrac{-172}{-86} = 2 \text{ and } y = \dfrac{F}{D} = \dfrac{86}{-86} = -1.$

60. $E = \det\begin{bmatrix} 25 & 5 \\ -3 & 4 \end{bmatrix} = 100 + 15 = 115; \quad F = \det\begin{bmatrix} -2 & 25 \\ 3 & -3 \end{bmatrix} = 6 - 75 = -69$

$D = \det\begin{bmatrix} -2 & 5 \\ 3 & 4 \end{bmatrix} = -8 - 15 = -23; \quad$ The solution is $x = \dfrac{E}{D} = \dfrac{115}{-23} = -5$ and $y = \dfrac{F}{D} = \dfrac{-69}{-23} = 3.$

61. $E = \det\begin{bmatrix} 1.5 & -6 \\ 8 & -5 \end{bmatrix} = -7.5 + 48 = 40.5; \quad F = \det\begin{bmatrix} 3 & 1.5 \\ 7 & 8 \end{bmatrix} = 24 - 10.5 = 13.5$

$D = \det\begin{bmatrix} 3 & -6 \\ 7 & -5 \end{bmatrix} = -15 + 42 = 27; \quad$ The solution is $x = \dfrac{E}{D} = \dfrac{40.5}{27} = \dfrac{3}{2}$ and $y = \dfrac{F}{D} = \dfrac{13.5}{27} = \dfrac{1}{2}.$

62. $E = \det\begin{bmatrix} -47 & 4 \\ 63 & -7 \end{bmatrix} = 329 - 252 = 77; \quad F = \det\begin{bmatrix} -5 & -47 \\ 6 & 63 \end{bmatrix} = -315 + 282 = -33$

$D = \det\begin{bmatrix} -5 & 4 \\ 6 & -7 \end{bmatrix} = 35 - 24 = 11; \quad$ The solution is $x = \dfrac{E}{D} = \dfrac{77}{11} = 7$ and $y = \dfrac{F}{D} = \dfrac{-33}{11} = -3.$

Applications

63. Let x and y represent pedestrian fatalities for 1994 and 2004 respectively. Then the system needed is

$x + y = 10{,}130$ and $x - y = 848.$ Adding the two equations will eliminate the variable y.

$\begin{aligned} x + y &= 10{,}130 \\ x - y &= 848 \\ \hline 2x &= 10{,}978 \end{aligned}$ Thus, $x = 5489.$ And so $(5489) + y = 10{,}130 \Rightarrow y = 4641.$

There were 5489 pedestrian fatalities in 1994 and 4641 in 2004.

64. Let x and y represent the time spent on the stair climber and the bicycle respectively. Then the system needed is $x + y = 30$ and $11.5x + 9y = 290.$ Multiplying the first equation by -9 and adding the two equations will eliminate the variable y.

$\begin{aligned} -9x - 9y &= -270 \\ 11.5x + 9y &= 290 \\ \hline 2.5x &= 20 \end{aligned}$ Thus, $x = 8.$ And so $(8) + y = 30 \Rightarrow y = 22.$

The athlete spent 8 minutes on the stair climber and 22 minutes on the stationary bicycle.

65. First note that the amounts of candy and cashews cannot be negative, so $x \geq 0$ and $y \geq 0$. Also, if the total cost must be less than or equal to $20 then the inequality $4x + 5y \leq 20$ must be satisfied. See Figure 65.

Figure 65

66. Let x and y represent the amounts of the unsubsidized and subsidized loans, respectively. Then the system of equations is $x + y = 4000$ and $x = y - 500.$ Substitute $x = y - 500$ into the first equation:

$y - 500 + y = 4000 \Rightarrow 2y = 4500 \Rightarrow y = 2250$, and so $x = 2250 - 500 \Rightarrow x = 1750$. The unsubsidized loan is for \$1750 and the subsidized loan is for \$2250.

67.   Let x and y represent the number of shirts and pants respectively. Since a shirt requires 20 minutes of cutting, pants require 10 minutes of cutting and the cutting machine is only available for 360 minutes each day, $20x + 10y \le 360$. Since a shirt requires 10 minutes of sewing, pants require 20 minutes of sewing and the sewing machine is only available for 480 minutes each day, $10x + 20y \le 480$. Since the number of shirts and pants cannot be negative $x \ge 0$ and $y \ge 0$. Here the profit function is $P = 20x + 25y$. From the graph of the region of feasible solutions (not shown), the vertices are (0, 0), (0, 24), (8, 20) and (18, 0). To find (8, 20) solve the system of equations $20x + 10y = 360$ and $10x + 20y = 480$.

The maximum value of P occurs at one of the vertices.

For $(0,\ 0)$, $P = 20(0) + 25(0) = 0$. For $(0,\ 24)$, $P = 20(0) + 25(24) = 600$.

For $(8,\ 20)$, $P = 20(8) + 25(20) = 660$. For $(18,\ 0)$, $P = 20(18) + 25(0) = 360$.

The maximum profit of \$660 is attained when 8 shirts and 20 pants are sold.

68.   Let x and y represent the number of gallons of 30% and 55% solution respectively. Then the system needed is $x + y = 4$ and $0.30x + 0.55y = 1.6$. Multiplying the first equation by –3, the second equation by 10 and adding the two equations will eliminate the variable x.

$$\begin{array}{r} -3x - 3y = -12 \\ 3x + 5.5y = 16 \\ \hline 2.5y = 4 \end{array}$$ Thus, $y = 1.6$. And so $x + (1.6) = 4 \Rightarrow x = 2.4$.

The mechanic should add 2.4 gallons of 30% solution and 1.6 gallons of 55% solution.

69.   Let x and y represent the speed of the boat and the current respectively. Using the formula $d = rt$ the system is $18 = (x + y)(1)$ and $18 = (x - y)(1.5)$. These equations may be written: $x + y = 18$ and $1.5x - 1.5y = 18$.

Multiplying the first equation by 1.5 and adding the equations together will eliminate the variable y.

$$\begin{array}{r} 1.5x + 1.5y = 27 \\ 1.5x - 1.5y = 18 \\ \hline 3x = 45 \end{array}$$ Thus, $x = 15$. And so $(15) + y = 18 \Rightarrow y = 3$.

The boat travels at 15 mph and the river flows at 3 mph.

70.   Let x and y represent the number of \$8 and \$12 tickets respectively. Then the system needed is $x + y = 480$ and $8x + 12y = 4620$. Note that $x + y = 480 \Rightarrow y = -x + 480$ and $8x + 12y = 4620 \Rightarrow y = -\dfrac{2}{3}x + 385$.

Multiplying the first equation by –8 and adding the two equations will eliminate the variable x.

$$\begin{array}{r} -8x - 8y = -3840 \\ 8x + 12y = 4620 \\ \hline 4y = 780 \end{array}$$ Thus, $y = 195$. And so $x + (195) = 480 \Rightarrow x = 285$. The solution is (285, 195).

There were 285 tickets sold costing \$8 each and 195 tickets sold costing \$12 each.

71. (a) $m + 3c + 5b = 14$
          $m + 2c + 4b = 11$
              $c + 3b = 5$

     (b) Using a graphing calculator to solve the system, the solution is (3, 2, 1).

          A malt costs $3.00, cones cost $2.00 and an ice cream bar costs $1.00.

72. Let x, y and z represent the measure of the largest, middle and smallest angle respectively. The system needed is:

     $x + y + z = 180$
     $x - y - z = 20$
     $x \quad - z = 85$

     Using a graphing calculator to solve the system, the solution is (100, 65, 15).

     The measures of the three angles are $100°$, $65°$ and $15°$.

73. Let x, y and z represent the amount of $1.50, $2.00 and $2.50 candy respectively. The system needed is:

     $x \quad + y \quad + z = 12$
     $1.50x + 2.00y + 2.50z = 26$
     $\quad -y \quad + z = 2$

     Using a graphing calculator to solve the system, the solution is (2, 4, 6).

     There should be 2 lb of $1.50 candy, 4 lb of $2.00 candy and 6 lb of $2.50 candy.

74. (a) $a + 202b + 63c = 40$
          $a + 365b + 70c = 50$
          $a + 446b + 77c = 55$

     (b) Using the graphing calculator to solve the system, the solution is $a \approx 27.134$, $b \approx 0.061$, $c \approx 0.009$.

          So the equation is $C \approx 27.134 + 0.061W + 0.009L$.

     (c) When $W = 300$ and $L = 68$, $C \approx 27.134 + 0.061(300) + 0.009(68) = 46.046 \approx 46$ inches.

Chapter 4 Test

1. Note that $2x + y = 7 \Rightarrow y = 7 - 2x$ and $3x - 2y = 7 \Rightarrow y = \dfrac{3x - 7}{2}$.

    Graph $Y_1 = 7 - 2X$ and $Y_2 = (3X - 7)/2$ in [–5, 5, 1] by [–5, 5, 1]. See Figure 1.

    The graphs intersect at (3, 1). The system is consistent. The equations are independent.

2. Note that $8x - 4y = 3 \Rightarrow y = 2x - \dfrac{3}{4}$ and $-4x + 2y = 6 \Rightarrow y = 2x + 3$.

    Graph $Y_1 = 2X - (3/4)$ and $Y_2 = 2X + 3$ in [–5, 5, 1] by [–5, 5, 1]. See Figure 2.

    The system is inconsistent since the lines are parallel. No solutions.

[–5, 5, 1] by [–5, 5, 1]   [–5, 5, 1] by [–5, 5, 1]

Figure 1   Figure 2

3. Note that $2x - 6y = 2 \Rightarrow y = \dfrac{-2x + 2}{-6}$ and $-3x + 9y = -3 \Rightarrow y = \dfrac{3x - 3}{9}$. Graph $Y_1 = (-2X + 2)/-6$ and

   $Y_2 = (3X - 3)/9$ in [–5, 5, 1] by [–5, 5, 1].

   The lines are identical, so the system is consistent and the equations are dependent. The solution is

   $\{(x, y) \mid x - 3y = 1\}$.

4. Note that $2x - 5y = 36 \Rightarrow y = \dfrac{-2x + 36}{-5}$ and $-4x + 3y = -23 \Rightarrow y = \dfrac{4x - 23}{3}$. Graph $Y_1 = (-2X + 36)/-5$ and

   $Y_2 = (4X - 23)/3$ in [–10, 10, 1] by [–10, 10, 1].

   The graphs intersect at $\left(\dfrac{1}{2}, -7\right)$. The system is consistent. The equations are independent.

5. Note that $2x + 5y = -1 \Rightarrow y = -\dfrac{2}{5}x - \dfrac{1}{5}$. Substituting $y = -\dfrac{2}{5}x - \dfrac{1}{5}$ into the second equation yields:

   $3x + 2\left(-\dfrac{2}{5}x - \dfrac{1}{5}\right) = -7 \Rightarrow \dfrac{11}{5}x = -\dfrac{33}{5} \Rightarrow x = -3$ and so $y = -\dfrac{2}{5}(-3) - \dfrac{1}{5} \Rightarrow y = 1$.

   The solution is (–3, 1).

6. (a) Let x and y represent the first and second number respectively. The system is $x - y = 34$ and $x - 2y = 0$.

   (b) Multiplying the first equation by –1 and adding the two equations will eliminate the variable x.

   $\begin{aligned} -x\ \ + y &= -34 \\ x - 2y &= 0 \\ \hline -y &= -34 \end{aligned}$ Thus, $y = 34$. And so $x - (34) = 34 \Rightarrow x = 68$. The solution is (68, 34).

7. Note that $-\pi x + \sqrt{3}y = 3.3 \Rightarrow y = \dfrac{\pi x + 3.3}{\sqrt{3}}$ and $\sqrt{5}x + (1 + \sqrt{2})y = 2.1 \Rightarrow y = \dfrac{-\sqrt{5}x + 2.1}{1 + \sqrt{2}}$. Graph

   $Y_1 = (\pi X + 3.3)/\sqrt{3}$ and $Y_2 = (-\sqrt{5}X + 2.1)/(1 + \sqrt{2})$ in [–5, 5, 1] by [–5, 5, 1].

The graphs intersect at approximately $(-0.378, 1.220)$.

8.   Note that $3x + y = 17 \Rightarrow y = -3x + 17$ and $2x - 3y = 37 \Rightarrow y = \dfrac{-2x + 37}{-3}$.

X	Y1	Y2
5	2	-9
6	-1	-8.333
7	-4	-7.667
8	-7	-7
9	-10	-6.333
10	-13	-5.667
11	-16	-5

X=8

The solution is $(8, -7)$.

9.   See Figure 9.

Figure 9   Figure 10   Figure 11

10.   See Figure 10.

11.   See Figure 11.

12.   Multiply the third equation by -1 and add the second and third equations to eliminate the variables y and z.

$$-2x + y + z = 5$$
$$\underline{ - y - z = 3}$$
$$-2x = 8$$

And so $x = -4$. Substitute $x = -4$ into the first equation: $(-4) + 3y = 2 \Rightarrow 3y = 6 \Rightarrow y = 2$

Substitute $x = -4$ and $y = 2$ into the second equation: $-2(-4) + (2) + z = 5 \Rightarrow z = -5$

The solution is $(-4, 2, -5)$.

13.   Add the first and second equations to eliminate the variable z.

$$x + y - z = 1$$
$$\underline{2x - 3y + z = 0}$$
$$3x - 2y = 1$$

Multiply the first equation by 2 and add the first and third equations to eliminate the variable z.

$$2x + 2y - 2z = 2$$
$$\underline{x - 4y + 2z = 2}$$
$$3x - 2y = 4$$

So the two new equations are $3x - 2y = 1$ and $3x - 2y = 4$. This is a contradiction, so there are no solutions.

14. The equation of a line through the points $(-2, 0)$ and $(0, 2)$ is $y = x + 2$. The equation of a line through the points $(0, -1)$ and $(1, 2)$ is $y = 3x - 1$. The system of inequalities is $y \le x + 2$ and $y \ge 3x - 1$.

15. (a) $\begin{bmatrix} 1 & 1 & 1 & | & 2 \\ 1 & -1 & -1 & | & 3 \\ 2 & 2 & 1 & | & 6 \end{bmatrix}$

(b) $\begin{bmatrix} 1 & 1 & 1 & | & 2 \\ 1 & -1 & -1 & | & 3 \\ 2 & 2 & 1 & | & 6 \end{bmatrix} \begin{array}{l} \\ R_2 - R_1 \to \\ R_3 - 2R_1 \to \end{array} \begin{bmatrix} 1 & 1 & 1 & | & 2 \\ 0 & -2 & -2 & | & 1 \\ 0 & 0 & -1 & | & 2 \end{bmatrix} \begin{array}{l} R_1 + (1/2)R_2 \to \\ (-1/2)R_2 \to \\ -1R_3 \to \end{array} \begin{bmatrix} 1 & 0 & 0 & | & \frac{5}{2} \\ 0 & 1 & 1 & | & -\frac{1}{2} \\ 0 & 0 & 1 & | & -2 \end{bmatrix}$

$R_2 - R_3 \to \begin{bmatrix} 1 & 0 & 0 & | & \frac{5}{2} \\ 0 & 1 & 0 & | & \frac{3}{2} \\ 0 & 0 & 1 & | & -2 \end{bmatrix}$ The solution is $\left(\frac{5}{2}, \frac{3}{2}, -2 \right)$.

16. $\det A = 3\left[(2)(-3) - (8)(-6) \right] - 6\left[(2)(-3) - (8)(-1) \right] + 0\left[(2)(-6) - (2)(-1) \right] = 126 - 12 + 0 = 114$

17. $E = \det \begin{bmatrix} 7 & -3 \\ 11 & 2 \end{bmatrix} = 14 - (-33) = 47; \quad F = \det \begin{bmatrix} 5 & 7 \\ -4 & 11 \end{bmatrix} = 55 - (-28) = 83$

$D = \det \begin{bmatrix} 5 & -3 \\ -4 & 2 \end{bmatrix} = 10 - 12 = -2;$ The solution is $x = \dfrac{E}{D} = \dfrac{47}{-2} = -\dfrac{47}{2}$ and $y = \dfrac{F}{D} = \dfrac{83}{-2} = -\dfrac{83}{2}$.

18. (a) Let x and y represent private and public tuition respectively. The system needed is

$x \quad - y = 12,636$

$x - 4.6y = 0$

(b) Note that $x - y = 12,636 \Rightarrow y = x - 12,636$. Substituting $y = x - 12,636$ into the second equation gives:

$x - 4.6(x - 12,636) = 0 \Rightarrow -3.6x = -58,125.6 \Rightarrow x = 16,146$ and so $y = 16,146 - 12,636 = 3510$.

Private tuition was \$16,146 and public tuition was \$3510.

19. Let x and y represent the time spent running and on the rowing machine respectively.

The system needed is $x + y = 60$ and $12x + 9y = 669$.

Multiplying the first equation by -9 and adding the two equations will eliminate the variable y.

$-9x - 9y = -540$

$\underline{12x + 9y = 669}$

$3x = 129$ Thus, $x = 43$. And so $(43) + y = 60 \Rightarrow y = 17$. The solution is $(43, 17)$.

The athlete spent 43 minutes running and 17 minutes on the rowing machine.

20. Let x and y represent the average speed of the plane and the wind respectively. Using the formula $d = rt$, the system is $600 = (x - y)(2.5)$ and $600 = (x + y)(2)$.

These equations may be written as follows: $x - y = 240$ and $x + y = 300$.

Adding the two equations together will eliminate the variable y.

$x - y = 240$

$\underline{x + y = 300}$

$2x = 540$ Thus, $x = 270$. And so $(270) - y = 240 \Rightarrow -y = -30 \Rightarrow y = 30$. The solution is $(270, 30)$.

The speed of the plane is 270 mph and the speed of the wind is 30 mph.

21.   Let x, y and z represent the measure of the largest, middle and smallest angle respectively. The system needed is:

$$\begin{aligned} x + y + z &= 180 \\ x \quad\ \ - z &= 50 \\ -x + y + z &= 10 \end{aligned} \quad \text{and so } [A] = \begin{bmatrix} 1 & 1 & 1 & | & 180 \\ 1 & 0 & -1 & | & 50 \\ -1 & 1 & 1 & | & 10 \end{bmatrix}; \text{rref}([A]) = \begin{bmatrix} 1 & 0 & 0 & | & 85 \\ 0 & 1 & 0 & | & 60 \\ 0 & 0 & 1 & | & 35 \end{bmatrix}$$

The solution is (85, 60, 35). The angles are $85°$, $60°$, and $35°$.

22.   From the graph of the region of feasible solutions (not shown), the vertices are (0, 0), (0, 2), and (3, 0).

The maximum value of R occurs at one of the vertices. For $(0,\ 0)$, $R = (0) + 2(0) = 0$.

For $(0,\ 2)$, $R = (0) + 2(2) = 4$. For $(3,\ 0)$, $R = (3) + 2(0) = 3$. The maximum value is $R = 4$.

23.   The constraint is $3x + 5y < 30$. See Figure 23.

Figure 23

24. x: amount of subsidized loan

$x - 700$: amount of unsubsidized loan

$x + x - 700 = 4400 \implies 2x - 700 = 4400 \implies x = 2550,\ x - 700 = 1850$

The unsubsidized loan is for \$2550 and the subsidized loan is for \$1850.

Chapter 4 Extended and Discovery Exercises

1. $D = 1\big[(1)(3) - (1)(2)\big] - 2\big[(1)(3) - (1)(1)\big] + 0\big[(1)(2) - (1)(1)\big] = 1 - 4 + 0 = -3$

$E = 6\big[(1)(3) - (1)(2)\big] - 9\big[(1)(3) - (1)(1)\big] + 9\big[(1)(2) - (1)(1)\big] = 6 - 18 + 9 = -3$

$F = 1\big[(9)(3) - (9)(2)\big] - 2\big[(6)(3) - (9)(1)\big] + 0\big[(6)(1) - (9)(1)\big] = 9 - 18 + 0 = -9$

$G = 1\big[(1)(9) - (1)(9)\big] - 2\big[(1)(9) - (1)(6)\big] + 0\big[(1)(9) - (1)(6)\big] = 0 - 6 + 0 = -6$

$x = \dfrac{E}{D} = \dfrac{-3}{-3} = 1,\quad y = \dfrac{F}{D} = \dfrac{-9}{-3} = 3,\quad z = \dfrac{G}{D} = \dfrac{-6}{-3} = 2.$ The solution is $(1,\ 3,\ 2)$.

2. $D = 0\big[(-1)(-1) - (1)(-1)\big] - 2\big[(1)(-1) - (1)(1)\big] + 1\big[(1)(-1) - (-1)(1)\big] = 0 + 4 + 0 = 4$

$E = 1\big[(-1)(-1) - (1)(-1)\big] - (-1)\big[(1)(-1) - (1)(1)\big] + 3\big[(1)(-1) - (-1)(1)\big] = 2 - 2 + 0 = 0$

$F = 0\big[(-1)(-1) - (3)(-1)\big] - 2\big[(1)(-1) - (3)(1)\big] + 1\big[(1)(-1) - (-1)(1)\big] = 0 + 8 + 0 = 8$

$G = 0[(-1)(3) - (1)(-1)] - 2[(1)(3) - (1)(1)] + 1[(1)(-1) - (-1)(1)] = 0 - 4 + 0 = -4$

$x = \dfrac{E}{D} = \dfrac{0}{4} = 0, \quad y = \dfrac{F}{D} = \dfrac{8}{4} = 2, \quad z = \dfrac{G}{D} = \dfrac{-4}{4} = -1.$ The solution is $(0, 2, -1)$.

3. $D = 1\left[(1)(2) - (1)(0)\right] - 1\left[(0)(2) - (1)(1)\right] + 0\left[(0)(0) - (1)(1)\right] = 2 + 1 + 0 = 3$

   $E = 2\left[(1)(2) - (1)(0)\right] - 0\left[(0)(2) - (1)(1)\right] + 1\left[(0)(0) - (1)(1)\right] = 4 + 0 - 1 = 3$

   $F = 1\left[(0)(2) - (1)(0)\right] - 1\left[(2)(2) - (1)(1)\right] + 0\left[(0)(2) - (1)(0)\right] = 0 - 3 + 0 = -3$

   $G = 1\left[(1)(1) - (1)(0)\right] - 1\left[(0)(1) - (1)(2)\right] + 0\left[(0)(0) - (1)(2)\right] = 1 + 2 + 0 = 3$

   $x = \dfrac{E}{D} = \dfrac{3}{3} = 1, \quad y = \dfrac{F}{D} = \dfrac{-3}{3} = -1, \quad z = \dfrac{G}{D} = \dfrac{3}{3} = 1.$ The solution is $(1, -1, 1)$.

4. $D = 1\left[(-2)(-3) - (1)(-3)\right] - (-1)\left[(1)(-3) - (1)(2)\right] + 0\left[(1)(-3) - (-2)(2)\right] = 9 - 5 + 0 = 4$

   $E = 1\left[(-2)(-3) - (1)(-3)\right] - (-2)\left[(1)(-3) - (1)(2)\right] + 5\left[(1)(-3) - (-2)(2)\right] = 9 - 10 + 5 = 4$

   $F = 1\left[(-2)(-3) - (5)(-3)\right] - (-1)\left[(1)(-3) - (5)(2)\right] + 0\left[(1)(-3) - (-2)(2)\right] = 21 - 13 + 0 = 8$

   $G = 1[(-2)(5) - (1)(-2)] - (-1)[(1)(5) - (1)(1)] + 0[(1)(-2) - (-2)(1)] = -8 + 4 + 0 = -4$

   $x = \dfrac{E}{D} = \dfrac{4}{4} = 1, \quad y = \dfrac{F}{D} = \dfrac{8}{4} = 2, \quad z = \dfrac{G}{D} = \dfrac{-4}{4} = -1.$ The solution is $(1, 2, -1)$.

5. $D = 1\left[(1)(2) - (-1)(1)\right] - (-1)\left[(0)(2) - (-1)(2)\right] + 2\left[(0)(1) - (1)(2)\right] = 3 + 2 - 4 = 1$

   $E = 7\left[(1)(2) - (-1)(1)\right] - 5\left[(0)(2) - (-1)(2)\right] + 6\left[(0)(1) - (1)(2)\right] = 21 - 10 - 12 = -1$

   $F = 1\left[(5)(2) - (6)(1)\right] - (-1)\left[(7)(2) - (6)(2)\right] + 2\left[(7)(1) - (5)(2)\right] = 4 + 2 - 6 = 0$

   $G = 1\left[(1)(6) - (-1)(5)\right] - (-1)\left[(0)(6) - (-1)(7)\right] + 2\left[(0)(5) - (1)(7)\right] = 11 + 7 - 14 = 4$

   $x = \dfrac{E}{D} = \dfrac{-1}{1} = -1, \quad y = \dfrac{F}{D} = \dfrac{0}{1} = 0, \quad z = \dfrac{G}{D} = \dfrac{4}{1} = 4.$ The solution is $(-1, 0, 4)$.

6. $D = 1\left[(-3)(-2) - (4)(-1)\right] - 2\left[(2)(-2) - (4)(3)\right] + 1\left[(2)(-1) - (-3)(3)\right] = 10 + 32 + 7 = 49$

   $E = -1\left[(-3)(-2) - (4)(-1)\right] - 12\left[(2)(-2) - (4)(3)\right] + (-12)\left[(2)(-1) - (-3)(3)\right] = -10 + 192 - 84 = 98$

   $F = 1\left[(12)(-2) - (-12)(-1)\right] - 2\left[(-1)(-2) - (-12)(3)\right] + 1\left[(-1)(-1) - (12)(3)\right] = -36 - 76 - 35 = -147$

   $G = 1\left[(-3)(-12) - (4)(12)\right] - 2\left[(2)(-12) - (4)(-1)\right] + 1\left[(2)(12) - (-3)(-1)\right] = -12 + 40 + 21 = 49$

   $x = \dfrac{E}{D} = \dfrac{98}{49} = 2, \quad y = \dfrac{F}{D} = \dfrac{-147}{49} = -3, \quad z = \dfrac{G}{D} = \dfrac{49}{49} = 1.$ The solution is $(2, -3, 1)$.

7. Since Denver is city 1 and Las Vegas is city 4, we look at either entry a_{14} or a_{41}. The distance is 760 miles.

8. Add entry a_{12} to entry a_{23}. The distance is 360 miles.

9. The dimension would be 20×20 and the matrix would contain 400 elements.

10.   The elements on the main diagonal represent the distance from a city to itself, which is always zero.

11. $a_{14} + a_{41} = 760 + 760 = 1520$ miles

12. $a_{11} + a_{44} = 0 + 0 = 0$ miles

13.   See Figure 13.

$$\begin{bmatrix} 0 & 130 & 95 & 75 \\ 130 & 0 & 186 & \star \\ 95 & 186 & 0 & 57 \\ 75 & \star & 57 & 0 \end{bmatrix} \qquad \begin{bmatrix} 0 & 97 & \star & \star & 59 \\ 97 & 0 & 113 & 118 & \star \\ \star & 113 & 0 & 94 & \star \\ \star & 118 & 94 & 0 & 177 \\ 59 & \star & \star & 177 & 0 \end{bmatrix}$$

Figure 13   Figure 14

14.   See Figure 14.

15.   All maps for adjacency matrix *A* must have the same distances between cities, but the location of each city may vary. The solution is not unique. One possible solution is shown in Figure 15.

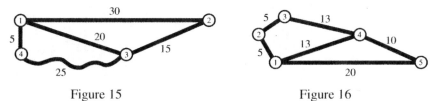

Figure 15   Figure 16

16.   All maps for adjacency matrix *A* must have the same distances between cities, but the location of each city may vary. The solution is not unique. One possible solution is shown in Figure 16.

17.   (a)
$$\begin{bmatrix} 1 & 19 & 57.5 & 32 & | & 125 \\ 1 & 26 & 65 & 42 & | & 316 \\ 1 & 30 & 72 & 48 & | & 436 \\ 1 & 30.5 & 75 & 54 & | & 514 \end{bmatrix}$$

(b) $a \approx -552.272,\ b \approx 8.733,\ c \approx 2.859,\ d \approx 10.843$

(c) $N = 24,\ L = 63$ and $C = 39,\ W \approx -552.272 + 8.733(24) + 2.859(63) + 10.843(39) \approx 260$

A bear with a 24-inch neck, 63-inch length and 39-inch chest weighs approximately 260 pounds.

Chapters 1–4 Cumulative Review Exercises

1.   Identity

2.   Associative

3. $\dfrac{1+2}{3-1} - 2^2 \cdot 4 = \dfrac{3}{2} - 4 \cdot 4 = 1.5 - 16 = -14.5$

4. $-1 + 8 - 19 + 12 = 0$

5. $-\dfrac{a}{b}$

6.   (a) $\left(\dfrac{4^2}{3}\right)^{-2} = \left(\dfrac{3}{4^2}\right)^2 = \dfrac{3^2}{4^4} = \dfrac{9}{256}$

(b) $\dfrac{(2ab^{-4})^2}{a^7(b^2)^{-3}} = \dfrac{4a^2b^{-8}}{a^7b^{-6}} = 4a^{2-7}b^{-8-(-6)} = 4a^{-5}b^{-2} = \dfrac{4}{a^5b^2}$

(c) $(x^2y^3)^{-2}(xy^2)^4 = x^{-4}y^{-6}x^4y^8 = x^0y^2 = y^2$

7.　$0.0056 = 5.6 \times 10^{-3}$

8.　$f(-2) = 5 - 4(-2) = 5 + 8 = 13$

9.　$V = \dfrac{1}{3}\pi(3)(2)^2 = \dfrac{1}{3}\pi(3)(4) = 4\pi$

10.　The denominator cannot equal zero, so $x \neq -\dfrac{1}{2}$.

11.　See Figure 11.

12.　See Figure 12.

Figure 11　　　　　　Figure 12

13.　(a) Yes. The graph passes the vertical line test.

　　(b) *D*: all real numbers; *R*: all real numbers

　　(c) $f(-1) = -1.5;\ f(2) = 0$

　　(d) *x*-intercept: 2; *y*-intercept: –1

　　(e) Two points on the line are (2, 0) and (0, –1).

$$m = \dfrac{y_2 - y_1}{x_2 - x_1} = \dfrac{-1-0}{0-2} = \dfrac{-1}{-2} = \dfrac{1}{2}$$

　　(f) $f(x) = \dfrac{1}{2}x - 1$

14.　The slope of a line perpendicular to $y = -\dfrac{3}{4}x$ is $m = \dfrac{4}{3}$.

$$y - (3) = \dfrac{4}{3}(x - (-6)) \Rightarrow y = \dfrac{4}{3}(x + 6) + 3 \Rightarrow y = \dfrac{4}{3}x + 11$$

15.　Two points on the graph are (0, 2) and (2, 10). $m = \dfrac{y_2 - y_1}{x_2 - x_1} = \dfrac{10-2}{2-0} = \dfrac{8}{2} = 4$; From the table, the *y*-intercept

is 2, so an equation of the line is $y = 4x + 2$. To find the *x*-intercept, let $y = 0$ and solve for

$x\colon 0 = 4x + 2 \Rightarrow -2 = 4x \Rightarrow x = -\dfrac{1}{2}$.

16. $\frac{1}{2}(1-x)+2x=3x+1 \Rightarrow \frac{1}{2}-\frac{1}{2}x+2x=3x+1$

$\Rightarrow -\frac{1}{2}x+2x-3x=-\frac{1}{2}+1 \Rightarrow -\frac{3}{2}x=\frac{1}{2} \Rightarrow x=-\frac{2}{3}\cdot\frac{1}{2} \Rightarrow x=-\frac{1}{3}$

17. $2(1-x)>4x-(2+x) \Rightarrow 2-2x>4x-2-x \Rightarrow -2x-4x+x>-2-2 \Rightarrow -5x>-4 \Rightarrow x<\frac{4}{5};$ the solutions are

$\left(-\infty, \frac{4}{5}\right).$

18. $x+1<2 \Rightarrow x<1$ or $x+1>4 \Rightarrow x>3 \Rightarrow (-\infty, 1) \cup (3, \infty)$

19. $-3\le 2-4x<5 \Rightarrow -5\le -4x<3 \Rightarrow \frac{5}{4}\ge x>-\frac{3}{4} \Rightarrow -\frac{3}{4}<x\le\frac{5}{4} \Rightarrow \left(-\frac{3}{4}, \frac{5}{4}\right]$

20. $|3x-2|=4 \Rightarrow 3x-2=4$ or $3x-2=-4 \Rightarrow 3x=6$ or $3x=-2 \Rightarrow x=2$ or $x=-\frac{2}{3}$

(b) $|3x-2|<4 \Rightarrow -4<3x-2<4 \Rightarrow -2<3x<6 \Rightarrow -\frac{2}{3}<x<2 \Rightarrow \left(-\frac{2}{3}, 2\right)$

(c) $|3x-2|>4 \Rightarrow 3x-2<-4$ or $3x-2>4 \Rightarrow 3x<-2$ or $3x>6 \Rightarrow x<-\frac{2}{3}$ or $x>2 \Rightarrow \left(-\infty, -\frac{2}{3}\right) \cup (2, \infty)$

21.   (a)   Note that $2x+y=3 \Rightarrow y=-2x+3$ and $x-2y=-1 \Rightarrow -2y=-x-1 \Rightarrow y=\frac{1}{2}x+\frac{1}{2}.$ Graph

$Y_1=-2X+3$ and $Y_2=1/2X+1/2$ in $[-5,5,1]$ by $[-5,5,1]$. The solution is $(1, 1)$.

(b)   Note that $4x+3y=8 \Rightarrow 3y=-4x+8 \Rightarrow y=-\frac{4}{3}x+\frac{8}{3}$ and $2x+7y=4 \Rightarrow 7y=-2x+4 \Rightarrow y=-\frac{2}{7}x+\frac{4}{7}.$

Table $Y_1=-4/3X+8/3$ and $Y_2=-2/7X+4/7$ with TblStart = 0 and ΔTbl = 1. The solution is $(2, 0)$.

X	Y1	Y2
0	2.6667	.57143
1	1.3333	.28571
2	0	0
3	-1.333	-.2857
4	-2.667	-.5714
5	-4	-.8571
6	-5.333	-1.143

X=2

22.   (a)   Add the two equations to eliminate the variable y.

$x+2y=4$

$\underline{3x-2y=-2}$

$4x \qquad = 2$ $\Rightarrow x=\frac{1}{2}.$ Substitute $x=\frac{1}{2}$ in the first equation and solve for

$y: \frac{1}{2}+2y=4 \Rightarrow 2y=\frac{7}{2} \Rightarrow y=\frac{7}{4}.$ The solution is $\left(\frac{1}{2}, \frac{7}{4}\right).$

(b)   Multiply the first equation by 2 and add the equations to eliminate the variables x and y.

$$-2x + 2y = 4$$
$$\underline{2x - 2y = 5}$$
$$0 = 9 \qquad \text{This is a contradiction. There are no solutions.}$$

23. (a) Note that $x + 2y < 3 \Rightarrow y < -\dfrac{1}{2}x + \dfrac{3}{2}$ See Figure 23a.

Figure 23a   Figure 23b

(b) Note that $x + y \le 2 \Rightarrow y \le -x + 2$ and $3x - y > 6 \Rightarrow y < 3x - 6$ See Figure 23b.

24. Add the second and third equations to eliminate the variable y.

$$3x + y + z = 12$$
$$\underline{x - y - 2z = -1}$$
$$4x \qquad - z = 11$$

Multiply the second equation by -2 and add to the first equation to eliminate the variable y.

$$-x + 2y + z = 2$$
$$\underline{-6x - 2y - 2z = -24}$$
$$-7x \qquad - z = -22$$

Multiply the result of the first sum by -1 and add to this new equation to eliminate the variable z.

$$-4x + z = -11$$
$$\underline{-7x - z = -22}$$
$$-11x \qquad = -33$$

$\Rightarrow x = 3$. Then $4(3) - z = 11 \Rightarrow 12 - z = 11 \Rightarrow z = 1$. Substitute the values $x = 3$ and $z = 1$ into the second equation and solve for y.

$$3(3) + y + (1) = 12 \Rightarrow 9 + y + 1 = 12 \Rightarrow y = 2.$$

The solution is $(3, 2, 1)$.

25. $\begin{bmatrix} 1 & 1 & 1 & | & -3 \\ 2 & -1 & 1 & | & -11 \\ -1 & -1 & 1 & | & -5 \end{bmatrix} \begin{matrix} -2R_1 + R_2 \to \\ R_1 + R_3 \to \end{matrix} \begin{bmatrix} 1 & 1 & 1 & | & -3 \\ 0 & -3 & -1 & | & -5 \\ 0 & 0 & 2 & | & -8 \end{bmatrix} \frac{1}{2}R_3 \to \begin{bmatrix} 1 & 1 & 1 & | & -3 \\ 0 & -3 & -1 & | & -5 \\ 0 & 0 & 1 & | & -4 \end{bmatrix} \begin{matrix} -R_3 + R_1 \to \\ R_3 + R_2 \to \end{matrix}$

$\begin{bmatrix} 1 & 1 & 0 & | & 1 \\ 0 & -3 & 0 & | & -9 \\ 0 & 0 & 1 & | & -4 \end{bmatrix} -\frac{1}{3}R_2 \to \begin{bmatrix} 1 & 1 & 0 & | & 1 \\ 0 & 1 & 0 & | & 3 \\ 0 & 0 & 1 & | & -4 \end{bmatrix} -R_2 + R_1 \to \begin{bmatrix} 1 & 0 & 0 & | & -2 \\ 0 & 1 & 0 & | & 3 \\ 0 & 0 & 1 & | & -4 \end{bmatrix};$

The solution is $(-2, 3, -4)$.

26. $1(0 \cdot 3 - 4 \cdot 4) - 2(-1 \cdot 3 - 2 \cdot 4) + 0(-1 \cdot 4 - 2 \cdot 0)$

$$= 1 (0-16) - 2(-3-8) + 0(-4-0)$$

$$= -16 - 2(-11) + 0 = -16 + 22 = 6$$

27.　(a)　$I(x) = 0.07x$

　　(b)　$I(500) = 0.07(500) = \$35$; the interest after one year for \$500 at 7% is \$35.

28.　(a)　$T(1990) = 572.3(1990 - 1980) + 3617 = 572.3(10) + 3617 = 5723 + 3617 = 9340$; average tuition and fees in 1990 were \$9340.

　　(b)　slope = 572.3; tuition and fees increased, on average, by \$572.30 per year from 1980 to 2000.

29.　Let x represent the width. Then $2(x) + 2(x+7) = 74 \Rightarrow 2x + 2x + 14 = 74 \Rightarrow 4x = 60 \Rightarrow x = 15$; the dimensions are 15 inches by 22 inches.

30.　$|P - 12.4| \leq 0.2$

31.　Let x, y, and z represent the amounts invested at 5%, 6%, and 8%, respectively. Then the system of equations is

$$\begin{aligned} x + y + z &= 5000 \\ z &= y + 500 \\ y &= x + z - 1000 \end{aligned} \qquad \Rightarrow \qquad \begin{aligned} x + y + z &= 5000 \\ -y + z &= 500 \\ -x + y - z &= -1000 \end{aligned}$$

Add the first and third equations to eliminate the variables x and z.

$$\begin{aligned} x + y + z &= 5000 \\ -x + y - z &= -1000 \\ \hline 2y &= 4000 \end{aligned} \qquad \Rightarrow y = 2000. \text{ Then } z = 2000 + 500 = 2500.$$

Substitute the values $y = 2000$ and $z = 2500$ into the first equation and solve for

x: $x + 2000 + 2500 = 5000 \Rightarrow x = 500$. So \$500 is invested at 5%, \$2000 is invested at 6% and \$2500 is invested at 8%.

32.　Let x and y represent the populations of Texas and Florida in 2002, respectively. Then the system needed is

$$\begin{aligned} x + y &= 38.5 \\ x &= y + 5.1 \end{aligned}$$

Substitute $x = y + 5.1$ into the first equation and solve for y: $y + 5.1 + y = 38.5 \Rightarrow 2y = 33.4 \Rightarrow y = 16.7$ and so $x = 16.7 + 5.1 = 21.8$. In 2002, the population of Texas was 21.8 million and the population of Florida was 16.7 million.

Critical Thinking Solutions for Chapter 4

Section 4.1

•　The tables for y_1 and y_2 would be identical. If the system of two equations is dependent, there are an infinite number of solutions.

•　The two y-values for a given x-value would never be equal.

Section 4.3

•　Yes. The point (2, 2) satisfies *both* inequalities. No. The point (2, 2) does *not* satisfy $2x - y < 2$.

• There are no solutions to this system. See Figure 1.

Figure 1

Section 4.5

• (a) There are no solutions. The planes are parallel.

(b) There are infinitely many solutions; the planes intersect in a line.

• As the number of adults increases, so does the number of fawns. However, as the severity of the winter increases, the number of fawns decreases.

Section 4.6

• The first matrix represents an inconsistent system and the second matrix represents a system of dependent equations.

Section 4.7

• The points are collinear; they all lie on the same line.

Chapter 5: Polynomial Expressions and Functions

5.1: Polynomial Functions

Concepts

1. $3x^2$; *Answers may vary.*

2.   The degree is 3. The leading coefficient is -1.

3.   No, the powers must match for each variable.

4. $x^4 - 3x + 5$; *Answers may vary.*

5.   No, the opposite is $-x^2 - 1$.

6. $4(2)^3(3) = 96$

7.   No; a function has only one output for each input.

8.   Yes; if the polynomial is linear.

9. $f(2) = (2)^2 + 2 = 4 + 2 = 6$

10. $(f + g)(x) = f(x) + g(x) = x^2 + 2x^2 = 3x^2$

Monomials and Polynomials

11.   Yes

12.   No, the exponent is negative.

13.   No, there are two terms.

14.   No, the variable is under a square root symbol.

15.   Yes

16.   Yes

17.   No, the variable is in a denominator.

18.   Yes

19.   No, the exponent is negative.

20.   No, the exponent is negative.

21. x^2

22. πd

23. πr^2

24. $\dfrac{3}{2}bh$

25. xy

26. wz

27.   The degree is 7. The coefficient is 3.

28.   The degree is 3. The coefficient is -5.

29. The degree is 7. The coefficient is –3.

30. The degree is 6. The coefficient is 1.

31. The degree is 6. The coefficient is –1.

32. The degree is 2. The coefficient is $\sqrt{2}$.

33. The degree is 2. The leading coefficient is 5.

34. The degree is 4. The leading coefficient is –9.

35. The degree is 3. The leading coefficient is $-\dfrac{2}{5}$.

36. The degree is 4. The leading coefficient is 4.

37. The degree is 5. The leading coefficient is 1.

38. The degree is 4. The leading coefficient is 7.

39. $x^2 + 4x^2 = 5x^2$

40. $-3z + 5z = 2z$

41. $6y^4 - 3y^4 = 3y^4$

42. $9xy - 7xy = 2xy$

43. Not possible

44. Not possible

45. $9x^2 - x + 4x - 6x^2 = 3x^2 + 3x$

46. $-xy^2 - \dfrac{1}{2}xy^2 = -\dfrac{3}{2}xy^2$

47. $x^2 + 9xy - y^2 + 4x^2 + y^2 = 5x^2 + 9xy$

48. $6xy + 4x - 6xy = 4x$

49. $4x + 7x^3y^7 - \dfrac{1}{2}x^3y^7 + 9x - \dfrac{3}{2}x^3y^7 = 5x^3y^7 + 13x$

50. $19x^3 + x^2 - 3x^3 + x - 4x^2 + 1 = 16x^3 - 3x^2 + x + 1$

51. $(3x + 1) + (-x + 1) = 2x + 2$

52. $\left(5y^3 + y\right) + \left(12y^3 - 5y\right) = 17y^3 - 4y$

53. $\left(x^2 - 2x + 15\right) + \left(-3x^2 + 5x - 7\right) = -2x^2 + 3x + 8$

54. $(4x) + (1 - 4.5x) = -0.5x + 1$

55. $\left(3x^3 - 4x + 3\right) + \left(5x^2 + 4x + 12\right) = 3x^3 + 5x^2 + 15$

56. $\left(y^5 + y\right) + \left(5 - y + \dfrac{1}{3}y^2\right) = y^5 + \dfrac{1}{3}y^2 + 5$

57. $\left(x^4 - 3x^2 - 4\right) + \left(-8x^4 + x - \dfrac{1}{2}\right) = -7x^4 - 3x^2 + x - \dfrac{9}{2}$

58. $\left(3z + z^4 + 2\right) + \left(-3z^4 - 5 + z^2\right) = -2z^4 + z^2 + 3z - 3$

59. $\left(4r^4 - r + 2\right) + \left(r^3 - 5r\right) = 4r^4 + r^3 - 6r + 2$

60. $\left(5t^3 + 3t\right) + \left(4t^4 - 3t^3 + 1\right) = 4t^4 + 2t^3 + 3t + 1$

61. $\left(4xy - x^2 + y^2\right) + \left(4y^2 - 8xy - x^2\right) = 5y^2 - 4xy - 2x^2$

62. $\left(3x^2 + 6xy - y^2\right) + \left(8y^2 - xy - 2x^2\right) = x^2 + 5xy + 7y^2$

63. $-6x^5$

64. $5y^7$

65. $-19x^5 + 5x^3 - 3x$

66. $x^2 + x + 5$

67. $7z^4 - z^2 + 8$

68. $-6 + 4x - 5x^2 + \dfrac{1}{10}x^3$

69. $(5x - 3) - (2x + 4) = 5x - 3 - 2x - 4 = 3x - 7$

70. $(10x + 5) - (-6x - 4) = 10x + 5 + 6x + 4 = 16x + 9$

71. $\left(x^2 - 3x + 1\right) - \left(-5x^2 + 2x - 4\right) = x^2 - 3x + 1 + 5x^2 - 2x + 4 = 6x^2 - 5x + 5$

72. $\left(-x^2 + x - 5\right) - \left(x^2 - x + 5\right) = -x^2 + x - 5 - x^2 + x - 5 = -2x^2 + 2x - 10$

73. $3\left(4x^4 + 2x^2 - 9\right) - 4\left(x^4 - 2x^2 - 5\right) = 12x^4 + 6x^2 - 27 - 4x^4 + 8x^2 + 20 = 8x^4 + 14x^2 - 7$

74. $2\left(8x^3 + 5x^2 - 3x + 1\right) - 5\left(-5x^3 + 6x - 11\right) = 16x^3 + 10x^2 - 6x + 2 + 25x^3 - 30x + 55$

    $= 41x^3 + 10x^2 - 36x + 57$

75. $4\left(x^4 - 1\right) - \left(4x^4 + 3x + 7\right) = 4x^4 - 4 - 4x^4 - 3x - 7 = -3x - 11$

76. $\left(5x^4 - 6x^3 + x^2 + 5\right) - \left(x^3 + 11x^2 + 9x - 3\right) = 5x^4 - 6x^3 + x^2 + 5 - x^3 - 11x^2 - 9x + 3$

    $= 5x^4 - 7x^3 - 10x^2 - 9x + 8$

77. Yes. This is a fourth degree polynomial.

78. Yes. The degree of the polynomial is 3. It is a cubic polynomial.

79. No, the exponent on the variable is not positive.

80. No, a polynomial may not contain an absolute value.

81. No, the variable is located in the denominator.

82.   Yes. The degree of the polynomial is 1. It is a linear polynomial.

83.   Yes. The degree of the polynomial is 2. It is a quadratic polynomial.

84.   No, the exponent on the variable is not positive.

Evaluating Polynomials

85. $-4(2)^2 = -4(4) = -16$

86. $-2(-3)^3 = -2(-27) = 54$

87. $2(2)^2(3) = 2(4)(3) = 24$

88. $-(4)(-1)^3 = -(4)(-1) = 4$

89. $(-3)^2(4) - (-3)(4)^2 = 9(4) + 3(16) = 36 + 48 = 84$

90. $3(-2)^3 + 2(3)^3 = 3(-8) + 2(27) = -24 + 54 = 30$

91.   When $x = 1$, $y = -1$ and so $f(1) = -1$. When $x = -2$, $y = 2$ and so $f(-2) = 2$.

92.   When $x = 0$, $y = -2$ and so $f(0) = -2$. When $x = 2$, $y = 4$ and so $f(2) = 4$.

93.   When $x = -1$, $y = -4$ and so $f(-1) = -4$. When $x = 2$, $y = 2$ and so $f(2) = 2$.

94.   When $x = -1$, $y = -1$ and so $f(-1) = -1$. When $x = 0$, $y = 2$ and so $f(0) = 2$.

95. $f(-2) = 3(-2)^2 = 3(4) = 12$

96. $f(3) = (3)^2 - 2(3) = 9 - 6 = 3$

97. $f\left(-\dfrac{1}{2}\right) = 5 - 4\left(-\dfrac{1}{2}\right) = 5 + 2 = 7$

98. $f(-3) = (-3)^2 + 4(-3) - 5 = 9 - 12 - 5 = -8$

99. $f(-1) = 0.5(-1)^4 - 0.3(-1)^3 + 5 = 0.5 + 0.3 + 5 = 5.8$

100. $f(0) = 6 - 2(0) + (0)^3 = 6 - 0 + 0 = 6$

101. $f(-1) = -(-1)^3 = -(-1) = 1$

102. $f\left(\dfrac{3}{10}\right) = 3 - 2\left(\dfrac{3}{10}\right) = 3 - \dfrac{3}{5} = \dfrac{12}{5} = 2.4$

103. $f(-3) = -(-3)^2 - 3(-3) = -9 + 9 = 0$

104. $f(1) = 2(1)^3 - 4(1) + 1 = 2 - 4 + 1 = -1$

105. $f(2.4) = 1 - 2(2.4) + (2.4)^2 = 1 - 4.8 + 5.76 = 1.96$

106. $f(1.8) = 4(1.8)^2 - 20(1.8) + 25 = 12.96 - 36 + 25 = 1.96$

107. $f(-1) = (-1)^5 - 5 = -1 - 5 = -6$

108. $f\left(\dfrac{3}{2}\right) = 1.2\left(\dfrac{3}{2}\right)^4 - 5.7\left(\dfrac{3}{2}\right) + 3 = 6.075 - 8.55 + 3 = 0.525$

109. $f(a) = a^2 - 2a$

110. $f(a+2) = 2(a+2) - 1 = 2a + 4 - 1 = 2a + 3$

111.   (a) $(f+g)(2) = (3(2)-1) + (5-(2)) = 6 - 1 + 5 - 2 = 8$

    (b) $(f-g)(-1) = (3(-1)-1) - (5-(-1)) = -3 - 1 - 5 - 1 = -10$

    (c) $(f+g)(x) = (3x-1) + (5-x) = 2x + 4$

    (d) $(f-g)(x) = (3x-1) - (5-x) = 3x - 1 - 5 + x = 4x - 6$

112.   (a) $(f+g)(2) = (-4(2)+3) + (5(2)) = -8 + 3 + 10 = 5$

    (b) $(f-g)(-1) = (-4(-1)+3) - (5(-1)) = 4 + 3 + 5 = 12$

    (c) $(f+g)(x) = (-4x+3) + (5x) = x + 3$

    (d) $(f-g)(x) = (-4x+3) - (5x) = -9x + 3$

113.   (a) $(f+g)(2) = \left(-3(2)^2\right) + \left((2)^2 + 1\right) = -3(4) + 4 + 1 = -7$

    (b) $(f-g)(-1) = \left(-3(-1)^2\right) - \left((-1)^2 + 1\right) = -3 - 1 - 1 = -5$

    (c) $(f+g)(x) = \left(-3x^2\right) + \left(x^2 + 1\right) = -2x^2 + 1$

    (d) $(f-g)(x) = \left(-3x^2\right) - \left(x^2 + 1\right) = -4x^2 - 1$

114.   (a) $(f+g)(2) = \left(2(2)^2 - 2\right) + \left(3 - (2)^2\right) = 2(4) - 2 + 3 - 4 = 5$

    (b) $(f-g)(-1) = \left(2(-1)^2 - 2\right) - \left(3 - (-1)^2\right) = 2 - 2 - 3 + 1 = -2$

    (c) $(f+g)(x) = \left(2x^2 - 2\right) + \left(3 - x^2\right) = x^2 + 1$

    (d) $(f-g)(x) = \left(2x^2 - 2\right) - \left(3 - x^2\right) = 3x^2 - 5$

115.   (a) $(f+g)(2) = \left(-(2)^3\right) + \left(3(2)^3\right) = -8 + 3(8) = 16$

    (b) $(f-g)(-1) = \left(-(-1)^3\right) - \left(3(-1)^3\right) = 1 - (-3) = 4$

    (c) $(f+g)(x) = \left(-x^3\right) + \left(3x^3\right) = 2x^3$

    (d) $(f-g)(x) = \left(-x^3\right) - \left(3x^3\right) = -4x^3$

116. (a) $(f+g)(2) = (2^3 + 2) + (2(2) - 3(2)^3) = 8 + 2 + 4 - 3(8) = -10$

     (b) $(f-g)(-1) = ((-1)^3 + (-1)) - (2(-1) - 3(-1)^3) = (-1) + (-1) - (-2) - 3 = -3$

     (c) $(f+g)(x) = (x^3 + x) + (2x - 3x^3) = -2x^3 + 3x$

     (d) $(f-g)(x) = (x^3 + x) - (2x - 3x^3) = 4x^3 - x$

117. (a) $(f+g)(2) = (2^2 - 2(2) + 1) + (4(2)^2 + 3(2)) = 4 - 4 + 1 + 16 + 6 = 23$

     (b) $(f-g)(-1) = ((-1)^2 - 2(-1) + 1) - (4(-1)^2 + 3(-1)) = 1 + 2 + 1 - 4 + 3 = 3$

     (c) $(f+g)(x) = (x^2 - 2x + 1) + (4x^2 + 3x) = 5x^2 + x + 1$

     (d) $(f-g)(x) = (x^2 - 2x + 1) - (4x^2 + 3x) = -3x^2 - 5x + 1$

118. (a) $(f+g)(2) = (3 + 2 - 2(2)^2) + (5(2) + 8) = 3 + 2 - 8 + 10 + 8 = 15$

     (b) $(f-g)(-1) = (3 + (-1) - 2(-1)^2) - (5(-1) + 8) = 3 - 1 - 2 + 5 - 8 = -3$

     (c) $(f+g)(x) = (3 + x - 2x^2) + (5x + 8) = -2x^2 + 6x + 11$

     (d) $(f-g)(x) = (3 + x - 2x^2) - (5x + 8) = -2x^2 - 4x - 5$

Applications

119. (a) When $x = 1980$ the y-value is about 1250. When $x = 1995$ the y-value is about 7250.

     In 1980 there were about 1250 women running. In 1995 there were about 7250.

     (b) In 1980 $x = 2$, and so $8.87(2)^2 + 232(2) + 769 = 1268.48 \approx 1268$.

     In 1995 $x = 17$, and so $8.87(17)^2 + 232(17) + 769 = 7276.43 \approx 7276$. The answers are similar.

     (c) In 1978 $x = 0$, in 1998 $x = 20$, and so

     $$\left(8.87(20)^2 + 232(20) + 769\right) - \left(8.87(0)^2 + 232(0) + 769\right) = 8188$$

120. For 2003, $x = 6$, so we have $0.7868(6)^2 + 12(6) + 79.5 \approx 180$ million personal computers.

121. Three rooms are 8 by x by y and two rooms are 8 by x by z. The polynomial is

     $3(8xy) + 2(8xz) = 24xy + 16xz$.

     When $x = 10$, $y = 12$ and $z = 7$, we have $24(10 \cdot 12) + 16(10 \cdot 7) = 4000$ ft^3

122. (a) $f(10) = 2.4(10)^2 - 14(10) + 23 = 240 - 140 + 23 = 123$ thousand, which is close to the actual value.

     (b) $f(17) = 2.4(17)^2 - 14(17) + 23 = 693.6 - 238 + 23 = 478.6$ thousand, which is too high. AIDS deaths did

     not continue to rise as rapidly as the model predicts.

123. The volume of one cube is s^3, so the volume of five identical cubes is $5s^3$.

124. The area of one rectangle is LW, so the area of six identical rectangles is $6LW$.

125. A square with side x has area x^2 and a circle with radius x has area πx^2. The polynomial is $x^2 + \pi x^2$.

    When $x = 10$ we have $10^2 + \pi \cdot 10^2 = 100 + 100\pi \approx 414.2 \text{ in}^2$.

126. The volume of one sphere with radius y is $\frac{4}{3}\pi y^3$. For 9 spheres the monomial is $9 \cdot \frac{4}{3}\pi y^3 = 12\pi y^3$.

    When $y = 3$ we have $12\pi(3)^3 = 324\pi \approx 1017.9 \text{ ft}^3$.

127. The table is shown in Figure 127. The athlete's heart rate is between 80 and 110 beats per minute from 4 to 8 minutes after exercise had stopped.

t	3	4	5	6	7	8	9
$y = f(t)$	126.875	110	96.875	87.5	81.875	80	81.875

Figure 127

128. (a) Let $f(x)$ represent the number of SUVs sold during year x. The line passes through the points

    (1991, 1) and (1999, 3.2). The slope is $a = \dfrac{3.2 - 1}{1999 - 1991} = \dfrac{2.2}{8} = 0.275$. Then since $f(x) = ax + b$,

    $1 = 0.275(1991) + b \Rightarrow b = -546.525$. The function needed is $f(x) = 0.275x - 546.525$.

    (b) $f(1995) = 0.275(1995) - 546.525 = 2.1$ million.

129. The best model is $f(x)$. This can be verified numerically using a table.

130. (a) April is month $x = 4$, and so $f(4) = -0.064(4)^3 + 0.56(4)^2 + 2.9(4) + 61 \approx 77.5°\text{F}$.

    (b) The peak of the graph appears to occur in late July when the temperature is about 87°F.

131. (a) $R(x) = 16x$

    (b) $P(x) = R(x) - C(x) = 16x - (4x + 2000) = 12x - 2000$

    (c) $P(3000) = 12(3000) - 2000 = 36,000 - 2000 = 34,000$; the profit is \$34,000 for selling 3000 CDs.

132. (a) $T(x) = (0.07 + 0.15)x = 0.22x$

    (b) $T(4000) = 0.22(4000) = 880$; state and federal taxes on \$4000 are \$880.

Group Activity Solutions

1. (a) $f(1983) = -0.002(1983)^2 + 8.042(1983) - 8078.908 = 3.8$

    $f(1993) = -0.002(1993)^2 + 8.042(1993) - 8078.908 = 4.7$

    $f(2003) = -0.002(2003)^2 + 8.042(2003) - 8078.908 = 5.2$

    (b) Table $Y_1 = -0.002X^2 + 8.042X - 8078.908$ with TblStart = 2004 and ΔTbl = 1. See Figure 1.

$f(2010) = -0.002(2010)^2 + 8.042(2010) - 8078.908 = 5.312$.   The model predicts that 5.312 million women will be attending 4-year institutions of higher education in 2010.   This is probably not accurate because this date is relatively far in the future.

(c)   Yes.   Estimating between data points is generally more reliable than estimating beyond data points.

(d)   No.   In 1959 there were women attending college as will be the case in 2062.

Figure 1

5.2: Multiplication of Polynomials

Concepts

1.   Distributive

2. $3x$; $2x - 7$; $x^2 - 3x + 1$;   *Answers may vary.*

3. $x^{3+5} = x^8$

4. $(2x)^3 = 2^3 \cdot x^3 = 8x^3$ and $\left(x^2\right)^3 = x^{2 \cdot 3} = x^6$

5. $a^2 - b^2$

6. $a^2 + 2ab + b^2$

7. $x^2 - x$

8.   No, it equals $x^2 + 2x + 1$.

Multiplying Polynomials

9. $x^4 \cdot x^8 = x^{4+8} = x^{12}$

10. $2x \cdot 4x^3 = 8x^{1+3} = 8x^4$

11. $-5y^7 \cdot 4y = -20y^{7+1} = -20y^8$

12. $3xy^2 \cdot 6x^3y^2 = 18x^{1+3} \cdot y^{2+2} = 18x^4y^4$

13. $(-xy)\left(4x^3y^5\right) = -4x^{1+3} \cdot y^{1+5} = -4x^4y^6$

14. $\left(4z^3\right)\left(-5z^2\right) = -20z^{3+2} = -20z^5$

15. $\left(5y^2z\right)\left(4x^2yz^5\right) = 20x^2 \cdot y^{2+1} \cdot z^{1+5} = 20x^2y^3z^6$

16. $x^2\left(-xy^2\right) = -x^{2+1} \cdot y^2 = -x^3y^2$

17. $5(y+2) = 5y + 10$

18. $4(y-7) = 4y - 28$

19. $-2(5x+9) = -10x-18$

20. $-3x(5+x) = -15x-3x^2$

21. $-6y(y-3) = -6y^2+18y$

22. $(2y-5)8y^3 = 16y^4-40y^3$

23. $(9-4x)3x = 27x-12x^2$

24. $-(5-x^2) = -5+x^2$

25. $-ab(a^2-b^2) = -a^3b+ab^3$

26. $a^2b^2(1-4ab) = a^2b^2-4a^3b^3$

27. $-5m(n^3+m) = -5mn^3-5m^2$

28. $7n(3n-2m^2) = 21n^2-14m^2n$

29. $x^2+x+2x+2 = x^2+3x+2;$ When $x=5,(5)^2+3(5)+2 = 25+15+2 = 42$ in^2.

30. $x^2+3x+4x+2 = x^2+7x+12;$ When $x=5,(5)^2+7(5)+12 = 25+35+12 = 72$ in^2.

31. $2x^2+2x+x+1 = 2x^2+3x+1;$ When $x=5, 2(5)^2+3(5)+1 = 50+15+1 = 66$ in^2.

32. $6x^2+12x+4x+8 = 6x^2+16x+8;$ When $x=5, 6(5)^2+16(5)+8 = 150+80+8 = 238$ in^2.

33. $(x+5)(x+6) = x^2+6x+5x+30 = x^2+11x+30$

34. $(x+1)(x+4) = x^2+4x+x+4 = x^2+5x+4$

35. $(2x+1)(2x+1) = 4x^2+2x+2x+1 = 4x^2+4x+1$

36. $(x+3)(2x+4) = 2x^2+4x+6x+12 = 2x^2+10x+12$

37. No, a square of a sum does not equal the sum of the squares.

38. No, a square of a difference does not equal the difference of the squares.

39. No, $(x-2)^2 = x^2-4x+4 \neq x^2-4$.

40. No, $(x+4)^2 = x^2+8x+16 \neq x^2+16$.

41. Yes, $(x+3)(x-2) = x^2+x-6$.

42. Yes, $(5x-1)^2 = 25x^2-10x+1$.

43. No, $2z(3z+1) = 6z^2+2z \neq 6z^2+1$.

44. No, $-(z^2+4z) = -z^2-4z \neq -z^2+4z$.

45. $(x+5)(x+10) = x^2+10x+5x+50 = x^2+15x+50$

46. $(x-5)(x-10) = x^2 - 10x - 5x + 50 = x^2 - 15x + 50$

47. $(x-3)(x-4) = x^2 - 4x - 3x + 12 = x^2 - 7x + 12$

48. $(x+3)(x+4) = x^2 + 4x + 3x + 12 = x^2 + 7x + 12$

49. $(2z-1)(z+2) = 2z^2 + 4z - z - 2 = 2z^2 + 3z - 2$

50. $(2z+1)(z-2) = 2z^2 - 4z + z - 2 = 2z^2 - 3z - 2$

51. $(y+3)(y-4) = y^2 - 4y + 3y - 12 = y^2 - y - 12$

52. $(2y+1)(5y+1) = 10y^2 + 2y + 5y + 1 = 10y^2 + 7y + 1$

53. $(4x-3)(4-9x) = 16x - 36x^2 - 12 + 27x = -36x^2 + 43x - 12$

54. $(1-x)(1+2x) = 1 + 2x - x - 2x^2 = -2x^2 + x + 1$

55. $(-2z+3)(z-2) = -2z^2 + 4z + 3z - 6 = -2z^2 + 7z - 6$

56. $(z-2)(4z+3) = 4z^2 + 3z - 8z - 6 = 4z^2 - 5z - 6$

57. $\left(z - \dfrac{1}{2}\right)\left(z + \dfrac{1}{4}\right) = z^2 + \dfrac{1}{4}z - \dfrac{1}{2}z - \dfrac{1}{8} = z^2 - \dfrac{1}{4}z - \dfrac{1}{8}$

58. $\left(z - \dfrac{1}{3}\right)\left(z - \dfrac{1}{6}\right) = z^2 - \dfrac{1}{6}z - \dfrac{1}{3}z + \dfrac{1}{18} = z^2 - \dfrac{1}{2}z + \dfrac{1}{18}$

59. $(x^2+1)(2x^2-1) = 2x^4 - x^2 + 2x^2 - 1 = 2x^4 + x^2 - 1$

60. $(x^2-2)(x^2+4) = x^4 + 4x^2 - 2x^2 - 8 = x^4 + 2x^2 - 8$

61. $(x+y)(x-2y) = x^2 - 2xy + xy - 2y^2 = x^2 - xy - 2y^2$

62. $(x^2+y^2)(x-y) = x^3 - x^2y + xy^2 - y^3$

63. $4x(x^2-2x-3) = 4x^3 - 8x^2 - 12x$

64. $2x(3-x+x^2) = 6x - 2x^2 + 2x^3 = 2x^3 - 2x^2 + 6x$

65. $-x(x^4-3x^2+1) = -x^5 + 3x^3 - x$

66. $-3m^2(4m^3+m^2-2m) = -12m^5 - 3m^4 + 6m^3$

67. $(2n^2-4n+1)(3n^2) = 6n^4 - 12n^3 + 3n^2$

68. $(x-y+5)(xy) = x^2y - xy^2 + 5xy$

69. $(x+1)(x^2+2x-3) = x^3 + 2x^2 - 3x + x^2 + 2x - 3 = x^3 + 3x^2 - x - 3$

70. $(2x-1)(3x^2-x+6) = 6x^3 - 2x^2 + 12x - 3x^2 + x - 6 = 6x^3 - 5x^2 + 13x - 6$

71. $z(2+z)(1-z-z^2) = (2z+z^2)(1-z-z^2) = 2z-2z^2-2z^3+z^2-z^3-z^4 = -z^4-3z^3-z^2+2z$

72. $z^2(1-z)(2+z) = (z^2-z^3)(2+z) = 2z^2+z^3-2z^3-z^4 = -z^4-z^3+2z^2$

73. $2ab^2(2a^2-ab+3b^2) = 4a^3b^2-2a^2b^3+6ab^4$

74. $2n(mn^2+2n)(3m^2n-3n) = (2mn^3+4n^2)(3m^2n-3n) = 6m^3n^4+12m^2n^3-6mn^4-12n^3$

75. $(2r-4t)(3r^2+rt-t^2) = 6r^3+2r^2t-2rt^2-12r^2t-4rt^2+4t^3 = 6r^3-10r^2t-6rt^2+4t^3$

76. $-2(x-y)(x^2+xy+y^2) = (-2x+2y)(x^2+xy+y^2) = -2x^3-2x^2y-2xy^2+2x^2y+2xy^2+2y^3$

    $= -2x^3+2y^3$

77. $(2^3)^2 = 2^{3\cdot2} = 2^6 = 64$

78. $(x^3)^5 = x^{3\cdot5} = x^{15}$

79. $2(z^3)^6 = 2z^{3\cdot6} = 2z^{18}$

80. $(5y)^3 = 5^3\cdot y^3 = 125y^3$

81. $(-5x)^2 = (-5)^2\cdot x^2 = 25x^2$

82. $(2y)^4 = 2^4\cdot y^4 = 16y^4$

83. $(-2xy^2)^3 = (-2)^3\cdot x^3\cdot y^{2\cdot3} = -8x^3y^6$

84. $(3x^2y^3)^4 = 3^4\cdot x^{2\cdot4}\cdot y^{3\cdot4} = 81x^8y^{12}$

85. $(-4a^2b^3)^2 = (-4)^2\cdot a^{2\cdot2}\cdot b^{3\cdot2} = 16a^4b^6$

86. $-(5r^3t)^2 = -5^2\cdot r^{3\cdot2}\cdot t^2 = -25r^6t^2$

87. $(x-3)(x+3) = x^2-9$

88. $(x+5)(x-5) = x^2-25$

89. $(3-2x)(3+2x) = 3^2-(2x)^2 = 9-4x^2$

90. $(4-5x)(4+5x) = 4^2-(5x)^2 = 16-25x^2$

91. $(x-y)(x+y) = x^2-y^2$

92. $(2x+2y)(2x-2y) = 4x^2-4y^2$

93. $(x+2)^2 = x^2+2(2x)+4 = x^2+4x+4$

94. $(y+5)^2 = y^2 + 2(5y) + 25 = y^2 + 10y + 25$

95. $(2x+1)^2 = 4x^2 + 2(2x) + 1 = 4x^2 + 4x + 1$

96. $(3x+5)^2 = 9x^2 + 2(15x) + 25 = 9x^2 + 30x + 25$

97. $(x-1)^2 = x^2 + 2(-x) + 1 = x^2 - 2x + 1$

98. $(x-7)^2 = x^2 + 2(-7x) + 49 = x^2 - 14x + 49$

99. $(3x-2)^2 = 9x^2 + 2(-6x) + 4 = 9x^2 - 12x + 4$

100. $(6x-5)^2 = 36x^2 + 2(-30x) + 25 = 36x^2 - 60x + 25$

101. $3x(x+1)(x-1) = 3x(x^2-1) = 3x^3 - 3x$

102. $-4x(3x-5)^2 = -4x(9x^2 - 30x + 25) = -36x^3 + 120x^2 - 100x$

103. $3rt(t-2r)(t+2r) = 3rt(t^2 - 4r^2) = 3rt^3 - 12r^3t$

104. $5r^2t^2(t-4)(t+4) = 5r^2t^2(t^2-16) = 5r^2t^4 - 80r^2t^2$

105. $(a^2 + 2b^2)(a^2 - 2b^2) = (a^2)^2 - (2b^2)^2 = a^4 - 4b^4$

106. $(2a + 5b^4)(2a - 5b^4) = (2a)^2 - (5b^4)^2 = 4a^2 - 25b^8$

107. $(3m^3 + 5n^2)^2 = (3m^3)^2 + 2(3m^3)(5n^2) + (5n^2)^2 = 9m^6 + 30m^3n^2 + 25n^4$

108. $(6m + 4n^2)^2 = (6m)^2 + 2(6m)(4n^2) + (4n^2)^2 = 36m^2 + 48mn^2 + 16n^4$

109. $(x^3 - 2y^3)^2 = (x^3)^2 - 2(x^3)(2y^3) + (2y^3)^2 = x^6 - 4x^3y^3 + 4y^6$

110. $(6m - n^4)^2 = (6m)^2 - 2(6m)(n^4) + (n^4)^2 = 36m^2 - 12mn^4 + n^8$

111. $((x-3)+y)((x-3)-y) = (x-3)^2 - y^2 = x^2 - 6x + 9 - y^2 = x^2 - 6x - y^2 + 9$

112. $((2m-1)+n)((2m-1)-n) = (2m-1)^2 - n^2 = 4m^2 - 4m + 1 - n^2 = 4m^2 - 4m - n^2 + 1$

113. $(r-(t+2))(r+(t+2)) = r^2 - (t+2)^2 = r^2 - (t^2 + 4t + 4) = r^2 - t^2 - 4t - 4$

114. $(y-(z+1))(y+(z+1)) = y^2 - (z+1)^2 = y^2 - (z^2 + 2z + 1) = y^2 - z^2 - 2z - 1$

115. $(102)(98) = (100+2)(100-2) = 100^2 - 2^2 = 10,000 - 4 = 9996$

116. $(51)(49) = (50+1)(50-1) = 50^2 - 1^2 = 2500 - 1 = 2499$

117. $(fg)(2) = (2+1)(2-2) = (3)(0) = 0;$

$$(fg)(x) = (x+1)(x-2) = x^2 - 2x + x - 2 = x^2 - x - 2$$

118. $(fg)(2) = (2(2)+3)(4-2) = (7)(2) = 14;$

$$(fg)(x) = (2x+3)(4-x) = 8x - 2x^2 + 12 - 3x = -2x^2 + 5x + 12$$

119. $(fg)(2) = ((2)^2)(3-5(2)) = (4)(-7) = -28;$

$$(fg)(x) = (x^2)(3-5x) = 3x^2 - 5x^3 = -5x^3 + 3x^2$$

120. $(fg)(2) = ((2)^2 - 4(2))((2)^2 - 5) = (-4)(-1) = 4;$

$$(fg)(x) = (x^2 - 4x)(x^2 - 5) = x^4 - 5x^2 - 4x^3 + 20x = x^4 - 4x^3 - 5x^2 + 20x$$

121. $(fg)(2) = (2(2)^2 + 1)((2)^2 + 2 - 3) = (9)(3) = 27;$

$$(fg)(x) = (2x^2 + 1)(x^2 + x - 3) = 2x^4 + 2x^3 - 6x^2 + x^2 + x - 3$$

$$= 2x^4 + 2x^3 - 5x^2 + x - 3$$

122. $(fg)(2) = ((2)^3 - 3(2)^2)(2(2)^2 + 4(2)) = (8-12)(8+8) = (-4)(16) = -64;$

$$(fg)(x) = (x^3 - 3x^2)(2x^2 + 4x) = 2x^5 + 4x^4 - 6x^4 - 12x^3 = 2x^5 - 2x^4 - 12x^3$$

Area

123. $x(x+4);$ When $x = 20, (20)(20+4) = 20(24) = 480 \text{ ft}^2.$

124. $\frac{1}{2}(x+1)(x-1);$ When $x = 20, \frac{1}{2}(20+1)(20-1) = \frac{1}{2}(21)(19) = 199.5 \text{ ft}^2.$

125. $(x+3)^2;$ When $x = 20, (20+3)^2 = 23^2 = 529 \text{ ft}^2.$

126. $\pi(2x+1)^2;$ When $x = 20, \pi(2 \cdot 20 + 1)^2 = \pi \cdot 41^2 = 1681\pi \approx 5281 \text{ ft}^2.$

127. (a) $D = 40 - \frac{1}{2}(20) = 40 - 10 = 30;$ demand is 30 thousand units.

(b) $R = Dp = \left(40 - \frac{1}{2}p\right)(p) = 40p - \frac{1}{2}p^2$

(c) $R = 40(30) - \frac{1}{2}(30)^2 = 1200 = \frac{1}{2}(900) = 1200 - 450 = 750;$ revenue is \$750 thousand.

128. (a) $D = 20 - \frac{1}{10}(20) = 20 - 2 = 18;$ demand is 18 thousand units.

(b) $R = Dp = \left(20 - \frac{1}{10}p\right)(p) = 20p - \frac{1}{10}p^2$

(c) $R = 20(30) - \frac{1}{10}(30)^2 = 600 - \frac{1}{10}(900) = 600 - 90 = 510;$ revenue is \$510 thousand.

Applications

129.   (a) $N(1+r)^2 = N(1+2r+r^2) = N+2Nr+Nr^2 = Nr^2+2Nr+N$

(b) $200(1+0.10)^2 = 242$ and $200(0.10)^2 + 2(200)(0.10)+200 = 2+40+200 = 242$;   The answers agree.

130.   (a) $100\left(1-\dfrac{x}{100}\right)^2 = 100\left(1-2(1)\left(\dfrac{x}{100}\right)+\left(\dfrac{x}{100}\right)^2\right) = 100\left(1-\dfrac{x}{50}+\dfrac{x^2}{10,000}\right) = 100-2x+\dfrac{x^2}{100}$

$= \dfrac{x^2}{100}-2x+100$

(b) $100\left(1-\dfrac{25}{100}\right)^2 = 100(0.75)^2 = 56.25\%$ and $\dfrac{1}{100}(25)^2 - 2(25)+100 = 6.25-50+100 = 56.25\%$

131. $x(x+1) = x^2+x$

132. $x(2y+1) = 2xy+x$

133.   Let l represent the length of the rectangle. Then since the perimeter is 100 feet, $2l+2x = 100 \Rightarrow l = 50-x$.

Since the area is given by $A = xl$, we may write the area as follows: $x(50-x) = 50x-x^2$.

134. $(x+y)(x-y) = x^2-y^2$

Checking Basic Concepts for Sections 5.1 & 5.2

1.   (a) $8x^2+4x-5x^2+3x = 3x^2+7x$

(b) $\left(5x^2-3x+2\right)-\left(3x^2-5x^3+1\right) = 5x^2-3x+2-3x^2+5x^3-1 = 5x^3+2x^2-3x+1$

2.   The polynomial is $x(x+120)$. When tickets cost \$10 each, the revenue will be $10(10+120) = \$1300$.

3.   (a) When exercise is stopped, $x = 0$, and so $f(0) = 2(0)^2 - 25(0)+160 = 0-0+160 = 160$ bpm.

(b) After 4 minutes, $x = 4$, and so $f(4) = 2(4)^2 - 25(4)+160 = 32-100+160 = 92$ bpm.

4.   (a) $-5(x-6) = -5x+30$

(b) $4x^3\left(3x^2-5x\right) = 12x^5 - 20x^4$

(c) $(2x-1)(x+3) = 2x^2+6x-x-3 = 2x^2+5x-3$

5.   (a) $(5x-6)(5x+6) = 25x^2-36$

(b) $(3x-4)^2 = 9x^2-24x+16$

6.   See Figure 6.

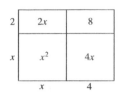

Figure 6

5.3: Factoring Polynomials

Concepts

1. To solve equations

2. Either $x = 0$ or $x - 3 = 0$; the zero-product property

3. Yes, $2x$ is a common factor of each term.

4. No, $4x^2$ is the greatest common factor.

5. No, since $\dfrac{1}{2}(4) = 2$, but $\dfrac{1}{2} \neq 2$ and $4 \neq 2$.

6. Yes, by the zero-product property.

Factoring and Equations

7. $10x - 15 = 5(2x - 3)$

8. $32 - 16x = 16(2 - x)$

9. $4x + 6y = 2(2x + 3y)$

10. $50a + 20b = 10(5a + 2b)$

11. $9r - 15t = 3(3r - 5t)$

12. $16m - 24n = 8(2m - 3n)$

13. $2x^3 - 5x = x(2x^2 - 5)$

14. $3y - 9y^2 = 3y(1 - 3y)$

15. $8a^3 + 10a = 2a(4a^2 + 5)$

16. $20b^3 + 25b^2 = 5b^2(4b + 5)$

17. $6r^3 - 18r^5 = 6r^3(1 - 3r^2)$

18. $7n^2 - 21n^4 = 7n^2(1 - 3n^2)$

19. $8x^3 - 4x^2 + 16x = 4x(2x^2 - x + 4)$

20. $5x^3 - x^2 + 4x = x(5x^2 - x + 4)$

21. $9n^4 - 6n^2 + 3n = 3n(3n^3 - 2n + 1)$

22. $5n^4 + 10n^2 - 25n = 5n\left(n^3 + 2n - 5\right)$

23. $6t^6 - 4t^4 + 2t^2 = 2t^2\left(3t^4 - 2t^2 + 1\right)$

24. $15t^6 + 25t^4 - 20t^2 = 5t^2\left(3t^4 + 5t^2 - 4\right)$

25. $5x^2y^2 - 15x^2y^3 = 5x^2y^2\left(1 - 3y\right)$

26. $21xy + 14x^3y^3 = 7xy\left(3 + 2x^2y^2\right)$

27. $6a^3b^2 - 15a^2b^3 = 3a^2b^2\left(2a - 5b\right)$

28. $45a^2b + 30a^3b^2 = 15a^2b\left(3 + 2ab\right)$

29. $18mn^2 + 12m^2n^3 = 6mn^2\left(3 + 2mn\right)$

30. $24m^2n^3 - 36m^3n^2 = 12m^2n^2\left(2n - 3m\right)$

31. $15x^2y + 10xy - 25x^2y^2 = 5xy\left(3x + 2 - 5xy\right)$

32. $14a^3b^2 - 21a^2b^2 + 35a^2b = 7a^2b\left(2ab - 3b + 5\right)$

33. $4a^2 - 2ab + 6ab^2 = 2a\left(2a - b + 3b^2\right)$

34. $5a^2 + 10a^2b^2 - 15ab = 5a\left(a + 2ab^2 - 3b\right)$

35. $-2x^2 + 4x - 6 = -2\left(x^2 - 2x + 3\right)$

36. $-7x^5 - 21x^3 - 14x^2 = -7x^2\left(x^3 + 3x + 2\right)$

37. $-8z^4 - 16z^3 = -8z^3\left(z + 2\right)$

38. $-8z^5 - 24z^4 = -8z^4\left(z + 3\right)$

39. $-4m^2n^3 - 6mn^2 - 8mn = -2mn\left(2mn^2 + 3n + 4\right)$

40. $-13m^4n^4 - 13m^3n^3 + 26m^2n^2 = -13m^2n^2\left(m^2n^2 + mn - 2\right)$

41. $m = 0$ or $n = 0$

42. $x = 0$ or $y = 0$ or $z = 0$

43. $3z = 0 \Rightarrow z = 0$ or $z + 4 = 0 \Rightarrow z = -4$

44. $2z = 0 \Rightarrow z = 0$ or $z - 1 = 0 \Rightarrow z = 1$

45. $r - 1 = 0 \Rightarrow r = 1$ or $r + 3 = 0 \Rightarrow r = -3$

46. $2r + 3 = 0 \Rightarrow 2r = -3 \Rightarrow r = -\dfrac{3}{2}$ or $r - 5 = 0 \Rightarrow r = 5$

47. $x + 2 = 0 \Rightarrow x = -2$ or $3x - 1 = 0 \Rightarrow 3x = 1 \Rightarrow x = \dfrac{1}{3}$

48. $4y - 3 = 0 \Rightarrow 4y = 3 \Rightarrow y = \dfrac{3}{4}$ or $2y + 1 = 0 \Rightarrow 2y = -1 \Rightarrow y = -\dfrac{1}{2}$

49. $3x = 0 \Rightarrow x = 0$ or $y - 6 = 0 \Rightarrow y = 6$

50. $7m = 0 \Rightarrow m = 0$ or $3n + 1 = 0 \Rightarrow 3n = -1 \Rightarrow n = -\dfrac{1}{3}$

51.   (a) The graph crossed the x-axis at -3 and 0.

       (b) $x^2 + 3x = 0 \Rightarrow x(x + 3) = 0 \Rightarrow x = 0$ or $x + 3 = 0$, that is $x = 0$ or $x = -3$.

       (c) The zeros of $P(x)$ are -3 and 0.

52.   (a) The graph crossed the x-axis at 0 and 1.

       (b) $2x - 2x^2 = 0 \Rightarrow 2x(1 - x) = 0 \Rightarrow 2x = 0$ or $1 - x = 0$, that is $x = 0$ or $x = 1$.

       (c) The zeros of $P(x)$ are 0 and 1.

53.   (a) The graph crossed the x-axis at 0 and 2.

       (b) $6x - 3x^2 = 0 \Rightarrow 3x(2 - x) = 0 \Rightarrow 3x = 0$ or $2 - x = 0$, that is $x = 0$ or $x = 2$.

       (c) The zeros of $P(x)$ are 0 and 2.

54.   (a) The graph crossed the x-axis at -2 and 0.

       (b) $x^2 + 2x = 0 \Rightarrow x(x + 2) = 0 \Rightarrow x = 0$ or $x + 2 = 0$, that is $x = 0$ or $x = -2$.

       (c) The zeros of $P(x)$ are -2 and 0.

55.   (a) The graph crossed the x-axis at -1 and 1.

       (b) $x^2 - 1 = 0 \Rightarrow (x + 1)(x - 1) = 0 \Rightarrow x + 1 = 0$ or $x - 1 = 0$, that is $x = -1$ or $x = 1$.

       (c) The zeros of $P(x)$ are -1 and 1.

56.   (a) The graph crossed the x-axis at -2 and 2.

       (b) $4 - x^2 = 0 \Rightarrow (2 + x)(2 - x) = 0 \Rightarrow 2 + x = 0$ or $2 - x = 0$, that is $x = -2$ or $x = 2$.

       (c) The zeros of $P(x)$ are -2 and 2.

57.   The graph of $y = x^2 - 2x$ (not shown) crosses the x-axis at 0 and 2. The solutions are 0 and 2.

58.   The graph of $y = x^2 + x$ (not shown) crosses the x-axis at -1 and 0. The solutions are -1 and 0.

59.   The graph of $y = x - x^2$ (not shown) crosses the x-axis at 0 and 1. The solutions are 0 and 1.

60.   The graph of $y = 3x - x^2$ (not shown) crosses the x-axis at 0 and 3. The solutions are 0 and 3.

61.   The graph of $y = x^2 + 4x$ (not shown) crosses the x-axis at -4 and 0. The solutions are -4 and 0.

62.   The graph of $y = x^2 - 4x$ (not shown) crosses the x-axis at 0 and 4. The solutions are 0 and 4.

63. $x^2 - x = 0 \Rightarrow x(x - 1) = 0 \Rightarrow$ Either $x = 0$ or $x - 1 = 0 \Rightarrow x = 1$.

64. $4x - 2x^2 = 0 \Rightarrow 2x(2-x) \Rightarrow$ Either $2x = 0 \Rightarrow x = 0$ or $2 - x = 0 \Rightarrow x = 2$.

65. $5x^2 - x = 0 \Rightarrow x(5x-1) \Rightarrow$ Either $x = 0$ or $5x - 1 = 0 \Rightarrow x = \dfrac{1}{5}$.

66. $4x^2 + 3x = 0 \Rightarrow x(4x+3) \Rightarrow$ Either $x = 0$ or $4x + 3 = 0 \Rightarrow x = -\dfrac{3}{4}$.

67. $10x^2 + 5x = 0 \Rightarrow 5x(2x+1) \Rightarrow$ Either $5x = 0 \Rightarrow x = 0$ or $2x + 1 = 0 \Rightarrow x = -\dfrac{1}{2}$.

68. $6x - 12x^2 = 0 \Rightarrow 6x(1-2x) \Rightarrow$ Either $6x = 0 \Rightarrow x = 0$ or $1 - 2x = 0 \Rightarrow x = \dfrac{1}{2}$.

69. $15x^2 = 10x \Rightarrow 15x^2 - 10x = 0 \Rightarrow 5x(3x-2) \Rightarrow$ Either $5x = 0 \Rightarrow x = 0$ or $3x - 2 = 0 \Rightarrow x = \dfrac{2}{3}$.

70. $4x = 8x^2 \Rightarrow 4x - 8x^2 = 0 \Rightarrow 4x(1-2x) \Rightarrow$ Either $4x = 0 \Rightarrow x = 0$ or $1 - 2x = 0 \Rightarrow x = \dfrac{1}{2}$.

71. $25x = 10x^2 \Rightarrow 25x - 10x^2 = 0 \Rightarrow 5x(5-2x) \Rightarrow$ Either $5x = 0 \Rightarrow x = 0$ or $5 - 2x = 0 \Rightarrow x = \dfrac{5}{2}$.

72. $34x^2 = 51x \Rightarrow 34x^2 - 51x = 0 \Rightarrow 17x(2x-3) = 0 \Rightarrow$ Either $17x = 0 \Rightarrow x = 0$ or $2x - 3 = 0 \Rightarrow x = \dfrac{3}{2}$.

73. $32x^4 - 16x^3 = 0 \Rightarrow 16x^3(2x-1) = 0 \Rightarrow$ Either $16x^3 = 0 \Rightarrow x = 0$ or $2x - 1 = 0 \Rightarrow x = \dfrac{1}{2}$.

74. $45x^4 - 30x^3 = 0 \Rightarrow 15x^3(3x-2) = 0 \Rightarrow$ Either $15x^3 = 0 \Rightarrow x = 0$ or $3x - 2 = 0 \Rightarrow x = \dfrac{2}{3}$.

75.   Numerically: Table $Y_1 = X^2 + 2X$ with Tblstart = –5 and ΔTbl = 1.

Figure 75a

Graphically: Graph $Y_1 = X^2 + 2X$ in $[-5,\ 5,\ 1]$ by $[-5, 5, 1]$.

Figure 75b

$x^2 + 2x = 0 \Rightarrow x(x+2) = 0 \Rightarrow x = 0$ or $x + 2 = 0 \Rightarrow x = -2$. The solutions are $-2, 0$.

76.   Numerically: Table $Y_1 = X^2 + 3X = 0$ with Tblstart = –5 and ΔTbl = 1.

Figure 76a

Graphically: Graph $Y_1 = X^2 + 3X$ in $[-5, 5, 1]$ by $[-5, 5, 1]$.

Figure 76b

$x^2 + 3x = 0 \Rightarrow x(x+3) = 0 \Rightarrow x = 0$ or $x + 3 = 0 \Rightarrow x = -3$. The solutions are $-3, 0$.

77.   Numerically: Table $Y_1 = 2X^2 - 3X$ with Tblstart $= -1$ and ΔTbl $= 0.5$.

Figure 77a

Graphically: Graph $Y_1 = 2X^2 - 3X$ in $[-5, 5, 1]$ by $[-5, 5, 1]$.

Figure 77b

$2x^2 - 3x = 0 \Rightarrow x(2x-3) = 0 \Rightarrow x = 0$ or $2x - 3 = 0 \Rightarrow x = \dfrac{3}{2}$. The solutions are $0, \dfrac{3}{2}$.

78.   Numerically: Table $Y_1 = 2X - 3X^2$ with Tblstart $= -1$ and ΔTbl $= 1/3$.

Figure 78a

Graphically: Graph $Y_1 = 2X - 3X^2$ in $[-3, 3, 1/3]$ by $[-3, 3, 1]$.

Figure 78b

$2x - 3x^2 = 0 \Rightarrow x(2-3x) = 0 \Rightarrow x = 0$ or $2 - 3x = 0 \Rightarrow x = \dfrac{2}{3}$. The solutions are $0, \dfrac{2}{3}$.

Factoring by Grouping

79. $2x(x+2)+3(x+2)=(2x+3)(x+2)$

80. $5(x-1)-2x(x-1)=(5-2x)(x-1)$

81. $(x-5)x^2-(x-5)2=(x-5)(x^2-2)$

82. $7x(x-1)-3(x-1)=(7x-3)(x-1)$

83. $x^3+3x^2+2x+6=x^2(x+3)+2(x+3)=(x+3)(x^2+2)$

84. $4x^3+3x^2+8x+6=x^2(4x+3)+2(4x+3)=(4x+3)(x^2+2)$

85. $6x^3-4x^2+9x-6=2x^2(3x-2)+3(3x-2)=(3x-2)(2x^2+3)$

86. $x^3-3x^2-5x+15=x^2(x-3)-5(x-3)=(x-3)(x^2-5)$

87. $2x^3-3x^2+2x-3=x^2(2x-3)+1(2x-3)=(x^2+1)(2x-3)$

88. $8x^3-2x^2+12x-3=2x^2(4x-1)+3(4x-1)=(2x^2+3)(4x-1)$

89. $x^3-7x^2-3x+21=x^2(x-7)-3(x-7)=(x^2-3)(x-7)$

90. $6x^3-15x^2-4x+10=3x^2(2x-5)-2(2x-5)=(3x^2-2)(2x-5)$

91. $3x^3-15x^2+5x-25=3x^2(x-5)+5(x-5)=(x-5)(3x^2+5)$

92. $2x^4-x^3+4x-2=x^3(2x-1)+2(2x-1)=(2x-1)(x^3+2)$

93. $xy+x+3y+3=x(y+1)+3(y+1)=(y+1)(x+3)$

94. $ax+bx-ay-by=x(a+b)-y(a+b)=(a+b)(x-y)$

95. $ab-3a+2b-6=a(b-3)+2(b-3)=(a+2)(b-3)$

96. $2ax-6bx-ay+3by=2x(a-3b)-y(a-3b)=(2x-y)(a-3b)$

97. Golf ball: graph b, because the height starts at 0, then increases until it reaches its highest point and then decreases until the height is 0 again.

    Yo – yo: graph a, because the height decreases until its lowest point, then it increases and returns to its starting position.

98. (a) $ab=5$ does not imply $a=5$ or $b=5$.

    (b) $ax^2-bx=0 \Rightarrow x(ax-b)=0 \Rightarrow x=0$ or $ax-b=0$

    $$\Rightarrow x=\frac{b}{a}, \text{ so } x=0 \text{ or } \frac{b}{a}.$$

Applications

99.   (a) $-16t^2 + 128t = 0 \Rightarrow -16t(t-8) = 0 \Rightarrow$ Either $-16t = 0 \Rightarrow t = 0$ or $t - 8 = 0 \Rightarrow t = 8$.

The golf ball hits the ground after 8 seconds.

(b) The graph crosses the *t*-axis at about 8 seconds.

(c) See Figure 99. Yes, the answer is the same.

(d) The maximum altitude given by either the graph or the table is 256 feet which is attained after 4 seconds.

t	3	4	5	6	7	8
$y = h(t)$	240	256	240	192	112	0

Figure 99

100. $-16t^2 + 96t = 0 \Rightarrow -16t(t-6) = 0 \Rightarrow -16t = 0$ or $t - 6 = 0$, that is $t = 0$ or $t = 6$. The ball strikes the ground after 6 seconds.

101. $f(47) = 0.0148(47)^2 + 0.686(47) + 315 \approx 380$; CO_2 concentration in 2005 was 380 ppm.

102.   <Insert graph calc screen shot of $Y_1 = 340$ and $Y_2 = 0.0148X^2 + 0.686X + 315$ in [0, 50, 10] by [300, 400, 20] show intersection at $X = 24.00802$, $Y = 340$>

$x = 24$; in 1982 the CO_2 concentration was 340 ppm.

103. $8y = \pi y^2 \Rightarrow 8y - \pi y^2 = 0 \Rightarrow y(8 - \pi y) = 0 \Rightarrow y = 0$ or $8 - \pi y = 0$, that is $y = 0$ or $y = \dfrac{8}{\pi}$.

The positive value is $\dfrac{8}{\pi}$.

104.   Graph $Y_1 = 4.1X^2 - 25X + 46$ and $Y_2 = 500$ in [4, 20, 1] by [0, 700, 100]. See Figure 104.

The cumulative number of AIDS cases reached 500 thousand in 1994.

[4, 20, 1] by [0, 700, 100]

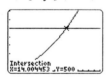

Figure 104

105.   (a) See Figure 105. It models the data quite well.

(b) From the table, the height is about 54,000 feet.

(c) $11t^2 + 6t = 0 \Rightarrow t(11t + 6) = 0 \Rightarrow$ Either $t = 0$ or $11t + 6 = 0 \Rightarrow t = -\dfrac{6}{11}$.

When $t = 0$ the shuttle has not yet left the ground. The value $t = -\dfrac{6}{11}$ has no physical meaning.

t	20	30	40	50	60	70	80
$y = f(t)$	4520	10,080	17,840	27,800	39,960	54,320	70,880

Figure 105

106. (a) For October, $x = 10$. $T(10) = 24(10) - 2(10)^2 = 240 - 200 = 40°F$

(b) $24x - 2x^2 = 0 \Rightarrow 2x(12 - x) = 0 \Rightarrow$ Either $2x = 0 \Rightarrow x = 0$ or $12 - x = 0 \Rightarrow x = 12$.

Both results correspond to December when the monthly average temperature is $0°F$.

(c) Graph $Y_1 = 24X - 2X^2$ in [0, 20, 1] by [0, 100, 10]. See Figure 106.

[0, 20, 1] by [0, 100, 10]

Figure 106

107. No, there are many possibilities such as 9×24, 8×27 or 13.5×16.

108. Yes, since $4x^2 + 8x = 4x(x + 2)$ the width is $x + 2$.

5.4: Factoring Trinomials

Concepts

1. A polynomial with 3 terms: $x^2 - x + 1$; *Answers may vary.*

2. The methods for factoring the given expression are symbolic and graphical, grouping and FOIL. *Answers may vary.*

3. $a = 3$, $b = -1$, $c = -3$

4. Yes, it checks using FOIL.

5. $(x + 3)(x - 1)$

6. $(6x - 3)(x - 2)$ or $3(2x - 1)(x - 2)$ or $6\left(x - \dfrac{1}{2}\right)(x - 2)$

Factoring Trinomials

7. Yes, it checks using FOIL.

8. Yes, it checks using FOIL.

9. No, $(x + 5)(x - 4) = x^2 + x - 20$.

10. No, $(x + 4)(x - 7) = x^2 - 3x - 28$.

11. Yes, it checks using FOIL.

12. No, $(2z - 4)(2z - 3) = 4z^2 - 14z + 12$.

13. No, $(5m + 2)(2m - 5) = 10m^2 - 21m - 10$.

14. Yes, it checks using FOIL.

15. $x^2 + 7x + 10 = (x + 2)(x + 5)$

16. $x^2 + 3x - 10 = (x - 2)(x + 5)$

17. $x^2 + 8x + 12 = (x+2)(x+6)$

18. $x^2 - 8x + 12 = (x-6)(x-2)$

19. $x^2 - 13x + 36 = (x-9)(x-4)$

20. $x^2 + 11x + 24 = (x+3)(x+8)$

21. $x^2 - 7x - 8 = (x-8)(x+1)$

22. $x^2 - 21x - 100 = (x-25)(x+4)$

23. $z^2 + z - 72 = (z-8)(z+9)$

24. $z^2 + 6z - 55 = (z-5)(z+11)$

25. $t^2 - 15t + 56 = (t-8)(t-7)$

26. $t^2 - 14t + 40 = (t-10)(t-4)$

27. $y^2 - 18y + 72 = (y-12)(y-6)$

28. $y^2 - 15y + 54 = (y-9)(y-6)$

29. $m^2 - 18m - 40 = (m-20)(m+2)$

30. $m^2 - 22m - 75 = (m-25)(m+3)$

31. $n^2 - 20n - 300 = (n-30)(n+10)$

32. $n^2 - 13n - 30 = (n-15)(n+2)$

33. $2x^2 + 7x + 3 = (x+3)(2x+1)$

34. $2x^2 - 5x - 3 = (x-3)(2x+1)$

35. $6x^2 - x - 2 = (2x+1)(3x-2)$

36. $10x^2 + 3x - 1 = (2x+1)(5x-1)$

37. $4z^2 + 19z + 12 = (z+4)(4z+3)$

38. $4z^2 + 17z + 4 = (z+4)(4z+1)$

39. $6t^2 - 17t + 12 = (2t-3)(3t-4)$

40. $6t^2 - 13t + 6 = (2t-3)(3t-2)$

41. $10y^2 + 13y - 3 = (2y+3)(5y-1)$

42. $10y^2 + 23y - 5 = (2y+5)(5y-1)$

43. $6m^2 - m - 12 = (2m-3)(3m+4)$

44. $20m^2 - m - 12 = (4m+3)(5m-4)$

45. $42n^2 + 5n - 25 = (6n+5)(7n-5)$

46. $42n^2 + 65n + 25 = (6n+5)(7n+5)$

47. $1 + x - 2x^2 = (1-x)(1+2x)$

48. $3 - 5x - 2x^2 = (3+x)(1-2x)$

49. $20 + 7x - 6x^2 = (5-2x)(4+3x)$

50. $4 + 13x - 12x^2 = (4-3x)(1+4x)$

51. $5y^2 + 5y - 30 = 5\left(y^2 + y - 6\right) = 5(y-2)(y+3)$

52. $3y^2 - 27y + 24 = 3\left(y^2 - 9y + 8\right) = 3(y-8)(y-1)$

53. $2z^2 + 12z + 16 = 2\left(z^2 + 6z + 8\right) = 2(z+2)(z+4)$

54. $4z^2 + 32z + 60 = 4\left(z^2 + 8z + 15\right) = 4(z+3)(z+5)$

55. $z^3 + 9z^2 + 14z = z\left(z^2 + 9z + 14\right) = z(z+2)(z+7)$

56. $z^3 + 7z^2 + 12z = z\left(z^2 + 7z + 12\right) = z(z+3)(z+4)$

57. $t^3 - 10t^2 + 21t = t\left(t^2 - 10t + 21\right) = t(t-7)(t-3)$

58. $t^3 - 11t^2 + 24t = t\left(t^2 - 11t + 24\right) = t(t-8)(t-3)$

59. $m^4 + 6m^3 + 5m^2 = m^2\left(m^2 + 6m + 5\right) = m^2(m+1)(m+5)$

60. $m^4 - m^3 - 2m^2 = m^2\left(m^2 - m - 2\right) = m^2(m-2)(m+1)$

61. $5x^3 + x^2 - 6x = x\left(5x^2 + x - 6\right) = x(x-1)(5x+6)$

62. $2x^3 + 8x^2 - 24x = 2x\left(x^2 + 4x - 12\right) = 2x(x-2)(x+6)$

63. $6x^3 + 21x^2 + 9x = 3x\left(2x^2 + 7x + 3\right) = 3x(x+3)(2x+1)$

64. $12x^3 - 8x^2 - 20x = 4x\left(3x^2 - 2x - 5\right) = 4x(x+1)(3x-5)$

65. $2x^3 - 14x^2 + 20x = 2x\left(x^2 - 7x + 10\right) = 2x(x-5)(x-2)$

66. $7x^3 + 35x^2 + 42x = 7x\left(x^2 + 5x + 6\right) = 7x(x+2)(x+3)$

67. $60z^3 + 230z^2 - 40z = 10z\left(6z^2 + 23z - 4\right) = 10z(z+4)(6z-1)$

68. $24z^3 + 8z^2 - 80z = 8z\left(3z^2 + z - 10\right) = 8z(z+2)(3z-5)$

69. $4x^4 + 10x^3 - 6x^2 = 2x^2\left(2x^2 + 5x - 3\right) = 2x^2\left(x + 3\right)\left(2x - 1\right)$

70. $30x^4 + 3x^3 - 9x^2 = 3x^2\left(10x^2 + x - 3\right) = 3x^2\left(2x - 1\right)\left(5x + 3\right)$

71. $x^2 + (2+3)x + 2\cdot3 = x^2 + 2x + 3x + 2\cdot3 = x(x+2) + 3(x+2) = (x+2)(x+3)$

72. $x^2 - (3+4)x + 3\cdot4 = x^2 - 3x - 4x + 3\cdot4 = x(x-3) - 4(x-3) = (x-3)(x-4)$

73. $x^2 + (a+b)x + ab = x^2 + ax + bx + ab = x(x+a) + b(x+a) = (x+a)(x+b)$

74. $x^2 - (a+b)x + ab = x^2 - ax - bx + ab = x(x-a) - b(x-a) = (x-a)(x-b)$

75. $x = 1,\ x = 2,\ x^2 + bx + c = 0 \Rightarrow (x-1)(x-2) = 0 \Rightarrow x^2 - 2x - x + 2 = 0$

    $\Rightarrow x^2 - 3x + 2 = 0 \Rightarrow b = -3,\ c = 2$

76. $x = -4,\ x^2 + bx = 0 \Rightarrow x(x+4) = 0 \Rightarrow x^2 + 4x = 0 \Rightarrow b = 4$

77. $h(x) = x^2 + 3x + 2 = (x+1)(x+2) \Rightarrow f(x) = x+1,\ g(x) = x+2$

78. $h(x) = x^2 - 4x + 3 = (x-1)(x-3) \Rightarrow f(x) = x-1,\ g(x) = x-3$

79. $h(x) = x^2 - 2x - 8 = (x+2)(x-4) \Rightarrow f(x) = x+2,\ g(x) = x-4$

80. $h(x) = x^2 + 3x - 10 = (x+5)(x-2) \Rightarrow f(x) = x+5,\ g(x) = x-2$

Factoring with Graphs and Tables

81. Since $x = 2$ and $x = 4$ are zeros of the polynomial, the factors are $(x-2)(x-4)$. This checks using FOIL.

82. Since $x = -2$ and $x = 3$ are zeros of the polynomial, the factors are $(x+2)(x-3)$. This checks using FOIL.

83. Since $x = -1$ and $x = 2$ are zeros of the polynomial, the factors are $2(x+1)(x-2)$. This checks using FOIL.

84. Since $x = -3$ and $x = 2$ are zeros of the polynomial, the factors are $3(x+3)(x-2)$. This checks using FOIL.

85. Since $x = -1$ and $x = 2$ are zeros of the polynomial, the factors are $-(x-2)(x+1)$. This checks using FOIL.

86. Since $x = -3$ and $x = 1$ are zeros of the polynomial, the factors are $-(x-1)(x+3)$. This checks using FOIL.

87. Since $Y_1 = 0$ when $x = -1$ and $x = 4$, the factors are $(x+1)(x-4)$. This checks using FOIL.

88. Since $Y_1 = 0$ when $x = 10$ and $x = 30$, the factors are $(x-10)(x-30)$. This checks using FOIL.

89. Since $Y_1 = 0$ when $x = -1$ and $x = 2$, the factors are $2(x+1)(x-2)$. This checks using FOIL.

90. Since $Y_1 = 0$ when $x = 2$ and $x = 4$, the factors are $3(x-2)(x-4)$. This checks using FOIL.

91. Table $Y_1 = X^2 + 3X - 10$ with TblStart $= -6.4$ and ΔTbl $= 1.4$. See Figure 91.

    Since $Y_1 = 0$ when $x = -5$ and $x = 2$, the factors are $(x-2)(x+5)$.

92. Table $Y_1 = X^2 + 7X + 12$ with TblStart $= -5$ and ΔTbl $= 0.5$. See Figure 92.

    Since $Y_1 = 0$ when $x = -4$ and $x = -3$, the factors are $(x+3)(x+4)$.

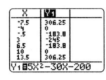

Figure 91   Figure 92   Figure 93   Figure 94

93.   Table $Y_1 = X^2 - 3X - 28$ with TblStart = –6.2 and ΔTbl = 2.2. See Figure 93.

Since $Y_1 = 0$ when $x = -4$ and $x = 7$, the factors are $(x - 7)(x + 4)$.

94.   Table $Y_1 = X^2 - 25X + 100$ with TblStart = 0 and ΔTbl = 5. See Figure 94.

Since $Y_1 = 0$ when $x = 5$ and $x = 20$, the factors are $(x - 20)(x - 5)$.

95.   Table $Y_1 = 2X^2 - 14X + 20$ with TblStart = 0 and ΔTbl = 1. See Figure 95.

Since $Y_1 = 0$ when $x = 2$ and $x = 5$, the factors are $2(x - 5)(x - 2)$.

96.   Table $Y_1 = 12X^2 - 6X - 6$ with TblStart = –1.5 and ΔTbl = 0.5. See Figure 96.

Since $Y_1 = 0$ when $x = -0.5$ and $x = 1$, the factors are $12(x - 1)(x + 0.5) = 6(x - 1)(2x + 1)$.

Figure 95   Figure 96   Figure 97   Figure 98

97.   Table $Y_1 = 5X^2 - 30X - 200$ with TblStart = –7.5 and ΔTbl = 3.5. See Figure 97.

Since $Y_1 = 0$ when $x = -4$ and $x = 10$, the factors are $5(x - 10)(x + 4)$.

98.   Table $Y_1 = 12X^2 - 30X + 12$ with TblStart = 0 and ΔTbl = 0.5. See Figure 98.

Since $Y_1 = 0$ when $x = 0.5$ and $x = 2$, the factors are $12(x - 2)(x - 0.5) = 6(x - 2)(2x - 1)$.

99.   Table $Y_1 = 8X^2 - 44X + 20$ with TblStart = –1 and ΔTbl = 1.5. See Figure 99.

Since $Y_1 = 0$ when $x = 0.5$ and $x = 5$, the factors are $8(x - 5)(x - 0.5) = 4(x - 5)(2x - 1)$.

Figure 99   Figure 100   Figure 105

100.   Table $Y_1 = 20X^2 + 3X - 9$ with TblStart = –1.02 and ΔTbl = 0.27. See Figure 100.

Since $Y_1 = 0$ when $x = -0.75$ and $x = 0.6$, the factors are $20(x - 0.6)(x + 0.75) = (5x - 3)(4x + 3)$.

Applications

101.   (a) $(35 - x)(1200 + 100x)$

(b) $(35 - x)(1200 + 100x) = 54{,}000 \Rightarrow 42{,}000 + 2300x - 100x^2 = 54{,}000 \Rightarrow x^2 - 23x + 120 = 0 \Rightarrow$

$(x-15)(x-8)=0 \Rightarrow$ Either $x-15=0 \Rightarrow x=15$ or $x-8=0 \Rightarrow x=8$

When $x=15$ the ticket price is $35-15=\$20$. When $x=8$ the ticket price is $35-8=\$27$.

102. (a) If x tickets are sold, the cost of each ticket is $300-5x$. The polynomial is $x(300-5x)=300x-5x^2$.

(b) $300(20)-5(20)^2=6000-2000=\$4000$

(c) $300x-5x^2=2500 \Rightarrow 5x^2-300x+2500=0 \Rightarrow x^2-60x+500=0 \Rightarrow (x-10)(x-50)=0 \Rightarrow$

Either $x=10$ or $x=50$. Since a group size of 50 is not allowed, the number of tickets sold was 10.

103. $x(x+6)=91 \Rightarrow x^2+6x-91=0 \Rightarrow (x+13)(x-7)=0 \Rightarrow$ Either $x=-13$ or $x=7$.

Since the width cannot be negative, the width is 7 feet and the length is $7+6=13$ feet.

104. Let x represent the height of the triangle. Then $x-2$ represents the length of the base. Since $A=\dfrac{1}{2}bh$,

$\dfrac{1}{2}x(x-2)=60 \Rightarrow x(x-2)=120 \Rightarrow x^2-2x-120=0 \Rightarrow (x-12)(x+10)=0 \Rightarrow$

Either $x=12$ or $x=-10$. Since the height cannot be negative, the height is 12 inches.

105. (a) $2t^2+88t=600 \Rightarrow t^2+44t-300=0 \Rightarrow (t+50)(t-6)=0 \Rightarrow$ Either $t=-50$ or $t=6$.

Since -50 seconds has no meaning, the car travels 600 feet in 6 seconds.

(b) Table $Y_1=2X^2+88X-600$ with TblStart $=2$ and ΔTbl $=1$. See Figure 105.

106. Let x represent the smaller number. Then the next consecutive number is $x+1$.

$x(x+1)=132 \Rightarrow x^2+x-132=0 \Rightarrow (x-11)(x+12)=0 \Rightarrow x=11$ or $x=-12$

The numbers are 11 and 12.

Checking Basic Concepts for Sections 5.3 & 5.4

1. (a) $3x^2-6x=3x(x-2)$

(b) $16x^3-8x^2+4x=4x(4x^2-2x+1)$

2. (a) $x^2-2x=0 \Rightarrow x(x-2)=0 \Rightarrow$ Either $x=0$ or $x-2=0 \Rightarrow x=2$.

(b) $9x^2=81x \Rightarrow 9x(x-9)=0 \Rightarrow$ Either $9x=0 \Rightarrow x=0$ or $x-9=0 \Rightarrow x=9$.

3. (a) $x^2+3x-10=(x-2)(x+5)$

(b) $x^2-3x-10=(x-5)(x+2)$

(c) $8x^2+14x+3=(2x+3)(4x+1)$

4. $x^2+3x+2=0 \Rightarrow (x+1)(x+2)=0 \Rightarrow$ Either $x+1=0 \Rightarrow x=-1$ or $x+2=0 \Rightarrow x=-2$

5. $-16t^2+64t+8=56 \Rightarrow -16t^2+64t-48=0 \Rightarrow -16(t-1)(t-3)=0 \Rightarrow t=1$ or $t=3$

After 1 and 3 seconds.

5.5: Special Types of Factoring

Concepts

1. $x^2 - 9$;   *Answers may vary.*

2. $x^2 - 8x + 16$;   *Answers may vary.*

3. $x^3 + 8$;   *Answers may vary.*

4. $a^2 - b^2 = (a-b)(a+b)$

5. $a^2 + 2ab + b^2 = (a+b)^2$

6. $a^3 - b^3 = (a-b)(a^2 + ab + b^2)$

Difference of Two Squares

7.   Yes; $x^2 - 25 = (x-5)(x+5)$

8.   Yes; $16x^2 - 100 = 4(4x^2 - 25) = 4(2x-5)(2x+5)$

9.   No; $x^3 + y^3 = (x+y)(x^2 - xy + y^2)$

10.   No; $9x^2 + 36y^2 = 9(x^2 + 4y^2)$

11. $x^2 - 36 = (x-6)(x+6)$

12. $y^2 - 144 = (y-12)(y+12)$

13. $25 - z^2 = (5-z)(5+z)$

14. $36 - y^2 = (6-y)(6+y)$

15.   The sum of squares cannot be factored.

16.   The sum of squares cannot be factored.

17. $36x^2 - 100 = 4(9x^2 - 25) = 4(3x-5)(3x+5)$

18. $4y^2 - 64 = 4(y^2 - 16) = 4(y-4)(y+4)$

19. $49a^2 - 64b^2 = (7a-8b)(7a+8b)$

20. $9x^2 - 4y^2 = (3x-2y)(3x+2y)$

21. $64z^2 - 25z^4 = z^2(64 - 25z^2) = z^2(8-5z)(8+5z)$

22. $64z^4 - 49z^2 = z^2(64z^2 - 49) = z^2(8z-7)(8z+7)$

23. $5x^3 - 125x = 5x(x^2 - 25) = 5x(x-5)(x+5)$

24. $100x^3 - x = x(100x^2 - 1) = x(10x-1)(10x+1)$

25.   The sum of squares cannot be factored.

26. $9t^4 - 25r^6 = \left(3t^2 - 5r^3\right)\left(3t^2 + 5r^3\right)$

27. $16t^4 - r^2 = \left(4t^2 - r\right)\left(4t^2 + r\right)$

28.   The sum of squares cannot be factored.

29. $(x+1)^2 - 25 = \left((x+1)-5\right)\left((x+1)+5\right) = (x-4)(x+6)$

30. $(x-2)^2 - 9 = \left((x-2)-3\right)\left((x-2)+3\right) = (x-5)(x+1)$

31. $100 - (n-4)^2 = \left(10-(n-4)\right)\left(10+(n-4)\right) = (14-n)(6+n)$

32. $81 - (n+3)^2 = \left(9-(n+3)\right)\left(9+(n+3)\right) = (6-n)(12+n)$

33. $y^4 - 16 = \left(y^2 - 4\right)\left(y^2 + 4\right) = (y-2)(y+2)\left(y^2 + 4\right)$

34. $16z^4 - 1 = \left(4z^2 - 1\right)\left(4z^2 + 1\right) = (2z-1)(2z+1)\left(4z^2 + 1\right)$

35. $16x^4 - y^4 = \left(4x^2 - y^2\right)\left(4x^2 + y^2\right) = (2x-y)(2x+y)\left(4x^2 + y^2\right)$

36. $r^4 - 81t^4 = \left(r^2 - 9t^2\right)\left(r^2 + 9t^2\right) = (r-3t)(r+3t)\left(r^2 + 9t^2\right)$

37. $x^3 + x^2 - x - 1 = x^2(x+1) - 1(x+1) = \left(x^2 - 1\right)(x+1) = (x-1)(x+1)(x+1) = (x-1)(x+1)^2$

38. $x^3 + x^2 - 9x - 9 = x^2(x+1) - 9(x+1) = \left(x^2 - 9\right)(x+1) = (x-3)(x+3)(x+1)$

39. $4x^3 - 8x^2 - x + 2 = 4x^2(x-2) - 1(x-2) = \left(4x^2 - 1\right)(x-2) = (2x-1)(2x+1)(x-2)$

40. $9x^3 - 18x^2 - 16x + 32 = 9x^2(x-2) - 16(x-2) = \left(9x^2 - 16\right)(x-2) = (3x-4)(3x+4)(x-2)$

Perfect Square Trinomials

41.   No, the middle term would need to be $8x$.

42.   No, the middle term would need to be $-20x$.

43.   Yes, $x^2 + 8x + 16 = (x+4)^2$

44.   Yes, $x^2 - 4x + 4 = (x-2)^2$

45.   Yes, $4z^2 - 4z + 1 = (2z-1)^2$

46.   No, the middle term would need to be $12z$.

47.   No, the middle term would need to be $-24t$.

48.   Yes, $4t^2 + 12t + 9 = (2t+3)^2$

49. $x^2 + 2x + 1 = (x+1)^2$

50. $x^2 - 6x + 9 = (x-3)^2$

51. $4x^2 + 20x + 25 = (2x + 5)^2$

52. $x^2 + 10x + 25 = (x + 5)^2$

53. $x^2 - 12x + 36 = (x - 6)^2$

54. $x^2 + 20x + 100 = (x + 10)^2$

55. $36z^2 + 12z + 1 = (6z + 1)^2$

56. $9z^2 - 24z + 16 = (3z - 4)^2$

57. $4y^4 + 4y^3 + y^2 = y^2(4y^2 + 4y + 1) = y^2(2y + 1)^2$

58. $16z^4 - 24z^3 + 9z^2 = z^2(16z^2 - 24z + 9) = z^2(4z - 3)^2$

59. $9z^3 - 6z^2 + z = z(9z^2 - 6z + 1) = z(3z - 1)^2$

60. $49y^2 + 42y + 9 = (7y + 3)^2$

61. $9x^2 + 6xy + y^2 = (3x + y)^2$

62. $25x^2 + 30xy + 9y^2 = (5x + 3y)^2$

63. $49a^2 - 28ab + 4b^2 = (7a - 2b)^2$

64. $64a^2 - 16ab + b^2 = (8a - b)^2$

65. $4x^4 - 4x^3y + x^2y^2 = x^2(4x^2 - 4xy + y^2) = x^2(2x - y)^2$

66. $4x^3y + 12x^2y^2 + 9xy^3 = xy(4x^2 + 12xy + 9y^2) = xy(2x + 3y)^2$

Sum and Difference of Two Cubes

67. $x^3 - 8 = (x - 2)(x^2 + 2x + 4)$

68. $x^3 + 8 = (x + 2)(x^2 - 2x + 4)$

69. $y^3 + z^3 = (y + z)(y^2 - yz + z^2)$

70. $y^3 - z^3 = (y - z)(y^2 + yz + z^2)$

71. $27x^3 - 8 = (3x - 2)(9x^2 + 6x + 4)$

72. $64 - y^3 = (4 - y)(16 + 4y + y^2)$

73. $64z^3 + 27t^3 = (4z + 3t)(16z^2 - 12zt + 9t^2)$

74. $125t^3 - 64r^3 = (5t - 4r)(25t^2 + 20tr + 16r^2)$

75. $8x^4 + 125x = x(8x^3 + 125) = x(2x+5)(4x^2 - 10x + 25)$

76. $x^3 y^2 + 8y^5 = y^2(x^3 + 8y^3) = y^2(x+2y)(x^2 - 2xy + 4y^2)$

77. $27y - 8x^3 y = y(27 - 8x^3) = y(3 - 2x)(9 + 6x + 4x^2)$

78. $x^3 y^3 + 1 = (xy+1)(x^2 y^2 - xy + 1)$

79. $z^6 - 27y^3 = (z^2 - 3y)(z^4 + 3z^2 y + 9y^2)$

80. $z^6 + 27y^3 = (z^2 + 3y)(z^4 - 3z^2 y + 9y^2)$

81. $125z^6 + 8y^9 = (5z^2 + 2y^3)(25z^4 - 10z^2 y^3 + 4y^6)$

82. $125z^6 - 8y^9 = (5z^2 - 2y^3)(25z^4 + 10z^2 y^3 + 4y^6)$

83. $5m^6 + 40n^3 = 5(m^6 + 8n^3) = 5(m^2 + 2n)(m^4 - 2m^2 n + 4n^2)$

84. $10m^9 - 270n^6 = 10(m^9 - 27n^6) = 10(m^3 - 3n^2)(m^6 + 3m^3 n^2 + 9n^4)$

General Factoring

85. $25x^2 - 64 = (5x - 8)(5x + 8)$

86. $25x^2 - 30x + 9 = (5x - 3)^2$

87. $x^3 + 27 = (x+3)(x^2 - 3x + 9)$

88. $4 - 16y^2 = 4(1 - 4y^2) = 4(1 - 2y)(1 + 2y)$

89. $64x^2 + 16x + 1 = (8x + 1)^2$

90. $2x^2 - 5x + 3 = (x - 1)(2x - 3)$

91. $3x^2 + 14x + 8 = (x + 4)(3x + 2)$

92. $125x^3 - 1 = (5x - 1)(25x^2 + 5x + 1)$

93. $x^4 + 8x = x(x^3 + 8) = x(x + 2)(x^2 - 2x + 4)$

94. $2x^3 - 12x^2 + 18x = 2x(x^2 - 6x + 9) = 2x(x - 3)^2$

95. $64x^3 + 8y^3 = 8(8x^3 + y^3) = 8(2x + y)(4x^2 - 2xy + y^2)$

96. $54 - 16x^3 = 2(27 - 8x^3) = 2(3 - 2x)(9 + 6x + 4x^2)$

97. $2r^2 - 8t^2 = 2(r^2 - 4t^2) = 2(r - 2t)(r + 2t)$

98. $a^3 - ab^2 = a(a^2 - b^2) = a(a - b)(a + b)$

99. $a^3 + 4a^2b + 4ab^2 = a\left(a^2 + 4ab + 4b^2\right) = a(a+2b)^2$

100. $8r^4 + rt^3 = r\left(8r^3 + t^3\right) = r(2r+t)\left(4r^2 - 2rt + t^2\right)$

101. $x^2 - 3x + 2 = (x-2)(x-1)$

102. $x^2 + 4x - 5 = (x+5)(x-1)$

103. $4z^2 - 25 = (2z-5)(2z+5)$

104. $(z+1)^2 - 49 = \left((z+1)-7\right)\left((z+1)+7\right) = (z-6)(z+8)$

105. $x^4 + 16x^3 + 64x^2 = x^2\left(x^2 + 16x + 64\right) = x^2(x+8)^2$

106. $4x^2 - 12xy + 9y^2 = (2x-3y)^2$

107. $z^3 - 1 = (z-1)\left(z^2 + z + 1\right)$

108. $8z^3 + 1 = (2z+1)\left(4z^2 - 2z + 1\right)$

109. $3t^2 - 5t - 8 = (t+1)(3t-8)$

110. $15t^2 - 11t + 2 = (3t-1)(5t-2)$

111. $7a^3 + 20a^2 - 3a = a\left(7a^2 + 20a - 3\right) = a(a+3)(7a-1)$

112. $b^3 - b^2 - 2b = b\left(b^2 - b - 2\right) = b(b-2)(b+1)$

113. $x^6 - y^6 = \left(x^3 - y^3\right)\left(x^3 + y^3\right) = (x-y)\left(x^2 + xy + y^2\right)(x+y)\left(x^2 - xy + y^2\right)$

114. $a^8 - b^8 = \left(a^4 - b^4\right)\left(a^4 + b^4\right) = \left(a^2 - b^2\right)\left(a^2 + b^2\right)\left(a^4 + b^4\right) = (a-b)(a+b)\left(a^2 + b^2\right)\left(a^4 + b^4\right)$

115. $100x^2 - 1 = (10x-1)(10x+1)$

116. $4x^2 + 28x + 49 = (2x+7)^2$

117. $p^3q^3 - 27 = (pq-3)\left(p^2q^2 + 3pq + 9\right)$

118. $a^2b^2 - c^2d^2 = (ab-cd)(ab+cd)$

Group Activity Solutions

When the rectangle is a square, the trinomial is a perfect square trinomial. This occurs in Exercises 3 and 4.

1. $x^2 + 3x + 2 = (x+1)(x+2)$; one side of the rectangle (not shown) is $x+1$ and the other side is $x+2$.

2. $x^2 + 6x + 5 = (x+1)(x+5)$; one side of the rectangle (not shown) is $x+1$ and the other side is $x+5$.

3. $4x^2 + 4x + 1 = (2x+1)(2x+1) = (2x+1)^2$; both sides of the rectangle (not shown) are $2x+1$.

4. $x^2 + 6x + 9 = (x+3)(x+3) = (x+3)^2$; both sides of the rectangle (not shown) are $x+3$.

5. $6x^2 + 29x + 20 = (x+4)(6x+5);$ one side of the rectangle (not shown) is $x+4$ and the other side is $6x+5$.

6. $8x^2 + 59x + 21 = (x+7)(8x+3);$ one side of the rectangle (not shown) is $x+7$ and the other side is $8x+3$.

5.6: Summary of Factoring

Concepts

1. Factor out the GCF.

2. $2x$

3. No; the sum of two squares cannot be factored.

4. Grouping

Warm Up

5. $a^2 - a = a(a-1)$

6. $2x - 4 = 2(x-2)$

7. $a^2 - 9 = (a-3)(a+3)$

8. $4b^2 - 1 = (2b-1)(2b+1)$

9. $x^2 - 2x + 1 = (x-1)^2$

10. $a^2 + 2ab + b^2 = (a+b)^2$

11. $x^3 - a^3 = (x-a)(x^2 + ax + a^2)$

12. $x^3 + a^3 = (x+a)(x^2 - ax + a^2)$

13. $a^2 + 4$ cannot be factored because it is a sum of squares.

14. $36x^2 + y^2$ cannot be factored because it is a sum of squares.

15. $x(x+2) - 3(x+2) = (x-3)(x+2)$

16. $2x(x-3) + (x-3) = (2x+1)(x-3)$

17. $x^3 + 2x^2 + x + 2 = x^2(x+2) + 1(x+2) = (x^2+1)(x+2)$

18. $x^3 - x^2 + 2x - 2 = x^2(x-1) + 2(x-1) = (x^2+2)(x-1)$

Factoring

19. $6x^2 - 14x = 2x(3x-7)$

20. $-27x^3 - 15x = -3x(9x^2 + 5)$

21. $2x^3 - 18x = 2x(x^2 - 9) = 2x(x-3)(x+3)$

22. $8x^2 - 18 = 2(4x^2 - 9) = 2(2x-3)(2x+3)$

23. $4a^4 - 64 = 4\left(a^4 - 16\right) = 4\left(a^2 - 4\right)\left(a^2 + 4\right) = 4(a-2)(a+2)\left(a^2 + 4\right)$

24. $b^4 - 81 = \left(b^2 - 9\right)\left(b^2 + 9\right) = (b-3)(b+3)\left(b^2 + 9\right)$

25. $6x^3 - 13x^2 - 15x = x\left(6x^2 - 13x - 15\right) = x(x-3)(6x+5)$

26. $10x^4 + 13x^3 - 3x^2 = x^2\left(10x^2 + 13x - 3\right) = x^2(5x-1)(2x+3)$

27. $2x^4 - 5x^3 - 25x^2 = x^2\left(2x^2 - 5x - 25\right) = x^2(x-5)(2x+5)$

28. $10x^3 + 28x^2 - 6x = 2x\left(5x^2 + 14x - 3\right) = 2x(5x-1)(x+3)$

29. $2x^4 + 5x^2 + 3 = \left(x^2 + 1\right)\left(2x^2 + 3\right)$

30. $2x^4 + 2x^2 - 4 = 2\left(x^4 + x^2 - 2\right) = 2\left(x^2 - 1\right)\left(x^2 + 2\right) = 2(x-1)(x+1)\left(x^2 + 2\right)$

31. $x^3 + 3x^2 + x + 3 = x^2(x+3) + 1(x+3) = \left(x^2 + 1\right)(x+3)$

32. $x^3 + 5x^2 + 4x + 20 = x^2(x+5) + 4(x+5) = \left(x^2 + 4\right)(x+5)$

33. $5x^3 - 5x^2 + 10x - 10 = 5\left(x^3 - x^2 + 2x - 2\right) = 5\left(x^2(x-1) + 2(x-1)\right)$

    $= 5\left(x^2 + 2\right)(x-1)$

34. $5x^4 - 20x^3 + 10x - 40 = 5\left(x^4 - 4x^3 + 2x - 8\right) = 5\left(x^3(x-4) + 2(x-4)\right)$

    $= 5\left(x^3 + 2\right)(x-4)$

35. $ax + bx - ay - by = x(a+b) - y(a+b) = (x-y)(a+b)$

36. $ax - bx - ay + by = x(a-b) - y(a-b) = (x-y)(a-b)$

37. $18x^2 + 12x + 2 = 2\left(9x^2 + 6x + 1\right) = 2(3x+1)^2$

38. $-3x^2 + 30x - 75 = -3\left(x^2 - 10x + 25\right) = -3(x-5)^2$

39. $-4x^3 + 24x^2 - 36x = -4x\left(x^2 - 6x + 9\right) = -4x(x-3)^2$

40. $18x^3 - 60x^2 + 50x = 2x\left(9x^2 - 30x + 25\right) = 2x(3x-5)^2$

41. $8x^3 - 27 = (2x-3)\left(4x^2 + 6x + 9\right)$

42. $27x^3 + 8 = (3x+2)\left(9x^2 - 6x + 4\right)$

43. $-x^4 - 8x = -x\left(x^3 + 8\right) = -x(x+2)\left(x^2 - 2x + 4\right)$

44. $x^5 - 27x^2 = x^2\left(x^3 - 27\right) = x^2(x-3)\left(x^2 + 3x + 9\right)$

45. $x^4 - 2x^3 - x + 2 = x^3(x-2) - 1(x-2) = (x^3 - 1)(x-2)$

$= (x-1)(x^2 + x + 1)(x-2)$

46. $x^4 + 3x^3 + x + 3 = x^3(x+3) + 1(x+3) = (x^3 + 1)(x+3)$

$= (x+1)(x^2 - x + 1)(x+3)$

47. $r^4 - 16 = (r^2 - 4)(r^2 + 4) = (r-2)(r+2)(r^2 + 4)$

48. $r^4 - 81 = (r^2 - 9)(r^2 + 9) = (r-3)(r+3)(r^2 + 9)$

49. $25x^2 - 4a^2 = (5x - 2a)(5x + 2a)$

50. $9y^2 - 16z^2 = (3y - 4z)(3y + 4z)$

51. $2x^4 - 2y^4 = 2(x^4 - y^4) = 2(x^2 - y^2)(x^2 + y^2) = 2(x-y)(x+y)(x^2 + y^2)$

52. $a^4 - b^4 = (a^2 - b^2)(a^2 + b^2) = (a-b)(a+b)(a^2 + b^2)$

53. $9x^3 + 6x^2 - 3x = 3x(3x^2 + 2x - 1) = 3x(3x - 1)(x+1)$

54. $8x^3 + 28x^2 - 16x = 4x(2x^2 + 7x - 4) = 4x(2x - 1)(x+4)$

55. $(z-2)^2 - 9 = ((z-2) - 3)((z-2) + 3) = (z-5)(z+1)$

56. $(y+2)^2 - 4 = ((y+2) - 2)((y+2) + 2) = y(y+4)$

57. $3x^5 - 27x^3 + 3x^2 - 27 = 3(x^5 - 9x^3 + x^2 - 9)$

$= 3(x^3(x^2 - 9) + 1(x^2 - 9)) = 3(x^3 + 1)(x^2 - 9)$

$= 3(x+1)(x^2 - x + 1)(x-3)(x+3)$

58. $2x^5 - 8x^3 - 16x^2 + 64 = 2(x^5 - 4x^3 - 8x^2 + 32)$

$= 2(x^3(x^2 - 4) - 8(x^2 - 4)) = 2(x^3 - 8)(x^2 - 4)$

$= 2(x-2)(x^2 + 2x + 4)(x-2)(x+2)$

$= 2(x-2)^2(x^2 + 2x + 4)(x+2)$

Applications

59.   (a) $x^3 - 380x^2 + 2x - 760 = x^2(x - 380) + 2(x - 380)$

$= (x^2 + 2)(x - 380)$

(b) $\left(x^2 + 2\right)(x - 380) = 0 \Rightarrow x^2 = -2$ (impossible) or $x = 380$; the record high amount was 380 ppm.

60. (a) $2x^3 - 620x^2 + x - 310 = 2x^2(x - 310) + 1(x - 310)$

$= \left(2x^2 + 1\right)(x - 310)$

(b) $\left(2x^2 + 1\right)(x - 310) = 0 \Rightarrow 2x^2 = -1$ (impossible) or $x = 310$; the amount in 1958 was 310 ppm.

61. (a) Volume $= x(x - 1)(x - 1 - 1) = x(x - 1)(x - 2)$

$= x\left(x^2 - 3x + 2\right) = x^3 - 3x^2 + 2x$

(b) $x^3 - 3x^2 + 2x = 6$

(c) $x^3 - 3x^2 + 2x = 6 \Rightarrow x^3 - 3x^2 + 2x - 6 = 0$

$\Rightarrow x^2(x - 3) + 2(x - 3) = 0 \Rightarrow \left(x^2 + 2\right)(x - 3) = 0$

$\Rightarrow x^2 = -2$ (impossible) or $x = 3$; the height is 3 feet.

62. (a) Area $= x(x + 2) = x^2 + 2x$

(b) $x^2 + 2x = 24$

(c) $x^2 + 2x - 24 = 0 \Rightarrow (x + 6)(x - 4) = 0 \Rightarrow x = -6$, which has no real meaning in this context, or $x = 4$; the width is 4 inches.

Checking Basic Concepts for Section 5.5 and 5.6

1. (a) $25x^2 - 16 = (5x - 4)(5x + 4)$

(b) $x^2 + 12x + 36 = (x + 6)^2$

(c) $9x^2 - 30x + 25 = (3x - 5)^2$

(d) $x^3 - 27 = (x - 3)\left(x^2 + 3x + 9\right)$

(e) $81x^4 - 16 = \left(9x^2 - 4\right)\left(9x^2 + 4\right) = (3x - 2)(3x + 2)\left(9x^2 + 4\right)$

2. (a) $x^3 - 2x^2 + 3x - 6 = x^2(x - 2) + 3(x - 2) = \left(x^2 + 3\right)(x - 2)$

(b) $x^2 - 4x - 21 = (x + 3)(x - 7)$

(c) $12x^3 + 2x^2 - 4x = 2x\left(6x^2 + x - 2\right) = 2x(2x - 1)(3x + 2)$

5.7: Polynomial Equations

Concepts

1. Factoring is important so that we can solve polynomial equations. *Answers may vary.*

2. multiplying

3.   Subtract 16 from each side.

4.   No. The left side of the equation should not be factored because the right side is not zero.

5.   Since $x - 1$ must equal zero, the solution is 1.

6.   No. This equation implies that $x^2 = -4$.

Solving Quadratic Equations

7.   The graph of $y = x^2 - 1$ (not shown) crosses the x-axis at $x = -1$ and $x = 1$. The solutions are -1 and 1.

8.   The graph of $y = x^2 - 9$ (not shown) crosses the x-axis at $x = -3$ and $x = 3$. The solutions are -3 and 3.

9.   The graph of $y = \frac{1}{4}x^2 - 1$ (not shown) crosses the x-axis at $x = -2$ and $x = 2$. The solutions are -2 and 2.

10.   The graph of $y = \frac{1}{16}x^2 - 1$ (not shown) crosses the x-axis at $x = -4$ and $x = 4$. The solutions are -4 and 4.

11.   The graph of $y = x^2 - x - 2$ (not shown) crosses the x-axis at $x = -1$ and $x = 2$. The solutions are -1 and 2.

12.   The graph of $y = x^2 - x - 6$ (not shown) crosses the x-axis at $x = -2$ and $x = 3$. The solutions are -2 and 3.

13. $z^2 - 64 = 0 \Rightarrow (z-8)(z+8) = 0 \Rightarrow z - 8 = 0$ or $z + 8 = 0 \Rightarrow z = 8$ or $z = -8$. The solutions are -8 and 8.

14. $z^2 - 100 = 0 \Rightarrow (z-10)(z+10) = 0 \Rightarrow z - 10 = 0$ or $z + 10 = 0 \Rightarrow z = 10$ or $z = -10$. The solutions are

-10 and 10.

15. $4y^2 - 1 = 0 \Rightarrow (2y-1)(2y+1) = 0 \Rightarrow 2y - 1 = 0$ or $2y + 1 = 0 \Rightarrow y = \frac{1}{2}$ or $y = -\frac{1}{2}$. The solutions are

$-\frac{1}{2}$ and $\frac{1}{2}$.

16. $9y^2 - 36 = 0 \Rightarrow (3y-6)(3y+6) = 0 \Rightarrow 3y - 6 = 0$ or $3y + 6 = 0 \Rightarrow y = 2$ or $y = -2$. The solutions are

-2 and 2.

17. $x^2 - 3x - 4 = 0 \Rightarrow (x-4)(x+1) = 0 \Rightarrow x - 4 = 0$ or $x + 1 = 0 \Rightarrow x = 4$ or $x = -1$. The solutions are

-1 and 4.

18. $x^2 - 8x + 7 = 0 \Rightarrow (x-7)(x-1) = 0 \Rightarrow x - 7 = 0$ or $x - 1 = 0 \Rightarrow x = 7$ or $x = 1$. The solutions are 1 and 7.

19. $x^2 + 4x - 12 = 0 \Rightarrow (x+6)(x-2) = 0 \Rightarrow x + 6 = 0$ or $x - 2 = 0 \Rightarrow x = -6$ or $x = 2$. The solutions are

-6 and 2.

20. $x^2 - 3x - 28 = 0 \Rightarrow (x-7)(x+4) = 0 \Rightarrow x - 7 = 0$ or $x + 4 = 0 \Rightarrow x = 7$ or $x = -4$. The solutions are

-4 and 7.

21. $2x^2 + 5x - 3 = 0 \Rightarrow (2x-1)(x+3) = 0 \Rightarrow 2x - 1 = 0$ or $x + 3 = 0 \Rightarrow x = \frac{1}{2}$ or $x = -3$. The solutions are

-3 and $\frac{1}{2}$.

22. $3x^2 + 8x + 4 = 0 \Rightarrow (3x+2)(x+2) = 0 \Rightarrow 3x+2 = 0$ or $x+2 = 0 \Rightarrow x = -\frac{2}{3}$ or $x = -2$. The solutions are

-2 and $-\frac{2}{3}$.

23. $2x^2 = 32 \Rightarrow 2x^2 - 32 = 0 \Rightarrow x^2 - 16 = 0 \Rightarrow (x-4)(x+4) = 0 \Rightarrow x-4 = 0$ or $x+4 = 0 \Rightarrow$

$x = 4$ or $x = -4$. The solutions are -4 and 4.

24. $4x^2 = 64 \Rightarrow 4x^2 - 64 = 0 \Rightarrow x^2 - 16 = 0 \Rightarrow (x-4)(x+4) = 0 \Rightarrow x-4 = 0$ or $x+4 = 0 \Rightarrow$

$x = 4$ or $x = -4$. The solutions are -4 and 4.

25. $z^2 + 14z + 49 = 0 \Rightarrow (z+7)^2 = 0 \Rightarrow z+7 = 0 \Rightarrow z = -7$. The solution is -7.

26. $z^2 + 64 = 16z \Rightarrow z^2 - 16z + 64 = 0 \Rightarrow (z-8)^2 = 0 \Rightarrow z-8 = 0 \Rightarrow z = 8$. The solution is 8.

27. $9t^2 + 1 = 6t \Rightarrow 9t^2 - 6t + 1 = 0 \Rightarrow (3t-1)^2 = 0 \Rightarrow 3t-1 = 0 \Rightarrow t = \frac{1}{3}$. The solution is $\frac{1}{3}$.

28. $49t^2 + 28t + 4 = 0 \Rightarrow (7t+2)^2 = 0 \Rightarrow 7t+2 = 0 \Rightarrow t = -\frac{2}{7}$. The solution is $-\frac{2}{7}$.

29. $15n^2 = 7n + 2 \Rightarrow 15n^2 - 7n - 2 = 0 \Rightarrow (5n+1)(3n-2) = 0 \Rightarrow 5n+1 = 0$ or $3n-2 = 0 \Rightarrow$

$n = -\frac{1}{5}$ or $n = \frac{2}{3}$. The solutions are $-\frac{1}{5}$ and $\frac{2}{3}$.

30. $7n^2 + 57n + 8 = 0 \Rightarrow (n+8)(7n+1) = 0 \Rightarrow n+8 = 0$ or $7n+1 = 0 \Rightarrow n = -8$ or $n = -\frac{1}{7}$

The solutions are -8 and $-\frac{1}{7}$.

31. $24m^2 + 23m = 12 \Rightarrow 24m^2 + 23m - 12 = 0 \Rightarrow (3m+4)(8m-3) = 0 \Rightarrow$

$3m+4 = 0$ or $8m-3 = 0 \Rightarrow m = -\frac{4}{3}$ or $m = \frac{3}{8}$. The solutions are $-\frac{4}{3}$ and $\frac{3}{8}$.

32. $11m^2 = 31m + 6 \Rightarrow 11m^2 - 31m - 6 = 0 \Rightarrow (11m+2)(m-3) = 0 \Rightarrow 11m+2 = 0$ or $m-3 = 0 \Rightarrow$

$m = -\frac{2}{11}$ or $m = 3$. The solutions are $-\frac{2}{11}$ and 3.

33. $x^2 + 12 = 0 \Rightarrow x^2 = -12$. There are no solutions.

34. $2x^2 + 3 = 0 \Rightarrow 2x^2 = -3 \Rightarrow x^2 = -\frac{3}{2}$. There are no solutions.

35. From the graph $x = -3$ or $x = 2$. $x^2 + x - 6 = 0 \Rightarrow (x+3)(x-2) = 0 \Rightarrow$ Either $x = -3$ or $x = 2$

36. From the graph $x = -1$ or $x = 3$. $x^2 - 2x - 3 = 0 \Rightarrow (x+1)(x-3) = 0 \Rightarrow$ Either $x = -1$ or $x = 3$

37. From the graph $x = -2$ or $x = 4$. $2x^2 - 4x - 16 = 0 \Rightarrow 2(x+2)(x-4) = 0 \Rightarrow$ Either $x = -2$ or $x = 4$

38.   From the graph $x = -2$ or $x = \dfrac{1}{2}$. $2x^2 + 3x - 2 = 0 \Rightarrow (x+2)(2x-1) = 0 \Rightarrow$ Either $x = -2$ or $x = \dfrac{1}{2}$

39.   The parabola should not cross the x-axis. See Figure 39.

40.   The parabola should just touch the x-axis at the vertex. See Figure 40.

    Figure 39   Figure 40   Figure 41

41.   The parabola should cross the x-axis two times. See Figure 41.

42.   It is not possible for a parabola to cross the x-axis three times.

Higher Degree Equations

43. $z^3 = 9z \Rightarrow z^3 - 9z = 0 \Rightarrow z\left(z^2 - 9\right) = 0 \Rightarrow z(z-3)(z+3) = 0 \Rightarrow z = 0$ or $z = 3$ or $z = -3$

    The solutions are -3, 0, and 3.

44. $2z^3 + 8z = 0 \Rightarrow 2z\left(z^2 + 4\right) = 0 \Rightarrow 2z = 0$ or $z^2 + 4 = 0 \Rightarrow z = 0$, $\left(z^2 = -4 \text{ is not possible}\right)$

    The solution is 0.

45. $x^3 + x = 0 \Rightarrow x\left(x^2 + 1\right) = 0 \Rightarrow x = 0$, $\left(x^2 = -1 \text{ is not possible}\right)$

    The solution is 0.

46. $x^3 = x \Rightarrow x^3 - x = 0 \Rightarrow x\left(x^2 - 1\right) = 0 \Rightarrow x(x-1)(x+1) = 0 \Rightarrow x = 0$ or $x = 1$ or $x = -1$

    The solutions are -1, 0, and 1.

47. $2x^3 - 6x^2 = 20x \Rightarrow 2x^3 - 6x^2 - 20x = 0 \Rightarrow 2x\left(x^2 - 3x - 10\right) = 0 \Rightarrow 2x(x-5)(x+2) = 0 \Rightarrow$

    $x = 0$ or $x = 5$ or $x = -2$. The solutions are -2, 0, and 5.

48. $3x^3 + 15x^2 + 12x = 0 \Rightarrow 3x\left(x^2 + 5x + 4\right) = 0 \Rightarrow 3x(x+1)(x+4) = 0 \Rightarrow x = 0$ or $x = -1$ or $x = -4$

    The solutions are -4, -1, and 0.

49. $t^4 - 4t^3 - 5t^2 = 0 \Rightarrow t^2\left(t^2 - 4t - 5\right) = 0 \Rightarrow t^2(t-5)(t+1) = 0 \Rightarrow t = 0$ or $t = 5$ or $t = -1$

    The solutions are -1, 0, and 5.

50. $2t^4 - 8t^3 + 6t^2 = 0 \Rightarrow 2t^2\left(t^2 - 4t + 3\right) = 0 \Rightarrow 2t^2(t-1)(t-3) = 0 \Rightarrow t = 0$ or $t = 1$ or $t = 3$

    The solutions are 0, 1, and 3.

51. $x^3 + 7x^2 - 4x - 28 = 0 \Rightarrow x^2(x+7) - 4(x+7) = 0 \Rightarrow \left(x^2 - 4\right)(x+7) = 0 \Rightarrow$

$(x-2)(x+2)(x+7)=0 \Rightarrow x=2$ or $x=-2$ or $x=-7$. The solutions are -7, -2, and 2.

52. $x^3+5x^2=9x+45 \Rightarrow x^3+5x^2-9x-45=0 \Rightarrow x^2(x+5)-9(x+5)=0 \Rightarrow$

$(x^2-9)(x+5)=0 \Rightarrow (x-3)(x+3)(x+5)=0 \Rightarrow x=3$ or $x=-3$ or $x=-5$

The solutions are -5, -3, and 3.

53. $n^3-2n^2-36n+72=0 \Rightarrow n^2(n-2)-36(n-2)=0 \Rightarrow (n^2-36)(n-2)=0 \Rightarrow$

$(n-6)(n+6)(n-2)=0 \Rightarrow n=6$ or $n=-6$ or $n=2$. The solutions are -6, 2, and 6.

54. $n^3-10n^2-4n+40=0 \Rightarrow n^2(n-10)-4(n-10)=0 \Rightarrow (n^2-4)(n-10)=0 \Rightarrow$

$(n-2)(n+2)(n-10)=0 \Rightarrow n=2$ or $n=-2$ or $n=10$. The solutions are -2, 2, and 10.

55. (a) $x^2-2x-15=0 \Rightarrow (x+3)(x-5)=0 \Rightarrow$ Either $x=-3$ or $x=5$

(b) Graph $Y_1=X^2-2X-15$ in $[-5, 7, 1]$ by $[-20, 10, 2]$. See Figures 55a & 55b. Either $x=-3$ or $x=5$.

(c) Table $Y_1=X^2-2X-15$ with TblStart $=-5$ and ΔTbl $= 2$. See Figure 55c. Either $x=-3$ or $x=5$.

$[-5, 7, 1]$ by $[-20, 10, 2]$ $[-5, 7, 1]$ by $[-20, 10, 2]$

Figure 55a   Figure 55b   Figure 55c

56. (a) $x^2+7x+10=0 \Rightarrow (x+5)(x+2)=0 \Rightarrow$ Either $x=-5$ or $x=-2$

(b) Graph $Y_1=X^2+7X+10$ in $[-8, 0, 1]$ by $[-4, 8, 1]$. See Figures 56a & 56b. Either $x=-5$ or $x=-2$.

(c) Table $Y_1=X^2+7X+10$ with TblStart $=-7$ and ΔTbl $= 1$. See Figure 56c. Either $x=-5$ or $x=-2$.

$[-8, 0, 1]$ by $[-4, 8, 1]$ $[-8, 0, 1]$ by $[-4, 8, 1]$

Figure 56a   Figure 56b   Figure 56c

57. (a) $2x^2-3x=2 \Rightarrow 2x^2-3x-2=0 \Rightarrow (2x+1)(x-2)=0 \Rightarrow$ Either $x=-\dfrac{1}{2}$ or $x=2$

(b) Graph $Y_1=2X^2-3X-2$ in $[-4, 4, 1]$ by $[-4, 4, 1]$. See Figures 57a & 57b. Either $x=-\dfrac{1}{2}$ or $x=2$.

(c) Table $Y_1=2X^2-3X-2$ with TblStart $=-1$ and ΔTbl $= 0.5$. See Figure 57c. Either $x=-\dfrac{1}{2}$ or $x=2$.

[–4, 4, 1] by [–4, 4, 1]   [–4, 4, 1] by [–4, 4, 1]

Figure 57a   Figure 57b   Figure 57c

58.   (a) $4t^2 + 25 = 20t \Rightarrow 4t^2 - 20t + 25 = 0 \Rightarrow (2t - 5)^2 = 0 \Rightarrow t = \dfrac{5}{2}$

(b) Graph $Y_1 = 4X^2 - 20X + 25$ in [0, 5, 1] by [–5, 10, 1]. See Figure 58b. Here $t = \dfrac{5}{2}$.

(c) Table $Y_1 = 4X^2 - 20X + 25$ with TblStart = 0 and ΔTbl = 0.5. See Figure 58c. Here $t = \dfrac{5}{2}$.

[0, 5, 1] by [–5, 10, 1]

Figure 58b   Figure 58c

59.   (a) $3t^2 + 18t + 15 = 0 \Rightarrow 3(t + 5)(t + 1) = 0 \Rightarrow$ Either $t = -5$ or $t = -1$

(b) Graph $Y_1 = 3X^2 + 18X + 15$ in [–6, 0, 1] by [–15, 5, 1]. See Figures 59a & 59b. Either $t = -5$ or $t = -1$.

(c) Table $Y_1 = 3X^2 + 18X + 15$ with TblStart = –6 and ΔTbl = 1. See Figure 59c. Either $t = -5$ or $t = -1$.

[–6, 0, 1] by [–15, 5, 1]   [–6, 0, 1] by [–15, 5, 1]

Figure 59a   Figure 59b   Figure 59c

60.   (a) $4z^2 = 16 \Rightarrow 4z^2 - 16 = 0 \Rightarrow 4(z + 2)(z - 2) = 0 \Rightarrow$ Either $z = -2$ or $z = 2$

(b) Graph $Y_1 = 4X^2 - 16$ in [–3, 3, 1] by [–20, 5, 5]. See Figures 60a & 60b. Either $z = -2$ or $z = 2$.

(c) Table $Y_1 = 4X^2 - 16$ with TblStart = –4 and ΔTbl = 1. See Figure 60c. Either $z = -2$ or $z = 2$.

[–3, 3, 1] by [–20, 5, 5]   [–3, 3, 1] by [–20, 5, 5]

Figure 60a   Figure 60b   Figure 60c

61.   (a) $4x^4 + 16x^2 = 16x^3 \Rightarrow 4x^4 - 16x^3 + 16x^2 = 0 \Rightarrow 4x^2 (x - 2)^2 = 0 \Rightarrow x = 0$ or $x = 2$

    (b) Graph $Y_1 = 4X^4 - 16X^3 + 16x^2$ in [–2, 4, 1] by [–2, 5, 1]. See Figures 61a & 61b. Here

        $x = 0$ or $x = 2$.

    (c) Table $Y_1 = 4X^4 - 16X^3 + 16x^2$ with TblStart = –2 and ΔTbl = 1. See Figure 61c. Here

        $x = 0$ or $x = 2$.

      [–2, 4, 1] by [–2, 5, 1]   [–2, 4, 1] by [–2, 5, 1]

        Figure 61a   Figure 61b   Figure 61c

62.   (a) $2x^3 + 12x^2 + 18x = 0 \Rightarrow 2x\left(x^2 + 6x + 9\right) = 0 \Rightarrow 2x\left(x + 3\right)^2 = 0 \Rightarrow$ Either $x = 0$ or $x = -3$

    (b) Graph $Y_1 = 2X^3 + 12X^2 + 18X$ in [–5, 1, 1] by [–10, 5, 1]. See Figures 62a & 62b. $x = 0$ or $x = -3$.

    (c) Table $Y_1 = 2X^3 + 12X^2 + 18X$ with TblStart = –5 and ΔTbl = 1. See Figure 62c. $x = 0$ or $x = -3$.

      [–5, 1, 1] by [–10, 5, 1]   [–5, 1, 1] by [–10, 5, 1]

        Figure 62a   Figure 62b   Figure 62c

Equations in Quadratic Form

63. $x^4 - 2x^2 - 8 = 0 \Rightarrow \left(x^2 - 4\right)\left(x^2 + 2\right) = 0 \Rightarrow \left(x - 2\right)\left(x + 2\right)\left(x^2 + 2\right) = 0 \Rightarrow$

      $x = 2$ or $x = -2$, $\left(x^2 = -2$ is not possible$\right)$. The solutions are –2 and 2.

64. $x^4 - 8x^2 - 9 = 0 \Rightarrow \left(x^2 - 9\right)\left(x^2 + 1\right) = 0 \Rightarrow \left(x - 3\right)\left(x + 3\right)\left(x^2 + 1\right) = 0 \Rightarrow$

      $x = 3$ or $x = -3$, $\left(x^2 = -1$ is not possible$\right)$. The solutions are –3 and 3.

65. $x^4 - 26x^2 + 25 = 0 \Rightarrow \left(x^2 - 25\right)\left(x^2 - 1\right) = 0 \Rightarrow \left(x - 5\right)\left(x + 5\right)\left(x - 1\right)\left(x + 1\right) = 0 \Rightarrow$

      $x = 5$ or $x = -5$ or $x = 1$ or $x = -1$. The solutions are –5, –1, 1, and 5.

66. $x^4 - 21x^2 - 100 = 0 \Rightarrow \left(x^2 - 25\right)\left(x^2 + 4\right) = 0 \Rightarrow \left(x - 5\right)\left(x + 5\right)\left(x^2 + 4\right) = 0 \Rightarrow$

      $x = 5$ or $x = -5$, $\left(x^2 = -4$ is not possible$\right)$. The solutions are –5 and 5.

67. $x^4 - 13x^2 + 36 = 0 \Rightarrow \left(x^2 - 9\right)\left(x^2 - 4\right) = 0 \Rightarrow \left(x - 3\right)\left(x + 3\right)\left(x - 2\right)\left(x + 2\right) = 0 \Rightarrow$

      $x = 3$ or $x = -3$ or $x = 2$ or $x = -2$. The solutions are –3, –2, 2, and 3.

68. $x^4 - 18x^2 + 81 = 0 \Rightarrow \left(x^2 - 9\right)\left(x^2 - 9\right) = 0 \Rightarrow \left(x - 3\right)\left(x + 3\right)\left(x - 3\right)\left(x + 3\right) = 0 \Rightarrow x = 3$ or $x = -3$. The solutions

      are –3 and 3.

69. $x^4 - 16 = 0 \Rightarrow (x^2 - 4)(x^2 + 4) = 0 \Rightarrow (x - 2)(x + 2)(x^2 + 4) = 0$

   $\Rightarrow x = 2$ or $x = -2$, $(x^2 = -4$ is not possible$)$. The solutions are -2 and 2.

70. $4x^4 = x^2 + 18 \Rightarrow 4x^4 - x^2 - 18 = 0 \Rightarrow (4x^2 - 9)(x^2 + 2) = 0 \Rightarrow (2x - 3)(2x + 3)(x^2 + 2) = 0 \Rightarrow$

   $x = \dfrac{3}{2}$ or $x = -\dfrac{3}{2}$, $(x^2 = -2$ is not possible$)$. The solutions are $-\dfrac{3}{2}$ and $\dfrac{3}{2}$.

71. $9x^4 - 13x^2 + 4 = 0 \Rightarrow (x^2 - 1)(9x^2 - 4) = 0 \Rightarrow (x - 1)(x + 1)(3x - 2)(3x + 2) = 0 \Rightarrow$

   $x = 1$ or $x = -1$ or $x = \dfrac{2}{3}$ or $x = -\dfrac{2}{3}$. The solutions are -1, $-\dfrac{2}{3}$, $\dfrac{2}{3}$, and 1.

72. $64x^4 - 180x^2 + 81 = 0 \Rightarrow (16x^2 - 9)(4x^2 - 9) = 0 \Rightarrow (4x - 3)(4x + 3)(2x - 3)(2x + 3) = 0 \Rightarrow$

   $x = \dfrac{3}{4}$ or $x = -\dfrac{3}{4}$ or $x = \dfrac{3}{2}$ or $x = -\dfrac{3}{2}$. The solutions are $-\dfrac{3}{2}$, $-\dfrac{3}{4}$, $\dfrac{3}{4}$, and $\dfrac{3}{2}$.

Applications

73.   Let x be the height of the picture and $x + 4$ be its width. The overall area is given by $(x + 4)(x + 8)$.

   $(x + 4)(x + 8) = 525 \Rightarrow x^2 + 12x + 32 = 525 \Rightarrow x^2 + 12x - 493 = 0 \Rightarrow (x - 17)(x + 29) = 0 \Rightarrow$

   $x = 17$ or $x = -29$. The only valid solution is 17. The dimensions are 17 inches by 21 inches.

74.   Let x be the width of the picture frame. The area of the picture is given by $(30 - 2x)(40 - 2x)$.

   $(30 - 2x)(40 - 2x) = 936 \Rightarrow 1200 - 140x + 4x^2 = 936 \Rightarrow 4x^2 - 140x + 264 = 0 \Rightarrow$

   $x^2 - 35x + 66 = 0 \Rightarrow (x - 2)(x - 33) = 0 \Rightarrow x = 2$ or $x = 33$

   The only valid solution is 2. The width of the frame is 2 inches.

75. $-0.0001x^2 + 500 = 400 \Rightarrow 0.0001x^2 - 100 = 0 \Rightarrow (0.01x - 10)(0.01x + 10) = 0 \Rightarrow x = 1000$ or $x = -1000$. The

   values are -1000 and 1000.

76. $(n + 3)^2 = 121 \Rightarrow n^2 + 6n + 9 = 121 \Rightarrow n^2 + 6n - 112 = 0 \Rightarrow (n - 8)(n + 14) = 0 \Rightarrow n = 8$ or $n = -14$. Because

   the number is positive, the only valid solution is 8.

77.   Let x be the width of the pool. The area of the pool is given by $x(x + 20)$ whereas the total area of the pool

   and the sidewalk is $(x + 10)(x + 30)$. Since the area of just the sidewalk portion is 900 square feet, we have

   $(x + 10)(x + 30) - x(x + 20) = 900 \Rightarrow x^2 + 40x + 300 - x^2 - 20x = 900 \Rightarrow 20x = 600 \Rightarrow x = 30$

   The pool is 30 feet by 50 feet.

78. $-16t^2 + 88t + 4 = 100 \Rightarrow 16t^2 - 88t + 96 = 0 \Rightarrow 2t^2 - 11t + 12 = 0 \Rightarrow (2t - 3)(t - 4) = 0 \Rightarrow$

   That is $t = 1.5$ or $t = 4$. The baseball is 100 feet in the air at 1.5 and 4 seconds.

79. $-16t^2 + 66t + 2 = 70 \Rightarrow 16t^2 - 66t + 68 = 0 \Rightarrow 8t^2 - 33t + 34 = 0 \Rightarrow (8t - 17)(t - 2) = 0 \Rightarrow$

That is $t = \dfrac{17}{8}$ or $t = 2$. The baseball is 70 feet in the air at 2 seconds and $\dfrac{17}{8} = 2.125$ seconds.

80.   Let x be the width of the rectangle. Then the area of the original rectangle is $x(x+2)$ and the area of the new

rectangle is given by $(x+3)(x+5)$. Since the area of the new rectangle is 183 square inches more than the

area of the original rectangle, $(x+3)(x+5) - x(x+2) = 183 \Rightarrow x^2 + 8x + 15 - x^2 - 2x = 183 \Rightarrow$

$6x + 15 = 183 \Rightarrow 6x = 168 \Rightarrow x = 28$. The dimensions of the original rectangle are 28 inches by 30 inches.

81. $\dfrac{1}{11}x^2 + \dfrac{11}{3}x = 220 \Rightarrow 3x^2 + 121x = 7260 \Rightarrow 3x^2 + 121x - 7260 = 0 \Rightarrow (x - 33)(3x + 220) = 0 \Rightarrow$

$x = 33$ or $x = -\dfrac{220}{3}$. The only valid solution is 33 mph.

82. $\dfrac{1}{11}x^2 + \dfrac{11}{3}x = 638 \Rightarrow 3x^2 + 121x = 21,054 \Rightarrow 3x^2 + 121x - 21,054 = 0 \Rightarrow (x - 66)(3x + 319) = 0 \Rightarrow$

$x = 66$ or $x = -\dfrac{319}{3}$. The only valid solution is 66 mph.

83.   Let x represent the thickness of the iPod. Then $5.904 = x(x+1.8)(x+3.5)$.

Graph $Y_1 = 5.904$ and $Y_2 = X(X+1.8)(X+3.5)$ in $[0,\ 2.5, 0.5]$ by $[0,\ 10,\ 1]$.

Figure 83

The solution is $x = 0.6$, so the dimensions of the iPod are 0.6 inches by 2.4 inches by 4.1 inches.

84.   Let x represent the thickness of the box. Then $286 = x(x+9)(x+11)$. Graph $Y_1 = 286$ and

$Y_2 = X(X+9)(X+11)$ in $[0,\ 5,\ 1]$ by $[0,\ 300, 50]$.

Figure 84

The solution is $x = 2$, so the dimensions of the box are 2 inches by 11 inches by 13 inches.

85.   (a)   The table is shown in Figure 85.

The elevation begins at 500 feet, decreases, and then increases back to 500 feet.

(b) $0.0002x^2 - 0.3x + 500 = 400 \Rightarrow 0.0002x^2 - 0.3x + 100 = 0 \Rightarrow x^2 - 1500x + 500,000 = 0 \Rightarrow$

$(x - 500)(x - 1000) = 0 \Rightarrow x = 500$ or $x = 1000$. The elevation is 400 feet at 500 feet and 1000 feet.

x	0	300	600	900	1200	1500
$y = E(x)$	500	428	392	392	428	500

Figure 85

86.   (a) Plot the data and Graph $Y_1 = -0.00138X^2 - 0.076X + 50.1$ in $[-10, 170, 10]$ by $[0, 55, 5]$. See Figure 86.

   (b) The equation models the data quite well.

   (c) From the graph, we may estimate that there were 10 worms remaining on about day 145.

   $[-10, 170, 10]$ by $[0, 55, 5]$

Figure 86

Checking Basic Concepts for Section 5.7

1.   The graph crosses the x-axis at $x = -3$ and $x = -1$. The solutions are -3 and -1.

   $x^2 + 4x + 3 = 0 \Rightarrow (x+3)(x+1) = 0 \Rightarrow x = -3$ or $x = -1$. The solutions are -3 and -1.

2.   The graph of $y = x^2 - 9$ (not shown) crosses the x-axis at $x = -3$ and $x = 3$. The solutions are -3 and 3.

   $x^2 - 9 = 0 \Rightarrow (x-3)(x+3) = 0 \Rightarrow x = 3$ or $x = -3$. The solutions are -3 and 3.

3.   (a) $x^2 + 9 = 6x \Rightarrow x^2 - 6x + 9 = 0 \Rightarrow (x-3)^2 = 0 \Rightarrow x - 3 = 0 \Rightarrow x = 3$

   (b) $x^2 + 9 = 0 \Rightarrow x^2 = -9$. There is no solution.

   (c) $12x^2 + 7x - 10 = 0 \Rightarrow (4x+5)(3x-2) = 0 \Rightarrow x = -\dfrac{5}{4}$ or $x = \dfrac{2}{3}$

4.   (a) $x^3 + 5x = 0 \Rightarrow x(x^2+5) = 0 \Rightarrow x = 0$, $\left(x^2 = -5 \text{ is not possible}\right)$. The only solution is 0.

   (b) $x^4 - 81 = 0 \Rightarrow (x^2-9)(x^2+9) = 0 \Rightarrow (x-3)(x+3)(x^2+9) = 0 \Rightarrow x = 3$ or $x = -3$

   $\left(x^2 = -9 \text{ is not possible}\right)$. The only solutions are -3 and 3.

   (c) $z^4 + z^2 = 20 \Rightarrow z^4 + z^2 - 20 = 0 \Rightarrow (z^2-4)(z^2+5) = 0 \Rightarrow (z-2)(z+2)(z^2+5) = 0 \Rightarrow$

   $z = 2$ or $z = -2$, $\left(z^2 = -5 \text{ is not possible}\right)$. The only solutions are -2 and 2.

   (d) $x^3 + 2x^2 - 49x = 98 \Rightarrow x^3 + 2x^2 - 49x - 98 = 0 \Rightarrow x^2(x+2) - 49(x+2) = 0$

   $\Rightarrow (x^2-49)(x+2) = 0 \Rightarrow (x-7)(x+7)(x+2) = 0 \Rightarrow x = 7, -7, \text{ or } -2$. The solutions are

   $-7, -2, \text{ and } 7$.

Chapter 5 Review Exercises

Section 5.1

1. $x + 5;\ x^2 - 3x + 1;$ *Answers may vary.*

2. $10xy^2;$ When $x = 5$ and $y = 8,$ $10(5)(8)^2 = 3200$ in^3.

3.   The degree is 5. The coefficient is –4.

4.   The degree is 3. The coefficient is 1.

5.   The degree is 7. The coefficient is 5.

6.   The degree is 10. The coefficient is –9.

7. $5x - 4x + 10x = 11x$

8. $9x^3 - 5x^3 + x^2 = 4x^3 + x^2$

9. $6x^3y - 4x^3 + 8x^3y + 5x^3 = 14x^3y + x^3$

10. $2(2)^3(-1)^2 - 3(-1) = 16 - (-3) = 16 + 3 = 19$

11.   The degree is 2. The leading coefficient is 5.

12.   The degree is 4. The leading coefficient is 2.

13. $\left(3x^2 - x + 7\right) + \left(5x^2 + 4x - 8\right) = 8x^2 + 3x - 1$

14. $\left(6z^3 + z\right) + \left(17z^3 - 4z^2\right) = 23z^3 - 4z^2 + z$

15. $\left(-4x^2 - 6x + 1\right) - \left(-3x^2 - 7x + 1\right) = -4x^2 - 6x + 1 + 3x^2 + 7x - 1 = -x^2 + x$

16. $\left(3x^3 - 5x + 7\right) - \left(8x^3 + x^2 - 2x + 1\right) = 3x^3 - 5x + 7 - 8x^3 - x^2 + 2x - 1 = -5x^3 - x^2 - 3x + 6$

17. $f(-1) = 2(-1)^2 - 3(-1) + 2 = 2 + 3 + 2 = 7$

18. $f(4) = 1 - (4) - 4(4)^3 = 1 - 4 - 256 = -259$

19.   When $x = 2,$ $y = -4$ and so $f(2) = -4.$

20. $(f + g)(-2) = \left((-2)^2 - 1\right) + \left((-2) - 3(-2)^2\right) = 4 - 1 + (-2) - 3(4) = -11;$

       $(f - g)(x) = \left(x^2 - 1\right) - \left(x - 3x^2\right) = x^2 - 1 - x + 3x^2 = 4x^2 - x - 1$

Section 5.2

21. $5(3x - 4) = 15x - 20$

22. $-2x\left(1 + x - 4x^2\right) = -2x - 2x^2 + 8x^3$

23. $x^3 \cdot x^5 = x^{3+5} = x^8$

24. $-2x^3 \cdot 3x = -6x^{3+1} = -6x^4$

25. $-7xy^7 \cdot 6xy = -42x^{1+1} \cdot y^{7+1} = -42x^2 y^8$

26. $12xy^4 \cdot 5x^2 y = 60x^{1+2} \cdot y^{4+1} = 60x^3 y^5$

27. $(x+4)(x+5) = x^2 + 5x + 4x + 20 = x^2 + 9x + 20$

28. $(x-7)(x-8) = x^2 - 8x - 7x + 56 = x^2 - 15x + 56$

29. $(6x+3)(2x-9) = 12x^2 - 54x + 6x - 27 = 12x^2 - 48x - 27$

30. $\left(y - \dfrac{1}{3}\right)\left(y + \dfrac{1}{3}\right) = y^2 - \left(\dfrac{1}{3}\right)^2 = y^2 - \dfrac{1}{9}$

31. $4x^2\left(2x^2 - 3x - 1\right) = 8x^4 - 12x^3 - 4x^2$

32. $-x\left(4 + 5x - 7x^2\right) = -4x - 5x^2 + 7x^3$

33. $(4x+y)(4x-y) = 16x^2 - y^2$

34. $(x+3)^2 = x^2 + 6x + 9$

35. $(2y-5)^2 = 4y^2 - 20y + 25$

36. $(a-b)\left(a^2 + ab + b^2\right) = a^3 - b^3$

37. $\left(5m - 2n^4\right)^2 = 25m^2 - 20mn^4 + 4n^8$

38. $\left((r-1)+t\right)\left((r-1)-t\right) = (r-1)^2 - t^2 = r^2 - 2r + 1 - t^2$

Section 5.3

39. $25x^2 - 30x = 5x(5x-6)$

40. $12x^4 + 8x^3 - 16x^2 = 4x^2\left(3x^2 + 2x - 4\right)$

41. $x^2 + 3x = 0 \Rightarrow x(x+3) = 0 \Rightarrow$ Either $x = 0$ or $x + 3 = 0 \Rightarrow x = -3$

42. $7x^4 = 28x^2 \Rightarrow 7x^4 - 28x^2 = 0 \Rightarrow 7x^2\left(x^2 - 4\right) = 0 \Rightarrow 7x^2(x-2)(x+2) \Rightarrow$ Either $x = 0$ or $x = 2$ or $x = -2$

43. $2t^2 - 3t + 1 = 0 \Rightarrow (2t-1)(t-1) = 0 \Rightarrow$ Either $2t - 1 = 0 \Rightarrow t = \dfrac{1}{2}$ or $t - 1 = 0 \Rightarrow t = 1$

44. $4z(z-3) + 4(z-3) = 0 \Rightarrow (z-3)(4z+4) = 0 \Rightarrow$ Either $z - 3 = 0 \Rightarrow z = 3$ or $4z + 4 = 0 \Rightarrow z = -1$

45. $2x^3 + 2x^2 - 3x - 3 = 2x^2(x+1) - 3(x+1) = (x+1)\left(2x^2 - 3\right)$

46. $z^3 + z^2 + z + 1 = z^2(z+1) + 1(z+1) = (z+1)\left(z^2 + 1\right)$

47. $ax - bx + ay - by = x(a-b) + y(a-b) = (a-b)(x+y)$

48. $(fg)(4) = (4+1)(4-3) = (5)(1) = 5; \quad (fg)(x) = (x+1)(x-3) = x^2 - 3x + x - 3 = x^2 - 2x - 3$

49.   (a) The graph crossed the x-axis at 0 and 3.

     (b) The solutions to $P(x) = 0$ are 0 and 3.

     (c) The zeros of $P(x)$ are 0 and 3.

50.   (a) The graph crossed the x-axis at -1 and 2.

     (b) The solutions to $P(x) = 0$ are -1 and 2.

     (c) The zeros of $P(x)$ are -1 and 2.

Section 5.4

51. $x^2 + 8x + 12 = (x+2)(x+6)$

52. $x^2 - 5x - 50 = (x-10)(x+5)$

53. $9x^2 + 25x - 6 = (x+3)(9x-2)$

54. $4x^2 - 22x + 10 = 2(2x^2 - 11x + 5) = 2(x-5)(2x-1)$

55. $x^3 - 4x^2 + 3x = x(x^2 - 4x + 3) = x(x-3)(x-1)$

56. $2x^4 + 14x^3 + 20x^2 = 2x^2(x^2 + 7x + 10) = 2x^2(x+2)(x+5)$

57. $5x^4 + 15x^3 - 90x^2 = 5x^2(x^2 + 3x - 18) = 5x^2(x-3)(x+6)$

58. $10x^3 - 90x^2 + 200x = 10x(x^2 - 9x + 20) = 10x(x-5)(x-4)$

59.   Since $Y_1 = 0$ when $x = -3$ and $x = 5$, the factors are $(x+3)(x-5)$. This checks using FOIL.

60.   Since $Y_1 = 0$ when $x = 11$ and $x = 13$, the factors are $(x-11)(x-13)$. This checks using FOIL.

61.   Since $x = -7$ and $x = 4$ are zeros of the polynomial, the factors are $(x+7)(x-4)$. This checks using FOIL.

62.   Since $x = 8$ and $x = 13$ are zeros of the polynomial, the solutions are 8 and 13. These solutions check.

Section 5.5

63. $t^2 - 49 = (t-7)(t+7)$

64. $4y^2 - 9x^2 = (2y - 3x)(2y + 3x)$

65. $x^2 + 4x + 4 = (x+2)^2$

66. $16x^2 - 8x + 1 = (4x-1)^2$

67. $x^3 - 27 = (x-3)(x^2 + 3x + 9)$

68. $64x^3 + 27y^3 = (4x + 3y)(16x^2 - 12xy + 9y^2)$

69. $10y^3 - 10y = 10y(y^2 - 1) = 10y(y-1)(y+1)$

70. $4r^4 - t^6 = \left(2r^2 - t^3\right)\left(2r^2 + t^3\right)$

71. $m^4 - 16n^4 = \left(m^2 - 4n^2\right)\left(m^2 + 4n^2\right) = (m - 2n)(m + 2n)\left(m^2 + 4n^2\right)$

72. $n^3 - 2n^2 - n + 2 = n^2(n - 2) - 1(n - 2) = \left(n^2 - 1\right)(n - 2) = (n - 1)(n + 1)(n - 2)$

73. $25a^2 - 30ab + 9b^2 = (5a - 3b)^2$

74. $2r^3 - 12r^2t + 18rt^2 = 2r\left(r^2 - 6rt + 9t^2\right) = 2r(r - 3t)^2$

75. $a^6 + 27b^3 = \left(a^2 + 3b\right)\left(a^4 - 3a^2b + 9b^2\right)$

76. $8p^6 - q^3 = \left(2p^2 - q\right)\left(4p^4 + 2p^2q + q^2\right)$

Section 5.6

77. $5x^3 - 10x^2 = 5x^2(x - 2)$

78. $-2x^3 + 32x = -2x\left(x^2 - 16\right) = -2x(x - 4)(x + 4)$

79. $x^4 - 16y^4 = \left(x^2 - 4y^2\right)\left(x^2 + 4y^2\right) = (x - 2y)(x + 2y)\left(x^2 + 4y^2\right)$

80. $4x^3 + 8x^2 - 12x = 4x\left(x^2 + 2x - 3\right) = 4x(x + 3)(x - 1)$

81. $-2x^3 + 11x^2 - 12x = -x\left(2x^2 - 11x + 12\right) = -x(2x - 3)(x - 4)$

82. $x^4 - 8x^2 - 9 = \left(x^2 + 1\right)\left(x^2 - 9\right) = \left(x^2 + 1\right)(x - 3)(x + 3)$

83. $64a^3 + b^3 = (4a + b)\left(16a^2 - 4ab + b^2\right)$

84. $8 - y^3 = (2 - y)\left(4 + 2y + y^2\right)$

85. $(z + 3)^2 - 16 = \left((z + 3) - 4\right)\left((z + 3) + 4\right) = (z - 1)(z + 7)$

86. $x^4 - 5x^3 - 4x^2 + 20x = x\left(x^3 - 5x^2 - 4x + 20\right) = x\left(x^2(x - 5) - 4(x - 5)\right)$

   $= x\left(x^2 - 4\right)(x - 5) = x(x - 2)(x + 2)(x - 5)$

Section 5.7

87. $x^2 - 16 = 0 \Rightarrow (x - 4)(x + 4) = 0 \Rightarrow x = 4$ or $x = -4$. The solutions are -4 and 4.

   The graph of $y = x^2 - 16$ (not shown) crosses the x-axis at $x = -4$ and $x = 4$. The solutions are -4 and 4.

88. $x^2 - 2x - 3 = 0 \Rightarrow (x - 3)(x + 1) = 0 \Rightarrow x = 3$ or $x = -1$. The solutions are -1 and 3.

   The graph of $y = x^2 - 2x - 3$ (not shown) crosses the x-axis at $x = -1$ and $x = 3$. The solutions are

   -1 and 3.

89. $4x^2 - 28x + 49 = 0 \Rightarrow (2x-7)^2 = 0 \Rightarrow 2x - 7 = 0 \Rightarrow x = \dfrac{7}{2}$

90. $x^2 + 8 = 0 \Rightarrow x^2 = -8.$ There are no solutions.

91. $3x^2 = 2x + 5 \Rightarrow 3x^2 - 2x - 5 = 0 \Rightarrow (x+1)(3x-5) = 0 \Rightarrow x = -1 \text{ or } x = \dfrac{5}{3}$

92. $4x^2 + 5x = 6 \Rightarrow 4x^2 + 5x - 6 = 0 \Rightarrow (x+2)(4x-3) = 0 \Rightarrow x = -2 \text{ or } x = \dfrac{3}{4}$

93. $x^3 = x \Rightarrow x^3 - x = 0 \Rightarrow x(x^2 - 1) = 0 \Rightarrow x(x-1)(x+1) = 0 \Rightarrow x = 0 \text{ or } x = 1 \text{ or } x = -1$

94. $x^3 - 6x^2 + 11x = 6 \Rightarrow x^3 - 6x^2 + 11x - 6 = 0;$ the graph of $y = x^3 - 6x^2 + 11x - 6$ (not shown) crosses the x-axis at $x = 1$, $x = 2$ and $x = 3$.

   The solutions are 1, 2 and 3.

95. $x^3 + x^2 - 72x = 0 \Rightarrow x(x^2 + x - 72) = 0 \Rightarrow x(x-8)(x+9) = 0 \Rightarrow x = 0 \text{ or } x = 8 \text{ or } x = -9$

96. $x^4 - 15x^3 + 56x^2 = 0 \Rightarrow x^2(x^2 - 15x + 56) = 0 \Rightarrow x^2(x-8)(x-7) = 0 \Rightarrow x = 0 \text{ or } x = 8 \text{ or } x = 7$

97. $x^4 = 16 \Rightarrow x^4 - 16 = 0 \Rightarrow (x^2 - 4)(x^2 + 4) = 0 \Rightarrow (x-2)(x+2)(x^2 + 4) = 0 \Rightarrow$

   $x = 2 \text{ or } x = -2,$ $(x^2 = -4 \text{ is not possible}).$ The only solutions are -2 and 2.

98. $x^4 + 5x^2 = 36 \Rightarrow x^4 + 5x^2 - 36 = 0 \Rightarrow (x^2 - 4)(x^2 + 9) = 0 \Rightarrow (x-2)(x+2)(x^2 + 9) = 0 \Rightarrow$

   $x = 2 \text{ or } x = -2,$ $(x^2 = -9 \text{ is not possible}).$ The only solutions are -2 and 2.

Applications

99. (a) $R(x) = 15x$

   (b) $P(x) = R(x) - C(x) = 15x - (3x + 9000) = 12x - 9000$

   (c) $P(4000) = 12(4000) - 9000 = 48{,}000 - 9000 = 39{,}000;$ the profit is \$39,000 for selling 4000 DVDs.

100. (a) Height $= x$, width $= x + 5$, length $= x + 5 + 5 = x + 10;$ volume $= x(x+5)(x+10)$

   (b) $x(x+5)(x+10) = 168$

   (c) $x(x^2 + 15x + 50) - 168 = 0 \Rightarrow x^3 + 15x^2 + 50x - 168 = 0$

   $\Rightarrow (x-2)(x^2 + 17x + 84) = 0 \Rightarrow x = 2,$ since $x^2 + 17x + 84 > 0$ for all x.

   The dimensions are 2 inches by 7 inches by 12 inches.

101. Let x represent the height of the picture, then the overall area of the picture and frame is

   $(x+6)(x+2+6) = (x+6)(x+8)$

   $= 224 \Rightarrow x^2 + 14x + 48 - 224 = 0 \Rightarrow x^2 + 14x - 176 = 0$

$$\Rightarrow (x-8)(x+22)=0 \Rightarrow x=8, \text{ since } x=-22 \text{ has no meaning in this context. The dimensions of the picture}$$

are 8 inches by 10 inches.

[1, 12, 1] by [30, 90, 10]

     Figure 103b   Figure 103c

102. $\dfrac{1}{2}(x+2)(x-3)=\dfrac{1}{2}\left(x^2-x-6\right)=\dfrac{1}{2}x^2-\dfrac{1}{2}x-3$

103.   (a)   In May, $x=5$; $f(5)=-1.466(5)^2+20.25(5)+9=73.6°\text{F}.$

      (b)   Table $Y_1=-1.466X^2+20.25X+9$ with TblStart = 1 and ΔTbl = 1. See Figure 103b. It is greatest in

          July.

      (c)   Graph $Y_1=-1.466X^2+20.25X+9$ in [1, 12, 1] by [30, 90, 10]. See Figure 103c. The temperature

          increases from January to July and then decreases from July to December.

104.   (a) $100\left(1-\dfrac{x}{100}\right)^2=100\left(1-2(1)\left(\dfrac{x}{100}\right)+\left(\dfrac{x}{100}\right)^2\right)=100\left(1-\dfrac{x}{50}+\dfrac{x^2}{10,000}\right)=100-2x+\dfrac{x^2}{100}$

          $=\dfrac{x^2}{100}-2x+100$

      (b) $100\left(1-\dfrac{70}{100}\right)^2=100(0.3)^2=9\%$ and $\dfrac{1}{100}(70)^2-2(70)+100=49-140+100=9\%$

105.   If x is the largest of three consecutive integers then the smallest is $x-2$ and the middle integer is $x-1$.

      The product is given by $(x-2)(x-1)x=\left(x^2-3x+2\right)x=x^3-3x^2+2x.$

106.   See Figure 106.

[−25, 20, 5] by [−160, 100, 10]

2	2x	14
x	x^2	7x
	x	7

    Figure 106   Figure 107a   Figure 107b

107.   Let x represent the width of the building. Then $x+7$ represents the length of the building. The equation

      needed is given by $x(x+7)=144 \Rightarrow x^2+7x-144=0.$

      (a)   Graph $Y_1=X^2+7X-144$ in [−25, 20, 5] by [−160, 100, 10]. See Figure 107a.

          Here $y=0$ when $x=9$. The dimensions are 9×16 feet.

      (b)   Table $Y_1=X^2+7X-144$ with TblStart = −1 and ΔTbl = 2. See Figure 107b.

Here $Y_1 = 0$ when $x = 9$. The dimensions are 9×16 feet.

(c) $x^2 + 7x - 144 = 0 \Rightarrow (x - 9)(x + 16) = 0 \Rightarrow$ Either $x - 9 = 0 \Rightarrow x = 9$ or $x + 16 = 0 \Rightarrow x = -16$. Since

$x = -16$ has no meaning in this problem, we know that $x = 9$. The dimensions are 9×16 feet.

108. Let l represent the length of the rectangle. Then since the perimeter is 50 feet,

$2l + 2x = 50 \Rightarrow l = 25 - x$. The area is $A = (25 - x)x = 25x - x^2$.

109. (a) $-16t^2 + 66t = 0 \Rightarrow 8t^2 - 33t = 0 \Rightarrow t(8t - 33) = 0 \Rightarrow t = 0$ or $8t - 33 = 0 \Rightarrow t = 0$ or $t = \dfrac{33}{8}$

The ball strikes the ground at $\dfrac{33}{8} = 4.125$ seconds.

(b) $-16t^2 + 66t = 50 \Rightarrow -16t^2 + 66t - 50 = 0 \Rightarrow 8t^2 - 33t + 25 = 0 \Rightarrow (t - 1)(8t - 25) \Rightarrow t = 1$ or $t = \dfrac{25}{8}$. The

ball is 50 feet high at 1 second and $\dfrac{25}{8} = 3.125$ seconds.

110. (a) $R(x) = (50 - x)(600 + 20x)$

(b) $(50 - x)(600 + 20x) = 32,000 \Rightarrow 30,000 + 400x - 20x^2 = 32,000 \Rightarrow x^2 - 20x + 100 = 0 \Rightarrow$

$(x - 10)^2 = 0 \Rightarrow x - 10 = 0 \Rightarrow x = 10$.

When $x = 10$ the ticket price is $50 - 10 = \$40$.

111. $-0.0001x^2 + 500 = 400 \Rightarrow 0.0001x^2 - 100 = 0 \Rightarrow (0.01x - 10)(0.01x + 10) = 0 \Rightarrow$

$0.01x - 10 = 0$ or $0.01 + 10 = 0 \Rightarrow x = 1000$ or $x = -1000$. The values are -1000 and 1000.

Chapter 5 Test

1. $x^2 y^2 - 4x + 9x - 5x^2 y^2 = 5x - 4x^2 y^2$

2. $\left(-2x^3 - 6x + 1\right) - \left(5x^3 - x^2 + x - 10\right) = -2x^3 - 6x + 1 - 5x^3 + x^2 - x + 10 = -7x^3 + x^2 - 7x + 11$

3. $f(-2) = 2(-2)^3 - (-2)^2 - 5(-2) + 2 = -16 - 4 + 10 + 2 = -8$

4.   Since $y = -2$ when $x = 2$, $f(2) = -2$.

5.   The degree is $3 + 1 = 4$. The coefficient is 3.

6. $8xyz$

7. $-(-2)^2 (3) + 3(-2)(3)^2 = -(4)(3) + 3(-2)(9)$

     $= -12 - 54 = -66$

8. $(f - g)(4) = 2(4) - 5 - \left(1 - 4^3\right) = 8 - 5 - (1 - 64)$

     $= 8 - 5 + 63 = 66$

     $(f + g)(x) = 2x - 5 + 1 - x^3 = -x^3 + 2x - 4$

9. $-\dfrac{2}{5}x^2(10x-5) = -4x^3 + 2x^2$

10. $2xy^7 \cdot 7xy = 14 \cdot x^{1+1} \cdot y^{7+1} = 14x^2 y^8$

11. $(2x+1)(5x-7) = 10x^2 - 14x + 5x - 7 = 10x^2 - 9x - 7$

12. $(5-3x)^2 = 25 - 30x + 9x^2 = 9x^2 - 30x + 25$

13. $(5x-4y)(5x+4y) = (5x)^2 - (4y)^2 = 25x^2 - 16y^2$

14. $-2x^2(x^2 - 3x + 2) = -2x^2 \cdot x^2 + 2x^2 \cdot 3x - 2x^2 \cdot 2$

    $= -2x^4 + 6x^3 - 4x^2$

15. $(x-2y)(x^2 + 2xy + 4y^2) = x \cdot x^2 + x \cdot 2xy + x \cdot 4y^2$

    $-2y \cdot x^2 - 2y \cdot 2xy - 2y \cdot 4y^2 = x^3 + 2x^2 y + 4xy^2 - 2x^2 y$

    $-4xy^2 - 8y^3 = x^3 - 8y^3$

16. $2x^2(x-1)(x+1) = 2x^2(x^2 - 1) = 2x^2 \cdot x^2 - 2x^2 \cdot 1 = 2x^4 - 2x^2$

17. $x^2 - 3x - 10 = (x-5)(x+2)$

18. $2x^3 + 6x = 2x(x^2 + 3)$

19. $3x^2 + 7x - 20 = (x+4)(3x-5)$

20. $5x^4 - 5x^2 = 5x^2(x^2 - 1) = 5x^2(x-1)(x+1)$

21. $2x^3 + x^2 - 10x - 5 = x^2(2x+1) - 5(2x+1) = (2x+1)(x^2 - 5)$

22. $49x^2 - 14x + 1 = (7x-1)^2$

23. $x^3 + 8 = (x+2)(x^2 - 2x + 4)$

24. $4x^2 y^4 + 8x^4 y^2 = 4x^2 y^2(y^2 + 2x^2)$

25. $a^2 - 3ab + 2b^2 = (a-b)(a-2b)$

26. The degree is 3. The leading coefficient is 1.

27. $(2m^3 - 4n^2)^2 = 4m^6 - 16m^3 n^2 + 16n^4$

28. Since $x = -8$ and $x = 6$ are zeros of the polynomial, the factors are $(x+8)(x-6)$.

29. If x is an even integer, the next consecutive even integer is $x+2$. The product is $x(x+2)$.

30. $5x^2 = 15x \Rightarrow 5x^2 - 15x = 0 \Rightarrow 5x(x-3) = 0 \Rightarrow$ Either $5x = 0 \Rightarrow x = 0$ or $x - 3 = 0 \Rightarrow x = 3$

31. $4t^2 + 19t - 5 = 0 \Rightarrow (4t-1)(t+5) = 0 \Rightarrow$ Either $4t - 1 = 0 \Rightarrow t = \dfrac{1}{4}$ or $t + 5 = 0 \Rightarrow t = -5$

32. $2z^4 - 8z^2 = 0 \Rightarrow 2z^2\left(z^2 - 4\right) = 0 \Rightarrow 2z^2(z-2)(z+2) = 0 \Rightarrow z = -2,\ 0,$ or 2

33. $x^4 - 2x^2 + 1 = 0 \Rightarrow \left(x^2 - 1\right)\left(x^2 - 1\right) = 0 \Rightarrow x^2 - 1 = 0$

 $\Rightarrow (x+1)(x-1) = 0 \Rightarrow$ Either $x = -1$ or $x = 1$

34. $x(x-3) + (x-3) = 0 \Rightarrow (x+1)(x-3) = 0 \Rightarrow$ Either

 $x = -1$ or $x = 3$

35. Let x represent the height of the frame. Then $x+4$ represents the width of the frame.

 (a) The equation needed is given by $x(x+4) = 221$.

 (b) $x(x+4) = 221 \Rightarrow x^2 + 4x - 221 = 0 \Rightarrow (x-13)(x+17) = 0 \Rightarrow x = 13$ or $x = -17$.

 Since $x = -17$ has no meaning in this problem, the height is 13 inches and the width is 17 inches.

 (c) The perimeter is $P = 2(13) + 2(17) = 26 + 34 = 60$ inches.

36. (a) For May, $x = 5;\ f(5) = -0.091(5)^3 + 0.66(5)^2 + 5.78(5) + 23.5 \approx 57.5°F$

 (b) The dew point starts at about 30°F in January and increases to a maximum of about 65°F in July

 Then it decreases to 30°F by the end of December.

37. (Get art from Instructor Answers: Chapter 5 Test #37)

2	2x	6
x	x^2	3x
	x	3

 $(x+2)(x+3) = x^2 + 2x + 3x + 6 = x^2 + 5x + 6$

38. $-16t^2 + 96t + 3 = 131 \Rightarrow -16t^2 + 96t - 128 = 0$

 $\Rightarrow -16\left(t^2 - 6t + 8\right) = 0 \Rightarrow (t-2)(t-4) = 0$

 $\Rightarrow$ Either $t = 2$ or $t = 4$

 The baseball was 131 feet in the air at 2 seconds and 4 seconds.

Chapter 5 Extended and Discovery Exercises

1. (a) The population of lynx oscillated during the recorded time period at nearly 10-year intervals.

 (b) The population of snowshoe hares oscillated during the recorded time period at nearly 10-year intervals.

(c) As the number of snowshoe hares increased, the lynx would have more plentiful prey and hence the lynx population would begin to increase. As the lynx population increased, the snowshoe hares would be killed in increasing numbers causing their population to begin to decrease. With a limited number of snowshoe hares available for food, the lynx population would decline. Now with fewer predators, the snowshoe hare population could begin to rise once again. This cycle repeated itself three times during the recorded time period.

2.   (a) Plot the data in [1, 10, 1] by [0, 30, 3]. See Figure 2a. The data appear to be nonlinear.

(b) Graph $Y_1 = X{\wedge}2.5$ in [1, 10, 1] by [0, 30, 3]. See Figure 2b. The model is only accurate for the first 3 planets.

(c) By trial and error, the model $y = x^{1.5}$ fits quite well.

(d) The orbit for Neptune is $y = (30.1)^{1.5} \approx 165.1$ years. The orbit for Pluto is $y = (39.4)^{1.5} \approx 247.3$ years.

[1, 10, 1] by [0, 30, 3]   [1, 10, 1] by [0, 30, 3]

Figure 2a   Figure 2b

3.   (a) Plot the data in [1890, 2000, 20] by [0, 60, 10]. See Figure 3. The data appear to be nonlinear.

(b) By trial and error the value is $k \approx 0.006$.

(c) In 2005 the number of women in the work force will be $y = 0.006(2005 - 1900)^2 + 5.3 \approx 71.5$ million.

4.   (a) Plot the data in [1993, 2005, 1] by [45, 115, 10]. See Figure 4.

(b) By trial and error the value is $k \approx 0.7$.

(c) In 2006 the number of Americans over 100 will be $y = 0.7(2006 - 1994)^2 + 50 \approx 150.8$ thousand.

[1890, 2000, 20] by [0, 60, 10]   [1993, 2005, 1] by [45, 115, 10]

Figure 3   Figure 4

5.   (a) $\begin{bmatrix} 10,000^2 & 10,000 & 1 & 412 \\ 40,000^2 & 40,000 & 1 & 843 \\ 100,000^2 & 100,000 & 1 & 2550 \end{bmatrix}$

(b) The results from a graphing calculator are $a \approx 1.56 \times 10^{-7}$, $b \approx 0.007$, and $c \approx 330.9$.

(c) $1.56 \times 10^{-7}(20,000)^2 + 0.007(20,000) + 330.9 \approx \$533.30$.

This is close to the actual value. Note that unrounded values for a, b, and c give \$524.37.

Chapters 1-5 Cumulative Review Exercises

1. $A = \dfrac{1}{2}(5)\left(\dfrac{3}{2}\right) = \dfrac{15}{4}$

2. $\dfrac{b-a}{a}$

3. (a) $\left(\dfrac{x^{-3}}{y}\right)^2 = \dfrac{x^{-6}}{y^2} = \dfrac{1}{x^6 y^2}$

   (b) $\dfrac{\left(3r^{-1}t\right)^{-4}}{r^2 \left(t^2\right)^{-2}} = \dfrac{3^{-4} r^4 t^{-4}}{r^2 t^{-4}} = \dfrac{1}{3^4} \cdot r^{4-2} \cdot t^{-4-(-4)}$

   $= \dfrac{1}{81} \cdot r^2 \cdot t^0 = \dfrac{r^2}{81}$

   (c) $\left(ab^{-2}\right)^4 \left(ab^3\right)^{-1} = a^4 b^{-8} a^{-1} b^{-3} = a^3 b^{-11} = \dfrac{a^3}{b^{11}}$

4. $5.859 \times 10^4 = 58,590$

5. $f(-3) = -2(-3)^2 + 3(-3) = -2(9) + 3(-3) = -18 - 9 = -27$

6. The radicand must be greater than or equal to zero.

   $D : x \geq 4$

7.

8.

9. (a) Yes. It passes the vertical line test.

   (b) D: all real numbers; $R : y \geq -4$

   (c) $f(1) = -4; f(2) = -3$

   (d) The graph crosses the x-axis at -1 and 3.

(e) The function has the value 0 where the graph crosses the x-axis at -1 and 3; $x = -1,\ 3$.

(f) $f(x) = (x+1)(x-3)$

10. $2x - y = 4 \Rightarrow y = 2x - 4$; so a line parallel to this line has slope $m = 2$. The line through $(-2,\ 5)$ with slope

$m = 2$ has equation $y - 5 = 2(x - (-2)) \Rightarrow y = 2x + 4 + 5$

$\Rightarrow y = 2x + 9.$

11.   Two points on the graph of f are $(-2,\ 12)$ and $(-1,\ 7)$.

$m = \dfrac{y_2 - y_1}{x_2 - x_1} = \dfrac{7 - 12}{-1 - (-2)} = \dfrac{-5}{1} = -5;\ y - 12 = -5(x - (-2))$

$\Rightarrow y = -5x - 10 + 12 \Rightarrow y = -5x + 2$

12. $-2(5x - 1) = 1 - (5 - x) \Rightarrow -10x + 2 = 1 - 5 + x$

$\Rightarrow -11x = -6 \Rightarrow x = \dfrac{6}{11}$

13. $3x + 4 \le x - 1 \Rightarrow 2x \le -5 \Rightarrow x \le -\dfrac{5}{2} \Rightarrow \left(-\infty,\ -\dfrac{5}{2}\right]$

14. $|5x - 10| > 5 \Rightarrow 5x - 10 < -5$ or $5x - 10 > 5 \Rightarrow$

$5x < 5$ or $5x > 15 \Rightarrow x < 1$ or $x > 3 \Rightarrow (-\infty,\ 1) \cup (3,\ \infty)$

15. $-2 < 2 - 7x \le 2 \Rightarrow -4 < -7x \le 0 \Rightarrow \dfrac{4}{7} > x \ge 0$

$\Rightarrow 0 \le x < \dfrac{4}{7} \Rightarrow \left[0,\ \dfrac{4}{7}\right)$

16.   Note that $4x + 2y = 10 \Rightarrow 2y = -4x + 10 \Rightarrow y = -2x + 5$ and $-x + 5y = 3 \Rightarrow 5y = x + 3 \Rightarrow y = \dfrac{1}{5}x + \dfrac{3}{5}.$

Graph $Y_1 = -2x + 5$ and $Y_2 = 1/5\,x + 3/5$ in $[-5,\ 5,\ 1]$ by $[-5,\ 5,\ 1]$. The solution is $(2,\ 1)$.

        Figure 16

17.   (a) $-x - 2y = 5 \Rightarrow -2y - 5 = x$. Substitute $x = -2y - 5$ into the second equation and solve for y:

        $2(-2y - 5) + 4y = -10 \Rightarrow -4y - 10 + 4y = -10 \Rightarrow -10 = -10.$

        This is an identity, so the equations are dependent.

        The solutions are $\{(x,\ y)\,|\,x + 2y = -5\}.$

        (b) Add the two equations to eliminate the variable y.

$$3x + 2y = 7$$
$$\underline{2x - 2y = 3}$$
$$5x \quad\quad = 10$$

$\Rightarrow x = 2.$ Substitute $x = 2$ into the first equation and solve for

$$y : 3(2) + 2y = 7 \Rightarrow 2y = 1$$

$\Rightarrow y = \dfrac{1}{2}.$ The solution is $\left(2,\ \dfrac{1}{2}\right).$

18.   Note that $2x + y \le 4 \Rightarrow y \le -2x + 4$ and $x - 2y < -2 \Rightarrow -2y < -x - 2 \Rightarrow y > \dfrac{1}{2}x + 1$

19.   Add the first two equations to eliminate the variables y and z.

$$x + y - z = -2$$
$$\underline{x - y + z = -6}$$
$$2x \quad\quad = -8 \quad \Rightarrow x = -4$$

Multiply the second equation by -1 and add to the third equation to eliminate the variables x and y.

$$-x + y\ - z = 6$$
$$\underline{\ x - y - 2z = 3}$$
$$-3z = 9 \Rightarrow z = -3 \quad \Rightarrow z = -3$$

Substitute $x = -4$ and $z = -3$ into the first equation and solve for $y : -4 + y - (-3) = -2 \Rightarrow y = -1.$

The solution is $(-4,\ -1,\ -3).$

20. $\begin{bmatrix} 1 & -1 & -1 & | & -2 \\ 2 & 1 & 1 & | & 8 \\ -1 & -1 & 2 & | & 0 \end{bmatrix} \begin{matrix} R_2 + R_1 \to \\ \\ 2R_3 + R_2 \to \end{matrix} \begin{bmatrix} 3 & 0 & 0 & | & 6 \\ 2 & 1 & 1 & | & 8 \\ 0 & -1 & 5 & | & 8 \end{bmatrix} \begin{matrix} \frac{1}{3}R_1 \to \\ \\ \\ \end{matrix} \begin{bmatrix} 1 & 0 & 0 & | & 2 \\ 2 & 1 & 1 & | & 8 \\ 0 & -1 & 5 & | & 8 \end{bmatrix} -2R_1 + R_2 \to$

$\begin{bmatrix} 1 & 0 & 0 & | & 2 \\ 0 & 1 & 1 & | & 4 \\ 0 & -1 & 5 & | & 8 \end{bmatrix} R_2 + R_3 \to \begin{bmatrix} 1 & 0 & 0 & | & 2 \\ 0 & 1 & 1 & | & 4 \\ 0 & 0 & 6 & | & 12 \end{bmatrix} \frac{1}{6}R_3 \to \begin{bmatrix} 1 & 0 & 0 & | & 2 \\ 0 & 1 & 1 & | & 4 \\ 0 & 0 & 1 & | & 2 \end{bmatrix} -R_3 + R_2 \to$

$\begin{bmatrix} 1 & 0 & 0 & | & 2 \\ 0 & 1 & 0 & | & 2 \\ 0 & 0 & 1 & | & 2 \end{bmatrix} \Rightarrow (2, 2, 2)$

21. $0(0 \cdot 0 - 1(-1)) - 1(1 \cdot 0 - 3(-1)) + (-3)(1 \cdot 1 - 3 \cdot 0)$

$= 0 - (0 + 3) - 3(1 - 0) = -3 - 3(1) = -3 - 3 = -6$

22. $x^2 + 4 = 0 \Rightarrow x^2 = -4,$ which is not possible for any real number x. There are no solutions.

23. $-2x(x^2 - 2x + 5) = -2x^3 + 4x^2 - 10x$

24. $(2a+b)(2a-b) = 4a^2 - 2ab + 2ab - b^2 = 4a^2 - b^2$

25. $(x-1)(x+1)(x+3) = (x^2-1)(x+3) = x^3 + 3x^2 - x - 3$

26. $(4x+9)(2x-1) = 8x^2 - 4x + 18x - 9 = 8x^2 + 14x - 9$

27. $(x^2+3y^3)^2 = (x^2+3y^3)(x^2+3y^3) = x^4 + 3x^2y^3 + 3x^2y^3 + 9y^6$

       $= x^4 + 6x^2y^3 + 9y^6$

28. $-2x(1-x^2) = -2x + 2x^3 = 2x^3 - 2x$

29. $x^2 - 8x - 33 = (x+3)(x-11)$

30. $10x^3 + 65x^2 - 35x = 5x(2x^2 + 13x - 7) = 5x(2x-1)(x+7)$

31. $4x^2 - 100 = 4(x^2 - 25) = 4(x-5)(x+5)$

32. $49x^2 - 70x + 25 = (7x-5)^2$

33. $r^4 - r = r(r^3 - 1) = r(r-1)(r^2 + r + 1)$

34. $x^3 + 2x^2 + x + 2 = x^2(x+2) + 1(x+2) = (x^2+1)(x+2)$

35. $4x^2 - 1 = 0 \Rightarrow (2x-1)(2x+1) = 0 \Rightarrow 2x-1 = 0$ or $2x+1 = 0$

       $\Rightarrow x = \dfrac{1}{2}$ or $x = -\dfrac{1}{2}$. The solutions are $-\dfrac{1}{2}$ and $\dfrac{1}{2}$.

36. $3x^2 + 14x - 5 = 0 \Rightarrow (3x-1)(x+5) = 0 \Rightarrow 3x-1 = 0$ or $x+5 = 0 \Rightarrow x = \dfrac{1}{3}$ or $x = -5$. The solutions are

       -5 and $\dfrac{1}{3}$.

37. $x^3 + 4x = 4x^2 \Rightarrow x^3 - 4x^2 + 4x = 0 \Rightarrow x(x^2 - 4x + 4) = 0$

       $\Rightarrow x(x-2)^2 = 0 \Rightarrow x = 0$ or $x-2 = 0 \Rightarrow x = 0$ or $x = 2$.

       The solutions are 0 and 2.

38. $x^4 = x^2 \Rightarrow x^4 - x^2 = 0 \Rightarrow x^2(x^2 - 1) = 0 \Rightarrow x^2(x-1)(x+1) = 0$

       $\Rightarrow x^2 = 0$ or $x-1 = 0$ or $x+1 = 0 \Rightarrow x = 0$ or $x = 1$ or $x = -1$.

       The solutions are $-1, 0,$ and 1.

39.   Graph $Y_1 = \sqrt{(2)}X - 1.1(X - \pi)$ and $Y_2 = 1 - 2X$ in $[-5, 5, 1]$ by $[-5, 5, 1]$. The solution is approximately

       $x = -1.1$.

Figure 39

40.   Graph $Y_1 = (\pi - 1) \times \wedge 2 - \sqrt{(3)}$ and $Y_2 = 5 - 1.3X$ in $[-10,\ 10,\ 1]$ by $[-10,\ 10,\ 1]$. The solutions are

approximately $x = -2.1$ and $x = 1.5$.

Figure 40a   Figure 40b

Applications

41.   Let x represent the amount invested at 6% interest. Then

$0.06x + 0.07(4000 - x) = 257 \Rightarrow 0.06x + 280 - 0.07x = 257$

$\Rightarrow -0.01x = -23 \Rightarrow x = 2300$. So \$2300 is invested at 6% and \$1700 is invested at 7%.

42.   (a) $C(1995) = 750(1995 - 1990) + 6800 = 750(5) + 6800 = 10{,}550;$

In 1995 the car cost \$10,550.

(b)   Slope = 750; The cost increased, on average, by \$750 per year from 1990 to 2005.

43.   Let x represent the length of a side of the square base.

$x^2(x - 5) = 1008 \Rightarrow x^3 - 5x^2 - 1008 = 0$

$\Rightarrow (x - 12)(x^2 + 7x + 84) = 0 \Rightarrow x = 12$, since $x^2 + 7x + 84$

is never zero. The dimensions are 12 inches by 12 inches by 7 inches.

44.   Let x, y, and z represent the measures of the angles of the triangle from smallest to largest. Then the system

needed is

$$\begin{array}{ll} x + y + z = 180 & x + y + z = 180 \\ z = x + y - 20 \quad \Rightarrow & -x - y + z = -20 \\ y + z = x + 100 & -x + y + z = 100 \end{array}$$

Add the first two equations to eliminate the variables x and y.

$$\begin{array}{l} x + y + z = 180 \\ \underline{-x - y + z = -20} \quad \Rightarrow z = 80 \\ 2z = 160 \end{array}$$

Add the first and third equations to eliminate the variable x.

$$\begin{array}{l} x + y + z = 180 \\ \underline{-x + y + z = 100} \quad \Rightarrow 2y + 2(80) = 280 \Rightarrow 2y = 120 \Rightarrow y = 60 \\ 2y + 2z = 280 \end{array}$$

Then $x + y + z = 180 \Rightarrow x + 60 + 80 = 180 \Rightarrow x = 40$. The angles are $40°, 60°,$ and $80°$.

Critical Thinking Solutions for Chapter 5

Section 5.1

• The volume of a cube is $V = l \cdot w \cdot h$. So one cube's volume is given by y^3. Volume for 4 cubes is $4y^3$.

• No, for example $\left(2x^2 + x\right) + \left(1 - 2x^2\right) = x + 1$.

Section 5.2

• If we let $x = 1$ the two expressions are not equal. *Answers may vary.*

Section 5.3

• $xy - 4x - 3y + 12 = 0 \Rightarrow x(y - 4) - 3(y - 4) = 0 \Rightarrow (y - 4)(x - 3) = 0 \Rightarrow y = 4$ or $x = 3$

Section 5.4

• Graph $Y_1 = 100X(100 - X)$ in [0, 100, 10] by [0, 300,000, 30,000]. This graph is not shown.

  The maximum occurs when $x = 50$. The price that maximizes revenue is \$50 per ticket.

• No. The trinomials shown cannot be factored using the methods discussed in this section.

Chapter 6: Rational Expressions and Functions

6.1: Introduction to Rational Functions and Equations

Concepts

1. A rational expression is a polynomial divided by a nonzero polynomial. Example: $\dfrac{x^2+1}{3x}$ *Answers may vary.*

2. $x = 4$

3. Multiply each side by $x+7$.

4. No, the equation is undefined when $x = 5$.

5. No, it simplifies to $5+x$.

6. 1

7. a

8. 0

9. Yes

10. Yes

11. Yes

12. No, $|x|$ is not a polynomial.

13. No, $\sqrt{x}$ is not a polynomial.

14. Yes

Rational Functions

15. $f(x) = \dfrac{x}{x+1}$

16. $f(x) = \dfrac{x+2}{x+5}$

17. $f(x) = \dfrac{x^2}{x-2}$

18. $f(x) = \dfrac{1}{2x}$

19. The denominator cannot equal zero, so $D = \{x \mid x \neq -2\}$.

20. The denominator cannot equal zero, so $D = \{x \mid x \neq 4\}$.

21. The denominator cannot equal zero, so $D = \left\{x \mid x \neq \frac{1}{3}\right\}$.

22. The denominator cannot equal zero, so $D = \left\{x \mid x \neq -\frac{4}{5}\right\}$.

23. The denominator cannot equal zero, and

$t^2 - 4 = 0 \Rightarrow (t-2)(t+2) = 0 \Rightarrow t = 2$ or $t = -2$, so $D = \{t \mid t \neq -2, t \neq 2\}$.

24. The denominator cannot equal zero, and

    $9 - t^2 = 0 \Rightarrow (3-t)(3+t) = 0 \Rightarrow 3 = t$ or $-3 = t$, so $D = \{t \mid t \neq -3, t \neq 3\}$.

25. The denominator cannot equal zero, and

    $x^2 - 3x + 2 = 0 \Rightarrow (x-2)(x-1) = 0 \Rightarrow x = 2$ or $x = 1$, so $D = \{x \mid x \neq 1, x \neq 2\}$.

26. The denominator cannot equal zero, and

    $2x^2 - x - 15 = 0 \Rightarrow (2x+5)(x-3) = 0 \Rightarrow x = -\frac{5}{2}$ or $x = 3$, so $D = \left\{x \mid x \neq -\frac{5}{2}, x \neq 3\right\}$.

27. The denominator cannot equal zero, and $x^3 - 4x = 0 \Rightarrow x(x^2 - 4) = 0 \Rightarrow x(x-2)(x+2) = 0 \Rightarrow x = 0$ or $x = 2$

    or $x = -2$, so $D = \{x \mid x \neq -2, x \neq 0, x \neq 2\}$.

28. The denominator cannot equal zero, and $9x - x^3 = 0 \Rightarrow x(9 - x^2) = 0 \Rightarrow x(3-x)(3+x) = 0 \Rightarrow x = 0$ or $x = 3$

    or $x = -3$, so $D = \{x \mid x \neq -3, x \neq 0, x \neq 3\}$.

29. See Figure 29. The denominator cannot equal zero, so $x - 1 \neq 0$. The domain is $\{x \mid x \neq 1\}$.

30. See Figure 30. The denominator cannot equal zero, so $x + 3 \neq 0$. The domain is $\{x \mid x \neq -3\}$.

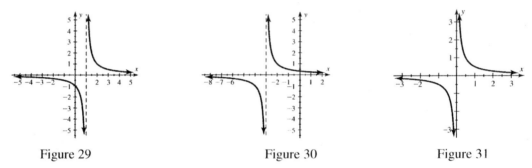

Figure 29   Figure 30   Figure 31

31. See Figure 31. The denominator cannot equal zero, so $2x \neq 0$. The domain is $\{x \mid x \neq 0\}$.

32. See Figure 32. The denominator cannot equal zero, so $x \neq 0$. The domain is $\{x \mid x \neq 0\}$.

33. See Figure 33. The denominator cannot equal zero, so $x + 2 \neq 0$. The domain is $\{x \mid x \neq -2\}$.

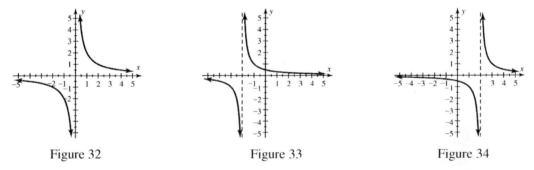

Figure 32   Figure 33   Figure 34

34. See Figure 34. The denominator cannot equal zero, so $x - 2 \neq 0$. The domain is $\{x \mid x \neq 2\}$.

35. See Figure 35. This denominator will never equal zero. The domain is $\{x \mid -\infty < x < \infty\}$.

36. See Figure 36. This denominator will never equal zero. The domain is $\{x \mid -\infty < x < \infty\}$.

Figure 35

Figure 36

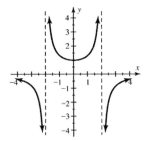

Figure 37

37.   See Figure 37. The denominator cannot equal zero, so $2x - 3 \neq 0$. The domain is $\left\{ x \mid x \neq \dfrac{3}{2} \right\}$.

38.   See Figure 38. The denominator cannot equal zero, so $3x + 2 \neq 0$. The domain is $\left\{ x \mid x \neq -\dfrac{2}{3} \right\}$.

Figure 38

Figure 39

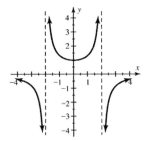

Figure 40

39.   The denominator cannot equal zero, so $x^2 - 1 = 0 \Rightarrow (x-1)(x+1) = 0 \Rightarrow x = 1$ or $x = -1$. The domain is

$\{x \mid x \neq -1,\ x \neq 1\}$.

40.   The denominator cannot equal zero, so $4 - x^2 = 0 \Rightarrow (2-x)(2+x) = 0 \Rightarrow x = 2$ or $x = -2$. The domain is

$\{x \mid x \neq -2,\ x \neq 2\}$.

41. $f(-2) = \dfrac{1}{(-2)-1} = -\dfrac{1}{3}$.

42. $f(2) = \dfrac{3(2)}{(2)^2 - 1} = \dfrac{6}{3} = 2$.

43. $f(-3) = \dfrac{(-3)+1}{(-3)-1} = \dfrac{-2}{-4} = \dfrac{1}{2}$.

44. $f(0) = \dfrac{2(0)+1}{3(0)-1} = \dfrac{1}{-1} = -1$.

45. $f(-2) = \dfrac{(-2)^2 - 3(-2) + 5}{(-2)^2 + 1} = \dfrac{15}{5} = 3$.

46. $f(-1) = \dfrac{5}{(-1)^2 - (-1)} = \dfrac{5}{2}$.

47. $f(-3) = 2$ and $f(1) = 0$; The equation on the vertical asymptote is $x = -1$.

48. $f(-3) = 1$ and $f(2)$ is undefined; The equation on the vertical asymptote is $x = 2$.

49. $f(-1) = 0$ and $f(2)$ is undefined; The equations on the vertical asymptotes are $x = -2$ and $x = 2$.

50. $f(-1) = 2$ and $f(1) = 2$; There are no vertical asymptotes.

51.

x	-2	-1	0	1	2
$f(x) = \dfrac{1}{x-1}$	$-\dfrac{1}{3}$	$-\dfrac{1}{2}$	-1	—	1

When $x = 1$, $\dfrac{1}{x-1} = \dfrac{1}{1-1} = \dfrac{1}{0}$, so f(1) is undefined.

52.

x	-2	-1	0	1	2
$f(x) = \dfrac{2x}{x+2}$	—	-2	0	$\dfrac{2}{3}$	1

When $x = -2$, $\dfrac{2x}{x+2} = \dfrac{2(-2)}{-2+2} = \dfrac{-4}{0}$, so $f(-2)$ is undefined.

$f(1) = \dfrac{2}{3}$

Rational Equations

53. $\dfrac{3}{x} = 5 \Rightarrow 3 = 5x \Rightarrow \dfrac{3}{5} = x \Rightarrow x = \dfrac{3}{5}$

54. $\dfrac{5}{x} = 7 \Rightarrow 5 = 7x \Rightarrow \dfrac{5}{7} = x \Rightarrow x = \dfrac{5}{7}$

55. $\dfrac{1}{x-2} = -1 \Rightarrow 1 = -1(x-2) \Rightarrow 1 = -x + 2 \Rightarrow -1 = -x \Rightarrow x = 1$

56. $\dfrac{-5}{x+4} = -5 \Rightarrow -5 = -5(x+4) \Rightarrow -5 = -5x - 20 \Rightarrow 15 = -5x \Rightarrow -3 = x \Rightarrow x = -3$

57. $\dfrac{x}{x+1} = 2 \Rightarrow x = 2(x+1) \Rightarrow x = 2x + 2 \Rightarrow -x = 2 \Rightarrow x = -2$

58. $\dfrac{3x}{x+3} = -6 \Rightarrow 3x = -6(x+3) \Rightarrow 3x = -6x - 18 \Rightarrow 9x = -18 \Rightarrow x = \dfrac{-18}{9} \Rightarrow x = -2$

59. $\dfrac{2x+1}{3x-2} = 1 \Rightarrow 2x+1 = 3x - 2 \Rightarrow 1 = x - 2 \Rightarrow 3 = x \Rightarrow x = 3$

60. $\dfrac{x+3}{4x+1} = \dfrac{3}{5} \Rightarrow 5(x+3) = 3(4x+1) \Rightarrow 5x + 15 = 12x + 3 \Rightarrow 12 = 7x \Rightarrow \dfrac{12}{7} = x \Rightarrow x = \dfrac{12}{7}$

61. $\dfrac{3}{x+2} = x \Rightarrow 3 = x(x+2) \Rightarrow x^2 + 2x - 3 = 0 \Rightarrow (x+3)(x-1) = 0 \Rightarrow x = -3$ or $x = 1$

62. $\dfrac{6}{2x+1}=x \Rightarrow 6=x(2x+1) \Rightarrow 2x^2+x-6=0 \Rightarrow (2x-3)(x+2)=0 \Rightarrow x=\dfrac{3}{2}$ or $x=-2$

63. $\dfrac{6}{x+1}=3x \Rightarrow \dfrac{2}{x+1}=x \Rightarrow 2=x(x+1) \Rightarrow x^2+x-2=0 \Rightarrow (x-1)(x+2) \Rightarrow x=1$ or $x=-2$

64. $\dfrac{4}{x-3}=x \Rightarrow 4=x(x-3) \Rightarrow x^2-3x-4=0 \Rightarrow (x+1)(x-4)=0 \Rightarrow x=-1$ or $x=4$

65. $\dfrac{1}{x^2-1}=-1 \Rightarrow 1=-1(x^2-1) \Rightarrow 1=-x^2+1 \Rightarrow 0=-x^2 \Rightarrow 0=x^2 \Rightarrow 0=x \Rightarrow x=0$

66. $\dfrac{5x}{x^2-5}=\dfrac{x+2}{x^2-5} \Rightarrow 5x=x+2 \Rightarrow 4x=2 \Rightarrow x=\dfrac{2}{4} \Rightarrow x=\dfrac{1}{2}$

67. $\dfrac{x}{x-5}=\dfrac{2x-5}{x-5} \Rightarrow x=2x-5 \Rightarrow -x=-5 \Rightarrow x=5$, but this solution does not check. No solution.

68. $\dfrac{x}{x+1}=\dfrac{2x+1}{x+1} \Rightarrow x=2x+1 \Rightarrow -x=1 \Rightarrow x=-1$, but this solution does not check. No solution.

69. $\dfrac{4x}{x+2}=\dfrac{-8}{2x+4} \Rightarrow \dfrac{4x}{x+2}=\dfrac{2(-4)}{2(x+2)} \Rightarrow \dfrac{4x}{x+2}=\dfrac{-4}{x+2} \Rightarrow 4x=-4 \Rightarrow x=-1$

70. $\dfrac{6x}{3x-2}=\dfrac{4}{4-6x} \Rightarrow \dfrac{6x}{3x-2}=\dfrac{-2(-2)}{-2(-2+3x)} \Rightarrow \dfrac{6x}{3x-2}=\dfrac{-2}{3x-2} \Rightarrow 6x=-2 \Rightarrow x=-\dfrac{1}{3}$

71. $\dfrac{2x}{x+2}=\dfrac{x-4}{x+2} \Rightarrow 2x=x-4 \Rightarrow x=-4$

72. $\dfrac{x+3}{x+1}=\dfrac{3x+4}{x+1} \Rightarrow x+3=3x+4 \Rightarrow -2x+3=4 \Rightarrow -2x=1 \Rightarrow x=-\dfrac{1}{2}$

73. Graph $Y_1=(4+X)/(2X)$ and $Y_2=-0.5$ in $[-4.7, 4.7, 1]$ by $[-3.1, 3.1, 1]$. See Figure 73. $x=-2$

74. Graph $Y_1=(2X-1)/(X-5)$ and $Y_2=-5/2$ in $[-9.4, 18.8, 2]$ by $[-6.2, 6.2, 1]$. See Figure 74. $x=3$

$[-4.7, 4.7, 1]$ by $[-3.1, 3.1, 1]$ $[-9.4, 18.8, 2]$ by $[-6.2, 6.2, 1]$

Figure 73   Figure 74

$[-9.4, 9.4, 1]$ by $[-3.1, 3.1, 1]$

Figure 75   Figure 76

75. Table $Y_1=(2X)/(X^2-4)$ and $Y_2=-2/3$ with TblStart $=-5$ and ΔTbl $=1$. See Figure 75. $x=-4$ or $x=1$

76. Graph $Y_1=(X-1)/(X+2)$ and $Y_2=X$ in $[-9.4, 9.4, 1]$ by $[-3.1, 3.1, 1]$. See Figure 76.   No solutions.

77.   Table $Y_1 = 1/(X-1)$ and $Y_2 = X-1$ with TblStart $= -3$ and ΔTbl $= 1$. See Figure 77. $x = 0$ or $x = 2$

Figure 77

Figure 78

78.   Table $Y_1 = 2/(X+2)$ and $Y_2 = X+1$ with TblStart $= -4$ and ΔTbl $= 1$. See Figure 78. $x = -3$ or $x = 0$

Using More Than One Method

79.   (a) Symbolic: $\dfrac{1}{x+2} = 1 \Rightarrow 1 = x+2 \Rightarrow -1 = x \Rightarrow x = -1$

    (b) Graphical: Graph $Y_1 = 1/(X+2)$ and $Y_2 = 1$ in $[-4.7, 4.7, 1]$ by $[-3.1, 3.1, 1]$. See Figure 79b. $x = -1$

    (c) Numerical: Table $Y_1 = 1/(X+2)$ and $Y_2 = 1$ with TblStart $= -3$ and ΔTbl $= 1$. See Figure 79c. $x = -1$

    $[-4.7, 4.7, 1]$ by $[-3.1, 3.1, 1]$

Figure 79b

Figure 79c

80.   (a) Symbolic: $\dfrac{3}{x-1} = 2 \Rightarrow 3 = 2(x-1) \Rightarrow 3 = 2x-2 \Rightarrow 5 = 2x \Rightarrow \dfrac{5}{2} = x \Rightarrow x = \dfrac{5}{2}$

    (b) Graphical: Graph $Y_1 = 3/(X-1)$ and $Y_2 = 2$ in $[-4.7, 4.7, 1]$ by $[-3.1, 3.1, 1]$. See Figure 80b. $x = \dfrac{5}{2}$

    (c) Numerical: Table $Y_1 = 3/(X-1)$ and $Y_2 = 2$ with TblStart $= 0$ and ΔTbl $= 0.5$. See Figure 80c. $x = \dfrac{5}{2}$

    $[-4.7, 4.7, 1]$ by $[-3.1, 3.1, 1]$

Figure 80b

Figure 80c

81.   (a) Symbolic: $\dfrac{x}{2x+1} = \dfrac{2}{5} \Rightarrow 5x = 2(2x+1) \Rightarrow 5x = 4x+2 \Rightarrow x = 2$

    (b) Graphical: Graph $Y_1 = X/(2X+1)$ and $Y_2 = 2/5$ in $[-2.35, 2.35, 1]$ by $[-1.55, 1.55, 1]$. See Figure 81b.

        $x = 2$

    (c) Numerical: Table $Y_1 = X/(2X+1)$ and $Y_2 = 2/5$ with TblStart $= 0$ and ΔTbl $= 1$. See Figure 81c. $x = 2$

$[-2.35, 2.35, 1]$ by $[-1.55, 1.55, 1]$

Figure 81b

Figure 81c

$[-9.4, 9.4, 1]$ by $[-6.2, 6.2, 1]$

Figure 82b

Figure 82c

82.   (a)   Symbolic: $\dfrac{4x-2}{x+1} = \dfrac{3}{2} \Rightarrow 2(4x-2) = 3(x+1) \Rightarrow 8x-4 = 3x+3 \Rightarrow 5x = 7 \Rightarrow x = \dfrac{7}{5}$

(b)   Graphical: Graph $Y_1 = (4X-2)/(X+1)$ and $Y_2 = 3/2$ in $[-9.4, 9.4, 1]$ by $[-6.2, 6.2, 1]$. See Figure 82b.

$x = \dfrac{7}{5}$

(c)   Numerical: Table $Y_1 = (4X-2)/(X+1)$ and $Y_2 = 3/2$ with TblStart $= 0.2$ and ΔTbl $= 0.2$. See Figure

82c. $x = \dfrac{7}{5}$

83.   Graph $Y_1 = X^3/(X-1)$ and $Y_2 = -1/(X+1)$ in $[-5, 5, 1]$ by $[-5, 5, 1]$. The solutions are approximately

$x = -1.62$ and $x = 0.62$

Figure 83a

Figure 83b

84.   Graph $Y_1 = (X^2-1)/(2X^2)$ and $Y_2 = (X+2)/(1-X)$ in $[-4.7, 4.7, 1]$ by $[-3.1, 3.1, 1]$. The solutions are

approximately $x = -1.41$.

Figure 84

85. $a = \dfrac{x}{b} \Rightarrow ba = b \cdot \dfrac{x}{b} \Rightarrow ab = x$

86. $\dfrac{a}{b} = \dfrac{c}{d} \Rightarrow bd \cdot \dfrac{a}{b} = bd \cdot \dfrac{c}{d} \Rightarrow ad = bc$

Operations on Functions

87.   (a) $(f+g)(3) = 5(3) + (3+1) = 15 + 4 = 19$

      (b) $(f-g)(-2) = 5(-2) - (-2+1) = -10 - (-1) = -9$

      (c) $(fg)(5) = (5 \cdot 5)(5+1) = 25(6) = 150$

      (d) $(f/g)(0) = (5 \cdot 0)/(0+1) = \dfrac{0}{1} = 0$

88.   (a) $(f+g)(3) = (3^2 + 2) + (-2 \cdot 3) = 9 + 2 + (-6) = 5$

      (b) $(f-g)(-2) = ((-2)^2 + 2) - (-2(-2)) = 4 + 2 - 4 = 2$

      (c) $(fg)(5) = (5^2 + 2)(-2 \cdot 5) = (27)(-10) = -270$

      (d) $(f/g)(0) = (0^2 + 2)/(-2.0) = \dfrac{2}{0}$, which is undefined

89.   (a) $(f+g)(3) = (2 \cdot 3 - 1) + (4 \cdot 3^2) = 6 - 1 + 4 \cdot 9 = 5 + 36 = 41$

      (b) $(f-g)(-2) = (2(-2) - 1) - (4(-2)^2) = -4 - 1 - 4(4) = -5 - 16 = -21$

      (c) $(fg)(5) = (2 \cdot 5 - 1)(4 \cdot 5^2) = (9)(100) = 900$

      (d) $(f/g)(0) = (2 \cdot 0 - 1)/(4 \cdot 0^2) = \dfrac{-1}{0}$, which is undefined

90.   (a) $(f+g)(3) = (3^2 - 1) + (3+2) = 9 - 1 + 5 = 13$

      (b) $(f-g)(-2) = ((-2)^2 - 1) - (-2+2) = 3 - 0 = 3$

      (c) $(fg)(5) = (5^2 - 1)(5+2) = (24)(7) = 168$

      (d) $(f/g)(0) = (0^2 - 1)/(0+2) = \dfrac{-1}{2} = -\dfrac{1}{2}$

91.   (a) $(f+g)(x) = (x+1) + (x+2) = 2x + 3$

      (b) $(f-g)(x) = (x+1) - (x+2) = -1$

      (c) $(fg)(x) = (x+1)(x+2) = x^2 + 3x + 2$

      (d) $(f/g)(x) = \dfrac{x+1}{x+2}$

92.   (a) $(f+g)(x) = (-3x) + (x-1) = -2x - 1$

      (b) $(f-g)(x) = (-3x) - (x-1) = -4x + 1$

      (c) $(fg)(x) = (-3x)(x-1) = -3x^2 + 3x$

      (d) $(f/g)(x) = \dfrac{-3x}{x-1}$

93.   (a) $(f+g)(x) = (1-x) + (x^2) = x^2 - x + 1$

(b) $(f-g)(x) = (1-x) - (x^2) = 1 - x - x^2$

(c) $(fg)(x) = (1-x)(x^2) = x^2 - x^3$

(d) $(f/g)(x) = \dfrac{1-x}{x^2}$

94. (a) $(f+g)(x) = (x^2 + 4) + (6x) = x^2 + 6x + 4$

(b) $(f-g)(x) = (x^2 + 4) - (6x) = x^2 - 6x + 4$

(c) $(fg)(x) = (x^2 + 4)(6x) = 6x^3 + 24x$

(d) $(f/g)(x) = \dfrac{x^2 + 4}{6x}$

Applications

95. The graph should increase quickly at first and then continue to increase at a slower rate. The answer is graph c.

96. The graph should decrease quickly at first and then continue to decrease at a slower rate. The answer is graph b.

97. The graph should increase slowly at first and then continue to increase at a faster rate. The answer is graph d.

98. The graph should increase at first but then decrease. The answer is graph a.

99. (a) $f(400) = \dfrac{2540}{400} = 6.35$; A curve with a radius of 400 feet will have an outer rail elevation of 6.35 inches.

(b) Table $Y_1 = 2540/X$ with TblStart = 100 and ΔTbl = 50. See Figure 99.

(c) If the radius of the curve doubles, the outer rail elevation is halved.

(d) $\dfrac{2540}{r} = 5 \Rightarrow 2540 = 5r \Rightarrow r = \dfrac{2540}{5} = 508$ feet

Figure 99

[0, 100, 10] by [0, 1, 0.1]

Figure 102

[0, 50, 10] by [0, 6, 1]

Figure 105

Figure 106

100. (a) $R(0.1) = \dfrac{1600}{15(0.1)+2} = \dfrac{1600}{3.5} \approx 457$; A curve with a slope of 0.1 will have a minimum radius of 457 feet.

(b) As the slope of the banking increases, the radius of the curve decreases.

(c) $320 = \dfrac{1600}{15m+2} \Rightarrow 320(15m+2) = 1600 \Rightarrow 4800m + 640 = 1600 \Rightarrow 4800m = 960 \Rightarrow m = 0.2$

101. (a) $D(0.05) = \dfrac{900}{10.5+30(0.05)} = \dfrac{900}{12} = 75;$ The braking distance is 75 feet when the uphill grade is 0.05.

(b) $60 = \dfrac{900}{10.5+30x} \Rightarrow 60(10.5+30x) = 900 \Rightarrow 630 + 1800x = 900 \Rightarrow 1800x = 270 \Rightarrow x = 0.15$

102. (a) $S(0.05) = \dfrac{900}{10.5-30(0.05)} = \dfrac{900}{9} = 100;$ The braking distance is 100 feet when the downhill grade is

0.05.

(b) Table $Y_1 = 900/(10.5+30X)$ and $Y_2 = 900/(10.5-30X)$ with TblStart = 0 and ΔTbl = 0.05. See Figure

102.

(c) The distances for downhill braking are farther than those for uphill breaking. This agrees with driving

experience.

103. (a) $T(4) = \dfrac{1}{5-(4)} = \dfrac{1}{1} = 1;$ When cars leave the ramp at a rate of 4 vehicles per minute, the wait is 1 minute.

(b) As more cars try to exit, the waiting time increases. This agrees with intuition.

(c) $3 = \dfrac{1}{5-x} \Rightarrow 3(5-x) = 1 \Rightarrow 15 - 3x = 1 \Rightarrow -3x = -14 \Rightarrow x = 4.\overline{6}$ vehicles per minute.

104. (a) $N(30) = \dfrac{(30)^2}{2500-50(30)} = \dfrac{900}{1000} = 0.9;$

When people arrive at a rate of 30 per hour, the line will be about 1 person long.

(b) As people arrive at a faster rate, the length of the line increases. This agrees with intuition.

(c) From the given graph, when $N = 8,$ the rate is about 45 people per hour.

105. (a) $P(1) = \dfrac{(1)-1}{(1)} = \dfrac{0}{1} = 0$ and $P(50) = \dfrac{(50)-1}{(50)} = \dfrac{49}{50} = 0.98$

When there is only 1 ball there is no chance of losing. With 50 balls there is a 98% chance of losing.

(b) Graph $Y_1 = (X-1)/X$ in [0, 100, 10] by [0, 1, 0.1]. See Figure 105.

Figure 105

(c) It increases. This agrees with intuition since there are more balls without the winning number.

(d) $0.975 = \dfrac{x-1}{x} \Rightarrow 0.975x = x-1 \Rightarrow -0.025x = -1 \Rightarrow x = 40$ balls

106. (a) $P(10) = \dfrac{5(10)+2}{(10)+1} = \dfrac{52}{11} = 4.\overline{72};$ After 10 months, there are about 4727 insects per acre.

(b) Graph $Y_1 = (5X+2)/(X+1)$ in [0, 50, 10] by [0, 6, 1]. See Figure 106.

Figure 106

(c) After several years the insect population stabilizes around 5000 insects per acre.

(d) $4.8 = \dfrac{5x+2}{x+1} \Rightarrow 4.8(x+1) = 5x+2 \Rightarrow 4.8x+4.8 = 5x+2 \Rightarrow -0.2x = -2.8 \Rightarrow x = 14$ months

Group Activity Solutions

(a) See Figure 1. Vertical asymptote: $x = 0$.

(b) It decreases. As the coefficient of friction increases to one, the road becomes less slippery.

(c) It increases. As the coefficient of friction decreases to zero, the road becomes more slippery.

(d) No, since there is always some friction. Otherwise, the car would never stop.

Figure 1

6.2: Multiplication and Division of Rational Expressions

Concepts

1.   1

2. $\dfrac{x-3}{3-x} = \dfrac{x-3}{-1(x-3)} = \dfrac{1}{-1} = -1$

3.   No, $\dfrac{x^2-1}{x-1} = \dfrac{(x-1)(x+1)}{x-1} = x+1.$

4.   No, it is equal to neither $\dfrac{1}{x}$ nor $1+\dfrac{3}{x}.$

5.   We multiply $\dfrac{2}{3}$ by $\dfrac{7}{5}.$

6. $\dfrac{ac}{bd}$

7. $\dfrac{ad}{bc}$

8. $\dfrac{a}{b}$

Review of Fractions

9. $\dfrac{1}{2} \cdot \dfrac{4}{5} = \dfrac{1}{1} \cdot \dfrac{2}{5} = \dfrac{2}{5}$

10. $\dfrac{5}{6} \cdot \dfrac{3}{10} = \dfrac{1}{2} \cdot \dfrac{1}{2} = \dfrac{1}{4}$

11. $\dfrac{7}{8} \cdot \dfrac{4}{3} \cdot (-3) = \dfrac{7}{2} \cdot \dfrac{1}{3} \cdot \dfrac{-3}{1} = \dfrac{7}{2} \cdot \dfrac{1}{1} \cdot \dfrac{-1}{1} = -\dfrac{7}{2}$

12. $4 \cdot \dfrac{7}{4} \cdot \dfrac{1}{2} = \dfrac{4}{1} \cdot \dfrac{7}{4} \cdot \dfrac{1}{2} = \dfrac{1}{1} \cdot \dfrac{7}{1} \cdot \dfrac{1}{2} = \dfrac{7}{2}$

13. $\dfrac{3}{8} \cdot 2 = \dfrac{3}{8} \cdot \dfrac{2}{1} = \dfrac{3}{4} \cdot \dfrac{1}{1} = \dfrac{3}{4}$

14. $-5 \cdot \dfrac{2}{7} = -\dfrac{5}{1} \cdot \dfrac{2}{7} = -\dfrac{10}{7}$

15. $-\dfrac{7}{11} \div 14 = -\dfrac{7}{11} \cdot \dfrac{1}{14} = -\dfrac{1}{11} \cdot \dfrac{1}{2} = -\dfrac{1}{22}$

16. $6 \div \dfrac{6}{5} = \dfrac{6}{1} \cdot \dfrac{5}{6} = \dfrac{1}{1} \cdot \dfrac{5}{1} = 5$

17. $\dfrac{5}{7} \div \dfrac{15}{14} = \dfrac{5}{7} \cdot \dfrac{14}{15} = \dfrac{1}{1} \cdot \dfrac{2}{3} = \dfrac{2}{3}$

18. $-\dfrac{2}{3} \div 2 = -\dfrac{2}{3} \cdot \dfrac{1}{2} = -\dfrac{1}{3} \cdot \dfrac{1}{1} = -\dfrac{1}{3}$

19. $6 \div \left(-\dfrac{1}{3}\right) = 6 \cdot (-3) = -18$

20. $\dfrac{10}{9} \div \dfrac{5}{3} = \dfrac{10}{9} \cdot \dfrac{3}{5} = \dfrac{2}{3} \cdot \dfrac{1}{1} = \dfrac{2}{3}$

Simplifying Rational Expressions

21. $\dfrac{5x}{x^2} = \dfrac{5}{x}$

22. $\dfrac{18t^3}{6t} = \dfrac{3t^2}{1} = 3t^2$

23. $\dfrac{3z+6}{z+2} = \dfrac{3(z+2)}{z+2} = 3$

24. $\dfrac{6}{16x+6} = \dfrac{6}{6(2x+1)} = \dfrac{1}{2x+1}$

25. $\dfrac{2z+2}{3z+3} = \dfrac{2(z+1)}{3(z+1)} = \dfrac{2}{3}$

26. $\dfrac{4x-12}{2x-6} = \dfrac{4(x-3)}{2(x-3)} = \dfrac{4}{2} = 2$

27. $\dfrac{(x-1)(x+1)}{x-1} = x+1$

28. $(x+2) \cdot \dfrac{x-6}{x+2} = x-6$

29. $\dfrac{x^2-4}{x+2} = \dfrac{(x-2)(x+2)}{x+2} = x-2$

30. $\dfrac{(x+2)(x-5)}{(x+10)(x+2)} = \dfrac{x-5}{x+10}$

31. $\dfrac{x(x-1)}{(x+1)(x-1)} = \dfrac{x}{x+1}$

32. $\dfrac{(2x-1)(x-3)}{(x-3)(2x+5)} = \dfrac{2x-1}{2x+5}$

33. $\dfrac{(3x+1)(x+2)}{(x+2)(5x-2)} = \dfrac{3x+1}{5x-2}$

34. $\dfrac{(3x+2)(x-7)}{x(x-7)} = \dfrac{3x+2}{x}$

35. $\dfrac{x+5}{x^2+2x-15} = \dfrac{x+5}{(x+5)(x-3)} = \dfrac{1}{x-3}$

36. $\dfrac{x^2-9}{x^2+6x+9} \cdot (x+3) = \dfrac{(x-3)(x+3)}{(x+3)(x+3)} \cdot \dfrac{x+3}{1} = x-3$

37. $\dfrac{x^2+2x}{x^2+3x+2} = \dfrac{x(x+2)}{(x+1)(x+2)} = \dfrac{x}{x+1}$

38. $\dfrac{x^2-3x-10}{x^2-6x+5} = \dfrac{(x-5)(x+2)}{(x-5)(x-1)} = \dfrac{x+2}{x-1}$

39. $\dfrac{6x^2+7x-5}{2x^2-11x+5} = \dfrac{(3x+5)(2x-1)}{(x-5)(2x-1)} = \dfrac{3x+5}{x-5}$

40. $\dfrac{30x^2-7x-15}{6x^2+7x-10} = \dfrac{(5x+3)(6x-5)}{(x+2)(6x-5)} = \dfrac{5x+3}{x+2}$

41. $\dfrac{a^2-b^2}{a-b} = \dfrac{(a-b)(a+b)}{a-b} = a+b$

42. $\dfrac{a^2 + 2ab + b^2}{a+b} = \dfrac{(a+b)^2}{a+b} = a+b$

43. $\dfrac{m^3 + n^3}{m+n} = \dfrac{(m+n)(m^2 - mn + n^2)}{m+n} = m^2 - mn + n^2$

44. $\dfrac{m^3 - n^3}{m-n} = \dfrac{(m-n)(m^2 + mn + n^2)}{m-n} = m^2 + mn + n^2$

45. $-\dfrac{4-t}{t-4} = \dfrac{-1(4-t)}{t-4} = \dfrac{t-4}{t-4} = 1$

46. $-\dfrac{t-r}{r-t} = \dfrac{-1(t-r)}{r-t} = \dfrac{r-t}{r-t} = 1$

47. $\dfrac{4m-n}{-4m+n} = \dfrac{4m-n}{-1(4m-n)} = \dfrac{1}{-1} = -1$

48. $\dfrac{2n+10m}{-n-5m} = \dfrac{2(n+5m)}{-1(n+5m)} = \dfrac{2}{-1} = -2$

49. $\dfrac{5-y}{y-5} = \dfrac{-1(y-5)}{y-5} = -1$

50. $\dfrac{a-b}{b-a} = \dfrac{a-b}{-1(a-b)} = \dfrac{1}{-1} = -1$

Reciprocals

51. $\dfrac{1}{4x}$

52. $\dfrac{1}{5x-2}$

53. $\dfrac{5b}{2a}$

54. $\dfrac{7a^2}{5b^3}$

55. $\dfrac{5-x}{3-x}$

56. $\dfrac{3x+1}{x^2-4}$

57. $\dfrac{x^2+1}{1} = x^2+1$

58. $\dfrac{5-x}{-1} = x-5$

Multiplication and Division of Rational Expressions

59. $\dfrac{2}{x} \cdot \dfrac{x-1}{3x} = \dfrac{2(x-1)}{3x^2}$

60. $\dfrac{2}{x-3} \cdot \dfrac{x}{x+1} = \dfrac{2x}{(x-3)(x+1)}$

61. $\dfrac{x-2}{x} \cdot \dfrac{x-3}{x+4} = \dfrac{(x-2)(x-3)}{x(x+4)}$

62. $\dfrac{x}{x+5} \cdot \dfrac{x-6}{x+4} = \dfrac{x(x-6)}{(x+5)(x+4)}$

63. $\dfrac{1}{2x} \cdot \dfrac{4x}{2} = \dfrac{1}{2x} \cdot \dfrac{2x}{1} = \dfrac{2x}{2x} = 1$

64. $\dfrac{5a^2}{7} \cdot \dfrac{7}{10a} = \dfrac{a}{1} \cdot \dfrac{1}{2} = \dfrac{a}{2}$

65. $\dfrac{5a}{4} \cdot \dfrac{12}{5a} = \dfrac{1}{1} \cdot \dfrac{3}{1} = 3$

66. $\dfrac{a^2b}{4c} \cdot \dfrac{8c^2}{3ab^2} = \dfrac{a}{1} \cdot \dfrac{2c}{3b} = \dfrac{2ac}{3b}$

67. $\dfrac{9x^2y^4}{8xy^6} \cdot \dfrac{\left(2xy^2\right)^3}{3\left(xy\right)^4} = \dfrac{9x^2y^4}{8xy^6} \cdot \dfrac{8x^3y^6}{3x^4y^4} = \dfrac{9 \cdot 8 \cdot x^5y^{10}}{8 \cdot 3 \cdot x^5y^{10}} = \dfrac{9}{3} = 3$

68. $\dfrac{\left(7rt\right)^2}{8} \cdot \dfrac{8r}{49\left(rt^2\right)^3} = \dfrac{49r^2t^2}{8} \cdot \dfrac{8r}{49r^3t^6} = \dfrac{8 \cdot 49r^3t^2}{8 \cdot 49r^3t^6} = \dfrac{1}{t^4}$

69. $\dfrac{x+1}{2x-5} \cdot \dfrac{2x-5}{x} = \dfrac{x+1}{1} \cdot \dfrac{1}{x} = \dfrac{x+1}{x}$

70. $\dfrac{x+1}{x} \cdot \dfrac{x}{x+2} = \dfrac{x+1}{1} \cdot \dfrac{1}{x+2} = \dfrac{x+1}{x+2}$

71. $\dfrac{b^2+1}{b^2-1} \cdot \dfrac{b-1}{b+1} = \dfrac{b^2+1}{(b-1)(b+1)} \cdot \dfrac{b-1}{b+1} = \dfrac{b^2+1}{b+1} \cdot \dfrac{1}{b+1} = \dfrac{b^2+1}{(b+1)^2}$

72. $\dfrac{\left(x-5\right)\left(x+3\right)}{3x-1} \cdot \dfrac{x\left(3x-1\right)}{\left(x-5\right)} = \dfrac{x+3}{1} \cdot \dfrac{x}{1} = x\left(x+3\right)$

73. $\dfrac{x^2-2x-35}{2x^3-3x^2} \cdot \dfrac{x^3-x^2}{2x-14} = \dfrac{(x-7)(x+5)}{x^2(2x-3)} \cdot \dfrac{x^2(x-1)}{2(x-7)} = \dfrac{x+5}{2x-3} \cdot \dfrac{x-1}{2} = \dfrac{(x-1)(x+5)}{2(2x-3)}$

74. $\dfrac{2x+4}{x+1} \cdot \dfrac{x^2+3x+2}{4x+2} = \dfrac{2(x+2)}{x+1} \cdot \dfrac{(x+1)(x+2)}{2(2x+1)} = \dfrac{x+2}{1} \cdot \dfrac{x+2}{2x+1} = \dfrac{(x+2)^2}{2x+1}$

75. $\dfrac{3n-9}{n^2-9} \cdot \left(n^3+27\right) = \dfrac{3(n-3) \cdot (n+3)\left(n^2-3n+9\right)}{(n+3)(n-3)} = \dfrac{3\left(n^2-3n+9\right)}{1} = 3\left(n^2-3n+9\right)$

76. $\left(10n+15\right) \cdot \dfrac{n+1}{6n+9} = \dfrac{5(2n+3)(n+1)}{3(2n+3)} = \dfrac{5(n+1)}{3}$

77. $\dfrac{3n-9}{n^2-9} \cdot \dfrac{n^3+27}{12} = \dfrac{3(n-3) \cdot (n+3)\left(n^2-3n+9\right)}{(n+3)(n-3) \cdot 12} = \dfrac{n^2-3n+9}{4}$

78. $\dfrac{10n+15}{n^2-1} \cdot \dfrac{n+1}{6n+9} = \dfrac{5(2n+3)(n+1)}{(n-1)(n+1) \cdot 3(2n+3)} = \dfrac{5}{3(n-1)}$

79. $\dfrac{x}{y} \cdot \dfrac{2y}{x} \cdot \dfrac{2}{xy} = \dfrac{x \cdot 2y \cdot 2}{y \cdot x \cdot xy} = \dfrac{4}{xy}$

80. $\dfrac{4z^2}{r^3} \cdot \dfrac{5r}{2z} \cdot \dfrac{r}{z} = \dfrac{4z^2 \cdot 5r \cdot r}{r^3 \cdot 2z \cdot z} = \dfrac{20r^2z^2}{2r^3z^2} = \dfrac{10}{r}$

81. $\dfrac{x-1}{y} \cdot \dfrac{y(x+y)}{2} \cdot \dfrac{y}{x+y} = \dfrac{(x-1) \cdot y^2(x+y)}{2y \cdot (x+y)} = \dfrac{y(x-1)}{2}$

82. $\dfrac{x}{y^2} \cdot \dfrac{y^3-y^2}{x+y} \cdot \dfrac{x^2+xy}{5x^2} = \dfrac{x \cdot y^2(y-1)x(x+y)}{y^2(x+y) \cdot 5x^2} = \dfrac{y-1}{5}$

83. $\dfrac{3x}{2} \div \dfrac{2x}{5} = \dfrac{3x}{2} \cdot \dfrac{5}{2x} = \dfrac{3}{2} \cdot \dfrac{5}{2} = \dfrac{15}{4}$

84. $\dfrac{x^2+x}{2x+6} \div \dfrac{x}{x+3} = \dfrac{x(x+1)}{2(x+3)} \cdot \dfrac{x+3}{x} = \dfrac{x+1}{2} \cdot \dfrac{1}{1} = \dfrac{x+1}{2}$

85. $\dfrac{8a^4}{3b} \div \dfrac{a^5}{9b^2} = \dfrac{8a^4}{3b} \cdot \dfrac{9b^2}{a^5} = \dfrac{8}{1} \cdot \dfrac{3b}{a} = \dfrac{24b}{a}$

86. $\dfrac{5m^4}{n^2} \div 5m = \dfrac{5m^4}{n^2} \cdot \dfrac{1}{5m} = \dfrac{m^3}{n^2} \cdot \dfrac{1}{1} = \dfrac{m^3}{n^2}$

87. $\left(2n+4\right) \div \dfrac{n+2}{n-1} = \dfrac{2(n+2)}{1} \cdot \dfrac{n-1}{n+2} = 2(n-1)$

88. $\dfrac{n+1}{n+3} \div \dfrac{n+1}{n+3} = \dfrac{n+1}{n+3} \cdot \dfrac{n+3}{n+1} = = \dfrac{1}{1} \cdot \dfrac{1}{1} = 1$

89. $\dfrac{6b}{b+2} \div \dfrac{3b^4}{2b+4} = \dfrac{6b}{b+2} \cdot \dfrac{2(b+2)}{3b^4} = \dfrac{2}{1} \cdot \dfrac{2}{b^3} = \dfrac{4}{b^3}$

90. $\dfrac{5x^5}{x-2} \div \dfrac{10x^3}{5x-10} = \dfrac{5x^5}{x-2} \cdot \dfrac{5(x-2)}{10x^3} = \dfrac{5x^2}{1} \cdot \dfrac{1}{2} = \dfrac{5x^2}{2}$

91. $\dfrac{3a+1}{a^7} \div \dfrac{a+1}{3a^8} = \dfrac{3a+1}{a^7} \cdot \dfrac{3a^8}{a+1} = \dfrac{3a+1}{1} \cdot \dfrac{3a}{a+1} = \dfrac{3a(3a+1)}{a+1}$

92. $\dfrac{16-x^2}{x+3} \div \dfrac{x+4}{9-x^2} = \dfrac{(4-x)(4+x)}{x+3} \cdot \dfrac{(3-x)(3+x)}{x+4} = \dfrac{4-x}{1} \cdot \dfrac{3-x}{1} = (4-x)(3-x) = (x-4)(x-3)$

93. $\dfrac{x+5}{x-x^3} \div \dfrac{25-x^2}{x^3} = \dfrac{x+5}{x(1-x^2)} \cdot \dfrac{x^3}{(5-x)(5+x)} = \dfrac{1}{1-x^2} \cdot \dfrac{x^2}{5-x} = \dfrac{x^2}{(x-5)(x^2-1)}$

94. $\dfrac{x^2+x-12}{2x^2-9x-5} \div \dfrac{x^2+7x+12}{2x^2-7x-4} = \dfrac{(x+4)(x-3)}{(2x+1)(x-5)} \cdot \dfrac{(2x+1)(x-4)}{(x+4)(x+3)} = \dfrac{x-3}{x-5} \cdot \dfrac{x-4}{x+3} = \dfrac{(x-4)(x-3)}{(x-5)(x+3)}$

95. $\dfrac{x^2-3x+2}{x^2+5x+6} \div \dfrac{x^2+x-2}{x^2+2x-3} = \dfrac{(x-2)(x-1)}{(x+2)(x+3)} \cdot \dfrac{(x+3)(x-1)}{(x+2)(x-1)} = \dfrac{(x-2)(x-1)}{(x+2)^2}$

96. $\dfrac{2x^2+x-1}{6x^2+x-2} \div \dfrac{2x^2+5x+3}{6x^2+13x+6} = \dfrac{(2x-1)(x+1)}{(3x+2)(2x-1)} \cdot \dfrac{(3x+2)(2x+3)}{(2x+3)(x+1)} = \dfrac{1}{1} = 1$

97. $\dfrac{x^2-4}{x^2+x-2} \div \dfrac{x-2}{x-1} = \dfrac{(x-2)(x+2)}{(x+2)(x-1)} \cdot \dfrac{x-1}{x-2} = 1$

98. $\dfrac{x^2+2x+1}{x-2} \div \dfrac{x+1}{2x-4} = \dfrac{(x+1)(x+1)}{x-2} \cdot \dfrac{2(x-2)}{x+1} = 2(x+1)$

99. $\dfrac{3y}{x^2} \div \dfrac{y^2}{x} \div \dfrac{y}{5x} = \dfrac{3y}{x^2} \cdot \dfrac{x}{y^2} \cdot \dfrac{5x}{y} = \dfrac{15x^2 y}{x^2 y^3} = \dfrac{15}{y^2}$

100. $\dfrac{x+1}{y-2} \div \dfrac{2x+2}{y-2} \div \dfrac{x}{y} = \dfrac{x+1}{y-2} \cdot \dfrac{y-2}{2(x+1)} \cdot \dfrac{y}{x} = \dfrac{y}{2x}$

101. $\dfrac{x-3}{x-1} \div \dfrac{x^2}{x-1} \div \dfrac{x-3}{x} = \dfrac{x-3}{x-1} \cdot \dfrac{x-1}{x^2} \cdot \dfrac{x}{x-3} = \dfrac{1}{x}$

102. $\dfrac{2x}{x-2} \div \dfrac{x+2}{x} \div \dfrac{7x}{x^2-4} = \dfrac{2x}{x-2} \cdot \dfrac{x}{x+2} \cdot \dfrac{(x-2)(x+2)}{7x} = \dfrac{2x}{7}$

Operations on Functions

103. $(fg)(x) = \dfrac{x+2}{x^2-3x+2} \cdot \dfrac{x-1}{x+2} = \dfrac{(x+2)(x-1)}{(x-2)(x-1)(x+2)} = \dfrac{1}{x-2}$

104. $(fg)(x) = \dfrac{2}{x^2-5x+4} \cdot \dfrac{x-4}{x+1} = \dfrac{2(x-4)}{(x-4)(x-1)(x+1)} = \dfrac{2}{x^2-1}$

105. $(f/g)(x) = \dfrac{x^2-1}{x+1} = \dfrac{(x-1)(x+1)}{x+1} = x-1$

106. $(f/g)(x) = \dfrac{2x-4}{5} \div \dfrac{4-2x}{15} = \dfrac{2x-4}{5} \cdot \dfrac{15}{-1(2x-4)} = -3$

Geometry

107. (a) $\dfrac{5x^2+12x+4}{x+2} = \dfrac{(5x+2)(x+2)}{x+2} = 5x+2$

   (b) If the width is 8 feet, $x+2=8 \Rightarrow x=6$. The length is $5(6)+2 = 32$ feet.

108.   (a) $\dfrac{x^2-1}{x-1} = \dfrac{(x-1)(x+1)}{x-1} = x+1$

(b) $15+1=16$ and $15-1=14$. The dimensions are 14 by 16. The area is $14 \cdot 16 = 224$ square units.

109.   (a) $\dfrac{4x^3+4x^2+x}{x} = 4x^2+4x+1$

(b)   Since $4x^2+4x+1 = (2x+1)^2$, a side of the bottom is $2(10)+1 = 21$. The dimensions are 21 by 21 by 10.

110.   One half of the height is $\dfrac{6x^2-x-15}{2x+3} = \dfrac{(3x-5)(2x+3)}{2x+3} = 3x-5$. The height is $2(3x-5)$.

Checking Basic Concepts for Sections 6.1 & 6.2

1.   (a) $f(2) = \dfrac{(2)}{(2)-1} = \dfrac{2}{1} = 2$

(b)   The denominator cannot equal zero, so $x-1 \neq 0$. The domain is $\{x \mid x \neq 1\}$.

(c)   See Figure 1. Vertical asymptote: $x = 1$.

Figure 1

2.   (a) $\dfrac{6}{2x+3} = 3 \Rightarrow 6 = 3(2x+3) \Rightarrow 6 = 6x+9 \Rightarrow 6x = -3 \Rightarrow x = -\dfrac{1}{2}$

(b) $\dfrac{2}{x-1} = x \Rightarrow 2 = x(x-1) \Rightarrow x^2-x-2 = 0 \Rightarrow (x+1)(x-2) = 0 \Rightarrow x = -1$ or $x = 2$

3. $\dfrac{x^2-6x-7}{x^2-1} = \dfrac{(x-7)(x+1)}{(x-1)(x+1)} = \dfrac{x-7}{x-1}$

4.   (a) $\dfrac{2x^2}{x^2-1} \cdot \dfrac{x+1}{4x} = \dfrac{2x^2}{(x-1)(x+1)} \cdot \dfrac{x+1}{4x} = \dfrac{x}{x-1} \cdot \dfrac{1}{2} = \dfrac{x}{2(x-1)}$

(b) $\dfrac{1}{x-2} \div \dfrac{3}{(x-2)(x+3)} = \dfrac{1}{x-2} \cdot \dfrac{(x-2)(x+3)}{3} = \dfrac{1}{1} \cdot \dfrac{x+3}{3} = \dfrac{x+3}{3}$

6.3: Addition and Subtraction of Rational Expressions

Concepts

1.   18

2.   18

3. $(x-5)(x+5)$

4. $(x-5)(x+5)$

5.   A common denominator

6.   A common denominator

7. $\dfrac{a+b}{c}$

8. $\dfrac{a-b}{c}$

Least Common Multiples

9. $10 = 2 \cdot 5$ and $15 = 3 \cdot 5$, the LCM is $2 \cdot 3 \cdot 5 = 30$.

10. $9 = 3 \cdot 3$ and $12 = 2 \cdot 2 \cdot 3$, the LCM is $2 \cdot 2 \cdot 3 \cdot 3 = 36$.

11. $34 = 2 \cdot 17$ and $51 = 3 \cdot 17$, the LCM is $2 \cdot 3 \cdot 17 = 102$.

12. $24 = 2 \cdot 2 \cdot 2 \cdot 3$ and $36 = 2 \cdot 2 \cdot 3 \cdot 3$, the LCM is $2 \cdot 2 \cdot 2 \cdot 3 \cdot 3 = 72$.

13. $6a = 2 \cdot 3 \cdot a$ and $9a^2 = 3 \cdot 3 \cdot a \cdot a$, the LCM is $2 \cdot 3 \cdot 3 \cdot a \cdot a = 18a^2$.

14. $12ab = 2 \cdot 2 \cdot 3 \cdot a \cdot b$ and $6a^2 = 2 \cdot 3 \cdot a \cdot a$, the LCM is $2 \cdot 2 \cdot 3 \cdot a \cdot a \cdot b = 12a^2b$.

15. $10x^2 = 2 \cdot 5 \cdot x \cdot x$ and $25\left(x^2 - x\right) = 5 \cdot 5 \cdot x \cdot (x-1)$, the LCM is $2 \cdot 5 \cdot 5 \cdot x \cdot x \cdot (x-1) = 50x^2(x-1)$.

16. $x^2 - 4 = (x-2) \cdot (x+2)$ and $x^2 + 2x = x \cdot (x+2)$, the LCM is $x \cdot (x-2) \cdot (x+2) = x(x-2)(x+2)$.

17. $x^2 + 2x + 1 = (x+1) \cdot (x+1)$ and $x^2 - 4x - 5 = (x-5) \cdot (x+1)$, the LCM is $(x-5)(x+1)^2$.

18. $4x^2 + 20x + 25 = (2x+5) \cdot (2x+5)$ and $2x^2 + 5x = x \cdot (2x+5)$, the LCM is $x(2x+5)^2$.

19.   The LCM is $(x+y)(x-y)$.

20. $(x-y)^2 = (x-y)(x-y)$ and $x^2 - y^2 = (x+y)(x-y)$, the LCM is $(x-y)(x-y)(x+y) = (x-y)^2(x+y)$.

Review of Fractions

21. $\dfrac{1}{7} + \dfrac{4}{7} = \dfrac{5}{7}$

22. $\dfrac{2}{5} + \dfrac{1}{2} = \dfrac{4}{10} + \dfrac{5}{10} = \dfrac{9}{10}$

23. $\dfrac{2}{3} + \dfrac{5}{6} + \dfrac{1}{4} = \dfrac{8}{12} + \dfrac{10}{12} + \dfrac{3}{12} = \dfrac{21}{12} = \dfrac{7}{4}$

24. $\dfrac{3}{11} + \dfrac{1}{2} + \dfrac{1}{6} = \dfrac{18}{66} + \dfrac{33}{66} + \dfrac{11}{66} = \dfrac{62}{66} = \dfrac{31}{33}$

25. $\dfrac{1}{10} - \dfrac{3}{10} = \dfrac{-2}{10} = -\dfrac{1}{5}$

26. $\dfrac{2}{9} - \dfrac{1}{11} = \dfrac{22}{99} - \dfrac{9}{99} = \dfrac{13}{99}$

27. $\dfrac{3}{2} - \dfrac{1}{8} = \dfrac{12}{8} - \dfrac{1}{8} = \dfrac{11}{8}$

28. $\dfrac{3}{12} - \dfrac{5}{16} = \dfrac{12}{48} - \dfrac{15}{48} = \dfrac{-3}{48} = -\dfrac{1}{16}$

Addition and Subtraction of Rational Expressions

29. $\dfrac{1}{x} + \dfrac{3}{x} = \dfrac{4}{x}$

30. $\dfrac{2}{x-1} + \dfrac{x}{x-1} = \dfrac{2+x}{x-1}$

31. $\dfrac{2}{x^2-4} - \dfrac{x+1}{x^2-4} = \dfrac{2-(x+1)}{x^2-4} = \dfrac{1-x}{x^2-4}$

32. $\dfrac{2x-1}{x^2+6} - \dfrac{2x+1}{x^2+6} = \dfrac{2x-1-(2x+1)}{x^2+6} = -\dfrac{2}{x^2+6}$

33. $\dfrac{4}{x^2} + \dfrac{5}{x^2} = \dfrac{9}{x^2}$

34. $\dfrac{8}{b^3} - \dfrac{5}{b^3} = \dfrac{3}{b^3}$

35. $\dfrac{4}{xy} - \dfrac{7}{xy} = -\dfrac{3}{xy}$

36. $\dfrac{9}{a^2 b} + \dfrac{1}{a^2 b} = \dfrac{10}{a^2 b}$

37. $\dfrac{x}{x+1} + \dfrac{1}{x+1} = \dfrac{x+1}{x+1} = 1$

38. $\dfrac{1}{2x-1} - \dfrac{2x}{2x-1} = \dfrac{1-2x}{2x-1} = -1$

39. $\dfrac{2z}{4-z} - \dfrac{3z-4}{4-z} = \dfrac{2z-(3z-4)}{4-z} = \dfrac{-z+4}{4-z} = \dfrac{4-z}{4-z} = 1$

40. $\dfrac{z}{z^2-9} - \dfrac{3}{z^2-9} = \dfrac{z-3}{z^2-9} = \dfrac{z-3}{(z-3)(z+3)} = \dfrac{1}{z+3}$

41. $\dfrac{4r}{5t^2} + \dfrac{r}{5t^2} = \dfrac{4r+r}{5t^2} = \dfrac{5r}{5t^2} = \dfrac{r}{t^2}$

42. $\dfrac{1}{2ab} + \dfrac{1}{2ab} = \dfrac{1+1}{2ab} = \dfrac{2}{2ab} = \dfrac{1}{ab}$

43. $\dfrac{3t}{t^2-t-6} + \dfrac{2-2t}{t^2-t-6} = \dfrac{3t+2-2t}{t^2-t-6} = \dfrac{t+2}{(t-3)(t+2)} = \dfrac{1}{t-3}$

44. $\dfrac{t}{t^2+5t}+\dfrac{5}{t^2+5t}=\dfrac{t+5}{t^2+5t}=\dfrac{t+5}{t(t+5)}=\dfrac{1}{t}$

45. $\dfrac{5b}{3a}-\dfrac{7b}{5a}=\dfrac{5b\cdot5}{15a}-\dfrac{7b\cdot3}{15a}=\dfrac{25b-21b}{15a}=\dfrac{4b}{15a}$

46. $\dfrac{a}{ab^2}-\dfrac{b}{a^2b}=\dfrac{a\cdot a}{a^2b^2}-\dfrac{b\cdot b}{a^2b^2}=\dfrac{a^2-b^2}{a^2b^2}$

47. $\dfrac{4}{n-4}+\dfrac{3}{2-n}=\dfrac{4}{n-4}-\dfrac{3}{n-2}=\dfrac{4(n-2)}{(n-4)(n-2)}-\dfrac{3(n-4)}{(n-4)(n-2)}=\dfrac{4n-8-3n+12}{(n-4)(n-2)}=\dfrac{n+4}{(n-4)(n-2)}$

48. $\dfrac{3}{2n-1}-\dfrac{3}{1-2n}=\dfrac{3}{2n-1}+\dfrac{3}{2n-1}=\dfrac{6}{2n-1}$

49. $\dfrac{x}{x+4}-\dfrac{x+1}{x}=\dfrac{x^2}{x(x+4)}-\dfrac{(x+1)(x+4)}{x(x+4)}=\dfrac{x^2-\left(x^2+5x+4\right)}{x(x+4)}=\dfrac{-5x-4}{x(x+4)}$

50. $\dfrac{4x}{x+2}+\dfrac{x-5}{x-2}=\dfrac{4x(x-2)}{(x+2)(x-2)}+\dfrac{(x+2)(x-5)}{(x+2)(x-2)}=\dfrac{4x^2-8x+x^2-3x-10}{(x+2)(x-2)}=\dfrac{5x^2-11x-10}{(x+2)(x-2)}$

51. $\dfrac{2}{x^2}-\dfrac{4x-1}{x}=\dfrac{2}{x^2}-\dfrac{x(4x-1)}{x^2}=\dfrac{2-\left(4x^2-x\right)}{x^2}=\dfrac{-4x^2+x+2}{x^2}$

52. $\dfrac{2x}{x-5}-\dfrac{x}{x+5}=\dfrac{2x(x+5)}{(x-5)(x+5)}-\dfrac{x(x-5)}{(x-5)(x+5)}=\dfrac{2x^2+10x-\left(x^2-5x\right)}{(x-5)(x+5)}=\dfrac{x(x+15)}{(x-5)(x+5)}$

53. $\dfrac{x+3}{x-5}+\dfrac{5}{x-3}=\dfrac{(x+3)(x-3)}{(x-5)(x-3)}+\dfrac{5(x-5)}{(x-5)(x-3)}=\dfrac{x^2-9+5x-25}{(x-5)(x-3)}=\dfrac{x^2+5x-34}{(x-5)(x-3)}$

54. $\dfrac{x}{2x-1}+\dfrac{1-x}{3x}=\dfrac{3x^2}{3x(2x-1)}+\dfrac{(1-x)(2x-1)}{3x(2x-1)}=\dfrac{3x^2-2x^2+3x-1}{3x(2x-1)}=\dfrac{x^2+3x-1}{3x(2x-1)}$

55. $\dfrac{4n}{n^2-9}-\dfrac{8}{n-3}=\dfrac{4n}{(n-3)(n+3)}-\dfrac{8(n+3)}{(n-3)(n+3)}=\dfrac{4n-8n-24}{(n-3)(n+3)}=-\dfrac{4(n+6)}{(n-3)(n+3)}$

56. $\dfrac{3n}{(4n-3)^2}-\dfrac{1}{4n-3}=\dfrac{3n}{(4n-3)^2}-\dfrac{1(4n-3)}{(4n-3)^2}=\dfrac{3n-4n+3}{(4n-3)^2}=\dfrac{3-n}{(4n-3)^2}$

57. $\dfrac{x}{x^2-9}+\dfrac{5x}{x-3}=\dfrac{x}{(x-3)(x+3)}+\dfrac{5x(x+3)}{(x-3)(x+3)}=\dfrac{x+5x^2+15x}{(x-3)(x+3)}=\dfrac{x(5x+16)}{(x-3)(x+3)}$

58. $\dfrac{a^2+1}{a^2-1}+\dfrac{a}{1-a^2}=\dfrac{a^2+1}{a^2-1}-\dfrac{a}{a^2-1}=\dfrac{a^2+1-a}{a^2-1}=\dfrac{a^2-a+1}{(a-1)(a+1)}$

59. $\dfrac{b}{2b-4}-\dfrac{b-1}{b-2}=\dfrac{b}{2(b-2)}-\dfrac{2(b-1)}{2(b-2)}=\dfrac{b-(2b-2)}{2(b-2)}=\dfrac{-(b-2)}{2(b-2)}=-\dfrac{1}{2}$

60. $\dfrac{y^2}{2-y} - \dfrac{y}{y^2-4} = \dfrac{-y^2(y+2)}{(y-2)(y+2)} - \dfrac{y}{(y-2)(y+2)} = \dfrac{-y^3-2y^2-y}{(y-2)(y+2)} = \dfrac{-y(y+1)^2}{(y-2)(y+2)}$

61. $\dfrac{2x}{x-5} + \dfrac{2x-1}{3x^2-16x+5} = \dfrac{2x(3x-1)}{(x-5)(3x-1)} + \dfrac{2x-1}{(x-5)(3x-1)} = \dfrac{6x^2-2x+2x-1}{(x-5)(3x-1)} = \dfrac{6x^2-1}{(x-5)(3x-1)}$

62. $\dfrac{x+3}{2x-1} + \dfrac{3}{10x^2-5x} = \dfrac{5x(x+3)}{5x(2x-1)} + \dfrac{3}{5x(2x-1)} = \dfrac{5x^2+15x+3}{5x(2x-1)}$

63. $\dfrac{4x}{x-y} - \dfrac{9}{x+y} = \dfrac{4x(x+y)}{(x-y)(x+y)} - \dfrac{9(x-y)}{(x-y)(x+y)} = \dfrac{4x^2+4xy-(9x-9y)}{(x-y)(x+y)} = \dfrac{4x^2+4xy-9x+9y}{(x-y)(x+y)}$

64. $\dfrac{1}{a-b} - \dfrac{3a}{a^2-b^2} = \dfrac{a+b}{(a-b)(a+b)} - \dfrac{3a}{(a-b)(a+b)} = \dfrac{a+b-3a}{(a-b)(a+b)} = \dfrac{b-2a}{(a-b)(a+b)}$

65. $\dfrac{3}{(x-1)(x-2)} + \dfrac{4x}{(x+1)(x-2)} = \dfrac{3(x+1)}{(x-2)(x-1)(x+1)} + \dfrac{4x(x-1)}{(x-2)(x-1)(x+1)}$

$= \dfrac{3x+3+4x^2-4x}{(x-2)(x-1)(x+1)} = \dfrac{4x^2-x+3}{(x-2)(x-1)(x+1)}$

66. $\dfrac{x}{(x-1)^2} - \dfrac{1}{(x-1)(x+3)} = \dfrac{x(x+3)}{(x-1)^2(x+3)} - \dfrac{1(x-1)}{(x-1)^2(x+3)}$

$= \dfrac{x^2+3x-x+1}{(x-1)^2(x+3)} = \dfrac{x^2+2x+1}{(x-1)^2(x+3)} = \dfrac{(x+1)^2}{(x-1)^2(x+3)}$

67. $\dfrac{3}{x^2-x-6} - \dfrac{2}{x^2+5x+6} = \dfrac{3}{(x-3)(x+2)} - \dfrac{2}{(x+3)(x+2)}$

$= \dfrac{3(x+3)}{(x-3)(x+2)(x+3)} - \dfrac{2(x-3)}{(x-3)(x+2)(x+3)} = \dfrac{3x+9-2x+6}{(x-3)(x+2)(x+3)}$

$= \dfrac{x+15}{(x-3)(x+2)(x+3)}$

68. $\dfrac{x}{x^2-5x+4} + \dfrac{2}{x^2-2x-8} = \dfrac{x}{(x-4)(x-1)} + \dfrac{2}{(x-4)(x+2)}$

$= \dfrac{x(x+2)}{(x-4)(x-1)(x+2)} + \dfrac{2(x-1)}{(x-4)(x-1)(x+2)} = \dfrac{x^2+2x+2x-2}{(x-4)(x-1)(x+2)}$

$= \dfrac{x^2+4x-2}{(x-4)(x-1)(x+2)}$

69. $\dfrac{3}{x^2-2x+1} + \dfrac{1}{x^2-3x+2} = \dfrac{3(x-2)}{(x-2)(x-1)^2} + \dfrac{x-1}{(x-2)(x-1)^2} = \dfrac{3x-6+x-1}{(x-2)(x-1)^2} = \dfrac{4x-7}{(x-2)(x-1)^2}$

70. $\dfrac{x}{x^2-4} - \dfrac{1}{x^2+4x+4} = \dfrac{x(x+2)}{(x-2)(x+2)^2} - \dfrac{x-2}{(x-2)(x+2)^2} = \dfrac{x^2+2x-(x-2)}{(x-2)(x+2)^2} = \dfrac{x^2+x+2}{(x-2)(x+2)^2}$

71. $\dfrac{3x}{x^2+2x-3}+\dfrac{1}{x^2-2x+1}=\dfrac{3x(x-1)}{(x+3)(x-1)(x-1)}+\dfrac{1(x+3)}{(x+3)(x-1)(x-1)}=\dfrac{3x^2-2x+3}{(x+3)(x-1)^2}$

72. $\dfrac{3x}{x-y}-\dfrac{3y}{x^2-2xy+y^2}=\dfrac{3x(x-y)}{(x-y)^2}-\dfrac{3y}{(x-y)^2}=\dfrac{3x^2-3xy-3y}{(x-y)^2}=\dfrac{3(x^2-xy-y)}{(x-y)^2}$

73. $\dfrac{4c}{ab}+\dfrac{3b}{ac}-\dfrac{2a}{bc}=\dfrac{4c^2}{abc}+\dfrac{3b^2}{abc}-\dfrac{2a^2}{abc}=\dfrac{4c^2+3b^2-2a^2}{abc}=\dfrac{-2a^2+3b^2+4c^2}{abc}$

74. $x+\dfrac{1}{x-1}-\dfrac{1}{x+1}=\dfrac{x(x-1)(x+1)}{(x-1)(x+1)}+\dfrac{1(x+1)}{(x-1)(x+1)}-\dfrac{1(x-1)}{(x-1)(x+1)}=\dfrac{x^3-x+x+1-x+1}{(x-1)(x+1)}=\dfrac{x^3-x+2}{(x-1)(x+1)}$

75. $5-\dfrac{6}{n^2-36}+\dfrac{3}{n-6}=\dfrac{5(n-6)(n+6)}{(n-6)(n+6)}-\dfrac{6}{(n-6)(n+6)}+\dfrac{3(n+6)}{(n-6)(n+6)}$

$=\dfrac{5n^2-180-6+3n+18}{(n-6)(n+6)}=\dfrac{5n^2+3n-168}{(n-6)(n+6)}$

76. $\dfrac{6}{t-1}+\dfrac{2}{t-2}+\dfrac{1}{t}=\dfrac{6t(t-2)}{t(t-2)(t-1)}+\dfrac{2t(t-1)}{t(t-2)(t-1)}+\dfrac{1(t-2)(t-1)}{t(t-2)(t-1)}$

$=\dfrac{6t^2-12t+2t^2-2t+t^2-3t+2}{t(t-2)(t-1)}=\dfrac{9t^2-17t+2}{t(t-2)(t-1)}$

77. $\dfrac{3}{x-5}-\dfrac{1}{x-3}-\dfrac{2x}{x-5}=\dfrac{3(x-3)}{(x-5)(x-3)}-\dfrac{x-5}{(x-5)(x-3)}-\dfrac{2x(x-3)}{(x-5)(x-3)}=\dfrac{-2(x^2-4x+2)}{(x-5)(x-3)}$

78. $\dfrac{2x+1}{x-1}-\dfrac{3}{x+1}+\dfrac{x}{x-1}=\dfrac{(2x+1)(x+1)}{(x-1)(x+1)}-\dfrac{3(x-1)}{(x-1)(x+1)}+\dfrac{x(x+1)}{(x-1)(x+1)}=\dfrac{3x^2+x+4}{(x-1)(x+1)}$

79. $\dfrac{5}{2x-3}+\dfrac{x}{x+1}-\dfrac{x}{2x-3}=\dfrac{5(x+1)}{(x+1)(2x-3)}+\dfrac{x(2x-3)}{(x+1)(2x-3)}-\dfrac{x(x+1)}{(x+1)(2x-3)}$

$=\dfrac{5x+5+2x^2-3x-x^2-x}{(x+1)(2x-3)}=\dfrac{x^2+x+5}{(x+1)(2x-3)}$

80. $\dfrac{1}{x-3}-\dfrac{2}{x+3}+\dfrac{x}{x^2-9}=\dfrac{1(x+3)}{(x-3)(x+3)}-\dfrac{2(x-3)}{(x-3)(x+3)}+\dfrac{x}{(x-3)(x+3)}$

$=\dfrac{x+3-2x+6+x}{(x-3)(x+3)}=\dfrac{9}{(x-3)(x+3)}$

81. $\dfrac{1}{x-1}-\dfrac{2}{x+1}+\dfrac{x}{x^2-1}=\dfrac{1(x+1)}{(x-1)(x+1)}-\dfrac{2(x-1)}{(x-1)(x+1)}+\dfrac{x}{(x-1)(x+1)}$

$=\dfrac{x+1-2x+2+x}{(x-1)(x+1)}=\dfrac{3}{(x-1)(x+1)}$

82. $\dfrac{2}{x-2}+\dfrac{1}{x+3}-\dfrac{1}{x-1}=\dfrac{2(x+3)(x-1)}{(x-2)(x-1)(x+3)}+\dfrac{(x-2)(x-1)}{(x-2)(x-1)(x+3)}$

$$-\frac{(x-2)(x+3)}{(x-2)(x-1)(x+3)} = \frac{2x^2+4x-6+x^2-3x+2-x^2-x+6}{(x-2)(x-1)(x+3)}$$

$$= \frac{2x^2+2}{(x-2)(x-1)(x+3)}$$

83. $\dfrac{a-b}{a+b} + \dfrac{a+b}{a-b} = \dfrac{(a-b)(a-b)}{(a+b)(a-b)} + \dfrac{(a+b)(a+b)}{(a+b)(a-b)} = \dfrac{a^2-2ab+b^2+a^2+2ab+b^2}{(a+b)(a-b)}$

$$= \frac{2a^2+2b^2}{(a+b)(a-b)}$$

84. $\dfrac{1}{a^2-b^2} - \dfrac{1}{a^2+b^2} = \dfrac{a^2+b^2}{(a^2-b^2)(a^2+b^2)} - \dfrac{a^2-b^2}{(a^2-b^2)(a^2+b^2)}$

$$= \frac{2b^2}{a^4-b^4}$$

Addition and Subtraction of Functions

85. $(f+g)(x) = \dfrac{1}{x+1} + \dfrac{x}{x+1} = \dfrac{1+x}{x+1} = 1$

$(f-g)(x) = \dfrac{1}{x+1} - \dfrac{x}{x+1} = \dfrac{1-x}{x+1}$

86. $(f+g)(x) = \dfrac{1}{2x} + \dfrac{3}{4x} = \dfrac{2}{4x} + \dfrac{3}{4x} = \dfrac{5}{4x}$

$(f-g)(x) = \dfrac{1}{2x} - \dfrac{3}{4x} = \dfrac{2}{4x} - \dfrac{3}{4x} = -\dfrac{1}{4x}$

87. $(f+g)(x) = \dfrac{1}{x+2} + \dfrac{1}{x-2} = \dfrac{x-2}{(x-2)(x+2)} + \dfrac{x+2}{(x-2)(x+2)} = \dfrac{2x}{(x-2)(x+2)}$

$(f-g)(x) = \dfrac{1}{x+2} - \dfrac{1}{x-2} = \dfrac{x-2}{(x-2)(x+2)} - \dfrac{x+2}{(x-2)(x+2)} = \dfrac{-4}{(x-2)(x+2)}$

88. $(f+g)(x) = \dfrac{1}{x+1} + \dfrac{1}{x} = \dfrac{x}{x(x+1)} + \dfrac{x+1}{x(x+1)} = \dfrac{2x+1}{x(x+1)}$

$(f-g)(x) = \dfrac{1}{x+1} - \dfrac{1}{x} = \dfrac{x}{x(x+1)} - \dfrac{x+1}{x(x+1)} = \dfrac{-1}{x(x+1)}$

Applications

89. Find the LCM of 12 and 30: $12 = 2 \cdot 2 \cdot 3$ and $30 = 2 \cdot 3 \cdot 5$, so the LCM is $2 \cdot 2 \cdot 3 \cdot 5 = 60$. The planets will be in alignment in 60 years.

90. Find the LCM of 6 and 10: $6 = 2 \cdot 3$ and $10 = 2 \cdot 5$, so the LCM is $2 \cdot 3 \cdot 5 = 30$. They work on the same day again in 30 days.

91. $\dfrac{1}{R} = \dfrac{1}{80} + \dfrac{1}{300} = \dfrac{30}{2400} + \dfrac{8}{2400} = \dfrac{38}{2400} = \dfrac{19}{1200}$ and so $R = \dfrac{1200}{19} \approx 63.2$ ohms

92. $\dfrac{1}{R} = \dfrac{1}{R_1} + \dfrac{1}{R_2} \Rightarrow RR_1R_2 \cdot \dfrac{1}{R} = \left(\dfrac{1}{R_1} + \dfrac{1}{R_2}\right) \cdot RR_1R_2 \Rightarrow R_1R_2 = R(R_1 + R_2) \Rightarrow R = \dfrac{R_1R_2}{R_1 + R_2}$

$R = \dfrac{80(300)}{80 + 300} = \dfrac{24,000}{380} = \dfrac{1200}{19} \approx 63.2$ ohms. The answers are the same.

93. $\dfrac{1}{S} = \dfrac{1}{0.1} - \dfrac{1}{10} \Rightarrow \dfrac{1}{S} = 10 - 0.1 \Rightarrow \dfrac{1}{S} = 9.9 \Rightarrow S = \dfrac{1}{9.9} \approx 0.101$ feet, or about 1.2 inches.

94. No, if $D < F$, we have that $\dfrac{1}{D} > \dfrac{1}{F}$ and so $\dfrac{1}{F} - \dfrac{1}{D} < 0$. That is, S must be negative. This is impossible.

95. $\dfrac{8}{d^2} + \dfrac{8}{d^2} = \dfrac{16}{d^2}$ W/m^2

96. $\dfrac{8}{d^2} + \dfrac{8}{(0.5d)^2} = \dfrac{8}{d^2} + \dfrac{8}{0.25d^2} = \dfrac{8}{d^2} + \dfrac{32}{d^2} = \dfrac{40}{d^2}$ W/m^2

6.4: Rational Equations

Concepts

1. Multiply each side by $x + 2$.

2. Multiply each side by the LCD.

3. $\dfrac{1}{2}$

4. bc

5. LCD

6. intersect

Solving Rational Equations

7. The factored denominators are x and 5. The LCD is $5x$.

8. The factored denominators are $x-1$ and $x+5$. The LCD is $(x-1)(x+5)$.

9. The factored denominators are $x-1$ and $(x-1)(x+1)$. The LCD is $(x-1)(x+1) = x^2 - 1$.

10. The factored denominators are $x(x-1)$ and $2x$. The LCD is $2x(x-1)$.

11. The factored denominators are 2 and $2x+1$ and $2(x-2)$. The LCD is $2(2x+1)(x-2)$.

12. The factored denominators are x and $x(x-4)$ and $2x$. The LCD is $2x(x-4)$.

13. The LCD is 6. The first step is to multiply both sides of the equation by the LCD.

$6 \cdot \left(\dfrac{x}{3} + \dfrac{1}{2}\right) = \dfrac{5}{6} \cdot 6 \Rightarrow 2x + 3 = 5 \Rightarrow 2x = 2 \Rightarrow x = \dfrac{2}{2} = 1$

14. The LCD is 8. The first step is to multiply both sides of the equation by the LCD.

$8 \cdot \left(\dfrac{7}{8} - \dfrac{x}{4}\right) = -\dfrac{11}{8} \cdot 8 \Rightarrow 7 - 2x = -11 \Rightarrow -2x = -18 \Rightarrow x = \dfrac{18}{2} = 9$

15. The LCD is $15x$. The first step is to multiply both sides of the equation by the LCD.

$$15x \cdot \left(\frac{2}{x} - \frac{7}{3}\right) = -\frac{29}{15} \cdot 15x \Rightarrow 30 - 35x = -29x \Rightarrow 30 = 6x \Rightarrow x = \frac{30}{6} = 5$$

16. The LCD is $15x$. The first step is to multiply both sides of the equation by the LCD.

$$15x \cdot \left(\frac{1}{3x} + \frac{1}{x}\right) = \frac{4}{15} \cdot 15x \Rightarrow 5 + 15 = 4x \Rightarrow 20 = 4x \Rightarrow x = \frac{20}{4} = 5$$

17. The LCD is $3(x-1)$. The first step is to multiply both sides of the equation by the LCD.

$$3(x-1) \cdot \frac{x}{x-1} = \frac{4}{3} \cdot 3(x-1) \Rightarrow 3x = 4x - 4 \Rightarrow x = 4$$

18. The LCD is $5x(x+1)$. The first step is to multiply both sides of the equation by the LCD.

$$5x(x+1) \cdot \frac{4}{5x} = -\frac{1}{x+1} \cdot 5x(x+1) \Rightarrow 4x + 4 = -5x \Rightarrow 9x = -4 \Rightarrow x = -\frac{4}{9}$$

19. The LCD is $6x$. The first step is to multiply both sides of the equation by the LCD.

$$6x \cdot \frac{1}{2x} - 6x \cdot \frac{5}{3x} = 1 \cdot 6x \Rightarrow 3 - 10 = 6x \Rightarrow -7 = 6x \Rightarrow x = -\frac{7}{6}$$

20. The LCD is $12x$. The first step is to multiply both sides of the equation by the LCD.

$$12x \cdot \frac{3}{4x} + 12x \cdot \frac{5}{6x} = -\frac{19}{12} \cdot 12x \Rightarrow 9 + 10 = -19x \Rightarrow 19 = -19x \Rightarrow x = -1$$

21. The LCD is $x+1$. The first step is to multiply both sides of the equation by the LCD.

$$(x+1) \cdot \frac{1}{x+1} - (x+1)(1) = \frac{3}{x+1} \cdot (x+1) \Rightarrow 1 - x - 1 = 3 \Rightarrow -x = 3 \Rightarrow x = -3$$

22. The LCD is $x-2$. The first step is to multiply both sides of the equation by the LCD.

$$(x-2) \cdot \frac{2}{x-2} + (x-2)(2) = \frac{4}{x-2} \cdot (x-2) \Rightarrow 2 + 2x - 4 = 4$$

$$\Rightarrow 2x - 2 = 4 \Rightarrow 2x = 6 \Rightarrow x = 3$$

23. The LCD is $x-3$. The first step is to multiply both sides of the equation by the LCD.

$$(x-3) \cdot \frac{1}{x-3} + (x-3) \cdot \frac{x}{x-3} = \frac{2x}{x-3} \cdot (x-3) \Rightarrow 1 + x = 2x \Rightarrow x = 1$$

24. The LCD is $x+2$. The first step is to multiply both sides of the equation by the LCD.

$$(x+2) \cdot \frac{6}{x+2} + (x+2) \cdot \frac{3x}{x+2} = \frac{3}{x+2} \cdot (x+2) \Rightarrow 6 + 3x = 3 \Rightarrow 3x = -3 \Rightarrow x = -1$$

25. The LCD is $(x-1)(x+4)$. The first step is to multiply both sides of the equation by the LCD.

$$(x-1)(x+4) \cdot \frac{3}{x-1} = \frac{6}{x+4} \cdot (x-1)(x+4) \Rightarrow 3x + 12 = 6x - 6 \Rightarrow 18 = 3x \Rightarrow x = \frac{18}{3} = 6$$

26. The LCD is $(x+5)(2x+1)$. The first step is to multiply both sides of the equation by the LCD.

$$(x+5)(2x+1) \cdot \frac{1}{x+5} = \frac{2}{2x+1} \cdot (x+5)(2x+1) \Rightarrow 2x + 1 = 2x + 10 \Rightarrow 1 = 10 \Rightarrow \text{ No solutions.}$$

27.   The LCD is $(3z+4)(2z-5)$. The first step is to multiply both sides of the equation by the LCD.

$$(3z+4)(2z-5)\cdot\frac{6}{3z+4}=\frac{4}{2z-5}\cdot(3z+4)(2z-5)\Rightarrow 12z-30=12z+16\Rightarrow -30=16\Rightarrow \text{No solutions.}$$

28.   The LCD is $(z-1)(z+1)$. The first step is to multiply both sides of the equation by the LCD.

$$(z-1)(z+1)\cdot\frac{2}{z-1}-(z-1)(z+1)\cdot\frac{5}{z+1}=\frac{4}{z^2-1}\cdot(z-1)(z+1)\Rightarrow$$

$$2z+2-5z+5=4\Rightarrow -3z+7=4\Rightarrow -3z=-3\Rightarrow z=1$$

Some expressions in the original equation are not defined when $z=1$. No solutions.

29.   The LCD is $(t-1)(t+2)$. The first step is to multiply both sides of the equation by the LCD.

$$(t-1)(t+2)\cdot\frac{5}{t-1}+(t-1)(t+2)\cdot\frac{2}{t+2}=\frac{15}{t^2+t-2}\cdot(t-1)(t+2)\Rightarrow$$

$$5t+10+2t-2=15\Rightarrow 7t+8=15\Rightarrow 7t=7\Rightarrow t=1$$

Some expressions in the original equation are not defined when $t=1$. No solutions.

30.   The LCD is $5t(t+1)$. The first step is to multiply both sides of the equation by the LCD.

$$5t(t+1)\cdot\frac{3}{5t}-5t(t+1)\cdot\frac{1}{t+1}=\frac{6}{5t^2+5t}\cdot 5t(t+1)\Rightarrow 3t+3-5t=6\Rightarrow -2t=3\Rightarrow t=-\frac{3}{2}$$

31.   The LCD is $6n$. The first step is to multiply both sides of the equation by the LCD.

$$6n\cdot\frac{1}{3n}-6n\cdot 2=\frac{1}{2n}\cdot 6n\Rightarrow 2-12n=3\Rightarrow -12n=1\Rightarrow n=-\frac{1}{12}$$

32.   The LCD is $3n$. The first step is to multiply both sides of the equation by the LCD.

$$3n\cdot\frac{4}{n}-3n\cdot 3=\frac{1}{3n}\cdot 3n\Rightarrow 12-9n=1\Rightarrow -9n=-11\Rightarrow n=\frac{11}{9}$$

33.   The LCD is x^2. The first step is to multiply both sides of the equation by the LCD.

$$x^2\cdot\left(\frac{1}{x}+\frac{1}{x^2}\right)=2\cdot x^2\Rightarrow x+1=2x^2\Rightarrow 2x^2-x-1=0\Rightarrow (2x+1)(x-1)=0\Rightarrow x=-\frac{1}{2}\text{ or }1$$

34.   The LCD is $56x(x+1)$. The first step is to multiply both sides of the equation by the LCD.

$$56x(x+1)\cdot\left(\frac{1}{x}-\frac{1}{x+1}\right)=\frac{1}{56}\cdot 56x(x+1)\Rightarrow 56x+56-56x=x(x+1)\Rightarrow 56=x^2+x\Rightarrow$$

$$x^2+x-56=0\Rightarrow (x+8)(x-7)=0\Rightarrow x=-8\text{ or }7$$

35.   The LCD is $(x+2)(x-3)$. The first step is to multiply both sides of the equation by the LCD.

$$(x+2)(x-3)\cdot\frac{x}{x+2}=\frac{4}{x-3}\cdot(x+2)(x-3)\Rightarrow x^2-3x=4x+8\Rightarrow x^2-7x-8=0\Rightarrow$$

$$(x+1)(x-8)=0\Rightarrow x=-1\text{ or }8$$

36.   The LCD is $x(1-x)$. The first step is to multiply both sides of the equation by the LCD.

$$x(1-x) \cdot \left(\frac{2x}{1-x} - \frac{1}{x}\right) = 0 \cdot x(1-x) \Rightarrow 2x^2 - (1-x) = 0 \Rightarrow 2x^2 + x - 1 = 0 \Rightarrow (x+1)(2x-1) = 0 \Rightarrow x = -1 \text{ or } \frac{1}{2}$$

37. $$\frac{2w+1}{3w} - \frac{4w-3}{w} = 0 \Rightarrow 3w \cdot \frac{2w+1}{3w} - 3w \cdot \frac{(4w-3)}{w} = 0 \cdot 3w \Rightarrow 2w + 1 - 12w + 9 = 0 \Rightarrow$$

$$-10w + 10 = 0 \Rightarrow -10w = -10 \Rightarrow w = 1$$

38. $$\frac{1}{2w} - \frac{2}{1-w} = -\frac{3}{2} \Rightarrow 2w(1-w) \cdot \frac{1}{2w} - 2w(1-w) \cdot \frac{2}{1-w} = -\frac{3}{2} \cdot 2w(1-w) \Rightarrow$$

$$1 - w - 4w = -3w + 3w^2 \Rightarrow 3w^2 + 2w - 1 = 0 \Rightarrow (3w-1)(w+1) = 0 \Rightarrow w = \frac{1}{3} \text{ or } w = -1$$

39. $$\frac{3}{2y} + \frac{2y}{y-4} = -\frac{11}{2} \Rightarrow 2y(y-4) \cdot \frac{3}{2y} + 2y(y-4) \cdot \frac{2y}{y-4} = -\frac{11}{2} \cdot 2y(y-4) \Rightarrow$$

$$3y - 12 + 4y^2 = -11y^2 + 44y \Rightarrow 15y^2 - 41y - 12 = 0 \Rightarrow (15y+4)(y-3) = 0 \Rightarrow y = -\frac{4}{15} \text{ or } y = 3$$

40. $$\frac{3}{y-2} + \frac{6y}{y+1} = 2 \Rightarrow (y-2)(y+1) \cdot \frac{3}{y-2} + (y-2)(y+1) \cdot \frac{6y}{y+1} = 2 \cdot (y-2)(y+1) \Rightarrow$$

$$3y + 3 + 6y^2 - 12y = 2y^2 - 2y - 4 \Rightarrow 4y^2 - 7y + 7 = 0$$

This quadratic equation has no real solutions (its graph does not cross the *x*-axis). No solutions.

41. $$\frac{1}{(x-1)^2} + \frac{3}{x^2-1} = \frac{5}{x^2-1} \Rightarrow 1(x+1) + 3(x-1) = 5(x-1) \Rightarrow x+1+3x-3 = 5x-5 \Rightarrow 4x-2 = 5x-5 \Rightarrow x = 3$$

42. $$\frac{1}{x^2-4} + \frac{1}{(x-2)^2} = \frac{2}{(x+2)^2} \Rightarrow 1(x-2)(x+2) + 1(x+2)^2 = 2(x-2)^2 \Rightarrow$$

$$x^2 - 4 + x^2 + 4x + 4 = 2x^2 - 8x + 8 \Rightarrow 12x = 8 \Rightarrow x = \frac{2}{3}$$

43. $$\frac{x^2+x-2}{x-2} - \frac{4}{x-2} = 0 \Rightarrow \frac{x^2+x-2-4}{x-2} = 0 \Rightarrow \frac{x^2+x-6}{x-2} = 0$$

$$\Rightarrow \frac{(x+3)(x-2)}{x-2} = 0 \Rightarrow x + 3 = 0 \Rightarrow x = -3$$

44. $$\frac{x^2-4x-5}{x-1} + \frac{8}{x-1} = 0 \Rightarrow \frac{x^2-4x-5+8}{x-1} = 0 \Rightarrow \frac{x^2-4x+3}{x-1} = 0$$

$$\Rightarrow \frac{(x-3)(x-1)}{x-1} = 0 \Rightarrow x - 3 = 0 \Rightarrow x = 3$$

45. $$\frac{4}{x+3} = \frac{x}{3-x} = \frac{18}{x^2-9} \Rightarrow (x-3)(x+3) \cdot \frac{4}{x+3} - (x-3)(x+3)\frac{-x}{x-3}$$

$$= \frac{18}{(x-3)(x+3)} \cdot (x-3)(x+3) \Rightarrow 4(x-3) - (-x)(x+3) = 18$$

$$\Rightarrow 4x - 12 + x^2 + 3x = 18 \Rightarrow x^2 + 7x - 30 = 0 \Rightarrow (x+10)(x-3) = 0$$

$\Rightarrow x = -10$ ($x = 3$ makes expressions in the original equation undefined)

46. $\dfrac{12}{x^2-9} + \dfrac{2}{x+3} = \dfrac{x}{3-x} \Rightarrow (x-3)(x+3)\cdot\dfrac{12}{(x-3)(x+3)} + (x-3)(x+3)\cdot\dfrac{2}{x+3}$

$= \dfrac{-x}{x-3}\cdot(x-3)(x+3) \Rightarrow 12 + 2(x-3) = -x(x+3) \Rightarrow 12 + 2x - 6 = -x^2 - 3x$

$\Rightarrow x^2 + 5x + 6 = 0 \Rightarrow (x+2)(x+3) = 0 \Rightarrow x = -2$ ($x = -3$ makes expressions in the original equation undefined)

47. $\dfrac{1}{x} - 4x = 0 \Rightarrow x\cdot\dfrac{1}{x} - x\cdot 4x = 0\cdot x \Rightarrow 1 - 4x^2 = 0$

$\Rightarrow (1-2x)(1+2x) = 0 \Rightarrow x = \dfrac{1}{2}$ or $x = -\dfrac{1}{2}$

48. $\dfrac{2-x}{x} + 2 = 0 \Rightarrow x\cdot\dfrac{2-x}{x} + x\cdot 2 = 0\cdot x \Rightarrow 2 - x + 2x = 0$

$\Rightarrow 2 + x = 0 \Rightarrow x = -2$

49. $\dfrac{a}{x} - \dfrac{b}{x} = c \Rightarrow \dfrac{a-b}{x} = c \Rightarrow x\cdot\dfrac{a-b}{x} = c\cdot x$

$\Rightarrow a - b = cx \Rightarrow \dfrac{a-b}{c} = x$

50. $\dfrac{ab}{x} - c = \dfrac{1}{x} \Rightarrow x\cdot\dfrac{ab}{x} - x\cdot c = \dfrac{1}{x}\cdot x \Rightarrow ab - cx = 1$

$\Rightarrow cx = ab - 1 \Rightarrow x = \dfrac{ab-1}{c}$

51. $y_1 = y_2$ when $x = 1$. By substitution of $x = 1$, this answer checks.

52. $y_1 = y_2$ when $x = 2$. By substitution of $x = 2$, this answer checks.

53. $y_1 = y_2$ when $x = 2$. By substitution of $x = 2$, this answer checks

54. $y_1 = y_2$ when $x = -1$. By substitution of $x = -1$, this answer checks.

55. Graph $Y_1 = 1/(X-1)$ and $Y_2 = 1/2$ in $[-4.7, 4.7, 1]$ by $[-3.1, 3.1, 1]$. See Figure 55.

    The solution is the x-coordinate of the intersection point, $x = 3$.

$[-4.7, 4.7, 1]$ by $[-3.1, 3.1, 1]$ $[-4.7, 4.7, 1]$ by $[-3.1, 3.1, 1]$

Figure 55   Figure 56

56. Graph $Y_1 = 1/(X+1)$ and $Y_2 = 2$ in $[-4.7, 4.7, 1]$ by $[-3.1, 3.1, 1]$. See Figure 56.

    The solution is the x-coordinate of the intersection point, $x = -\dfrac{1}{2}$.

57.   Graph $Y_1 = 3/(X+2)$ and $Y_2 = X$ in $[-4.7, 4.7, 1]$ by $[-6.2, 6.2, 1]$. See Figures 57a & 57b.

The solutions are the *x*-coordinates of the intersection points, $x = -3$ or $x = 1$.

$[-4.7, 4.7, 1]$ by $[-6.2, 6.2, 1]$ $[-4.7, 4.7, 1]$ by $[-6.2, 6.2, 1]$

Figure 57a   Figure 57b

$[-4.7, 4.7, 1]$ by $[-6.2, 6.2, 1]$ $[-4.7, 4.7, 1]$ by $[-6.2, 6.2, 1]$

Figure 58a   Figure 58b

58.   Graph $Y_1 = 3/(X-2)$ and $Y_2 = X$ in $[-4.7, 4.7, 1]$ by $[-6.2, 6.2, 1]$. See Figures 58a & 58b.

The solutions are the *x*-coordinates of the intersection points, $x = -1$ or $x = 3$.

59.   Graph $Y_1 = 1/(X-2)$ and $Y_2 = 2$ in $[-4.7, 4.7, 1]$ by $[-3.1, 3.1, 1]$. See Figure 59.

The solution is the *x*-coordinate of the intersection point, $x = 2.5$.

60.   Graph $Y_1 = (2X)/(X+1)$ and $Y_2 = 3$ in $[-4.7, 4.7, 1]$ by $[-6.2, 6.2, 1]$. See Figure 60.

The solution is the *x*-coordinate of the intersection point, $x = -3$.

$[-4.7, 4.7, 1]$ by $[-3.1, 3.1, 1]$ $[-4.7, 4.7, 1]$ by $[-6.2, 6.2, 1]$

Figure 59   Figure 60

$[-4.7, 4.7, 1]$ by $[-6.2, 6.2, 1]$ $[-4.7, 4.7, 1]$ by $[-6.2, 6.2, 1]$

Figure 61a   Figure 61b

61.   Graph $Y_1 = 1/X + 1/X^2$ and $Y_2 = 15/4$ in $[-4.7, 4.7, 1]$ by $[-6.2, 6.2, 1]$. See Figures 61a & 61b.

The solutions are the *x*-coordinates of the intersection points, $x = -0.4$ or $x \approx 0.67$.

62.   Graph $Y_1 = 1/X + 1/(2X)$ and $Y_2 = 2X$ in $[-2.35, 2.35, 1]$ by $[-6.2, 6.2, 1]$. See Figures 62a & 62b.

The solutions are the *x*-coordinates of the intersection points, $x \approx \pm 0.87$.

[−2.35, 2.35, 1] by [−6.2, 6.2, 1]

Figure 62a

[−2.35, 2.35, 1] by [−6.2, 6.2, 1]

Figure 62b

[−4.7, 4.7, 1] by [−3.1, 3.1, 1]

Figure 63a

[−4.7, 4.7, 1] by [−3.1, 3.1, 1]

Figure 63b

63.   Graph $Y_1 = 1/(X+2) - 1/(X-2)$ and $Y_2 = 4/3$ in [−4.7, 4.7, 1] by [−3.1, 3.1, 1]. See Figures 63a & 63b.

The solutions are the *x*-coordinates of the intersection points, $x = -1$ or $x = 1$.

64.   Graph $Y_1 = X/(2X+4) - (2X)/(X^2 - 4)$ and $Y_2 = 2.7$ in [−4.7, 4.7, 1] by [−3.1, 3.1, 1]. See Figures 64a & 64b.

The solutions are the *x*-coordinates of the intersection points, $x = -3$ or $x \approx 1.64$.

[−4.7, 4.7, 1] by [−3.1, 3.1, 1]

Figure 64a

[−4.7, 4.7, 1] by [−3.1, 3.1, 1]

Figure 64b

[−4.7, 4.7, 1] by [−1.55, 1.55, 1]

Figure 65a

Figure 65b

Using More Than One Method

65.   Symbolic: The LCD is $3x$. The first step is to multiply both sides of the equation by the LCD.

$$3x \cdot \left(\frac{1}{x} + \frac{2}{3} \right) = 1 \cdot 3x \Rightarrow 3 + 2x = 3x \Rightarrow 3 = x \Rightarrow x = 3$$

Graphical: Graph $Y_1 = 1/X + 2/3$ and $Y_2 = 1$ in [−4.7, 4.7, 1] by [−1.55, 1.55, 1]. See Figure 65a.

The solution is the *x*-coordinate of the intersection point, $x = 3$.

Numerical: Table $Y_1 = 1/X + 2/3$ and $Y_2 = 1$ with TblStart $= 0$ and ΔTbl $= 1$. See Figure 65b.

The solution is the *x*-value when $Y_1 = Y_2$, $x = 3$.

66.   Symbolic: The LCD is x^2. The first step is to multiply both sides of the equation by the LCD.

$$x^2 \cdot \left(\frac{1}{x} - \frac{1}{x^2} \right) = -2 \cdot x^2 \Rightarrow x - 1 = -2x^2 \Rightarrow 2x^2 + x - 1 = 0 \Rightarrow$$

$$(x+1)(2x-1) = 0 \Rightarrow x = -1 \text{ or } x = \frac{1}{2}$$

Graphical: Graph $Y_1 = 1/X + 1/X^2$ and $Y_2 = -2$ in $[-4.7, 4.7, 1]$ by $[-6.2, 3.1, 1]$. See Figures 66a & 66b.

The solutions are the x-coordinates of the intersection points, $x = -1$ or $x = \frac{1}{2}$.

Numerical: Table $Y_1 = 1/X - 1/X^2$ and $Y_2 = -2$ with TblStart $= -2$ and ΔTbl $= 0.5$. See Figure 66c.

The solutions are the x-values when $Y_1 = Y_2$, $x = -1$ or $x = \frac{1}{2}$.

$[-4.7, 4.7, 1]$ by $[-6.2, 3.1, 1]$ $[-4.7, 4.7, 1]$ by $[-6.2, 3.1, 1]$

Figure 66a   Figure 66b   Figure 66c

67.   Symbolic: The LCD is $3x(x+2)$. The first step is to multiply both sides of the equation by the LCD.

$$3x(x+2) \cdot \left(\frac{1}{x} + \frac{1}{x+2} \right) = \frac{4}{3} \cdot 3x(x+2) \Rightarrow 3x + 6 + 3x = 4x^2 + 8x \Rightarrow 4x^2 + 2x - 6 = 0 \Rightarrow$$

$$2(2x+3)(x-1) = 0 \Rightarrow x = -\frac{3}{2} \text{ or } x = 1$$

Graphical: Graph $Y_1 = 1/X + 1/(X+2)$ and $Y_2 = 4/3$ in $[-4.7, 4.7, 1]$ by $[-3.1, 3.1, 1]$. See Figures 67a & 67b.

The solutions are the x-coordinates of the intersection points, $x = -\frac{3}{2}$ or $x = 1$.

Numerical: Table $Y_1 = 1/X + 1/(X+2)$ and $Y_2 = 4/3$ with TblStart $= -2$ and ΔTbl $= 0.5$. See Figure 67c.

The solutions are the x-values when $Y_1 = Y_2$, $x = -\frac{3}{2}$ or $x = 1$.

$[-4.7, 4.7, 1]$ by $[-3.1, 3.1, 1]$ $[-4.7, 4.7, 1]$ by $[-3.1, 3.1, 1]$

Figure 67a   Figure 67b   Figure 67c

68.   Symbolic: The LCD is $3x(x-2)(x+2)$. The first step is to multiply both sides of the equation by the LCD.

$$3(x-2)(x+2) \cdot \left(\frac{1}{x-2} + \frac{1}{x+2} \right) = -\frac{2}{3} \cdot 3(x-2)(x+2) \Rightarrow 3x + 6 + 3x - 6 = -2x^2 + 8 \Rightarrow$$

$$-2x^2 - 6x + 8 = 0 \Rightarrow -2(x+4)(x-1) = 0 \Rightarrow x = -4 \text{ or } x = 1$$

Graphical: Graph $Y_1 = 1/(X-2)$ and $Y_2 = -2/3$ in $[-9.4, 9.4, 1]$ by $[-1.55, 1.55, 1]$.

    See Figures 68a & 68b. The solutions are the x-coordinates of the intersection points, $x = -4$ or $x = 1$.

Numerical: Table $Y_1 = 1/(X-2)$ and $Y_2 = -2/3$ with TblStart = -5 and ΔTbl = 1.

    See Figure 68c. The solutions are the x-values when $Y_1 = Y_2$, $x = -4$ or $x = 1$.

$[-9.4, 9.4, 1]$ by $[-1.55, 1.55, 1]$ $[-9.4, 9.4, 1]$ by $[-1.55, 1.55, 1]$

Figure 68a   Figure 68b   Figure 68c

69.   Graph $Y_1 = X/(X^2 - 1) - 3/(X+2)$ and $Y_2 = 2$ in $[-4, 4, 1]$ by $[-1, 4, 1]$. The solutions are the x-coordinates

     of the intersection points, approximately $x = -3.28$, $x = -0.90$, or $x = 1.18$.

     Figure 69a   Figure 69b   Figure 69c

70.   Graph $Y_1 = 2.2/(X - 0.1) + X/(0.4X - 1)$ and $Y_2 = 1$ in $[-4.7, 4.7, 1]$ by $[-3.1, 3.1, 1]$. The solutions are the

     x-coordinates of the intersection points, approximately $x = -3.99$ or $x = 0.96$.

     Figure 70a   Figure 70b

Solving an Equation for a Variable

71. $t = \dfrac{d}{r} \Rightarrow rt = d \Rightarrow r = \dfrac{d}{t}$

72. $r = \dfrac{C}{2\pi} \Rightarrow 2\pi r = C \Rightarrow C = 2\pi r$

73. $h = \dfrac{2A}{b} \Rightarrow bh = 2A \Rightarrow b = \dfrac{2A}{h}$

74. $P = VT \Rightarrow \dfrac{P}{V} = T \Rightarrow T = \dfrac{P}{V}$

75. $\dfrac{1}{2a} = \dfrac{1}{b} \Rightarrow 2a = b \Rightarrow a = \dfrac{b}{2}$

76. $\dfrac{a}{b} = \dfrac{c}{d} \Rightarrow ad = bc \Rightarrow d = \dfrac{bc}{a}$

77. $\dfrac{1}{R} = \dfrac{1}{R_1} + \dfrac{1}{R_2} \Rightarrow R_1R_2 = RR_2 + RR_1 \Rightarrow R_1R_2 - RR_1 = RR_2 \Rightarrow R_1\left(R_2 - R\right) = RR_2 \Rightarrow R_1 = \dfrac{RR_2}{R_2 - R}$

78. $S = \dfrac{5}{8H} \Rightarrow 8HS = 5 \Rightarrow H = \dfrac{5}{8S}$

79. $T = \dfrac{1}{15 - x} \Rightarrow T\left(15 - x\right) = 1 \Rightarrow 15 - x = \dfrac{1}{T} \Rightarrow -x = \dfrac{1}{T} - 15 \Rightarrow x = 15 - \dfrac{1}{T}$

80. $h = \dfrac{V}{\pi r^2} \Rightarrow \pi r^2 h = V \Rightarrow V = \pi r^2 h$

81. $\dfrac{1}{r} = \dfrac{1}{t+1} \Rightarrow t + 1 = r \Rightarrow t = r - 1$

82. $R = \dfrac{R_1R_2}{R_1 + R_2} \Rightarrow RR_1 + RR_2 = R_1R_2 \Rightarrow RR_1 = R_1R_2 - RR_2 \Rightarrow RR_1 = \left(R_1 - R\right)R_2 \Rightarrow R_2 = \dfrac{RR_1}{R_1 - R}$

83. $\dfrac{1}{r} = \dfrac{a}{a+b} \Rightarrow a + b = ar \Rightarrow b = ar - a \Rightarrow b = a\left(r - 1\right)$

84. $\dfrac{1}{t+1} = \dfrac{a}{a-b} \Rightarrow a - b = at + a \Rightarrow -b = at \Rightarrow b = -at$

Applications

85. (a) $N = 8 \Rightarrow 8 = \dfrac{x^2}{3600 - 60x} \Rightarrow \left(3600 - 60x\right)\left(8\right) = \dfrac{x^2}{3600 - 60x} \cdot \left(3600 - 60x\right)$

    $\Rightarrow 28{,}800 - 480x = x^2 \Rightarrow x^2 + 480x - 28{,}800 = 0$

    Graph $Y_1 = X^2 + 480X - 28{,}800$ and $Y_2 = 0$ in [0, 75, 5] by [−10,000, 10,000, 1000]. The solution is the x-coordinate of the intersection point, $x \approx 54$ cars. See Figure 85.

    Figure 85   Figure 86

    (b) If cars arrive, on average, at 54 per hour, the line will be, on average, 8 cars long.

86. (a) $T = 0.5 \Rightarrow 0.5 = \dfrac{1}{x - 80}$. Graph $Y_1 = 0.5$ and $Y_2 = 1/(X - 80)$ in [0, 100, 10] by [0, 2, 0.5]. The solution is the x-coordinate of the intersection point, $x = 82$ per hour. See Figure 86.

    (b) The wait gets very long.

87. (a) $\dfrac{x}{5} + \dfrac{x}{2} = 1$

    (b) The LCD is 10. The first step is to multiply both sides of the equation by the LCD.

    $10 \cdot \left(\dfrac{x}{5} + \dfrac{x}{2}\right) = 1 \cdot 10 \Rightarrow 2x + 5x = 10 \Rightarrow 7x = 10 \Rightarrow x = \dfrac{10}{7}$ hours.

(c) Graph $Y_1 = X/5 + X/2$ and $Y_2 = 1$ in $[-4.7, 4.7, 1]$ by $[-3.1, 3.1, 1]$. See Figure 87.

The solution is the x-coordinate of the intersection point, $x \approx 1.43$ hours.

$[-4.7, 4.7, 1]$ by $[-3.1, 3.1, 1]$ $[-37.6, 37.6, 4]$ by $[-3.1, 3.1, 1]$

Figure 87   Figure 88

88.   (a) $\dfrac{x}{40} + \dfrac{x}{70} = 1$

(b) The LCD is 280. The first step is to multiply both sides of the equation by the LCD.

$$280 \cdot \left(\frac{x}{40} + \frac{x}{70} \right) = 1 \cdot 280 \Rightarrow 7x + 4x = 280 \Rightarrow 11x = 280 \Rightarrow x = \frac{280}{11} = 25.\overline{45} \text{ hours.}$$

(c) Graph $Y_1 = X/40 + X/70$ and $Y_2 = 1$ in $[-37.6, 37.6, 4]$ by $[-3.1, 3.1, 1]$. See Figure 88.

The solution is the x-coordinate of the intersection point, $x = 25.\overline{45}$ hours.

89.   Let x represent the speed of the winner. Then $x - 2$ represents the speed of the second-place runner.

Since $t = \dfrac{d}{r}$, the time needed for the winner to finish is $\dfrac{5}{x}$ and the time for the second-place runner is $\dfrac{5}{x-2}$.

Since the winner finished 7.5 minutes $\left(\dfrac{1}{8} \text{ hour} \right)$ ahead of second place, the equation is $\dfrac{5}{x-2} - \dfrac{5}{x} = \dfrac{1}{8}$.

The LCD is $8x(x-2)$. The first step is to multiply both sides of the equation by the LCD.

$$8x(x-2) \cdot \left(\frac{5}{x-2} - \frac{5}{x} \right) = \frac{1}{8} \cdot 8x(x-2) \Rightarrow 40x - 40x + 80 = x^2 - 2x \Rightarrow x^2 - 2x - 80 = 0 \Rightarrow$$

$(x-10)(x+8) = 0 \Rightarrow x = 10 \text{ or } x = -8$

Since the value $x = -8$ has no meaning, the solutions are winner: 10 mph, second-place: $10 - 2 = 8$ mph.

90.   Let x represent the number of gallons pumped each hour by the large pump. Then $x - 100$ represents the number of gallons pumped each hour by the small pump. The time needed for the large pump to finish is

$\dfrac{10,000}{x}$ and the time for the small pump is $\dfrac{10,000}{x-100}$.

Since the large pump can finish 5 hours ahead of the small pump, the equation is $\dfrac{10,000}{x-100} - \dfrac{10,000}{x} = 5$.

The LCD is $x(x-100)$. The first step is to multiply both sides of the equation by the LCD.

$$x(x-100) \cdot \left(\frac{10,000}{x-100} - \frac{10,000}{x} \right) = 5 \cdot x(x-100) \Rightarrow 10,000x - 10,000x + 1,000,000 = 5x^2 - 500x \Rightarrow$$

$5x^2 - 500x - 1,000,000 = 0 \Rightarrow 5(x-500)(x+400) = 0 \Rightarrow x = 500 \text{ or } x = -400$

Since the value $x = -400$ has no meaning, the solutions are large pump: 500, small pump: $500 - 100 = 400$.

91. $\dfrac{1}{10,000} = \dfrac{0.625}{H} \Rightarrow H = 0.625(10,000) = 6250$ feet.

92. (a) Lower. At a lower height a photograph would show a smaller area, giving a larger scale.

(b) $\dfrac{1}{5000} = \dfrac{0.625}{H} \Rightarrow H = 0.625(5000) = 3125$ feet.

93. Let x represent the speed of the current. Then $15-x$ represents the boat's upstream speed and $15+x$ represents the boat's downstream speed. Since $t = \dfrac{d}{r}$, the equation is $\dfrac{36}{15-x} + \dfrac{36}{15+x} = 5$.

The LCD is $(15-x)(15+x)$. The first step is to multiply both sides of the equation by the LCD.

$$(15-x)(15+x)\cdot\left(\dfrac{36}{15-x} + \dfrac{36}{15+x}\right) = 5\cdot(15-x)(15+x) \Rightarrow 540 + 36x + 540 - 36x = 1125 - 5x^2$$

$\Rightarrow 5x^2 - 45 = 0 \Rightarrow 5x^2 = 45 \Rightarrow x^2 = 9 \Rightarrow x = \pm\sqrt{9} \Rightarrow x = 3$ mph (the value $x = -3$ has no meaning)

94. Let x represent the speed of the wind. Then $200-x$ represents the plane's speed into the wind and $200+x$ represents the plane's speed with the wind. Since $t = \dfrac{d}{r}$, the equation is $\dfrac{800}{200-x} + \dfrac{800}{200+x} = \dfrac{25}{3}$.

The LCD is $3(200-x)(200+x)$. The first step is to multiply both sides of the equation by the LCD.

$$3(200-x)(200+x)\cdot\left(\dfrac{800}{200-x} + \dfrac{800}{200+x}\right) = \dfrac{25}{3}\cdot 3(200-x)(200+x) \Rightarrow$$

$480,000 + 2400x + 480,000 - 2400x = 1,000,000 - 25x^2 \Rightarrow 25x^2 - 40,000 = 0 \Rightarrow$

$25x^2 = 40,000 \Rightarrow x^2 = 1600 \Rightarrow x = \pm\sqrt{1600} \Rightarrow x = 40$ mph (the value $x = -40$ has no meaning)

95. Let x represent the plane's speed with no wind. Then $x+50$ represents the plane's speed with the wind and $x-50$ represents the plane's speed into the wind. Since $t = \dfrac{d}{r}$, the equation is $\dfrac{675}{x+50} = \dfrac{450}{x-50}$.

The LCD is $(x+50)(x-50)$. The first step is to multiply both sides of the equation by the LCD.

$$(x+50)(x-50)\cdot\dfrac{675}{x+50} = \dfrac{450}{x-50}\cdot(x+50)(x-50) \Rightarrow 675x - 33,750 = 450x + 22,500 \Rightarrow$$

$225x = 56,250 \Rightarrow x = 250$ mph

96. (a) $5 = \dfrac{1}{25-x} \Rightarrow 125 - 5x = 1 \Rightarrow -5x = -124 \Rightarrow x = 24.8$; The wait is 5 hours when people arrive at a rate of 24.8 per hour.

(b) Table $Y_1 = 1/(25-X)$ and $Y_2 = 5$ with TblStart $= 24$ and ΔTbl $= 0.2$. See Figure 96.

The solution is the x-value when $Y_1 = Y_2$, $x = 24.8$.

Figure 96

97. Let x and $x+3$ represent the time needed by the faster employee and the slower employee respectively.

$$\frac{1}{x}+\frac{1}{x+3}=\frac{1}{2} \Rightarrow 2(x+3)+2x = x(x+3) \Rightarrow 2x+6+2x = x^2+3x \Rightarrow x^2-x-6=0 \Rightarrow$$

$(x-3)(x+2)=0 \Rightarrow x=3$ or $x=-2$. The value $x=-2$ has no physical meaning.

The faster employee can mow the field in 3 hours. The slower employee takes 6 hours.

98. Let x and $x+20$ represent the time needed by the faster painter and the slower painter respectively.

$$\frac{1}{x}+\frac{1}{x+20}=\frac{1}{24} \Rightarrow 24(x+20)+24x = x(x+20) \Rightarrow 24x+480+24x = x^2+20x \Rightarrow$$

$x^2-28x-480=0 \Rightarrow (x-40)(x+12)=0 \Rightarrow x=40$ or $x=-12$. The value $x=-12$ has no physical

meaning. The faster painter can paint the house in 40 hours. The slower painter takes 60 hours.

99. Let x and $x-1$ represent the speed of the faster person and the slower person respectively.

$$\frac{12}{x}=\frac{9}{x-1} \Rightarrow 12x-12=9x \Rightarrow 3x=12 \Rightarrow x=4$$

The faster parson walks 4 mph. The slower person walks 3 mph.

100. Let x and $x-5$ represent the speed of the faster car and the slower car respectively.

$$\frac{340}{x}=\frac{315}{x-5} \Rightarrow 340x-1700=315x \Rightarrow 25x=1700 \Rightarrow x=68$$

The faster car is traveling 68 mph. The slower car is traveling 63 mph.

101. Let x represent the time needed to empty the pool.

$$\frac{x}{40}-\frac{x}{60}=1 \Rightarrow 3x-2x=120 \Rightarrow x=120 \text{ hours. The pool is empty in 120 hours.}$$

102. Let x represent the time needed to empty the boat.

$$\frac{x}{3}-\frac{x}{5}=\frac{1}{2} \Rightarrow 10x-6x=15 \Rightarrow 4x=15 \Rightarrow x=3.75 \text{ hours. The boat is empty in 3 hours 45 minutes.}$$

103. Yes; the value is slightly greater than 2.

104. Yes; the value is slightly less than 2.

Checking Basic Concepts for Sections 6.3 & 6.4

1. (a) $\dfrac{x}{x^2-1}+\dfrac{1}{x^2-1}=\dfrac{x+1}{(x-1)(x+1)}=\dfrac{1}{x-1}$

   (b) $\dfrac{1}{x-2}-\dfrac{3}{x}=\dfrac{x}{x(x-2)}-\dfrac{3(x-2)}{x(x-2)}=\dfrac{x-(3x-6)}{x(x-2)}=\dfrac{-2x+6}{x(x-2)}=\dfrac{-2(x-3)}{x(x-2)}=-\dfrac{2(x-3)}{x(x-2)}$

(c) $\dfrac{1}{x(x-1)}+\dfrac{1}{x^2-1}-\dfrac{2}{x(x+1)}=\dfrac{1(x+1)+1x-2(x-1)}{x(x-1)(x+1)}=\dfrac{3}{x(x-1)(x+1)}$

2. (a) $\dfrac{6}{x}-\dfrac{1}{2}=1\Rightarrow 12-x=2x\Rightarrow 12=3x\Rightarrow x=4$

(b) $\dfrac{3}{2x-1}=\dfrac{2}{x+1}\Rightarrow 3(x+1)=2(2x-1)\Rightarrow 3x+3=4x-2\Rightarrow x=5$

(c) $\dfrac{2}{x-1}+\dfrac{3}{x+2}=\dfrac{x}{x^2+x-2}\Rightarrow 2(x+2)+3(x-1)=x\Rightarrow 5x+1=x\Rightarrow 4x=-1\Rightarrow x=-\dfrac{1}{4}$

3. $\dfrac{x}{12}+\dfrac{x}{28}=1\Rightarrow 7x+3x=84\Rightarrow 10x=84\Rightarrow x=8.4$ min

4. $\dfrac{1}{S}=\dfrac{1}{F}-\dfrac{1}{D}\Rightarrow DF=SD-SF\Rightarrow DF=S(D-F)\Rightarrow \dfrac{DF}{D-F}=S\Rightarrow S=\dfrac{DF}{D-F}$

6.5: Complex Fractions

Concepts

1. $\dfrac{5}{7}\cdot\dfrac{11}{3}=\dfrac{55}{21}$

2. $\dfrac{a}{b}\cdot\dfrac{d}{c}$

3. Multiply both the numerator and the denominator by $x-1$. *Answers may vary.*

4. A complex fraction is a rational expression with fractions in its numerator, denominator or both.

5. $\dfrac{z+\dfrac{3}{4}}{z-\dfrac{3}{4}}$

6. $\dfrac{\dfrac{a}{b}}{\dfrac{a-b}{a+b}}$

Simplifying Complex Fractions

7. $\dfrac{\dfrac{1}{5}}{\dfrac{4}{7}}=\dfrac{1}{5}\cdot\dfrac{7}{4}=\dfrac{7}{20}$

8. $\dfrac{\dfrac{3}{7}}{\dfrac{2}{9}}=\dfrac{3}{7}\cdot\dfrac{9}{2}=\dfrac{27}{14}$

9. $\dfrac{1+\dfrac{1}{3}}{1-\dfrac{1}{3}} = \dfrac{1+\dfrac{1}{3}}{1-\dfrac{1}{1}} \cdot \dfrac{3}{3} = \dfrac{3+1}{3-1} = \dfrac{4}{2} = 2$

10. $\dfrac{\dfrac{1}{2}-3}{\dfrac{1}{2}+3} = \dfrac{\dfrac{1}{2}-3}{\dfrac{1}{2}+3} \cdot \dfrac{2}{2} = \dfrac{1-6}{1+6} = \dfrac{-5}{7} = -\dfrac{5}{7}$

11. $\dfrac{2+\dfrac{2}{3}}{2-\dfrac{1}{4}} = \dfrac{2+\dfrac{2}{3}}{2-\dfrac{1}{4}} \cdot \dfrac{12}{12} = \dfrac{24+8}{24-3} = \dfrac{32}{21}$

12. $\dfrac{\dfrac{1}{2}+\dfrac{3}{4}}{\dfrac{1}{2}-\dfrac{3}{4}} = \dfrac{\dfrac{1}{2}+\dfrac{3}{4}}{\dfrac{1}{2}-\dfrac{3}{4}} \cdot \dfrac{8}{8} = \dfrac{4+6}{4-6} = \dfrac{10}{-2} = -5$

13. $\dfrac{\dfrac{a}{b}}{\dfrac{3a}{2b^2}} = \dfrac{a}{b} \cdot \dfrac{2b^2}{3a} = \dfrac{2b}{3}$

14. $\dfrac{\dfrac{7}{y}}{\dfrac{14}{y}} = \dfrac{7}{y} \cdot \dfrac{y}{14} = \dfrac{1}{2}$

15. $\dfrac{\dfrac{x}{2y}}{\dfrac{2x}{3y}} = \dfrac{x}{2y} \cdot \dfrac{3y}{2x} = \dfrac{3}{4}$

16. $\dfrac{\dfrac{ab^2}{2c}}{\dfrac{a}{4bc}} = \dfrac{ab^2}{2c} \cdot \dfrac{4bc}{a} = 2b^3$

17. $\dfrac{\dfrac{8}{n+1}}{\dfrac{4}{n-1}} = \dfrac{8}{n+1} \cdot \dfrac{n-1}{4} = \dfrac{2(n-1)}{n+1}$

18. $\dfrac{\dfrac{n}{m-2}}{\dfrac{3n}{m-2}} = \dfrac{n}{m-2} \cdot \dfrac{m-2}{3n} = \dfrac{1}{3}$

19. $\dfrac{\dfrac{2k+3}{k}}{\dfrac{k-4}{k}} = \dfrac{2k+3}{k} \cdot \dfrac{k}{k-4} = \dfrac{2k+3}{k-4}$

20. $\dfrac{\dfrac{2k}{k-7}}{\dfrac{1}{(k-7)^2}} = \dfrac{2k}{k-7} \cdot \dfrac{(k-7)^2}{1} = 2k(k-7)$

21. $\dfrac{\dfrac{3}{z^2-4}}{\dfrac{z}{z^2-4}} = \dfrac{3}{z^2-4} \cdot \dfrac{z^2-4}{z} = \dfrac{3}{z}$

22. $\dfrac{\dfrac{z}{(z-2)^2}}{\dfrac{2z}{z^2-4}} = \dfrac{z}{(z-2)^2} \cdot \dfrac{z^2-4}{2z} = \dfrac{z^2-4}{2(z-2)^2} = \dfrac{(z-2)(z+2)}{2(z-2)(z-2)} = \dfrac{z+2}{2(z-2)}$

23. $\dfrac{\dfrac{x}{x^2-16}}{\dfrac{1}{x-4}} = \dfrac{x}{x^2-16} \cdot \dfrac{x-4}{1} = \dfrac{x(x-4)}{x^2-16} = \dfrac{x(x-4)}{(x-4)(x+4)} = \dfrac{x}{x+4}$

24. $\dfrac{\dfrac{4y}{x-y}}{\dfrac{1}{x^2-y^2}} = \dfrac{4y}{x-y} \cdot \dfrac{x^2-y^2}{1} = \dfrac{4y(x^2-y^2)}{x-y} = \dfrac{4y(x-y)(x+y)}{x-y} = 4y(x+y)$

25. $\dfrac{1+\dfrac{1}{x}}{x+1} = \dfrac{1+\dfrac{1}{x}}{x+1} \cdot \dfrac{x}{x} = \dfrac{x+1}{x(x+1)} = \dfrac{1}{x}$

26. $\dfrac{2-x}{\dfrac{1}{x}-\dfrac{1}{2}} = \dfrac{2-x}{\dfrac{1}{x}-\dfrac{1}{2}} \cdot \dfrac{2x}{2x} = \dfrac{2x(2-x)}{2-x} = 2x$

27. $\dfrac{\dfrac{1}{x-3}}{\dfrac{1}{x}-\dfrac{3}{x-3}} = \dfrac{\dfrac{1}{x-3}}{\dfrac{1}{x}-\dfrac{3}{x-3}} \cdot \dfrac{x(x-3)}{x(x-3)} = \dfrac{x}{x-3-3x} = \dfrac{x}{-2x-3} = -\dfrac{x}{2x+3}$

28. $\dfrac{5+\dfrac{1}{x-1}}{\dfrac{1}{x-1}-\dfrac{1}{4}} = \dfrac{5+\dfrac{1}{x-1}}{\dfrac{1}{x-1}-\dfrac{1}{4}} \cdot \dfrac{4(x-1)}{4(x-1)} = \dfrac{20x-20+4}{4-(x-1)} = \dfrac{20x-16}{5-x} = \dfrac{4(5x-4)}{5-x} = -\dfrac{4(5x-4)}{x-5}$

29. $\dfrac{\dfrac{1}{x}+\dfrac{2}{x^2}}{\dfrac{3}{x}-\dfrac{1}{x^2}} = \dfrac{\dfrac{1}{x}+\dfrac{2}{x^2}}{\dfrac{3}{x}-\dfrac{1}{x^2}} \cdot \dfrac{x^2}{x^2} = \dfrac{x+2}{3x-1}$

30. $\dfrac{\dfrac{1}{x-1}+\dfrac{2}{x}}{2-\dfrac{1}{x}} = \dfrac{\dfrac{1}{x-1}+\dfrac{2}{x}}{2-\dfrac{1}{x}} \cdot \dfrac{x(x-1)}{x(x-1)} = \dfrac{x+2(x-1)}{2x(x-1)-(x-1)} = \dfrac{x+2x-2}{2x^2-2x-x+1} = \dfrac{3x-2}{(x-1)(2x-1)}$

31.
$$\frac{\dfrac{1}{x+3}+\dfrac{2}{x-3}}{2-\dfrac{1}{x-3}}=\frac{\dfrac{1}{x+3}+\dfrac{2}{x-3}}{2-\dfrac{1}{x-3}}\cdot\frac{(x-3)(x+3)}{(x-3)(x+3)}=\frac{x-3+2(x+3)}{2(x-3)(x+3)-(x+3)}=\frac{3(x+1)}{(x+3)(2x-7)}$$

32.
$$\frac{\dfrac{1}{x}+\dfrac{2}{x}}{\dfrac{1}{x-1}+\dfrac{x}{2}}=\frac{\dfrac{1}{x}+\dfrac{2}{x}}{\dfrac{1}{x-1}+\dfrac{x}{2}}\cdot\frac{2x(x-1)}{2x(x-1)}=\frac{2(x-1)+4(x-1)}{2x+x^2(x-1)}=\frac{2x-2+4x-4}{2x+x^3-x^2}=\frac{6(x-1)}{x\left(x^2-x+2\right)}$$

33.
$$\frac{\dfrac{4}{x-5}}{\dfrac{1}{x+5}+\dfrac{1}{x}}=\frac{\dfrac{4}{x-5}}{\dfrac{1}{x+5}+\dfrac{1}{x}}\cdot\frac{x(x-5)(x+5)}{x(x-5)(x+5)}=\frac{4x(x+5)}{x(x-5)+(x-5)(x+5)}=\frac{4x(x+5)}{(x-5)(2x+5)}$$

34.
$$\frac{\dfrac{1}{x-4}+\dfrac{1}{x-4}}{1-\dfrac{1}{x+4}}=\frac{\dfrac{1}{x-4}+\dfrac{1}{x-4}}{1-\dfrac{1}{x+4}}\cdot\frac{(x-4)(x+4)}{(x-4)(x+4)}=\frac{x+4+x+4}{(x-4)(x+4)-(x-4)}=\frac{2(x+4)}{(x-4)(x+3)}$$

35.
$$\frac{\dfrac{1}{p^2q}+\dfrac{1}{pq^2}}{\dfrac{1}{p^2q}-\dfrac{1}{pq^2}}=\frac{\dfrac{1}{p^2q}+\dfrac{1}{pq^2}}{\dfrac{1}{p^2q}-\dfrac{1}{pq^2}}\cdot\frac{p^2q^2}{p^2q^2}=\frac{q+p}{q-p}=\frac{p+q}{q-p}$$

36.
$$\frac{\dfrac{1}{p-1}}{\dfrac{1}{p-1}+2}=\frac{\dfrac{1}{p-1}}{\dfrac{1}{p-1}+2}\cdot\frac{p-1}{p-1}=\frac{1}{1+2(p-1)}=\frac{1}{1+2p-2}=\frac{1}{2p-1}$$

37,
$$\frac{\dfrac{1}{a}+\dfrac{1}{b}}{\dfrac{1}{b}-\dfrac{1}{a}}=\frac{\dfrac{1}{a}+\dfrac{1}{b}}{\dfrac{1}{b}-\dfrac{1}{a}}\cdot\frac{ab}{ab}=\frac{b+a}{a-b}=\frac{a+b}{a-b}$$

38.
$$\frac{\dfrac{1}{a}+\dfrac{1}{b}+\dfrac{1}{c}}{\dfrac{1}{ab}+\dfrac{1}{bc}}=\frac{\dfrac{1}{a}+\dfrac{1}{b}+\dfrac{1}{c}}{\dfrac{1}{ab}+\dfrac{1}{bc}}\cdot\frac{abc}{abc}=\frac{bc+ac+ab}{c+a}$$

39.
$$\frac{\dfrac{1}{x}+\dfrac{1}{x+1}}{\dfrac{2}{x+1}-\dfrac{1}{x+1}}=\frac{\dfrac{1}{x}+\dfrac{1}{x+1}}{\dfrac{1}{x+1}}=\frac{\dfrac{1}{x}+\dfrac{1}{x+1}}{\dfrac{1}{x+1}}\cdot\frac{x(x+1)}{x(x+1)}=\frac{x+1+x}{x}=\frac{2x+1}{x}$$

40.
$$\frac{\dfrac{2}{x-1}-4}{\dfrac{1}{x-1}+\dfrac{1}{x-2}}=\frac{\dfrac{2-4(x-1)}{x-1}}{\dfrac{1}{x-1}+\dfrac{1}{x-2}}\cdot\frac{(x-1)(x-2)}{(x-1)(x-2)}=\frac{(2-4(x-1))(x-2)}{x-2+x-1}=\frac{(-4x+6)(x-2)}{2x-3}$$

$$=\frac{-2(2x-3)(x-2)}{2x-3}=-2(x-2)$$

41. $\dfrac{3^{-1}-4^{-1}}{5^{-1}+4^{-1}} = \dfrac{\dfrac{1}{3}-\dfrac{1}{4}}{\dfrac{1}{5}+\dfrac{1}{4}} = \dfrac{\dfrac{4}{12}-\dfrac{3}{12}}{\dfrac{4}{20}+\dfrac{5}{20}} = \dfrac{\dfrac{1}{12}}{\dfrac{9}{20}} = \dfrac{1}{12}\cdot\dfrac{20}{9} = \dfrac{5}{27}$

42. $\dfrac{1+2^{-3}}{2^{-3}-1} = \dfrac{1+\dfrac{1}{8}}{\dfrac{1}{8}-1} = \dfrac{\dfrac{9}{8}}{-\dfrac{7}{8}} = \dfrac{9}{8}\cdot\dfrac{-8}{7} = -\dfrac{9}{7}$

43. $\dfrac{m^{-1}-2n^{-2}}{1+(mn)^{-2}} = \dfrac{\dfrac{1}{m}-\dfrac{2}{n^2}}{1+\dfrac{1}{m^2n^2}} = \dfrac{\dfrac{1}{m}-\dfrac{2}{n^2}}{1+\dfrac{1}{m^2n^2}}\cdot\dfrac{m^2n^2}{m^2n^2} = \dfrac{mn^2-2m^2}{m^2n^2+1}$

44. $\dfrac{1+p^{-2}}{1-p^{-2}} = \dfrac{1+\dfrac{1}{p^2}}{1-\dfrac{1}{p^2}} = \dfrac{1+\dfrac{1}{p^2}}{1-\dfrac{1}{p^2}}\cdot\dfrac{p^2}{p^2} = \dfrac{p^2+1}{p^2-1}$

45. $\dfrac{1-(2n+1)^{-1}}{1+(2n+1)^{-1}} = \dfrac{1-\dfrac{1}{2n+1}}{1+\dfrac{1}{2n+1}} = \dfrac{1-\dfrac{1}{2n+1}}{1+\dfrac{1}{2n+1}}\cdot\dfrac{2n+1}{2n+1} = \dfrac{2n+1-1}{2n+1+1} = \dfrac{2n}{2(n+1)} = \dfrac{n}{n+1}$

46. $\dfrac{(a+b)^{-1}-(a-b)^{-1}}{1+(a-b)^{-1}} = \dfrac{\dfrac{1}{a+b}-\dfrac{1}{a-b}}{1+\dfrac{1}{a-b}} = \dfrac{\dfrac{1}{a+b}-\dfrac{1}{a-b}}{1+\dfrac{1}{a-b}}\cdot\dfrac{(a+b)(a-b)}{(a+b)(a-b)}$

$= \dfrac{a-b-a-b}{(a+b)(a-b)+(a+b)} = \dfrac{-2b}{a^2-b^2+a-b} = -\dfrac{2b}{a^2-b^2+a-b}$

47. $\dfrac{\dfrac{x}{x^2-4}-\dfrac{1}{x^2-4}}{\dfrac{1}{x+4}} = \dfrac{\dfrac{x-1}{x^2-4}}{\dfrac{1}{x+4}} = \dfrac{x-1}{x^2-4}\cdot\dfrac{x+4}{1} = \dfrac{(x-1)(x+4)}{x^2-4}$

48. $\dfrac{\dfrac{1}{x^2+2x+1}-\dfrac{1}{x^2-2x+1}}{(x+1)(x-1)} = \dfrac{\dfrac{1}{(x+1)^2}-\dfrac{1}{(x-1)^2}}{(x+1)(x-1)}\cdot\dfrac{(x+1)^2(x-1)^2}{(x+1)^2(x-1)^2} = \dfrac{(x-1)^2-(x+1)^2}{(x+1)^3(x-1)^3}$

$\dfrac{x^2-2x+1-x^2-2x-1}{(x+1)^3(x-1)^3} = -\dfrac{4x}{(x+1)^3(x-1)^3}$

Applications

49. $\dfrac{P\left(1+\dfrac{r}{12}\right)^{24}-P}{\dfrac{r}{12}}$

50. $$\dfrac{P\left(1+\dfrac{r}{12}\right)^{24}-P}{\dfrac{r}{12}} \Rightarrow \dfrac{250\left(1+\dfrac{0.06}{12}\right)^{24}-250}{\dfrac{0.06}{12}} \approx 6357.99$$

Depositing \$250 each month into an account paying 6% annual interest will result in a total of \$6357.99 after 2 years.

51. $$R = \dfrac{1}{\dfrac{1}{R_1}+\dfrac{1}{R_2}} = \dfrac{1}{\dfrac{1}{R_1}+\dfrac{1}{R_2}} \cdot \dfrac{R_1 R_2}{R_1 R_2} = \dfrac{R_1 R_2}{R_2 + R_1} \Rightarrow R = \dfrac{R_1 R_2}{R_1 + R_2}$$

52. $$R = \dfrac{R_1 R_2}{R_1 + R_2} \Rightarrow = \dfrac{(75)(100)}{75+100} = \dfrac{7500}{175} \approx 42.9 \text{ ohms}$$

6.6: Modeling with Proportions and Variation

Concepts

1. A proportion is a statement that two ratios are equal.

2. $\dfrac{5}{6} = \dfrac{x}{7}$

3. It doubles.

4. It is reduced by half.

5. constant

6. constant

7. kxy

8. $kx^2 y^3$

9. It would vary directly. If the number of people doubled, the food bill would double.

10. It would vary inversely. Increasing the number of painters would decrease the time needed to paint the building.

Proportions

11. $\dfrac{x}{14} = \dfrac{5}{7} \Rightarrow 7x = 70 \Rightarrow x = \dfrac{70}{10} = 10$

12. $\dfrac{x}{5} = \dfrac{4}{9} \Rightarrow 9x = 20 \Rightarrow x = \dfrac{20}{9}$

13. $\dfrac{8}{x} = \dfrac{2}{3} \Rightarrow 2x = 24 \Rightarrow x = \dfrac{24}{2} = 12$

14. $\dfrac{5}{11} = \dfrac{9}{x} \Rightarrow 5x = 99 \Rightarrow x = \dfrac{99}{5}$

15. $\dfrac{6}{13} = \dfrac{h}{156} \Rightarrow 13h = 936 \Rightarrow h = \dfrac{936}{13} = 72$

16. $\dfrac{25}{a} = \dfrac{15}{8} \Rightarrow 15a = 200 \Rightarrow a = \dfrac{200}{15} = \dfrac{40}{3}$

17. $\dfrac{7}{4z} = \dfrac{5}{3} \Rightarrow 20z = 21 \Rightarrow z = \dfrac{21}{20}$

18. $\dfrac{3}{2} = \dfrac{2x}{9} \Rightarrow 4x = 27 \Rightarrow x = \dfrac{27}{4}$

19. $\dfrac{2}{3x+1} = \dfrac{5}{x} \Rightarrow 2x = 5(3x+1) \Rightarrow 2x = 15x+5 \Rightarrow -13x = 5 \Rightarrow x = -\dfrac{5}{13}$

20. $\dfrac{7}{x-1} = -\dfrac{5}{3x} \Rightarrow -21x = 5(x-1) \Rightarrow -21x = 5x-5 \Rightarrow -26x = -5 \Rightarrow x = \dfrac{5}{26}$

21. $\dfrac{4}{x} = \dfrac{x}{9} \Rightarrow 36 = x^2 \Rightarrow x^2 - 36 = 0 \Rightarrow (x-6)(x+6) = 0 \Rightarrow x = 6 \text{ or } x = -6$

22. $\dfrac{2x}{5} = \dfrac{40}{x} \Rightarrow 2x^2 = 200 \Rightarrow x^2 = 100 \Rightarrow x^2 - 100 = 0 \Rightarrow (x-10)(x+10) = 0 \Rightarrow x = 10 \text{ or } x = -10$

23. (a) $\dfrac{7}{9} = \dfrac{10}{x}$

    (b) $\dfrac{7}{9} = \dfrac{10}{x} \Rightarrow 7x = 90 \Rightarrow x = \dfrac{90}{7}$

24. (a) $\dfrac{x}{11} = \dfrac{9}{2}$

    (b) $\dfrac{x}{11} = \dfrac{9}{2} \Rightarrow 2x = 99 \Rightarrow x = \dfrac{99}{2}$

25. (a) $\dfrac{5}{3} = \dfrac{x}{6}$

    (b) $\dfrac{5}{3} = \dfrac{x}{6} \Rightarrow 3x = 30 \Rightarrow x = \dfrac{30}{3} = 10$

26. (a) $\dfrac{8}{14} = \dfrac{x}{9}$

    (b) $\dfrac{8}{14} = \dfrac{x}{9} \Rightarrow 14x = 72 \Rightarrow x = \dfrac{72}{14} = \dfrac{36}{7}$

27. (a) $\dfrac{78}{6} = \dfrac{x}{8}$

    (b) $\dfrac{78}{6} = \dfrac{x}{8} \Rightarrow 6x = 624 \Rightarrow x = \dfrac{624}{6} = \$104$

28. (a) $\dfrac{12}{1.2} = \dfrac{18}{x}$

    (b) $\dfrac{12}{1.2} = \dfrac{18}{x} \Rightarrow 12x = 21.6 \Rightarrow x = \dfrac{21.6}{12} = 1.8 \text{ gal}$

29.   (a) $\dfrac{2}{90} = \dfrac{5}{x}$

      (b) $\dfrac{2}{90} = \dfrac{5}{x} \Rightarrow 2x = 450 \Rightarrow x = \dfrac{450}{2} = 225 \ \text{min}$

30.   (a) $\dfrac{30}{8} = \dfrac{17}{x}$

      (b) $\dfrac{30}{8} = \dfrac{17}{x} \Rightarrow 30x = 136 \Rightarrow x = \dfrac{136}{30} = \dfrac{68}{15} \approx 4.53 \ \text{min}$

Variation

31.   (a) $y = kx \Rightarrow 6 = 3k \Rightarrow k = 2$

      (b) $y = 2x \Rightarrow y = 2(7) = 14$

32.   (a) $y = kx \Rightarrow 7 = 14k \Rightarrow k = 0.5$

      (b) $y = 0.5x \Rightarrow y = 0.5(7) = 3.5$

33.   (a) $y = kx \Rightarrow 5 = 2k \Rightarrow k = 2.5$

      (b) $y = 2.5x \Rightarrow y = 2.5(7) \Rightarrow 17.5$

34.   (a) $y = kx \Rightarrow 11 = 22k \Rightarrow k = 0.5$

      (b) $y = 0.5x \Rightarrow y = 0.5(7) = 3.5$

35.   (a) $y = kx \Rightarrow -120 = 16k \Rightarrow k = -7.5$

      (b) $y = -7.5x \Rightarrow y = -7.5(7) = -52.5$

36.   (a) $y = kx \Rightarrow -34 = 17k \Rightarrow k = -2$

      (b) $y = -2x \Rightarrow y = -2(7) = -14$

37.   (a) $y = \dfrac{k}{x} \Rightarrow 5 = \dfrac{k}{4} \Rightarrow k = 20$

      (b) $y = \dfrac{20}{x} \Rightarrow y = \dfrac{20}{10} = 2$

38.   (a) $y = \dfrac{k}{x} \Rightarrow 2 = \dfrac{k}{30} \Rightarrow k = 60$

      (b) $y = \dfrac{60}{x} \Rightarrow y = \dfrac{60}{10} = 6$

39.   (a) $y = \dfrac{k}{x} \Rightarrow 100 = \dfrac{k}{\frac{1}{2}} \Rightarrow k = 50$

      (b) $y = \dfrac{50}{x} \Rightarrow y = \dfrac{50}{10} = 5$

40.   (a) $y = \dfrac{k}{x} \Rightarrow \dfrac{1}{4} = \dfrac{k}{40} \Rightarrow k = 10$

      (b) $y = \dfrac{10}{x} \Rightarrow y = \dfrac{10}{10} = 1$

41.   (a) $y = \dfrac{k}{x} \Rightarrow 20 = \dfrac{k}{20} \Rightarrow k = 400$

      (b) $y = \dfrac{400}{x} \Rightarrow y = \dfrac{400}{10} = 40$

42.   (a) $y = \dfrac{k}{x} \Rightarrow \dfrac{45}{4} = \dfrac{k}{8} \Rightarrow k = 90$

      (b) $y = \dfrac{90}{x} \Rightarrow y = \dfrac{90}{10} = 9$

43.   (a) $z = kxy \Rightarrow 6 = 3(8)k \Rightarrow 6 = 24k \Rightarrow k = 0.25$

      (b) $z = 0.25xy \Rightarrow z = 0.25(5)(7) = 8.75$

44.   (a) $z = kxy \Rightarrow 135 = 2.5(9)k \Rightarrow 135 = 22.5k \Rightarrow k = 6$

      (b) $z = 6xy \Rightarrow z = 6(5)(7) = 210$

45.   (a) $z = kxy \Rightarrow 5775 = 25(21)k \Rightarrow 5775 = 525k \Rightarrow k = 11$

      (b) $z = 11xy \Rightarrow z = 11(5)(7) = 385$

46.   (a) $z = kxy \Rightarrow 1530 = 22.5(4)k \Rightarrow 1530 = 90k \Rightarrow k = 17$

      (b) $z = 17xy \Rightarrow z = 17(5)(7) = 595$

47.   (a) $z = kxy \Rightarrow 25 = \dfrac{1}{2}(5)k \Rightarrow 25 = \dfrac{5}{2}k \Rightarrow k = 10$

      (b) $z = 10xy \Rightarrow z = 10(5)(7) = 350$

48.   (a) $z = kxy \Rightarrow 12 = \dfrac{1}{4}(12)k \Rightarrow 12 = 3k \Rightarrow k = 4$

      (b) $z = 4xy \Rightarrow z = 4(5)(7) = 140$

49.   (a)   Direct. The ratios $\dfrac{y}{x}$ always equal 1.5.

      (b) $y = kx \Rightarrow 3 = 2k \Rightarrow k = 1.5;$ The equation is $y = 1.5x.$

      (c)   See Figure 49.

Figure 49

Figure 50

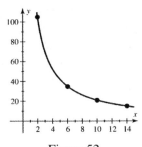

Figure 52

50. (a) Inverse. The products xy always equal 36.

  (b) $y = \dfrac{k}{x} \Rightarrow 12 = \dfrac{k}{3} \Rightarrow k = 36;$ The equation is $y = \dfrac{36}{x}.$

  (c) See Figure 50.

51. (a) Neither. The products xy do not remain constant.

  (b) N/A

  (c) N/A

52. (a) Inverse. The products xy always equal 210.

  (b) $y = \dfrac{k}{x} \Rightarrow 105 = \dfrac{k}{2} \Rightarrow k = 210;$ The equation is $y = \dfrac{210}{x}.$

  (c) See Figure 52.

53. (a) Neither. The ratios $\dfrac{y}{x}$ do not remain constant.

  (b) N/A

  (c) N/A

54. (a) Direct. The ratios $\dfrac{y}{x}$ always equal 6.

  (b) $y = kx \Rightarrow 6 = 1k \Rightarrow k = 6;$ The equation is $y = 6x.$

  (c) See Figure 54.

Figure 54

Figure 71

55. (a) Direct. The ratios $\dfrac{y}{x}$ always equal $-2b.$

  (b) $y = kx \Rightarrow -2b = 1k \Rightarrow k = -2b.$ The equation is $y = -2bx.$

56.   (a) Inverse. The products xy always equal $2ab$.

(b) $y = \dfrac{k}{x} \Rightarrow 2b = \dfrac{k}{a} \Rightarrow k = 2ab.$ The equation is $y = \dfrac{2ab}{x}.$

57.   Direct. The ratios $\dfrac{y}{x}$ always equal 1. $y = kx \Rightarrow 1 = 1k \Rightarrow k = 1$

58.   Inverse. The products xy always equal 6. $y = \dfrac{k}{x} \Rightarrow 6 = \dfrac{k}{1} \Rightarrow k = 6$

59.   Neither. The ratios $\dfrac{y}{x}$ do not remain constant.

60.   Neither. The products xy do not remain constant.

61.   Direct. The ratios $\dfrac{y}{x}$ always equal 2. $y = kx \Rightarrow 2 = 1k \Rightarrow k = 2$

62.   Inverse. The products xy always equal 8. $y = \dfrac{k}{x} \Rightarrow 8 = \dfrac{k}{1} \Rightarrow k = 8$

Applications

63. $\dfrac{6}{7} = \dfrac{x}{27} \Rightarrow 7x = 162 \Rightarrow x = \dfrac{162}{7} \approx 23.1$ feet

64. $\dfrac{600}{68} = \dfrac{360}{x} \Rightarrow 600x = 24,480 \Rightarrow x = \dfrac{24,480}{600} = 40.8$ min

65. $\dfrac{8}{1} = \dfrac{11}{x} \Rightarrow 8x = 11 \Rightarrow x = \dfrac{11}{8} = 1.375$ inches

66. $\dfrac{143}{11} = \dfrac{x}{17} \Rightarrow 11x = 2431 \Rightarrow x = \dfrac{2431}{11} = \$221$

67.   Let x be the total number of largemouth bass in the population.

$$\dfrac{300}{x} = \dfrac{17}{112} \Rightarrow 17x = 33,600 \Rightarrow x \approx 2000$$

68.   Let x be the total number of bald eagles in the population.

$$\dfrac{22}{x} = \dfrac{7}{56} \Rightarrow 7x = 1232 \Rightarrow x = 176$$

69. $d = kx^2; \ 300 = k(60)^2 \Rightarrow 300 = 3600k \Rightarrow k = \dfrac{1}{12}; \ d = \dfrac{1}{12}x^2, x = 30 \Rightarrow d = \dfrac{1}{12}(30)^2 = 75$ feet

70.   Let x represent the total points for the season.

$$\dfrac{132}{11} = \dfrac{x}{20} \Rightarrow 11x = 2640 \Rightarrow x = 240 \text{ points}$$

71.   (a) Direct; The ratios $\dfrac{R}{W}$ always equal 0.012.

(b) $R = 0.012W.$ See Figure 71.

(c) $R = 0.012(3200) = 38.4$ lb

72.   Here $6000 = \dfrac{k}{0.75} \Rightarrow k = 4500,$ that is $y = \dfrac{4500}{x}.$ When the toll is \$0.40, there will be $\dfrac{4500}{0.40} = 11{,}250$ users.

73.   (a) Direct; The ratios $\dfrac{G}{A}$ always equal 27.

      (b) $G = 27A.$ See Figure 73.

      (c) For each square inch increase in the cross-sectional area of the hose, the flow increases by 27 gal/min.

Figure 73

74.   (a) Direct; The ratios $\dfrac{D}{W}$ always equal 0.75.

      (b) $D = 0.75W$

      (c) $D = 0.75(11) = 8.25$ inches

75.   (a) $F = \dfrac{k}{L} \Rightarrow 150 = \dfrac{k}{8} \Rightarrow k = 1200$ and so $F = \dfrac{1200}{L}$

      (b) $F = \dfrac{1200}{20} = 60$ lb

76. $\dfrac{6}{435} = \dfrac{11}{x} \Rightarrow 6x = 4785 \Rightarrow \$797.50;$ In this problem k represents the tuition cost per credit.

77.   (a) Direct

      (b) $y = kx \Rightarrow -95 = 5k \Rightarrow k = -19$ and so $y = -19x$

      (c) It is negative. For each one mile increase in altitude the temperature decreases by 19°F.

      (d) $y = -19(3.5) = -66.5;$ The temperature decreases by 66.5°F.

78.   (a) Direct

      (b) $y = kx \Rightarrow 12 = 8k \Rightarrow k = 1.5$ and so $y = 1.5x$

      (c) $y = 1.5(7) = 10.5\ \%$

79. $\dfrac{35}{2} = \dfrac{25}{x} \Rightarrow 35x = 50 \Rightarrow x \approx 1.43$ ohms

80. $I = \dfrac{k}{R} \Rightarrow 0.8 = \dfrac{k}{150} \Rightarrow k = 120$ and so $I = \dfrac{120}{R};$ When $R = 40,\ I = \dfrac{120}{40} = 3$ amps

81. $z = kx^2 y^3 \Rightarrow 31.9 = (2)^2 (2.5)^3 k \Rightarrow 31.9 = 62.5k \Rightarrow k = 0.5104$ and so $z = 0.5104 x^2 y^3$

82. $P = kd^2 w^3 \Rightarrow 15,392 = (10)^2 (16)^3 k \Rightarrow 15,392 = 409,600k \Rightarrow k = \dfrac{15,392}{409,600}$ and so $P = \dfrac{15,392}{409,600} d^2 w^3$

When $d = 12$ and $w = 15$, $P = \dfrac{15,392}{409,600}(12)^2 (15)^3 \approx 18,263$ watts.

83. $S = kwt^2 \Rightarrow 300 = k(5)(3)^2 \Rightarrow 300 = 45k \Rightarrow k = \dfrac{20}{3}$ and so $S = \dfrac{20}{3} wt^2$

When $w = 5$ and $t = 2$, $S = \dfrac{20}{3}(5)(2)^2 \approx 133$ lb.

84. $C = kwl \Rightarrow 539 = k(11)(14) \Rightarrow 539 = 154k \Rightarrow k = 3.5$ and so $C = 3.5wl$

When $w = 17$ and $l = 19$, $C = 3.5(17)(19) = \$1130.50$; k represents a \$3.50 per square foot cost.

85. $W_m = kW_E \Rightarrow 28 = 175k \Rightarrow k = 0.16$; so $W_m = 0.16W_E$

A 220-pound person would weigh $W_m = 0.16(220) = 35.2$ pounds on the moon.

86. $W = \dfrac{k}{d^2} \Rightarrow 200 = \dfrac{k}{4000^2} \Rightarrow k = 3,200,000,000$; so $W = \dfrac{3,200,000,000}{d^2}$

The person would weigh $W = \dfrac{3,200,000,000}{7000^2} \approx 65.3$ pounds.

87. $V = kIR \Rightarrow 220 = (10)(22)k \Rightarrow k = 1$; so $V = IR$

When $I = 15$ and $R = 50$ the voltage is $V = (15)(50) = 750$.

88. $R = kxp \Rightarrow 24,000 = (3000)(8)k \Rightarrow k = 1$; so $R = xp$. That is $x = \dfrac{R}{p}$.

When $R = 30,000$ and $p = 6$ the number sold is $x = \dfrac{30,000}{6} = 5000$.

Checking Basic Concepts for Sections 6.5 & 6.6

1.   (a) $\dfrac{3 - \dfrac{1}{x^2}}{3 + \dfrac{1}{x^2}} = \dfrac{3 - \dfrac{1}{x^2}}{3 + \dfrac{1}{x^2}} \cdot \dfrac{x^2}{x^2} = \dfrac{3x^2 - 1}{3x^2 + 1}$

(b) $\dfrac{\dfrac{2}{x-1} - \dfrac{2}{x+1}}{\dfrac{4}{x^2 - 1}} = \dfrac{\dfrac{2}{x-1} - \dfrac{2}{x+1}}{\dfrac{4}{x^2 - 1}} \cdot \dfrac{(x-1)(x+1)}{(x-1)(x+1)} = \dfrac{2(x+1) - 2(x-1)}{4} = \dfrac{4}{4} = 1$

2.   (a) $y = kx \Rightarrow 6 = 8k \Rightarrow k = 0.75$

(b) $y = 0.75x \Rightarrow y = 0.75(11) = 8.25$

3.   (a) Direct. The ratios $\dfrac{y}{x}$ always equal 0.4. The equation is $y = 0.4x$.

      (b) Inverse. The products xy always equal 120. The equation is $y = \dfrac{120}{x}$.

6.7: Division of Polynomials

Concepts

1.   term

2. $\dfrac{a}{c} + \dfrac{b}{c}$

3. $5 \cdot 4 + 1$

4. $(3x - 5) \cdot (x - 2) + (-2)$

5.   No, the divisor is not of the form $x - k$.

6.   The remainder is the last number in the third row.

Division by a Monomial

7. $\dfrac{4x - 6}{2} = \dfrac{4x}{2} - \dfrac{6}{2} = 2x - 3$

      Table $Y_1 = (4X - 6)/2$ and $Y_2 = 2X - 3$ with TblStart = 0 and ΔTbl = 1. See Figure 7.

8. $\dfrac{4x^2 - 8x + 12}{4} = \dfrac{4x^2}{4} - \dfrac{8x}{4} + \dfrac{12}{4} = x^2 - 2x + 3$

      Table $Y_1 = (4X^2 - 8X + 12)/4$ and $Y_2 = X^2 - 2X + 3$ with TblStart = 0 and ΔTbl = 1. See Figure 8.

   Figure 7   Figure 8   Figure 9   Figure 10

9. $\dfrac{6x^3 - 9x}{3x} = \dfrac{6x^3}{3x} - \dfrac{9x}{3x} = 2x^2 - 3$

      Table $Y_1 = (6X \wedge 3 - 9X)/(3X)$ and $Y_2 = 2X^2 - 3$ with TblStart = 0 and ΔTbl = 1. See Figure 9.

10. $\dfrac{3x^4 + x^2}{6x^2} = \dfrac{3x^4}{6x^2} + \dfrac{x^2}{6x^2} = \dfrac{1}{2}x^2 + \dfrac{1}{6}$

      Table $Y_1 = (3X \wedge 4 + X^2)/(6X^2)$ and $Y_2 = (1/2)X^2 + (1/6)$ with TblStart = 0 and ΔTbl = 1. See Figure 10.

11. $(4x^2 - x + 1) \div 2x^2 = \dfrac{4x^2}{2x^2} - \dfrac{x}{2x^2} + \dfrac{1}{2x^2} = 2 - \dfrac{1}{2x} + \dfrac{1}{2x^2}$

      Table $Y_1 = (4X^2 - X + 1)/(2X^2)$ and $Y_2 = 2 - 1/(2X) + 1/(2X^2)$ with TblStart = 0 and ΔTbl = 1. See Figure 11.

Figure 11   Figure 12

12. $\left(5x^3 - 4x + 2\right) \div 20x = \dfrac{5x^3}{20x} - \dfrac{4x}{20x} + \dfrac{2}{20x} = \dfrac{1}{4}x^2 - \dfrac{1}{5} + \dfrac{1}{10x}$

Table $Y_1 = \left(5X^\wedge 3 - 4X + 2\right)/\left(20X\right)$ and $Y_2 = \left(1/4\right)X^2 - 1/5 + 1/\left(10X\right)$ with TblStart $= 0$ and ΔTbl $= 1$.

See Figure 12.

13. $\dfrac{9x^2 - 12x - 3}{3} = \dfrac{9x^2}{3} - \dfrac{12x}{3} - \dfrac{3}{3} = 3x^2 - 4x - 1$

14. $\dfrac{10x^3 - 15x^2 + 5x}{5} = \dfrac{10x^3}{5} - \dfrac{15x^2}{5} + \dfrac{5x}{5} = 2x^3 - 3x^2 + x$

15. $\dfrac{12a^3 - 18a}{6a} = \dfrac{12a^3}{6a} - \dfrac{18a}{6a} = 2a^2 - 3$

16. $\dfrac{50x^4 + 25x^2 + 100x}{25x} = \dfrac{50x^4}{25x} + \dfrac{25x^2}{25x} + \dfrac{100x}{25x} = 2x^3 + x + 4$

17. $\left(16x^3 - 24x\right) \div \left(12x\right) = \dfrac{16x^3}{12x} - \dfrac{24x}{12x} = \dfrac{4}{3}x^2 - 2$

18. $\left(2y^4 - 4y^2 + 16\right) \div 2y^2 = \dfrac{2y^4}{2y^2} - \dfrac{4y^2}{2y^2} + \dfrac{16}{2y^2} = y^2 - 2 + \dfrac{8}{y^2}$

19. $\left(a^2b^2 - 4ab + ab^2\right) \div ab = \dfrac{a^2b^2}{ab} - \dfrac{4ab}{ab} + \dfrac{ab^2}{ab} = ab - 4 + b$

20. $\left(10x^3y^2 + 5x^2y^3\right) \div \left(5x^2y^2\right) = \dfrac{10x^3y^2}{5x^2y^2} + \dfrac{5x^2y^3}{5x^2y^2} = 2x + y$

21. $\dfrac{6m^4n^4 + 3m^2n^2 - 12}{3m^2n^2} = \dfrac{6m^4n^4}{3m^2n^2} + \dfrac{3m^2n^2}{3m^2n^2} - \dfrac{12}{3m^2n^2} = 2m^2n^2 + 1 - \dfrac{4}{m^2n^2}$

22. $\dfrac{6p^2q^4 - 9p^6q^2}{-3pq} = \dfrac{6p^2q^4}{-3pq} - \dfrac{9p^6q^2}{-3pq} = -2pq^3 + 3p^5q$

Division by a Polynomial

23. $3x - 7$ The solution is: $3x - 7$

$$x - 3 \overline{)3x^2 - 16x + 21}$$

$$\underline{3x^2 - 9x}$$

$$-7x + 21$$

$$\underline{-7x + 21}$$

$$0$$

24.

$$
\begin{array}{r}
4x-9 \\
x+2\overline{\smash{\big)}\,4x^2 - x - 18} \\
\underline{4x^2 + 8x} \\
-9x-18 \\
\underline{-9x-18} \\
0
\end{array}
$$

The solution is: $4x-9$

25.

$$
\begin{array}{r}
x^2 - 1 \\
2x+3\overline{\smash{\big)}\,2x^3 + 3x^2 - 2x - 2} \\
\underline{2x^3 + 3x^2} \\
-2x-2 \\
\underline{-2x-3} \\
1
\end{array}
$$

The solution is: $x^2 - 1 + \dfrac{1}{2x+3}$

26.

$$
\begin{array}{r}
2x^2 - 3x - 6 \\
x-2\overline{\smash{\big)}\,2x^3 - 7x^2 + 0x + 8} \\
\underline{2x^3 - 4x^2} \\
-3x^2 + 0x \\
\underline{-3x^2 + 6x} \\
-6x+8 \\
\underline{-6x+12} \\
-4
\end{array}
$$

The solution is: $2x^2 - 3x - 6 - \dfrac{4}{x-2}$

27.

$$
\begin{array}{r}
10x + 10 \\
x-1\overline{\smash{\big)}\,10x^2 + 0x - 5} \\
\underline{10x^2 - 10x} \\
10x - 5 \\
\underline{10x - 10} \\
5
\end{array}
$$

The solution is: $10x + 10 + \dfrac{5}{x-1}$

28.

$$
\begin{array}{r}
3x - 1 \\
2x-3\overline{\smash{\big)}\,6x^2 - 11x + 4} \\
\underline{6x^2 - 9x} \\
-2x + 4 \\
\underline{-2x + 3} \\
1
\end{array}
$$

The solution is: $3x - 1 + \dfrac{1}{2x-3}$

29.

$$\begin{array}{r} 4x^2-1 \\ x+2\overline{\smash{\big)}4x^3+8x^2-x-2} \\ \underline{4x^3+8x^2} \\ 0-x-2 \\ \underline{-x-2} \\ 0 \end{array}$$

The solution is: $4x^2-1$

30.

$$\begin{array}{r} 3x^2-x+2 \\ x-1\overline{\smash{\big)}3x^3-4x^2+3x-2} \\ \underline{3x^3-3x^2} \\ -x^2+3x \\ \underline{-x^2+x} \\ 2x-2 \\ \underline{2x-2} \\ 0 \end{array}$$

The solution is: $3x^2-x+2$

31.

$$\begin{array}{r} x^2-4x+19 \\ x+4\overline{\smash{\big)}x^3+0x^2+3x-4} \\ \underline{x^3+4x^2} \\ -4x^2+\ 3x \\ \underline{-4x^2-16x} \\ 19x-4 \\ \underline{19x+76} \\ -80 \end{array}$$

The solution is: $x^2-4x+19-\dfrac{80}{x+4}$

32.

$$\begin{array}{r} 2x^2+3x+6 \\ x-2\overline{\smash{\big)}2x^3-x^2+0x+5} \\ \underline{2x^3-4x^2} \\ 3x^2+0x \\ \underline{3x^2-6x} \\ 6x+5 \\ \underline{6x-12} \\ 17 \end{array}$$

The solution is: $2x^2+3x+6+\dfrac{17}{x-2}$

33.

$$\begin{array}{r} x^2 + 3x - 6 \\ 3x-1{\overline{\smash{\big)}\,3x^3 + 8x^2 - 21x + 7}} \\ \underline{3x^3 - x^2} \\ 9x^2 - 21x \\ \underline{9x^2 - 3x} \\ -18x + 7 \\ \underline{-18x + 6} \\ 1 \end{array}$$

The solution is: $x^2 + 3x - 6 + \dfrac{1}{3x-1}$

34.

$$\begin{array}{r} 2x^2 + x - 1 \\ 7x-2{\overline{\smash{\big)}\,14x^3 + 3x^2 - 9x + 3}} \\ \underline{14x^3 - 4x^2} \\ 7x^2 - 9x \\ \underline{7x^2 - 2x} \\ -7x + 3 \\ \underline{-7x + 2} \\ 1 \end{array}$$

The solution is: $2x^2 + x - 1 + \dfrac{1}{7x-2}$

35.

$$\begin{array}{r} a^3 - a \\ 2a+5{\overline{\smash{\big)}\,2a^4 + 5a^3 - 2a^2 - 5a}} \\ \underline{2a^4 + 5a^3} \\ 0 - 2a^2 - 5a \\ \underline{-2a^2 - 5a} \\ 0 \end{array}$$

The solution is: $a^3 - a$

36.

$$\begin{array}{r} 2b^3 + 4b^2 - 3b \\ 2b+1{\overline{\smash{\big)}\,4b^4 + 10b^3 - 2b^2 - 3b + 5}} \\ \underline{4b^4 + 2b^3} \\ 8b^3 - 2b^2 \\ \underline{8b^3 + 4b^2} \\ -6b^2 - 3b \\ \underline{-6b^2 - 3b} \\ 0 + 5 \end{array}$$

The solution is: $2b^3 + 4b^2 - 3b + \dfrac{5}{2b+1}$

37.

$$
\begin{array}{r}
3x + 4 \\
x^2 + 0x - 4 \overline{\smash{)}3x^3 + 4x^2 - 12x - 16} \\
\underline{3x^3 + 0x^2 - 12x} \\
4x^2 + 0x - 16 \\
\underline{4x^2 + 0x - 16} \\
0
\end{array}
$$

The solution is: $3x + 4$

38.

$$
\begin{array}{r}
x^2 - 4 \\
2x^2 - x + 3 \overline{\smash{)}2x^4 - x^3 - 5x^2 + 4x - 12} \\
\underline{2x^4 - x^3 + 3x^2} \\
-8x^2 + 4x - 12 \\
\underline{-8x^2 + 4x - 12} \\
0
\end{array}
$$

The solution is: $x^2 - 4$

39.

$$
\begin{array}{r}
x + 1 \\
x^2 + 0x - 1 \overline{\smash{)}x^3 + x^2 - x + 0} \\
\underline{x^3 + 0x^2 - x} \\
x^2 + 0x + 0 \\
\underline{x^2 + 0x - 1} \\
1
\end{array}
$$

The solution is: $x + 1 + \dfrac{1}{x^2 - 1}$

40.

$$
\begin{array}{r}
x + 3 \\
x^2 - 2x \overline{\smash{)}x^3 + x^2 - 6x} \\
\underline{x^3 - 2x^2} \\
3x^2 - 6x \\
\underline{3x^2 - 6x} \\
0
\end{array}
$$

The solution is: $x + 3$

41.

$$
\begin{array}{r}
2a^2 - a + 3 \\
a^2 - a + 5 \overline{\smash{)}2a^4 - 3a^3 + 14a^2 - 8a + 10} \\
\underline{2a^4 - 2a^3 + 10a^2} \\
-a^3 + 4a^2 - 8a + 10 \\
\underline{-a^3 + a^2 - 5a} \\
3a^2 - 3a + 10 \\
\underline{3a^2 - 3a + 15} \\
-5
\end{array}
$$

The solution is: $2a^2 - a + 3 - \dfrac{5}{a^2 - a + 5}$

42.

$$z^2 + 0z - 1 \overline{)\begin{array}{c} 2z + 3 \\ 2z^3 + 3z^2 - 9z - 12 \end{array}}$$

$$\underline{2z^3 + 0z^2 - 2z}$$
$$3z^2 - 7z - 12$$
$$\underline{3z^2 + 0z - 3}$$
$$-7z - 9$$

The solution is: $2z + 3 - \dfrac{7z + 9}{z^2 - 1}$

43. $\left(a^2 + ab + b^2\right)(a - b) + 1 = a^3 + a^2 b + ab^2 - a^2 b - ab^2 - b^3 + 1$

$= a^3 - b^3 + 1$

44. $\left(x^3 + x^2 - 3x - 2\right) - 1 = x^3 + x^2 - 3x - 3$

$$x^2 - 3 \overline{)\begin{array}{c} x + 1 \\ x^3 + x^2 - 3x - 3 \end{array}}$$

$$\underline{x^3 + 0x^2 - 3x}$$
$$x^2 + 0x - 3$$
$$\underline{x^2 + 0x - 3}$$
$$0$$

The divisor is $x + 1$.

Synthetic Division

45.

$$\begin{array}{r|rrr} 1 & 1 & 3 & -1 \\ & & 1 & 4 \\ \hline & 1 & 4 & 3 \end{array}$$

The solution is: $x + 4 + \dfrac{3}{x - 1}$

46.

$$\begin{array}{r|rrr} 3 & 2 & 1 & -1 \\ & & 6 & 21 \\ \hline & 2 & 7 & 20 \end{array}$$

The solution is: $2x + 7 + \dfrac{20}{x - 3}$

47.

$$\begin{array}{r|rrr} 7 & 3 & -22 & 7 \\ & & 21 & -7 \\ \hline & 3 & -1 & 0 \end{array}$$

The solution is: $3x - 1$

48.

$$\begin{array}{r|rrr} -6 & 5 & 29 & -6 \\ & & -30 & 6 \\ \hline & 5 & -1 & 0 \end{array}$$

The solution is: $5x - 1$

49.

$$\begin{array}{r|rrrr} -4 & 1 & 7 & 14 & 8 \\ & & -4 & -12 & -8 \\ \hline & 1 & 3 & 2 & 0 \end{array}$$

The solution is: $x^2 + 3x + 2$

50.

$$\begin{array}{r|rrrr} -1 & 2 & 3 & 2 & 4 \\ & & -2 & -1 & -1 \\ \hline & 2 & 1 & 1 & 3 \end{array}$$

The solution is: $2x^2 + x + 1 + \dfrac{3}{x + 1}$

51.

$$\begin{array}{r|rrrr} 2 & 2 & 1 & 0 & -1 \\ & & 4 & 10 & 20 \\ \hline & 2 & 5 & 10 & 19 \end{array}$$

The solution is: $2x^2 + 5x + 10 + \dfrac{19}{x - 2}$

52. $-3 \rfloor$ $\begin{array}{rrrr} 1 & 0 & 1 & -2 \\ & -3 & 9 & -30 \\ \hline 1 & -3 & 10 & -32 \end{array}$ The solution is: $x^2 - 3x + 10 - \dfrac{32}{x+3}$

53. $-2 \rfloor$ $\begin{array}{rrrrr} 2 & 0 & 3 & 0 & -4 \\ & -4 & 8 & -22 & 44 \\ \hline 2 & -4 & 11 & -22 & 40 \end{array}$ The solution is: $2x^3 - 4x^2 + 11x - 22 + \dfrac{40}{x+2}$

54. $4 \rfloor$ $\begin{array}{rrrr} 1 & -2 & -2 & 4 \\ & 4 & 8 & 24 \\ \hline 1 & 2 & 6 & 28 \end{array}$ The solution is: $x^2 + 2x + 6 + \dfrac{28}{x-4}$

55. $1 \rfloor$ $\begin{array}{rrrrr} 1 & 0 & 0 & 0 & -1 \\ & 1 & 1 & 1 & 1 \\ \hline 1 & 1 & 1 & 1 & 0 \end{array}$ The solution is: $b^3 + b^2 + b + 1$

56. $-2.5 \rfloor$ $\begin{array}{rrr} 1 & 1 & 0 \\ & -2.5 & 3.75 \\ \hline 1 & -1.5 & 3.75 \end{array}$ The solution is: $a - 1.5 + \dfrac{3.75}{a+2.5}$

Geometry

57. Use polynomial division to find $\left(6x^2 + 7x - 5\right) \div \left(2x - 1\right) = 3x + 5$. That is, $L = 3x + 5$.

When $x = 8$, $L = 3(8) + 5 = 29$ feet.

58. Use polynomial division to find $\left(12x^2 + x - 2\right) \div \left(4x + 3\right) = 3x - 2 + \dfrac{4}{4x+3}$.

That is, $W = 3x - 2 + \dfrac{4}{4x+3}$. When $x = 20$, $W = 3(20) - 2 + \dfrac{4}{4(20)+3} = 58 + \dfrac{4}{83} = 58\dfrac{4}{83}$ feet.

59. The volume of a box is $V = lwh$, so $h = \dfrac{V}{lw}$. Divide the volume by the length times the width.

Use polynomial division to find $\left(x^3 + 7x^2 + 14x + 8\right) \div \left(x^2 + 5x + 4\right) = x + 2$. That is, $h = x + 2$.

60. The area of a triangle is $A = \dfrac{1}{2}bh$, so $b = \dfrac{2A}{h}$. Divide twice the area by the height.

Use polynomial division to find $\left(24x^2 - 10x - 6\right) \div \left(3x + 1\right) = 8x - 6$. That is, $b = 8x - 6$.

61. (a) By synthetic division the remainder for $\left(x^2 - 3x + 2\right) \div \left(x - 1\right)$ is 0.

$p(1) = (1)^2 - 3(1) + 2 = 0$

(b) By synthetic division the remainder for $\left(3x^2 + 5x - 2\right) \div \left(x + 2\right)$ is 0.

$p(-2) = 3(-2)^2 + 5(-2) - 2 = 0$

(c) By synthetic division the remainder for $\left(3x^3 - 4x^2 - 5x + 3\right) \div \left(x - 2\right)$ is 1.

$p(2) = 3(2)^3 - 4(2)^2 - 5(2) + 3 = 1$

(d) By synthetic division the remainder for $\left(x^3 - 2x^2 - x + 2\right) \div \left(x + 1\right)$ is 0.

$$p(-1) = (-1)^3 - 2(-1)^2 - (-1) + 2 = 0$$

(e) By synthetic division the remainder for $\left(x^4 - 5x^2 - 1\right) \div (x - 3)$ is 35.

$$p(3) = (3)^4 - 5(3)^2 - 1 = 35$$

62.   If $\dfrac{p(x)}{x-k}$ has remainder r, then $p(k) = r$.

63.   (a) $p(2) = (2)^2 + (2) - 6 = 0$

Yes, it is a factor because by synthetic division $\left(x^2 + x - 6\right) \div (x - 2) = x + 3$.

(b) $p(1) = (1)^2 + 4(1) - 5 = 0$

Yes, it is a factor because by synthetic division $\left(x^2 + 4x - 5\right) \div (x - 1) = x + 5$.

(c) $p(-2) = (-2)^2 + 8(-2) + 11 = -1$

No, it is not a factor because by synthetic division $\left(x^2 + 8x + 11\right) \div (x + 2) = x + 6$ Remainder -1.

(d) $p(-1) = (-1)^3 + (-1)^2 + (-1) + 1 = 0$

Yes, it is a factor because by synthetic division $\left(x^3 + x^2 + x + 1\right) \div (x + 1) = x^2 + 1$.

(e) $p(2) = (2)^3 - 3(2)^2 - (2) - 3 = -9$

No, it is not a factor because $\left(x^3 - 3x^2 - x - 3\right) \div (x - 2) = x^2 - x - 3$ Remainder -9.

64.   If $p(k) = 0$, then $x - k$ is a factor of $p(x)$.

Checking Basic Concepts for Section 6.7

1.
(a) $\dfrac{2x - x^2}{x^2} = \dfrac{2x}{x^2} - \dfrac{x^2}{x^2} = \dfrac{2}{x} - 1$

(b) $\dfrac{6a^2 - 9a + 15}{3a} = \dfrac{6a^2}{3a} - \dfrac{9a}{3a} + \dfrac{15}{3a} = 2a - 3 + \dfrac{5}{a}$

2.
$$\begin{array}{r} 5x - 3 \\ 2x+1\overline{)10x^2 - x + 4} \\ \underline{10x^2 + 5x} \\ -6x + 4 \\ \underline{-6x - 3} \\ 7 \end{array}$$

The solution is: $5x - 3 + \dfrac{7}{2x+1}$

3.
(a)
$$\begin{array}{r} 1\underline{|} 2 \quad -5 \quad\ 0 \quad -1 \\ 2 \quad -3 \quad -3 \\ \hline 2 \quad -3 \quad -3 \quad -4 \end{array}$$

The solution is: $2x^2 - 3x - 3 - \dfrac{4}{x-1}$

(b) $\dfrac{-2|\quad 2 \quad -5 \quad 0 \quad -1}{\begin{array}{cccc} & -4 & 18 & -36 \\ \hline 2 & -9 & 18 & -37 \end{array}}$ The solution is: $2x^2 - 9x + 18 - \dfrac{37}{x+2}$

Chapter 6 Review Exercises

Section 6.1

1.   Symbolic: $f(x) = \dfrac{1}{x-1}$

2.   Symbolic: $f(x) = \dfrac{x-3}{x}$

3.   See Figure 3. Because the denominator cannot be equal to 0, the domain is $\{x \mid x \neq -2\}$.

Figure 3

4. $f(3) = \dfrac{1}{(3)^2 - 1} = \dfrac{1}{9-1} = \dfrac{1}{8}$; The values $x = \pm 1$ are not in the domain of f.

5. $f(-3) = \dfrac{3}{(-3)+2} = \dfrac{3}{-1} = -3$ and $f(2) = \dfrac{3}{(2)+2} = \dfrac{3}{4} = 0.75$

6. $f(-2) = \dfrac{2(-2)}{(-2)^2 - 4} = \dfrac{-4}{0}$ is undefined and $f(3) = \dfrac{2(3)}{(3)^2 - 4} = \dfrac{6}{5} = 1.2$

7. $f(0) = 3$ and $f(2) = 1$; The equation of the vertical asymptote is $x = 1$.

8. $f(-3) = 2$ and $f(-2)$ is undefined; The equation of the vertical asymptote is $x = -2$.

9.   The LCD is x. The first step is to multiply both sides of the equation by the LCD.

$$x \cdot \left(\frac{3-x}{x} \right) = 2 \cdot x \Rightarrow 3 - x = 2x \Rightarrow 3 = 3x \Rightarrow x = 1$$

10.   The LCD is $5(x+3)$. The first step is to multiply both sides of the equation by the LCD.

$$5(x+3) \cdot \left(\frac{1}{x+3} \right) = \frac{1}{5} \cdot 5(x+3) \Rightarrow 5 = x + 3 \Rightarrow x = 2$$

11.   The LCD is $x - 2$. The first step is to multiply both sides of the equation by the LCD.

$$(x-2) \cdot \left(\frac{x}{x-2} \right) = (x-2) \cdot \frac{2x-2}{x-2} \Rightarrow x = 2x - 2 \Rightarrow x = 2$$

Some expressions in the original equation are not defined when $x = 2$. No solutions.

12.   The LCD is $2-3x$. The first step is to multiply both sides of the equation by the LCD.

$$(2-3x)\cdot\left(\frac{4}{2-3x}\right)=-1\cdot(2-3x)\Rightarrow 4=3x-2\Rightarrow 3x=6\Rightarrow x=2$$

13.   (a) $(f+g)(3)=\left(2(3)^2-3(3)\right)+(2(3)-3)=(2(9)-9)+(6-3)=(18-9)+3=9+3=12$

       (b) $(fg)(3)=\left(2(3)^2-3(3)\right)(2(3)-3)=(2(9)-9)(6-3)=(18-9)(3)=9(3)=27$

14.   (a) $(f-g)(x)=\left(x^2-1\right)-(x-1)=x^2-x$

       (b) $(f/g)(x)=\frac{x^2-1}{x-1}=\frac{(x-1)(x+1)}{x-1}=x+1$

Section 6.2

15. $\dfrac{4a}{6a^4}=\dfrac{2}{3a^3}$

16. $\dfrac{(x-3)(x+2)}{(x+1)(x-3)}=\dfrac{x+2}{x+1}$

17. $\dfrac{x^2-4}{x-2}=\dfrac{(x-2)(x+2)}{x-2}=x+2$

18. $\dfrac{x^2-6x-7}{2x^2-x-3}=\dfrac{(x-7)(x+1)}{(2x-3)(x+1)}=\dfrac{x-7}{2x-3}$

19. $\dfrac{8-x}{x-8}=\dfrac{-1(x-8)}{x-8}=-1$

20. $-\dfrac{3-2x}{2x-3}=\dfrac{-1(3-2x)}{2x-3}=\dfrac{2x-3}{2x-3}=1$

21. $\dfrac{1}{2y}\cdot\dfrac{4y^2}{8}=\dfrac{1}{2}\cdot\dfrac{y}{2}=\dfrac{y}{4}$

22. $\dfrac{x+2}{x-5}\cdot\dfrac{x-5}{x+1}=\dfrac{x+2}{1}\cdot\dfrac{1}{x+1}=\dfrac{x+2}{x+1}$

23. $\dfrac{x^2+1}{x^2-1}\cdot\dfrac{x-1}{x+1}=\dfrac{x^2+1}{(x-1)(x+1)}\cdot\dfrac{x-1}{x+1}=\dfrac{x^2+1}{x+1}\cdot\dfrac{1}{x+1}=\dfrac{x^2+1}{(x+1)^2}$

24. $\dfrac{x^2+2x+1}{x^2-9}\cdot\dfrac{x+3}{x+1}=\dfrac{(x+1)(x+1)}{(x-3)(x+3)}\cdot\dfrac{x+3}{x+1}=\dfrac{x+1}{x-3}\cdot\dfrac{1}{1}=\dfrac{x+1}{x-3}$

25. $\dfrac{1}{3y}\div\dfrac{1}{9y^4}=\dfrac{1}{3y}\cdot\dfrac{9y^4}{1}=\dfrac{1}{1}\cdot\dfrac{3y^3}{1}=3y^3$

26. $\dfrac{2x+2}{3x-3}\div\dfrac{x+1}{x-1}=\dfrac{2(x+1)}{3(x-1)}\cdot\dfrac{x-1}{x+1}=\dfrac{2}{3}\cdot\dfrac{1}{1}=\dfrac{2}{3}$

27. $\dfrac{x^2+2x}{x^2-25} \div \dfrac{x+2}{x+5} = \dfrac{x(x+2)}{(x-5)(x+5)} \cdot \dfrac{x+5}{x+2} = \dfrac{x}{x-5} \cdot \dfrac{1}{1} = \dfrac{x}{x-5}$

28. $\dfrac{x^2+2x-15}{x^2+4x+3} \div \dfrac{x-3}{x+1} = \dfrac{(x+5)(x-3)}{(x+3)(x+1)} \cdot \dfrac{x+1}{x-3} = \dfrac{x+5}{x+3} \cdot \dfrac{1}{1} = \dfrac{x+5}{x+3}$

29. $\dfrac{x^2+x-2}{2x^2-7x+3} \cdot \dfrac{x^2-3x}{x^2+2x-3} = \dfrac{(x+2)(x-1)}{(2x-1)(x-3)} \cdot \dfrac{x(x-3)}{(x+3)(x-1)} = \dfrac{x(x+2)}{(2x-1)(x+3)}$

30. $\dfrac{x^2+3x+2}{x^2+7x+12} \div \dfrac{x^2+4x+4}{x^2+4x+3} = \dfrac{(x+2)(x+1)}{(x+3)(x+4)} \cdot \dfrac{(x+3)(x+1)}{(x+2)(x+2)} = \dfrac{(x+1)^2}{(x+2)(x+4)}$

Section 6.3

31. $36 = 2 \cdot 2 \cdot 3 \cdot 3$ and $24 = 2 \cdot 2 \cdot 2 \cdot 3$ and $16 = 2 \cdot 2 \cdot 2 \cdot 2$. The LCM is $2 \cdot 2 \cdot 2 \cdot 2 \cdot 3 \cdot 3 = 144$.

32. $4ab = 2 \cdot 2 \cdot a \cdot b$ and $a^2b = a \cdot a \cdot b$. The LCM is $2 \cdot 2 \cdot a \cdot a \cdot b = 4a^2b$.

33. $9x^2y = 3 \cdot 3 \cdot x \cdot x \cdot y$ and $6xy^3 = 2 \cdot 3 \cdot x \cdot y \cdot y \cdot y$. The LCM is $2 \cdot 3 \cdot 3 \cdot x \cdot x \cdot y \cdot y \cdot y = 18x^2y^3$.

34. $x-1 = (x-1)$ and $x+2 = (x+2)$. The LCM is $(x-1)(x+2)$.

35. $x^2-9 = (x-3)(x+3)$ and $x(x+3) = x(x+3)$. The LCM is $x(x-3)(x+3)$.

36. $x^2 = x \cdot x$ and $x-3 = (x-3)$ and $x^2-6x+9 = (x-3)^2$. The LCM is $x^2(x-3)^2$.

37. $\dfrac{1}{x+4} + \dfrac{3}{x+4} = \dfrac{1+3}{x+4} = \dfrac{4}{x+4}$

38. $\dfrac{2}{x} + \dfrac{x-3}{x} = \dfrac{2+x-3}{x} = \dfrac{x-1}{x}$

39. $\dfrac{1}{x+1} - \dfrac{x}{x+1} = \dfrac{1-x}{x+1}$

40. $\dfrac{2x}{x-2} - \dfrac{2}{x-2} = \dfrac{2x-2}{x-2}$

41. $\dfrac{4}{1-t} + \dfrac{t}{t-1} = \dfrac{4}{-1(t-1)} + \dfrac{t}{t-1} = \dfrac{-4}{t-1} + \dfrac{t}{t-1} = \dfrac{t-4}{t-1}$

42. $\dfrac{2}{y-2} - \dfrac{2}{y+2} = \dfrac{2(y+2)}{(y-2)(y+2)} - \dfrac{2(y-2)}{(y-2)(y+2)} = \dfrac{2y+4-2y+4}{(y-2)(y+2)} = \dfrac{8}{(y-2)(y+2)}$

43. $\dfrac{4b}{a^2c} - \dfrac{3a}{b^2c} = \dfrac{4b^3}{a^2b^2c} - \dfrac{3a^3}{a^2b^2c} = \dfrac{4b^3-3a^3}{a^2b^2c}$

44. $\dfrac{r}{5t^2} + \dfrac{t}{5r^2} = \dfrac{r^3}{5r^2t^2} + \dfrac{t^3}{5r^2t^2} = \dfrac{r^3+t^3}{5r^2t^2}$

45. $\dfrac{4}{a^2-b^2} - \dfrac{2}{a+b} = \dfrac{4}{(a-b)(a+b)} - \dfrac{2(a-b)}{(a-b)(a+b)} = \dfrac{4-2a+2b}{(a-b)(a+b)} = -\dfrac{2(a-b-2)}{(a-b)(a+b)}$

46. $\dfrac{a}{a-b}+\dfrac{b}{a+b}=\dfrac{a(a+b)}{(a-b)(a+b)}+\dfrac{b(a-b)}{(a-b)(a+b)}=\dfrac{a^2+2ab-b^2}{(a-b)(a+b)}$

47. $\dfrac{1}{x^2-3x+2}+\dfrac{1}{x^2+x-2}=\dfrac{1}{(x-2)(x-1)}+\dfrac{1}{(x+2)(x-1)}$

$=\dfrac{x+2}{(x-2)(x-1)(x+2)}+\dfrac{x-2}{(x-2)(x-1)(x+2)}=\dfrac{x+2+x-2}{(x-2)(x-1)(x+2)}$

$=\dfrac{2x}{(x-2)(x-1)(x+2)}$

48. $\dfrac{1}{x^2-5x+6}-\dfrac{1}{x^2+x-6}=\dfrac{1}{(x-2)(x-3)}-\dfrac{1}{(x+3)(x-2)}$

$=\dfrac{x+3}{(x-3)(x-2)(x+3)}-\dfrac{x-3}{(x-3)(x-2)(x+3)}=\dfrac{x+3-x+3}{(x-3)(x-2)(x+3)}$

$=\dfrac{6}{(x-3)(x-2)(x+3)}$

49. $\dfrac{1}{x-2}+\dfrac{2}{x+2}-\dfrac{x}{x-2}=\dfrac{x+2}{(x-2)(x+2)}+\dfrac{2(x-2)}{(x-2)(x+2)}-\dfrac{x(x+2)}{(x-2)(x+2)}$

$=\dfrac{x+2+2x-4-x^2-2x}{(x-2)(x+2)}=\dfrac{-x^2+x-2}{(x-2)(x+2)}$

50. $\dfrac{2x}{2x-1}-\dfrac{3}{2x+1}-\dfrac{1}{2x-1}=\dfrac{2x(2x+1)}{(2x-1)(2x+1)}-\dfrac{3(2x-1)}{(2x-1)(2x+1)}-\dfrac{2x+1}{(2x-1)(2x+1)}$

$=\dfrac{4x^2+2x-6x+3-2x-1}{(2x-1)(2x+1)}=\dfrac{4x^2-6x+2}{(2x-1)(2x+1)}=\dfrac{2(x-1)(2x-1)}{(2x-1)(2x+1)}$

$=\dfrac{2x-2}{2x+1}$

Section 6.4

51. The LCD is $2x$. The first step is to multiply both sides of the equation by the LCD.

$\dfrac{4}{x}-\dfrac{5}{2x}=\dfrac{1}{2}\Rightarrow 2x\cdot\dfrac{4}{x}-2x\cdot\dfrac{5}{2x}=\dfrac{1}{2}\cdot 2x\Rightarrow 8-5=x\Rightarrow x=3$

52. Cross multiply to obtain the following.

$\dfrac{1}{x-4}=\dfrac{3}{2x-1}\Rightarrow 3(x-4)=1(2x-1)\Rightarrow 3x-12=2x-1\Rightarrow x=11$

53. The LCD is x^2. The first step is to multiply both sides of the equation by the LCD.

$x^2\cdot\left(\dfrac{2}{x^2}-\dfrac{1}{x}\right)=1\cdot x^2\Rightarrow 2-x=x^2\Rightarrow x^2+x-2=0\Rightarrow (x+2)(x-1)=0\Rightarrow x=-2 \text{ or } x=1$

54. The LCD is $x(x+4)$. The first step is to multiply both sides of the equation by the LCD.

$$x(x+4)\cdot\left(\frac{1}{x+4}-\frac{1}{x}\right)=1\cdot x(x+4)\Rightarrow x-(x+4)=x^2+4x\Rightarrow x^2+4x+4=0\Rightarrow (x+2)(x+2)=0\Rightarrow x=-2$$

55. The LCD is $3(x-1)(x+1)$. The first step is to multiply both sides of the equation by the LCD.

$$3(x-1)(x+1)\cdot\left(\frac{1}{x^2-1}-\frac{1}{x-1}\right)=\frac{2}{3}\cdot 3(x-1)(x+1)\Rightarrow 3-3(x+1)=2(x-1)(x+1)\Rightarrow$$

$$3-3x-3=2x^2-2\Rightarrow 2x^2+3x-2=0\Rightarrow (x+2)(2x-1)=0\Rightarrow x=-2 \text{ or } x=\frac{1}{2}$$

56. The LCD is $(x-3)(x+3)$. The first step is to multiply both sides of the equation by the LCD.

$$(x^2-9)\cdot\left(\frac{1}{x-3}+\frac{1}{x+3}\right)=\frac{-5}{x^2-9}\cdot(x^2-9)\Rightarrow x+3+x-3=-5\Rightarrow 2x=-5\Rightarrow x=-\frac{5}{2}$$

57. The LCD is $(x+2)(x-2)^2$. The first step is to multiply both sides of the equation by the LCD.

$$(x+2)(x-2)^2\cdot\frac{1}{(x-2)^2}-(x+2)(x-2)^2\cdot\frac{1}{x^2-4}=\frac{2}{(x-2)^2}\cdot(x+2)(x-2)^2\Rightarrow$$

$$x+2-(x-2)=2(x+2)\Rightarrow 4=2x+4\Rightarrow 2x=0\Rightarrow x=0$$

58. The LCD is $2(x+1)(x+2)$. The first step is to multiply both sides of the equation by the LCD.

$$2(x+1)(x+2)\cdot\frac{1}{x^2+3x+2}+2(x+1)(x+2)\cdot\frac{x}{x+2}=\frac{1}{2}\cdot 2(x+1)(x+2)\Rightarrow$$

$$2+2x(x+1)=(x+1)(x+2)\Rightarrow 2x^2+2x+2=x^2+3x+2\Rightarrow x^2-x=0\Rightarrow x=0 \text{ or } x=1$$

59. $$\frac{-3x-3}{x-3}+\frac{x^2+x}{x-3}=7x+7\Rightarrow \frac{-3x-3+x^2+x}{x-3}=7x+7$$

$$\Rightarrow \frac{x^2-2x-3}{x-3}=7x+7\Rightarrow \frac{(x-3)(x+1)}{x-3}=7x+7$$

$$\Rightarrow x+1=7x+7\Rightarrow -6x=6\Rightarrow x=-1$$

60. $$\frac{1}{x-4}+\frac{x}{x+4}=\frac{8}{x^2-4}\Rightarrow (x-4)(x+4)\cdot\frac{1}{x-4}+(x-4)(x+4)\cdot\frac{x}{x+4}$$

$$=\frac{8}{(x-4)(x+4)}\cdot(x-4)(x+4)\Rightarrow x+4+x(x-4)=8$$

$$\Rightarrow x+4+x^2-4x=8\Rightarrow x^2-3x-4=0\Rightarrow (x-4)(x+1)=0$$

$$\Rightarrow x-4=0 \text{ or } x+1=0\Rightarrow x=-1 \text{ } (x=4 \text{ is not a solution because this value makes expressions in the}$$

original equation undefined)

61. $y_1=y_2$ when $x=2$. By substitution of $x=2$, this answer checks.

62. $y_1=y_2$ when $x=-2$ and $x=3$. By substitution of $x=-2$ and $x=3$, these answers check.

63. $\quad m = \dfrac{y_2 - y_1}{x_2 - x_1} \Rightarrow m\left(x_2 - x_1\right) = y_2 - y_1 \Rightarrow m\left(x_2 - x_1\right) + y_1 = y_2 \Rightarrow y_2 = m\left(x_2 - x_1\right) + y_1$

64. $\quad T = \dfrac{a}{b+2} \Rightarrow T\left(b+2\right) = a \Rightarrow a = T\left(b+2\right)$

65. $\quad \dfrac{1}{f} = \dfrac{1}{p} + \dfrac{1}{q} \Rightarrow pq = fq + fp \Rightarrow pq - fp = fq \Rightarrow p\left(q - f\right) = fq \Rightarrow p = \dfrac{fq}{q - f}$

66. $\quad I = \dfrac{2a + 3b}{ab} \Rightarrow abI = 2a + 3b \Rightarrow abI - 3b = 2a \Rightarrow b\left(aI - 3\right) = 2a \Rightarrow b = \dfrac{2a}{aI - 3}$

Section 6.5

67. $\quad \dfrac{\dfrac{3}{5}}{\dfrac{10}{13}} = \dfrac{3}{5} \cdot \dfrac{13}{10} = \dfrac{39}{50}$

68. $\quad \dfrac{\dfrac{4}{ab}}{\dfrac{2}{bc}} = \dfrac{4}{ab} \cdot \dfrac{bc}{2} = \dfrac{2c}{a}$

69. $\quad \dfrac{\dfrac{2n-1}{n}}{\dfrac{3n}{2n+1}} = \dfrac{2n-1}{n} \cdot \dfrac{2n+1}{3n} = \dfrac{4n^2 - 1}{3n^2}$

70. $\quad \dfrac{\dfrac{1}{x-y}}{\dfrac{1}{x^2 - y^2}} = \dfrac{1}{x-y} \cdot \dfrac{x^2 - y^2}{1} = \dfrac{(x-y)(x+y)}{x-y} = x + y$

71. $\quad \dfrac{2 + \dfrac{3}{x}}{2 - \dfrac{3}{x}} = \dfrac{2 + \dfrac{3}{x}}{2 - \dfrac{3}{x}} \cdot \dfrac{x}{x} = \dfrac{2x + 3}{2x - 3}$

72. $\quad \dfrac{\dfrac{1}{x} + \dfrac{1}{2}}{\dfrac{1}{4} - \dfrac{2}{x}} = \dfrac{\dfrac{1}{x} + \dfrac{1}{2}}{\dfrac{1}{4} - \dfrac{2}{x}} \cdot \dfrac{4x}{4x} = \dfrac{4 + 2x}{x - 8} = \dfrac{2(2 + x)}{x - 8}$

73. $\quad \dfrac{\dfrac{4}{x} + \dfrac{1}{x-1}}{\dfrac{1}{x} - \dfrac{2}{x-1}} = \dfrac{\dfrac{4}{x} + \dfrac{1}{x-1}}{\dfrac{1}{x} - \dfrac{2}{x-1}} \cdot \dfrac{x(x-1)}{x(x-1)} = \dfrac{4(x-1) + x}{x - 1 - 2x} = \dfrac{5x - 4}{-x - 1} = \dfrac{5x - 4}{-1(x+1)} = \dfrac{4 - 5x}{x + 1}$

74. $\quad \dfrac{\dfrac{1}{x+3} - \dfrac{1}{x-3}}{\dfrac{4}{x+3} - \dfrac{2}{x-3}} = \dfrac{\dfrac{1}{x+3} - \dfrac{1}{x-3}}{\dfrac{4}{x+3} - \dfrac{2}{x-3}} \cdot \dfrac{(x+3)(x-3)}{(x+3)(x-3)} = \dfrac{x - 3 - (x+3)}{4(x-3) - 2(x+3)} = \dfrac{-6}{2x - 18} = \dfrac{-3}{x - 9}$

Section 6.6

75. $\dfrac{x}{6} = \dfrac{6}{20} \Rightarrow 20x = 36 \Rightarrow x = \dfrac{36}{20} \Rightarrow x = \dfrac{9}{5}$

76. $\dfrac{11}{x} = \dfrac{5}{7} \Rightarrow 5x = 77 \Rightarrow x = \dfrac{77}{5}$

77. $\dfrac{x+1}{5} = \dfrac{x}{3} \Rightarrow 5x = 3x + 3 \Rightarrow 2x = 3 \Rightarrow x = \dfrac{3}{2}$

78. $\dfrac{3}{7} = \dfrac{4}{x-1} \Rightarrow 3x - 3 = 28 \Rightarrow 3x = 31 \Rightarrow x = \dfrac{31}{3}$

79. $\dfrac{x+1}{5} = \dfrac{10}{15} \Rightarrow 15x + 15 = 50 \Rightarrow 15x = 35 \Rightarrow x = \dfrac{35}{15} = \dfrac{7}{3}$

80. $\dfrac{7}{8} = \dfrac{11}{x} \Rightarrow 7x = 88 \Rightarrow x = \dfrac{88}{7} \approx 12.6$

81. $y = kx \Rightarrow 8 = 2k \Rightarrow k = 4 \Rightarrow y = 4x$, so when $x = 7$, $y = 4(7) = 28$

82. $y = \dfrac{k}{x} \Rightarrow 5 = \dfrac{k}{10} \Rightarrow k = 50 \Rightarrow y = \dfrac{50}{x}$, so when $x = 25$, $y = \dfrac{50}{25} = 2$

83. $z = kxy \Rightarrow 483 = k(23)(7) \Rightarrow 483 = 161k \Rightarrow k = \dfrac{483}{161} \Rightarrow k = 3$

84. $z = kxy^2 \Rightarrow 891 = k(22)(3)^2 \Rightarrow 891 = 198k \Rightarrow k = \dfrac{891}{198} \Rightarrow k = \dfrac{9}{2} \Rightarrow z = \dfrac{9}{2}xy^2$

        So when $x = 10$ and $y = 4$, $z = \dfrac{9}{2}(10)(4)^2 = 720$

85.   Inverse. The products xy always equal 200. $y = \dfrac{k}{x} \Rightarrow 100 = \dfrac{k}{2} \Rightarrow k = 200$; The equation is $y = \dfrac{200}{x}$.

86.   Direct. The ratios $\dfrac{y}{x}$ always equal 3. $y = kx \Rightarrow 9 = 3k \Rightarrow k = 3$; The equation is $y = 3x$.

87.   Direct. The ratios $\dfrac{y}{x}$ always equal $\dfrac{1}{2}$. The constant of variation is $k = \dfrac{1}{2}$.

88.   Inverse. The products xy always equal 6. The constant of variation is $k = 6$.

Section 6.7

89. $\dfrac{10x+15}{5} = \dfrac{10x}{5} + \dfrac{15}{5} = 2x + 3$

90. $\dfrac{2x^2 + x}{x} = \dfrac{2x^2}{x} + \dfrac{x}{x} = 2x + 1$

91. $\left(4x^3 - x^2 + 2x\right) \div 2x^2 = \dfrac{4x^3 - x^2 + 2x}{2x^2} = \dfrac{4x^3}{2x^2} - \dfrac{x^2}{2x^2} + \dfrac{2x}{2x^2} = 2x - \dfrac{1}{2} + \dfrac{1}{x}$

92. $\left(4a^3b - 6ab^2\right) \div \left(2a^2b^2\right) = \dfrac{4a^3b - 6ab^2}{2a^2b^2} = \dfrac{4a^3b}{2a^2b^2} - \dfrac{6ab^2}{2a^2b^2} = \dfrac{2a}{b} - \dfrac{3}{a}$

93.
$$
\begin{array}{r}
2x - 3 \\
x+1 \overline{\smash{\big)}\ 2x^2 - x - 2} \\
\underline{2x^2 + 2x} \\
-3x - 2 \\
\underline{-3x - 3} \\
1
\end{array}
$$

The solution is: $2x - 3 + \dfrac{1}{x+1}$

94.
$$
\begin{array}{r}
x^2 - x + 2 \\
x+1 \overline{\smash{\big)}\ x^3 + 0x^2 + x - 1} \\
\underline{x^3 + x^2} \\
-x^2 + x \\
\underline{-x^2 - x} \\
2x - 1 \\
\underline{2x + 2} \\
-3
\end{array}
$$

The solution is: $x^2 - x + 2 - \dfrac{3}{x+1}$

95.
$$
\begin{array}{r}
2x^2 - x + 1 \\
3x-2 \overline{\smash{\big)}\ 6x^3 - 7x^2 + 5x - 1} \\
\underline{6x^3 - 4x^2} \\
-3x^2 + 5x \\
\underline{-3x^2 + 2x} \\
3x - 1 \\
\underline{3x - 2} \\
1
\end{array}
$$

The solution is: $2x^2 - x + 1 + \dfrac{1}{3x-2}$

96.
$$
\begin{array}{r}
2x - 9 \\
x^2 + 0x - 2 \overline{\smash{\big)}\ 2x^3 - 9x^2 + 21x - 21} \\
\underline{2x^3 + 0x^2 - 4x} \\
-9x^2 + 25x - 21 \\
\underline{-9x^2 + 0x + 18} \\
25x - 39
\end{array}
$$

The solution is: $2x - 9 + \dfrac{25x - 39}{x^2 - 2}$

97.
$$
\begin{array}{r|rrr}
3 & 2 & -11 & 13 \\
  &   & 6 & -15 \\
\hline
  & 2 & -5 & -2
\end{array}
$$

The solution is: $2x - 5 - \dfrac{2}{x-3}$

98.
$$
\begin{array}{r|rrrr}
-4 & 3 & 10 & -4 & 19 \\
   &   & -12 & 8 & -16 \\
\hline
   & 3 & -2 & 4 & 3
\end{array}
$$

The solution is: $3x^2 - 2x + 4 + \dfrac{3}{x+4}$

Applications

99.   (a) $D(0) = \dfrac{1600}{9.6-30(0)} = \dfrac{1600}{9.6} = 166.\overline{6}; \; D(0.1) = \dfrac{1600}{9.6-30(0.1)} = \dfrac{1600}{6.6} = 242.\overline{42}$

The downhill grade adds $242.\overline{42} - 166.\overline{6} \approx 75.8$ feet to the braking distance.

(b) $200 = \dfrac{1600}{9.6-30x} \Rightarrow 200(9.6-30x) = 1600 \Rightarrow 9.6-30x = 8 \Rightarrow -30x = -1.6 \Rightarrow x = 0.05\overline{3}$

100.   (a) Table $Y_1 = 1/(10-X)$ with TblStart $= 9$ and ΔTbl $= 0.1$. See Figure 100.

(b) As x approaches 10 the waiting time increases. As vehicles arrive at a faster rate, the wait in line increases.

101.   (a) $N(14) = \dfrac{14^2}{225-15(14)} = \dfrac{196}{15} \approx 13$ cars

(b) As x increases the number of cars in line increases. This agrees with intuition.

102.   (a) $P(0) = \dfrac{5}{(0)^2 +1} = \dfrac{5}{1} = 5;$ Initially there were 5000 fish in the lake.

(b) Graph $Y_1 = 5/(X^2 +1)$ in [0, 6, 1] by [0, 6, 1]. See Figure 102.

(c) Over this 6-year period, the fish population decreased.

(d) $1 = \dfrac{5}{x^2+1} \Rightarrow x^2+1 = 5 \Rightarrow x^2 = 4 \Rightarrow x = 2$ (the value $x = -2$ has no physical meaning)

The population was 1 thousand after 2 years.

	[0, 6, 1] by [0, 6, 1]	[0, 2, 1] by [0, 2, 1]
Figure 100	Figure 102	Figure 103

103.   (a) $\dfrac{x}{2} + \dfrac{x}{3} = 1$

(b) $6 \cdot \left(\dfrac{x}{2} + \dfrac{x}{3} \right) = 1 \cdot 6 \Rightarrow 3x + 2x = 6 \Rightarrow 5x = 6 \Rightarrow x = \dfrac{6}{5} = 1.2$ hours

(c) Graph $Y_1 = X/2 + X/3$ and $Y_2 = 1$ in [0, 2, 1] by [0, 2, 1]. See Figure 103. $x = 1.2$ hours

104.   Let x represent the speed of the current. Then $12-x$ represents the boat's upstream speed and $12+x$ represents the boat's downstream speed. Since $t = \dfrac{d}{r}$, the equation is $\dfrac{48}{12-x} + \dfrac{48}{12+x} = 9.$

The LCD is $(12-x)(12+x)$. The first step is to multiply both sides of the equation by the LCD.

$(12-x)(12+x) \cdot \left(\dfrac{48}{12-x} + \dfrac{48}{12+x} \right) = 9 \cdot (12-x)(12+x) \Rightarrow 576 + 48x + 576 - 48x = 1296 - 9x^2$

$\Rightarrow 9x^2 - 144 = 0 \Rightarrow 9x^2 = 144 \Rightarrow x^2 = 16 \Rightarrow x = \pm\sqrt{16} \Rightarrow x = 4$ mph ($x = -4$ has no meaning)

105. $\dfrac{650}{74} = \dfrac{387}{x} \Rightarrow 650x = 28,638 \Rightarrow x = \dfrac{28,638}{650} \approx 44$ minutes

106. $\dfrac{5}{3} = \dfrac{x}{26} \Rightarrow 3x = 130 \Rightarrow x = \dfrac{130}{3} \approx 43.3$ feet

107. (a) Plot the data in [0, 300, 50] by [0, 250, 50]. See Figure 107. The data represent inverse variation.

 (b) $R = \dfrac{k}{x} \Rightarrow 242 = \dfrac{k}{50} \Rightarrow k = 12,100$; Equation: $R = \dfrac{12,100}{W}$

 (c) $R = \dfrac{12,100}{55} = 220$ ohms

Figure 107

108. (a) $D = kW \Rightarrow 0.3 = 5k \Rightarrow k = 0.06$; Equation: $D = 0.06W$

 (b) $D = 0.06(7) = 0.42$ inches

109. The change in temperature is 18°F so $\dfrac{18}{4000} = \dfrac{x}{6000} \Rightarrow 4000x = 108,000 \Rightarrow x = 27\,^{\circ}$ change at 6000 feet.

 The temperature at 6000 feet is $80 - 27 = 53$°F.

110. (a) Direct. The ratios $\dfrac{y}{x}$ always equal $\dfrac{7}{2}$.

 (b) $y = kx \Rightarrow 3.5 = 1k \Rightarrow k = 3.5$, Equation: $y = 3.5x$

 (c) $y = 3.5(2.3) = 8.05\%$

Chapter 6 Test

1. $f(x) = \dfrac{x}{x+2}$

2. (a) $f(-2) = \dfrac{1}{4(-2)^2 - 1} = \dfrac{1}{16 - 1} = \dfrac{1}{15}$

 (b) Here $4x^2 - 1 \neq 0 \Rightarrow x \neq -\dfrac{1}{2}$ and $x \neq \dfrac{1}{2}$. The domain is $\left\{ x \mid x \neq \dfrac{1}{2},\ x \neq -\dfrac{1}{2} \right\}$.

3. See Figure 3.

Figure 3

4. $\dfrac{2a^3}{4a^2} = \dfrac{a}{2}$

5. $\dfrac{1-2t}{2t-1} = \dfrac{-1(2t-1)}{2t-1} = -1$

6. $\dfrac{x^2-2x-15}{2x^2-x-21} = \dfrac{(x-5)(x+3)}{(2x-7)(x+3)} = \dfrac{x-5}{2x-7}$

7. $\dfrac{x^2+4}{x^2-4} \cdot \dfrac{x-2}{x+2} = \dfrac{x^2+4}{(x-2)(x+2)} \cdot \dfrac{x-2}{x+2} = \dfrac{x^2+4}{x+2} \cdot \dfrac{1}{x+2} = \dfrac{x^2+4}{(x+2)^2}$

8. $\dfrac{1}{4y^2} \div \dfrac{1}{8y^4} = \dfrac{1}{4y^2} \cdot \dfrac{8y^4}{1} = \dfrac{1}{1} \cdot \dfrac{2y^2}{1} = 2y^2$

9. $\dfrac{x}{x+5} + \dfrac{1-x}{x+5} = \dfrac{x+1-x}{x+5} = \dfrac{1}{x+5}$

10. $\dfrac{2x}{x-2} - \dfrac{1}{x+2} = \dfrac{2x(x+2)}{(x-2)(x+2)} - \dfrac{x-2}{(x-2)(x+2)} = \dfrac{2x(x+2)-(x-2)}{(x-2)(x+2)}$

    $= \dfrac{2x^2+4x-x+2}{(x-2)(x+2)} = \dfrac{2x^2+3x+2}{(x-2)(x+2)}$

11. $\dfrac{a^2}{3b} - \dfrac{2b^3}{5a} = \dfrac{a^2}{3b} \cdot \dfrac{5a}{5a} - \dfrac{2b^3}{5a} \cdot \dfrac{3b}{3b} = \dfrac{5a^3}{15ab} - \dfrac{6b^4}{15ab}$

    $= \dfrac{5a^3 - 6b^4}{15ab}$

12. $\dfrac{x}{x-2} - \dfrac{4}{x^2} - \dfrac{2}{x} = \dfrac{x}{(x-2)} \cdot \dfrac{x^2}{x^2} - \dfrac{4}{x^2} \cdot \dfrac{x-2}{x-2} - \dfrac{2}{x} \cdot \dfrac{x(x-2)}{x(x-2)}$

    $= \dfrac{x^3}{x^2(x-2)} - \dfrac{4x-8}{x^2(x-2)} - \dfrac{2x^2-4x}{x^2(x-2)}$

    $= \dfrac{x^3 - 4x + 8 - 2x^2 + 4x}{x^2(x-2)} = \dfrac{x^3 - 2x^2 + 8}{x^2(x-2)}$

13. $\dfrac{3+\dfrac{3}{x}}{3-\dfrac{3}{x}}=\dfrac{3+\dfrac{3}{x}}{3-\dfrac{3}{x}}\cdot\dfrac{x}{x}=\dfrac{3x+3}{3x-3}=\dfrac{3(x+1)}{3(x-1)}=\dfrac{x+1}{x-1}$

14. $\dfrac{1}{z+4}-\dfrac{z}{(z+4)^2}=\dfrac{z+4}{(z+4)(z+4)}-\dfrac{z}{(z+4)(z+4)}=\dfrac{z+4-z}{(z+4)(z+4)}=\dfrac{4}{(z+4)^2}$

15. $\dfrac{\dfrac{1}{x-2}+\dfrac{x}{x-2}}{\dfrac{1}{3}-\dfrac{5}{x-2}}=\dfrac{\dfrac{1}{x-2}+\dfrac{x}{x-2}}{\dfrac{1}{3}-\dfrac{5}{x-2}}\cdot\dfrac{3(x-2)}{3(x-2)}=\dfrac{3+3x}{x-2-15}=\dfrac{3x+3}{x-17}=\dfrac{3(x+1)}{x-17}$

16. The LCD is $7(5t+1)$. The first step is to multiply both sides of the equation by the LCD.

$$7(5t+1)\cdot\dfrac{t}{5t+1}=\dfrac{2}{7}\cdot 7(5t+1)\Rightarrow 7t=10t+2\Rightarrow -3t=2\Rightarrow t=-\dfrac{2}{3}$$

17. The LCD is $(2x-1)(x+4)$. The first step is to multiply both sides of the equation by the LCD.

$$(2x-1)(x+4)\cdot\dfrac{x}{2x-1}=\dfrac{x+2}{x+4}\cdot(2x-1)(x+4)$$

$$\Rightarrow(x+4)x=(x+2)(2x-1)\Rightarrow x^2+4x=2x^2+3x-2$$

$$\Rightarrow 0=x^2-x-2\Rightarrow 0=(x+1)(x-2)\Rightarrow \text{Either } x=-1 \text{ or}$$

$$x=2$$

18. The LCD is $2-x$. The first step is to multiply both sides of the equation by the LCD.

$$(2-x)\cdot\left(\dfrac{x+4}{2-x}-\dfrac{2x-1}{2-x}\right)=0\cdot(2-x)$$

$$\Rightarrow x+4-(2x-1)=0\Rightarrow x+4-2x+1=0\Rightarrow x=5$$

19. The LCD is $(x-2)(x+2)$. The first step is to multiply both sides of the equation by the LCD.

$$(x-2)(x+2)\cdot\left(\dfrac{1}{x^2-4}-\dfrac{1}{x-2}\right)=\dfrac{1}{x+2}\cdot(x-2)(x+2)\Rightarrow 1-(x+2)=x-2\Rightarrow$$

$$-x-1=x-2\Rightarrow -2x=-1\Rightarrow x=\dfrac{1}{2}$$

20. $F=\dfrac{Gm}{r^2}\Rightarrow Fr^2=Gm\Rightarrow m=\dfrac{Fr^2}{G}$

21. Graph $Y_1=\sqrt{2}\big/\left(X^2+2\right)-(1.7X)\big/(X-1.2)$ and $Y_2=\sqrt{3}$ in $[-5,5,1]$ by $[-5,5,1]$.

Figure 21

The solution is approximately 0.47.

22. $(f-g)(2) = (2-1) - (2^2 - 2(2)+1) = 1 - (4-4+1) = 1-1 = 0;$

$$(f/g)(x) = \frac{x-1}{x^2 - 2x + 1} = \frac{x-1}{(x-1)(x-1)} = \frac{1}{x-1}$$

23. $\dfrac{7}{12} = \dfrac{x}{20} \Rightarrow 12x = 140 \Rightarrow x = \dfrac{140}{12} = \dfrac{35}{3}$

24. $y = kx \Rightarrow 8 = 23k \Rightarrow k = \dfrac{8}{23} \Rightarrow y = \dfrac{8}{23}x$, so when $x = 10$, $y = \dfrac{8}{23}(10) = \dfrac{80}{23}$

25. Inverse. The products xy always equal 100. $y = \dfrac{k}{x} \Rightarrow 50 = \dfrac{k}{2} \Rightarrow k = 100$; The equation is $y = \dfrac{100}{x}$.

26. Direct. The ratios $\dfrac{y}{x}$ always equal 1.5. $y = kx \Rightarrow 3 = 2k \Rightarrow k = 1.5$; The equation is $y = 1.5x$.

27. $\dfrac{4a^3 + 10a}{2a} = \dfrac{4a^3}{2a} + \dfrac{10a}{2a} = 2a^2 + 5$

28. Using synthetic division:

$$\begin{array}{r|rrrr} -2 & 3 & 5 & 0 & -2 \\ & & -6 & 2 & -4 \\ \hline & 3 & -1 & 2 & -6 \end{array}$$

The solution is: $3x^2 - x + 2 - \dfrac{6}{x+2}$

29. $\dfrac{73}{50} = \dfrac{x}{180} \Rightarrow 50x = 13,140 \Rightarrow x = \dfrac{13,140}{50} = 262.8$ inches, or $\dfrac{262.8}{12} = 21.9$ feet

30. (a) Graph $Y_1 = 1/(25 - X)$ in [0, 25, 5] by [0, 2, 0.5]. Vertical asymptote: $x = 25$. See Figure 30.

    (b) $1 = \dfrac{1}{25 - x} \Rightarrow 25 - x = 1 \Rightarrow -x = -24 \Rightarrow x = 24$ vehicles per minute

    [0, 25, 5] by [0, 2, 0.5]

    Figure 30

31. (a) $\dfrac{x}{24} + \dfrac{x}{30} = 1$

    (b) The LCD is 120. The first step is to multiply both sides of the equation by the LCD.

    $$120 \cdot \left(\frac{x}{24} + \frac{x}{30}\right) = 1 \cdot 120 \Rightarrow 5x + 4x = 120 \Rightarrow 9x = 120 \Rightarrow x = \frac{120}{9} = \frac{40}{3} \approx 13.3 \text{ hours}$$

32. The change in dew point is 11°F so $\dfrac{11}{10,000} = \dfrac{x}{7500} \Rightarrow 10,000x = 82,500 \Rightarrow x = 8.25°$ change at 7500 feet.

    The temperature at 7500 feet is $80 - 8.25 = 41.75°F$.

Chapter 6 Extended and Discovery Exercises

1.   (a) The matching graph is iii. Graph $Y_1 = \sqrt{(X)}$ in [0, 15, 1] by [0, 8, 1]. See Figure 1a.

Graph $Y_1 = \left(10X^2 + 80X + 32\right)\big/\left(X^2 + 40X + 80\right)$ in [0, 15, 1] by [0, 8, 1]. See Figure 1-iii.

[0, 15, 1] by [0, 8, 1]   [0, 15, 1] by [0, 8, 1]   [0, 15, 1] by [0, 8, 1]   [0, 15, 1] by [0, 8, 1]

                              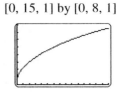

Figure 1a   Figure 1-iii   Figure 1b   Figure 1-ii

(b) The matching graph is ii. Graph $Y_1 = \sqrt{(4X+1)}$ in [0, 15, 1] by [0, 8, 1]. See Figure 1b.

Graph $Y_1 = \left(15X^2 + 75X + 33\right)\big/\left(X^2 + 23X + 31\right)$ in [0, 15, 1] by [0, 8, 1]. See Figure 1-ii.

(c) The matching graph is iv. Graph $Y_1 = \sqrt[3]{(X)}$ in [0, 15, 1] by [0, 8, 1]. See Figure 1c.

Graph $Y_1 = \left(7X{\wedge}3 + 42X^2 + 30X + 2\right)\big/\left(2X{\wedge}3 + 30X^2 + 42X + 7\right)$ in [0, 15, 1] by [0, 8, 1]. See Figure

1-iv.

[0, 15, 1] by [0, 8, 1]   [0, 15, 1] by [0, 8, 1]   [0, 15, 1] by [−1, 1, 1]   [0, 15, 1] by [−1, 1, 1]

Figure 1c   Figure 1-iv   Figure 1d   Figure 1-i

(d) The matching graph is i. Graph $Y_1 = \left(1 - \sqrt{(X)}\right)\big/\left(1 + \sqrt{(X)}\right)$ in [0, 15, 1] by [−1, 1, 1]. See Figure 1d.

Graph $Y_1 = \left(2 - 2X^2\right)\big/\left(3X^2 + 10X + 3\right)$ in [0, 15, 1] by [−1, 1, 1]. See Figure 1-i.

2.   It quadruples.

3.   It doubles.

4.   (a) $1.125 = k(2.1)^{1.25} \Rightarrow k = \dfrac{1.125}{2.1^{1.25}} \approx 0.445$

(b) $0.8 = 0.445x^{1.25} \Rightarrow x^{1.25} = \dfrac{0.8}{0.445} \Rightarrow \left(x^{1.25}\right)^{0.8} = \left(\dfrac{0.8}{0.445}\right)^{0.8} \Rightarrow x \approx 1.60$ grams

5. $V = kr^2 \Rightarrow 150 = k(5)^2 \Rightarrow 150 = 25k \Rightarrow k = \dfrac{150}{25} = 6 \Rightarrow V = 6r^2$ so when $r = 7$, $V = 6(7)^2 = 294$ in^3

6.   It is reduced to $\frac{1}{4}$ of its value.

7.   It is reduced to $\frac{1}{8}$ of its value.

8. (a) $200 = \dfrac{k}{4000^2} \Rightarrow k = 200\left(4000^2\right) = 3.2 \times 10^9$

    (b) Graph $Y_1 = \left(3.2 \times 10^{\wedge}9\right)\big/X^2$ in [0, 10,000, 1000] by [0, 200, 50]. See Figure 8.

         Fifty pounds is $\frac{1}{4}$ of 200 pounds and so the person should be twice as far or 8000 miles from Earth's

         center.

    (c) One percent is $\frac{1}{100}$ of the weight of the object on Earth's surface, thus the object must be 10 times as far

         or 40,000 miles from Earth's center.

         [0, 10,000, 1000] by [0, 200, 50]   [0, 5, 1] by [0, 30, 5]

                Figure 8   Figure 9

9. (a) Since $k = I \cdot d^2$, $k = 31.68\left(0.5\right)^2 = 7.92$.

    (b) Graph $Y_1 = 7.92\big/X^2$ in [0, 5, 1] by [0, 30, 5]. See Figure 9.

         As the distance from the light bulb increases the intensity decreases.

    (c) When the distance is doubled, the intensity is reduced to $\frac{1}{4}$ of its value.

    (d) $1 = \dfrac{7.92}{d^2} \Rightarrow d^2 = 7.92 \Rightarrow d = \sqrt{7.92} \approx 2.81$ meters

Chapters 1-6 Cumulative Review Exercises

1. $y = \sqrt{74 + (7)} = \sqrt{81} = 9$

2. $r = 16 - (-4)^2 = 16 - 16 = 0$

3. Natural: 1; Whole: 0, 1; Integer: $-\dfrac{12}{4}, 0, 1$; Rational: $-\dfrac{12}{4}, 0, 1, 2.\overline{11}, \dfrac{13}{2}$; Irrational: $\sqrt{3}$

4. By substitution of values, the formula that best fits the data is (i).

5. $\dfrac{18x^{-2}y^3}{3x^2y^{-3}} = 6x^{-2-2}y^{3-(-3)} = 6x^{-4}y^6 = \dfrac{6y^6}{x^4}$

6. $\left(\dfrac{2c^2}{3d^3}\right)^{-2} = \left(\dfrac{3d^3}{2c^2}\right)^2 = \dfrac{3^2\left(d^3\right)^2}{2^2\left(c^2\right)^2} = \dfrac{9d^6}{4c^4}$

7. Move the decimal point 10 places to the left: $67,300,000,000 = 6.73 \times 10^{10}$.

8. The domain corresponds to the x-coordinates and the range corresponds to the y-coordinates.

    $D = \{-3, -1, 0, 4\}; \ R = \{-2, 0, 1, 5\}$

9. When $x = -2$, $y = 3(-2)^2 - 1 = -7$. The other ordered pairs can be found similarly.

The ordered pairs are $(-2, -7), (-1, -4), (0, -1), (1, 2), (2, 5)$. See Figure 9.

10.   When $x = -2$, $y = \dfrac{4-(-2)^2}{2} = \dfrac{4-4}{2} = \dfrac{0}{2} = 0$. The other ordered pairs can be found similarly.

The ordered pairs are $(-2, 0), \left(-1, \dfrac{3}{2}\right), (0, 2), \left(1, \dfrac{3}{2}\right), (2, 0)$. See Figure 10.

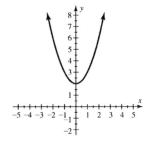

        Figure 9   Figure 10   Figure 11

11.   See Figure 11.

12.   The function is defined for all values of the variable except 1. The domain is $\{x \mid x \ne 1\}$.

13.   The slope is $m = \dfrac{3-(-5)}{2-(-2)} = \dfrac{8}{4} = 2$. Since $f(x) = -1$ when $x = 0$ the y-intercept is -1. Here $f(x) = 2x - 1$.

14.   See Figure 14.

        Figure 14   Figure 17

15.   The equation is in the form $f(x) = mx + b$. The slope is -3 and the y-intercept is 2.

16. $m = \dfrac{9-(-3)}{2-6} = \dfrac{12}{-4} = -3$

17.   See Figure 17.

18.   The graph falls 1 unit for each 2 units of run. The slope is $-\dfrac{1}{2}$. The y-intercept is 2. So $y = -\dfrac{1}{2}x + 2$.

19.   Since the line is parallel to $y = 2x + 3$, the slope is $m = 2$. Using the point-slope form gives

$$y = 2(x-1) + 4 \Rightarrow y = 2x - 2 + 4 \Rightarrow y = 2x + 2$$

20. Since the line is perpendicular to $y = \frac{2}{3}x - 2$, the slope is $m = -\frac{3}{2}$. Using the point-slope form gives

$$y = -\frac{3}{2}(x-2)+1 \Rightarrow y = -\frac{3}{2}x+3+1 \Rightarrow y = -\frac{3}{2}x+4$$

21. $\frac{2}{5}(x+1)-6 = -4 \Rightarrow \frac{2}{5}(x+1) = 2 \Rightarrow x+1 = 5 \Rightarrow x = 4$

22. $\frac{1}{4}\left(\frac{t-5}{3}\right)-6 = \frac{2}{3}t-(3t+7) \Rightarrow t-5-72 = 8t-12(3t+7) \Rightarrow t-77 = -28t-84 \Rightarrow 29t = -7 \Rightarrow t = -\frac{7}{29}$

23. The graphs intersect at the point $(3, -2)$, so $y_1 = y_2$ when $x = 3$.

24. $\frac{2x+3}{4} \le \frac{1}{3} \Rightarrow 6x+9 \le 4 \Rightarrow 6x \le -5 \Rightarrow x \le -\frac{5}{6}$. The interval is $\left(-\infty, -\frac{5}{6}\right]$.

25. $\frac{1}{2}z-5 > \frac{3}{4}z-(2z+5) \Rightarrow 2z-20 > 3z-4(2z+5) \Rightarrow 7z > 0 \Rightarrow z > 0$. The interval is $(0, \infty)$.

26. $-6 \le -\frac{2}{3}x-4 < -2 \Rightarrow -2 \le -\frac{2}{3}x < 2 \Rightarrow 3 \ge x > -3 \Rightarrow -3 < x \le 3$.

The interval is $(-3, 3]$. See Figure 26.

27. $3x-1 \le 5$ or $2x+5 > 13 \Rightarrow 3x \le 6$ or $2x > 8 \Rightarrow x \le 2$ or $x > 4$.

The interval is $(-\infty, 2] \cup (4, \infty)$. See Figure 27.

Figure 26   Figure 27

28. $\left|\frac{1}{3}x+6\right| = 4 \Rightarrow \frac{1}{3}x+6 = -4 \Rightarrow \frac{1}{3}x = -10 \Rightarrow x = -30$ or $\frac{1}{3}x+6 = 4 \Rightarrow \frac{1}{3}x = -2 \Rightarrow x = -6$

29. The solutions to $|2x-3| < 11$ satisfy $c < x < d$ where c and d are the solutions to $|2x-3| = 11$.

$|2x-3| = 11$ is equivalent to $2x-3 = -11 \Rightarrow x = -4$ and $2x-3 = 11 \Rightarrow x = 7$. The interval is $(-4, 7)$.

30. First divide each side of $-3|t-5| \le -18$ by -3 to obtain $|t-5| \ge 6$.

The solutions to $|t-5| \ge 6$ satisfy $t \le c$ or $t \ge d$ where c and d are the solutions to $|t-5| = 6$.

$|t-5| = 6$ is equivalent to $t-5 = -6 \Rightarrow t = -1$ and $t-5 = 6 \Rightarrow t = 11$.

The interval is $(-\infty, -1] \cup [11, \infty)$.

31. By substitution, $(-8, -1)$ is a solution to the given system of equations.

32. See Figure 32.

Figure 32

33. Multiplying the second equation by 4 and adding the two equations will eliminate the variable y.

$$2x - 8y = 5$$
$$16x + 8y = 4$$
$$\overline{18x = 9}$$

Thus, $x = \dfrac{1}{2}$. And so $2\left(\dfrac{1}{2}\right) - 8y = 5 \Rightarrow y = -\dfrac{1}{2}$. The solution is $\left(\dfrac{1}{2}, -\dfrac{1}{2}\right)$.

34. Multiplying the second equation by 2 and adding the two equations will eliminate the variable x.

$$2x - 3y = 12$$
$$-2x + 4y = -12$$
$$\overline{y = 0}$$

Thus, $y = 0$. And so $2x - 3(0) = 12 \Rightarrow x = 6$. The solution is $(6, 0)$.

35. From the graph of the region of feasible solutions (not shown), the vertices are (0, 0), (0, 3), (2, 2), and (3, 0).

The maximum value of R occurs at one of the vertices. For $(0, 0)$, $R = 2(0) + 3(0) = 0$.

For $(0, 3)$, $R = 2(0) + 3(3) = 9$. For $(2, 2)$, $R = 2(2) + 3(2) = 10$. For $(3, 0)$, $R = 2(3) + 3(0) = 6$.

The maximum value is $R = 10$.

36. Multiply the second equation by 3 and add the first and second equations to eliminate the variable y.

$$2x + 3y - z = 3$$
$$9x - 3y + 12z = 30$$
$$\overline{11x + 11z = 33}$$
or $x + z = 3$

Add the second and third equations together to eliminate the variable y.

$$3x - y + 4z = 10$$
$$2x + y - 2z = -1$$
$$\overline{5x + 2z = 9}$$

Multiply the first *new* equation by –2 and add the first *new* equation and second *new* equation to eliminate z.

$$-2x - 2z = -6$$
$$5x + 2z = 9$$
$$\overline{3x = 3}$$

And so $x = 1$. Substitute $x = 1$ into the first *new* equation: $(1) + z = 3 \Rightarrow z = 2$

Substitute $x = 1$ and $z = 2$ into the *original* first equation: $2(1) + 3y - (2) = 3 \Rightarrow y = 1$

The solution is (1, 1, 2).

37. $\begin{bmatrix} 1 & 1 & -1 & | & 4 \\ -1 & -1 & -1 & | & 0 \\ 1 & -2 & 1 & | & -9 \end{bmatrix} \begin{matrix} R_2 + R_1 \to \\ R_3 - R_1 \to \end{matrix} \begin{bmatrix} 1 & 1 & -1 & | & 4 \\ 0 & 0 & -2 & | & 4 \\ 0 & -3 & 2 & | & -13 \end{bmatrix} \begin{matrix} Exchange \\ R_2 \leftrightarrow R_3 \end{matrix} \begin{bmatrix} 1 & 1 & -1 & | & 4 \\ 0 & -3 & 2 & | & -13 \\ 0 & 0 & -2 & | & 4 \end{bmatrix}$

$$(-1/2)R_3 \rightarrow \begin{bmatrix} 1 & 1 & -1 & | & 4 \\ 0 & -3 & 2 & | & -13 \\ 0 & 0 & 1 & | & -2 \end{bmatrix} \begin{matrix} R_1 + R_3 \rightarrow \\ R_2 - 2R_3 \rightarrow \end{matrix} \begin{bmatrix} 1 & 1 & 0 & | & 2 \\ 0 & -3 & 0 & | & -9 \\ 0 & 0 & 1 & | & -2 \end{bmatrix} \begin{matrix} R_1 + (1/3)R_2 \rightarrow \\ (-1/3)R_2 \rightarrow \end{matrix} \begin{bmatrix} 1 & 0 & 0 & | & -1 \\ 0 & 1 & 0 & | & 3 \\ 0 & 0 & 1 & | & -2 \end{bmatrix}$$

The solution is $(-1, 3, -2)$.

38. $\det A = 4(3) - 1(-2) = 12 + 2 = 14$

39. The triangle has vertices $(-3, 2)$, $(2, 1)$ and $(1, -2)$. The matrix needed is $A = \begin{bmatrix} -3 & 2 & 1 \\ 2 & 1 & -2 \\ 1 & 1 & 1 \end{bmatrix}$.

The area is $D = \left| \frac{1}{2} \det([A]) \right| = 8 \text{ in}^2$.

40. $E = \det \begin{bmatrix} 8 & 7 \\ 18 & 5 \end{bmatrix} = 40 - 126 = -86; \quad F = \det \begin{bmatrix} 6 & 8 \\ -8 & 18 \end{bmatrix} = 108 + 64 = 172$

$D = \det \begin{bmatrix} 6 & 7 \\ -8 & 5 \end{bmatrix} = 30 + 56 = 86;$ The solution is $x = \dfrac{E}{D} = \dfrac{-86}{86} = -1$ and $y = \dfrac{F}{D} = \dfrac{172}{86} = 2$.

41. $3x^2(x^3 + 5x - 2) = 3x^5 + 15x^3 - 6x^2$

42. $(2x - 5)(x + 3) = 2x^2 + 6x - 5x - 15 = 2x^2 + x - 15$

43. $6x + 3x^2 = 0 \Rightarrow 3x(2 + x) = 0 \Rightarrow$ Either $3x = 0 \Rightarrow x = 0$ or $2 + x = 0 \Rightarrow x = -2$

44. $3a^3 - a^2 + 15a - 5 = a^2(3a - 1) + 5(3a - 1) = (3a - 1)(a^2 + 5)$

45. $4x^2 + 5x - 6 = (4x - 3)(x + 2)$

46. $6x^3 - 9x^2 - 6x = 3x(2x^2 - 3x - 2) = 3x(x - 2)(2x + 1)$

47. $9a^2 - 4b^2 = (3a - 2b)(3a + 2b)$

48. $64t^3 + 27 = (4t + 3)(16t^2 - 12t + 9)$

49. $3x^2 - 11x = 4 \Rightarrow 3x^2 - 11x - 4 = 0 \Rightarrow (3x + 1)(x - 4) = 0 \Rightarrow x = -\dfrac{1}{3}$ or $x = 4$

50. $x^4 - x^3 - 30x^2 = 0 \Rightarrow x^2(x^2 - x - 30) = 0 \Rightarrow x^2(x + 5)(x - 6) = 0 \Rightarrow x = 0$ or $x = -5$ or $x = 6$

51. $\dfrac{x^2 + 3x - 10}{x^2 - 4} \cdot \dfrac{x - 2}{x + 5} = \dfrac{(x + 5)(x - 2)(x - 2)}{(x - 2)(x + 2)(x + 5)} = \dfrac{x - 2}{x + 2}$

52. $\dfrac{x^2 + 2x - 24}{x^2 + 3x - 18} \div \dfrac{x + 3}{x^2 - 9} = \dfrac{x^2 + 2x - 24}{x^2 + 3x - 18} \cdot \dfrac{x^2 - 9}{x + 3} = \dfrac{(x + 6)(x - 4)(x - 3)(x + 3)}{(x + 6)(x - 3)(x + 3)} = x - 4$

53. $\dfrac{2}{t + 2} - \dfrac{t}{t^2 - 4} = \dfrac{2(t - 2)}{(t - 2)(t + 2)} - \dfrac{t}{(t - 2)(t + 2)} = \dfrac{2t - 4 - t}{(t - 2)(t + 2)} = \dfrac{t - 4}{t^2 - 4}$

54. $\dfrac{4a}{3ab^2} + \dfrac{b}{a^2 c} = \dfrac{4a^2 c}{3a^2 b^2 c} + \dfrac{3b^3}{3a^2 b^2 c} = \dfrac{4a^2 c + 3b^3}{3a^2 b^2 c}$

55. $\dfrac{1}{x+4}+\dfrac{1}{x-4}=\dfrac{-7}{x^2-16}\Rightarrow 1(x-4)+1(x+4)=-7\Rightarrow 2x=-7\Rightarrow x=-\dfrac{7}{2}$

56. $\dfrac{1}{y^2+3y-4}-\dfrac{y}{y-1}=-1\Rightarrow 1-y(y+4)=-1(y+4)(y-1)\Rightarrow 1-y^2-4y=-y^2-3y+4\Rightarrow$

    $1-4y=4-3y\Rightarrow y=-3$

57. $J=\dfrac{y+z}{z}\Rightarrow Jz=y+z\Rightarrow Jz-z=y\Rightarrow z(J-1)=y\Rightarrow z=\dfrac{y}{J-1}$

58. $\dfrac{\dfrac{4}{x^2}+\dfrac{1}{x}}{\dfrac{4}{x^2}-\dfrac{1}{x}}=\dfrac{\dfrac{4}{x^2}+\dfrac{1}{x}}{\dfrac{4}{x^2}-\dfrac{1}{x}}\cdot\dfrac{x^2}{x^2}=\dfrac{4+x}{4-x}$

59. $y=\dfrac{k}{x}\Rightarrow 2=\dfrac{k}{4}\Rightarrow k=8\Rightarrow y=\dfrac{8}{x}$, so when $x=16$, $y=\dfrac{8}{16}=\dfrac{1}{2}$

60.
$$
\begin{array}{r}
x^2-2x+6 \\
x+2\overline{\smash{\big)}\,x^3+0x^2+2x+11} \\
\underline{x^3+2x^2} \\
-2x^2+2x \\
\underline{-2x^2-4x} \\
6x+11 \\
\underline{6x+12} \\
-1
\end{array}
$$

The solution is: $x^2-2x+6-\dfrac{1}{x+2}$

61. $(f+g)(3)=\left(3^2-3(3)+2\right)+(3-2)=(9-9+2)+1=2+1=3$

62. $(f/g)(x)=\dfrac{x^2-3x+2}{x-2}=\dfrac{(x-2)(x-1)}{x-2}=x-1$

63. (a) See Figure 63. These data are linear.

    (b) $m=\dfrac{100-0}{212-32}=\dfrac{100}{180}=\dfrac{5}{9}$. Letting $h=32$ and $k=0$, the function is $f(x)=\dfrac{5}{9}(x-32)$.

    (c) $f(104)=\dfrac{5}{9}(104-32)=\dfrac{5}{9}(72)=40°C$

Figure 63

64.   Let x represent the length of each of the shorter sides. Then $\frac{1}{2}x+7$ represents the length of the longer side.

The perimeter is 22 so $x+x+\frac{1}{2}x+7 = 22 \Rightarrow \frac{5}{2}x = 15 \Rightarrow x = 6$. The sides are 6, 6, and 10 inches.

65.   Let x and y represent the time spent on the stair climber and the bicycle respectively. Then the system needed is $x+y = 1.5$ and $690x+540y = 885$. Multiplying the first equation by -540 and adding the two equations will eliminate the variable y.

$$\begin{array}{r} -540x-540y = -810 \\ \underline{690x+540y =\ \ \ 885} \\ 150x = 75 \end{array}$$ Thus, $x = 0.5$. And so $(0.5)+y = 1.5 \Rightarrow y = 1$.

The athlete spent 0.5 hour on the stair climber and 1 hour on the stationary bicycle.

66.   Let x and y represent the number of $2 and $5 tickets respectively. Then the system needed is $x+y = 30$ and $2x+5y = 78$. Multiplying the first equation by -2 and adding the two equations will eliminate the x.

$$\begin{array}{r} -2x-2y = -60 \\ \underline{2x+5y =\ \ 78} \\ 3y = 18 \end{array}$$ Thus, $y = 6$. And so $x+(6) = 30 \Rightarrow x = 24$. There were 24 children and 6 adults.

67.   Let x represent the width of the rectangle. Then $x+4$ represents the length.

$$x(x+4) = 165 \Rightarrow x^2+4x-165 = 0 \Rightarrow (x-11)(x+15) = 0 \Rightarrow x = 11 \text{ or } x = -15$$

The solution $x = -15$ has no physical meaning. The rectangle is 11 feet by 15 feet.

68.   (a) $-16t^2+44t = 0 \Rightarrow 4t^2-11t = 0 \Rightarrow t(4t-11) = 0 \Rightarrow t = 0 \text{ or } 4t-11 = 0 \Rightarrow t = 0 \text{ or } t = \frac{11}{4}$

The ball strikes the ground at $\frac{11}{4} = 2.75$ seconds.

(b) $-16t^2+44t = 18 \Rightarrow -16t^2+44t-18 = 0 \Rightarrow 8t^2-22t+9 = 0 \Rightarrow (2t-1)(4t-9) \Rightarrow t = \frac{1}{2} \text{ or } t = \frac{9}{4}$. The

ball is 18 feet high at $\frac{1}{2}$ second and $\frac{9}{4} = 2.25$ seconds.

69.   (a) $\frac{x}{15}+\frac{x}{10} = 1$

(b) $\frac{x}{15}+\frac{x}{10} = 1 \Rightarrow 2x+3x = 30 \Rightarrow 5x = 30 \Rightarrow x = 6$ hours

70. $\frac{6}{4} = \frac{x}{32} \Rightarrow 4x = 192 \Rightarrow x = 48$ feet

Critical Thinking Solutions for Chapter 6

Section 6.3

•   No, for example $\frac{1}{2} = \frac{1}{4}+\frac{1}{4}$, but $2 \neq 4+4$.

Section 6.4

• At 6 miles per hour the bicyclist rides 1 mile up hill in $\dfrac{1}{6}$ hour. At 12 miles per hour the bicyclist rides 1 mile

  down hill in $\dfrac{1}{12}$ hour. Thus the bicyclist rides a total of 2 miles in $\dfrac{1}{6}+\dfrac{1}{12}=\dfrac{2}{12}+\dfrac{1}{12}=\dfrac{3}{12}=\dfrac{1}{4}$ hour.

  The average speed of the bicyclist is $2\div\dfrac{1}{4}=8$ miles per hour.

Section 6.5

• No, $\dfrac{\dfrac{x}{y}}{2+\dfrac{x}{y}}=\dfrac{\dfrac{x}{y}}{2+\dfrac{x}{y}}\cdot\dfrac{y}{y}=\dfrac{x}{2y+x}$. No, $\dfrac{2+\dfrac{x}{y}}{\dfrac{x}{y}}=\dfrac{2+\dfrac{x}{y}}{\dfrac{x}{y}}\cdot\dfrac{y}{y}=\dfrac{2y+x}{x}$.

Section 6.6

• If the width doubles the strength doubles, whereas if the thickness doubles, the strength quadruples. If both triple, the strength increases by 27 times.

Section 6.7

• 1. Since $x-k$ is a factor, $p(x)=(x-k)(\text{some other factor})$. So $P(k)=(k-k)(\text{some other factor})=0$.

  2. Since $p(k)=0$, an x-intercept on the graph must be k.

Chapter 7: Radical Expressions and Functions

7.1: Radical Expressions and Rational Exponents

Concepts

1. ± 3

2.   3

3.   2

4.   Yes

5.   b

6. $\sqrt{x} = x^{1/2}$

7. $\sqrt[3]{a^4} = a^{4/3}$

8. $\sqrt[n]{a}$

9. $\left(\sqrt[n]{a}\right)^m$ or $\sqrt[n]{a^m}$

10.   Yes

Radical Expressions

11. $\sqrt{9} = 3$

12. $\sqrt{121} = 11$

13. $\sqrt{0.36} = 0.6$

14. $\sqrt{0.64} = 0.8$

15. $\sqrt{\dfrac{16}{25}} = \dfrac{4}{5}$

16. $\sqrt{\dfrac{9}{49}} = \dfrac{3}{7}$

17. $\sqrt{x^2} = x$ since $x > 0$

18. $\sqrt{(x-1)^2} = x - 1$, since $x > 1 \Rightarrow x - 1 > 0$

19. $\sqrt[3]{27} = 3$

20. $\sqrt[3]{64} = 4$

21. $\sqrt[3]{-64} = -4$

22. $-\sqrt[3]{-1} = -(-1) = 1$

23. $\sqrt[3]{\dfrac{8}{27}} = \dfrac{2}{3}$

24. $\sqrt[3]{-\dfrac{1}{25}} = -\dfrac{1}{5}$

25. $-\sqrt[3]{x^9} = -\sqrt[3]{\left(x^3\right)^3} = -x^3$

26. $\sqrt[3]{(x+1)^6} = \sqrt[3]{\left((x+1)^2\right)^3} = (x+1)^2$

27. $\sqrt[3]{(2x)^6} = \sqrt[3]{\left((2x)^2\right)^3} = (2x)^2 = 4x^2$

28. $\sqrt[3]{27x^3} = 3x$

29. $\sqrt[4]{81} = 3$

30. $\sqrt[5]{-1} = -1$

31. $\sqrt[5]{-243} = \sqrt[5]{(-3)^5} = -5$

32. $\sqrt[4]{625} = \sqrt[4]{(5)^4} = 5$

33. $\sqrt[4]{-16}$ is not possible to evaluate over the real numbers since the index is even and the radicand is negative.

34. $\sqrt[6]{-64}$ is not possible to evaluate over the real numbers since the index is even and the radicand is negative.

35. $-\sqrt{5} \approx -2.24$

36. $\sqrt{11} \approx 3.32$

37. $\sqrt[3]{5} \approx 1.71$

38. $\sqrt[3]{-13} \approx -2.35$

39. $\sqrt[5]{-7} \approx -1.48$

40. $\sqrt[4]{6} \approx 1.57$

41. $16^{1/5} \approx 1.74$

42. $7^{1/4} \approx 1.63$

43. $5^{1/3} \approx 1.71$

44. $11^{1/2} \approx 3.32$

45. $9^{3/5} \approx 3.74$

46. $13^{5/4} \approx 24.68$

47. $4^{-3/7} \approx 0.55$

48. $2^{-3/4} \approx 0.59$

49. $9^{1/2} = \sqrt{9} = 3$

50. $100^{1/2} = \sqrt{100} = 10$

51. $8^{1/3} = \sqrt[3]{8} = 2$

52. $(-8)^{1/3} = \sqrt[3]{-8} = -2$

53. $\left(\dfrac{4}{9}\right)^{1/2} = \sqrt{\dfrac{4}{9}} = \dfrac{2}{3}$

54. $\left(\dfrac{64}{27}\right)^{1/3} = \sqrt[3]{\dfrac{64}{27}} = \dfrac{4}{3}$

55. $(-8)^{2/3} = \sqrt[3]{(-8)^2} = \sqrt[3]{64} = 4$

56. $(16)^{3/2} = \left(\sqrt{16}\right)^3 = 4^3 = 64$

57. $\left(\dfrac{1}{8}\right)^{-1/3} = 8^{1/3} = \sqrt[3]{8} = 2$

58. $\left(\dfrac{1}{81}\right)^{-1/4} = 81^{1/4} = \sqrt[4]{81} = 3$

59. $16^{-3/4} = \dfrac{1}{\sqrt[4]{16^3}} = \dfrac{1}{\left(\sqrt[4]{16}\right)^3} = \dfrac{1}{(2)^3} = \dfrac{1}{8}$

60. $(32)^{-2/5} = \dfrac{1}{\sqrt[5]{32^2}} = \dfrac{1}{\left(\sqrt[5]{32}\right)^2} = \dfrac{1}{2^2} = \dfrac{1}{4}$

61. $\left(4^{1/2}\right)^{-3} = \dfrac{1}{\left(\sqrt{4}\right)^3} = \dfrac{1}{2^3} = \dfrac{1}{8}$

62. $\left(8^{1/3}\right)^{-2} = \left(\sqrt[3]{8}\right)^{-2} = 2^{-2} = \dfrac{1}{2^2} = \dfrac{1}{4}$

63. $z^{1/4} = \sqrt[4]{z}$

64. $b^{1/3} = \sqrt[3]{b}$

65. $y^{-2/5} = \dfrac{1}{\sqrt[5]{y^2}}$

66. $z^{-3/4} = \dfrac{1}{\sqrt[4]{z^3}}$

67. $(3x)^{1/3} = \sqrt[3]{3x}$

68. $(5x)^{1/2} = \sqrt{5x}$

69. $\sqrt{y} = y^{1/2}$

70. $\sqrt{z+1} = (z+1)^{1/2}$

71. $\sqrt{x} \cdot \sqrt{x} = \left(x^{1/2}\right)^2 = x$

72. $\sqrt[3]{x} \cdot \sqrt[3]{x} = \left(\sqrt[3]{x}\right)^2 = x^{2/3}$

73. $\sqrt[3]{8x^2} = \sqrt[3]{8} \cdot \sqrt[3]{x^2} = 2x^{2/3}$

74. $\sqrt[3]{27z} = \sqrt[3]{27} \cdot \sqrt[3]{z} = 3z^{1/3}$

75. $\dfrac{\sqrt{49x}}{\sqrt[3]{x^2}} = \dfrac{\sqrt{49} \cdot \sqrt{x}}{x^{2/3}} = 7x^{1/2-2/3} = 7x^{-1/6} = \dfrac{7}{x^{1/6}}$

76. $\dfrac{\sqrt[3]{8x}}{\sqrt[4]{x^3}} = \dfrac{\sqrt[3]{8} \cdot \sqrt[3]{x}}{x^{3/4}} = 2x^{1/3-3/4}\ 2x^{-5/12} = \dfrac{2}{x^{5/12}}$

77. $\left(b^{1/a}\, b^{2/a}\right)^a = \left(b^{1/a+2/a}\right)^a = \left(b^{3/a}\right)^a = b^{\frac{3}{a} \cdot a} = b^3$

78. $b^{(b-1)/b} \cdot \sqrt[b]{b} = b^{(b-1)/b} \cdot b^{1/b} = b^{(b-1)/b+1/b} = b^{b/b} = b^1 = b$

79. $\left(x^2\right)^{3/2} = x^{2 \cdot 3/2} = x^3$

80. $\left(y^4\right)^{1/2} = y^{4 \cdot 1/2} = y^2$

81. $\sqrt[3]{x^3 y^6} = \left(x^3 y^6\right)^{1/3} = x^{3 \cdot 1/3} \cdot y^{6 \cdot 1/3} = xy^2$

82. $\sqrt{16x^4} = \left(16x^4\right)^{1/2} = 16^{1/2} \cdot x^{4 \cdot 1/2} = \sqrt{16} \cdot x^2 = 4x^2$

83. $\sqrt{\dfrac{y^4}{x^2}} = \left(\dfrac{y^4}{x^2}\right)^{1/2} = \dfrac{y^{4 \cdot 1/2}}{x^{2 \cdot 1/2}} = \dfrac{y^2}{x}$

84. $\sqrt[3]{\dfrac{x^{12}}{z^6}} = \left(\dfrac{x^{12}}{z^6}\right)^{1/3} = \dfrac{x^{12 \cdot 1/3}}{z^{6 \cdot 1/3}} = \dfrac{x^4}{z^2}$

85. $\sqrt{y^3} \cdot \sqrt[3]{y^2} = (y^3)^{1/2} \cdot (y^2)^{1/3} = y^{3 \cdot 1/2} \cdot y^{2 \cdot 1/3} = y^{3/2} \cdot y^{2/3} = y^{3/2+2/3} = y^{13/6}$

86. $\left(\dfrac{x^6}{81}\right)^{1/4} = \dfrac{x^{6 \cdot 1/4}}{81^{1/4}} = \dfrac{x^{3/2}}{\sqrt[4]{81}} = \dfrac{x^{3/2}}{3}$

87. $\left(\dfrac{x^6}{27}\right)^{2/3} = \dfrac{x^{6 \cdot 2/3}}{27^{2/3}} = \dfrac{x^4}{\left(\sqrt[3]{27}\right)^2} = \dfrac{x^4}{3^2} = \dfrac{x^4}{9}$

88. $\left(\dfrac{1}{x^8}\right)^{-1/4} = \left(x^8\right)^{1/4} = x^{8 \cdot 1/4} = x^2$

89. $\left(\dfrac{x^2}{y^6}\right)^{-1/2} = \left(\dfrac{y^6}{x^2}\right)^{1/2} = \dfrac{y^{6 \cdot 1/2}}{x^{2 \cdot 1/2}} = \dfrac{y^3}{x}$

90. $\dfrac{\sqrt{x}}{\sqrt[3]{27x^6}} = \dfrac{x^{1/2}}{\left(27x^6\right)^{1/3}} = \dfrac{x^{1/2}}{\sqrt[3]{27} \cdot x^{6 \cdot 1/3}} = \dfrac{x^{1/2}}{3x^2} = \dfrac{x^{1/2-2}}{3} = \dfrac{x^{-3/2}}{3} = \dfrac{1}{3x^{3/2}}$

91. $\sqrt{\sqrt{y}} = \left(y^{1/2}\right)^{1/2} = y^{1/2 \cdot 1/2} = y^{1/4}$

92. $\sqrt{\sqrt[3]{(3x)^2}} = \left((3x)^{2/3}\right)^{1/2} = (3x)^{1/3}$

93. $\left(a^{-1/2}\right)^{4/3} = a^{-1/2 \cdot 4/3} = a^{-2/3} = \dfrac{1}{a^{2/3}}$

94. $\left(x^{-3/2}\right)^{2/3} = x^{-3/2 \cdot 2/3} = x^{-1} = \dfrac{1}{x}$

95. $\dfrac{\left(k^{1/2}\right)^{-3}}{\left(k^2\right)^{1/4}} = \dfrac{k^{-3/2}}{k^{1/2}} = k^{-3/2-1/2} = k^{-4/2} = k^{-2} = \dfrac{1}{k^2}$

96. $\dfrac{\left(b^{3/4}\right)^4}{\left(b^{4/5}\right)^{-5}} = \dfrac{b^3}{b^{-4}} = b^{3-(-4)} = b^7$

97. $\sqrt{b} \cdot \sqrt[4]{b} = b^{1/2} \cdot b^{1/4} = b^{1/2+1/4} = b^{3/4}$

98. $\sqrt[3]{t} \cdot \sqrt[5]{t} = t^{1/3} \cdot t^{1/5} = t^{1/3+1/5} = t^{8/15}$

99. $p^{1/2}\left(p^{3/2} + p^{1/2}\right) = p^{1/2+3/2} + p^{1/2+1/2} = p^2 + p$

100. $d^{3/4}\left(d^{1/4} - d^{-1/4}\right) = d^{3/4+1/4} - d^{3/4+(-1/4)} = d - d^{1/2}$

101. $\sqrt[3]{x}\left(\sqrt{x} - \sqrt[3]{x^2}\right) = x^{1/3}\left(x^{1/2} - x^{2/3}\right) = x^{1/3+1/2} - x^{1/3+2/3} = x^{5/6} - x$

102. $\dfrac{1}{2}\sqrt{x}\left(\sqrt{x} + \sqrt[4]{x^2}\right) = \dfrac{1}{2}x^{1/2}\left(x^{1/2} + x^{2/4}\right) = \dfrac{1}{2}x^{1/2}\left(2x^{1/2}\right) = \dfrac{1}{2} \cdot 2 \cdot x^{1/2+1/2} = x$

103. $\sqrt{(-4)^2} = \sqrt{16} = 4$

104. $\sqrt{9^2} = \sqrt{81} = 9$

105. $\sqrt{y^2} = |y|$

106. $\sqrt{z^4} = \left(z^4\right)^{1/2} = z^{4 \cdot 1/2} = z^2$

107. $\sqrt{(x-5)^2} = |x-5|$

108. $\sqrt{(2x-1)^2} = |2x-1|$

109. $\sqrt{x^2 - 2x + 1} = \sqrt{(x-1)^2} = |x-1|$

110. $\sqrt{4x^2 + 4x + 1} = \sqrt{(2x+1)^2} = |2x+1|$

111. $\sqrt[4]{y^4} = \left(y^4\right)^{1/4} = y^{4 \cdot 1/4} = |y|$

112. $\sqrt[4]{x^8 z^4} = \left(x^8 z^4\right)^{1/4} = x^{8 \cdot 1/4} z^{4 \cdot 1/4} = x^2 |z|$

113. $\sqrt[4]{x^{12}} = \left(x^{12}\right)^{1/4} = x^{12 \cdot 1/4} = \left|x^3\right|$

114. $\sqrt[6]{x^6} = \left(x^6\right)^{1/6} = x^{6 \cdot 1/6} = |x|$

115. $\sqrt[5]{x^5} = \left(x^5\right)^{1/5} = x^{5 \cdot 1/5} = x$

116. $\sqrt[5]{32(x+4)^5} = \left(32(x+4)^5\right)^{1/5} = 32^{1/5} \cdot (x+4)^{5 \cdot 1/5} = 2(x+4)$

Applications

117. $15\pi R^2 = 65 \;\Rightarrow\; R^2 = \dfrac{65}{15\pi} \;\Rightarrow\; R = \sqrt{\dfrac{65}{15\pi}} \approx 1.17$ miles

118. (a) The higher note has twice the frequency of the lower note.

    (b) The frequency is $2^{1/12} \cdot 2^{1/12} \cdot 2^{1/12} = 2^{3/12} = 2^{1/4}$ times greater or $220 \cdot 2^{1/4} \approx 261.6$ cycles per second.

119. $N(h) = 1.6 h^{-1/2} = 1.6(2.5)^{-1/2} = \dfrac{1.6}{\sqrt{2.5}} \approx 1.01$; The stepping frequency is about 1 step per second.

120. $N(w) = 885 w^{-1/2} = 885(800)^{-1/2} = \dfrac{885}{\sqrt{800}} \approx 31.29$; The heart rate is about 31 beats per minute.

121. $s = \dfrac{1}{2}(3+4+5) = 6 \;\Rightarrow\; A = \sqrt{6(6-3)(6-4)(6-5)} = \sqrt{6(3)(2)(1)} = \sqrt{36} = 6$

122. $s = \dfrac{1}{2}(5+9+10) = 12 \;\Rightarrow\; A = \sqrt{12(12-5)(12-9)(12-10)} = \sqrt{12(7)(3)(2)} = \sqrt{504} \approx 22.45$

7.2: Simplifying Radical Expressions

Concepts

1. Yes

2. No

3. $\sqrt[3]{ab}$

4. $\dfrac{a}{b}$

5. $\dfrac{a}{b}$

6. $\dfrac{\sqrt{3}}{\sqrt{27}} = \sqrt{\dfrac{3}{27}} = \sqrt{\dfrac{1}{9}} = \dfrac{1}{3}$

7.   No; $\sqrt{50} = \sqrt{25 \cdot 2} = \sqrt{25} \cdot \sqrt{2} = 5\sqrt{2}$ and $\sqrt{25} + \sqrt{25}$

$= 5 + 5 = 2(5)$ or 10

8.   Yes; $\sqrt{50} = \sqrt{25 \cdot 2} = \sqrt{25} \cdot \sqrt{2} = 5\sqrt{2}$

9.   No, because $1^3 \neq 3$.

10.   Yes, because $4^3 = 64$.

Multiplying and Dividing

11. $\sqrt{3} \cdot \sqrt{3} = \sqrt{3 \cdot 3} = \sqrt{9} = 3$

12. $\sqrt{2} \cdot \sqrt{18} = \sqrt{2 \cdot 18} = \sqrt{36} = 6$

13. $\sqrt{2} \cdot \sqrt{50} = \sqrt{2 \cdot 50} = \sqrt{100} = 10$

14. $\sqrt[3]{-2} \cdot \sqrt[3]{-4} = \sqrt[3]{(-2)(-4)} = \sqrt[3]{8} = 2$

15. $\sqrt[3]{4} \cdot \sqrt[3]{16} = \sqrt[3]{4 \cdot 16} = \sqrt[3]{64} = 4$

16. $\sqrt[3]{x} \cdot \sqrt[3]{x^2} = \sqrt[3]{x \cdot x^2} = \sqrt[3]{x^3} = x$

17. $\sqrt{\dfrac{9}{25}} = \dfrac{\sqrt{9}}{\sqrt{25}} = \dfrac{3}{5}$

18. $\sqrt[3]{\dfrac{x}{8}} = \dfrac{\sqrt[3]{x}}{\sqrt[3]{8}} = \dfrac{\sqrt[3]{x}}{2}$

19. $\sqrt{\dfrac{1}{2}} \cdot \sqrt{\dfrac{1}{8}} = \sqrt{\dfrac{1 \cdot 1}{2 \cdot 8}} = \sqrt{\dfrac{1}{16}} = \dfrac{\sqrt{1}}{\sqrt{16}} = \dfrac{1}{4}$

20. $\sqrt{\dfrac{5}{3}} \cdot \sqrt{\dfrac{1}{3}} = \sqrt{\dfrac{5 \cdot 1}{3 \cdot 3}} = \sqrt{\dfrac{5}{9}} = \dfrac{\sqrt{5}}{\sqrt{9}} = \dfrac{\sqrt{5}}{3}$

21. $\sqrt[3]{\dfrac{2}{3}} \cdot \sqrt[3]{\dfrac{4}{3}} \cdot \sqrt[3]{\dfrac{1}{3}} = \sqrt[3]{\dfrac{2}{3} \cdot \dfrac{4}{3} \cdot \dfrac{1}{3}} = \sqrt[3]{\dfrac{8}{27}} = \dfrac{2}{3}$

22. $\sqrt[4]{\dfrac{8}{3}} \cdot \sqrt[4]{\dfrac{4}{9}} \cdot \sqrt[4]{\dfrac{8}{3}} = \sqrt[4]{\dfrac{8}{3} \cdot \dfrac{4}{9} \cdot \dfrac{8}{3}} = \sqrt[4]{\dfrac{256}{81}} = \dfrac{\sqrt[4]{256}}{\sqrt[4]{81}} = \dfrac{4}{3}$

23. $\sqrt{x^3} \cdot \sqrt{x^3} = \sqrt{x^3 \cdot x^3} = \sqrt{x^6} = x^{6/2} = x^3$

24. $\sqrt{z} \cdot \sqrt{z^7} = \sqrt{z \cdot z^7} = \sqrt{z^8} = z^{8/2} = z^4$

25. $\sqrt[3]{\dfrac{7}{27}} = \dfrac{\sqrt[3]{7}}{\sqrt[3]{27}} = \dfrac{\sqrt[3]{7}}{3}$

26. $\sqrt[3]{\dfrac{9}{64}} = \dfrac{\sqrt[3]{9}}{\sqrt[3]{64}} = \dfrac{\sqrt[3]{9}}{4}$

27. $\sqrt[4]{\dfrac{x}{81}} = \dfrac{\sqrt[4]{x}}{\sqrt[4]{81}} = \dfrac{\sqrt[4]{x}}{3}$

28. $\sqrt[4]{\dfrac{16x}{81}} = \dfrac{\sqrt[4]{16} \cdot \sqrt[4]{x}}{\sqrt[4]{81}} = \dfrac{2\sqrt[4]{x}}{3}$

29. $\sqrt{\dfrac{9}{z^2}} = \dfrac{\sqrt{9}}{\sqrt{z^2}} = \dfrac{3}{z}$

30. $\sqrt{\dfrac{x^2}{81}} = \dfrac{\sqrt{x^2}}{\sqrt{81}} = \dfrac{x}{9}$

31. $\sqrt{\dfrac{x}{2}} \cdot \sqrt{\dfrac{x}{8}} = \sqrt{\dfrac{x \cdot x}{2 \cdot 8}} = \sqrt{\dfrac{x^2}{16}} = \dfrac{\sqrt{x^2}}{\sqrt{16}} = \dfrac{x}{4}$

32. $\sqrt{\dfrac{4}{y}} \cdot \sqrt{\dfrac{y}{5}} = \sqrt{\dfrac{4 \cdot y}{y \cdot 5}} = \sqrt{\dfrac{4y}{5y}} = \sqrt{\dfrac{4}{5}} = \dfrac{\sqrt{4}}{\sqrt{5}} = \dfrac{2}{\sqrt{5}}$

33. $\dfrac{\sqrt{45}}{\sqrt{5}} = \sqrt{\dfrac{45}{5}} = \sqrt{9} = 3$

34. $\dfrac{\sqrt{7}}{\sqrt{28}} = \sqrt{\dfrac{7}{28}} = \sqrt{\dfrac{1}{4}} = \dfrac{\sqrt{1}}{\sqrt{4}} = \dfrac{1}{2}$

35. $\sqrt[3]{-4} \cdot \sqrt[3]{-16} = \sqrt[3]{-4 \cdot (-16)} = \sqrt[3]{64} = 4$

36. $\sqrt[3]{9} \cdot \sqrt[3]{3} = \sqrt[3]{9 \cdot 3} = \sqrt[3]{27} = 3$

37. $\sqrt[4]{9} \cdot \sqrt[4]{9} = \sqrt[4]{9 \cdot 9} = \sqrt[4]{81} = 3$

38. $\sqrt[5]{16} \cdot \sqrt[5]{-2} = \sqrt[5]{16 \cdot (-2)} = \sqrt[5]{-32} = -2$

39. $\dfrac{\sqrt[5]{64}}{\sqrt[5]{-2}} = \sqrt[5]{\dfrac{64}{-2}} = \sqrt[5]{-32} = -2$

40. $\dfrac{\sqrt[4]{324}}{\sqrt[4]{4}} = \sqrt[4]{\dfrac{324}{4}} = \sqrt[4]{81} = 3$

41. $\dfrac{\sqrt{a^2 b}}{\sqrt{b}} = \sqrt{\dfrac{a^2 b}{b}} = \sqrt{a^2} = a$

42. $\dfrac{\sqrt{4xy^2}}{\sqrt{x}} = \sqrt{\dfrac{4xy^2}{x}} = \sqrt{4y^2} = \sqrt{4} \cdot \sqrt{y^2} = 2y$

43. $\dfrac{\sqrt[3]{54}}{\sqrt[3]{2}} = \sqrt[3]{\dfrac{54}{2}} = \sqrt[3]{27} = 3$

44. $\dfrac{\sqrt[3]{x^3 y^7}}{\sqrt[3]{y^4}} = \sqrt[3]{\dfrac{x^3 y^7}{y^4}} = \sqrt[3]{x^3 y^3} = \sqrt[3]{x^3} \cdot \sqrt[3]{y^3} = xy$

45. $\sqrt{4x^4} = \sqrt{4} \cdot \sqrt{\left(x^2\right)^2} = 2x^2$

46. $\sqrt[3]{-8y^3} = \sqrt[3]{-8} \cdot \sqrt[3]{y^3} = -2y$

47. $\sqrt[3]{-5a^6} = \sqrt[3]{-5} \cdot \sqrt[3]{(a^2)^3} = \sqrt[3]{-5} \cdot a^2 = -a^2\sqrt[3]{5}$

48. $\sqrt{9x^2y} = \sqrt{9} \cdot \sqrt{x^2} \cdot \sqrt{y} = 3x\sqrt{y}$

49. $\sqrt[4]{16x^4y} = \sqrt[4]{16} \cdot \sqrt[4]{x^4} \cdot \sqrt[4]{y} = 2x\sqrt[4]{y}$

50. $\sqrt[3]{8xy^3} = \sqrt[3]{8} \cdot \sqrt[3]{x} \cdot \sqrt[3]{y^3} = 2\sqrt[3]{x} \cdot y = 2y\sqrt[3]{x}$

51. $\sqrt{3x} \cdot \sqrt{12x} = \sqrt{3 \cdot 12 \cdot x \cdot x} = \sqrt{36x^2} = \sqrt{36} \cdot \sqrt{x^2} = 6x$

52. $\sqrt{6x^5} \cdot \sqrt{6x} = \sqrt{6 \cdot 6 \cdot x^5 \cdot x} = \sqrt{36x^6} = \sqrt{36} \cdot \sqrt{(x^3)^2} = 6x^3$

53. $\sqrt[3]{8x^6y^3z^9} = \sqrt[3]{8} \cdot \sqrt[3]{(x^2)^3} \cdot \sqrt[3]{y^3} \cdot \sqrt[3]{(z^3)^3} = 2x^2yz^3$

54. $\sqrt{16x^4y^6} = \sqrt{16} \cdot \sqrt{(x^2)^2} \cdot \sqrt{(y^3)^2} = 4x^2y^3$

55. $\sqrt[4]{\dfrac{3}{4}} \cdot \sqrt[4]{\dfrac{27}{4}} = \sqrt[4]{\dfrac{3}{4} \cdot \dfrac{27}{4}} = \sqrt[4]{\dfrac{81}{16}} = \dfrac{\sqrt[4]{81}}{\sqrt[4]{16}} = \dfrac{3}{2}$

56. $\sqrt[5]{\dfrac{4}{-9}} \cdot \sqrt[5]{\dfrac{8}{-27}} = \sqrt[5]{\dfrac{4}{-9} \cdot \dfrac{8}{-27}} = \sqrt[5]{\dfrac{32}{243}} = \dfrac{2}{3}$

57. $\sqrt[3]{12} \cdot \sqrt[3]{ab} = \sqrt[3]{12ab}$

58. $\sqrt{5x} \cdot \sqrt{5z} = \sqrt{25xz} = \sqrt{25} \cdot \sqrt{xz} = 5\sqrt{xz}$

59. $\sqrt[4]{25z} \cdot \sqrt[4]{25z} = \sqrt[4]{625z^2} = \sqrt[4]{625} \cdot \sqrt[4]{z^2} = 5\sqrt{z}$

60. $\sqrt[5]{3z^2} \cdot \sqrt[5]{7z} = \sqrt[5]{21z^3}$

61. $\sqrt[5]{\dfrac{7a}{b^2}} \cdot \sqrt[5]{\dfrac{b^2}{7a^6}} = \sqrt[5]{\dfrac{7ab^2}{7a^6b^2}} = \sqrt[5]{\dfrac{1}{a^5}} = \dfrac{1}{a}$

62. $\sqrt[3]{\dfrac{8m}{n}} \cdot \sqrt[3]{\dfrac{n^4}{m^2}} = \sqrt[3]{\dfrac{8mn^4}{nm^2}} = \sqrt[3]{\dfrac{8n^3}{m}} = \dfrac{\sqrt[3]{8n^3}}{\sqrt[3]{m}} = \dfrac{2n}{\sqrt[3]{m}}$

63. $\sqrt{x+4} \cdot \sqrt{x-4} = \sqrt{(x+4)(x-4)} = \sqrt{x^2-16}$

64. $\sqrt[3]{x-1} \cdot \sqrt[3]{x^2+x+1} = \sqrt[3]{(x-1)(x^2+x+1)} = \sqrt[3]{x^3-1}$

65. $\sqrt[3]{a+1} \cdot \sqrt[3]{a^2-a+1} = \sqrt[3]{(a+1)(a^2-a+1)} = \sqrt[3]{a^3+1}$

66. $\sqrt{b-1} \cdot \sqrt{b+1} = \sqrt{(b-1)(b+1)} = \sqrt{b^2-1}$

67. $\dfrac{\sqrt{x^2+2x+1}}{\sqrt{x+1}} = \sqrt{\dfrac{x^2+2x+1}{x+1}} = \sqrt{\dfrac{(x+1)(x+1)}{x+1}} = \sqrt{x+1}$

68. $\dfrac{\sqrt{x^2-4x+4}}{\sqrt{x-2}} = \sqrt{\dfrac{x^2-4x+4}{x-2}} = \sqrt{\dfrac{(x-2)(x-2)}{x-2}} = \sqrt{x-2}$

69. $\sqrt{500} = \sqrt{100 \cdot 5} = \sqrt{100} \cdot \sqrt{5} = 10\sqrt{5}$; the answer is 10.

70. $\sqrt{28} = \sqrt{4 \cdot 7} = \sqrt{4} \cdot \sqrt{7} = 2\sqrt{7}$; the answer is 2.

71. $\sqrt{8} = \sqrt{4 \cdot 2} = \sqrt{4} \cdot \sqrt{2} = 2\sqrt{2}$; the answer is 2.

72. $\sqrt{99} = \sqrt{9 \cdot 11} = \sqrt{9} \cdot \sqrt{11} = 3\sqrt{11}$; the answer is 3.

73. $\sqrt{45} = \sqrt{9 \cdot 5} = \sqrt{9} \cdot \sqrt{5} = 3\sqrt{5}$; the answer is 3.

74. $\sqrt{243} = \sqrt{81 \cdot 3} = \sqrt{81} \cdot \sqrt{3} = 9\sqrt{3}$; the answer is 9.

75. $\sqrt{200} = \sqrt{100 \cdot 2} = \sqrt{100} \cdot \sqrt{2} = 10\sqrt{2}$

76. $\sqrt{72} = \sqrt{36 \cdot 2} = \sqrt{36} \cdot \sqrt{2} = 6\sqrt{2}$

77. $\sqrt[3]{81} = \sqrt[3]{27 \cdot 3} = \sqrt[3]{27} \cdot \sqrt[3]{3} = 3\sqrt[3]{3}$

78. $\sqrt[3]{256} = \sqrt[3]{64 \cdot 4} = \sqrt[3]{64} \cdot \sqrt[3]{4} = 4\sqrt[3]{4}$

79. $\sqrt[4]{64} = \sqrt[4]{16 \cdot 4} = \sqrt[4]{16} \cdot \sqrt[4]{4} = 2\sqrt[4]{4} = 2\sqrt[4]{2^2} = 2\sqrt{2}$

80. $\sqrt[5]{27 \cdot 81} = \sqrt[5]{3^3 \cdot 3^4} = \sqrt[5]{3^7} = \sqrt[5]{3^5 \cdot 3^2} = \sqrt[5]{3^5} \cdot \sqrt[5]{3^2} = 3\sqrt[5]{9}$

81. $\sqrt[5]{-64} = \sqrt[5]{-2^6} = \sqrt[5]{-2^5 \cdot 2} = \sqrt[5]{-2^5} \cdot \sqrt[5]{2} = -2\sqrt[5]{2}$

82. $\sqrt[3]{-81} = \sqrt[3]{-3^4} = \sqrt[3]{-3^3 \cdot 3} = \sqrt[3]{-3^3} \cdot \sqrt[3]{3} = -3\sqrt[3]{3}$

83. $\sqrt{b^5} = \sqrt{\left(b^2\right)^2 \cdot b} = \sqrt{\left(b^2\right)^2} \cdot \sqrt{b} = b^2\sqrt{b}$

84. $\sqrt{t^3} = \sqrt{t^2 \cdot t} = \sqrt{t^2} \cdot \sqrt{t} = t\sqrt{t}$

85. $\sqrt{8n^3} = \sqrt{\left(2n\right)^2 \cdot 2n} = \sqrt{\left(2n\right)^2} \cdot \sqrt{2n} = 2n\sqrt{2n}$

86. $\sqrt{32a^2} = \sqrt{\left(4a\right)^2 \cdot 2} = \sqrt{\left(4a\right)^2} \cdot \sqrt{2} = 4a\sqrt{2}$

87. $\sqrt{12a^2b^5} = \sqrt{\left(2ab^2\right)^2 \cdot 3b} = \sqrt{\left(2ab^2\right)^2} \cdot \sqrt{3b} = 2ab^2\sqrt{3b}$

88. $\sqrt{20a^3b^2} = \sqrt{\left(2ab\right)^2 \cdot 5a} = \sqrt{\left(2ab\right)^2} \cdot \sqrt{5a} = 2ab\sqrt{5a}$

89. $\sqrt[3]{-125x^4y^5} = \sqrt[3]{\left(-5xy\right)^3 \cdot xy^2} = \sqrt[3]{\left(-5xy\right)^3} \cdot \sqrt[3]{xy^2} = -5xy\sqrt[3]{xy^2}$

90. $\sqrt[3]{-81a^5b^2} = \sqrt[3]{\left(-3a\right)^3 \cdot 3a^2b^2} = \sqrt[3]{\left(-3a\right)^3} \cdot \sqrt[3]{3a^2b^2} = -3a\sqrt[3]{3a^2b^2}$

91. $\sqrt[3]{5t} \cdot \sqrt[3]{125t} = \sqrt[3]{625t^2} = \sqrt[3]{5^4t^2} = \sqrt[3]{5^3 \cdot 5t^2} = \sqrt[3]{5^3} \cdot \sqrt[3]{5t^2} = 5\sqrt[3]{5t^2}$

92. $\sqrt[4]{4bc^3} \cdot \sqrt[4]{64ab^3c^2} = \sqrt[4]{256ab^4c^5} = \sqrt[4]{4^4ab^4c^5} = \sqrt[4]{\left(4bc\right)^4 \cdot ac} = \sqrt[4]{\left(4bc\right)^4} \cdot \sqrt[4]{ac} = 4bc\sqrt[4]{ac}$

93. $\sqrt[4]{\dfrac{9t^5}{r^8}} \cdot \sqrt[4]{\dfrac{9r}{5t}} = \sqrt[4]{\dfrac{81rt^5}{5r^8t}} = \sqrt[4]{\dfrac{81t^4}{5r^7}} = \dfrac{\sqrt[4]{(3t)^4}}{\sqrt[4]{r^4 \cdot 5r^3}} = \dfrac{3t}{r\sqrt[4]{5r^3}}$

94. $\sqrt[5]{\dfrac{4t^6}{r}} \cdot \sqrt[5]{\dfrac{8t}{r^6}} = \sqrt[5]{\dfrac{32t^7}{r^7}} = \dfrac{\sqrt[5]{(2t)^5 \cdot t^2}}{\sqrt[5]{r^5 \cdot r^2}} = \dfrac{2t\sqrt[5]{t^2}}{r\sqrt[5]{r^2}} = \dfrac{2t}{r}\sqrt[5]{\dfrac{t^2}{r^2}}$

95. $\sqrt[3]{\dfrac{27x^2}{y^3}} = \dfrac{\sqrt[3]{27} \cdot \sqrt[3]{x^2}}{\sqrt[3]{y^3}} = \dfrac{3\sqrt[3]{x^2}}{y}$

96. $\sqrt[4]{\dfrac{32x^8}{z^4}} = \dfrac{\sqrt[4]{32} \cdot \sqrt[4]{x^8}}{\sqrt[4]{z^4}} = \dfrac{\sqrt[4]{16} \cdot \sqrt[4]{2} \cdot x^{8/4}}{z} = \dfrac{2x^2\sqrt[4]{2}}{z}$

97. $\sqrt{\dfrac{7a^2}{27}} \cdot \sqrt{\dfrac{7a}{3}} = \sqrt{\dfrac{49a^3}{81}} = \dfrac{\sqrt{49} \cdot \sqrt{a^3}}{\sqrt{81}} = \dfrac{7\sqrt{a^2} \cdot \sqrt{a}}{9}$

    $= \dfrac{7a\sqrt{a}}{9}$

98. $\sqrt{\dfrac{8a}{125}} \cdot \sqrt{\dfrac{2a}{5}} = \sqrt{\dfrac{16a^2}{625}} = \dfrac{\sqrt{16} \cdot \sqrt{a^2}}{\sqrt{625}} = \dfrac{4a}{25}$

99. $\left(\sqrt[mn]{a^m b^m}\right)^n = \left(\sqrt[m]{a^m b^m}\right)^{n/n} = \sqrt[m]{(ab)^m} = (ab)^{m/m} = ab$

100. $\sqrt[mn]{a^n b^m} \cdot \sqrt[mn]{a^m b^n} = \sqrt[mn]{a^n} \cdot \sqrt[mn]{b^m} \cdot \sqrt[mn]{a^m} \cdot \sqrt[mn]{b^n}$

    $= \sqrt[m]{a} \cdot \sqrt[n]{b} \cdot \sqrt[n]{a} \cdot \sqrt[m]{b} = \sqrt[m]{a} \cdot \sqrt[m]{b} \cdot \sqrt[n]{a} \sqrt[n]{b}$

    $= \sqrt[m]{ab} \cdot \sqrt[n]{ab}$

101. $\sqrt{3} \cdot \sqrt[3]{3} = 3^{1/2} \cdot 3^{1/3} = 3^{1/2+1/3} = 3^{5/6} = \sqrt[6]{3^5}$

102. $\sqrt{5} \cdot \sqrt[3]{5} = 5^{1/2} \cdot 5^{1/3} = 5^{1/2+1/3} = 5^{5/6} = \sqrt[6]{5^5}$

103. $\sqrt[4]{8} \cdot \sqrt[3]{4} = \sqrt[4]{2^3} \cdot \sqrt[3]{2^2} = 2^{3/4} \cdot 2^{2/3} = 2^{3/4+2/3} = 2^{17/12} = 2^{12/12+5/12} = 2 \cdot 2^{5/12} = 2\sqrt[12]{2^5}$

104. $\sqrt[5]{16} \cdot \sqrt{2} = \sqrt[5]{2^4} \cdot \sqrt{2} = 2^{4/5} \cdot 2^{1/2} = 2^{4/5+1/2} = 2^{13/10} = 2^{10/10} \cdot 2^{3/10} = 2\sqrt[10]{2^3}$

105. $\sqrt[4]{27} \cdot \sqrt[3]{9} \cdot \sqrt{3} = \sqrt[4]{3^3} \cdot \sqrt[3]{3^2} \cdot \sqrt{3} = 3^{3/4} \cdot 3^{2/3} \cdot 3^{1/2} = 3^{3/4+2/3+1/2} = 3^{23/12} = 3^{12/12} \cdot 3^{11/12} = 3\sqrt[12]{3^{11}}$

106. $\sqrt[5]{16} \cdot \sqrt[3]{16} = 16^{1/5} \cdot 16^{1/3} = 16^{1/5+1/3} = 16^{8/15} = \left(2^4\right)^{8/15} = 2^{32/15} = 2^{30/15} \cdot 2^{2/15} = 2^2 \cdot 2^{2/15} = 4\sqrt[15]{2^2}$

107. $\sqrt[4]{x^3} \cdot \sqrt[3]{x} = x^{3/4} \cdot x^{1/3} = x^{3/4+1/3} = x^{13/12} = x^{12/12} \cdot x^{1/12} = x\sqrt[12]{x}$

108. $\sqrt[4]{x^3} \cdot \sqrt{x} = x^{3/4} \cdot x^{1/2} = x^{3/4+1/2} = x^{5/4} = x^{4/4} \cdot x^{1/4} = x \cdot x^{1/4} = x\sqrt[4]{x}$

109. $\sqrt[4]{rt} \cdot \sqrt[3]{r^2 t} = (rt)^{1/4} \cdot \left(r^2 t\right)^{1/3} = r^{1/4} t^{1/4} \cdot r^{2/3} t^{1/3} = r^{1/4+2/3} t^{1/4+1/3} = r^{11/12} t^{7/12} = \sqrt[12]{r^{11} t^7}$

110. $\sqrt[3]{a^3 b^2} \cdot \sqrt{a^2 b} = \left(a^3 b^2\right)^{1/3} \cdot \left(a^2 b\right)^{1/2} = ab^{2/3} \cdot ab^{1/2} = a^{1+1} b^{2/3+1/2} = a^2 b^{7/6} = a^2 b^{6/6} \cdot b^{1/6} = a^2 b\sqrt[6]{b}$

Applications

111.   (a) $A = 100\sqrt[3]{8^2} = 100\sqrt[3]{64} = 100 \cdot 4 = 400$ square inches

      (b) $A = 100\sqrt[3]{W^2} \;\Rightarrow\; A = 100W^{2/3}$

112.   (a) $T = \sqrt{30^3} = \sqrt{27{,}000} \approx 164.3$ years

      (b) $T = \sqrt{D^3} \;\Rightarrow\; T = D^{3/2}$

Checking Basic Concepts for Sections 7.1 & 7.2

1.   (a) ± 7

    (b)   7

2.   (a) $\sqrt[3]{-8} = -2$

    (b) $-\sqrt[4]{81} = -3$

3.   (a) $x^{3/2} = \sqrt{x^3}$ or $\left(\sqrt{x}\right)^3$

    (b) $x^{2/3} = \sqrt[3]{x^2}$ or $\left(\sqrt[3]{x}\right)^2$

    (c) $x^{-2/5} = \dfrac{1}{\sqrt[5]{x^2}}$ or $\dfrac{1}{\left(\sqrt[5]{x}\right)^2}$

4. $\sqrt{(x-1)^2} = |x-1|$

5.   (a) $\left(64^{-3/2}\right)^{1/3} = 64^{-3/2 \cdot 1/3} = 64^{-1/2} = \dfrac{1}{64^{1/2}} = \dfrac{1}{\sqrt{64}} = \dfrac{1}{8}$

    (b) $\sqrt{5} \cdot \sqrt{20} = \sqrt{5 \cdot 20} = \sqrt{100} = 10$

    (c) $\sqrt[3]{-8x^4 y} = \sqrt[3]{(-2x)^3 \cdot xy} = -2x\sqrt[3]{xy}$

    (d) $\sqrt{\dfrac{4b}{5}} \cdot \sqrt{\dfrac{4b^3}{5}} = \sqrt{\dfrac{4b \cdot 4b^3}{5 \cdot 5}} = \dfrac{\sqrt{16b^4}}{\sqrt{25}} = \dfrac{4b^2}{5}$

6. $\sqrt[3]{7} \cdot \sqrt{7} = 7^{1/3} \cdot 7^{1/2} = 7^{1/3 + 1/2} = 7^{5/6} = \sqrt[6]{7^5}$

7.3: Operations on Radical Expressions

Concepts

1. $2\sqrt{a}$

2. $3\sqrt[3]{b}$

3.   like

4.   Yes, these are like radicals. $4\sqrt{15} - 3\sqrt{15} = (4-3)\sqrt{15} = \sqrt{15}$

5.   No; 6 and $3\sqrt{5}$ are not like radicals.

6. $\dfrac{\sqrt{7}}{\sqrt{7}}$

7. $\sqrt{t}+5$

8.   The conjugate of the denominator over itself: $\dfrac{5+\sqrt{2}}{5+\sqrt{2}}$

Like Radicals

9.   Not possible, since $\sqrt{12}=2\sqrt{3}$ and $\sqrt{24}=2\sqrt{6}$.

10. Not possible, since $\sqrt{18}=3\sqrt{2}$ and $\sqrt{27}=3\sqrt{3}$.

11. Since $\sqrt{28}=\sqrt{4\cdot7}=\sqrt{4}\cdot\sqrt{7}=2\sqrt{7}$ and $\sqrt{63}=\sqrt{9\cdot7}=\sqrt{9}\cdot\sqrt{7}=3\sqrt{7}$, the like radicals are $\sqrt{7},2\sqrt{7}$, and $3\sqrt{7}$.

12. Not possible, since $\sqrt{200}=10\sqrt{2}$, $\sqrt{300}=10\sqrt{3}$, and $\sqrt{500}=10\sqrt{5}$.

13. Since $\sqrt[3]{16}=\sqrt[3]{8\cdot2}=\sqrt[3]{8}\cdot\sqrt[3]{2}=2\sqrt[3]{2}$ and $\sqrt[3]{-54}=\sqrt[3]{-27\cdot2}=\sqrt[3]{-27}\cdot\sqrt[3]{2}=-3\sqrt[3]{2}$, the like radicals are $2\sqrt[3]{2}$ and $-3\sqrt[3]{2}$.

14. Since $\sqrt[3]{80}=\sqrt[3]{8\cdot10}=\sqrt[3]{8}\cdot\sqrt[3]{10}=2\sqrt[3]{10}$, the like radicals are $2\sqrt[3]{10}$ and $\sqrt[3]{10}$.

15. Not possible, since $\sqrt{x^2y}=x\sqrt{y}$ and $\sqrt{4y^2}=2y$.

16. Since $\sqrt{x^5y^3}=\sqrt{\left(x^2y\right)^2\cdot xy}=\sqrt{\left(x^2y\right)^2}\cdot\sqrt{xy}=x^2y\sqrt{xy}$ and $\sqrt{9xy}=\sqrt{9}\cdot\sqrt{xy}=3\sqrt{xy}$, the like radicals are $x^2y\sqrt{xy}$ and $3\sqrt{xy}$.

17. Since $\sqrt[3]{8xy}=\sqrt[3]{8}\cdot\sqrt[3]{xy}=2\sqrt[3]{xy}$ and $\sqrt[3]{x^4y^4}=\sqrt[3]{\left(xy\right)^3\cdot xy}=\sqrt[3]{\left(xy\right)^3}\cdot\sqrt[3]{xy}=xy\sqrt[3]{xy}$, the like radicals are $2\sqrt[3]{xy}$ and $xy\sqrt[3]{xy}$.

18. Since $\sqrt[3]{64x^4}=\sqrt[3]{\left(4x\right)^3\cdot x}=\sqrt[3]{\left(4x\right)^3}\cdot\sqrt[3]{x}=4x\sqrt[3]{x}$ and $\sqrt[3]{-8x}=\sqrt[3]{-8}\cdot\sqrt[3]{x}=-2\sqrt[3]{x}$, the like radicals are $4x\sqrt[3]{x}$ and $-2\sqrt[3]{x}$.

Addition and Subtraction of Radicals

19. $2\sqrt{3}+7\sqrt{3}=9\sqrt{3}$

20. $8\sqrt{7}+2\sqrt{7}=10\sqrt{7}$

21. $4\sqrt[3]{5}+2\sqrt[3]{5}=6\sqrt[3]{5}$

22. $\sqrt[3]{13}+3\sqrt[3]{13}=4\sqrt[3]{13}$

23. Not possible, since 7 and $4\sqrt{7}$ are not like radicals

24. Not possible, since 8 and $-4\sqrt{3}$ are not like radicals

25. Not possible, since $2\sqrt{3}$ and $3\sqrt{2}$ are not like radicals

26. Not possible, since $\sqrt{6}$ and $\sqrt{17}$ are not like radicals

27. Not possible, since $\sqrt{3}$ and $\sqrt[3]{3}$ are not like radicals

28. Not possible, since $\sqrt{6}$ and $\sqrt[4]{6}$ are not like radicals

29. $\sqrt[3]{16} + 3\sqrt[3]{2} = \sqrt[3]{8 \cdot 2} + 3\sqrt[3]{2} = \sqrt[3]{8} \cdot \sqrt[3]{2} + 3\sqrt[3]{2} = 2\sqrt[3]{2} + 3\sqrt[3]{2} = 5\sqrt[3]{2}$

30. $\sqrt[3]{24} + \sqrt[3]{81} = \sqrt[3]{8 \cdot 3} + \sqrt[3]{27 \cdot 3} = \sqrt[3]{8} \cdot \sqrt[3]{3} + \sqrt[3]{27} \cdot \sqrt[3]{3} = 2\sqrt[3]{3} + 3\sqrt[3]{3} = 5\sqrt[3]{3}$

31. $\sqrt{2} + \sqrt{18} + \sqrt{32} = \sqrt{2} + \sqrt{9 \cdot 2} + \sqrt{16 \cdot 2} = \sqrt{2} + \sqrt{9} \cdot \sqrt{2} + \sqrt{16} \cdot \sqrt{2} = \sqrt{2} + 3\sqrt{2} + 4\sqrt{2} = 8\sqrt{2}$

32. $2\sqrt{3} + \sqrt{12} + \sqrt{27} = 2\sqrt{3} \cdot \sqrt{4 \cdot 3} + \sqrt{9 \cdot 3} = 2\sqrt{3} + \sqrt{4} \cdot \sqrt{3} + \sqrt{9} \cdot \sqrt{3} = 2\sqrt{3} + 2\sqrt{3} + 3\sqrt{3} = 7\sqrt{3}$

33. $11\sqrt{11} - 5\sqrt{11} = 6\sqrt{11}$

34. $9\sqrt{5} + \sqrt{2} - \sqrt{5} = 8\sqrt{5} + \sqrt{2}$

35. $\sqrt{x} + \sqrt{x} - \sqrt{y} = 2\sqrt{x} - \sqrt{y}$

36. $\sqrt{xy^2} - \sqrt{x} = \sqrt{x} \cdot \sqrt{y^2} - \sqrt{x} = y\sqrt{x} - \sqrt{x} = (y-1)\sqrt{x}$

37. $\sqrt[3]{z} + \sqrt[3]{z} = 2\sqrt[3]{z}$

38. $\sqrt[3]{y} - \sqrt[3]{y} = 0$

39. $2\sqrt[3]{6} - 7\sqrt[3]{6} = -5\sqrt[3]{6}$

40. $18\sqrt[3]{3} + 3\sqrt[3]{3} = 21\sqrt[3]{3}$

41. $\sqrt[3]{y^6} - \sqrt[3]{y^3} = \sqrt[3]{\left(y^2\right)^3} - \sqrt[3]{y^3} = y^2 - y$

42. $2\sqrt{20} + 7\sqrt{5} + 3\sqrt{2} = 2\sqrt{4 \cdot 5} + 7\sqrt{5} + 3\sqrt{2} = 2 \cdot 2\sqrt{5} + 7\sqrt{5} + 3\sqrt{2} = 11\sqrt{5} + 3\sqrt{2}$

43. $3\sqrt{28} + 3\sqrt{7} = 3\sqrt{4 \cdot 7} + 3\sqrt{7} = 3 \cdot 2\sqrt{7} + 3\sqrt{7} = 9\sqrt{7}$

44. $9\sqrt{18} - 2\sqrt{8} = 9\sqrt{9 \cdot 2} - 2\sqrt{4 \cdot 2} = 9 \cdot 3\sqrt{2} - 2 \cdot 2\sqrt{2} = 23\sqrt{2}$

45. $\sqrt[4]{48} + 4\sqrt[4]{3} = \sqrt[4]{16 \cdot 3} + 4\sqrt[4]{3} = \sqrt[4]{16} \cdot \sqrt[4]{3} + 4\sqrt[4]{3} = 2\sqrt[4]{3} + 4\sqrt[4]{3} = 6\sqrt[4]{3}$

46. $\sqrt[4]{32} + \sqrt[4]{16} = \sqrt[4]{16 \cdot 2} + 2 = \sqrt[4]{16} \cdot \sqrt[4]{2} + 2 = 2\sqrt[4]{2} + 2$

47. $\sqrt{9x} + \sqrt{16x} = \sqrt{9} \cdot \sqrt{x} + \sqrt{16} \cdot \sqrt{x} = 3\sqrt{x} + 4\sqrt{x} = 7\sqrt{x}$

48. $-3\sqrt{x} + 5\sqrt{x} = 2\sqrt{x}$

49. $3\sqrt{2k} + \sqrt{8k} + \sqrt{18k} = 3\sqrt{2k} + \sqrt{4 \cdot 2k} + \sqrt{9 \cdot 2k} = 3\sqrt{2k} + \sqrt{4} \cdot \sqrt{2k} + \sqrt{9} \cdot \sqrt{2k}$

    $= 3\sqrt{2k} + 2\sqrt{2k} + 3\sqrt{2k} = 8\sqrt{2k}$

50. $3\sqrt{k} + 2\sqrt{4k} + \sqrt{9k} = 3\sqrt{k} + 2\sqrt{4} \cdot \sqrt{k} + \sqrt{9} \cdot \sqrt{k} = 3\sqrt{k} + 2 \cdot 2\sqrt{k} + 3\sqrt{k} = 10\sqrt{k}$

51. $\sqrt{44} - 4\sqrt{11} = \sqrt{4 \cdot 11} - 4\sqrt{11} = 2\sqrt{11} - 4\sqrt{11} = -2\sqrt{11}$

52. $\sqrt[4]{5} + 2\sqrt[4]{5} = 3\sqrt[4]{5}$

53. $2\sqrt[3]{16} + \sqrt[3]{2} - \sqrt{2} = 2\sqrt[3]{8 \cdot 2} + \sqrt[3]{2} - \sqrt{2} = 2 \cdot 2\sqrt[3]{2} + \sqrt[3]{2} - \sqrt{2} = 5\sqrt[3]{2} - \sqrt{2}$

54. $5\sqrt[3]{x} - 2\sqrt[3]{x} = 2\sqrt[3]{x}$

55. $\sqrt[3]{xy} - 2\sqrt[3]{xy} = -\sqrt[3]{xy}$

56. $3\sqrt{x^3} - \sqrt{x} = 3\sqrt{x^2 \cdot x} - \sqrt{x} = 3\sqrt{x^2} \cdot \sqrt{x} - \sqrt{x} = 3x\sqrt{x} - \sqrt{x} = (3x-1)\sqrt{x}$

57. $\sqrt{4x+8} + \sqrt{x+2} = \sqrt{4(x+2)} + \sqrt{x+2} = 2\sqrt{x+2} + \sqrt{x+2} = 3\sqrt{x+2}$

58. $\sqrt{2a+1} + \sqrt{8a+4} = \sqrt{2a+1} + \sqrt{4(2a+1)} = \sqrt{2a+1} + 2\sqrt{2a+1} = 3\sqrt{2a+1}$

59. $\sqrt{25x^3} - \sqrt{x^3} = \sqrt{25} \cdot \sqrt{x^2} \cdot \sqrt{x} - \sqrt{x^2} \cdot \sqrt{x} = 5x\sqrt{x} - x\sqrt{x} = 4x\sqrt{x}$

60. $\sqrt{36x^5} - \sqrt{25x^5} = \sqrt{36} \cdot \sqrt{x^4} \cdot \sqrt{x} - \sqrt{25} \cdot \sqrt{x^4} \cdot \sqrt{x} = 6x^2\sqrt{x} - 5x^2\sqrt{x} = x^2\sqrt{x}$

61. $\sqrt[3]{\dfrac{7x}{8}} - \dfrac{\sqrt[3]{7x}}{3} = \dfrac{\sqrt[3]{7x}}{\sqrt[3]{8}} - \dfrac{\sqrt[3]{7x}}{3} = \dfrac{\sqrt[3]{7x}}{2} - \dfrac{\sqrt[3]{7x}}{3} = \dfrac{3\sqrt[3]{7x}}{6} - \dfrac{2\sqrt[3]{7x}}{6} = \dfrac{\sqrt[3]{7x}}{6}$

62. $\sqrt[3]{\dfrac{8x^2}{27}} - \sqrt[3]{\dfrac{x^2}{8}} = \dfrac{\sqrt[3]{8} \cdot \sqrt[3]{x^2}}{\sqrt[3]{27}} - \dfrac{\sqrt[3]{x^2}}{\sqrt[3]{8}} = \dfrac{2\sqrt[3]{x^2}}{3} - \dfrac{\sqrt[3]{x^2}}{2} = \dfrac{4\sqrt[3]{x^2}}{6} - \dfrac{3\sqrt[3]{x^2}}{6} = \dfrac{\sqrt[3]{x^2}}{6}$

63. $\dfrac{4\sqrt{3}}{3} + \dfrac{\sqrt{3}}{6} = \dfrac{4\sqrt{3}}{3} \cdot \dfrac{2}{2} + \dfrac{\sqrt{3}}{6} = \dfrac{8\sqrt{3}}{6} + \dfrac{\sqrt{3}}{6} = \dfrac{8\sqrt{3} + \sqrt{3}}{6} = \dfrac{9\sqrt{3}}{6} = \dfrac{3\sqrt{3}}{2}$

64. $\dfrac{8\sqrt{5}}{7} + \dfrac{4\sqrt{5}}{2} = \dfrac{8\sqrt{5}}{7} \cdot \dfrac{2}{2} + \dfrac{4\sqrt{5}}{2} \cdot \dfrac{7}{7} = \dfrac{16\sqrt{5}}{14} + \dfrac{28\sqrt{5}}{14} = \dfrac{16\sqrt{5} + 28\sqrt{5}}{14} = \dfrac{44\sqrt{5}}{14} = \dfrac{22\sqrt{5}}{7}$

65. $\dfrac{15\sqrt{8}}{4} - \dfrac{2\sqrt{2}}{5} = \dfrac{15 \cdot 2\sqrt{2}}{4} \cdot \dfrac{5}{5} - \dfrac{2\sqrt{2}}{5} \cdot \dfrac{4}{4} = \dfrac{150\sqrt{2}}{20} - \dfrac{8\sqrt{2}}{20} = \dfrac{150\sqrt{2} - 8\sqrt{2}}{20} = \dfrac{142\sqrt{2}}{20} = \dfrac{71\sqrt{2}}{10}$

66. $\dfrac{23\sqrt{11}}{2} - \dfrac{\sqrt{44}}{8} = \dfrac{23\sqrt{11}}{2} \cdot \dfrac{4}{4} - \dfrac{2\sqrt{11}}{8} = \dfrac{92\sqrt{11}}{8} - \dfrac{2\sqrt{11}}{8} = \dfrac{92\sqrt{11} - 2\sqrt{11}}{8} = \dfrac{90\sqrt{11}}{8} = \dfrac{45\sqrt{11}}{4}$

67. $2\sqrt[4]{64} - \sqrt[4]{324} + \sqrt[4]{4} = 2\sqrt[4]{16 \cdot 4} - \sqrt[4]{81 \cdot 4} + \sqrt[4]{4} = 4\sqrt[4]{4} - 3\sqrt[4]{4} + \sqrt[4]{4} = 2\sqrt[4]{4} = 2\sqrt{2}$

68. $2\sqrt[3]{16} - 5\sqrt[3]{54} + 10\sqrt[3]{2} = 2\sqrt[3]{8 \cdot 2} - 5\sqrt[3]{27 \cdot 2} + 10\sqrt[3]{2} = 4\sqrt[3]{2} - 15\sqrt[3]{2} + 10\sqrt[3]{2} = -\sqrt[3]{2}$

69. $5\sqrt[4]{x^5} - \sqrt[4]{x} = 5\sqrt[4]{x^4 \cdot x} - \sqrt[4]{x} = 5x\sqrt[4]{x} - \sqrt[4]{x} = (5x-1)\sqrt[4]{x}$

70. $20\sqrt[3]{b^4} - 4\sqrt[3]{b} = 20\sqrt[3]{b^3 \cdot b} - 4\sqrt[3]{b} = 20b\sqrt[3]{b} - 4\sqrt[3]{b} = 4\sqrt[3]{b}(5b-1)$

71. $\sqrt{64x^3} - \sqrt{x} + 3\sqrt{x} = \sqrt{(8x)^2 \cdot x} - \sqrt{x} + 3\sqrt{x} = 8x\sqrt{x} - \sqrt{x} + 3\sqrt{x} = 2\sqrt{x}(4x+1)$

72. $2\sqrt{3z} + 3\sqrt{12z} + 3\sqrt{48z} = 2\sqrt{3z} + 3\sqrt{4 \cdot 3z} + 3\sqrt{16 \cdot 3z} = 2\sqrt{3z} + 6\sqrt{3z} + 12\sqrt{3z} = 20\sqrt{3z}$

73. $\sqrt[4]{81a^5b^5} - \sqrt[4]{ab} = \sqrt[4]{(3ab)^4 \cdot ab} - \sqrt[4]{ab} = 3ab\sqrt[4]{ab} - \sqrt[4]{ab} = (3ab-1)\sqrt[4]{ab}$

74. $\sqrt[4]{xy^5} - \sqrt[4]{x^5y} = \sqrt[4]{y^4 \cdot xy} - \sqrt[4]{x^4 \cdot xy} = y\sqrt[4]{xy} - x\sqrt[4]{xy} = (y-x)\sqrt[4]{xy}$

75. $5\sqrt[3]{\dfrac{n^4}{125}} - 2\sqrt[3]{n} = 5\sqrt[3]{\dfrac{n^3}{125} \cdot n} - 2\sqrt[3]{n} = 5 \cdot \dfrac{n}{5}\sqrt[3]{n} - 2\sqrt[3]{n} = n\sqrt[3]{n} - 2\sqrt[3]{n} = (n-2)\sqrt[3]{n}$

76. $\sqrt[3]{\dfrac{8x}{27}} - \dfrac{2\sqrt[3]{x}}{3} = \dfrac{\sqrt[3]{8x}}{\sqrt[3]{27}} - \dfrac{2\sqrt[3]{x}}{3} = \dfrac{2\sqrt[3]{x}}{3} - \dfrac{2\sqrt[3]{x}}{3} = 0$

Multiplying Binomials Containing Radicals

77. $\left(\sqrt{x} - 3\right)\left(\sqrt{x} + 2\right) = \left(\sqrt{x}\right)^2 + 2\sqrt{x} - 3\sqrt{x} - 6 = x - \sqrt{x} - 6$

78. $\left(2\sqrt{x} + 1\right)\left(\sqrt{x} + 4\right) = 2\left(\sqrt{x}\right)^2 + 8\sqrt{x} + \sqrt{x} + 4 = 2x + 9\sqrt{x} + 4$

79. $\left(3 + \sqrt{7}\right)\left(3 - \sqrt{7}\right) = 3^2 - \left(\sqrt{7}\right)^2 = 9 - 7 = 2$

80. $\left(5 - \sqrt{5}\right)\left(5 + \sqrt{5}\right) = 5^2 - \left(\sqrt{5}\right)^2 = 25 - 5 = 20$

81. $\left(11 - \sqrt{2}\right)\left(11 + \sqrt{2}\right) = 11^2 - \left(\sqrt{2}\right)^2 = 121 - 2 = 119$

82. $\left(6 + \sqrt{3}\right)\left(6 - \sqrt{3}\right) = 6^2 - \left(\sqrt{3}\right)^2 = 36 - 3 = 33$

83. $\left(\sqrt{x} + 8\right)\left(\sqrt{x} - 8\right) = \left(\sqrt{x}\right)^2 - 8^2 = x - 64$

84. $\left(\sqrt{ab} - 3\right)\left(\sqrt{ab} + 3\right) = \left(\sqrt{ab}\right)^2 - 3^2 = ab - 9$

85. $\left(\sqrt{ab} - \sqrt{c}\right)\left(\sqrt{ab} + \sqrt{c}\right) = \left(\sqrt{ab}\right)^2 - \left(\sqrt{c}\right)^2 = ab - c$

86. $\left(\sqrt{2x} + \sqrt{3y}\right)\left(\sqrt{2x} - \sqrt{3y}\right) = \left(\sqrt{2x}\right)^2 - \left(\sqrt{3y}\right)^2 = 2x - 3y$

87. $\left(\sqrt{x} - 7\right)\left(\sqrt{x} + 8\right) = \left(\sqrt{x}\right)^2 + 8\sqrt{x} - 7\sqrt{x} - 56 = x + \sqrt{x} - 56$

88. $\left(\sqrt{ab} - 1\right)\left(\sqrt{ab} - 2\right) = \left(\sqrt{ab}\right)^2 - 2\sqrt{ab} - \sqrt{ab} + 2 = ab - 3\sqrt{ab} + 2$

Rationalizing the Denominator

89. $\dfrac{1}{\sqrt{7}} = \dfrac{1}{\sqrt{7}} \cdot \dfrac{\sqrt{7}}{\sqrt{7}} = \dfrac{\sqrt{7}}{\left(\sqrt{7}\right)^2} = \dfrac{\sqrt{7}}{7}$

90. $\dfrac{1}{\sqrt{23}} = \dfrac{1}{\sqrt{23}} \cdot \dfrac{\sqrt{23}}{\sqrt{23}} = \dfrac{\sqrt{23}}{\left(\sqrt{23}\right)^2} = \dfrac{\sqrt{23}}{23}$

91. $\dfrac{4}{\sqrt{3}} = \dfrac{4}{\sqrt{3}} \cdot \dfrac{\sqrt{3}}{\sqrt{3}} = \dfrac{4\sqrt{3}}{\left(\sqrt{3}\right)^2} = \dfrac{4\sqrt{3}}{3}$

92. $\dfrac{8}{\sqrt{2}} = \dfrac{8}{\sqrt{2}} \cdot \dfrac{\sqrt{2}}{\sqrt{2}} = \dfrac{8\sqrt{2}}{\left(\sqrt{2}\right)^2} = \dfrac{8\sqrt{2}}{2} = 4\sqrt{2}$

93. $\dfrac{5}{3\sqrt{5}} = \dfrac{5}{3\sqrt{5}} \cdot \dfrac{\sqrt{5}}{\sqrt{5}} = \dfrac{5\sqrt{5}}{3\left(\sqrt{5}\right)^2} = \dfrac{5\sqrt{5}}{3\cdot 5} = \dfrac{\sqrt{5}}{3}$

94. $\dfrac{6}{11\sqrt{3}} = \dfrac{6}{11\sqrt{3}} \cdot \dfrac{\sqrt{3}}{\sqrt{3}} = \dfrac{6\sqrt{3}}{11\left(\sqrt{3}\right)^2} = \dfrac{6\sqrt{3}}{11\cdot 3} = \dfrac{2\sqrt{3}}{11}$

95. $\sqrt{\dfrac{b}{12}} = \dfrac{\sqrt{b}}{\sqrt{12}} \cdot \dfrac{\sqrt{12}}{\sqrt{12}} = \dfrac{\sqrt{12b}}{\left(\sqrt{12}\right)^2} = \dfrac{\sqrt{4\cdot 3b}}{12} = \dfrac{\sqrt{4}\cdot\sqrt{3b}}{12} = \dfrac{2\sqrt{3b}}{12} = \dfrac{\sqrt{3b}}{6}$

96. $\sqrt{\dfrac{5b}{72}} = \dfrac{\sqrt{5b}}{\sqrt{72}} = \dfrac{\sqrt{5b}}{\sqrt{36\cdot 2}} = \dfrac{\sqrt{5b}}{6\sqrt{2}} \cdot \dfrac{\sqrt{2}}{\sqrt{2}} = \dfrac{\sqrt{10b}}{6\left(\sqrt{2}\right)^2} = \dfrac{\sqrt{10b}}{6\cdot 2} = \dfrac{\sqrt{10b}}{12}$

97. $\dfrac{rt}{2\sqrt{r^3}} = \dfrac{rt}{2\sqrt{r^2}\cdot\sqrt{r}} \cdot \dfrac{\sqrt{r}}{\sqrt{r}} = \dfrac{rt\sqrt{r}}{2r\left(\sqrt{r}\right)^2} = \dfrac{t\sqrt{r}}{2r}$

98. $\dfrac{m^2 n}{2\sqrt{m^5}} = \dfrac{m^2 n}{2\sqrt{m^4}\cdot\sqrt{m}} \cdot \dfrac{\sqrt{m}}{\sqrt{m}} = \dfrac{m^2 n\sqrt{m}}{2m^2\left(\sqrt{m}\right)^2} = \dfrac{n\sqrt{m}}{2m}$

99. $\dfrac{1}{3-\sqrt{2}} = \dfrac{1}{3-\sqrt{2}} \cdot \dfrac{3+\sqrt{2}}{3+\sqrt{2}} = \dfrac{3+\sqrt{2}}{9-2} = \dfrac{3+\sqrt{2}}{7}$

100. $\dfrac{1}{\sqrt{3}-2} = \dfrac{1}{\sqrt{3}-2} \cdot \dfrac{\sqrt{3}+2}{\sqrt{3}+2} = \dfrac{\sqrt{3}+2}{3-4} = \dfrac{\sqrt{3}+2}{-1} = -\sqrt{3}-2$

101. $\dfrac{\sqrt{2}}{\sqrt{5}+2} = \dfrac{\sqrt{2}}{\sqrt{5}+2} \cdot \dfrac{\sqrt{5}-2}{\sqrt{5}-2} = \dfrac{\sqrt{10}-2\sqrt{2}}{5-4} = \dfrac{\sqrt{10}-2\sqrt{2}}{1} = \sqrt{10}-2\sqrt{2}$

102. $\dfrac{\sqrt{3}}{\sqrt{3}+2} = \dfrac{\sqrt{3}}{\sqrt{3}+2} \cdot \dfrac{\sqrt{3}-2}{\sqrt{3}-2} = \dfrac{\sqrt{3}-2\sqrt{3}}{3-4} = \dfrac{3-2\sqrt{3}}{-1} = 2\sqrt{3}-3$

103. $\dfrac{\sqrt{7}-2}{\sqrt{7}+2} = \dfrac{\sqrt{7}-2}{\sqrt{7}+2} \cdot \dfrac{\sqrt{7}-2}{\sqrt{7}-2} = \dfrac{7-4\sqrt{7}+4}{7-4} = \dfrac{11-4\sqrt{7}}{3}$

104. $\dfrac{\sqrt{3}-1}{\sqrt{3}+1} = \dfrac{\sqrt{3}-1}{\sqrt{3}+1} \cdot \dfrac{\sqrt{3}-1}{\sqrt{3}-1} = \dfrac{3-2\sqrt{3}+1}{3-1} = \dfrac{4-2\sqrt{3}}{2} = 2-\sqrt{3}$

105. $\dfrac{1}{\sqrt{7}-\sqrt{6}} = \dfrac{1}{\sqrt{7}-\sqrt{6}} \cdot \dfrac{\sqrt{7}+\sqrt{6}}{\sqrt{7}+\sqrt{6}} = \dfrac{\sqrt{7}+\sqrt{6}}{7-6} = \dfrac{\sqrt{7}+\sqrt{6}}{1} = \sqrt{7}+\sqrt{6}$

106. $\dfrac{1}{\sqrt{8}-\sqrt{7}} = \dfrac{1}{\sqrt{8}-\sqrt{7}} \cdot \dfrac{\sqrt{8}+\sqrt{7}}{\sqrt{8}+\sqrt{7}} = \dfrac{\sqrt{8}+\sqrt{7}}{8-7} = \dfrac{\sqrt{8}+\sqrt{7}}{1} = \sqrt{8}+\sqrt{7}$

107. $\dfrac{\sqrt{z}}{\sqrt{z}-3} = \dfrac{\sqrt{z}}{\sqrt{z}-3} \cdot \dfrac{\sqrt{z}+3}{\sqrt{z}+3} = \dfrac{z+3\sqrt{z}}{z-9}$

108. $\dfrac{2\sqrt{z}}{2-\sqrt{z}} = \dfrac{2\sqrt{z}}{2-\sqrt{z}} \cdot \dfrac{2+\sqrt{z}}{2+\sqrt{z}} = \dfrac{4\sqrt{z}+2z}{4-z}$

109. $\dfrac{\sqrt{a}+\sqrt{b}}{\sqrt{a}-\sqrt{b}} = \dfrac{\sqrt{a}+\sqrt{b}}{\sqrt{a}-\sqrt{b}} \cdot \dfrac{\sqrt{a}+\sqrt{b}}{\sqrt{a}+\sqrt{b}} = \dfrac{a+2\sqrt{ab}+b}{a-b}$

110. $\dfrac{\sqrt{x}-2\sqrt{y}}{\sqrt{x}+2\sqrt{y}} = \dfrac{\sqrt{x}-2\sqrt{y}}{\sqrt{x}+2\sqrt{y}} \cdot \dfrac{\sqrt{x}-2\sqrt{y}}{\sqrt{x}-2\sqrt{y}} = \dfrac{x-4\sqrt{xy}+4y}{x-4y}$

111. $\dfrac{1}{\sqrt{x+1}-\sqrt{x}} = \dfrac{1}{\sqrt{x+1}-\sqrt{x}} \cdot \dfrac{\sqrt{x+1}+\sqrt{x}}{\sqrt{x+1}+\sqrt{x}} = \dfrac{\sqrt{x+1}+\sqrt{x}}{x+1-x} = \dfrac{\sqrt{x+1}+\sqrt{x}}{1} = \sqrt{x+1}+\sqrt{x}$

112. $\dfrac{1}{\sqrt{a+1}+\sqrt{a}} = \dfrac{1}{\sqrt{a+1}+\sqrt{a}} \cdot \dfrac{\sqrt{a+1}-\sqrt{a}}{\sqrt{a+1}-\sqrt{a}} = \dfrac{\sqrt{a+1}-\sqrt{a}}{a+1-a} = \dfrac{\sqrt{a+1}-\sqrt{a}}{1} = \sqrt{a+1}-\sqrt{a}$

113. $\dfrac{3}{\sqrt[3]{x}} = \dfrac{3}{x^{1/3}} \cdot \dfrac{x^{2/3}}{x^{2/3}} = \dfrac{3x^{2/3}}{x} = \dfrac{3\sqrt[3]{x^2}}{x}$

114. $\dfrac{6}{5\sqrt[3]{x}} = \dfrac{6}{5x^{1/3}} \cdot \dfrac{x^{2/3}}{x^{2/3}} = \dfrac{6x^{2/3}}{5x} = \dfrac{6\sqrt[3]{x^2}}{5x}$

115. $\dfrac{1}{\sqrt[3]{x^2}} = \dfrac{1}{x^{2/3}} \cdot \dfrac{x^{1/3}}{x^{1/3}} = \dfrac{x^{1/3}}{x} = \dfrac{\sqrt[3]{x}}{x}$

116. $\dfrac{2}{\sqrt[3]{(x-2)^2}} = \dfrac{2}{(x-2)^{2/3}} \cdot \dfrac{(x-2)^{1/3}}{(x-2)^{1/3}} = \dfrac{2(x-2)^{1/3}}{x-2} = \dfrac{2\sqrt[3]{x-2}}{x-2}$

Geometry

117. $\sqrt{27}+\sqrt{48}+\sqrt{75} = \sqrt{9\cdot3}+\sqrt{16\cdot3}+\sqrt{25\cdot3} = 3\sqrt{3}+4\sqrt{3}+5\sqrt{3} = 12\sqrt{3} \approx 20.8$ cm

118. $2\sqrt{8}+2\sqrt{18} = 2\sqrt{4\cdot2}+2\sqrt{9\cdot2} = 2\cdot2\sqrt{2}+2\cdot3\sqrt{2} = 4\sqrt{2}+6\sqrt{2} = 10\sqrt{2} \approx 14.1$ cm

Group Activity Solutions

1. (a) $S = \pi(1.5)\sqrt{(1.5)^2+(4)^2} \approx 20.13$ in^2

   (b) No. The answers are 20.13 and 25.92. The square root of a sum does not equal the sum of square roots.

   (c) *Answers may vary.*

   (d) No. See Figure 1.

a	b	$\sqrt{a+b}$	$\sqrt{a}+\sqrt{b}$
0	4	2	2
4	0	2	2
5	4	3	4.24
9	7	4	5.65
4	16	4.47	6
25	100	11.18	15

Figure 1

7.4: Radical Functions

Concepts

1. See Figure 1.

Figure 1

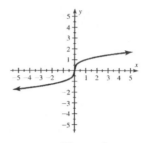

Figure 2

2.   See Figure 2.

3. $\{x \mid x \geq 0\}$

4.   All real numbers

5. $f(x) = x^p$, where p is rational

6. $f(x) = \sqrt[n]{x}$, where n is an integer and $n \geq 2$

7.   The variable cannot be negative. The domain is $\{x \mid x \geq 0\}$.

8.   All real numbers.

Root Functions

9. $f(10) = \sqrt{10-1} = \sqrt{9} = 3$; $f(0)$ is not possible because $\sqrt{0-1} = \sqrt{-1}$

10. $f(-4) = \sqrt{4-3(-4)} = \sqrt{4+12} = \sqrt{16} = 4$; $f(1) = \sqrt{4-3(1)} = \sqrt{4-3} = \sqrt{1} = 1$

11. $f(-1) = \sqrt{3-3(-1)} = \sqrt{3+3} = \sqrt{6}$; $f(5)$ is not possible because $\sqrt{3-3(5)} = \sqrt{3-15} = \sqrt{-12}$

12. $f(-1)$ is not possible because $\sqrt{-1-5} = \sqrt{-6}$; $f(5) = \sqrt{5-5} = \sqrt{0} = 0$

13. $f(-4) = \sqrt{(-4)^2 - (-4)} = \sqrt{16+4} = \sqrt{20} = \sqrt{4 \cdot 5} = 2\sqrt{5}$;

      $f(3) = \sqrt{3^2 - 3} = \sqrt{9-3} = \sqrt{6}$

14. $f(-1)$ is not possible because $\sqrt{2(-1)^2 - 3} = \sqrt{2-3} = \sqrt{-1}$;

      $f(2) = \sqrt{2(2)^2 - 3} = \sqrt{8-3} = \sqrt{5}$

15. $f(-3) = \sqrt[3]{(-3)^2 - 8} = \sqrt[3]{9-8} = \sqrt[3]{1} = 1$; $f(4) = \sqrt[3]{4^2 - 8} = \sqrt[3]{16-8} = \sqrt[3]{8} = 2$

16. $f(-2) = \sqrt[3]{2(-2)^2} = \sqrt[3]{8} = 2$; $f(2) = \sqrt[3]{2(2)^2} = \sqrt[3]{8} = 2$

17. $f(1) = \sqrt[3]{1-9} = \sqrt[3]{-8} = -2$; $f(10) = \sqrt[3]{10-9} = \sqrt[3]{1} = 1$

18. $f(-5) = \sqrt[3]{5(-5) - 2} = \sqrt[3]{-25-2} = \sqrt[3]{-27} = -3$;

      $f(2) = \sqrt[3]{5(2) - 2} = \sqrt[3]{10-2} = \sqrt[3]{8} = 2$

19. $f(-2) = \sqrt[3]{3 - (-2)^2} = \sqrt[3]{3-4} = \sqrt[3]{-1} = -1$;

      $f(3)\sqrt[3]{3 - 3^2} = \sqrt[3]{3-9} = \sqrt[3]{-6}$ or $-\sqrt[3]{6}$

20. $f(0) = \sqrt[3]{-1-0^2} = \sqrt[3]{-1} = -1; f(3) = \sqrt[3]{-1-3^2} = \sqrt[3]{-1-9} = \sqrt[3]{-10} \text{ or } -\sqrt[3]{10}$

21. $T(64) = \dfrac{1}{2}\sqrt{64} = \dfrac{1}{2}(8) = 4$

22. $L(23) = 2\sqrt{23+2} = 2\sqrt{25} = 2 \cdot 5 = 10$

23. $f(4) = \sqrt{4+5} + \sqrt{4} = \sqrt{9} + \sqrt{4} = 3+2 = 5$

24. $f(9) = \dfrac{\sqrt{9-5} - \sqrt{9}}{2} = \dfrac{\sqrt{4} - \sqrt{9}}{2} = \dfrac{2-3}{2} = -\dfrac{1}{2}$

25. $f(x) = \sqrt{x} + 1$

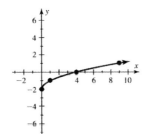

x	$\sqrt{x}+1$
-1	—
0	1
1	2
4	3
9	4

26. $f(x) = \sqrt{x} - 2$

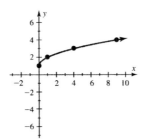

x	$\sqrt{x}-2$
-1	—
0	-2
1	-1
4	0
9	1

27. $f(x) = \sqrt{3x}$

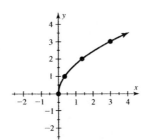

x	$\sqrt{3x}$
-1	——
0	0
$\frac{1}{3}$	1
$\frac{4}{3}$	2
3	3

28. $f(x) = \sqrt{x+1}$

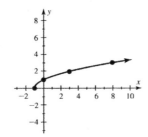

x	$\sqrt{x+1}$
-2	—
-1	0
0	1
3	2
8	3

29. $f(x) = 2\sqrt[3]{x}$

x	$2\sqrt[3]{x}$
–8	–4
–1	–2
0	0
1	2
8	4

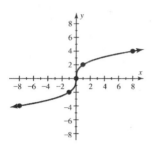

30. $f(x) = \sqrt[3]{4x}$

x	$\sqrt[3]{4x}$
–2	–2
$-\frac{1}{4}$	–1
0	0
$\frac{1}{4}$	1
2	2

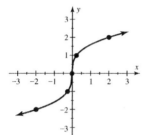

31. $f(x) = \sqrt[3]{x-1}$

x	$\sqrt[3]{x-1}$
–7	–2
0	–1
1	0
2	1
9	2

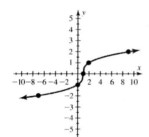

32. $f(x) = \sqrt[3]{x}+1$

x	$\sqrt[3]{x}+1$
–8	–1
–1	0
0	1
1	2
8	3

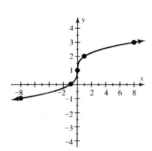

33. $x+2 \geq 0 \Rightarrow x \geq -2 \Rightarrow$ Domain: $[-2, \infty)$

34. $x-1 \geq 0 \Rightarrow x \geq 1 \Rightarrow$ Domain: $[1, \infty)$

35. $x-2 \geq 0 \Rightarrow x \geq 2 \Rightarrow$ Domain: $[2, \infty)$

36. $x+1 \geq 0 \Rightarrow x \geq -1 \Rightarrow$ Domain: $[-1, \infty)$

37. $2x-4 \geq 0 \Rightarrow 2x \geq 4 \Rightarrow x \geq 2 \Rightarrow$ Domain: $[2, \infty)$

38. $4x+2 \geq 0 \Rightarrow 4x \geq -2 \Rightarrow x \geq -\frac{1}{2} \Rightarrow$ Domain: $\left[-\frac{1}{2}, \infty\right)$

39. $1 - x \geq 0 \;\Rightarrow\; -x \geq -1 \Rightarrow x \leq 1 \Rightarrow$ Domain: $(-\infty, 1]$

40. $6 - 3x \geq 0 \Rightarrow -3x \geq -6 \;\Rightarrow\; x \leq 2 \Rightarrow$ Domain: $(-\infty,\; 2]$

41. $8 - 5x \geq 0 \Rightarrow -5x \geq -8 \Rightarrow x \leq \dfrac{8}{5} \Rightarrow$ Domain: $\left(-\infty, \dfrac{5}{8}\right]$

42. $3 - 2x \geq 0 \;\Rightarrow\; -2x \geq -3 \Rightarrow x \leq \dfrac{3}{2} \Rightarrow$ Domain: $\left(-\infty, \dfrac{3}{2}\right]$

43. $3x^2 + 4 \geq 0 \Rightarrow 3x^2 \geq -4 \;\Rightarrow\; x^2 \geq -\dfrac{4}{3} \Rightarrow$ Domain: $(-\infty, \infty)$

44. $1 + 2x^2 \geq 0 \;\Rightarrow\; 2x^2 \geq -1 \;\Rightarrow\; x^2 \geq -\dfrac{1}{2} \Rightarrow$ Domain: $(-\infty, \infty)$

45. $2x + 1 > 0 \;\Rightarrow\; 2x > -1 \;\Rightarrow\; x > -\dfrac{1}{2} \;\Rightarrow$ Domain: $\left(-\dfrac{1}{2},\; \infty\right)$

46. $x - 1 > 0 \;\Rightarrow\; x > 1 \;\Rightarrow$ Domain: $(1, \infty)$

47.   See Figure 47. This graph is shifted 2 units left.

48.   See Figure 48. This graph is shifted 1 unit right.

| Figure 47 | Figure 48 | Figure 49 |

49.   See Figure 49. This graph is shifted 2 units upward.

50.   See Figure 50. This graph is shifted 2 units upward.

51.   See Figure 51. This graph is shifted 2 units left.

| Figure 50 | Figure 51 | Figure 52 |

52.   See Figure 52. This graph is shifted 1 unit downward.

Power Functions

53. $f(x) = x^{1/2} = \sqrt{x}$

54. $f(x) = x^{1/3} = \sqrt[3]{x}$

55. $f(x) = x^{2/3} = \sqrt[3]{x^2}$

56. $f(x) = x^{3/4} = \sqrt[4]{x^3}$

57. $f(x) = x^{-1/5} = \dfrac{1}{x^{1/5}} = \dfrac{1}{\sqrt[5]{x}}$

58. $f(x) = x^{-2/5} = \dfrac{1}{x^{2/5}} = \dfrac{1}{\sqrt[5]{x^2}}$

59. $f(4) = 4^{5/2} = \left(\sqrt{4}\right)^5 = 2^5 = 32;\ f(5) = 5^{5/2} \approx 55.90$

60. $f(1) = 1^{-3/4} = 1;\ f(3) = 3^{-3/4} = \dfrac{1}{3^{3/4}} \approx 0.44$

61. $f(-32) = (-32)^{7/5} = \dfrac{1}{(-32)^{7/5}} = \dfrac{1}{\left(\sqrt[5]{-32}\right)^7} = \dfrac{1}{(-2)^7} = -\dfrac{1}{128} \approx -0.01;\ f(10) = 10^{-7/5} = \dfrac{1}{10^{7/5}} \approx 0.04$

62. $f(-8) = (-8)^{4/3} = \left(\sqrt[3]{-8}\right)^4 = (-2)^4 = 16;\ f(27) = 27^{4/3} = \left(\sqrt[3]{27}\right)^4 = 3^4 = 81$

63. $f(256) = 256^{1/4} = \sqrt[4]{256} = 4;\ f(-10) = (-10)^{1/4} = \sqrt[4]{-10} \Rightarrow$ Not possible

64. $f(16) = 16^{3/4} = \left(\sqrt[4]{16}\right)^3 = 2^3 = 8;\ f(-1) = (-1)^{3/4} = \left(\sqrt[4]{-1}\right)^3 \Rightarrow$ Not possible

65. $f(32) = 32^{2/5} = \left(\sqrt[5]{32}\right)^2 = 2^2 = 4;\ f(-32) = (-32)^{2/5} = \left(\sqrt[5]{-32}\ \right)^2 = (-2)^2 = 4$

66. $f(-5) = (-5)^{5/6} = \left(\sqrt[6]{-5}\right)^5 \Rightarrow$ Not possible; $f(64) = 64^{5/6} = \left(\sqrt[6]{64}\right)^5 = 2^5 = 32$

67. Graph $Y_1 = X^{\wedge}(1/5)$ and $Y_2 = X^{\wedge}(1/3)$ in [0, 6, 1] by [0, 6, 1]. See Figure 67. Function $g(x)$ increases faster.

68. Graph $Y_1 = X^{\wedge}(4/5)$ and $Y_2 = X^{\wedge}(5/4)$ in [0, 6, 1] by [0, 6, 1]. See Figure 68. Function $g(x)$ increases faster.

[0, 6, 1] by [0, 6, 1]   [0, 6, 1] by [0, 6, 1]   [0, 6, 1] by [0, 6, 1]   [0, 6, 1] by [0, 6, 1]

Figure 67   Figure 68   Figure 69   Figure 70

69. Graph $Y_1 = X^{\wedge}1.2$ and $Y_2 = X^{\wedge}0.45$ in [0, 6, 1] by [0, 6, 1]. See Figure 69. Function $f(x)$ increases faster.

70. Graph $Y_1 = X^{\wedge}(-1.4)$ and $Y_2 = X^{\wedge}1.4$ in [0, 6, 1] by [0, 6, 1]. See Figure 70. Function $g(x)$ increases faster.

71. $x^p > x^q$

72. $x^p < x^q$

73. (a) $(f+g)(2) = \sqrt{8 \cdot 2} + \sqrt{2 \cdot 2} = \sqrt{16} + \sqrt{4} = 4 + 2 = 6$

(b) $(f-g)(x) = \sqrt{8x} - \sqrt{2x} = \sqrt{4 \cdot 2x} - \sqrt{2x} = 2\sqrt{2x} - \sqrt{2x} = \sqrt{2x}$

(c) $(fg)(x) = \left(\sqrt{8x}\right)\left(\sqrt{2x}\right) = \sqrt{8x \cdot 2x} = \sqrt{16x^2} = 4|x|$

(d) $(f/g)(x) = \dfrac{\sqrt{8x}}{\sqrt{2x}} = \sqrt{\dfrac{8x}{2x}} = \sqrt{4} = 2$

74. (a) $(f+g)(2) = \sqrt{9 \cdot 2 + 18} + \sqrt{4 \cdot 2 + 8} = \sqrt{36} + \sqrt{16} = 6 + 4 = 10$

(b) $(f-g)(x) = \sqrt{9x+18} - \sqrt{4x+8} = \sqrt{9(x+2)} - \sqrt{4(x+2)} = 3\sqrt{x+2} - 2\sqrt{x+2} = \sqrt{x+2}$

(c) $(f\,g)(x) = \sqrt{9x+18} \cdot \sqrt{4x+8} = \sqrt{(9x+18)(4x+8)} = \sqrt{9(x+2) \cdot 4(x+2)} = \sqrt{36(x+2)^2} = 6|x+2|$

(d) $(f/g)(x) = \dfrac{\sqrt{9x+18}}{\sqrt{4x+8}} = \dfrac{\sqrt{9(x+2)}}{\sqrt{4(x+2)}} = \dfrac{3\sqrt{x+2}}{2\sqrt{x+2}} = \dfrac{3}{2}$

75. b

76. d

77. c

78. a

Applications

79. $T(4) = \dfrac{\sqrt{4}}{2} = \dfrac{2}{2} = 1$ second

80. $T(80) = \dfrac{\sqrt{80}}{2} = \dfrac{4\sqrt{5}}{2} = 2\sqrt{5} \approx 4.5$ seconds

81. (a) $T(0.8c) = 10\sqrt{1 - (0.8c/c)^2} = 10\sqrt{1 - 0.8^2} = 10\sqrt{1 - 0.64} = 10\sqrt{0.36} = 10 \cdot 0.6 = 6$ years

(b) The twin in the spaceship will be 4 years younger than the twin on Earth.

82. (a) $W(0.6c) = \dfrac{220}{\sqrt{1 - (0.6c/c)^2}} = \dfrac{220}{\sqrt{1 - 0.6^2}} = \dfrac{220}{\sqrt{1 - 0.36}} = \dfrac{220}{\sqrt{0.64}} = \dfrac{220}{0.8} = 275$ pounds

(b) A 220-pound person traveling at 60% of the speed of light weighs 275 pounds.

83. (a)

[0, 5, 1] by [0, 0.5, 0.1]

(b) $A(2) = k(2)^{2/3} = 0.254 \Rightarrow k = \dfrac{0.254}{2^{2/3}} \Rightarrow k \approx 0.16$

(c)

[0, 5, 1] by [0, 0.5, 0.1]

Yes

(d) $A(2.5) = 0.16(2.5)^{2/3} \approx 0.295$ square meters

84.   (a)   As animal size increases, the pulse rate decreases.

(b)   Plot the data in [0, 1600, 400] by [0, 220, 20]. See Figure 84.

(c) $R = kW^{-1/2} \Rightarrow 198 = k \cdot 20^{-1/2} \Rightarrow 198 = \dfrac{k}{20^{1/2}} \Rightarrow k = 198 \cdot 20^{1/2} \approx 885$

(d) $R = 885(700)^{-1/2} \approx 33$;   A 700-pound animal will have a pulse rate of about 33 bpm.

85.   (a) $L = kW^{1/3} \Rightarrow 0.422 = k \cdot 0.1^{1/3} \Rightarrow k = \dfrac{0.422}{0.1^{1/3}} \approx 0.91$

(b)   Plot the data and graph $Y_1 = 0.91X^\wedge(1/3)$ in [0, 1.5, 0.1] by [0, 1, 0.1]. See Figure 85. It increases.

(c) $L = 0.91(0.7)^{1/3} \approx 0.808$ meters

(d) $L = 0.91(0.65)^{1/3} \approx 0.788$;   A bird weighing 0.65 kg has a wing span of about 0.788 meters.

[0, 1.5, 0.1] by [0, 1, 0.1]   [0, 1600, 400] by [0, 220, 20]

          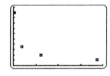

Figure 84   Figure 85

86.   (a) $340 = k\sqrt{0.01} \Rightarrow k = \dfrac{340}{\sqrt{0.01}} = 3400$

(b) $R = 3400\sqrt{0.04} = 680$;   It doubles to 680 ft^3/sec.

87. $S(150) = 342(150)^{0.425} \approx 2877$ square inches

88. $S(200) = 342(200)^{0.425} \approx 3251$ square inches

Checking Basic Concepts for Sections 7.3 & 7.4

1.   (a) $\sqrt{3} \cdot \sqrt{12} = \sqrt{3 \cdot 12} = \sqrt{36} = 6$

(b) $\dfrac{\sqrt[3]{81}}{\sqrt[3]{3}} = \sqrt[3]{\dfrac{81}{3}} = \sqrt[3]{27} = 3$

(c) $\sqrt{36x^6} = \sqrt{36} \cdot \sqrt{\left(x^3\right)^2} = 6x^3$

2.   (a) $5\sqrt{6} + 2\sqrt{6} + \sqrt{7} = 7\sqrt{6} + \sqrt{7}$

(b) $8\sqrt[3]{x} - 3\sqrt[3]{x} = 5\sqrt[3]{x}$

(c) $\sqrt{9x} - \sqrt{4x} = \sqrt{9} \cdot \sqrt{x} - \sqrt{4} \cdot \sqrt{x} = 3\sqrt{x} - 2\sqrt{x} = \sqrt{x}$

3.   (a) $\sqrt[3]{xy^4} - \sqrt[3]{x^4 y} = \sqrt[3]{y^3 \cdot xy} - \sqrt[3]{x^3 \cdot xy} = y\sqrt[3]{xy} - x\sqrt[3]{xy} = (y - x)\sqrt[3]{xy}$

(b) $\left(4 - \sqrt{2}\right)\left(4 + \sqrt{2}\right) = 4^2 - \left(\sqrt{2}\right)^2 = 16 - 2 = 14$

4. $\dfrac{6}{2\sqrt{6}} = \dfrac{6}{2\sqrt{6}} \cdot \dfrac{\sqrt{6}}{\sqrt{6}} = \dfrac{6\sqrt{6}}{2 \cdot 6} = \dfrac{\sqrt{6}}{2}$

5. $\dfrac{2}{\sqrt{5} - 1} = \dfrac{2}{\sqrt{5} - 1} \cdot \dfrac{\sqrt{5} + 1}{\sqrt{5} + 1} = \dfrac{2\left(\sqrt{5} + 1\right)}{5 - 1} = \dfrac{2\left(\sqrt{5} + 1\right)}{4} = \dfrac{\sqrt{5} + 1}{2}$

6.   (a) See Figure 6a. $f(-1)$ is undefined

(b) See Figure 6b. $f(-1) = -1$

(c) See Figure 6c. $f(-1) = 1$

Figure 6a

Figure 6b

Figure 6c

7. $f(64) = 0.2(64)^{2/3} = 0.2\left(\sqrt[3]{64}\right)^2 = 0.2(4)^2 = 0.2 \cdot 16 = 3.2$

8. $x - 4 \geq 0 \Rightarrow x \geq 4 \Rightarrow$ Domain: $[4, \infty)$

7.5: Equations Involving Radical Expressions

Concepts

1.   Square each side.

2.   Cube each side.

3.   Yes

4.   We must check the answers.

5.   The Pythagorean theorem is used to find an unknown side of a right triangle. *Answers may vary.*

6. $c^2 = 3^2 + 4^2 \Rightarrow c^2 = 9 + 16 \Rightarrow c^2 = 25 \Rightarrow c = \sqrt{25} = 5$

7. $d = \sqrt{\left(x_2 - x_1\right)^2 + \left(y_2 - y_1\right)^2}$

8. $x^{1/2} + x^{3/4} = 2$

9. $\sqrt{2} \cdot \sqrt{2} = \sqrt{2 \cdot 2} = \sqrt{4} = 2$

10. $\sqrt{5} \cdot \sqrt{5} = \sqrt{5 \cdot 5} = \sqrt{25} = 5$

11. $\sqrt{x} \cdot \sqrt{x} = \sqrt{x \cdot x} = \sqrt{x^2} = x$

12. $\sqrt{2x} \cdot \sqrt{2x} = \sqrt{2x \cdot 2x} = \sqrt{4x^2} = 2x$

13. $\left(\sqrt{2x+1}\right)^2 = 2x+1$

14. $\left(\sqrt{7x}\right)^2 = 7x$

15. $\left(\sqrt[3]{5x^2}\right)^3 = 5x^2$

16. $\left(\sqrt[3]{(2x-5)}\right)^3 = 2x-5$

Symbolic Solutions

17. $\sqrt{x} = 8 \Rightarrow \left(\sqrt{x}\right)^2 = 8^2 \Rightarrow x = 64$

18. $\sqrt{3z} = 6 \Rightarrow \left(\sqrt{3z}\right)^2 = 6^2 \Rightarrow 3z = 36 \Rightarrow z = 12$

19. $\sqrt[4]{x} = 3 \Rightarrow \left(\sqrt[4]{x}\right)^4 = 3^4 \Rightarrow x = 81$

20. $\sqrt[3]{x-4} = 2 \Rightarrow \left(\sqrt[3]{x-4}\right)^3 = 2^3 \Rightarrow x-4 = 8 \Rightarrow x = 12$

21. $\sqrt{2t+4} = 4 \Rightarrow \left(\sqrt{2t+4}\right)^2 = 4^2 \Rightarrow 2t+4 = 16 \Rightarrow 2t = 12 \Rightarrow t = 6$

22. $\sqrt{y+4} = 3 \Rightarrow \left(\sqrt{y+4}\right)^2 = 3^2 \Rightarrow y+4 = 9 \Rightarrow y = 5$

23. $\sqrt{x+1} - 3 = 4 \Rightarrow \sqrt{x+1} = 7 \Rightarrow x+1 = 7^2 \Rightarrow x = 49 - 1 \Rightarrow x = 48$

24. $\sqrt{2x+5} + 2 = 5 \Rightarrow \sqrt{2x+5} = 3 \Rightarrow 2x+5 = 3^2 \Rightarrow 2x = 9 - 5 \Rightarrow 2x = 4 \Rightarrow x = 2$

25. $2\sqrt{x-2} + 1 = 5 \Rightarrow 2\sqrt{x-2} = 4 \Rightarrow \sqrt{x-2} = 2 \Rightarrow x-2 = 2^2 \Rightarrow x = 4 + 2 \Rightarrow x = 6$

26. $-\sqrt{x+7} - 1 = -7 \Rightarrow -\sqrt{x+7} = -6 \Rightarrow \sqrt{x+7} = 6 \Rightarrow x+7 = 6^2 \Rightarrow x = 36 - 7 \Rightarrow x = 29$

27. $\sqrt{x+6} = x \Rightarrow \left(\sqrt{x+6}\right)^2 = x^2 \Rightarrow x+6 = x^2 \Rightarrow x^2 - x - 6 = 0 \Rightarrow (x+2)(x-3) = 0 \Rightarrow x = -2 \text{ or } x = 3.$ The

    solution $x = -2$ does not check. The solution is $x = 3$.

28. $\sqrt{z} + 6 = z \Rightarrow \sqrt{z} = z - 6 \Rightarrow \left(\sqrt{z}\right)^2 = (z-6)^2 \Rightarrow z = z^2 - 12z + 36 \Rightarrow z^2 - 13z + 36 = 0 \Rightarrow$

    $(z-4)(z-9) = 0 \Rightarrow z = 4 \text{ or } z = 9.$ The solution $z = 4$ does not check. The solution is $z = 9$.

29. $\sqrt[3]{x} = 3 \Rightarrow \left(\sqrt[3]{x}\right)^3 = 3^3 \Rightarrow x = 27$

30. $\sqrt[3]{x+10} = 4 \Rightarrow \left(\sqrt[3]{x+10}\right)^3 = 4^3 \Rightarrow x+10 = 64 \Rightarrow x = 54$

31. $\sqrt[3]{2z-4} = -2 \Rightarrow 2z - 4 = (-2)^3 \Rightarrow 2z - 4 = -8 \Rightarrow 2z = -4 \Rightarrow z = -2$

32. $\sqrt[3]{z-1} = -3 \Rightarrow z - 1 = (-3)^3 \Rightarrow z - 1 = -27 \Rightarrow z = -26$

33. $\sqrt[4]{t+1} = 2 \Rightarrow t + 1 = 2^4 \Rightarrow t + 1 = 16 \Rightarrow t = 15$

34. $\sqrt[4]{5t} = 5 \Rightarrow 5t = 5^4 \Rightarrow 5t = 625 \Rightarrow t = 125$

35. $\sqrt{5z-1} = \sqrt{z+1} \Rightarrow \left(\sqrt{5z-1}\right)^2 = \left(\sqrt{z+1}\right)^2 \Rightarrow 5z - 1 = z + 1 \Rightarrow 4z = 2 \Rightarrow z = \frac{1}{2}$

36. $y = \sqrt{y+1} + 1 \Rightarrow \sqrt{y+1} = y - 1 \Rightarrow \left(\sqrt{y+1}\right)^2 = (y-1)^2 \Rightarrow y + 1 = y^2 - 2y + 1 \Rightarrow$

    $y^2 - 3y = 0 \Rightarrow y(y-3) = 0 \Rightarrow y = 0$ or $y = 3$. The solution $y = 0$ does not check. The solution is $y = 3$.

37. $\sqrt{1-x} = 1 - x \Rightarrow \left(\sqrt{1-x}\right)^2 = (1-x)^2 \Rightarrow 1 - x = 1 - 2x + x^2 \Rightarrow x^2 - x = 0 \Rightarrow x(x-1) = 0 \Rightarrow x = 0$ or $x = 1$

38. $\sqrt[3]{4x} = x \Rightarrow \left(\sqrt[3]{4x}\right)^3 = x^3 \Rightarrow 4x = x^3 \Rightarrow x^3 - 4x = 0 \Rightarrow x(x^2 - 4) = 0 \Rightarrow x(x-2)(x+2) = 0 \Rightarrow$

    $x = 0$ or $x = -2$ or $x = 2$

39. $\sqrt{b^2 - 4} = b - 2 \Rightarrow \left(\sqrt{b^2 - 4}\right)^2 = (b-2)^2 \Rightarrow b^2 - 4 = b^2 - 4b + 4 \Rightarrow 4b = 8 \Rightarrow b = 2$

40. $\sqrt{b^2 - 2b + 1} = b \Rightarrow \left(\sqrt{b^2 - 2b + 1}\right)^2 = b^2 \Rightarrow b^2 - 2b + 1 = b^2 \Rightarrow 2b = 1 \Rightarrow b = \frac{1}{2}$

41. $\sqrt{1-2x} = x + 7 \Rightarrow \left(\sqrt{1-2x}\right)^2 = (x+7)^2 \Rightarrow 1 - 2x = x^2 + 14x + 49 \Rightarrow x^2 + 16x + 48 = 0 \Rightarrow$

    $(x+12)(x+4) = 0 \Rightarrow x = -12$ or $x = -4$. The solution $x = -12$ does not check. The solution is $x = -4$.

42. $\sqrt{4-y} = y - 2 \Rightarrow \left(\sqrt{4-y}\right)^2 = (y-2)^2 \Rightarrow 4 - y = y^2 - 4y + 4 \Rightarrow y^2 - 3y = 0 \Rightarrow$

    $y(y-3) = 0 \Rightarrow y = 0$ or $y = 3$. The solution $y = 0$ does not check. The solution is $y = 3$.

43. $\sqrt{x} = \sqrt{x-5} + 1 \Rightarrow \left(\sqrt{x}\right)^2 = \left(\sqrt{x-5} + 1\right)^2 \Rightarrow x = (x-5) + 2\sqrt{x-5} + 1 \Rightarrow$

    $2\sqrt{x-5} = 4 \Rightarrow \left(2\sqrt{x-5}\right)^2 = 4^2 \Rightarrow 4(x-5) = 16 \Rightarrow 4x - 20 = 16 \Rightarrow 4x = 36 \Rightarrow x = 9$

44. $\sqrt{x-1} = \sqrt{x+4} - 1 \Rightarrow \left(\sqrt{x-1}\right)^2 = \left(\sqrt{x+4} - 1\right)^2 \Rightarrow x - 1 = (x+4) - 2\sqrt{x+4} + 1 \Rightarrow$

    $2\sqrt{x+4} = 6 \Rightarrow \left(2\sqrt{x+4}\right)^2 = 6^2 \Rightarrow 4(x+4) = 36 \Rightarrow 4x + 16 = 36 \Rightarrow 4x = 20 \Rightarrow x = 5$

45. $\sqrt{2t-2} + \sqrt{t} = 7 \Rightarrow \sqrt{2t-2} = 7 - \sqrt{t} \Rightarrow \left(\sqrt{2t-2}\right)^2 = \left(7 - \sqrt{t}\right)^2 \Rightarrow 2t - 2 = 49 - 14\sqrt{t} + t \Rightarrow$

    $14\sqrt{t} = 51 - t \Rightarrow \left(14\sqrt{t}\right)^2 = (51-t)^2 \Rightarrow 196t = 2601 - 102t + t^2 \Rightarrow t^2 - 298t + 2601 = 0 \Rightarrow$

    $(t-9)(t-289) = 0 \Rightarrow t = 9$ or $t = 289$. The solution $t = 289$ does not check. The solution is $t = 9$.

46. $\sqrt{x+1}-\sqrt{x-6}=1 \Rightarrow \sqrt{x+1}=1+\sqrt{x-6} \Rightarrow \left(\sqrt{x+1}\right)^2 = \left(1+\sqrt{x-6}\right)^2 \Rightarrow$

   $x+1=1+2\sqrt{x-6}+(x-6) \Rightarrow 2\sqrt{x-6}=6 \Rightarrow \left(2\sqrt{x-6}\right)^2 = 6^2 \Rightarrow 4(x-6)=36 \Rightarrow$

   $4x-24=36 \Rightarrow 4x=60 \Rightarrow x=15$

47. $x^2 = 49 \Rightarrow \sqrt{x^2} = \sqrt{49} \Rightarrow |x|=7 \Rightarrow x=\pm 7$

48. $x^2 = 9 \Rightarrow \sqrt{x^2} = \sqrt{9} \Rightarrow |x|=3 \Rightarrow x=\pm 3$

49. $2z^2 = 200 \Rightarrow z^2 = 100 \Rightarrow \sqrt{z^2} = \sqrt{100} \Rightarrow |z|=10 \Rightarrow z=\pm 10$

50. $3z^2 = 48 \Rightarrow z^2 = 16 \Rightarrow \sqrt{z^2} = \sqrt{16} \Rightarrow |z|=4 \Rightarrow z=\pm 4$

51. $(t+1)^2 = 16 \Rightarrow \sqrt{(t+1)^2} = \sqrt{16} \Rightarrow |t+1|=4 \Rightarrow t+1=\pm 4$

   $\Rightarrow t=3 \text{ or } t=-5$

52. $(t-5)^2 = 81 \Rightarrow \sqrt{(t-5)^2} = \sqrt{81} \Rightarrow |t-5|=9 \Rightarrow t-5=\pm 9$

   $\Rightarrow t=14 \text{ or } t=-4$

53. $(4-2x)^2 = 100 \Rightarrow \sqrt{(4-2x)^2} = \sqrt{100} \Rightarrow |4-2x|=10 \Rightarrow 4-2x=\pm 10$

   $\Rightarrow 4-2x=10 \text{ or } 4-2x=-10 \Rightarrow -2x=6 \text{ or } -2x=-14 \Rightarrow x=-3 \text{ or } x=7$

54. $(3x-6)^2 = 25 \Rightarrow \sqrt{(3x-6)^2} = \sqrt{25} \Rightarrow |3x-6|=5 \Rightarrow 3x-6=\pm 5$

   $\Rightarrow 3x-6=5 \text{ or } 3x-6=-5 \Rightarrow 3x=11 \text{ or } 3x=1 \Rightarrow x=\dfrac{11}{3} \text{ or } x=\dfrac{1}{3}$

55. $b^3 = 64 \Rightarrow \sqrt[3]{b^3} = \sqrt[3]{64} \Rightarrow b=4$

56. $a^3 = 1000 \Rightarrow \sqrt[3]{a^3} = \sqrt[3]{1000} \Rightarrow a=10$

57. $2t^3 = -128 \Rightarrow t^3 = -64 \Rightarrow \sqrt[3]{t^3} = \sqrt[3]{-64} \Rightarrow t=-4$

58. $3t^3 = -81 \Rightarrow t^3 = -27 \Rightarrow \sqrt[3]{t^3} = \sqrt[3]{-27} \Rightarrow t=-3$

59. $(x+1)^3 = 8 \Rightarrow \sqrt[3]{(x+1)^3} = \sqrt[3]{8} \Rightarrow x+1=2 \Rightarrow x=1$

60. $(4-x)^3 = -1 \Rightarrow \sqrt[3]{(4-x)^3} = \sqrt[3]{(-1)} \Rightarrow 4-x=-1 \Rightarrow -x=-5 \Rightarrow x=5$

61. $(2-5z)^3 = -125 \Rightarrow \sqrt[3]{(2-5z)^3} = \sqrt[3]{-125} \Rightarrow 2-5z=-5 \Rightarrow -5z=-7 \Rightarrow z=\dfrac{7}{5}$

62. $(2x+4)^3 = 125 \Rightarrow \sqrt[3]{(2x+4)^3} = \sqrt[3]{125} \Rightarrow 2x+4=5 \Rightarrow 2x=1 \Rightarrow x=\dfrac{1}{2}$

63. $x^4 = 16 \Rightarrow \sqrt[4]{x^4} = \sqrt[4]{16} \Rightarrow |x|=2 \Rightarrow x=\pm 2$

64. $x^4 = 7 \Rightarrow \sqrt[4]{x^4} = \sqrt[4]{7} \Rightarrow |x| = \sqrt[4]{7} \Rightarrow x = \pm\sqrt[4]{7}$

65. $x^5 = 12 \Rightarrow \sqrt[5]{x^5} = \sqrt[5]{12} \Rightarrow x = \sqrt[5]{12}$

66. $x^5 = -32 \Rightarrow \sqrt[5]{x^5} = \sqrt[5]{-32} \Rightarrow x = -2$

67. $2(x+2)^4 = 162 \Rightarrow (x+2)^4 = 81 \Rightarrow \sqrt[4]{(x+2)^4} = \sqrt[4]{81}$

   $\Rightarrow |x+2| = 3 \Rightarrow x+2 = \pm 3 \Rightarrow x = 1 \text{ or } x = -5$

68. $\dfrac{1}{2}(x-1)^5 = 16 \Rightarrow (x-1)^5 = 32 \Rightarrow \sqrt[5]{(x-1)^5} = \sqrt[5]{32} \Rightarrow x-1 = 2 \Rightarrow x = 3$

Graphical Solutions

69. Graphical: Graph $Y_1 = \sqrt[3]{(X+5)}$ and $Y_2 = 2$ in $[-7, 7, 1]$ by $[0, 4, 1]$. See Figure 69. The solution is $x = 3$.

70. Graphical: Graph $Y_1 = \sqrt[3]{(X)} + \sqrt{(X)}$ and $Y_2 = 3.43$ in $[0, 4, 1]$ by $[0, 4, 1]$. See Figure 70.

   The solution is $x \approx 3.60$.

$[-7, 7, 1]$ by $[0, 4, 1]$ $[0, 4, 1]$ by $[0, 4, 1]$ $[0, 3, 1]$ by $[-2, 2, 1]$

Figure 69   Figure 70   Figure 71

71. Graphical: Graph $Y_1 = \sqrt{(2X-3)}$ and $Y_2 = \sqrt{(X)} - (1/2)$ in $[0, 3, 1]$ by $[-2, 2, 1]$. See Figure 71.

   The solution is $x \approx 1.88$.

72. Graphical: Graph $Y_1 = X^{(4/3)} - 1$ and $Y_2 = 2$ in $[-4, 4, 1]$ by $[-4, 4, 1]$. See Figures 72a & 72b.

   The solutions are $x \approx \pm 2.28$.

$[-4, 4, 1]$ by $[-4, 4, 1]$ $[-4, 4, 1]$ by $[-4, 4, 1]$

Figure 72a   Figure 72b

$[-4, 4, 1]$ by $[-4, 4, 1]$ $[-4, 4, 1]$ by $[-4, 4, 1]$

Figure 73a   Figure 73b

73. Graphical: Graph $Y_1 = X^{(5/3)}$ and $Y_2 = 2 - 3X^2$ in $[-4, 4, 1]$ by $[-4, 4, 1]$. See Figures 73a & 73b.

   The solutions are $x = -1$ or $x \approx 0.70$.

74.   Graphical: Graph $Y_1 = X^{\wedge}(3/2)$ and $Y_2 = \sqrt{(X+2)} - 2$ in [–3, 3, 1] by [–3, 3, 1]. See Figure 74.

Since the two graphs do not intersect, there are no solutions.

75.   Graphical: Graph $Y_1 = X^{\wedge}(1/3) - 1$ and $Y_2 = 2 - X$ in [–3, 3, 1] by [–3, 3, 1]. See Figure 75.

The solution is $z \approx 1.79$.

[–3, 3, 1] by [–3, 3, 1]   [–3, 3, 1] by [–3, 3, 1]

Figure 74   Figure 75

76.   Graphical: Graph $Y_1 = X^{\wedge}(3/2) - 2X^{\wedge}(1/2) - 1$ and $Y_2 = 0$ in [–1, 4, 1] by [–3, 3, 1]. See Figure 76.

The solution is $z \approx 2.62$.

77.   Graphical: Graph $Y_1 = \sqrt{(X+2)} + \sqrt{(3X+2)}$ and $Y_2 = 2$ in [–2, 2, 1] by [0, 5, 1]. See Figure 77.

The solution is $y \approx -0.47$.

78.   Graphical: Graph $Y_1 = \sqrt{(X+1)} - \sqrt{(X-1)}$ and $Y_2 = 4$ in [0, 10, 1] by [0, 5, 1]. See Figure 78.

Since the two graphs do not intersect, there are no solutions.

[–1, 4, 1] by [–3, 3, 1]   [–2, 2, 1] by [0, 5, 1]   [0, 10, 1] by [0, 5, 1]

Figure 76   Figure 77   Figure 78

Using More Than One Method

79.   (a) $2\sqrt{x} = 8 \Rightarrow \left(2\sqrt{x}\right)^2 = 8^2 \Rightarrow 4x = 64 \Rightarrow x = 16$

(b)   Graph $Y_1 = 2\sqrt{(X)}$ and $Y_2 = 8$ in [0, 30, 5] by [0, 10, 1]. See Figure 79b. The solution is $x = 16$.

(c)   Table $Y_1 = 2\sqrt{(X)}$ and $Y_2 = 8$ with TblStart = 0 and ΔTbl = 4. See Figure 79c. The solution is $x = 16$.

[0, 30, 5] by [0, 10, 1]   [–10, 10, 1] by [–3, 3, 1]

Figure 79b   Figure 79c   Figure 80b   Figure 80c

80.   (a) $\sqrt[3]{5-x} = 2 \Rightarrow \left(\sqrt[3]{5-x}\right)^3 = 2^3 \Rightarrow 5 - x = 8 \Rightarrow -x = 3 \Rightarrow x = -3$

(b)   Graph $Y_1 = \sqrt[3]{(5-X)}$ and $Y_2 = 2$ in [–10, 10, 1] by [–3, 3, 1]. See Figure 80b. The solution is $x = -3$.

(c) Table $Y_1 = \sqrt[3]{(5-X)}$ and $Y_2 = 2$ with TblStart $= -5$ and ΔTbl $= 1$. See Figure 80c. The solution is $x = -3$.

81. (a) $\sqrt{6z-2} = 8 \Rightarrow \left(\sqrt{6z-2}\right)^2 = 8^2 \Rightarrow 6z-2 = 64 \Rightarrow 6z = 66 \Rightarrow z = 11$

(b) Graph $Y_1 = \sqrt{(6X-2)}$ and $Y_2 = 8$ in [0, 20, 2] by [0, 10, 1]. See Figure 81b. The solution is $z = 11$.

(c) Table $Y_1 = \sqrt{(6X-2)}$ and $Y_2 = 8$ with TblStart $= 7$ and ΔTbl $= 1$. See Figure 81c. The solution is $z = 11$.

[0, 20, 2] by [0, 10, 1]

Figure 81b   Figure 81c

82. (a) $\sqrt{y+4} = \dfrac{y}{3} \Rightarrow 3\sqrt{y+4} = y \Rightarrow \left(3\sqrt{y+4}\right)^2 = y^2 \Rightarrow 9(y+4) = y^2 \Rightarrow 9y+36 = y^2 \Rightarrow$

$y^2 - 9y - 36 = 0 \Rightarrow (y+3)(y-12) = 0 \Rightarrow y = -3$ or $y = 12$. The solution $y = -3$ does not check. The solution is $y = 12$.

(b) Graph $Y_1 = \sqrt{(X+4)}$ and $Y_2 = X/3$ in [−5, 20, 5] by [−5, 10, 1]. See Figure 82b. The solution is $y = 12$.

(c) Table $Y_1 = \sqrt{(X+4)}$ and $Y_2 = X/3$ with TblStart $= 10$ and ΔTbl $= 1$. See Figure 82c. The solution is $y = 12$

[−5, 20, 5] by [−5, 10, 1]

Figure 82b   Figure 82c

Solving an Equation for a Variable

83. $T = 2\pi\sqrt{\dfrac{L}{32}} \Rightarrow \dfrac{T}{2\pi} = \sqrt{\dfrac{L}{32}} \Rightarrow \left(\dfrac{T}{2\pi}\right)^2 = \dfrac{L}{32} \Rightarrow \dfrac{T^2}{4\pi^2} = \dfrac{L}{32} \Rightarrow 32 \cdot \dfrac{T^2}{4\pi^2} = L \Rightarrow L = \dfrac{8T^2}{\pi^2}$

84. $Z = \sqrt{L^2 + R^2} \Rightarrow Z^2 = L^2 + R^2 \Rightarrow R^2 = Z^2 - L^2 \Rightarrow R = \pm\sqrt{Z^2 - L^2}$

85. $r = \sqrt{\dfrac{A}{\pi}} \Rightarrow r^2 = \dfrac{A}{\pi} \Rightarrow \pi r^2 = A \Rightarrow A = \pi r^2$

86. $F = \dfrac{1}{2\pi\sqrt{LC}} \Rightarrow F\sqrt{LC} = \dfrac{1}{2\pi} \Rightarrow \sqrt{LC} = \dfrac{1}{2\pi F} \Rightarrow LC = \left(\dfrac{1}{2\pi F}\right)^2 \Rightarrow LC = \dfrac{1}{4\pi^2 F^2} \Rightarrow C = \dfrac{1}{4\pi^2 L F^2}$

Pythagorean Theorem

87.   Yes, since $6^2 + 8^2 = 10^2$. That is $36 + 64 = 100$.

88.   Yes, since $5^2 + 12^2 = 13^2$. That is $25 + 144 = 169$.

89.   Yes, since $\left(\sqrt{5}\right)^2 + \left(\sqrt{9}\right)^2 = \left(\sqrt{14}\right)^2$. That is $5 + 9 = 14$.

90.   No, since $4^2 + 5^2 \neq 7^2$. That is $16 + 25 \neq 49$.

91.   Yes, since $7^2 + 24^2 = 25^2$. That is $49 + 576 = 625$.

92.   Yes, since $1^2 + \left(\sqrt{3}\right)^2 = 2^2$. That is $1 + 3 = 4$.

93.   No, since $8^2 + 8^2 \neq 16^2$. That is $64 + 64 \neq 256$.

94.   Yes, since $11^2 + 60^2 = 61^2$. That is $121 + 3600 = 3721$.

95. $4^2 + 4^2 = c^2 \Rightarrow c^2 = 16 + 16 \Rightarrow c^2 = 32 \Rightarrow c = \sqrt{32} = 4\sqrt{2}$

96. $a^2 + 6^2 = 10^2 \Rightarrow a^2 + 36 = 100 \Rightarrow a^2 = 64 \Rightarrow a = \sqrt{64} = 8$

97. $24^2 + b^2 = 25^2 \Rightarrow 576 + b^2 = 625 \Rightarrow b^2 = 49 \Rightarrow b = \sqrt{49} = 7$

98. $4^2 + b^2 = 8^2 \Rightarrow 16 + b^2 = 64 \Rightarrow b^2 = 48 \Rightarrow b = \sqrt{48} = 4\sqrt{3}$

99. $3^2 + 4^2 = c^2 \Rightarrow c^2 = 9 + 16 \Rightarrow c^2 = 25 \Rightarrow c = \sqrt{25} = 5$

100. $4^2 + 7^2 = c^2 \Rightarrow c^2 = 16 + 49 \Rightarrow c^2 = 65 \Rightarrow c = \sqrt{65}$

101. $\left(\sqrt{3}\right)^2 + b^2 = 8^2 \Rightarrow 3 + b^2 = 64 \Rightarrow b^2 = 61 \Rightarrow b = \sqrt{61}$

102. $\left(\sqrt{6}\right)^2 + b^2 = \left(\sqrt{10}\right)^2 \Rightarrow 6 + b^2 = 10 \Rightarrow b^2 = 4 \Rightarrow b = \sqrt{4} = 2$

103. $a^2 + 48^2 = 50^2 \Rightarrow a^2 + 2304 = 2500 \Rightarrow a^2 = 196 \Rightarrow a = \sqrt{196} = 14$

104. $a^2 + 10^2 = 26^2 \Rightarrow a^2 + 100 = 676 \Rightarrow a^2 = 576 \Rightarrow a = \sqrt{576} = 24$

Distance Formula

105.   From $(-2, 1)$ to $(2, 3)$, $d = \sqrt{\left(2 - (-2)\right)^2 + \left(3 - 1\right)^2} = \sqrt{4^2 + 2^2} = \sqrt{16 + 4} = \sqrt{20} = 2\sqrt{5}$.

106.   From $(-3, 3)$ to $(2, -2)$, $d = \sqrt{\left(2 - (-3)\right)^2 + \left(-2 - 3\right)^2} = \sqrt{5^2 + (-5)^2} = \sqrt{25 + 25} = \sqrt{50} = 5\sqrt{2}$.

107.   From $(10, 40)$ to $(30, -20)$,

$$d = \sqrt{\left(30 - 10\right)^2 + \left(-20 - 40\right)^2} = \sqrt{20^2 + (-60)^2} = \sqrt{400 + 3600} = \sqrt{4000} = 20\sqrt{10}.$$

108.   From $(-75, -50)$ to $(75, -25)$,

$$d = \sqrt{\left(75 - (-75)\right)^2 + \left(-25 - (-50)\right)^2} = \sqrt{150^2 + 25^2} = \sqrt{22,500 + 625} = \sqrt{23,125} = 25\sqrt{37}.$$

109. $d = \sqrt{\left(4 - (-1)\right)^2 + \left(10 - 2\right)^2} = \sqrt{5^2 + 8^2} = \sqrt{25 + 64} = \sqrt{89}$.

110. $d = \sqrt{(-6-5)^2 + (20-(-40))^2} = \sqrt{(-11)^2 + 60^2} = \sqrt{121+3600} = \sqrt{3721} = 61.$

111. $d = \sqrt{(4-0)^2 + (0-(-3))^2} = \sqrt{4^2 + 3^2} = \sqrt{16+9} = \sqrt{25} = 5.$

112. $d = \sqrt{(-4-3)^2 + (2-9)^2} = \sqrt{(-7)^2 + (-7)^2} = \sqrt{49+49} = \sqrt{98} = 7\sqrt{2}.$

113. $\sqrt{(0-x)^2 + (6-3)^2} = 5 \Rightarrow \sqrt{(-x)^2 + 3^2} = 5 \Rightarrow \sqrt{x^2+9} = 5 \Rightarrow \left(\sqrt{x^2+9}\right)^2 = 5^2 \Rightarrow$

$x^2 + 9 = 25 \Rightarrow x^2 = 16 \Rightarrow x = \sqrt{16} = \pm 4.$ Since x is positive, $x = 4$.

114. $\sqrt{(6-x)^2 + (11-(-1))^2} = 13 \Rightarrow \sqrt{(6-x)^2 + 12^2} = 13 \Rightarrow \sqrt{(36-12x+x^2)+144} = 13 \Rightarrow$

$\sqrt{x^2-12x+180} = 13 \Rightarrow (\sqrt{x^2-12x+180})^2 = 13^2 \Rightarrow x^2-12x+180 = 169 \Rightarrow$

$x^2-12x+11 = 0 \Rightarrow (x-1)(x-11) = 0 \Rightarrow x = 1 \text{ or } x = 11$

115. $\sqrt{(62-x)^2 + (6-(-5))^2} = 61 \Rightarrow \sqrt{(62-x)^2 + 11^2} = 61 \Rightarrow \sqrt{(3844-124x+x^2)+121} = 61 \Rightarrow$

$\sqrt{x^2-124x+3965} = 61 \Rightarrow \left(\sqrt{x^2-124x+3965}\right)^2 = 61^2 \Rightarrow x^2-124x+3965 = 3721 \Rightarrow$

$x^2-124x+244 = 0 \Rightarrow (x-2)(x-122) = 0 \Rightarrow x = 2 \text{ or } x = 122$

116. $\sqrt{(12-x)^2 + (-4-3)^2} = 25 \Rightarrow \sqrt{(12-x)^2 + (-7)^2} = 25 \Rightarrow \sqrt{(144-24x+x^2)+49} = 25 \Rightarrow$

$\sqrt{x^2-24x+193} = 25 \Rightarrow \left(\sqrt{x^2-24x+193}\right)^2 = 25^2 \Rightarrow x^2-24x+193 = 625 \Rightarrow$

$x^2-24x-432 = 0 \Rightarrow (x+12)(x-36) = 0 \Rightarrow x = -12 \text{ or } x = 36.$ Since x is positive, $x = 36$.

Applications

117. $400 = 100\sqrt[3]{W^2} \Rightarrow \dfrac{400}{100} = \sqrt[3]{W^2} \Rightarrow 4 = \sqrt[3]{W^2} \Rightarrow 4^3 = \left(\sqrt[3]{W^2}\right)^3 \Rightarrow 64 = W^2 \Rightarrow W = 8 \text{ lb}$

118. $1000 = 100\sqrt[3]{W^2} \Rightarrow \dfrac{1000}{100} = \sqrt[3]{W^2} \Rightarrow 10 = \sqrt[3]{W^2} \Rightarrow 10^3 = \left(\sqrt[3]{W^2}\right)^3 \Rightarrow 1000 = W^2 \Rightarrow W = \sqrt{1000} \approx 31.6 \text{ lb}$

119. $D(6) = 1.22\sqrt{6} \approx 2.988 \approx 3 \text{ miles}$

120. $D(29,028) = 1.22\sqrt{29,028} \approx 207.859 \approx 208 \text{ miles}$

121. $1.22\sqrt{h} = 20 \Rightarrow \sqrt{h} = \dfrac{20}{1.22} \Rightarrow \left(\sqrt{h}\right)^2 = \left(\dfrac{20}{1.22}\right)^2 \Rightarrow h \approx 268.745 \approx 269 \text{ feet}$

122. $1.22\sqrt{h} = 100 \Rightarrow \sqrt{h} = \dfrac{100}{1.22} \Rightarrow \left(\sqrt{h}\right)^2 = \left(\dfrac{100}{1.22}\right)^2 \Rightarrow h \approx 6718.62 \approx 6719 \text{ feet}$

123. $d^2 = 11.4^2 + 15.2^2 \Rightarrow d^2 = 129.96 + 231.04 \Rightarrow d^2 = 361 \Rightarrow d = \sqrt{361} = 19 \text{ inches}$

124. Let x represent the width of the television screen. Then $\frac{3}{4}x$ represents the height.

$$x^2 + \left(\frac{3}{4}x\right)^2 = 13^2 \Rightarrow x^2 + \frac{9}{16}x^2 = 169 \Rightarrow \frac{25}{16}x^2 = 169 \Rightarrow x^2 = 169\left(\frac{16}{25}\right) \Rightarrow$$

$$x^2 = \frac{2704}{25} \Rightarrow x = \sqrt{\frac{2704}{25}} = 10.4 \text{ inches.} \quad \text{The height is } \frac{3}{4} \cdot 10.4 = 7.8 \text{ inches.} \quad \text{It is } 10.4 \text{ inches by } 7.8 \text{ inches.}$$

125. The height can be found using proportions: $\frac{16}{9} = \frac{29}{x} \Rightarrow 16x = 261 \Rightarrow x = \frac{261}{16} \approx 16.3$ inches.

Then $d^2 = 29^2 + 16.3^2 \Rightarrow d^2 = 841 + 265.69 \Rightarrow d^2 = 1106.69 \Rightarrow d = \sqrt{1106.69} \approx 33.3$ inches.

126. (a) $Q = 3.32(20)\left(5^{3/2}\right) \approx 742 \text{ ft}^3/\text{sec}$

(b) $3.32(30)D^{3/2} = 2690 \Rightarrow D^{3/2} = \frac{2690}{99.6} \Rightarrow \left(D^{3/2}\right)^{2/3} = \left(\frac{2690}{99.6}\right)^{2/3} \Rightarrow D \approx 9$ feet

127. (a) $\frac{60}{11}\sqrt{d} = 60 \Rightarrow \sqrt{d} = 60\left(\frac{11}{60}\right) \Rightarrow \sqrt{d} = 11 \Rightarrow \left(\sqrt{d}\right)^2 = 11^2 \Rightarrow d = 121$ feet

(b) $\frac{60}{11}\sqrt{d} = 100 \Rightarrow \sqrt{d} = 100\left(\frac{11}{60}\right) \Rightarrow \sqrt{d} = \frac{55}{3} \Rightarrow \left(\sqrt{d}\right)^2 = \left(\frac{55}{3}\right)^2 \Rightarrow d \approx 336$ feet

128. $L^2 = 30^2 + 10^2 \Rightarrow L^2 = 900 + 100 \Rightarrow L^2 = 1000 \Rightarrow L = \sqrt{1000} \approx 31.6$ feet

129. (a) $V = 30\sqrt{\frac{285}{178}} \approx 38$ mph. The accident vehicle was traveling about 38 mph.

(b) $45\sqrt{\frac{D}{255}} = 60 \Rightarrow \sqrt{\frac{D}{255}} = \frac{60}{45} \Rightarrow \left(\sqrt{\frac{D}{255}}\right)^2 = \left(\frac{4}{3}\right)^2 \Rightarrow \frac{D}{255} = \frac{16}{9} \Rightarrow D = 255\left(\frac{16}{9}\right) \approx 453$ feet

130. (a) $L = 1.5\sqrt{400} = 1.5 \cdot 20 = 30$ mph

(b) It increases by a factor of $\sqrt{2} \approx 1.4$, since $L = 1.5\sqrt{2R} \Rightarrow L = 1.5\sqrt{2}\sqrt{R} \Rightarrow L = \sqrt{2}\left(1.5\sqrt{R}\right)$.

(c) $1.5\sqrt{R} = 40 \Rightarrow \sqrt{R} = \frac{40}{1.5} \Rightarrow \left(\sqrt{R}\right)^2 = \left(\frac{40}{1.5}\right)^2 \Rightarrow R \approx 711$ feet

131. (a) $W(2v) = 3.8(2v)^3 = 3.8 \cdot 8 \cdot v^3 = 8 \cdot \left(3.8v^3\right)$; The wattage generated increases by a factor of 8.

(b) $W = 3.8v^3 \Rightarrow \frac{W}{3.8} = v^3 \Rightarrow \sqrt[3]{\frac{W}{3.8}} = \sqrt[3]{v^3} \Rightarrow v = \sqrt[3]{\frac{W}{3.8}}$

(c) $v = \sqrt[3]{\frac{30,400}{3.8}} = \sqrt[3]{8000} = 20$ mph

132. Let w represent weight and h represent height.

Then $w = kh^3$, so if $w_1 = 2w_2$, then $h_1 = \sqrt[3]{2}\, h_2$ because $w_1 = k\left(h_1\right)^3 \Rightarrow$

$$2w_2 = k\left(\sqrt[3]{2}\, h_2\right)^3 \Rightarrow 2w_2 = k(2)\left(h_2\right)^3 \Rightarrow w_2 = k\left(h_2\right)^3.$$

So the heavier person's height is greater by a factor of $\sqrt[3]{2} \approx 1.26$.

133. $c^2 = a^2 + a^2 \Rightarrow c^2 = 2a^2 \Rightarrow c = \sqrt{2a^2} = a\sqrt{2}$

134. $a^2 + b^2 = c^2 \Rightarrow \left(\dfrac{1}{2}c\right)^2 + b^2 = c^2 \Rightarrow \dfrac{1}{4}c^2 + b^2 = c^2 \Rightarrow b^2 = \dfrac{3}{4}c^2 \Rightarrow b = \sqrt{\dfrac{3}{4}c^2} = \dfrac{\sqrt{3}}{2}c$

That is, $a = \dfrac{1}{2}c$ and $b = \dfrac{\sqrt{3}}{2}c.$

Group Activity Solutions

(a) $T = 2\pi\sqrt{\dfrac{L}{g}} \Rightarrow \dfrac{T}{2\pi} = \sqrt{\dfrac{L}{g}} \Rightarrow \left(\dfrac{T}{2\pi}\right)^2 = \dfrac{L}{g} \Rightarrow \dfrac{T^2}{4\pi^2} = \dfrac{L}{g} \Rightarrow g \cdot \dfrac{T^2}{4\pi^2} = L \Rightarrow g = \dfrac{4\pi^2 L}{T^2}$

(b) Substituting the values $L = 1$ and $T = 1.11$ from the table, $g = \dfrac{4\pi^2(1)}{(1.11)^2} \approx 32.$

(c) For each second that an object falls, its speed increases by 32 feet per second.

7.6 Complex Numbers

Concepts

1. $2 + 3i$; *Answers may vary.*

2. No, any real number a can be written as $a + 0i$.

3. i

4. -1

5. $i\sqrt{a}$

6. $10 - 7i$

7. $a + bi$

8. $\dfrac{2 + 4i}{2} = \dfrac{2}{2} + \dfrac{4}{2}i = 1 + 2i$

9. 4

10. -5

11. 0

12. pure

Complex Numbers

13. $\sqrt{-5} = i\sqrt{5}$

14. $\sqrt{-21} = i\sqrt{21}$

15. $\sqrt{-100} = i\sqrt{100} = i \cdot 10 = 10i$

16. $\sqrt{-49} = i\sqrt{49} = i \cdot 7 = 7i$

17. $\sqrt{-144} = i\sqrt{144} = i \cdot 12 = 12i$

18. $\sqrt{-64} = i\sqrt{64} = i \cdot 8 = 8i$

19. $\sqrt{-12} = i\sqrt{12} = i \cdot \sqrt{4 \cdot 3} = i \cdot \sqrt{4} \cdot \sqrt{3} = i \cdot 2 \cdot \sqrt{3} = 2i\sqrt{3}$

20. $\sqrt{-8} = i\sqrt{8} = i \cdot \sqrt{4 \cdot 2} = i \cdot \sqrt{4} \cdot \sqrt{2} = i \cdot 2 \cdot \sqrt{2} = 2i\sqrt{2}$

21. $\sqrt{-18} = i\sqrt{18} = i \cdot \sqrt{9 \cdot 2} = i \cdot \sqrt{9} \cdot \sqrt{2} = i \cdot 3 \cdot \sqrt{2} = 3i\sqrt{2}$

22. $\sqrt{-48} = i\sqrt{48} = i \cdot \sqrt{16 \cdot 3} = i \cdot \sqrt{16} \cdot \sqrt{3} = i \cdot 4 \cdot \sqrt{3} = 4i\sqrt{3}$

23. $(5+3i)+(-2-3i) = (5+(-2))+(3+(-3))i = 3+0i = 3$

24. $(1-i)+(5-7i) = (1+5)+(-1+(-7))i = 6-8i$

25. $(2i)+(-8+5i) = (0+(-8))+(2+5)i = -8+7i$

26. $(-3i)+(5i) = (-3+5)i = 2i$

27. $(2-7i)-(1+2i) = (2-1)+(-7-2)i = 1-9i$

28. $(1+8i)-(3+9i) = (1-3)+(8-9)i = -2-i$

29. $(5i)-(10-2i) = (0-10)+(5-(-2))i = -10+7i$

30. $-3(4-3i) = -12+9i$

31. $(3+2i)(-1+5i) = -3+15i-2i+10i^2 = -3+13i+10(-1) = -3+13i-10 = -13+13i$

32. $(1+i)-(1-i) = (1-1)+(1-(-1))i = 0+2i = 2i$

33. $4(5-3i) = 20-12i$

34. $(1+2i)(-6-i) = -6-i-12i-2i^2 = -6-13i-2(-1) = -6-13i+2 = -4-13i$

35. $(5+4i)(5-4i) = 25-16i^2 = 25-16(-1) = 25+16 = 41$

36. $(3+5i)(3-5i) = 9-25i^2 = 9-25(-1) = 9+25 = 34$

37. $(-4i)(5i) = -4 \cdot 5 \cdot i^2 = -20(-1) = 20$

38. $(-6i)(-4i) = -6 \cdot (-4) \cdot i^2 = 24(-1) = -24$

39. $3i+(2-3i)-(1-5i) = 3i+2-3i-1+5i = 1+5i$

40. $4-(5-7i)+(3+7i) = 4-5+7i+3+7i = 2+14i$

41. $(2+i)^2 = 4+4i+i^2 = 4+4i-1 = 3+4i$

42. $(-1+2i)^2 = 1 - 4i + 4i^2 = 1 - 4i + 4(-1) = 1 - 4i - 4 = -3 - 4i$

43. $2i(-3+i) = -6i + 2i^2 = -6i + 2(-1) = -2 - 6i$

44. $5i(1-9i) = 5i - 45i^2 = 5i - 45(-1) = 45 + 5i$

45. $i(1+i)^2 = i(1 + 2i + i^2) = i(1 + 2i - 1) = i(2i) = 2i^2 = 2(-1) = -2$

46. $2i(1-i)^2 = 2i(1 - 2i + i^2) = 2i(1 - 2i - 1) = 2i(-2i) = -4i^2 = -4(-1) = 4$

47. $(a+3bi)(a-3bi) = a^2 - 9b^2i^2 = a^2 - 9b^2(-1) = a^2 + 9b^2$

48. $(a+bi) - (a-bi) = a - a + bi + bi = 2bi$

49. When 11 is divided by 4, the result is 2 with remainder 3. Thus $i^{11} = i^3 = -i$.

50. When 50 is divided by 4, the result is 12 with remainder 2. Thus $i^{50} = i^2 = -1$.

51. When 21 is divided by 4, the result is 5 with remainder 1. Thus $i^{21} = i^1 = i$.

52. When 103 is divided by 4, the result is 25 with remainder 3. Thus $i^{103} = i^3 = -i$.

53. When 58 is divided by 4, the result is 14 with remainder 2. Thus $i^{58} = i^2 = -1$.

54. When 61 is divided by 4, the result is 15 with remainder 1. Thus $i^{64} = i^1 = i$.

55. When 64 is divided by 4, the result is 16 with remainder 0. Thus $i^{64} = i^0 = 1$.

56. When 28 is divided by 4, the result is 7 with remainder 0. Thus $i^{28} = i^0 = 1$.

57. $3 - 4i$

58. $1 + 4i$

59. Since $-6i = 0 - 6i$, the complex conjugate is $0 + 6i = 6i$.

60. Since $-10 = -10 + 0i$, the complex conjugate is $-10 - 0i = -10$.

61. $5 + 4i$

62. $7 - 2i$

63. Since $-1 = -1 + 0i$, the complex conjugate is $-1 - 0i = -1$.

64. Since $19i = 0 + 19i$, the complex conjugate is $0 - 19i = -19i$.

65. $\dfrac{2}{1+i} = \dfrac{2}{1+i} \cdot \dfrac{1-i}{1-i} = \dfrac{2(1-i)}{1^2 - i^2} = \dfrac{2-2i}{1+1} = \dfrac{2-2i}{2} = \dfrac{2}{2} - \dfrac{2}{2}i = 1 - i$

66. $\dfrac{-6}{2-i} = \dfrac{-6}{2-i} \cdot \dfrac{2+i}{2+i} = \dfrac{-6(2+i)}{2^2 - i^2} = \dfrac{-12-6i}{4+1} = \dfrac{-12-6i}{5} = -\dfrac{12}{5} - \dfrac{6}{5}i$

67. $\dfrac{3i}{5-2i} = \dfrac{3i}{5-2i} \cdot \dfrac{5+2i}{5+2i} = \dfrac{3i(5+2i)}{5^2 - 4i^2} = \dfrac{15i + 6i^2}{25+4} = \dfrac{15i-6}{29} = -\dfrac{6}{29} + \dfrac{15}{29}i$

68. $\dfrac{-8}{2i} = \dfrac{-8}{2i} \cdot \dfrac{-2i}{-2i} = \dfrac{-8(-2i)}{-4i^2} = \dfrac{16i}{4} = \dfrac{16}{4}i = 4i$

69. $\dfrac{8+9i}{5+2i} = \dfrac{8+9i}{5+2i} \cdot \dfrac{5-2i}{5-2i} = \dfrac{40-16i+45i-18i^2}{5^2-4i^2} = \dfrac{40+29i-18(-1)}{25+4} = \dfrac{58+29i}{29} = 2+i$

70. $\dfrac{3-2i}{1+4i} = \dfrac{3-2i}{1+4i} \cdot \dfrac{1-4i}{1-4i} = \dfrac{3-12i-2i+8i^2}{1^2-16i^2} = \dfrac{3-14i+8(-1)}{1+16} = \dfrac{-5-14i}{17} = -\dfrac{5}{17} - \dfrac{14}{17}i$

71. $\dfrac{5+7i}{1-i} = \dfrac{5+7i}{1-i} \cdot \dfrac{1+i}{1+i} = \dfrac{5+5i+7i+7i^2}{1^2-i^2} = \dfrac{5+12i+7(-1)}{1+1} = \dfrac{-2+12i}{2} = -1+6i$

72. $\dfrac{-7+4i}{3-2i} = \dfrac{-7+4i}{3-2i} \cdot \dfrac{3+2i}{3+2i} = \dfrac{-21-14i+12i+8i^2}{3^2-4i^2} = \dfrac{-21-2i+8(-1)}{9+4} = \dfrac{-29-2i}{13} = -\dfrac{29}{13} - \dfrac{2}{13}i$

73. $\dfrac{2-i}{i} = \dfrac{2-i}{i} \cdot \dfrac{-i}{-i} = \dfrac{-2i+i^2}{-i^2} = \dfrac{-2i+(-1)}{-(-1)} = \dfrac{-2i-1}{1} = -1-2i$

74. $\dfrac{3+2i}{-i} = \dfrac{3+2i}{-i} \cdot \dfrac{i}{i} = \dfrac{3i+2i^2}{-i^2} = \dfrac{3i+2(-1)}{-(-1)} = \dfrac{3i-2}{1} = -2+3i$

75. $\dfrac{1}{i} + \dfrac{1}{2i} = \dfrac{2}{2i} + \dfrac{1}{2i} = \dfrac{3}{2i} = \dfrac{3}{2i} \cdot \dfrac{-2i}{-2i} = \dfrac{-6i}{-4i^2} = \dfrac{-6i}{-4(-1)} = \dfrac{-6i}{4} = -\dfrac{3}{2}i$

76. $\dfrac{3}{4i} + \dfrac{2}{i} = \dfrac{3}{4i} + \dfrac{8}{4i} = \dfrac{11}{4i} = \dfrac{11}{4i} \cdot \dfrac{-4i}{-4i} = \dfrac{-44i}{-16i^2} = \dfrac{-44i}{-16(-1)} = \dfrac{-44i}{16} = -\dfrac{11}{4}i$

77. $\dfrac{1}{-1+i} - \dfrac{2}{i} = \dfrac{i}{i(-1+i)} - \dfrac{2(-1+i)}{i(-1+i)} = \dfrac{i}{-1-i} - \dfrac{-2+2i}{-1-i} = \dfrac{i+2-2i}{-1-i} = \dfrac{2-i}{-1-i}$

$= \dfrac{2-i}{-1-i} \cdot \dfrac{-1+i}{-1+i} = \dfrac{-2+2i+i-i^2}{1-i^2} = \dfrac{-2+3i-(-1)}{1-(-1)} = \dfrac{-1+3i}{2} = -\dfrac{1}{2} + \dfrac{3}{2}i$

78. $-\dfrac{3}{2i} - \dfrac{2}{1+i} = -\dfrac{3(1+i)}{2i(1+i)} - \dfrac{2(2i)}{2i(1+i)} = \dfrac{-3-3i-4i}{2i(1+i)} = \dfrac{-3-7i}{2i+2i^2} = \dfrac{-3-7i}{2i+2(-1)} = \dfrac{-3-7i}{-2+2i}$

$= \dfrac{-3-7i}{-2+2i} \cdot \dfrac{-2-2i}{-2-2i} = \dfrac{6+6i+14i+14i^2}{4-4i^2} = \dfrac{6+20i+14(-1)}{4-4(-1)} = \dfrac{-8+20i}{8} = -1 + \dfrac{5}{2}i$

Applications

79. $Z = \dfrac{40+70i}{2+3i} = \dfrac{40+70i}{2+3i} \cdot \dfrac{2-3i}{2-3i} = \dfrac{80-120i+140i-210i^2}{2^2-9i^2} = \dfrac{290+20i}{13} = \dfrac{290}{13} + \dfrac{20}{13}i$

80. $Z = \dfrac{10+20i}{3+7i} = \dfrac{10+20i}{3+7i} \cdot \dfrac{3-7i}{3-7i} = \dfrac{30-70i+60i-140i^2}{3^2-49i^2} = \dfrac{170-10i}{58} = \dfrac{170}{58} - \dfrac{10}{58}i = \dfrac{85}{29} - \dfrac{5}{29}i$

Checking Basic Concepts for Sections 7.5 & 7.6

1. (a) $\sqrt{2x-4} = 2 \Rightarrow \left(\sqrt{2x-4}\right)^2 = 2^2 \Rightarrow 2x-4 = 4 \Rightarrow 2x = 8 \Rightarrow x = 4$

   (b) $\sqrt[3]{x-1} = 3 \Rightarrow \left(\sqrt[3]{x-1}\right)^3 = 3^3 \Rightarrow x-1 = 27 \Rightarrow x = 28$

   (c) $\sqrt{3x} = 1 + \sqrt{x+1} \Rightarrow \left(\sqrt{3x}\right)^2 = \left(1+\sqrt{x+1}\right)^2 \Rightarrow 3x = 1 + 2\sqrt{x+1} + x + 1 \Rightarrow$

$$3x = x+2+2\sqrt{x+1} \Rightarrow 2x-2 = 2\sqrt{x+1} \Rightarrow x-1 = \sqrt{x+1} \Rightarrow (x-1)^2 = \left(\sqrt{x+1}\right)^2 \Rightarrow$$

$$x^2 - 2x + 1 = x + 1 \Rightarrow x^2 - 3x = 0 \Rightarrow x(x-3) = 0 \Rightarrow x = 0 \text{ or } x = 3$$

The solution $x = 0$ does not check. The solution is $x = 3$.

2. $d = \sqrt{(2-(-3))^2 + (-7-5)^2} = \sqrt{5^2 + (-12)^2} = \sqrt{25+144} = \sqrt{169} = 13$

3. $h^2 + 12.8^2 = 16^2 \Rightarrow h^2 + 163.84 = 256 \Rightarrow h^2 = 92.16 \Rightarrow h = \sqrt{92.16} = 9.6$ inches

4. $(x+1)^4 = 16 \Rightarrow \sqrt[4]{(x+1)^4} = \sqrt[4]{16} \Rightarrow |x+1| = 2 \Rightarrow x+1 = \pm 2 \Rightarrow x = -3 \text{ or } x = 1$

5.   (a) $\sqrt{-64} = i\sqrt{64} = i(8) = 8i$

       (b) $\sqrt{-17} = i\sqrt{17}$

6.   (a) $(2-3i)+(1-i) = (2+1)+(-3+(-1))i = 3-4i$

       (b) $4i - (2+i) = (0-2)+(4-1)i = -2+3i$

       (c) $(3-2i)(1+i) = 3+3i-2i-2i^2 = 3+i-2(-1) = 3+i+2 = 5+i$

       (d) $\dfrac{3}{2-2i} = \dfrac{3}{2-2i} \cdot \dfrac{2+2i}{2+2i} = \dfrac{3(2+2i)}{2^2-4i^2} = \dfrac{6+6i}{4+4} = \dfrac{6+6i}{8} = \dfrac{6}{8}+\dfrac{6}{8}i = \dfrac{3}{4}+\dfrac{3}{4}i$

Chapter 7 Review Exercises

Section 7.1

1. $\sqrt{4} = 2$

2. $\sqrt{36} = 6$

3. $\sqrt{9x^2} = \sqrt{9} \cdot \sqrt{x^2} = 3|x|$

4. $\sqrt{(x-1)^2} = |x-1|$

5. $\sqrt[3]{-64} = -4$

6. $\sqrt[3]{-125} = -5$

7. $\sqrt[3]{x^6} = \sqrt[3]{(x^2)^3} = x^2$

8. $\sqrt[3]{27x^3} = \sqrt[3]{27} \cdot \sqrt[3]{x^3} = 3x$

9. $\sqrt[4]{16} = 2$

10. $\sqrt[5]{-1} = -1$

11. $\sqrt[4]{x^8} = \sqrt[4]{(x^2)^4} = x^2$

12. $\sqrt[5]{(x+1)^5} = x+1$

13. $14^{1/2} = \sqrt{14}$

14. $(-5)^{1/3} = \sqrt[3]{-5}$

15. $\left(\dfrac{x}{y}\right)^{3/2} = \left(\sqrt{\dfrac{x}{y}}\right)^3$ or $\sqrt{\left(\dfrac{x}{y}\right)^3}$

16. $(xy)^{-2/3} = \dfrac{1}{(xy)^{2/3}} = \dfrac{1}{\sqrt[3]{(xy)^2}}$ or $\dfrac{1}{\left(\sqrt[3]{xy}\right)^2}$

17. $(-27)^{2/3} = \left(\sqrt[3]{-27}\right)^2 = (-3)^2 = 9$

18. $16^{1/4} = \sqrt[4]{16} = 2$

19. $16^{3/2} = \left(\sqrt{16}\right)^3 = 4^3 = 64$

20. $81^{3/4} = \left(\sqrt[4]{81}\right)^3 = 3^3 = 27$

21. $\left(z^3\right)^{2/3} = z^{3 \cdot 2/3} = z^2$

22. $\left(x^2 y^4\right)^{1/2} = x^{2 \cdot 1/2} \cdot y^{4 \cdot 1/2} = xy^2$

23. $\left(\dfrac{x^2}{y^6}\right)^{3/2} = \dfrac{x^{2 \cdot 3/2}}{y^{6 \cdot 3/2}} = \dfrac{x^3}{y^9}$

24. $\left(\dfrac{x^3}{y^6}\right)^{-1/3} = \dfrac{x^{3 \cdot (-1/3)}}{y^{6 \cdot (-1/3)}} = \dfrac{x^{-1}}{y^{-2}} = \dfrac{y^2}{x}$

Section 7.2

25. $\sqrt{2} \cdot \sqrt{32} = \sqrt{64} = 8$

26. $\sqrt[3]{-4} \cdot \sqrt[3]{2} = \sqrt[3]{-8} = -2$

27. $\sqrt[3]{x^4} \cdot \sqrt[3]{x^2} = \sqrt[3]{x^6} = \sqrt[3]{\left(x^2\right)^3} = x^2$

28. $\dfrac{\sqrt{80}}{\sqrt{20}} = \sqrt{\dfrac{80}{20}} = \sqrt{4} = 2$

29. $\sqrt[3]{-\dfrac{x}{8}} = -\dfrac{\sqrt[3]{x}}{\sqrt[3]{8}} = -\dfrac{\sqrt[3]{x}}{2}$

30. $\sqrt{\dfrac{1}{3}} \cdot \sqrt{\dfrac{1}{3}} = \left(\sqrt{\dfrac{1}{3}}\right)^2 = \dfrac{1}{3}$

31. $\sqrt{48} = \sqrt{16 \cdot 3} = \sqrt{16} \cdot \sqrt{3} = 4\sqrt{3}$

32. $\sqrt{54} = \sqrt{9 \cdot 6} = \sqrt{9} \cdot \sqrt{6} = 3\sqrt{6}$

33. $\sqrt[3]{\dfrac{3}{x}} \cdot \sqrt[3]{\dfrac{9}{x^2}} = \sqrt[3]{\dfrac{3 \cdot 9}{x \cdot x^2}} = \sqrt[3]{\dfrac{27}{x^3}} = \dfrac{\sqrt[3]{27}}{\sqrt[3]{x^3}} = \dfrac{3}{x}$

34. $\sqrt{32a^3b^2} = \sqrt{(4ab)^2 \cdot 2a} = \sqrt{(4ab)^2} \cdot \sqrt{2a} = 4ab\sqrt{2a}$

35. $\sqrt{3xy} \cdot \sqrt{27xy} = \sqrt{3 \cdot 27 \cdot xy \cdot xy} = \sqrt{81(xy)^2} = \sqrt{(9xy)^2} = 9xy$

36. $\sqrt[3]{-25z^2} \cdot \sqrt[3]{-5z^2} = \sqrt[3]{-25 \cdot (-5) \cdot z^2 \cdot z^2} = \sqrt[3]{125z^4} = \sqrt[3]{(5z)^3 \cdot z} = \sqrt{(5z)^3} \cdot \sqrt[3]{z} = 5z\sqrt[3]{z}$

37. $\sqrt{x^2 + 2x + 1} = \sqrt{(x+1)^2} = x + 1$

38. $\sqrt[4]{\dfrac{2a^2}{b}} \cdot \sqrt[4]{\dfrac{8a^3}{b^3}} = \sqrt[4]{\dfrac{16a^5}{b^4}} = \sqrt[4]{\left(\dfrac{2a}{b}\right)^4 \cdot a} = \sqrt[4]{\left(\dfrac{2a}{b}\right)^4} \cdot \sqrt[4]{a} = \dfrac{2a\sqrt[4]{a}}{b}$

39. $2\sqrt{x} \cdot \sqrt[3]{x} = 2x^{1/2} \cdot x^{1/3} = 2x^{1/2 + 1/3} = 2x^{5/6} = 2\sqrt[6]{x^5}$

40. $\sqrt[3]{rt} \cdot \sqrt[4]{r^2t^4} = (rt)^{1/3} \cdot \left(r^2t^4\right)^{1/4} = r^{1/3}t^{1/3} \cdot r^{1/2}t = r^{1/3+1/2}t^{1/3+1} = r^{5/6}t^{4/3} = r^{5/6}t^{8/6} = \sqrt[6]{r^5t^8} \text{ or } t\sqrt[6]{r^5t^2}$

Section 7.3

41. $3\sqrt{3} + \sqrt{3} = 4\sqrt{3}$

42. $\sqrt[3]{x} + 2\sqrt[3]{x} = 3\sqrt[3]{x}$

43. $3\sqrt[3]{5} - 6\sqrt[3]{5} = -3\sqrt[3]{5}$

44. $\sqrt[4]{y} - 2\sqrt[4]{y} = -\sqrt[4]{y}$

45. $2\sqrt{12} + 7\sqrt{3} = 2\sqrt{4 \cdot 3} + 7\sqrt{3} = 2\sqrt{4} \cdot \sqrt{3} + 7\sqrt{3} = 4\sqrt{3} + 7\sqrt{3} = 11\sqrt{3}$

46. $3\sqrt{18} - 2\sqrt{2} = 3\sqrt{9 \cdot 2} - 2\sqrt{2} = 3\sqrt{9} \cdot \sqrt{2} - 2\sqrt{2} = 9\sqrt{2} - 2\sqrt{2} = 7\sqrt{2}$

47. $7\sqrt[3]{16} - \sqrt[3]{2} = 7\sqrt[3]{8 \cdot 2} - \sqrt[3]{2} = 7\sqrt[3]{8} \cdot \sqrt[3]{2} - \sqrt[3]{2} = 14\sqrt[3]{2} - \sqrt[3]{2} = 13\sqrt[3]{2}$

48. $\sqrt{4x + 4} + \sqrt{x + 1} = \sqrt{4(x+1)} + \sqrt{x+1} = \sqrt{4} \cdot \sqrt{x+1} + \sqrt{x+1} = 3\sqrt{x+1}$

49. $\sqrt{4x^3} - \sqrt{x} = \sqrt{(2x)^2 \cdot x} - \sqrt{x} = \sqrt{(2x)^2} \cdot \sqrt{x} - \sqrt{x} = 2x\sqrt{x} - \sqrt{x} = (2x - 1)\sqrt{x}$

50. $\sqrt[3]{ab^4} + 2\sqrt[3]{a^4b} = \sqrt[3]{b^3 \cdot ab} + 2\sqrt[3]{a^3 \cdot ab} = \sqrt[3]{b^3} \cdot \sqrt[3]{ab} + 2\sqrt[3]{a^3} \cdot \sqrt[3]{ab} = (b + 2a)\sqrt[3]{ab}$

51. $\left(1 + \sqrt{2}\right)\left(3 + \sqrt{2}\right) = 3 + \sqrt{2} + 3\sqrt{2} + \left(\sqrt{2}\right)^2 = 3 + 4\sqrt{2} + 2 = 5 + 4\sqrt{2}$

52. $\left(7 - \sqrt{5}\right)\left(1 + \sqrt{3}\right) = 7 + 7\sqrt{3} - \sqrt{5} + \sqrt{15}$

53. $\left(3 + \sqrt{6}\right)\left(3 - \sqrt{6}\right) = 3^2 - \left(\sqrt{6}\right)^2 = 9 - 6 = 3$

54. $\left(10 - \sqrt{5}\right)\left(10 + \sqrt{5}\right) = 10^2 - \left(\sqrt{5}\right)^2 = 100 - 5 = 95$

55. $\left(\sqrt{a}+\sqrt{2b}\right)\left(\sqrt{a}-\sqrt{2b}\right) = \left(\sqrt{a}\right)^2 - \left(\sqrt{2b}\right)^2 = a - 2b$

56. $\left(\sqrt{xy}-1\right)\left(\sqrt{xy}+2\right) = \left(\sqrt{xy}\right)^2 + 2\sqrt{xy} - \sqrt{xy} - 2 = xy + \sqrt{xy} - 2$

57. $\dfrac{4}{\sqrt{5}} = \dfrac{4}{\sqrt{5}} \cdot \dfrac{\sqrt{5}}{\sqrt{5}} = \dfrac{4\sqrt{5}}{5}$

58. $\dfrac{r}{2\sqrt{t}} = \dfrac{r}{2\sqrt{t}} \cdot \dfrac{\sqrt{t}}{\sqrt{t}} = \dfrac{r\sqrt{t}}{2t}$

59. $\dfrac{1}{\sqrt{2}+3} = \dfrac{1}{\sqrt{2}+3} \cdot \dfrac{\sqrt{2}-3}{\sqrt{2}-3} = \dfrac{\sqrt{2}-3}{2-9} = \dfrac{\sqrt{2}-3}{-7} = \dfrac{3-\sqrt{2}}{7}$

60. $\dfrac{2}{5-\sqrt{7}} = \dfrac{2}{5-\sqrt{7}} \cdot \dfrac{5+\sqrt{7}}{5+\sqrt{7}} = \dfrac{10+2\sqrt{7}}{25-7} = \dfrac{10+2\sqrt{7}}{18} = \dfrac{5+\sqrt{7}}{9}$

61. $\dfrac{1}{\sqrt{8}-\sqrt{7}} = \dfrac{1}{\sqrt{8}-\sqrt{7}} \cdot \dfrac{\sqrt{8}+\sqrt{7}}{\sqrt{8}+\sqrt{7}} = \dfrac{\sqrt{8}+\sqrt{7}}{8-7} = \dfrac{\sqrt{8}+\sqrt{7}}{1} = \sqrt{8}+\sqrt{7}$

62. $\dfrac{\sqrt{a}-\sqrt{b}}{\sqrt{a}+\sqrt{b}} = \dfrac{\sqrt{a}-\sqrt{b}}{\sqrt{a}+\sqrt{b}} \cdot \dfrac{\sqrt{a}-\sqrt{b}}{\sqrt{a}-\sqrt{b}} = \dfrac{a-2\sqrt{ab}+b}{a-b}$

Section 7.4

63. See Figure 63.

64. See Figure 64.

        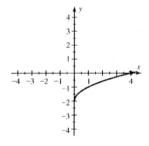

Figure 63   Figure 64   Figure 67

65. $f(x) = x^{1/2} = \sqrt{x}; \; f(4) = 4^{1/2} = \sqrt{4} = 2$

66. $f(x) = x^{2/7} = \sqrt[7]{x^2}; \; f(4) = 4^{2/7} = \sqrt[7]{4^2} = \sqrt[7]{16}$

67. See Figure 67. This graph is shifted 2 units downward.

68. See Figure 68. This graph is shifted 1 unit to the right.

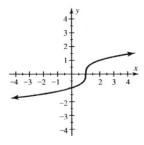

Figure 68

69. $x - 1 \geq 0 \Rightarrow x \geq 1 \Rightarrow \text{Domain}: [1, \infty)$

70. $6 - 2x \geq 0 \Rightarrow -2x \geq -6 \Rightarrow x \leq 3 \Rightarrow \text{Domain}: (-\infty, 3]$

71. $x^2 + 1 \geq 0 \Rightarrow x^2 \geq -1 \Rightarrow \text{Domain}: (-\infty, \infty)$

72. $x + 2 > 0 \Rightarrow x > -2 \Rightarrow \text{Domain}: (-2, \infty)$

Section 7.5

73. $\sqrt{x+2} = x \Rightarrow \left(\sqrt{x+2}\right)^2 = x^2 \Rightarrow x + 2 = x^2 \Rightarrow x^2 - x - 2 = 0 \Rightarrow (x-2)(x+1) = 0 \Rightarrow x = 2 \text{ or } x = -1.$ The

solution $x = -1$ does not check. The solution is $x = 2$.

74. $\sqrt{2x-1} = \sqrt{x+3} \Rightarrow \left(\sqrt{2x-1}\right)^2 = \left(\sqrt{x+3}\right)^2 \Rightarrow 2x - 1 = x + 3 \Rightarrow x = 4$

75. $\sqrt[3]{x-1} = 2 \Rightarrow \left(\sqrt[3]{x-1}\right)^3 = 2^3 \Rightarrow x - 1 = 8 \Rightarrow x = 9$

76. $\sqrt[3]{3x} = 3 \Rightarrow \left(\sqrt[3]{3x}\right)^3 = 3^3 \Rightarrow 3x = 27 \Rightarrow x = 9$

77. $\sqrt{2x} = x - 4 \Rightarrow \left(\sqrt{2x}\right)^2 = (x-4)^2 \Rightarrow 2x = x^2 - 8x + 16 \Rightarrow x^2 - 10x + 16 = 0 \Rightarrow$

$(x-2)(x-8) = 0 \Rightarrow x = 2 \text{ or } x = 8.$ The solution $x = 2$ does not check. The solution is $x = 8$.

78. $\sqrt{x} + 1 = \sqrt{x+2} \Rightarrow \left(\sqrt{x}+1\right)^2 = \left(\sqrt{x+2}\right)^2 \Rightarrow x + 2\sqrt{x} + 1 = x + 2 \Rightarrow 2\sqrt{x} = 1 \Rightarrow$

$\left(2\sqrt{x}\right)^2 = 1^2 \Rightarrow 4x = 1 \Rightarrow x = \dfrac{1}{4}$

79. Graph $Y_1 = (2X-1)^{\wedge}(1/3)$ and $Y_2 = 2$ in [–4, 6, 1] by [–3, 3, 1]. See Figure 79. The solution is $x = 4.5$.

[–4, 6, 1] by [–3, 3, 1]   [–5, 5, 1] by [–5, 5, 1]

Figure 79   Figure 80

80. Graph $Y_1 = X^{\wedge}(2/3)$ and $Y_2 = 3 - X$ in [–5, 5, 1] by [–5, 5, 1]. See Figure 80. The solution is $x \approx 1.62$.

81. $c^2 = 4^2 + 7^2 \Rightarrow c^2 = 16 + 49 \Rightarrow c^2 = 65 \Rightarrow c = \sqrt{65}$

82. $5^2 + b^2 = 8^2 \Rightarrow 25 + b^2 = 64 \Rightarrow b^2 = 39 \Rightarrow b = \sqrt{39}$

83. $d = \sqrt{\left(2-(-2)\right)^2 + \left(-2-3\right)^2} = \sqrt{4^2 + \left(-5\right)^2} = \sqrt{16+25} = \sqrt{41}$

84. $d = \sqrt{\left(-4-2\right)^2 + \left(1-(-3)\right)^2} = \sqrt{\left(-6\right)^2 + 4^2} = \sqrt{36+16} = \sqrt{52} = 2\sqrt{13}$

85. $x^2 = 121 \Rightarrow x = \pm\sqrt{121} \Rightarrow x = \pm 11$

86. $2z^2 = 32 \Rightarrow z^2 = 16 \Rightarrow z = \pm\sqrt{16} \Rightarrow z = \pm 4$

87. $\left(x-1\right)^2 = 16 \Rightarrow x-1 = \pm\sqrt{16} \Rightarrow x-1 = \pm 4 \Rightarrow x = 1 \pm 4 \Rightarrow x = -3 \text{ or } x = 5$

88. $x^3 = 64 \Rightarrow x = \sqrt[3]{64} \Rightarrow x = 4$

89. $\left(x-1\right)^3 = 8 \Rightarrow x-1 = \sqrt[3]{8} \Rightarrow x-1 = 2 \Rightarrow x = 3$

90. $\left(2x-1\right)^3 = 27 \Rightarrow 2x-1 = \sqrt[3]{27} \Rightarrow 2x-1 = 3 \Rightarrow 2x = 4 \Rightarrow x = 2$

91. $x^4 = 256 \Rightarrow \sqrt[4]{x^4} = \sqrt[4]{256} \Rightarrow |x| = 4 \Rightarrow x = \pm 4$

92. $x^5 = -1 \Rightarrow \sqrt[5]{x^5} = \sqrt[5]{-1} \Rightarrow x = -1$

93. $\left(x-3\right)^5 = -32 \Rightarrow \sqrt[5]{\left(x-3\right)^5} = \sqrt[5]{-32} \Rightarrow x-3 = -2 \Rightarrow x = 1$

94. $3\left(x+1\right)^4 = 3 \Rightarrow \left(x+1\right)^4 = 1 \Rightarrow \sqrt[4]{\left(x+1\right)^4} = \sqrt[4]{1}$

$\Rightarrow |x+1| = 1 \Rightarrow x+1 = \pm 1 \Rightarrow x = -2 \text{ or } x = 0$

Section 7.6

95. $\left(1-2i\right) + \left(-3+2i\right) = \left(1+(-3)\right) + \left(-2+2\right)i = -2 + 0i = -2$

96. $\left(1+3i\right) - \left(3-i\right) = \left(1-3\right) + \left(3-(-1)\right)i = -2 + 4i$

97. $\left(1-i\right)\left(2+3i\right) = 2 + 3i - 2i - 3i^2 = 2 + i - 3(-1) = 2 + i + 3 = 5 + i$

98. $\dfrac{3+i}{1-i} = \dfrac{3+i}{1-i} \cdot \dfrac{1+i}{1+i} = \dfrac{3+3i+i+i^2}{1^2 - i^2} = \dfrac{3+4i-1}{1+1} = \dfrac{2+4i}{2} = \dfrac{2}{2} + \dfrac{4}{2}i = 1 + 2i$

99. $\dfrac{i\left(4+i\right)}{2-3i} = \dfrac{4i+i^2}{2-3i} = \dfrac{-1+4i}{2-3i} = \dfrac{-1+4i}{2-3i} \cdot \dfrac{2+3i}{2+3i} = \dfrac{-2-3i+8i+12i^2}{4-9i^2} = \dfrac{-2+5i+12(-1)}{4-9(-1)}$

$= \dfrac{-14+5i}{13} = -\dfrac{14}{13} + \dfrac{5}{13}i$

100. $\left(1-i\right)^2\left(1+i\right) = \left(1-2i+i^2\right)\left(1+i\right) = \left(1-2i-1\right)\left(1+i\right) = -2i\left(1+i\right) = -2i - 2i^2 = 2 - 2i$

Applications

101. $\dfrac{\sqrt{h}}{2} = 4.6 \Rightarrow \sqrt{h} = 9.2 \Rightarrow \left(\sqrt{h}\right)^2 = 9.2^2 \Rightarrow h = 84.64 \approx 85 \text{ feet}$

102. $d^2 = 90^2 + 90^2 \Rightarrow d^2 = 8100 + 8100 \Rightarrow d^2 = 16,200 \Rightarrow d = \sqrt{16,200} \approx 127.3 \text{ feet}$

103. $T = \frac{1}{4}\sqrt{10} \approx 0.79$ seconds

104.   (a) $A = s^2 = \left(\sqrt{5}\right)^2 = 5$ square units

     (b) $V = s^3 = \left(\sqrt{5}\right)^3 = 5\sqrt{5}$ cubic units

     (c) $d^2 = \left(\sqrt{5}\right)^2 + \left(\sqrt{5}\right)^2 \Rightarrow d^2 = 5+5 \Rightarrow d^2 = 10 \Rightarrow d = \sqrt{10}$ units

     (d) $d^2 = \left(\sqrt{5}\right)^2 + \left(\sqrt{10}\right)^2 \Rightarrow d^2 = 5+10 \Rightarrow d^2 = 15 \Rightarrow d = \sqrt{15}$ units

105. $2\pi\sqrt{\dfrac{L}{32.2}} = 1 \Rightarrow \sqrt{\dfrac{L}{32.2}} = \dfrac{1}{2\pi} \Rightarrow \left(\sqrt{\dfrac{L}{32.2}}\right)^2 = \left(\dfrac{1}{2\pi}\right)^2 \Rightarrow \dfrac{L}{32.2} = \dfrac{1}{4\pi^2} \Rightarrow L = \dfrac{32.2}{4\pi^2} \approx 0.82$ feet

106. $2\pi\sqrt{\dfrac{L}{5.1}} = 1 \Rightarrow \sqrt{\dfrac{L}{5.1}} = \dfrac{1}{2\pi} \Rightarrow \left(\sqrt{\dfrac{L}{5.1}}\right)^2 = \left(\dfrac{1}{2\pi}\right)^2 \Rightarrow \dfrac{L}{5.1} = \dfrac{1}{4\pi^2} \Rightarrow L = \dfrac{5.1}{4\pi^2} \approx 0.13$ feet.   It is shorter.

107. $4(1+r)^{210} = 281 \Rightarrow (1+r)^{210} = \dfrac{281}{4} \Rightarrow \left((1+r)^{210}\right)^{1/210} = \left(\dfrac{281}{4}\right)^{1/210} \Rightarrow 1+r = \left(\dfrac{281}{4}\right)^{1/210} \Rightarrow$

     $r = \left(\dfrac{281}{4}\right)^{1/210} - 1 \approx 0.02$.   From 1790 to 2000 the annual percentage growth rate was about 2%.

108.   (a) $L = \sqrt{3.75(500)} = \sqrt{1875} \approx 43$ mph

     (b) $L = 1.5\sqrt{500} \approx 34$ mph.   A steeper bank allows for a higher speed limit. This agrees with intuition.

109. $x^2 = 7 \Rightarrow x = \sqrt{7} \approx 2.65$ feet

110. $S = \pi(11)\sqrt{11^2 + 60^2} = 11\pi\sqrt{121+3600} = 11\pi\sqrt{3721} \approx 2108$ in^2

111.   (a) $2^{-5700/5700} = 2^{-1} = \dfrac{1}{2}$

     (b) $2^{-20,000/5700} = 2^{-200/57} \approx 0.09 = \dfrac{9}{100}$

Chapter 7 Test

1. $\sqrt[3]{-27} = \sqrt[3]{(-3)^3} = -3$

2. $\sqrt{(z+1)^2} = |z+1|$

3. $\sqrt{25x^4} = \sqrt{25} \cdot \sqrt{\left(x^2\right)^2} = 5x^2$

4. $\sqrt[3]{8z^6} = \sqrt[3]{8} \cdot \sqrt[3]{\left(z^2\right)^3} = 2z^2$

5. $\sqrt[4]{16x^4 y^5} = \sqrt[4]{(2xy)^4 \cdot y} = \sqrt[4]{(2xy)^4} \cdot \sqrt[4]{y} = 2xy\sqrt[4]{y}$

6. $\left(\sqrt{3}-\sqrt{2}\right)\left(\sqrt{3}+\sqrt{2}\right)=\left(\sqrt{3}\right)^{2}-\left(\sqrt{2}\right)^{2}=3-2=1$

7. $7^{2/5}=\sqrt[5]{7^{2}}$ or $\left(\sqrt[5]{7}\right)^{2}$

8. $\left(\dfrac{x}{y}\right)^{-2/3}=\left(\dfrac{y}{x}\right)^{2/3}=\sqrt[3]{\left(\dfrac{y}{x}\right)^{2}}$ or $\left(\sqrt[3]{\dfrac{y}{x}}\right)^{2}$

9. $(-8)^{4/3}=\left(\sqrt[3]{-8}\right)^{4}=(-2)^{4}=16$

10. $36^{-3/2}=\dfrac{1}{36^{3/2}}=\dfrac{1}{\left(\sqrt{36}\right)^{3}}=\dfrac{1}{6^{3}}=\dfrac{1}{216}$

11. $\sqrt[3]{x^{4}}=x^{4/3}$

12. $\sqrt{x}\cdot\sqrt[5]{x}=x^{1/2}\cdot x^{1/5}=x^{(1/2+1/5)}=x^{7/10}$

13. $4-x\ge 0\Rightarrow -x\ge -4\Rightarrow x\le 4\Rightarrow \text{Domain}:(-\infty,4]$

14. See Figure 14.

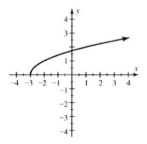

Figure 14

15. $\left(2z^{1/2}\right)^{3}=2^{3}\cdot z^{1/2\cdot 3}=8z^{3/2}$

16. $\left(\dfrac{y^{2}}{z^{3}}\right)^{-1/3}=\left(\dfrac{z^{3}}{y^{2}}\right)^{1/3}=\dfrac{z^{3\cdot 1/3}}{y^{2\cdot 1/3}}=\dfrac{z}{y^{2/3}}$

17. $\sqrt{3}\cdot\sqrt{27}=\sqrt{81}=9$

18. $\dfrac{\sqrt{y^{3}}}{\sqrt{4y}}=\sqrt{\dfrac{y^{3}}{4y}}=\sqrt{\dfrac{y^{2}}{4}}=\dfrac{\sqrt{y^{2}}}{\sqrt{4}}=\dfrac{y}{2}$

19. $7\sqrt{7}-3\sqrt{7}+\sqrt{5}=4\sqrt{7}+\sqrt{5}$

20. $7\sqrt[3]{x}-\sqrt[3]{x}=6\sqrt[3]{x}$

21. $4\sqrt{18}+\sqrt{8}=4(3)\sqrt{2}+2\sqrt{2}=(12+2)\sqrt{2}=14\sqrt{2}$

22. $\dfrac{\sqrt[3]{32}}{\sqrt[3]{4}}=\dfrac{\sqrt[3]{8\cdot 4}}{\sqrt[3]{4}}=\dfrac{2\sqrt[3]{4}}{\sqrt[3]{4}}=2$

23. (a) $\sqrt{x-2}=5\Rightarrow\left(\sqrt{x-2}\right)^{2}=5^{2}\Rightarrow x-2=25\Rightarrow x=27$

(b) $\sqrt[3]{x+1} = 2 \Rightarrow \left(\sqrt[3]{x+1}\right)^3 = 2^3 \Rightarrow x+1 = 8 \Rightarrow x = 7$

(c) $(x-1)^3 = 8 \Rightarrow \sqrt[3]{(x-1)^3} = \sqrt[3]{8} \Rightarrow x-1 = 2 \Rightarrow x = 3$

(d) $\sqrt{2x+2} = x-11 \Rightarrow \left(\sqrt{2x+2}\right)^2 = (x-11)^2 \Rightarrow 2x+2 = x^2 - 22x$

$+121 \Rightarrow x^2 - 24x + 119 = 0 \Rightarrow (x-7)(x-17) = 0$

$\Rightarrow x = 7$ or $x = 17$. The value $x = 7$ does not check. $x = 17$

24. (a) $\dfrac{2}{3\sqrt{7}} = \dfrac{2}{3\sqrt{7}} \cdot \dfrac{\sqrt{7}}{\sqrt{7}} = \dfrac{2\sqrt{7}}{21}$

(b) $\dfrac{1}{1+\sqrt{5}} = \dfrac{1}{1+\sqrt{5}} \cdot \dfrac{1-\sqrt{5}}{1-\sqrt{5}} = \dfrac{1-\sqrt{5}}{1-5} = \dfrac{1-\sqrt{5}}{-4} = \dfrac{-1+\sqrt{5}}{4}$

25. Graph $Y_1 = \sqrt{3X} - X + 1$ and $Y_2 = (X-1)^\wedge(1/3)$ in $[-5, 5, 1]$ by $[-5, 5, 1]$

Figure 25

The solution is approximately $x = 2.63$.

26. $7^2 + b^2 = 13^2 \Rightarrow 49 + b^2 = 169 \Rightarrow b^2 = 120 \Rightarrow b = \sqrt{120} \approx 10.95$

27. $d = \sqrt{\left(-1-(-3)\right)^2 + (7-5)^2} = \sqrt{2^2 + 2^2} = \sqrt{4+4} = \sqrt{8} = 2\sqrt{2}$

28. $(-5+i) + (7-20i) = (-5+7) + (1+(-20))i = 2 - 19i$

29. $(3i) - (6-5i) = (0-6) + (3-(-5))i = -6 + 8i$

30. $\left(\dfrac{1}{2} - i\right)\left(\dfrac{1}{2} + i\right) = \dfrac{1}{4} + \dfrac{1}{2}i - \dfrac{1}{2}i - i^2 = \dfrac{1}{4} - (-1) = \dfrac{5}{4}$

31. $\dfrac{2i}{5+2i} = \dfrac{2i}{5+2i} \cdot \dfrac{5-2i}{5-2i} = \dfrac{2i(5-2i)}{5^2 - 4i^2} = \dfrac{10i - 4i^2}{25+4} = \dfrac{4+10i}{29} = \dfrac{4}{29} + \dfrac{10}{29}i$

32. (a) $V = \dfrac{4}{3}\pi r^3 \Rightarrow r^3 = \dfrac{3V}{4\pi} \Rightarrow \sqrt[3]{r^3} = \sqrt[3]{\dfrac{3V}{4\pi}} \Rightarrow r = \sqrt[3]{\dfrac{3V}{4\pi}}$

(b) $r = \sqrt[3]{\dfrac{3(50)}{4\pi}} \approx 2.29$ inches

33. $27.4W^{1/3} = 30 \Rightarrow W^{1/3} = \dfrac{30}{27.4} \Rightarrow \left(W^{1/3}\right)^3 = \left(\dfrac{30}{27.4}\right)^3 \Rightarrow W = \left(\dfrac{30}{27.4}\right)^3 \approx 1.31$ lb

Chapter 7 Extended and Discovery Exercises

1. By trial and error $\dfrac{m}{n} = \dfrac{3}{2}$. Plot the data and graph $Y_1 = 0.0002X \wedge (3/2)$ in [0, 2000, 500] by [0, 20, 2]. See Figure 1.

[0, 2000, 500] by [0, 20, 2]   [0, 1000, 100] by [40,000, 60,000, 5000]

    Figure 1   Figure 4

2. (a) $k(47)^{1.12}(11)^{1.98} = 11.4 \Rightarrow k = \dfrac{11.4}{(47)^{1.12}(11)^{1.98}} \approx 0.001325$

    (b) $V = 0.001325(105)^{1.12}(20)^{1.98} \approx 91.6 \text{ ft}^3$

3. (a) $S = 15.7(154)^{0.425}(65)^{0.725} \approx 2753.963261 \approx 2754 \text{ in}^2$

    (b) It increases by a factor of $2^{0.425} \approx 1.34$.

    (c) It increases by a factor of $2^{0.725} \approx 1.65$.

4. (a) Since the segment AB is on land, the expression is $30x$.

    (b) The legs of right triangle BCD have lengths $CB = 1000 - x$ and $CD = 500$. Let $d = BD$.

    $d^2 = (1000 - x)^2 + 500^2 \Rightarrow d = \sqrt{(1000 - x)^2 + 500^2}$.

    (c) Since the segment BD is underwater, the expression is $50\sqrt{(1000 - x)^2 + 500^2}$.

    (d) The expression is $30x + 50\sqrt{(1000 - x)^2 + 500^2}$.

    (e) Graph $Y_1 = 30X + 50\sqrt{((100 - X)^2 + 500^2)}$ in [0, 1000, 100] by [40,000, 60,000, 5000]. See Figure 4.

    The minimum cost is \$50,000 when $x = 625$ feet.

Chapters 1–7 Cumulative Review Exercises

1. $S = 4\pi(3)^2 = 4\pi(9) = 36\pi$

2. $D = \{-1,\ 0,\ 1\};\ R = \{2,\ 4\}$

3. (a) $\left(\dfrac{ab^2}{b^{-1}}\right)^{-3} = \dfrac{a^{-3}b^{-6}}{b^3} = a^{-3}b^{-6-3} = a^{-3}b^{-9} = \dfrac{1}{a^3 b^9}$

    (b) $\dfrac{(x^2 y)^3}{x^2 (y^2)^{-3}} = \dfrac{x^6 y^3}{x^2 y^{-6}} = x^{6-2} y^{3-(-6)} = x^4 y^9$

(c) $(rt)^2 \left(r^2 t\right)^3 = r^2 t^2 r^6 t^3 = r^{2+6} t^{2+3} = r^8 t^5$

4. $0.00043 = 4.3 \times 10^{-4}$

5. $f(3) = \dfrac{3}{3-2} = \dfrac{3}{1} = 3$; the denominator cannot equal 0, so $x \neq 2$.

6.   All real numbers

7.   See Figure 7.   8.   See Figure 8.   9.   See Figure 9.

         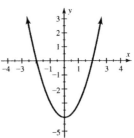

       Figure 7   Figure 8   Figure 9

(a) D: All real numbers; $R : y \geq -4$

(b) $f(-2) = (-2)^2 - 4 = 4 - 4 = 0$

(c)   The x-intercepts are -2 and 2.

(d) $x^2 - 4 = 0 \Rightarrow (x-2)(x+2) = 0 \Rightarrow x = 2$ or $x = -2$

10.   The line perpendicular to $y = -2x$ has slope $m = \dfrac{1}{2}$.

$$y - 2 = \frac{1}{2}\left(x - (-1)\right) \Rightarrow y = \frac{1}{2}x + \frac{1}{2} + 2 \Rightarrow y = \frac{1}{2}x + \frac{5}{2}$$

11. $m = \dfrac{-5 - 7}{2 - (-2)} = \dfrac{-12}{4} = -3$; $y - (-5) = -3(x - 2)$

      $\Rightarrow y = -3x + 6 - 5 \Rightarrow y = -3x + 1$; $f(x) = 1 - 3x$

12.   See Figure 12.

        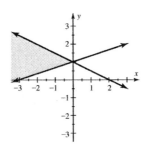

       Figure 12   Figure 18

13. $5x - (3 - x) = \dfrac{1}{2}x \Rightarrow 5x - 3 + x - \dfrac{1}{2}x = 0 \Rightarrow \dfrac{11}{2}x - 3 = 0 \Rightarrow \dfrac{11}{2}x = 3 \Rightarrow x = \dfrac{6}{11}$

14. $2x - 5 \leq 4 - x \Rightarrow 3x \leq 9 \Rightarrow x \leq 3; \, (-\infty, 3]$

15. $|x-2| \le 3 \Rightarrow x-2 \le 3$ and $x-2 \ge -3 \Rightarrow x \le 5$ and $x \ge -1$; $[-1, 5]$

16. $-1 \le 1-2x \le 6 \Rightarrow -2 \le -2x \le 5 \Rightarrow 1 \ge x \ge -\dfrac{5}{2} \Rightarrow -\dfrac{5}{2} \le x \le 1$; $\left[-\dfrac{5}{2}, 1\right]$

17. (a) Add the equations.

$$2x - y = 4$$
$$\underline{x + y = 8}$$
$$3x \quad = 12 \Rightarrow x = 4$$

$$x + y = 8 \Rightarrow 4 + y = 8 \Rightarrow y = 4.$$

The solution is $(4, 4)$.

(b) Multiply the second equation by -3 and add to the first equation.

$$3x - 4y = 2$$
$$\underline{-3x + 4y = -3}$$
$$0 = -1$$

contradiction; there are no solutions.

18. Note that $x + 2y \le 2 \Rightarrow y \le -\dfrac{1}{2}x + 1$ and $-x + 3y \ge 3 \Rightarrow y \ge \dfrac{1}{3}x + 1$. See Figure 18.

19. Add the first two equations to eliminate the variable z.

$$x + 2y - z = 6$$
$$\underline{x - 3y + z = -2}$$
$$2x - y \quad = 4$$

Add the first and third equations to eliminate the variable z.

$$x + 2y - z = 6$$
$$\underline{x + y + z = 6}$$
$$2x + 3y \quad = 12$$

Multiply this new equation by -1 and add it to the result of the first sum.

$$-2x - 3y = -12$$
$$\underline{2x - y = 4}$$
$$-4y = -8$$

$\Rightarrow y = 2$; $2x - 2 = 4 \Rightarrow 2x = 6 \Rightarrow x = 3$

Substitute $x = 3$ and $y = 2$ into the third equation to solve for z:

$3 + 2 + z = 6 \Rightarrow 5 + z = 6 \Rightarrow z = 1$. The solution is $(3, 2, 1)$.

20. $4(1 \cdot 1 - (-2) \cdot 0) - 2(2 \cdot 1 - 0 \cdot 0) + (-1)(2(-2) - 0 \cdot 1)$

$= 4(1 - 0) - 2(2 - 0) - 1(-4 - 0) = 4(1) - 2(2) - 1(-4) = 4 - 4 + 4 = 4$

21. $4x(4 - x^3) = 16x - 4x^4 = -4x^4 + 16x$

22. $(x - 4)(x + 4) = x^2 - 16$

23. $(5x+3)(x-2) = 5x^2 - 10x + 3x - 6 = 5x^2 - 7x - 6$

24. $(4x+9)^2 = (4x)^2 + 2(4x)(9) + (9)^2 = 16x^2 + 72x + 81$

25. $9x^2 - 16 = (3x-4)(3x+4)$

26. $x^2 - 4x + 4 = (x-2)(x-2) = (x-2)^2$

27. $15x^3 - 9x^2 = 3x^2(5x-3)$

28. $12x^2 - 5x - 3 = (4x-3)(3x+1)$

29. $r^3 - 1 = (r-1)(r^2 + r + 1)$

30. $x^3 - 3x^2 + 5x - 15 = x^2(x-3) + 5(x-3) = (x-3)(x^2+5)$

31. $x^2 - 3x + 2 = 0 \Rightarrow (x-2)(x-1) = 0 \Rightarrow x = 2 \text{ or } x = 1$

32. $x^3 = 4x \Rightarrow x^3 - 4x = 0 \Rightarrow x(x^2-4) = 0 \Rightarrow x(x-2)(x+2) = 0$

    $\Rightarrow x = 0 \text{ or } x = 2 \text{ or } x = -2$

33. $\dfrac{x^2+3x+2}{x-3} \div \dfrac{x+1}{2x-6} = \dfrac{(x+2)(x+1)}{x-3} \cdot \dfrac{2(x-3)}{x+1} = 2(x+2)$

34. $\dfrac{2}{x-1} + \dfrac{5}{x} = \dfrac{2}{x-1} \cdot \dfrac{x}{x} + \dfrac{5}{x} \cdot \dfrac{x-1}{x-1} = \dfrac{2x+5(x-1)}{x(x-1)} = \dfrac{2x+5x-5}{x(x-1)} = \dfrac{7x-5}{x(x-1)}$

35. $\sqrt{36x^2} = \sqrt{36} \cdot \sqrt{x^2} = 6x$

36. $\sqrt[3]{64} = 4$

37. $16^{-3/2} = (\sqrt{16})^{-3} = 4^{-3} = \dfrac{1}{4^3} = \dfrac{1}{64}$

38. $\sqrt[4]{625} = \sqrt[4]{(5)^4} = 5$

39. $\sqrt{2x} \cdot \sqrt{8x} = \sqrt{(2x)(8x)} = \sqrt{16x^2} = 4x$

40. $\sqrt{x} \cdot \sqrt[4]{x} = x^{1/2} \cdot x^{1/4} = x^{3/4} \text{ or } \sqrt[4]{x^3}$

41. $\dfrac{\sqrt[3]{16x^4}}{\sqrt[3]{2x}} = \sqrt[3]{\dfrac{16x^4}{2x}} = \sqrt[3]{8x^3} = 2x$

42. $4\sqrt{12x} - 2\sqrt{3x} = 4\sqrt{4 \cdot 3x} - 2\sqrt{3x} = 4\sqrt{4} \cdot \sqrt{3x} - 2\sqrt{3x}$

    $= 4(2)\sqrt{3x} - 2\sqrt{3x} = 8\sqrt{3x} - 2\sqrt{3x} = 6\sqrt{3x}$

43. $(2x+\sqrt{3})(x-\sqrt{3}) = 2x^2 - 2x\sqrt{3} + x\sqrt{3} - (\sqrt{3})^2$

    $= 2x^2 - x\sqrt{3} - 3$

44. The radicand must be greater than or equal to $0 \Rightarrow 1 - x \geq 0 \Rightarrow x \leq 1;\ (-\infty, 1]$

45. See Figure 45.

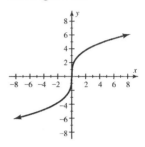

Figure 45

46. $d = \sqrt{(x_2 - x_1)^2 + (y_2 - y_1)^2} = \sqrt{(1-(-2))^2 + (2-3)^2} = \sqrt{3^2 + (-1)^2} = \sqrt{9+1} = \sqrt{10}$

47. $(1-i)(2+3i) = 2 + 3i - 2i - 3i^2 = 2 + i - 3(-1) = 2 + 3 + i = 5 + i$

48. Use the Pythagorean Theorem: $a^2 + b^2 = c^2 \Rightarrow 5^2 + 12^2 = c^2 \Rightarrow 25 + 144 = c^2 \Rightarrow 169 = c^2 \Rightarrow c = 13$

49. $2\sqrt{x+3} = x \Rightarrow \sqrt{x+3} = \dfrac{x}{2} \Rightarrow x + 3 = \left(\dfrac{x}{2}\right)^2 \Rightarrow x + 3 = \dfrac{x^2}{4}$

$\Rightarrow 4(x+3) = 4\left(\dfrac{x^2}{4}\right) \Rightarrow 4x + 12 = x^2 \Rightarrow x^2 - 4x - 12 = 0$

$\Rightarrow (x-6)(x+2) = 0 \Rightarrow x = 6\ (x = -2 \text{ does not check}).$

50. $\sqrt[3]{x-1} = 3 \Rightarrow x - 1 = 3^3 \Rightarrow x - 1 = 27 \Rightarrow x = 28$

51. $\sqrt{x} + 4 = 2\sqrt{x+5} \Rightarrow \left(\sqrt{x} + 4\right)^2 = 4(x+5) \Rightarrow x + 8\sqrt{x} + 16 = 4x + 20 \Rightarrow 8\sqrt{x} = 3x + 4 \Rightarrow 64x = (3x+4)^2$

$\Rightarrow 64x = 9x^2 + 24x + 16 \Rightarrow 9x^2 - 40x + 16 = 0 \Rightarrow (9x-4)(x-4) = 0 \Rightarrow x = \dfrac{4}{9} \text{ or } x = 4$

52. $\dfrac{1}{3}x^4 = 27 \Rightarrow x^4 = 81 \Rightarrow x = \sqrt[4]{81} \Rightarrow x = \pm 3$

53. Graph $Y_1 = (X^2 - 2)^{(1/3)} + X$ and $Y_2 = \sqrt{(X)}$ in $[-4.7, 4.7, 1]$ by $[-3.1, 3.1, 1]$. The solution is $x \approx 1.41.$

Figure 53

54. Graph $Y_1 = X - X^{\left(1/3\right)}$ and $Y_2 = \sqrt{(X+2)}$ in $[-6, 6, 1]$ by $[-4, 4, 1]$. The solution is $x \approx 4.06.$

Figure 54

Applications

55.   Water is leaving the tank at 15 gallons per minute.

56.   See Figure 56.

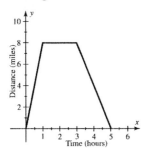

Figure 56

57.   Let x represent the amount invested at 5%. Then $0.05x + 0.04(2000 - x) = 93 \Rightarrow 0.05x + 80 - 0.04x = 93$

$\Rightarrow 0.01x = 13 \Rightarrow x = 1300$; $1300 is invested at 5% and $700 is invested at 4%.

58.   Let x represent the length of a side of the base. Then $x^2(x - 4) = 256 \Rightarrow x^3 - 4x^2 - 256 = 0$

Table $Y_1 = X^3 - 4X^2 - 256$ with TblStart $= 1$ and ΔTbl $= 1$ (not shown). $x = 8$, so the dimensions are 8 inches by 8 inches by 4 inches.

59.   5 feet 3 inches $=$ 5.25 feet; let h represent the height of the building; $\dfrac{5.25}{7.5} = \dfrac{h}{3.2}$

$\Rightarrow (5.25)(32) = 7.5h \Rightarrow 168 = 7.5h \Rightarrow h = 22.4$ feet

60.   Let x, y, z, represent the measures of the angles of the triangle from smallest to largest, respectively. The system needed is

$x + y + z = 180$
$z = x + y - 20$
$y + z = x + 90$

Substitute $z = x + y - 20$ into the third equation:

$y + x + y - 20 = x + 90 \Rightarrow 2y = 110 \Rightarrow y = 55$

Substitute $y = 55$ and $z = x + y - 20$ into the first equation:

$x + 55 + x + 55 - 20 = 180 \Rightarrow 2x + 90 = 180 \Rightarrow 2x = 90 \Rightarrow x = 45$

Then $z = x + y - 20 \Rightarrow z = 45 + 55 - 20 \Rightarrow z = 80$.

The angle measures are 45°, 55°, and 80°.

Critical Thinking Solutions for Chapter 7

Section 7.1

- $\sqrt[6]{(-2)^6} = |-2| = 2$; $\sqrt[3]{(-2)^3} = -2$; n even $\Rightarrow \sqrt[n]{x^n} = |x|$ and n odd $\Rightarrow \sqrt[n]{x^n} = x$

Section 7.4

- Since hang time increases by a factor of $\sqrt{h}$, we would need 4 times the height to double the hang time.

  $4(50) = 200$ feet

Chapter 8: Quadratic Functions and Equations

8.1: Quadratic Functions and Their Graphs

Concepts

1.   parabola

2.   the vertex

3.   axis of symmetry

4. $(0, 0)$

5.   See Figure 5. *Answers may vary.*

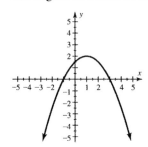

Figure 5

6. $-\dfrac{b}{2a}$

7.   narrower

8.   reflected

9. $ax^2 + bx + c$ with $a \neq 0$

10.   vertex

11. $f(-2) = 0$ and $f(0) = -4$

12. $f(-2) = 4$ and $f(2) = -4$

13. $f(-3) = -2$ and $f(1) = -2$

14. $f(-1) = -2$ and $f(2) = 1$

Graphs of Quadratic Functions

15.   The vertex is $(1,\ -2)$. The axis of symmetry is $x = 1$. The parabola opens upward.

   The graph is increasing when $x \geq 1$ and decreasing when $x \leq 1$.

16.   The vertex is $(0,\ 4)$. The axis of symmetry is $x = 0$. The parabola opens downward.

   The graph is increasing when $x \leq 0$ and decreasing when $x \geq 0$.

17.   The vertex is $(-2,\ 3)$. The axis of symmetry is $x = -2$. The parabola opens downward.

   The graph is increasing when $x \leq -2$ and decreasing when $x \geq -2$.

18.   The vertex is $(3,\ -5)$. The axis of symmetry is $x = 3$. The parabola opens upward.

   The graph is increasing when $x \geq 3$ and decreasing when $x \leq 3$.

19. (a) See Figure 19.

     (b) The vertex is (0, 0). The axis of symmetry is $x = 0$.

     (c) $f(-2) = \frac{1}{2}(-2)^2 = \frac{1}{2}(4) = 2$ and $f(3) = \frac{1}{2}(3)^2 = \frac{1}{2}(9) = 4.5$

Figure 19   Figure 20

20. (a) See Figure 20.

     (b) The vertex is (0, 0). The axis of symmetry is $x = 0$.

     (c) $f(-2) = -3(-2)^2 = -3(4) = -12$ and $f(3) = -3(3)^2 = -3(9) = -27$

21. (a) See Figure 21.

     (b) The vertex is $(0, \ -2)$. The axis of symmetry is $x = 0$.

     (c) $f(-2) = (-2)^2 - 2 = 4 - 2 = 2$ and $f(3) = (3)^2 - 2 = 9 - 2 = 7$

22. (a) See Figure 22.

     (b) The vertex is $(0, \ -1)$. The axis of symmetry is $x = 0$.

     (c) $f(-2) = (-2)^2 - 1 = 4 - 1 = 3$ and $f(3) = (3)^2 - 1 = 9 - 1 = 8$

            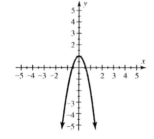

Figure 21   Figure 22   Figure 23

23. (a) See Figure 23.

     (b) The vertex is $(0, \ 1)$. The axis of symmetry is $x = 0$.

     (c) $f(-2) = -3(-2)^2 + 1 = -12 + 1 = -11$ and $f(3) = -3(3)^2 + 1 = -27 + 1 = -26$

24. (a) See Figure 24.

     (b) The vertex is $(0, \ 2)$. The axis of symmetry is $x = 0$.

     (c) $f(-2) = \frac{1}{2}(-2)^2 + 2 = 2 + 2 = 4$ and $f(3) = \frac{1}{2}(3)^2 + 2 = 4.5 + 2 = 6.5$

25. (a) See Figure 25.

(b) The vertex is $(1, 0)$. The axis of symmetry is $x = 1$.

(c) $f(-2) = ((-2) - 1)^2 = (-3)^2 = 9$ and $f(3) = ((3) - 1)^2 = (2)^2 = 4$

Figure 24

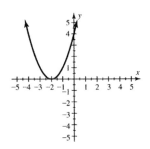

Figure 25

Figure 26

26. (a) See Figure 26.

(b) The vertex is $(-2, 0)$. The axis of symmetry is $x = -2$.

(c) $f(-2) = ((-2) + 2)^2 = (0)^2 = 0$ and $f(3) = ((3) + 2)^2 = (5)^2 = 25$

27. (a) See Figure 27.

(b) The vertex is $(-2, 0)$. The axis of symmetry is $x = -2$.

(c) $f(-2) = -(-2 + 2)^2 = -(0)^2 = 0$ and $f(3) = -(3 + 2)^2 = -(5)^2 = -25$

Figure 27

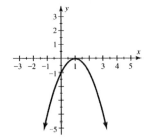

Figure 28

28. (a) See Figure 28.

(b) The vertex is $(1, 0)$. The axis of symmetry is $x = 1$.

(c) $f(-2) = -(-2 - 1)^2 = -(-3)^2 = -9$ and $f(3) = -(3 - 1)^2 = -(2)^2 = -4$

29. (a) See Figure 29.

(b) The vertex is $(-0.5, -2.25)$. The axis of symmetry is $x = -0.5$.

(c) $f(-2) = (-2)^2 + (-2) - 2 = 4 - 2 - 2 = 0$ and $f(3) = (3)^2 + (3) - 2 = 9 + 3 - 2 = 10$

30. (a) See Figure 30.

(b) The vertex is $(1, 1)$. The axis of symmetry is $x = 1$.

(c) $f(-2) = (-2)^2 - 2(-2) + 2 = 4 + 4 + 2 = 10$ and $f(3) = (3)^2 - 2(3) + 2 = 9 - 6 + 2 = 5$

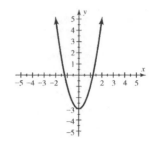

      Figure 29   Figure 30   Figure 31

31.   (a)   See Figure 31.

      (b)   The vertex is $(0,\ -3)$. The axis of symmetry is $x = 0$.

      (c) $f(-2) = 2(-2)^2 - 3 = 8 - 3 = 5$ and $f(3) = 2(3)^2 - 3 = 18 - 3 = 15$

32.   (a)   See Figure 32.

      (b)   The vertex is $(0,\ 1)$. The axis of symmetry is $x = 0$.

      (c) $f(-2) = 1 - 2(-2)^2 = 1 - 8 = -7$ and $f(3) = 1 - 2(3)^2 = 1 - 18 = -17$

33.   (a)   See Figure 33.

      (b)   The vertex is $(1,\ 1)$. The axis of symmetry is $x = 1$.

      (c) $f(-2) = 2(-2) - (-2)^2 = -4 - 4 = -8$ and $f(3) = 2(3) - (3)^2 = 6 - 9 = -3$

           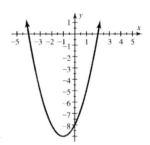

      Figure 32   Figure 33   Figure 34

34.   (a)   See Figure 34.

      (b)   The vertex is $(-1,\ -9)$. The axis of symmetry is $x = -1$.

      (c) $f(-2) = (-2)^2 + 2(-2) - 8 = 4 - 4 - 8 = -8$ and $f(3) = (3)^2 + 2(3) - 8 = 9 + 6 - 8 = 7$

35.   (a)   See Figure 35.

      (b)   The vertex is $(1,\ 1)$. The axis of symmetry is $x = 1$.

      (c) $f(-2) = -2(-2)^2 + 4(-2) - 1 = -8 - 8 - 1 = -17$ and $f(3) = -2(3)^2 + 4(3) - 1 = -18 + 12 - 1 = -7$

36.   (a)   See Figure 36.

      (b)   The vertex is $(2,\ -1)$. The axis of symmetry is $x = 2$.

      (c) $f(-2) = -\dfrac{1}{2}(-2)^2 + 2(-2) - 3 = -2 - 4 - 3 = -9$ and $f(3) = -\dfrac{1}{2}(3)^2 + 2(3) - 3 = -4.5 + 6 - 3 = -1.5$

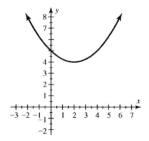

Figure 35   Figure 36   Figure 37

37.   (a) See Figure 37.

(b) The vertex is $(2,\ 4)$. The axis of symmetry is $x = 2$.

(c) $f(-2) = \dfrac{1}{4}(-2)^2 - (-2) + 5 = 1 + 2 + 5 = 8$ and $f(3) = \dfrac{1}{4}(3)^2 - (3) + 5 = 2.25 - 3 + 5 = 4.25$

38.   (a) See Figure 38.

(b) The vertex is $(-0.75,\ 5.25)$. The axis of symmetry is $x = -0.75$.

(c) $f(-2) = 3 - 6(-2) - 4(-2)^2 = 3 + 12 - 16 = -1$ and $f(3) = 3 - 6(3) - 4(3)^2 = 3 - 18 - 36 = -51$

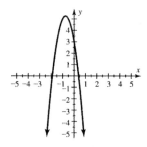

Figure 38

39. $x = -\dfrac{b}{2a} = -\dfrac{(-4)}{2(1)} = 2$, $f(2) = (2)^2 - 4(2) - 2 = 4 - 8 - 2 = -6$; The vertex is $(2, -6)$.

40. $x = -\dfrac{b}{2a} = -\dfrac{(6)}{2(2)} = -\dfrac{3}{2}$, $f\left(-\dfrac{3}{2}\right) = 2\left(-\dfrac{3}{2}\right)^2 + 6\left(-\dfrac{3}{2}\right) - 3 = \dfrac{9}{2} - 9 - 3 = -\dfrac{15}{2}$; The vertex is $\left(-\dfrac{3}{2},\ -\dfrac{15}{2}\right)$

41. $x = -\dfrac{b}{2a} = -\dfrac{(-2)}{2(-\frac{1}{3})} = -3$, $f(-3) = -\dfrac{1}{3}(-3)^2 - 2(-3) + 1 = -3 + 6 + 1 = 4$; The vertex is $(-3, 4)$.

42. $x = -\dfrac{b}{2a} = -\dfrac{(-4)}{2(1)} = 2$, $f(2) = 5 - 4(2) + (2)^2 = 5 - 8 + 4 = 1$; The vertex is $(2, 1)$.

43. $x = -\dfrac{b}{2a} = -\dfrac{(0)}{2(-2)} = 0$, $f(0) = 3 - 2(0)^2 = 3 - 0 = 3$; The vertex is $(0, 3)$.

44. $x = -\dfrac{b}{2a} = -\dfrac{(-3)}{2(\frac{1}{4})} = 6$, $f(6) = \dfrac{1}{4}(6)^2 - 3(6) - 2 = 9 - 18 - 2 = -11$; The vertex is $(6, -11)$.

45. $x = -\dfrac{b}{2a} = -\dfrac{(0.6)}{2(-0.3)} = 1$, $f(1) = -0.3(1)^2 + 0.6(1) + 1.1 = -0.3 + 0.6 + 1.1 = 1.4$; The vertex is $(1, 1.4)$.

46. $x = -\dfrac{b}{2a} = -\dfrac{(-10)}{2(20)} = \dfrac{1}{4}$, $f\left(\dfrac{1}{4}\right) = 25 - 10\left(\dfrac{1}{4}\right) + 20\left(\dfrac{1}{4}\right)^2 = \dfrac{100}{4} - \dfrac{10}{4} + \dfrac{5}{4} = \dfrac{95}{4}$; The vertex is $\left(\dfrac{1}{4},\ \dfrac{95}{4}\right)$.

47.   See Figure 47. Compared to $y = x^2$, the graph is reflected across the x-axis.

48.   See Figure 48. Compared to $y = x^2$, the graph is reflected across the x-axis and is narrower.

Figure 47

Figure 48

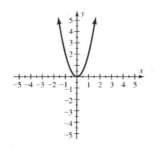

Figure 49

49.   See Figure 49. Compared to $y = x^2$, the graph is narrower.

50.   See Figure 50. Compared to $y = x^2$, the graph is narrower.

51.   See Figure 51. Compared to $y = x^2$, the graph is wider.

Figure 50

Figure 51

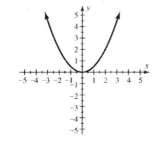

Figure 52

52.   See Figure 52. Compared to $y = x^2$, the graph is wider.

53.   See Figure 53. Compared to $y = x^2$, the graph is reflected across the x-axis and is wider.

Figure 53

Figure 54

54.   See Figure 54. Compared to $y = x^2$, the graph is reflected across the x-axis and is narrower.

55.   Because $-\dfrac{b}{2a} = -\dfrac{2}{2(1)} = -1$ and $f(-1) = (-1)^2 + 2(-1) - 1 = -2$, the vertex is $(-1,\ -2)$.

The minimum y-value on the graph is -2. The graph is increasing when $x \geq -1$ and decreasing when $x \leq -1$.

56.   Because $-\dfrac{b}{2a} = -\dfrac{6}{2(1)} = -3$ and $f(-3) = (-3)^2 + 6(-3) + 2 = -7$, the vertex is $(-3, -7)$.

The minimum y-value on the graph is -7. The graph is increasing when $x \geq -3$ and decreasing when $x \leq -3$.

57.   Because $-\dfrac{b}{2a} = -\dfrac{-5}{2(1)} = \dfrac{5}{2}$ and $f\left(\dfrac{5}{2}\right) = \left(\dfrac{5}{2}\right)^2 - 5\left(\dfrac{5}{2}\right) = -\dfrac{25}{4}$, the vertex is $\left(\dfrac{5}{2}, -\dfrac{25}{4}\right)$.

The minimum y-value on the graph is $-\dfrac{25}{4}$. The graph is increasing when $x \geq \dfrac{5}{2}$ and decreasing when $x \leq \dfrac{5}{2}$.

58.   Because $-\dfrac{b}{2a} = -\dfrac{-3}{2(1)} = \dfrac{3}{2}$ and $f\left(\dfrac{3}{2}\right) = \left(\dfrac{3}{2}\right)^2 - 3\left(\dfrac{3}{2}\right) = -\dfrac{9}{4}$, the vertex is $\left(\dfrac{3}{2}, -\dfrac{9}{4}\right)$.

The minimum y-value on the graph is $-\dfrac{9}{4}$. The graph is increasing when $x \geq \dfrac{3}{2}$ and decreasing when $x \leq \dfrac{3}{2}$.

59.   Because $-\dfrac{b}{2a} = -\dfrac{2}{2(2)} = -\dfrac{1}{2}$ and $f\left(-\dfrac{1}{2}\right) = 2\left(-\dfrac{1}{2}\right)^2 + 2\left(-\dfrac{1}{2}\right) - 3 = -\dfrac{7}{2}$, the vertex is $\left(-\dfrac{1}{2}, -\dfrac{7}{2}\right)$.

The minimum y-value on the graph is $-\dfrac{7}{2}$. The graph is increasing when $x \geq -\dfrac{1}{2}$ and decreasing when $x \leq -\dfrac{1}{2}$.

60.   Because $-\dfrac{b}{2a} = -\dfrac{-3}{2(3)} = \dfrac{1}{2}$ and $f\left(\dfrac{1}{2}\right) = 3\left(\dfrac{1}{2}\right)^2 - 3\left(\dfrac{1}{2}\right) + 7 = \dfrac{25}{4}$, the vertex is $\left(\dfrac{1}{2}, \dfrac{25}{4}\right)$.

The minimum y-value on the graph is $\dfrac{25}{4}$. The graph is increasing when $x \geq \dfrac{1}{2}$ and decreasing when $x \leq \dfrac{1}{2}$.

61.   Because $-\dfrac{b}{2a} = -\dfrac{2}{2(-1)} = 1$ and $f(1) = -(1)^2 + 2(1) + 5 = 6$, the vertex is $(1, 6)$.

The maximum y-value on the graph is 6. The graph is increasing when $x \leq 1$ and decreasing when $x \geq 1$.

62.   Because $-\dfrac{b}{2a} = -\dfrac{4}{2(-1)} = 2$ and $f(2) = -(2)^2 + 4(2) - 3 = 1$, the vertex is $(2, 1)$.

The maximum y-value on the graph is 1. The graph is increasing when $x \leq 2$ and decreasing when $x \geq 2$.

63.   Because $-\dfrac{b}{2a} = -\dfrac{4}{2(-1)} = 2$ and $f(2) = 4(2) - (2)^2 = 4$, the vertex is $(2, 4)$.

The maximum y-value on the graph is 4. The graph is increasing when $x \leq 2$ and decreasing when $x \geq 2$.

64.   Because $-\dfrac{b}{2a} = -\dfrac{6}{2(-1)} = 3$ and $f(3) = 6(3) - (3)^2 = 9$, the vertex is $(3,\ 9)$.

The maximum y-value on the graph is 9. The graph is increasing when $x \le 3$ and decreasing when $x \ge 3$.

65.   Because $-\dfrac{b}{2a} = -\dfrac{1}{2(-2)} = \dfrac{1}{4}$ and $f\left(\dfrac{1}{4}\right) = -2\left(\dfrac{1}{4}\right)^2 + \left(\dfrac{1}{4}\right) - 5 = -\dfrac{39}{8}$, the vertex is $\left(\dfrac{1}{4},\ -\dfrac{39}{8}\right)$.

The maximum y-value on the graph is $-\dfrac{39}{8}$. The graph is increasing when $x \le \dfrac{1}{4}$ and decreasing when

$x \ge \dfrac{1}{4}$.

66.   Because $-\dfrac{b}{2a} = -\dfrac{15}{2(-5)} = \dfrac{3}{2}$ and $f\left(\dfrac{3}{2}\right) = -5\left(\dfrac{3}{2}\right)^2 + 15\left(\dfrac{3}{2}\right) - 2 = \dfrac{37}{4}$, the vertex is $\left(\dfrac{3}{2}, \dfrac{37}{4}\right)$.

The maximum y-value on the graph is $\dfrac{37}{4}$. The graph is increasing when $x \le \dfrac{3}{2}$ and decreasing when $x \ge \dfrac{3}{2}$.

67.   (a) $a = \dfrac{1}{2}$, so $a > 0$ and the graph opens upward. Because $0 < |a| < 1$, the graph is wider than the graph of

$y = x^2$.

(b)   The axis of symmetry is $x = -\dfrac{b}{2a} = -\dfrac{1}{2\left(\frac{1}{2}\right)} = -\dfrac{1}{1} = -1$.

$f(-1) = \dfrac{1}{2}(-1)^2 + (-1) - \dfrac{3}{2} = \dfrac{1}{2}(1) - \dfrac{3}{2} = \dfrac{1}{2} - \dfrac{2}{2} - \dfrac{3}{2} = -\dfrac{4}{2} = -2$ so the vertex is $(-1, -2)$.

(c)   The y-intercept is $c = -\dfrac{3}{2}$. To find the x-intercepts, let $y = 0$ and solve for x:

$\dfrac{1}{2}x^2 + x - \dfrac{3}{2} = 0 \Rightarrow 2\left(\dfrac{1}{2}x^2 + x - \dfrac{3}{2}\right) = 2(0) \Rightarrow x^2 + 2x - 3 = 0 \Rightarrow (x+3)(x-1) = 0 \Rightarrow x = -3$ or $x = 1$.

(d)   See Figure 67.

Figure 67   Figure 68   Figure 69

68.   (a) $a = -1$, so $a < 0$ and the graph opens downward. Because $|a| = 1$, the graph has the same width as the

graph of $y = x^2$.

(b) The axis of symmetry is $x = -\dfrac{b}{2a} = -\dfrac{4}{2(-1)} = -\dfrac{4}{-2} = 2$. $f(2) = -(2)^2 + 4(2) + 5 = -4 + 8 + 5 = 9$ so the

vertex is (2, 9).

(c) The y-intercept is $c = 5$. To find the x-intercepts, let $y = 0$ and solve for x:

$$-x^2 + 4x + 5 = 0 \Rightarrow x^2 - 4x - 5 = 0 \Rightarrow (x-5)(x+1) = 0 \Rightarrow x = 5 \text{ or } x = -1.$$

(d) See Figure 68.

69.   (a) $a = -1$, so $a < 0$ and the graph opens downward. Because $|a| = 1$, the graph has the same width as the

graph of $y = x^2$.

(b) The axis of symmetry is $x = -\dfrac{b}{2a} = -\dfrac{2}{2(-1)} = -\dfrac{2}{-2} = 1$. $f(1) = 2(1) - 1^2 = 2 - 1 = 1$, so the vertex is (1, 1).

(c) The y-intercept is $c = 0$. To find the x-intercepts, let $y = 0$ and solve for x:

$$2x - x^2 = 0 \Rightarrow x(2 - x) = 0 \Rightarrow x = 0 \text{ and } x = 2.$$

(d) See Figure 69.

70.   (a) $a = -2$, so $a < 0$ and the graph opens downward. Because $|a| > 1$, the graph is narrower than the graph of

$y = x^2$.

(b) The axis of symmetry is $x = -\dfrac{b}{2a} = -\dfrac{1}{2(-2)} = -\dfrac{1}{-4} = \dfrac{1}{4}$.

$$f\left(\frac{1}{4}\right) = \frac{1}{4} - 2\left(\frac{1}{4}\right)^2 = \frac{1}{4} - 2\left(\frac{1}{16}\right) = \frac{4}{16} - \frac{2}{16} = \frac{2}{16} = \frac{1}{8} \text{ so the vertex is } \left(\frac{1}{4}, \frac{1}{8}\right).$$

(c) The y-intercept is $c = 0$. To find the x-intercepts, let $y = 0$ and solve for x:

$$x - 2x^2 = 0 \Rightarrow x(1 - 2x) = 0 \Rightarrow x = 0 \text{ or } x = \frac{1}{2}.$$

(d) See Figure 70.

Figure 70

Figure 71

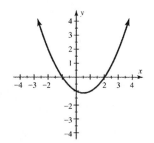

Figure 72

71.   (a) $a = 2$, so $a > 0$ and the graph opens upward. Because $|a| > 1$, the graph is narrower than the graph of

$y = x^2$.

(b) The axis of symmetry is $x = -\dfrac{b}{2a} = -\dfrac{2}{2(2)} = -\dfrac{2}{4} = -\dfrac{1}{2}$.

$f\left(-\dfrac{1}{2}\right) = 2\left(-\dfrac{1}{2}\right)^2 + 2\left(-\dfrac{1}{2}\right) - 4 = 2\left(\dfrac{1}{4}\right) - 1 - 4 = \dfrac{1}{2} - \dfrac{2}{2} - \dfrac{8}{2} = -\dfrac{9}{2}$ so the vertex is $\left(-\dfrac{1}{2}, -\dfrac{9}{2}\right)$.

(c) The y-intercept is $c = -4$. To find the x-intercepts, let $y = 0$ and solve for x:

$2x^2 + 2x - 4 = 0 \Rightarrow 2(x^2 + x - 2) = 0 \Rightarrow 2(x + 2)(x - 1) = 0 \Rightarrow x = -2$ or $x = 1$.

(d) See Figure 71.

72. (a) $a = \dfrac{1}{2}$, so $a > 0$ and the graph opens upward. Because $0 < |a| < 1$, the graph is wider than the graph of

$y = x^2$.

(b) The axis of symmetry is $x = -\dfrac{b}{2a} = -\dfrac{\left(-\frac{1}{2}\right)}{2\left(\frac{1}{2}\right)} = \dfrac{\frac{1}{2}}{1} = \dfrac{1}{2}$.

$f\left(\dfrac{1}{2}\right) = \dfrac{1}{2}\left(\dfrac{1}{2}\right)^2 - \dfrac{1}{2}\left(\dfrac{1}{2}\right) - 1 = \dfrac{1}{2}\left(\dfrac{1}{4}\right) - \dfrac{1}{4} - 1 = \dfrac{1}{8} - \dfrac{2}{8} - \dfrac{8}{8} = -\dfrac{9}{8}$ so the vertex is $\left(\dfrac{1}{2}, -\dfrac{9}{8}\right)$.

(c) The y-intercept is $c = -1$. To find the x-intercepts, let $y = 0$ and solve for x:

$\dfrac{1}{2}x^2 - \dfrac{1}{2}x - 1 = 0 \Rightarrow 2\left(\dfrac{1}{2}x^2 - \dfrac{1}{2}x - 1\right) = 2(0) \Rightarrow x^2 - x - 2 = 0 \Rightarrow (x - 2)(x + 1) = 0 \Rightarrow x = 2$ or $x = -1$.

(d) See Figure 72.

73. (a) Let x be one of the numbers, then $20 - x$ is the other number. $x(20 - x) = 20x - x^2$. The graph of

$y = -x^2 + 20x$ is a parabola that opens downward, so its vertex is the maximum point on the graph. The

x-value of the vertex is on the axis of symmetry, so $x = -\dfrac{b}{2a} = -\dfrac{20}{2(-1)} = -\dfrac{20}{-2} = 10$. So the numbers are

10 and 10.

74. Let x be one of the numbers, then $k - x$ is the other number. $x(k - x) = kx - x^2$. The graph of $y = -x^2 + kx$ is

a parabola that opens downward, so its vertex is the maximum point on the graph. The x-value of the vertex

is on the axis of symmetry, so $x = -\dfrac{b}{2a} = -\dfrac{k}{2(-1)} = \dfrac{k}{2}$. So the numbers are $\dfrac{k}{2}$ and $\dfrac{k}{2}$.

Applications

75. d. The stone's distance from the ground would increase and then decrease.

76. b. The number of people attending the movie would initially be large but would then decrease.

77. a. The temperature would first decrease but after the repair, it would increase.

78. c. The population has been increasing over the given time period.

79. (a) When the ball is hit, $t = 0$. Then $h(0) = -16(0)^2 + 64(0) + 2 = 2$ feet .

(b) Find the x-coordinate of the vertex. $-\dfrac{b}{2a} = -\dfrac{64}{2(-16)} = 2$ seconds

(c) Find the y-coordinate of the vertex. $h(2) = -16(2)^2 + 64(2) + 2 = 66$ feet .

80. (a) When the ball is hit, $t = 0$. Then $h(0) = -16(0)^2 + 128(0) = 0$ feet .

   (b) Find the x-coordinate of the vertex. $-\dfrac{b}{2a} = -\dfrac{128}{2(-16)} = 4$ seconds

   (c) Find the y-coordinate of the vertex. $h(4) = -16(4)^2 + 128(4) = 256$ feet .

81. The x-coordinate of the vertex represents the time when the ball reaches its maximum height. Here we have

   $x = \dfrac{-b}{2a} = \dfrac{-66}{2(-16)} = \dfrac{66}{32} \approx 2$ seconds. The maximum height is $h(2) = -16(2)^2 + 66(2) + 6 \approx 74$ feet.

82. The x-coordinate of the vertex represents the time when the ball reaches its maximum height.

   Here we have $x = \dfrac{-b}{2a} = -\dfrac{66}{2(-2.55)} = \dfrac{66}{5.1} \approx 12.9$ seconds.

   The maximum height is $h(12.9) = -2.55(12.9)^2 + 66(12.9) + 6 \approx 433$ feet.

   The ball goes about $433 - 74 = 359$ feet higher on the moon.

83. (a) The revenue is increasing when $x \le 50$, and it is decreasing when $x \ge 50$.

   (b) From the graph, the maximum revenue is $2500 when 50 tickets are sold.

   (c) If x represents the number of tickets sold, then $100 - x$ represents the price of one ticket.

      The total revenue is given by $f(x) = x(100 - x)$.

   (d) Since $f(x) = -x^2 + 100x$, the number of tickets that should be sold to maximize revenue is

      $-\dfrac{b}{2a} = -\dfrac{100}{2(-1)} = 50$.

      The maximum revenue is $f(50) = 50(100 - 50) = 50(50) = \$2500$.

84. (a) The price per passenger for x passengers is $300 - 1.50x$. The formula is $f(x) = x(300 - 1.50x)$.

   (b) Since $f(x) = -1.50x^2 + 300x$, $x = -\dfrac{b}{2a} = -\dfrac{300}{2(-1.5)} = 100$, $f(100) = 100(300 - 1.50(100)) = 15{,}000$.

      The maximum revenue is $15,000 when 100 tickets are sold.

85. Because there are 1200 feet of fence and the width of the enclosure is x, the length is given by $1200 - 2x$.

   The area of the enclosure is $A(x) = x(1200 - 2x)$ or $A(x) = -2x^2 + 1200x$. The value of x that will maximize

   the area is the x-coordinate of the vertex, $-\dfrac{b}{2a} = -\dfrac{1200}{2(-2)} = 300$. Thus the width is 300 feet and the length is

   $1200 - 2(300) = 1200 - 600 = 600$ feet . The enclosure measures 300 feet by 600 feet.

86. (a) The other two sides have length $\dfrac{1}{2}(60 - 2x) = 30 - x$. The formula is $f(x) = x(30 - x)$.

(b) The function is $f(x) = -x^2 + 30x$. Since the x-coordinate of the vertex is $x = \dfrac{-b}{2a} = \dfrac{-30}{2(-1)} = 15$, one side

has length 15 feet. The other side has length $30 - 15 = 15$ feet. The maximum area is $15(15) = 225 \text{ ft}^2$

when the pen has dimensions 15×15 feet.

87. (a) Graph $Y_1 = -0.095X^2 + 5.4X - 52.2$ in [20, 40, 5] by [0, 30, 5]. See Figure 87a.

(b) Since the x-coordinate of the vertex is $x \approx 28.4$, the temperature resulting in the greatest height for the

melon seedling is about 28.4°C. See Figure 87b.

(c) $x = -\dfrac{b}{2a} = -\dfrac{5.4}{2(-0.095)} \approx 28.4°C$

[20, 40, 5] by [0, 30, 5]   [20, 40, 5] by [0, 30, 5]

Figure 87a   Figure 87b

88. (a) The value of x that represents the year when games were longest is the x-coordinate of the vertex,

$-\dfrac{b}{2a} = -\dfrac{8000}{2(-2)} = 2000$. The year with the longest games was 2000.

(b) $L(2000) = -2(2000)^2 + 8000(2000) - 7,999,820 = 180$ minutes

89. $S(8) = -0.227(8)^2 + 8.155(8) - 8.8 \approx 42$ inches

90. $S(12) = -0.227(12)^2 + 8.155(12) - 8.8 \approx 56$ inches

8.2: Parabolas and Modeling

Concepts

1. $x^2 + 2$

2. $(x-2)^2$

3. $(1, 2)$

4. $(-1, -2)$

5. $f(x) = ax^2 + bx + c$ or $f(x) = a(x-h)^2 + k$

6. $y = a(x-h)^2 + k$; (h, k)

7. downward

8. $-\dfrac{b}{2a}$

Graphs of Parabolas

9.   (a)   The vertex form of the function is $f(x) = (x-0)^2 + (-4)$. See Figure 9.

(b)   The vertex is $(0, -4)$.

(c)   Compared to the graph of $y = x^2$, the graph is shifted down 4 units.

10.   (a)   The vertex form of the function is $f(x) = (x-0)^2 + (-1)$. See Figure 10.

(b)   The vertex is $(0, -1)$.

(c)   Compared to the graph of $y = x^2$, the graph is shifted down 1 unit.

Figure 9

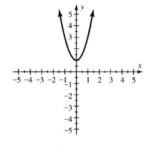

Figure 10

Figure 11

11.   (a)   The vertex form of the function is $f(x) = 2(x-0)^2 + 1$. See Figure 11.

(b)   The vertex is $(0, 1)$.

(c)   Compared to the graph of $y = x^2$, the graph is narrower and is shifted up 1 unit.

12.   (a)   The vertex form of the function is $f(x) = \frac{1}{2}(x-0)^2 + 1$. See Figure 12.

(b)   The vertex is $(0, 1)$.

(c)   Compared to the graph of $y = x^2$, the graph is wider and is shifted up 1 unit.

13.   (a)   The vertex form of the function is $f(x) = (x-3)^2 + 0$. See Figure 13.

(b)   The vertex is $(3, 0)$.

(c)   Compared to the graph of $y = x^2$, the graph is shifted right 3 units.

Figure 12

Figure 13

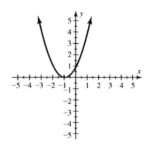

Figure 14

14.   (a)   The vertex form of the function is $f(x) = (x-(-1))^2 + 0$. See Figure 14.

(b)   The vertex is $(-1, 0)$.

(c) Compared to the graph of $y = x^2$, the graph is shifted left 1 unit.

15. (a) The vertex form of the function is $f(x) = -(x-0)^2 + 0$. See Figure 15.

    (b) The vertex is $(0, 0)$.

    (c) Compared to the graph of $y = x^2$, the graph is reflected across the *x*-axis.

16. (a) The vertex form of the function is $f(x) = -(x-(-2))^2 + 0$. See Figure 16.

    (b) The vertex is $(-2, 0)$.

    (c) Compared to the graph of $y = x^2$, the graph is reflected across the *x*-axis and shifted left 2 units.

Figure 15

Figure 16

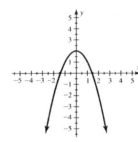

Figure 17

17. (a) The vertex form of the function is $f(x) = -(x-0)^2 + 2$. See Figure 17.

    (b) The vertex is $(0, 2)$.

    (c) Compared to the graph of $y = x^2$, the graph is reflected across the *x*-axis and shifted up 2 units.

18. (a) The vertex form of the function is $f(x) = (x-1)^2 + 0$. See Figure 18.

    (b) The vertex is $(1, 0)$.

    (c) Compared to the graph of $y = x^2$, the graph is shifted right 1 unit.

19. (a) The vertex form of the function is $f(x) = (x-(-2))^2 + 0$. See Figure 19.

    (b) The vertex is $(-2, 0)$.

    (c) Compared to the graph of $y = x^2$, the graph is shifted left 2 units.

Figure 18

Figure 19

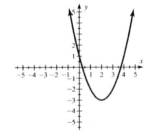

Figure 20

20. (a) The vertex form of the function is $f(x) = (x-2)^2 + (-3)$. See Figure 20.

    (b) The vertex is $(2, -3)$.

(c) Compared to the graph of $y = x^2$, the graph is shifted right 2 units and down 3 units.

21. (a) The vertex form of the function is $f(x) = (x-(-1))^2 +(-2)$. See Figure 21.

   (b) The vertex is $(-1, -2)$.

   (c) Compared to the graph of $y = x^2$, the graph is shifted left 1 unit and down 2 units.

22. (a) The vertex form of the function is $f(x) = (x-3)^2 +1$. See Figure 22.

   (b) The vertex is $(3, 1)$.

   (c) Compared to the graph of $y = x^2$, the graph is shifted right 3 units and up 1 unit.

Figure 21

Figure 22

Figure 23

23. (a) The vertex form of the function is $f(x) = (x-1)^2 +2$. See Figure 23.

   (b) The vertex is $(1, 2)$.

   (c) Compared to the graph of $y = x^2$, the graph is shifted right 1 unit and up 2 units.

24. (a) The vertex form of the function is $f(x) = \dfrac{1}{2}(x-(-3))^2 +(-3)$. See Figure 24.

   (b) The vertex is $(-3, -3)$.

   (c) Compared to the graph of $y = x^2$, the graph is wider, shifted left 3 units and down 3 units.

25. (a) The vertex form of the function is $f(x) = 2(x-5)^2 +(-4)$. See Figure 25.

   (b) The vertex is $(5, -4)$.

   (c) Compared to the graph of $y = x^2$, the graph is narrower, shifted right 5 units and down 4 units.

Figure 24

Figure 25

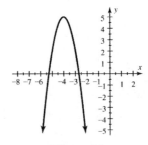
Figure 26

26. (a) The vertex form of the function is $f(x) = -3(x-(-4))^2 +5$. See Figure 26.

(b) The vertex is $(-4, 5)$.

(c) Compared to the graph of $y = x^2$, the graph is narrower, reflected across the x-axis, left 4 units and up 5 units.

27. (a) The vertex form of the function is $f(x) = -\dfrac{1}{2}(x - (-3))^2 + 1$. See Figure 27.

(b) The vertex is $(-3, 1)$.

(c) Compared to the graph of $y = x^2$, the graph is wider, reflected across the x-axis, left 3 units and up 1 unit.

Figure 27

Figure 28

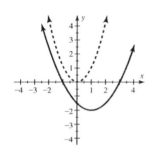

Figure 29

28. (a) The vertex form of the function is $f(x) = 2(x - 5)^2 + 10$. See Figure 28.

(b) The vertex is $(5, 10)$.

(c) Compared to the graph of $y = x^2$, the graph is narrower, shifted right 5 units and up 10 units.

29. The graph of $f(x)$ is the graph of $y = x^2$ translated 1 unit right and 2 units downward. The graph of $f(x)$ is wider. See Figure 29.

30. The graph of $f(x)$ is the graph of $y = x^2$ translated 2 units left and 1 unit downward. The graph of $f(x)$ is narrower. See Figure 30.

Figure 30

Figure 31

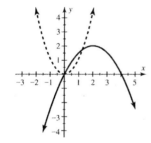

Figure 32

31. The graph of $f(x)$ is the graph of $y = x^2$ translated 1 unit left and 3 units upward. The graph of $f(x)$ opens downward and is narrower. See Figure 31.

32. The graph of $f(x)$ is the graph of $y = x^2$ translated 2 units right and 2 units upward. The graph of $f(x)$ opens downward and is wider. See Figure 32.

33. See Figure 33.

[–20, 20, 2] by [–20, 20, 2]   [–10, 20, 2] by [–100, 100, 10]

Figure 33   Figure 34

34.   See Figure 34.

Vertex Form

35.   Since $h = 3$, $k = 4$ and $a = 3$, the equation is $y = 3(x-3)^2 + 4$. Expand to obtain the other form:

$$y = 3(x^2 - 6x + 9) + 4 \Rightarrow y = 3x^2 - 18x + 27 + 4 \Rightarrow y = 3x^2 - 18x + 31$$

36.   Since $h = -1$, $k = 3$ and $a = -5$, the equation is $y = -5(x+1)^2 + 3$. Expand to obtain the other form:

$$y = -5(x^2 + 2x + 1) + 3 \Rightarrow y = -5x^2 - 10x - 5 + 3 \Rightarrow y = -5x^2 - 10x - 2$$

37.   Since $h = 5$, $k = -2$ and $a = -\dfrac{1}{2}$, the equation is $y = -\dfrac{1}{2}(x-5)^2 - 2$. Expand to obtain the other form:

$$y = -\frac{1}{2}(x^2 - 10x + 25) - 2 \Rightarrow y = -\frac{1}{2}x^2 + 5x - \frac{25}{2} - 2 \Rightarrow y = -\frac{1}{2}x^2 + 5x - \frac{29}{2}$$

38.   Since $h = -2$, $k = -6$ and $a = \dfrac{3}{4}$, the equation is $y = \dfrac{3}{4}(x+2)^2 - 6$. Expand to obtain the other form:

$$y = \frac{3}{4}(x^2 + 4x + 4) - 6 \Rightarrow y = \frac{3}{4}x^2 + 3x + 3 - 6 \Rightarrow y = \frac{3}{4}x^2 + 3x - 3$$

39.   Since $h = 1$, $k = 2$ and $a = 1$, the equation is $y = (x-1)^2 + 2$.

40.   Since $h = -1$, $k = -2$ and $a = -1$, the equation is $y = -(x+1)^2 - 2$.

41.   Since $h = 0$, $k = -3$ and $a = -1$, the equation is $y = -(x-0)^2 - 3$ or $y = -x^2 - 3$.

42.   Since $h = 5$, $k = -4$ and $a = 1$, the equation is $y = (x-5)^2 - 4$.

43.   Since $h = 0$, $k = -3$ and $a = 1$, the equation is $y = (x-0)^2 - 3$ or $y = x^2 - 3$.

44.   Since $h = 2$, $k = -3$ and $a = 1$, the equation is $y = (x-2)^2 - 3$.

45.   Since $h = -1$, $k = 2$ and $a = -1$, the equation is $y = -(x+1)^2 + 2$.

46.   Since $h = -3$, $k = -1$ and $a = -1$, the equation is $y = -(x+3)^2 - 1$.

47. $y = x^2 + 2x - 3 \Rightarrow y = (x^2 + 2x + 1) - 3 - 1 \Rightarrow y = (x+1)^2 - 4$. The vertex is $(-1, \ -4)$.

48. $y = x^2 + 4x + 1 \Rightarrow y = (x^2 + 4x + 4) + 1 - 4 \Rightarrow y = (x+2)^2 - 3$. The vertex is $(-2, \ -3)$.

49. $y = x^2 - 4x + 5 \Rightarrow y = (x^2 - 4x + 4) + 5 - 4 \Rightarrow y = (x-2)^2 + 1$. The vertex is $(2, 1)$.

50. $y = x^2 - 8x + 10 \Rightarrow y = (x^2 - 8x + 16) + 10 - 16 \Rightarrow y = (x-4)^2 - 6$. The vertex is $(4, \ -6)$.

51. $y = x^2 + 3x - 2 \Rightarrow y = \left(x^2 + 3x + \dfrac{9}{4}\right) - 2 - \dfrac{9}{4} \Rightarrow y = \left(x + \dfrac{3}{2}\right)^2 - \dfrac{17}{4}$. The vertex is $\left(-\dfrac{3}{2}, \ -\dfrac{17}{4}\right)$.

52. $y = x^2 + 5x - 4 \Rightarrow y = \left(x^2 + 5x + \dfrac{25}{4}\right) - 4 - \dfrac{25}{4} \Rightarrow y = \left(x + \dfrac{5}{2}\right)^2 - \dfrac{41}{4}$. The vertex is $\left(-\dfrac{5}{2}, \ -\dfrac{41}{4}\right)$.

53. $y = x^2 - 7x + 1 \Rightarrow y = \left(x^2 - 7x + \dfrac{49}{4}\right) + 1 - \dfrac{49}{4} \Rightarrow y = \left(x - \dfrac{7}{2}\right)^2 - \dfrac{45}{4}$. The vertex is $\left(\dfrac{7}{2}, \ -\dfrac{45}{4}\right)$.

54. $y = x^2 - 3x + 5 \Rightarrow y = \left(x^2 - 3x + \dfrac{9}{4}\right) + 5 - \dfrac{9}{4} \Rightarrow y = \left(x - \dfrac{3}{2}\right)^2 + \dfrac{11}{4}$. The vertex is $\left(\dfrac{3}{2}, \dfrac{11}{4}\right)$.

55. $y = 3x^2 + 6x - 1 \Rightarrow y = 3(x^2 + 2x + 1) - 1 - 3 \Rightarrow y = 3(x + 1)^2 - 4$. The vertex is $(-1, \ -4)$.

56. $y = 2x^2 + 4x - 9 \Rightarrow y = 2(x^2 + 2x + 1) - 9 - 2 \Rightarrow y = 2(x + 1)^2 - 11$. The vertex is $(-1, \ -11)$.

57. $y = 2x^2 - 3x \Rightarrow y = 2\left(x^2 - \dfrac{3}{2}x + \dfrac{9}{16}\right) - \dfrac{9}{8} \Rightarrow y = 2\left(x - \dfrac{3}{4}\right)^2 - \dfrac{9}{8}$. The vertex is $\left(\dfrac{3}{4}, \ -\dfrac{9}{8}\right)$.

58. $y = 3x^2 - 7x \Rightarrow y = 3\left(x^2 - \dfrac{7}{3}x + \dfrac{49}{36}\right) - \dfrac{49}{12} \Rightarrow y = 3\left(x - \dfrac{7}{6}\right)^2 - \dfrac{49}{12}$. The vertex is $\left(\dfrac{7}{6}, \ -\dfrac{49}{12}\right)$.

59. $y = -2x^2 - 8x + 5 \Rightarrow y = -2(x^2 + 4x + 4) + 5 + 8 \Rightarrow y = -2(x + 2)^2 + 13$. The vertex is $(-2, \ 13)$.

60. $y = -3x^2 + 6x + 1 \Rightarrow y = -3(x^2 - 2x + 1) + 1 + 3 \Rightarrow y = -3(x - 1)^2 + 4$. The vertex is $(1, 4)$.

Modeling Data

61. Since $y = 2$ when $x = 1$, $2 = a(1)^2 \Rightarrow 2 = 1a \Rightarrow a = 2$.

62. Since $y = 6$ when $x = -2$, $6 = a(-2)^2 \Rightarrow 6 = 4a \Rightarrow a = \dfrac{3}{2}$.

63. Since $y = 1.2$ when $x = 2$, $1.2 = a(2)^2 \Rightarrow 1.2 = 4a \Rightarrow a = 0.3$.

64. Since $y = 17.5$ when $x = 5$, $17.5 = a(5)^2 \Rightarrow 17.5 = 25a \Rightarrow a = 0.7$.

65. A scatterplot of the data (not shown) indicates that the data point $(1, -3)$ is the vertex of the parabola. The function has the form $f(x) = a(x - 1)^2 - 3$. By trial and error, $a = 2$. Thus $f(x) = 2(x - 1)^2 - 3$.

66. A scatterplot of the data (not shown) indicates that the data point $(-2, 5)$ is the vertex of the parabola. The function has the form $f(x) = a(x + 2)^2 + 5$. By trial and error, $a = -3$. Thus $f(x) = -3(x + 2)^2 + 5$.

67. A scatterplot of the data (not shown) indicates that the data point $(1980, 6)$ is the vertex of the parabola. The function has the form $f(x) = a(x - 1980)^2 + 6$. By trial and error, $a = 0.5$. So

   $f(x) = 0.5(x - 1980)^2 + 6$.

68. A scatterplot of the data (not shown) indicates that the data point $(1990, 10)$ is the vertex of the parabola.

The function has the form $f(x) = a(x-1990)^2 + 10$. By trial and error, $a = 2$. Thus

$$f(x) = 2(x-1990)^2 + 10.$$

69.   (a) See Figure 69.

      (b) Since $D = 12$ when $x = 12$, we have $12 = a(12)^2 \Rightarrow 12 = 144a \Rightarrow a = \dfrac{12}{144} \Rightarrow a = \dfrac{1}{12}$.

          The function is $D(x) = \dfrac{1}{12}x^2$.

            Figure 69   Figure 70

70.   (a) See Figure 64.

      (b) The scatterplot of the data indicates that the data point (1996, 1) is the vertex of the parabola. The

          function has the form $C(x) = a(x-1996)^2 + 1$. By trial and error, $a \approx 0.65$. So

          $C(x) = 0.65(x-1996)^2 + 1$.

71.   (a) Graph the data (not shown) to see that the data point (1982, 1) is near the vertex of a parabola. Graph

          $Y_1 = (X-1982) \wedge 2 + 1$ to see if it is a reasonable model. A better model is

          $f(x) = 2(x-1982)^2 + 1$. *Answers may vary.*

      (b) Using the model, $f(1992) = 2(1992-1982)^2 + 1 = 2(10)^2 + 1 = 2(100) + 1 = 201$. The model predicts 201

          thousand deaths in 1992, which is close to the actual value of 202 thousand. *Answers may vary.*

72.   (a) Graph the data (not shown) to see that the data point (1980, 376) is near the vertex of a parabola. Graph

          $Y_1 = (X-1980) \wedge 2 + 376$ to see if it is a reasonable model. A better model in

          $f(x) = 1.7(x-1980)^2 + 376$. *Answers may vary.*

      (b) Using the model,

          $f(1990) = 1.7(1990-1980)^2 + 376 = 1.7(10)^2 + 376 = 1.7(100) + 376 = 170 + 376 = 546$. The model

          predicts 546 thousand students in 1990, which is close to the actual value of 541 thousand. *Answers may*

          vary.

Checking Basic Concepts for Sections 8.1 & 8.2

1.   (a) See Figure 1a. The vertex is $(0, -2)$, and the axis of symmetry is $x = 0$.

      (b) See Figure 1b. The vertex is $(1, -3)$, and the axis of symmetry is $x = 1$.

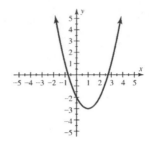

Figure 1a   Figure 1b

2.   The graph of y_1 opens upward whereas y_2 opens downward. Also, y_1 is narrower than y_2.

3.   Because $-\dfrac{b}{2a} = -\dfrac{12}{2(-3)} = 2$ and $f(2) = -3(2)^2 + 12(2) - 5 = 7$, the vertex is $(2, 7)$.

The maximum y-value on the graph is 7. The graph is increasing when $x \le 2$ and decreasing when $x \ge 2$.

4.   (a) See Figure 4a. Compared to the graph of $y = x^2$, the graph is shifted right 1 unit and up 2 units.

(b) See Figure 4b. Compared to the graph of $y = x^2$, the graph is reflected across the x-axis and left 3 units.

Figure 4a   Figure 4b

5.   (a) $y = x^2 + 14x - 7 \Rightarrow y = (x^2 + 14x + 49) - 7 - 49 \Rightarrow y = (x + 7)^2 - 56$.

(b) $y = 4x^2 + 8x - 2 \Rightarrow y = 4(x^2 + 2x + 1) - 2 - 4 \Rightarrow y = 4(x + 1)^2 - 6$.

8.3: Quadratic Equations

Concepts

1. $x^2 + 3x - 2 = 0$; *Answers may vary.* A quadratic equation can have 0, 1 or 2 solutions.

2.   Nonlinear

3.   Factoring, square root property, completing the square

4.   See Figure 4. *Answers may vary.*

5.   See Figure 5. *Answers may vary.*

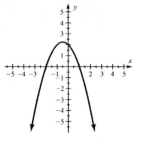

Figure 4   Figure 5

6.   The equation has two solutions. The solutions are the *x*-intercepts.

7. $x = \pm 8$; the square root property.

8. $\left(\dfrac{b}{2}\right)^2$

9.   Yes

10.   Yes

11.   No, there is no x^2 term.

12.   No, the degree of this polynomial is 3.

13.   Yes

14.   Yes

15.   No, the term $\sqrt{x}$ is not allowed in a quadratic equation.

16.   No, the variable *x* is located in the denominator.

17.   (a) $1 \pm \sqrt{7} \approx 1 \pm 2.65 = 3.65 \text{ or } -1.65$

      (b) $-2 \pm \sqrt{11} \approx -2 \pm 3.32 = 1.32 \text{ or } -5.32$

18.   (a) $\pm \dfrac{\sqrt{3}}{2} \approx \pm 0.87$

      (b) $\pm \dfrac{2\sqrt{5}}{7} \approx \pm 0.64$

19.   (a) $\dfrac{3 \pm \sqrt{13}}{5} \approx \dfrac{3 \pm 3.61}{5} = \dfrac{6.61}{5} \text{ or } -\dfrac{0.61}{5} \approx 1.32 \text{ or } -0.12$

      (b) $\dfrac{-5 \pm \sqrt{6}}{9} \approx \dfrac{-5 \pm 2.45}{9} = \dfrac{-2.55}{9} \text{ or } \dfrac{-7.45}{9} \approx -0.28 \text{ or } -0.83$

20.   (a) $\dfrac{2}{5} \pm \dfrac{\sqrt{5}}{5} \approx 0.4 \pm 0.45 = 0.85 \text{ or } -0.05$

      (b) $-\dfrac{3}{7} \pm \dfrac{\sqrt{3}}{7} \approx -\dfrac{3}{7} \pm 0.25 \approx -0.18 \text{ or } -0.68$

Solving Quadratic Equations

21.   –2, 1

22.   –2

23. No real solutions

24. $-3, 0$

25. $-2, 3$

26. $-6, 4$

27. -0.5

28. $-3, 1$

29. $x^2 - 4x - 5 = 0 \Rightarrow (x+1)(x-5) = 0 \Rightarrow x+1 = 0 \text{ or } x-5 = 0 \Rightarrow x = -1 \text{ or } 5$

    A graph of $y = x^2 - 4x - 5$ (not shown) intersects the x-axis at -1 and 5.

30. $x^2 - x - 6 = 0 \Rightarrow (x+2)(x-3) = 0 \Rightarrow x+2 = 0 \text{ or } x-3 = 0 \Rightarrow x = -2 \text{ or } 3$

    A graph of $y = x^2 - x - 6$ (not shown) intersects the x-axis at -2 and 3.

31. $x^2 + 2x = 3 \Rightarrow x^2 + 2x - 3 = 0 \Rightarrow (x+3)(x-1) = 0 \Rightarrow x+3 = 0 \text{ or } x-1 = 0 \Rightarrow x = -3 \text{ or } 1$

    A graph of $y = x^2 + 2x - 3$ (not shown) intersects the x-axis at -3 and 1.

32. $x^2 + 4x = 5 \Rightarrow x^2 + 4x - 5 = 0 \Rightarrow (x+5)(x-1) = 0 \Rightarrow x+5 = 0 \text{ or } x-1 = 0 \Rightarrow x = -5 \text{ or } 1$

    A graph of $y = x^2 + 4x - 5$ (not shown) intersects the x-axis at -5 and 1.

33. $x^2 = 9 \Rightarrow x^2 - 9 = 0 \Rightarrow (x+3)(x-3) = 0 \Rightarrow x+3 = 0 \text{ or } x-3 = 0 \Rightarrow x = -3 \text{ or } 3$

    A graph of $y = x^2 - 9$ (not shown) intersects the x-axis at -3 and 3.

34. $x^2 = 4 \Rightarrow x^2 - 4 = 0 \Rightarrow (x+2)(x-2) = 0 \Rightarrow x+2 = 0 \text{ or } x-2 = 0 \Rightarrow x = -2 \text{ or } 2$

    A graph of $y = x^2 - 4$ (not shown) intersects the x-axis at -2 and 2.

35. $4x^2 - 4x - 3 = 0 \Rightarrow (2x+1)(2x-3) = 0 \Rightarrow 2x+1 = 0 \text{ or } 2x-3 = 0 \Rightarrow x = -\dfrac{1}{2} \text{ or } \dfrac{3}{2}$

    A graph of $y = 4x^2 - 4x - 3$ (not shown) intersects the x-axis at $-\dfrac{1}{2}$ and $\dfrac{3}{2}$.

36. $2x^2 + x = 1 \Rightarrow 2x^2 + x - 1 = 0 \Rightarrow (x+1)(2x-1) = 0 \Rightarrow x+1 = 0 \text{ or } 2x-1 = 0 \Rightarrow x = -1 \text{ or } \dfrac{1}{2}$

    A graph of $y = 2x^2 + x - 1$ (not shown) intersects the x-axis at -1 and $\dfrac{1}{2}$.

37. $x^2 + 2x = -1 \Rightarrow x^2 + 2x + 1 = 0 \Rightarrow (x+1)(x+1) = 0 \Rightarrow x+1 = 0 \Rightarrow x = -1$. A graph of $y = x^2 + 2x + 1$ (not shown) intersects the x-axis at -1.

38. $4x^2 - 4x + 1 = 0 \Rightarrow (2x-1)(2x-1) = 0 \Rightarrow 2x-1 = 0 \Rightarrow x = \dfrac{1}{2}$. A graph of $y = 4x^2 - 4x + 1$ (not shown) intersects the x-axis at $\dfrac{1}{2}$.

39. $x^2 + 2 = 0$ has no real solutions. A graph of $y = x^2 + 2$ (not shown) does not intersect the x-axis.

40. $-4x^2 - 1 = 2 \Rightarrow 4x^2 + 3 = 0$ has no real solutions. A graph of $y = 4x^2 + 3$ does not intersect the x-axis.

41. $x^2 + 2x - 35 = 0 \Rightarrow (x+7)(x-5) = 0 \Rightarrow$ Either $x + 7 = 0 \Rightarrow x = -7$ or $x - 5 = 0 \Rightarrow x = 5$

42. $2x^2 - 7x + 3 = 0 \Rightarrow (2x-1)(x-3) = 0 \Rightarrow$ Either $2x - 1 = 0 \Rightarrow x = \dfrac{1}{2}$ or $x - 3 = 0 \Rightarrow x = 3$

43. $6x^2 - x - 1 = 0 \Rightarrow (3x+1)(2x-1) = 0 \Rightarrow$ Either $3x + 1 = 0 \Rightarrow x = -\dfrac{1}{3}$ or $2x - 1 = 0 \Rightarrow x = \dfrac{1}{2}$

44. $x^2 + 7x + 6 = 0 \Rightarrow (x+6)(x+1) = 0 \Rightarrow$ Either $x + 6 = 0 \Rightarrow x = -6$ or $x + 1 = 0 \Rightarrow x = -1$

45. $2x^2 - 5x + 3 = 0 \Rightarrow (x-1)(2x-3) = 0 \Rightarrow$ Either $x - 1 = 0 \Rightarrow x = 1$ or $2x - 3 = 0 \Rightarrow x = \dfrac{3}{2}$

46. $6x^2 - x - 15 = 0 \Rightarrow (2x+3)(3x-5) = 0 \Rightarrow$ Either $2x + 3 = 0 \Rightarrow x = -\dfrac{3}{2}$ or $3x - 5 = 0 \Rightarrow x = \dfrac{5}{3}$

47. $25x^2 - 350 = 125x \Rightarrow 25x^2 - 125x - 350 = 0 \Rightarrow 25(x^2 - 5x - 14) = 0 \Rightarrow 25(x-7)(x+2) = 0$

    $\Rightarrow$ Either $x - 7 = 0 \Rightarrow x = 7$ or $x + 2 = 0 \Rightarrow x = -2$

48. $20x^2 + 150 = 130x \Rightarrow 20x^2 - 130x + 150 = 0 \Rightarrow 10(2x^2 - 13x + 15) = 0 \Rightarrow 10(2x-3)(x-5) = 0$

    $\Rightarrow$ Either $2x - 3 = 0 \Rightarrow x = \dfrac{3}{2}$ or $x - 5 = 0 \Rightarrow x = 5$

49. $10x^2 - 27x + 18 = 0 \Rightarrow (5x-6)(2x-3) = 0 \Rightarrow$ Either $5x - 6 = 0 \Rightarrow x = \dfrac{6}{5}$ or $2x - 3 = 0 \Rightarrow x = \dfrac{3}{2}$

50. $45x^2 + 15x - 10 = 0 \Rightarrow 5(3x+2)(3x-1) = 0 \Rightarrow$ Either $3x + 2 = 0 \Rightarrow x = -\dfrac{2}{3}$ or $3x - 1 = 0 \Rightarrow x = \dfrac{1}{3}$

51. $x^2 = 144 \Rightarrow x = \pm\sqrt{144} \Rightarrow x = \pm 12$

52. $4x^2 - 5 = 0 \Rightarrow 4x^2 = 5 \Rightarrow x^2 = \dfrac{5}{4} \Rightarrow x = \pm\sqrt{\dfrac{5}{4}} \Rightarrow x = \pm\dfrac{\sqrt{5}}{2}$

53. $5x^2 - 64 = 0 \Rightarrow 5x^2 = 64 \Rightarrow x^2 = \dfrac{64}{5} \Rightarrow x = \pm\sqrt{\dfrac{64}{5}} \Rightarrow x = \pm\dfrac{8}{\sqrt{5}}$ or $\pm\dfrac{8\sqrt{5}}{5}$

54. $3x^2 = 7 \Rightarrow x^2 = \dfrac{7}{3} \Rightarrow x = \pm\sqrt{\dfrac{7}{3}}$ or $\pm\dfrac{\sqrt{21}}{3}$

55. $(x+1)^2 = 25 \Rightarrow x + 1 = \pm\sqrt{25} \Rightarrow x + 1 = \pm 5 \Rightarrow x = -1 \pm 5 \Rightarrow x = -6$ or 4

56. $(x+4)^2 = 9 \Rightarrow x + 4 = \pm\sqrt{9} \Rightarrow x + 4 = \pm 3 \Rightarrow x = -4 \pm 3 \Rightarrow x = -7$ or -1

57. $(x-1)^2 = 64 \Rightarrow x - 1 = \pm\sqrt{64} \Rightarrow x - 1 = \pm 8 \Rightarrow x = 1 \pm 8 \Rightarrow x = -7$ or 9

58. $(x-3)^2 = 0 \Rightarrow x - 3 = \pm\sqrt{0} \Rightarrow x - 3 = 0 \Rightarrow x = 3$

59. $(2x-1)^2 = 5 \Rightarrow 2x - 1 = \pm\sqrt{5} \Rightarrow 2x = 1 \pm \sqrt{5} \Rightarrow x = \dfrac{1 \pm \sqrt{5}}{2}$

60. $(5x+3)^2 = 7 \Rightarrow 5x+3 = \pm\sqrt{7} \Rightarrow 5x = -3 \pm \sqrt{7} \Rightarrow x = \dfrac{-3 \pm \sqrt{7}}{5}$

61. $10(x-5)^2 = 50 \Rightarrow (x-5)^2 = 5 \Rightarrow x-5 = \pm\sqrt{5} \Rightarrow x = 5 \pm \sqrt{5}$

62. $7(3x+1)^2 = 14 \Rightarrow (3x+1)^2 = 2 \Rightarrow 3x+1 = \pm\sqrt{2} \Rightarrow 3x = -1 \pm \sqrt{2} \Rightarrow x = \dfrac{-1 \pm \sqrt{2}}{3}$

Completing the Square

63. $\left(\dfrac{4}{2}\right)^2 = 2^2 = 4$

64. $\left(\dfrac{-6}{2}\right)^2 = (-3)^2 = 9$

65. $\left(\dfrac{-5}{2}\right)^2 = \dfrac{25}{4}$

66. $\left(\dfrac{3}{2}\right)^2 = \dfrac{9}{4}$

67.   The term needed to complete the square is $\left(\dfrac{-8}{2}\right)^2 = (-4)^2 = 16$. The resulting perfect square is $(x-4)^2$.

68.   The term needed to complete the square is $\left(\dfrac{-5}{2}\right)^2 = \dfrac{25}{4}$. The resulting perfect square is $\left(x-\dfrac{5}{2}\right)^2$.

69.   The term needed to complete the square is $\left(\dfrac{9}{2}\right)^2 = \dfrac{81}{4}$. The resulting perfect square is $\left(x+\dfrac{9}{2}\right)^2$.

70.   The term needed to complete the square is $\left(\dfrac{1}{2}\right)^2 = \dfrac{1}{4}$. The resulting perfect square is $\left(x+\dfrac{1}{2}\right)^2$.

71. $x^2 - 2x = 24 \Rightarrow x^2 - 2x + 1 = 24 + 1 \Rightarrow (x-1)^2 = 25 \Rightarrow x-1 = \pm\sqrt{25} \Rightarrow x-1 = \pm 5 \Rightarrow x = 1 \pm 5 \Rightarrow x = -4$ or 6

72. $x^2 - 2x + \dfrac{1}{2} = 0 \Rightarrow x^2 - 2x + 1 = -\dfrac{1}{2} + 1 \Rightarrow (x-1)^2 = \dfrac{1}{2} \Rightarrow x-1 = \pm\sqrt{\dfrac{1}{2}} \Rightarrow x = 1 \pm \dfrac{1}{\sqrt{2}}$ or $1 \pm \dfrac{\sqrt{2}}{2}$

73. $x^2 + 6x - 2 = 0 \Rightarrow x^2 + 6x + 9 = 2 + 9 \Rightarrow (x+3)^2 = 11 \Rightarrow x+3 = \pm\sqrt{11} \Rightarrow x = -3 \pm \sqrt{11}$

74. $x^2 - 16x = 5 \Rightarrow x^2 - 16x + 64 = 5 + 64 \Rightarrow (x-8)^2 = 69 \Rightarrow x-8 = \pm\sqrt{69} \Rightarrow x = 8 \pm \sqrt{69}$

75. $x^2 - 3x = 5 \Rightarrow x^2 - 3x + \dfrac{9}{4} = 5 + \dfrac{9}{4} \Rightarrow \left(x-\dfrac{3}{2}\right)^2 = \dfrac{29}{4} \Rightarrow x-\dfrac{3}{2} = \pm\sqrt{\dfrac{29}{4}} \Rightarrow x = \dfrac{3}{2} \pm \dfrac{\sqrt{29}}{2} = \dfrac{3 \pm \sqrt{29}}{2}$

76. $x^2 + 5x = 2 \Rightarrow x^2 + 5x + \dfrac{25}{4} = 2 + \dfrac{25}{4} \Rightarrow \left(x+\dfrac{5}{2}\right)^2 = \dfrac{33}{4} \Rightarrow x+\dfrac{5}{2} = \pm\sqrt{\dfrac{33}{4}} \Rightarrow x = -\dfrac{5}{2} \pm \dfrac{\sqrt{33}}{2} = \dfrac{-5 \pm \sqrt{33}}{2}$

77. $x^2 - 5x + 1 = 0 \Rightarrow x^2 - 5x = -1 \Rightarrow x^2 - 5x + \dfrac{25}{4} = -1 + \dfrac{25}{4} \Rightarrow \left(x - \dfrac{5}{2}\right)^2 = \dfrac{21}{4} \Rightarrow$

$x - \dfrac{5}{2} = \pm\sqrt{\dfrac{21}{4}} \Rightarrow x = \dfrac{5}{2} \pm \dfrac{\sqrt{21}}{2} = \dfrac{5 \pm \sqrt{21}}{2}$

78. $x^2 - 9x + 7 = 0 \Rightarrow x^2 - 9x = -7 \Rightarrow x^2 - 9x + \dfrac{81}{4} = -7 + \dfrac{81}{4} \Rightarrow \left(x - \dfrac{9}{2}\right)^2 = \dfrac{53}{4} \Rightarrow$

$x - \dfrac{9}{2} = \pm\sqrt{\dfrac{53}{4}} \Rightarrow x = \dfrac{9}{2} \pm \dfrac{\sqrt{53}}{2} = \dfrac{9 \pm \sqrt{53}}{2}$

79. $x^2 - 4 = 2x \Rightarrow x^2 - 2x = 4 \Rightarrow x^2 - 2x + 1 = 4 + 1 \Rightarrow (x-1)^2 = 5 \Rightarrow x - 1 = \pm\sqrt{5} \Rightarrow x = 1 \pm \sqrt{5}$

80. $x^2 + 1 = 7x \Rightarrow x^2 - 7x = -1 \Rightarrow x^2 - 7x + \dfrac{49}{4} = -1 + \dfrac{49}{4} \Rightarrow \left(x - \dfrac{7}{2}\right)^2 = \dfrac{45}{4} \Rightarrow$

$x - \dfrac{7}{2} = \pm\sqrt{\dfrac{45}{4}} \Rightarrow x = \dfrac{7}{2} \pm \dfrac{\sqrt{45}}{2} = \dfrac{7 \pm \sqrt{45}}{2} = \dfrac{7 \pm 3\sqrt{5}}{2}$

81. $2x^2 - 3x = 4 \Rightarrow x^2 - \dfrac{3}{2}x = 2 \Rightarrow x^2 - \dfrac{3}{2}x + \dfrac{9}{16} = 2 + \dfrac{9}{16} \Rightarrow \left(x - \dfrac{3}{4}\right)^2 = \dfrac{41}{16} \Rightarrow x - \dfrac{3}{4} = \pm\sqrt{\dfrac{41}{16}} \Rightarrow$

$x = \dfrac{3}{4} \pm \dfrac{\sqrt{41}}{4} = \dfrac{3 \pm \sqrt{41}}{4}$

82. $3x^2 + 6x - 5 = 0 \Rightarrow 3(x^2 + 2x + 1) = 5 + 3 \Rightarrow 3(x+1)^2 = 8 \Rightarrow (x+1)^2 = \dfrac{8}{3} \Rightarrow$

$x + 1 = \pm\sqrt{\dfrac{8}{3}} \Rightarrow x = -1 \pm \dfrac{\sqrt{8}}{\sqrt{3}} = -\dfrac{\sqrt{3}}{\sqrt{3}} \pm \dfrac{\sqrt{8}}{\sqrt{3}} = \dfrac{-\sqrt{3} \pm \sqrt{8}}{\sqrt{3}} = \dfrac{-\sqrt{3} \pm \sqrt{8}}{\sqrt{3}} \cdot \dfrac{\sqrt{3}}{\sqrt{3}} = \dfrac{-3 \pm 2\sqrt{6}}{3}$

83. $4x^2 - 8x - 7 = 0 \Rightarrow x^2 - 2x - \dfrac{7}{4} = 0 \Rightarrow x^2 - 2x + 1 = \dfrac{7}{4} + 1 \Rightarrow (x-1)^2 = \dfrac{11}{4} \Rightarrow$

$x - 1 = \pm\sqrt{\dfrac{11}{4}} \Rightarrow x = 1 \pm \dfrac{\sqrt{11}}{2} \Rightarrow x = \dfrac{2 \pm \sqrt{11}}{2}$

84. $25x^2 - 20x - 1 = 0 \Rightarrow x^2 - \dfrac{4}{5}x - \dfrac{1}{25} = 0 \Rightarrow x^2 - \dfrac{4}{5}x + \dfrac{4}{25} = \dfrac{1}{25} + \dfrac{4}{25} \Rightarrow \left(x - \dfrac{2}{5}\right)^2 = \dfrac{1}{5} \Rightarrow$

$x - \dfrac{2}{5} = \pm\sqrt{\dfrac{1}{5}} \Rightarrow x = \dfrac{2}{5} \pm \dfrac{1}{\sqrt{5}} \Rightarrow x = \dfrac{2 \pm \sqrt{5}}{5}$

85. $36x^2 + 18x + 1 = 0 \Rightarrow 36\left(x^2 + \dfrac{1}{2}x + \dfrac{1}{16}\right) = -1 + \dfrac{36}{16} \Rightarrow 36\left(x + \dfrac{1}{4}\right)^2 = \dfrac{20}{16} \Rightarrow$

$\left(x + \dfrac{1}{4}\right)^2 = \dfrac{20}{576} \Rightarrow x + \dfrac{1}{4} = \pm\sqrt{\dfrac{20}{576}} \Rightarrow x = -\dfrac{1}{4} \pm \dfrac{\sqrt{20}}{24} = \dfrac{-6 \pm 2\sqrt{5}}{24} = \dfrac{-3 \pm \sqrt{5}}{12}$

86. $12x^2 + 8x - 2 = 0 \Rightarrow 12\left(x^2 + \frac{2}{3}x + \frac{1}{9}\right) = 2 + \frac{12}{9} \Rightarrow 12\left(x + \frac{1}{3}\right)^2 = \frac{10}{3} \Rightarrow$

$\left(x + \frac{1}{3}\right)^2 = \frac{10}{36} \Rightarrow x + \frac{1}{3} = \pm\sqrt{\frac{10}{36}} \Rightarrow x = -\frac{1}{3} \pm \frac{\sqrt{10}}{6} = \frac{-2 \pm \sqrt{10}}{6}$

87. $3x^2 + 12x = 36 \Rightarrow 3x^2 + 12x - 36 = 0 \Rightarrow 3(x^2 + 4x - 12) = 0 \Rightarrow 3(x+6)(x-2) = 0 \Rightarrow$

Either $x + 6 = 0 \Rightarrow x = -6$ or $x - 2 = 0 \Rightarrow x = 2$

88. $6x^2 + 9x = 27 \Rightarrow 6x^2 + 9x - 27 = 0 \Rightarrow 3(2x^2 + 3x - 9) = 0 \Rightarrow 3(2x - 3)(x + 3) = 0 \Rightarrow$ Either $2x - 3 = 0 \Rightarrow x = \frac{3}{2}$

or $x + 3 = 0 \Rightarrow x = -3$

89. $x^2 + 4x = -2 \Rightarrow x^2 + 4x + 4 = -2 + 4 \Rightarrow (x+2)^2 = 2 \Rightarrow x + 2 = \pm\sqrt{2} \Rightarrow x = -2 \pm \sqrt{2}$

90. $x^2 + 6x + 3 = 0 \Rightarrow x^2 + 6x = -3 \Rightarrow x^2 + 6x + 9 = -3 + 9 \Rightarrow (x+3)^2 = 6 \Rightarrow x + 3 = \pm\sqrt{6} \Rightarrow x = -3 \pm \sqrt{6}$

91. $3x^2 - 4 = 2 \Rightarrow 3x^2 = 6 \Rightarrow x^2 = 2 \Rightarrow x = \pm\sqrt{2}$

92. $-2x^2 + 3 = 1 \Rightarrow -2x^2 = -2 \Rightarrow x^2 = 1 \Rightarrow x = \pm\sqrt{1} \Rightarrow x = \pm 1$

93. $-6x^2 + 70 = 16x \Rightarrow -6x^2 - 16x + 70 = 0 \Rightarrow -2(3x^2 + 8x - 35) = 0 \Rightarrow -2(3x - 7)(x + 5) = 0 \Rightarrow$

Either $3x - 7 = 0 \Rightarrow x = \frac{7}{3}$ or $x + 5 = 0 \Rightarrow x = -5$

94. $-15x^2 + 25x + 10 = 0 \Rightarrow -5(3x^2 - 5x - 2) = 0 \Rightarrow -5(3x + 1)(x - 2) = 0 \Rightarrow$

Either $3x + 1 = 0 \Rightarrow x = -\frac{1}{3}$ or $x - 2 = 0 \Rightarrow x = 2$

95. $-3x(x-8) = 6 \Rightarrow -3x^2 + 24x = 6 \Rightarrow x^2 - 8x = -2 \Rightarrow x^2 - 8x + 16 = -2 + 16 \Rightarrow (x-4)^2 = 14$

$\Rightarrow x - 4 = \pm\sqrt{14} \Rightarrow x = 4 \pm \sqrt{14}$

96. $-2x(4-x) = 8 \Rightarrow -8x + 2x^2 = 8 \Rightarrow 2(x^2 - 4x) = 8 \Rightarrow x^2 - 4x = 4 \Rightarrow x^2 - 4x + 4 = 4 + 4$

$\Rightarrow (x-2)^2 = 8 \Rightarrow x - 2 = \pm\sqrt{8} \Rightarrow x = 2 \pm \sqrt{8} \Rightarrow x = 2 \pm 2\sqrt{2}$

97. $ax^2 - c = 0 \Rightarrow ax^2 = c \Rightarrow x^2 = \frac{c}{a} \Rightarrow x = \pm\sqrt{\frac{c}{a}}$

98. $ax^2 + bx = 0 \Rightarrow x(ax + b) = 0 \Rightarrow$ Either $x = 0$ or $ax + b = 0 \Rightarrow x = -\frac{b}{a}$

Solving Equations by More Than One Method

99. (a) $x^2 - 3x - 18 = 0 \Rightarrow (x+3)(x-6) = 0 \Rightarrow$ Either $x + 3 = 0 \Rightarrow x = -3$ or $x - 6 = 0 \Rightarrow x = 6$

(b) Graph $Y_1 = X^2 - 3X - 18$ in $[-5, 8, 1]$ by $[-25, 5, 5]$. See Figures 99a & 99b.

The solutions are the x-intercepts, $x = -3$ or $x = 6$.

(c) Table $Y_1 = X^2 - 3X - 18$ with TblStart = -6 and ΔTbl = 3. See Figure 99c.

Since $Y_1 = 0$ when $x = -3$ or when $x = 6$, the solutions are $x = -3$ or $x = 6$.

$[-5, 8, 1]$ by $[-25, 5, 5]$ $[-5, 8, 1]$ by $[-25, 5, 5]$

Figure 99a   Figure 99b   Figure 99c

100. (a) $\frac{1}{2}x^2 + 2x - 6 = 0 \Rightarrow (x+6)\left(\frac{1}{2}x - 1\right) = 0 \Rightarrow$ Either $x + 6 = 0 \Rightarrow x = -6$ or $\frac{1}{2}x - 1 = 0 \Rightarrow x = 2$

(b) Graph $Y_1 = (1/2)X^2 + 2X - 6$ in $[-10, 10, 1]$ by $[-10, 10, 1]$. See Figures 100a & 100b.

The solutions are the x-intercepts, $x = -6$ or $x = 2$.

(c) Table $Y_1 = (1/2)X^2 + 2X - 6$ with TblStart = –8 and ΔTbl = 2. See Figure 100c.

Since $Y_1 = 0$ when $x = -6$ or when $x = 2$, the solutions are $x = -6$ or $x = 2$.

$[-10, 10, 1]$ by $[-10, 10, 1]$ $[-10, 10, 1]$ by $[-10, 10, 1]$

Figure 100a   Figure 100b   Figure 100c

101. (a) $x^2 - 8x + 15 = 0 \Rightarrow (x-3)(x-5) = 0 \Rightarrow$ Either $x - 3 = 0 \Rightarrow x = 3$ or $x - 5 = 0 \Rightarrow x = 5$

(b) Graph $Y_1 = X^2 - 8X + 15$ in $[-10, 0, 1]$ by $[-5, 10, 1]$. See Figures 101a & 101b.

The solutions are the x-intercepts, $x = 3$ or $x = 5$.

(c) Table $Y_1 = X^2 - 8X + 15$ with TblStart = 1 and ΔTbl = 1. See Figure 101c.

Since $Y_1 = 0$ when $x = 3$ or when $x = 5$, the solutions are $x = 3$ or $x = 5$.

$[-10, 0, 1]$ by $[-5, 10, 1]$ $[-10, 0, 1]$ by $[-5, 10, 1]$

Figure 101a   Figure 101b   Figure 101c

102. (a) $2x^2 - 7x + 3 = 0 \Rightarrow (2x-1)(x-3) = 0 \Rightarrow$ Either $2x - 1 = 0 \Rightarrow x = \frac{1}{2}$ or $x - 3 = 0 \Rightarrow x = 3$

(b) Graph $Y_1 = 2X^2 - 7X + 3$ in $[-2, 5, 1]$ by $[-5, 10, 1]$. See Figures 102a & 102b.

The solutions are the x-intercepts, $x = \frac{1}{2}$ or $x = 3$.

(c) Table $Y_1 = 2X^2 - 7X + 3$ with TblStart = 0 and ΔTbl = 0.5. See Figure 102c.

Since $Y_1 = 0$ when $x = 0.5$ or when $x = 3$, the solutions are $x = \dfrac{1}{2}$ or $x = 3$.

[–2, 5, 1] by [–5, 10, 1]   [–2, 5, 1] by [–5, 10, 1]

Figure 102a   Figure 102b   Figure 102c

103.   (a) $4(x^2 + 35) = 48x \Rightarrow x^2 + 35 = 12x \Rightarrow x^2 - 12x + 35 = 0 \Rightarrow (x-5)(x-7) = 0 \Rightarrow$

Either $x - 5 = 0 \Rightarrow x = 5$ or $x - 7 = 0 \Rightarrow x = 7$

(b)   Graph $Y_1 = 4(X^2 + 35) - 48X$ in [–2, 10, 1] by [–6, 6, 1]. See Figures 103a & 103b.

The solutions are the x-intercepts, $x = 5$ or $x = 7$.

(c)   Table $Y_1 = 4(X^2 + 35) - 48X$ with TblStart = 3 and ΔTbl = 1. See Figure 103c.

Since $Y_1 = 0$ when $x = 5$ or when $x = 7$, the solutions are $x = 5$ or $x = 7$.

[–3, 3, 1] by [–3, 3, 1]   [–3, 3, 1] by [–3, 3, 1]

Figure 103a   Figure 103b   Figure 103c

104.   (a) $4x^2 - 8x - 5 = 0 \Rightarrow (2x+1)(2x-5) = 0 \Rightarrow$ Thus $2x+1 = 0 \Rightarrow x = -\dfrac{1}{2}$ or $2x-5 = 0 \Rightarrow x = \dfrac{5}{2}$

(b)   Graph $Y_1 = 4X(2 - X) + 5$ in [–3, 3, 1] by [–5, 10, 1]. See Figures 104a & 104b.

The solutions are the x-intercepts, $x = -\dfrac{1}{2}$ or $x = \dfrac{5}{2}$.

(c)   Table $Y_1 = 4X(2 - X) + 5$ with TblStart = –1.5 and ΔTbl = 1. See Figure 104c.

Since $Y_1 = 0$ when $x = -0.5$ or when $x = 2.5$, the solutions are $x = -\dfrac{1}{2}$ or $x = \dfrac{5}{2}$.

[–3, 3, 1] by [–5, 10, 1]   [–3, 3, 1] by [–5, 10, 1]

Figure 104a   Figure 104b   Figure 104c

Solving an Equation for a Variable

105. $x = y^2 - 1 \Rightarrow x + 1 = y^2 \Rightarrow \pm\sqrt{x+1} = y \Rightarrow y = \pm\sqrt{x+1}$

106. $x = 9y^2 \Rightarrow \dfrac{x}{9} = y^2 \Rightarrow \pm\sqrt{\dfrac{x}{9}} = y \Rightarrow y = \pm\dfrac{\sqrt{x}}{3}$

107. $K = \dfrac{1}{2}mv^2 \Rightarrow 2K = mv^2 \Rightarrow \dfrac{2K}{m} = v^2 \Rightarrow \pm\sqrt{\dfrac{2K}{m}} = v \Rightarrow v = \pm\sqrt{\dfrac{2K}{m}}$

108. $c^2 = a^2 + b^2 \Rightarrow c^2 - a^2 = b^2 \Rightarrow \pm\sqrt{c^2 - a^2} = b \Rightarrow b = \pm\sqrt{c^2 - a^2}$

109. $E = \dfrac{k}{r^2} \Rightarrow Er^2 = k \Rightarrow r^2 = \dfrac{k}{E} \Rightarrow r = \pm\sqrt{\dfrac{k}{E}}$

110. $W = I^2 R \Rightarrow \dfrac{W}{R} = I^2 \Rightarrow \pm\sqrt{\dfrac{W}{R}} = I \Rightarrow I = \pm\sqrt{\dfrac{W}{R}}$

111. $LC = \dfrac{1}{(2\pi f)^2} \Rightarrow 4\pi^2 f^2 LC = 1 \Rightarrow f^2 = \dfrac{1}{4\pi^2 LC} \Rightarrow f = \pm\sqrt{\dfrac{1}{4\pi^2 LC}} \Rightarrow f = \pm\dfrac{1}{2\pi\sqrt{LC}}$

112. $F = \dfrac{KmM}{r^2} \Rightarrow r^2 F = KmM \Rightarrow r^2 = \dfrac{KmM}{F} \Rightarrow r = \pm\sqrt{\dfrac{KmM}{F}}$

Applications

113. (a) $\dfrac{1}{2}x^2 = 450 \Rightarrow x^2 = 900 \Rightarrow x = \pm\sqrt{900} \Rightarrow x = 30$ mph ($x = -30$ has no physical meaning)

   (b) $\dfrac{1}{2}x^2 = 800 \Rightarrow x^2 = 1600 \Rightarrow x = \pm\sqrt{1600} \Rightarrow x = 40$ mph ($x = -40$ has no physical meaning)

114. (a) $\dfrac{1}{9}x^2 = 25 \Rightarrow x^2 = 225 \Rightarrow x = \pm\sqrt{225} \Rightarrow x = 15$ mph ($x = -15$ has no physical meaning)

   (b) $\dfrac{1}{9}x^2 = 361 \Rightarrow x^2 = 3249 \Rightarrow x = \pm\sqrt{3249} \Rightarrow x = 57$ mph ($x = -57$ has no physical meaning)

   (c) $\dfrac{1}{9}x^2 = 784 \Rightarrow x^2 = 7056 \Rightarrow x = \pm\sqrt{7056} \Rightarrow x = 84$ mph ($x = -84$ has no physical meaning)

115. $60 - 16t^2 = 0 \Rightarrow -16t^2 = -60 \Rightarrow t^2 = \dfrac{60}{16} \Rightarrow t = \pm\sqrt{\dfrac{60}{16}} \Rightarrow t = \dfrac{\sqrt{60}}{4} \approx 1.9$ seconds. The value $t \approx -1.9$ seconds

   has no physical meaning. The toy takes about 1.9 seconds to hit he ground. This is not twice the time it takes
   to fall from a height of 30 feet.

116. (a) $-16t^2 - 22t + 100 = 62 \Rightarrow 16t^2 + 22t - 38 = 0 \Rightarrow 2(8t + 19)(t - 1) \Rightarrow t = 1$ second.

   The value $t = -\dfrac{19}{8}$ seconds has no physical meaning.

   (b) Graph $Y_1 = -16X^2 - 22X + 100$ and $Y_2 = 62$ in $[0, 2, 1]$ by $[0, 100, 10]$. See Figure 116.

   The solution is the *x*-coordinate of the intersection point, $x = 1$. The height is 62 feet after 1 second.

   (c) $-16t^2 + 22t + 100 = 80 \Rightarrow 16t^2 - 22t - 20 = 0 \Rightarrow 2(8t + 5)(t - 2) \Rightarrow t = 2$ seconds.

   The value $t = -\dfrac{5}{8}$ second has no physical meaning.

[0, 2, 1] by [0, 100, 10]

Figure 116

117. $S = 42 \Rightarrow 42 = -0.227x^2 + 8.155x - 8.8$

$\Rightarrow -0.227x^2 + 8.155x = 50.8$

$\Rightarrow -0.227(x^2 - 35.925x) = 50.8$

$\Rightarrow x^2 - 35.925x = -223.789$

$\Rightarrow x^2 - 35.925x + 322.651 = -223.789 + 322.651$

$\Rightarrow (x - 17.9625)^2 = 98.862$

$\Rightarrow x - 17.9625 = \pm 9.943$

$\Rightarrow x = 17.9625 \pm 9.943$

$\Rightarrow x \approx 28 \text{ or } 8$

28 feet from the screen is not reasonable, so the answer is about 8 feet.

118. $S = 50 \Rightarrow 50 = -0.227x^2 + 8.155x - 8.8$

$\Rightarrow -0.227x^2 + 8.155x = 58.8$

$\Rightarrow -0.227(x^2 - 35.925x) = 58.8$

$\Rightarrow x^2 - 35.925x = -259.031$

$\Rightarrow x^2 - 35.925x + 322.651 = -259.031 + 322.651$

$\Rightarrow (x - 17.9625)^2 = 63.62$

$\Rightarrow x - 17.9625 = \pm 7.976$

$\Rightarrow x = 17.9625 \pm 7.976$

$\Rightarrow x \approx 10 \text{ or } 26$

26 feet from the screen is not reasonable, so the answer is about 10 feet.

119.   Let x represent the number of hours the athletes run. The athletes are running along the legs of a right triangle.

The distance between them is given by the length of the hypotenuse. One athlete runs $6x$ miles while the other runs $8x$ miles. By the Pythagorean Theorem we have the following

$(6x)^2 + (8x)^2 = 20^2 \Rightarrow 36x^2 + 64x^2 = 400 \Rightarrow 100x^2 = 400 \Rightarrow x^2 = 4 \Rightarrow x = \pm 2$.

The athletes are 20 miles apart after 2 hours.

120.   Let x represent the height of the triangle. Then $x + 3$ represents the base and $\frac{1}{2}x(x+3)$ represents the area.

$\frac{1}{2}x(x+3) = 35 \Rightarrow x(x+3) = 70 \Rightarrow x^2 + 3x - 70 = 0 \Rightarrow (x-7)(x+10) = 0 \Rightarrow x = 7 \text{ or } -10$

Since the value -10 has no physical meaning, the height is 7 inches and the base is $7 + 3 = 10$ inches.

121.   (a) Let x represent the width of the lot. Then $x + 6$ represents the length. So $x(x+6) = 520$.

The quadratic equation is $x^2 + 6x - 520 = 0$.

(b) $x^2 + 6x - 520 = 0 \Rightarrow (x + 26)(x - 20) = 0 \Rightarrow x = -26$ or 20

Since the value -26 has no physical meaning, the width is 20 feet.

122.   The ball was 25 feet above the ground at about 0.5 and 2.5 seconds.

123.   The height of the seedling was about 22 centimeters when the temperature was about $23°C$ and $34°C$.

124.   We must find the value of x for which $0.976x^2 - 4.643x + 0.238 = 150$.

    Graph $Y_1 = 0.976X^2 - 4.643X + 0.238$ and $Y_2 = 150$ in [5, 17, 2] by [0, 200, 10]. See Figure 124.

    The solution is the x-coordinate of the intersection point, $x \approx 15$. The year is 2005.

    [5, 17, 2] by [0, 200, 10]

       Figure 124

125.   (a)   The rate of increase each 20-year period is not constant.

     (b)   The vertex is (1800, 5). In 1800 the population was 5 million.

     (c) $0.0066(x - 1800)^2 + 5 = 85 \Rightarrow 0.0066(x - 1800)^2 = 80 \Rightarrow (x - 1800)^2 \approx 12{,}121 \Rightarrow$

       $x - 1800 \approx \sqrt{12{,}121} \Rightarrow x - 1800 \approx 110 \Rightarrow x \approx 1910$. The population was 85 million in 1910.

126.   By trial and substitution $f(x) = 164$ when $x = 1998$.

Group Activity Solutions

(a)   Make a scatterplot In [1930, 2010, 10] by [0, 6, 1]. See Figure 1.

(b)   If we use the point (1940, 0.25) as the vertex and the point (1997, 5.15) for x- and y-values,

    $5.15 = a(1997 - 1940)^2 + 0.25 \Rightarrow 5.40 = 3249a \Rightarrow a \approx 0.0015$.

    The function is $f(x) = 0.0015(x - 1940)^2 + 0.25$.

(c) $f(1976) = 0.0015(1976 - 1940)^2 + 0.25 = 2.194 \approx \$2.19$

    The function's value for 1976 was lower than the actual value by \$0.11.

(d) $0.0015(x - 1940)^2 + 0.25 = 1 \Rightarrow 0.0015(x - 1940)^2 = 0.75 \Rightarrow (x - 1940)^2 = 500 \Rightarrow$

    $x - 1940 \approx 22.36 \Rightarrow x \approx 1962.36$. Minimum wage was \$1.00 during 1962.

(e) $f(2009) = 0.0015(2009 - 1940)^2 + 0.25 \approx 7.39 = \$7.39$

    If the trend were to continue, the minimum wage in 2009 will be about \$7.39 per hour, higher than the projected value.

[1930, 2010, 10] by [0, 6, 1]

Figure 1

8.4: The Quadratic Formula

Concepts

1.   We use the quadratic formula to solve equations of the form $ax^2 + bx + c = 0$.

2.   Completing the square

3. $b^2 - 4ac$

4.   The quadratic equation has only one solution.

5.   Factoring, square root property, completing the square and the quadratic formula

6.   No. When $b^2 - 4ac < 0$, there are no real solutions.

7. $x^2 - 4 = 0 \Rightarrow x^2 = 4 \Rightarrow x = \pm\sqrt{4} \Rightarrow x = \pm 2$

8. $x^2 + 4 = 0 \Rightarrow x^2 = -4 \Rightarrow x = \pm\sqrt{-4} \Rightarrow x = \pm 2i$

The Quadratic Formula

9. $x = \dfrac{-11 \pm \sqrt{(11)^2 - 4(2)(-6)}}{2(2)} = \dfrac{-11 \pm \sqrt{169}}{4} = \dfrac{-11 \pm 13}{4} \Rightarrow x = -6$ or $x = \dfrac{1}{2}$

Graph $Y_1 = 2X^2 + 11X - 6$ in [−10, 5, 1] by [−25, 10, 5]. See Figures 9a & 9b. $x = -6$ or $x = \dfrac{1}{2}$

Table $Y_1 = 2X^2 + 11X - 6$ with TblStart = −7.3 and ΔTbl = 1.3. See Figure 9c. $x = -6$ or $x = \dfrac{1}{2}$

[−10, 5, 1] by [−25, 10, 5]   [−10, 5, 1] by [−25, 10, 5]

Figure 9a   Figure 9b   Figure 9c

10. $x = \dfrac{-2 \pm \sqrt{(2)^2 - 4(1)(-24)}}{2(1)} = \dfrac{-2 \pm \sqrt{100}}{2} = \dfrac{-2 \pm 10}{2} \Rightarrow x = -6$ or $x = 4$

Graph $Y_1 = X^2 + 2X - 24$ in [−7, 5, 1] by [−25, 10, 5]. See Figures 10a & 10b. $x = -6$ or $x = 4$

Table $Y_1 = X^2 + 2X - 24$ with TblStart = −8 and ΔTbl = 2. See Figure 10c. $x = -6$ or $x = 4$

[–7, 5, 1] by [–25, 10, 5]   [–7, 5, 1] by [–25, 10, 5]

Figure 10a   Figure 10b   Figure 10c

11. $x = \dfrac{-2 \pm \sqrt{(2)^2 - 4(-1)(-1)}}{2(-1)} = \dfrac{-2 \pm \sqrt{0}}{-2} = \dfrac{-2}{-2} \Rightarrow x = 1$

Graph $Y_1 = -X^2 + 2X - 1$ in [–5, 5, 1] by [–5, 5, 1]. See Figure 11a. $x = 1$

Table $Y_1 = -X^2 + 2X - 1$ with TblStart = –2 and ΔTbl = 1. See Figure 11b. $x = 1$

[–5, 5, 1] by [–5, 5, 1]   [–5, 5, 1] by [–5, 5, 1]

Figure 11a   Figure 11b   Figure 12a   Figure 12b

12. $x = \dfrac{-(-1) \pm \sqrt{(-1)^2 - 4(3)(1)}}{2(3)} = \dfrac{1 \pm \sqrt{-11}}{6} \Rightarrow$ No real solutions.

Graph $Y_1 = 3X^2 - X + 1$ in [–5, 5, 1] by [–5, 5, 1]. See Figure 12a. No real solutions.

Table $Y_1 = 3X^2 - X + 1$ with TblStart = –2 and ΔTbl = 1. See Figure 12b. No real solutions.

13. $x = \dfrac{-(-6) \pm \sqrt{(-6)^2 - 4(1)(-16)}}{2(1)} = \dfrac{6 \pm \sqrt{100}}{2} = \dfrac{6 \pm 10}{2} \Rightarrow x = -2 \text{ or } x = 8$

14. $x = \dfrac{-(-9) \pm \sqrt{(-9)^2 - 4(2)(7)}}{2(2)} = \dfrac{9 \pm \sqrt{25}}{4} = \dfrac{9 \pm 5}{4} \Rightarrow x = 1 \text{ or } x = \dfrac{7}{2}$

15. $x = \dfrac{-(-1) \pm \sqrt{(-1)^2 - 4(4)(-1)}}{2(4)} = \dfrac{1 \pm \sqrt{17}}{8}$

16. $x = \dfrac{-2 \pm \sqrt{(2)^2 - 4(-1)(1)}}{2(-1)} = \dfrac{-2 \pm \sqrt{8}}{-2} = \dfrac{-2 \pm 2\sqrt{2}}{-2} = \dfrac{-2(1 \pm \sqrt{2})}{-2} = 1 \pm \sqrt{2}$

17. $x = \dfrac{-2 \pm \sqrt{(2)^2 - 4(-3)(-1)}}{2(-3)} = \dfrac{-2 \pm \sqrt{-8}}{-6} \Rightarrow$ No real solutions.

18. $x = \dfrac{-1 \pm \sqrt{(1)^2 - 4(1)(3)}}{2(1)} = \dfrac{-1 \pm \sqrt{-11}}{2} \Rightarrow$ No real solutions.

19. $x = \dfrac{-(-36) \pm \sqrt{(-36)^2 - 4(36)(9)}}{2(36)} = \dfrac{36 \pm \sqrt{0}}{72} = \dfrac{36}{72} = \dfrac{1}{2}$

20. $x = \dfrac{-(-5.6) \pm \sqrt{(-5.6)^2 - 4(4)(1.96)}}{2(4)} = \dfrac{5.6 \pm \sqrt{0}}{8} = \dfrac{5.6}{8} \Rightarrow x = 0.7$

21. $x = \dfrac{-(-6) \pm \sqrt{(-6)^2 - 4(2)(-2)}}{2(2)} = \dfrac{6 \pm \sqrt{52}}{4} = \dfrac{6 \pm 2\sqrt{13}}{4} = \dfrac{2(3 \pm \sqrt{13})}{2(2)} = \dfrac{3 \pm \sqrt{13}}{2}$

22. $x = \dfrac{-2 \pm \sqrt{(2)^2 - 4(1)(-5)}}{2(1)} = \dfrac{-2 \pm \sqrt{24}}{2} = \dfrac{-2 \pm 2\sqrt{6}}{2} = \dfrac{2(-1 \pm \sqrt{6})}{2} = -1 \pm \sqrt{6}$

23. $x = \dfrac{-(-4) \pm \sqrt{(-4)^2 - 4(1)(1)}}{2(1)} = \dfrac{4 \pm \sqrt{12}}{2} = \dfrac{4 \pm 2\sqrt{3}}{2} = \dfrac{2(2 \pm \sqrt{3})}{2} = 2 \pm \sqrt{3}$

24. $x = \dfrac{-(-\frac{1}{2}) \pm \sqrt{(-\frac{1}{2})^2 - 4(1)(4)}}{2(1)} = \dfrac{\frac{1}{2} \pm \sqrt{-\frac{63}{4}}}{2} \Rightarrow$ No real solutions.

25. $x = \dfrac{-(-\frac{1}{2}) \pm \sqrt{(-\frac{1}{2})^2 - 4(\frac{3}{2})(-\frac{3}{2})}}{2(\frac{3}{2})} = \dfrac{\frac{1}{2} \pm \sqrt{\frac{37}{4}}}{3} = \dfrac{\frac{1}{2} \pm \frac{\sqrt{37}}{2}}{3} = \dfrac{1 \pm \sqrt{37}}{6}$

26. $x = \dfrac{-(-\frac{5}{4}) \pm \sqrt{(-\frac{5}{4})^2 - 4(\frac{1}{2})(\frac{1}{2})}}{2(\frac{1}{2})} = \dfrac{\frac{5}{4} \pm \sqrt{\frac{9}{16}}}{1} = \dfrac{5}{4} \pm \dfrac{3}{4} \Rightarrow x = \dfrac{1}{2}$ or $x = 2$

27. $x = \dfrac{-(-2) \pm \sqrt{(-2)^2 - 4(2)(-7)}}{2(2)} = \dfrac{2 \pm \sqrt{60}}{4} = \dfrac{2 \pm 2\sqrt{15}}{4} = \dfrac{2(1 \pm \sqrt{15})}{4} = \dfrac{1 \pm \sqrt{15}}{2}$

28. $x = \dfrac{-(-12) \pm \sqrt{(-12)^2 - 4(3)(-4)}}{2(3)} = \dfrac{12 \pm \sqrt{192}}{6} = \dfrac{12 \pm 8\sqrt{3}}{6} = \dfrac{2(6 \pm 4\sqrt{3})}{6} = \dfrac{6 \pm 4\sqrt{3}}{3}$

29. $x = \dfrac{-10 \pm \sqrt{(10)^2 - 4(-3)(-5)}}{2(-3)} = \dfrac{-10 \pm \sqrt{40}}{-6} = \dfrac{-10 \pm 2\sqrt{10}}{-6} = \dfrac{-2(5 \pm \sqrt{10})}{-6} = \dfrac{5 \pm \sqrt{10}}{3}$

30. $x = \dfrac{-4 \pm \sqrt{(4)^2 - 4(-2)(-1)}}{2(-2)} = \dfrac{-4 \pm \sqrt{8}}{-4} = \dfrac{-4 \pm 2\sqrt{2}}{-4} = \dfrac{-2(2 \pm \sqrt{2})}{-4} = \dfrac{2 \pm \sqrt{2}}{2}$

The Discriminant

31. (a) Since the parabola opens upward, $a > 0$.

    (b) The solutions are the x-intercepts, $x = -1$ or $x = 2$

    (c) Since there are two real solutions, the discriminant is positive.

32. (a) Since the parabola opens upward, $a > 0$.

    (b) The solution is the x-intercept, $x = -1$

    (c) Since there is one real solution, the discriminant is zero.

33. (a) Since the parabola opens upward, $a > 0$.

    (b) Since there are no x-intercepts, there are no real solutions.

    (c) Since there are no real solutions, the discriminant is negative.

34. (a) Since the parabola opens downward, $a < 0$.

(b) Since there are no x-intercepts, there are no real solutions.

(c) Since there are no real solutions, the discriminant is negative.

35.   (a) Since the parabola opens downward, $a < 0$.

(b) The solution is the x-intercept, $x = 2$

(c) Since there is one real solution, the discriminant is zero.

36.   (a) Since the parabola opens downward, $a < 0$.

(b) The solutions are the x-intercepts, $x = 0$ or $x = 3$

(c) Since there are two real solutions, the discriminant is positive.

37.   (a) $(1)^2 - 4(3)(-2) = 25$

(b) Since the discriminant is positive, there are two real solutions.

(c) Graph $Y_1 = 3X^2 + X - 2$ in $[-3, 3, 1]$ by $[-3, 3, 1]$. See Figure 37. There are two x-intercepts.

38.   (a) $(-13)^2 - 4(5)(6) = 49$

(b) Since the discriminant is positive, there are two real solutions.

(c) Graph $Y_1 = 5X^2 - 13X + 6$ in $[-3, 3, 1]$ by $[-3, 3, 1]$. See Figure 38. There are two x-intercepts.

$[-3, 3, 1]$ by $[-3, 3, 1]$ $[-3, 3, 1]$ by $[-3, 3, 1]$

Figure 37   Figure 38

$[0, 4, 1]$ by $[-3, 3, 1]$ $[0, 8, 1]$ by $[-1, 5, 1]$

Figure 39   Figure 40

39.   (a) $(-4)^2 - 4(1)(4) = 0$

(b) Since the discriminant is zero, there is only one real solution.

(c) Graph $Y_1 = X^2 - 4X + 4$ in $[0, 4, 1]$ by $[-3, 3, 1]$. See Figure 39. There is one x-intercept.

40.   (a) $(-2)^2 - 4\left(\frac{1}{4}\right)(4) = 0$

(b) Since the discriminant is zero, there is only one real solution.

(c) Graph $Y_1 = (1/4)X^2 - 2X + 4$ in $[0, 8, 1]$ by $[-1, 5, 1]$. See Figure 40. There is one x-intercept.

41.   (a) $\left(\frac{3}{2}\right)^2 - 4\left(\frac{1}{2}\right)(2) = -\frac{7}{4}$

(b) Since the discriminant is negative, there are no real solutions.

(c) Graph $Y_1 = (1/2)X^2 + (3/2)X + 2$ in $[-10, 10, 1]$ by $[0, 10, 1]$. See Figure 41. There are no x-intercepts.

42.   (a) $(-1)^2 - 4(2)(3) = -23$

(b) Since the discriminant is negative, there are no real solutions.

(c) Graph $Y_1 = 2X^2 - X + 3$ in $[-3, 3, 1]$ by $[0, 10, 1]$. See Figure 42. There are no x-intercepts.

$[-10, 10, 1]$ by $[0, 10, 1]$ $[-3, 3, 1]$ by $[0, 10, 1]$

Figure 41   Figure 42

$[-5, 5, 1]$ by $[-8, 5, 1]$ $[-10, 10, 1]$ by $[-100, 100, 10]$

Figure 43   Figure 44

43.   (a) $(3)^2 - 4(1)(-3) = 21$

(b) Since the discriminant is positive, there are two real solutions.

(c) Graph $Y_1 = X^2 + 3X - 3$ in $[-5, 5, 1]$ by $[-8, 5, 1]$. See Figure 43. There are two x-intercepts.

44.   (a) $(-13)^2 - 4(4)(28) = -279$

(b) Since the discriminant is negative, there are no real solutions.

(c) Graph $Y_1 = 4X^2 - 13X + 28$ in $[-10, 10, 1]$ by $[-100, 100, 10]$. See Figure 44. There are no x-intercepts.

45. $x = \dfrac{-(-2) \pm \sqrt{(-2)^2 - 4(1)(-1)}}{2(1)} = \dfrac{2 \pm \sqrt{8}}{2} = \dfrac{2 \pm 2\sqrt{2}}{2} = \dfrac{2(1 \pm \sqrt{2})}{2} = 1 \pm \sqrt{2}$

46. $x = \dfrac{-3 \pm \sqrt{(3)^2 - 4(1)(1)}}{2(1)} = \dfrac{-3 \pm \sqrt{5}}{2}$

47. $x = \dfrac{-(-1) \pm \sqrt{(-1)^2 - 4(-2)(3)}}{2(-2)} = \dfrac{1 \pm \sqrt{25}}{-4} = \dfrac{1 \pm 5}{-4} = -\dfrac{3}{2}$ or 1

48. $x = \dfrac{-(-1) \pm \sqrt{(-1)^2 - 4(-3)(4)}}{2(-3)} = \dfrac{1 \pm \sqrt{49}}{-6} = \dfrac{1 \pm 7}{-6} = -\dfrac{4}{3}$ or 1

49. $x = \dfrac{-1 \pm \sqrt{(1)^2 - 4(1)(5)}}{2(1)} = \dfrac{-1 \pm \sqrt{-19}}{2} \Rightarrow$ No real solutions. No x-intercepts.

50. $x = \dfrac{-(-2) \pm \sqrt{(-2)^2 - 4(3)(5)}}{2(3)} = \dfrac{2 \pm \sqrt{-56}}{6} \Rightarrow$ No real solutions. No x-intercepts.

51. $x = \dfrac{-(0) \pm \sqrt{(0)^2 - 4(1)(9)}}{2(1)} = \dfrac{0 \pm \sqrt{-36}}{2} \Rightarrow$ No real solutions. No x-intercepts.

52. $x = \dfrac{-(0) \pm \sqrt{(0)^2 - 4(1)(11)}}{2(1)} = \dfrac{0 \pm \sqrt{-44}}{2} \Rightarrow$ No real solutions. No x-intercepts.

53. $x = \dfrac{-4 \pm \sqrt{(4)^2 - 4(3)(-2)}}{2(3)} = \dfrac{-4 \pm \sqrt{40}}{6} = \dfrac{-4 \pm 2\sqrt{10}}{6} = \dfrac{2(-2 \pm \sqrt{10})}{6} = \dfrac{-2 \pm \sqrt{10}}{3}$

54. $x = \dfrac{-(-2) \pm \sqrt{(-2)^2 - 4(4)(-3)}}{2(4)} = \dfrac{2 \pm \sqrt{52}}{8} = \dfrac{2 \pm 2\sqrt{13}}{8} = \dfrac{2(1 \pm \sqrt{13})}{8} = \dfrac{1 \pm \sqrt{13}}{4}$

Complex Solutions

55. $x^2 + 9 = 0 \Rightarrow x^2 = -9 \Rightarrow x = \pm\sqrt{-9} \Rightarrow x = \pm 3i$

56. $x^2 + 16 = 0 \Rightarrow x^2 = -16 \Rightarrow x = \pm\sqrt{-16} \Rightarrow x = \pm 4i$

57. $x^2 + 80 = 0 \Rightarrow x^2 = -80 \Rightarrow x = \pm\sqrt{-80} \Rightarrow x = \pm\sqrt{-16 \cdot 5} \Rightarrow x = \pm 4i\sqrt{5}$

58. $x^2 + 20 = 0 \Rightarrow x^2 = -20 \Rightarrow x = \pm\sqrt{-20} \Rightarrow x = \pm\sqrt{-4 \cdot 5} \Rightarrow x = \pm 2i\sqrt{5}$

59. $x^2 + \dfrac{1}{4} = 0 \Rightarrow x^2 = -\dfrac{1}{4} \Rightarrow x = \pm\sqrt{-\dfrac{1}{4}} \Rightarrow x = \pm\dfrac{1}{2}i$

60. $x^2 + \dfrac{9}{4} = 0 \Rightarrow x^2 = -\dfrac{9}{4} \Rightarrow x = \pm\sqrt{-\dfrac{9}{4}} \Rightarrow x = \pm\dfrac{3}{2}i$

61. $16x^2 + 9 = 0 \Rightarrow 16x^2 = -9 \Rightarrow x^2 = -\dfrac{9}{16} \Rightarrow x = \pm\sqrt{-\dfrac{9}{16}} \Rightarrow x = \pm\dfrac{3}{4}i$

62. $25x^2 + 36 = 0 \Rightarrow 25x^2 = -36 \Rightarrow x^2 = -\dfrac{36}{25} \Rightarrow x = \pm\sqrt{-\dfrac{36}{25}} \Rightarrow x = \pm\dfrac{6}{5}i$

63. $x^2 = -6 \Rightarrow x = \pm\sqrt{-6} \Rightarrow x = \pm i\sqrt{6}$

64. $x^2 = -75 \Rightarrow x = \pm\sqrt{-75} \Rightarrow x = \pm\sqrt{-25 \cdot 3} \Rightarrow x = \pm 5i\sqrt{3}$

65. $x^2 - 3 = 0 \Rightarrow x^2 = 3 \Rightarrow x = \pm\sqrt{3}$

66. $x^2 - 8 = 0 \Rightarrow x^2 = 8 \Rightarrow x = \pm\sqrt{8} \Rightarrow x = \pm 2\sqrt{2}$

67. $x^2 + 2 = 0 \Rightarrow x^2 = -2 \Rightarrow x = \pm\sqrt{-2} \Rightarrow x = \pm i\sqrt{2}$

68. $x^2 + 4 = 0 \Rightarrow x^2 = -4 \Rightarrow x = \pm\sqrt{-4} \Rightarrow x = \pm i\sqrt{4} \Rightarrow x = \pm 2i$

69. $x = \dfrac{-(-1) \pm \sqrt{(-1)^2 - 4(1)(2)}}{2(1)} = \dfrac{1 \pm \sqrt{-7}}{2} = \dfrac{1 \pm i\sqrt{7}}{2} = \dfrac{1}{2} \pm i\dfrac{\sqrt{7}}{2}$

70. $x = \dfrac{-2 \pm \sqrt{2^2 - 4(1)(3)}}{2(1)} = \dfrac{-2 \pm \sqrt{-8}}{2} = \dfrac{-2 \pm i\sqrt{8}}{2} = \dfrac{-2 \pm 2i\sqrt{2}}{2} = \dfrac{-2}{2} \pm \dfrac{2\sqrt{2}}{2}i = -1 \pm i\sqrt{2}$

71. $x = \dfrac{-3 \pm \sqrt{3^2 - 4(2)(4)}}{2(2)} = \dfrac{-3 \pm \sqrt{-23}}{4} = \dfrac{-3 \pm i\sqrt{23}}{4} = -\dfrac{3}{4} \pm i\dfrac{\sqrt{23}}{4}$

72. $x = \dfrac{-(-1) \pm \sqrt{(-1)^2 - 4(3)(-1)}}{2(3)} = \dfrac{1 \pm \sqrt{13}}{6}$

73. $x = \dfrac{-(-4) \pm \sqrt{(-4)^2 - 4(1)(1)}}{2(1)} = \dfrac{4 \pm \sqrt{12}}{2} = \dfrac{4 \pm 2\sqrt{3}}{2} = 2 \pm \sqrt{3}$

74. $x = \dfrac{-(-1) \pm \sqrt{(-1)^2 - 4(3)(2)}}{2(3)} = \dfrac{1 \pm \sqrt{-23}}{6} = \dfrac{1 \pm i\sqrt{23}}{6} = \dfrac{1}{6} \pm i\dfrac{\sqrt{23}}{6}$

75. $x = \dfrac{-1 \pm \sqrt{1^2 - 4(1)(2)}}{2(1)} = \dfrac{-1 \pm \sqrt{-7}}{2} = \dfrac{-1 \pm i\sqrt{7}}{2} = -\dfrac{1}{2} \pm i\dfrac{\sqrt{7}}{2}$

76. $x = \dfrac{-(-4) \pm \sqrt{(-4)^2 - 4(1)(8)}}{2(1)} = \dfrac{4 \pm \sqrt{-16}}{2} = \dfrac{4 \pm i\sqrt{16}}{2} = \dfrac{4 \pm 4i}{2} = 2 \pm 2i$

77. $x = \dfrac{-2 \pm \sqrt{(2)^2 - 4(5)(4)}}{2(5)} = \dfrac{-2 \pm \sqrt{-76}}{10} = \dfrac{-2 \pm 2i\sqrt{19}}{10} = -\dfrac{1}{5} \pm i\dfrac{\sqrt{19}}{5}$

78. $x = \dfrac{-(-2) \pm \sqrt{(-2)^2 - 4(7)(4)}}{2(7)} = \dfrac{2 \pm \sqrt{-108}}{14} = \dfrac{2 \pm 6i\sqrt{3}}{14} = \dfrac{1}{7} \pm \dfrac{3}{7}i\sqrt{3}$

79. $x = \dfrac{-\frac{3}{4} \pm \sqrt{\left(\frac{3}{4}\right)^2 - 4\left(\frac{1}{2}\right)(1)}}{2\left(\frac{1}{2}\right)} = \dfrac{-\frac{3}{4} \pm \sqrt{-\frac{23}{16}}}{1} = -\dfrac{3}{4} \pm \sqrt{\dfrac{-23}{16}} = -\dfrac{3}{4} \pm \dfrac{\sqrt{-23}}{4} = -\dfrac{3}{4} \pm i\dfrac{\sqrt{23}}{4}$

80. $x = \dfrac{-1 \pm \sqrt{(1)^2 - 4\left(-\frac{1}{3}\right)(-2)}}{2\left(-\frac{1}{3}\right)} = \dfrac{-1 \pm \sqrt{-\frac{5}{3}}}{-\frac{2}{3}} = \left(-1 \pm \sqrt{\dfrac{-5}{3}}\right) \cdot \left(-\dfrac{3}{2}\right) = \dfrac{3}{2} \pm \dfrac{3\sqrt{-5}}{2\sqrt{3}} = \dfrac{3}{2} \pm i\dfrac{\sqrt{15}}{2}$

81. $x = \dfrac{-1 \pm \sqrt{(1)^2 - 4(1)(4)}}{2(1)} = \dfrac{-1 \pm \sqrt{-15}}{2} = -\dfrac{1}{2} \pm i\dfrac{\sqrt{15}}{2}$

82. $x = \dfrac{-1 \pm \sqrt{(1)^2 - 4(4)(5)}}{2(4)} = \dfrac{-1 \pm \sqrt{-79}}{8} = -\dfrac{1}{8} \pm i\dfrac{\sqrt{79}}{8}$

83. $x = \dfrac{-(-2) \pm \sqrt{(-2)^2 - 4(2)(-1)}}{2(2)} = \dfrac{2 \pm \sqrt{12}}{4} = \dfrac{2 \pm 2\sqrt{3}}{4} = \dfrac{2(1 \pm \sqrt{3})}{4} = \dfrac{1 \pm \sqrt{3}}{2}$

84. $2x = x(3 - 4x) \Rightarrow 4x^2 - x = 0 \Rightarrow x(4x - 1) = 0 \Rightarrow x = 0 \text{ or } \dfrac{1}{4}$

85. $x = \dfrac{-(-1) \pm \sqrt{(-1)^2 - 4(2)(2)}}{2(2)} = \dfrac{1 \pm \sqrt{-15}}{4} = \dfrac{1 \pm i\sqrt{15}}{4} = \dfrac{1}{4} \pm i\dfrac{\sqrt{15}}{4}$

86. $x = \dfrac{-(-10) \pm \sqrt{(-10)^2 - 4(4)(8)}}{2(4)} = \dfrac{10 \pm \sqrt{-28}}{8} = \dfrac{10 \pm 2i\sqrt{7}}{8} = \dfrac{2(5 \pm i\sqrt{7})}{8} = \dfrac{5}{4} \pm i\dfrac{\sqrt{7}}{4}$

You Decide the Method

87. $x^2 - 3x + 2 = 0 \Rightarrow (x-1)(x-2) = 0 \Rightarrow x = 1 \text{ or } x = 2$

88. $x^2 + 2x + 1 = 0 \Rightarrow (x+1)(x+1) = 0 \Rightarrow x = -1$

89. Multiply both sides of the equation by 4 to obtain the following result.

$$0.5x^2 - 1.75x - 1 = 0 \Rightarrow 2x^2 - 7x - 4 = 0 \Rightarrow (2x+1)(x-4) = 0 \Rightarrow x = -\frac{1}{2} \text{ or } x = 4$$

90. Multiply both sides of the equation by $\frac{10}{3}$ to obtain the following result.

$$\frac{3}{5}x^2 + \frac{9}{10}x - \frac{3}{5} = 0 \Rightarrow 2x^2 + 3x - 2 = 0 \Rightarrow (x+2)(2x-1) = 0 \Rightarrow x = -2 \text{ or } x = \frac{1}{2}$$

91. $x = \dfrac{-(-5) \pm \sqrt{(-5)^2 - 4(1)(2)}}{2(1)} = \dfrac{5 \pm \sqrt{17}}{2}$; Quadratic formula or completing the square.

92. $x = \dfrac{-(-1) \pm \sqrt{(-1)^2 - 4(2)(-4)}}{2(2)} = \dfrac{1 \pm \sqrt{33}}{4}$; Quadratic formula or completing the square.

93. $x = \dfrac{-1 \pm \sqrt{(1)^2 - 4(2)(8)}}{2(2)} = \dfrac{-1 \pm \sqrt{-63}}{4} = \dfrac{-1 \pm 3i\sqrt{7}}{4} = -\dfrac{1}{4} \pm \dfrac{3}{4} i\sqrt{7}$; Quadratic formula.

94. $x = \dfrac{-(-2) \pm \sqrt{(-2)^2 - 4(4)(3)}}{2(4)} = \dfrac{2 \pm \sqrt{-44}}{8} = \dfrac{2 \pm 2i\sqrt{11}}{8} = \dfrac{1}{4} \pm i\dfrac{\sqrt{11}}{4}$; Quadratic formula.

95. $4x^2 - 1 = 0 \Rightarrow (2x-1)(2x+1) = 0 \Rightarrow \text{Either } 2x - 1 = 0 \Rightarrow x = \dfrac{1}{2} \text{ or } 2x + 1 = 0 \Rightarrow x = -\dfrac{1}{2}$

96. $3x^2 = 9 \Rightarrow x^2 = 3 \Rightarrow x = \pm\sqrt{3}$

97. $3x^2 + 6 = 0 \Rightarrow 3(x^2 + 2) = 0 \Rightarrow x^2 + 2 = 0 \Rightarrow x^2 = -2 \Rightarrow x = \pm\sqrt{-2} \Rightarrow x = \pm i\sqrt{2}$

98. $4x^2 + 7 = 0 \Rightarrow 4x^2 = -7 \Rightarrow x^2 = -\dfrac{7}{4} \Rightarrow x = \pm\sqrt{-\dfrac{7}{4}} \Rightarrow x = \pm i\dfrac{\sqrt{7}}{\sqrt{4}} \Rightarrow x = \pm i\dfrac{\sqrt{7}}{2} \text{ or } x = \pm\dfrac{1}{2} i\sqrt{7}$

99. $9x^2 + 1 = 6x \Rightarrow 9x^2 - 6x + 1 = 0 \Rightarrow (3x-1)(3x-1) = 0 \Rightarrow 3x - 1 = 0 \Rightarrow x = \dfrac{1}{3}$

100. $10x^2 + 15x = 25 \Rightarrow 10x^2 + 15x - 25 = 0 \Rightarrow 5(2x^2 + 3x - 5) = 0 \Rightarrow 5(2x+5)(x-1) = 0 \Rightarrow$

   $\text{Either } 2x + 5 = 0 \Rightarrow x = -\dfrac{5}{2} \text{ or } x - 1 = 0 \Rightarrow x = 1$

Applications

101. $\dfrac{1}{9}x^2 + \dfrac{11}{3}x - 42 = 0 \Rightarrow x^2 + 33x - 378 = 0 \Rightarrow x = (x-9)(x+42) = 0 \Rightarrow x = 9 \text{ mph}$

   The value $x = -42$ has no physical meaning.

102. $\dfrac{1}{9}x^2 + \dfrac{11}{3}x - 152 = 0 \Rightarrow x^2 + 33x - 1368 = 0 \Rightarrow x = (x-24)(x+57) = 0 \Rightarrow x = 24 \text{ mph}$

The value $x = -57$ has no physical meaning.

103. $\dfrac{1}{9}x^2 + \dfrac{11}{3}x - 390 = 0 \Rightarrow x^2 + 33x - 3510 = 0 \Rightarrow x = (x-45)(x+78) = 0 \Rightarrow x = 45$ mph

The value $x = -78$ has no physical meaning.

104. $\dfrac{1}{9}x^2 + \dfrac{11}{3}x - 726 = 0 \Rightarrow x^2 + 33x - 6534 = 0 \Rightarrow x = (x-66)(x+99) = 0 \Rightarrow x = 66$ mph

The value $x = -99$ has no physical meaning.

105. $2.39x^2 + 5.04x + 5.1 = 200 \Rightarrow 2.39x^2 + 5.04x - 194.9 = 0$

$x = \dfrac{-5.04 \pm \sqrt{(5.04)^2 - 4(2.39)(-194.9)}}{2(2.39)} = \dfrac{-5.04 \pm \sqrt{1888.6456}}{4.78} \Rightarrow x \approx 8.04$; about 1992

The value $x \approx -10.15$ has no meaning in this problem. Our answer agrees with the graph.

106.   Let x represent the average speed of the canoe in still water. The trip downstream takes $\dfrac{2}{x+2}$ hours. The

trip upstream takes $\dfrac{4}{x-1}$ hours. The total is $\dfrac{2}{x+2} + \dfrac{4}{x-1} = 3$. Solve this equation for x.

$\dfrac{2}{x+2} + \dfrac{4}{x-1} = 3 \Rightarrow 2(x-1) + 4(x+2) = 3(x+2)(x-1) \Rightarrow 6x + 6 = 3x^2 + 3x - 6 \Rightarrow$

$3x^2 - 3x - 12 = 0 \Rightarrow x^2 - x - 4 = 0 \Rightarrow x = \dfrac{-(-1) \pm \sqrt{(-1)^2 - 4(1)(-4)}}{2(1)} = \dfrac{1 \pm \sqrt{17}}{2} \approx 2.6$ mph

107.   Use the Pythagorean Theorem to write the equation: $x^2 + (x+10)^2 = 50^2 \Rightarrow x^2 + x^2 + 20x + 100 = 2500 \Rightarrow$

$2x^2 + 20x - 2400 = 0 \Rightarrow x^2 + 10x - 1200 = 0 \Rightarrow (x+40)(x-30) = 0 \Rightarrow x = 30$ ($x = -40$ is not

reasonable). The cars traveled 30 miles and 40 miles.

108.   Let x represent the speed of the airplane without wind. The first trip takes $\dfrac{500}{x-20}$ hours. The second trip

takes $\dfrac{500}{x+10}$ hours. The total is $\dfrac{500}{x-20} + \dfrac{500}{x+10} = 4$. Solve this equation for x.

$\dfrac{500}{x-20} + \dfrac{500}{x+10} = 4 \Rightarrow \dfrac{125}{x-20} + \dfrac{125}{x+10} = 1 \Rightarrow 125(x+10) + 125(x-20) = (x-20)(x+10) \Rightarrow$

$250x - 1250 = x^2 - 10x - 200 \Rightarrow x^2 - 260x + 1050 = 0 \Rightarrow$

$x = \dfrac{-(-260) \pm \sqrt{(-260)^2 - 4(1)(1050)}}{2(1)} = \dfrac{260 \pm \sqrt{63,400}}{2} = 130 \pm \sqrt{634} \approx 256$ mph

109.   Let x represent the height of the screen. Then $x+3$ represents the width. The equation is $x(x+3) = 154$.

(a) Graph $Y_1 = X^2 + 3X - 154$ in $[-20, 20, 2]$ by $[-200, 100, 50]$. See Figure 109a. $x = 11$

(b) Table $Y_1 = X^2 + 3X - 154$ with TblStart = 7 and ΔTbl = 1. See Figure 109b. $x = 11$

(c) $x^2 + 3x - 154 = 0 \Rightarrow (x - 11)(x + 14) = 0 \Rightarrow x = 11$;   The value $x = -14$ has no physical meaning.

The screen is 11 inches by 14 inches.

[−20, 20, 2] by [−200, 100, 50]

Figure 109a   Figure 109b

110.   Let x represent the width of the sidewalk. Then the area of the sidewalk is

$(40 + 2x)(30 + 2x) - (40)(30) = 624 \Rightarrow 1200 + 80x + 60x + 4x^2 - 1200 = 624$

$\Rightarrow 4x^2 + 140x - 624 = 0 \Rightarrow x^2 + 35x - 156 = 0 \Rightarrow (x + 39)(x - 4) = 0 \Rightarrow x = 4$ ($x = -39$ is not reasonable).

The sidewalk should be 4 feet wide.

111.   (a)   The rate of change is not constant.

(b)   From the table, the height was 7 centimeters after about 75 seconds. *Answers may vary.*

(c) $x = \dfrac{-(-0.15) \pm \sqrt{(0.15)^2 - 4(0.0004)(9)}}{2(0.0004)} = \dfrac{0.15 \pm \sqrt{0.0081}}{0.0008} = \dfrac{0.15 \pm 0.09}{0.0008} \Rightarrow x = 75$ seconds

The value $x = 300$ is not possible for this problem.

112.   (a)   The number of hospitals increased from 1945 to 1970 and then decreased from 1970 to 2000.

(b)   The vertex gives the year of the maximum number of hospitals as well as the maximum number of hospitals.

(c) $f(30) = -1.38(30)^2 + 84(30) + 5865 = 7143$ hospitals. This is about the same as the graph.

(d) $-1.38x^2 + 84x + 5865 = 6300 \Rightarrow -1.38x^2 + 84x - 435 = 0 \Rightarrow$

$x = \dfrac{-84 \pm \sqrt{(84)^2 - 4(-1.38)(-435)}}{2(-1.38)} \approx 5.7$ and 55.2. The years were about 1946 and 1995.

This agrees with the graph.

Checking Basic Concepts for Sections 8.3 & 8.4

1.   Symbolic:

$2x^2 - 7x + 3 = 0 \Rightarrow (2x - 1)(x - 3) = 0 \Rightarrow$ Either $2x - 1 = 0 \Rightarrow x = \dfrac{1}{2}$ or $x - 3 = 0 \Rightarrow x = 3$

Graphical: Graph $Y_1 = 2X^2 - 7X + 3$ in [−5, 5, 1] by [−5, 5, 1]. See Figures 1a & 1b. $x = \dfrac{1}{2}$ or $x = 3$

[-5, 5, 1] by [-5, 5, 1]   [-5, 5, 1] by [-5, 5, 1]

Figure 1a   Figure 1b

2. $x^2 = 5 \Rightarrow x = \pm\sqrt{5}$

3. $x^2 - 4x + 1 = 0 \Rightarrow x^2 - 4x + 4 = -1 + 4 \Rightarrow (x-2)^2 = 3 \Rightarrow x - 2 = \pm\sqrt{3} \Rightarrow x = 2 \pm \sqrt{3}$

4. $x^2 + y^2 = 1 \Rightarrow y^2 = 1 - x^2 \Rightarrow y = \pm\sqrt{1 - x^2}$

5.   (a) $2x^2 = 3x + 1 \Rightarrow 2x^2 - 3x - 1 = 0 \Rightarrow x = \dfrac{-(-3) \pm \sqrt{(-3)^2 - 4(2)(-1)}}{2(2)} = \dfrac{3 \pm \sqrt{17}}{4}$

      (b) $9x^2 - 24x + 16 = 0 \Rightarrow x = \dfrac{-(-24) \pm \sqrt{(-24)^2 - 4(9)(16)}}{2(9)} = \dfrac{24 \pm \sqrt{0}}{18} = \dfrac{24}{18} = \dfrac{4}{3}$

      (c) $x = \dfrac{-1 \pm \sqrt{1^2 - 4(1)(2)}}{2(1)} = \dfrac{-1 \pm \sqrt{-7}}{2} = \dfrac{-1 \pm i\sqrt{7}}{2} = -\dfrac{1}{2} \pm i\dfrac{\sqrt{7}}{2}$

6.   (a) $(-5)^2 - 4(1)(5) = 5$; Since the discriminant is positive, there are two real solutions.

      (b) $(-5)^2 - 4(2)(4) = -7$; Since the discriminant is negative, there are no real solutions.

      (c) $(-56)^2 - 4(49)(16) = 0$; Since the discriminant is zero, there is one real solution.

8.5: Quadratic Inequalities

Concepts

1.   An inequality has an inequality sign rather than an equals sign.

2.   No, they often have an infinite number of solutions.

3.   No, since $9 \not< 7$.

4.   Yes, since $25 \geq 25$.

5. $-2 < x < 4$

6. $x < -3$ or $x > 1$

7.   Yes

8.   No, the degree of the polynomial on the right side is 3.

9.   Yes

10.   Yes

11.   No, this inequality is linear.

12.   No, the degree of the polynomial on the left side is 3.

13.   Yes, since $2(3)^2 + (3) - 1 = 20$ and $20 > 0$.

14.   Yes, since $(2)^2 - 3(2) + 2 = 0$ and $0 \leq 0$.

15.   No, since $(0)^2 + 2 = 2$ and $2 \not\leq 0$.

16.   No, since $2(1)(1-3) = -4$ and $-4 \not\geq 0$.

17.   No, since $(-3)^2 - 3(-3) = 18$ and $18 \not\leq 1$.

18.   No, since $4(-2)^2 - 5(-2) + 1 = 27$ and $27 \not> 30$.

Solving Quadratic Inequalities

19.   (a) The solutions are the *x*-intercepts, $x = -3$ or $x = 2$.

        (b) $-3 < x < 2$

        (c) $x < -3$ or $x > 2$

20.   (a) The solutions are the *x*-intercepts, $x = -2$ or $x = 0$.

        (b) $-2 < x < 0$

        (c) $x < -2$ or $x > 0$

21.   (a) The solutions are the *x*-intercepts, $x = -2$ or $x = 2$.

        (b) $-2 < x < 2$

        (c) $x < -2$ or $x > 2$

22.   (a) There are no *x*-intercepts, so there are no real solutions.

        (b) No real solutions.

        (c) All real numbers.

23.   (a) The solutions are the *x*-intercepts, $x = -10$ or $x = 5$.

        (b) $x < -10$ or $x > 5$

        (c) $-10 < x < 5$

24.   (a) The solutions are the *x*-intercepts, $x = -8$ or $x = 4$.

        (b) $x < -8$ or $x > 4$

        (c) $-8 < x < 4$

25.   (a) The solutions are $x = -2$ or $x = 2$.

        (b) $-2 < x < 2$

        (c) $x < -2$ or $x > 2$

26.   (a) The solutions are $x = -1$ or $x = 2$.

        (b) $-1 < x < 2$

        (c) $x < -1$ or $x > 2$

27.   (a) The solutions are $x = -4$ or $x = 0$.

        (b) $-4 < x < 0$

        (c) $x < -4$ or $x > 0$

28.   (a) The solutions are $x = -1.5$ or $x = 0.5$.

        (b) $x < -1.5$ or $x > 0.5$

        (c) $-1.5 < x < 0.5$

29. First replace the inequality symbol with an equals sign and solve the resulting equation.

    $x^2 + 4x + 3 = 0 \Rightarrow (x+3)(x+1) = 0 \Rightarrow x = -3$ or -1. The parabola given by $y = x^2 + 4x + 3$ lies below the x-axis when $-3 < x < -1$. The interval is $(-3, -1)$.

30. First replace the inequality symbol with an equals sign and solve the resulting equation.

    $x^2 + x - 2 = 0 \Rightarrow (x+2)(x-1) = 0 \Rightarrow x = -2$ or 1. The parabola given by $y = x^2 + x - 2$ lies below the x-axis when $-2 \le x \le 1$. The interval is $[-2, 1]$.

31. First replace the inequality symbol with an equals sign and solve the resulting equation.

    $2x^2 - x - 15 = 0 \Rightarrow (2x+5)(x-3) = 0 \Rightarrow x = -2.5$ or 3. The parabola given by $y = 2x^2 - x - 15$ lies above the x-axis when $x \le -2.5$ or $x \ge 3$. The interval is $(-\infty, -2.5] \cup [3, \infty)$.

32. First replace the inequality symbol with an equals sign and solve the resulting equation.

    $3x^2 - 3x - 6 = 0 \Rightarrow 3(x+1)(x-2) = 0 \Rightarrow x = -1$ or 2. The parabola given by $y = 3x^2 - 3x - 6$ lies above the x-axis when $x < -1$ or $x > 2$. The interval is $(-\infty, -1) \cup (2, \infty)$.

33. First replace the inequality symbol with an equals sign and solve the resulting equation.

    $2x^2 = 8 \Rightarrow x^2 = 4 \Rightarrow x^2 - 4 = 0 \Rightarrow (x+2)(x-2) = 0 \Rightarrow x = -2$ or 2. The parabola given by $y = 2x^2 - 8$ lies below the x-axis when $-2 \le x \le 2$. The interval is $[-2, 2]$.

34. First replace the inequality symbol with an equals sign and solve the resulting equation.

    $x^2 = 9 \Rightarrow x^2 - 9 = 0 \Rightarrow (x+3)(x-3) = 0 \Rightarrow x = -3$ or 3. The parabola given by $y = x^2 - 9$ lies below the x-axis when $-3 < x < 3$. The interval is $(-3, 3)$.

35. The value of x^2 is greater than -5 for all values of x. The parabola given by $y = x^2 + 5$ lies entirely above the x-axis. The interval is $(-\infty, \infty)$.

36. The value of $-x^2$ is never greater than 1. The parabola given by $y = -x^2 - 1$ lies entirely below the x-axis. There are no solutions.

37. First replace the inequality symbol with an equals sign and solve the resulting equation.

    $-x^2 + 3x = 0 \Rightarrow -x(x-3) = 0 \Rightarrow x = 0$ or 3. The parabola given by $y = -x^2 + 3x$ lies above the x-axis when $0 < x < 3$. The interval is $(0, 3)$.

38. First replace the inequality symbol with an equals sign and solve the resulting equation.

    $-8x^2 - 2x + 1 = 0 \Rightarrow -(2x+1)(4x-1) = 0 \Rightarrow x = -0.5$ or 0.25. The parabola given by $y = -8x^2 - 2x + 1$ lies below the x-axis when $x \le -0.5$ or $x \ge 0.25$. The interval is $(-\infty, -0.5] \cup [0.25, \infty)$.

39. $x^2 + 2 \le 0$ has no solutions; the left side of the inequality is always greater than or equal to 2.

40. $x^2 + 3 \ge -5 \Rightarrow x^2 \ge -8$; the value of x^2 is greater than -8 for all values of x. The parabola given by $y = x^2 + 8$ lies entirely above the x-axis. The interval is $(-\infty, \infty)$.

41. $(x-2)^2 \le 0 \Rightarrow (x-2)^2 = 0$ because $(x-2)^2$ can never be less than 0. $(x-2)^2 = 0 \Rightarrow x-2 = 0 \Rightarrow x = 2$.

42. $(x+2)^2 \le 0 \Rightarrow (x+2)^2 = 0$ because $(x+2)^2$ can never be less than 0. $(x+2)^2 = 0 \Rightarrow x+2 = 0 \Rightarrow x = -2$.

43. First replace the inequality symbol with an equals sign and solve the resulting equation.

     $(x+1)^2 = 0 \Rightarrow x+1 = 0 \Rightarrow x = -1$. The parabola given by $y = (x+1)^2$ lies above the x-axis when $x < -1$ or

     $x > -1$. The interval is $(-\infty, -1) \cup (-1, \infty)$.

44. First replace the inequality symbol with an equals sign and solve the resulting equation.

     $(x-3)^2 = 0 \Rightarrow x-3 = 0 \Rightarrow x = 3$. The parabola given by $y = (x-3)^2$ lies above the x-axis when $x < 3$ or

     $x > 3$. The interval is $(-\infty, 3) \cup (3, \infty)$.

45. $x(1-x) \ge -2 \Rightarrow x(1-x)+2 \ge 0$. Replace the inequality symbol with an equals sign and solve the resulting

     equation. $x(1-x)+2 = 0 \Rightarrow x-x^2+2 = 0 \Rightarrow -x^2+x+2 = 0 \Rightarrow (-x+2)(x+1) = 0 \Rightarrow x = 2$ or $x = -1$. The

     parabola given by $y = -x^2+x+2$ lies above or on the x-axis when $-1 \le x \le 2$. The interval is $[-1, 2]$.

46. $x(x-2) < 3 \Rightarrow x^2-2x-3 < 0$. Replace the inequality symbol with an equals sign and solve the resulting

     equation. $x^2-2x-3 = 0 \Rightarrow (x-3)(x+1) = 0 \Rightarrow x = 3$ or $x = -1$. The parabola given by $y = x^2-2x-3$ lies

     below the x-axis when $-1 < x < 3$. The interval is $(-1, 3)$.

47. (a) $x^2-4 = 0 \Rightarrow x^2 = 4 \Rightarrow x = -2$ or $x = 2$

     (b) Since the parabola opens upward, the solution is $-2 < x < 2$.

     (c) Since the parabola opens upward, the solution is $x < -2$ or $x > 2$.

48. (a) $x^2-5 = 0 \Rightarrow x^2 = 5 \Rightarrow x = -\sqrt{5}$ or $x = \sqrt{5}$

     (b) Since the parabola opens upward, the solution is $-\sqrt{5} \le x \le \sqrt{5}$.

     (c) Since the parabola opens upward, the solution is $x \le -\sqrt{5}$ or $x \ge \sqrt{5}$.

49. (a) $x^2+x-1 = 0 \Rightarrow x = \dfrac{-1 \pm \sqrt{(1)^2-4(1)(-1)}}{2(1)} \Rightarrow x = \dfrac{-1 \pm \sqrt{5}}{2}$

     (b) Since the parabola opens upward, the solution is $\dfrac{-1-\sqrt{5}}{2} < x < \dfrac{-1+\sqrt{5}}{2}$.

     (c) Since the parabola opens upward, the solution is $x < \dfrac{-1-\sqrt{5}}{2}$ or $x > \dfrac{-1+\sqrt{5}}{2}$.

50. (a) $x^2+4x-5 = 0 \Rightarrow (x+5)(x-1) = 0 \Rightarrow x = -5$ or $x = 1$

     (b) Since the parabola opens upward, the solution is $-5 \le x \le 1$.

     (c) Since the parabola opens upward, the solution is $x \le -5$ or $x \ge 1$.

51. $x^2+10x+21 = 0 \Rightarrow (x+7)(x+3) = 0 \Rightarrow x = -7$ or $x = -3$

     Since the parabola opens upward, the solution is $[-7, -3]$.

52. $x^2 - 7x - 18 = 0 \Rightarrow (x + 2)(x - 9) = 0 \Rightarrow x = -2$ or $x = 9$

Since the parabola opens upward, the solution is $(-2, 9)$.

53. $3x^2 - 9x + 6 = 0 \Rightarrow 3(x - 1)(x - 2) = 0 \Rightarrow x = 1$ or $x = 2$

Since the parabola opens upward, the solution is $(-\infty, 1) \cup (2, \infty)$.

54. $7x^2 + 34x - 5 = 0 \Rightarrow (x + 5)(7x - 1) = 0 \Rightarrow x = -5$ or $x = \dfrac{1}{7}$

Since the parabola opens upward, the solution is $(-\infty, -5] \cup \left[\dfrac{1}{7}, \infty\right)$.

55. $x^2 = 10 \Rightarrow x = -\sqrt{10}$ or $x = \sqrt{10}$

Since the parabola opens upward, the solution is $(-\sqrt{10}, \sqrt{10})$.

56. $x^2 = 64 \Rightarrow x = -8$ or $x = 8$

Since the parabola opens upward, the solution is $(-\infty, -8] \cup [8, \infty)$.

57. $x(x - 6) = 0 \Rightarrow x = 0$ or $x = 6$

Since the parabola opens upward, the solution is $(-\infty, 2) \cup (6, \infty)$.

58. $1 - x^2 = 0 \Rightarrow (1 + x)(1 - x) = 0 \Rightarrow x = -1$ or $x = 1$

Since the parabola opens downward, the solution is $(-\infty, -1] \cup [1, \infty)$.

59. $x(4 - x) = 2 \Rightarrow -x^2 + 4x - 2 = 0 \Rightarrow x = \dfrac{-4 \pm \sqrt{(4)^2 - 4(-1)(-2)}}{2(-1)} = 2 \pm \sqrt{2}$

Since the parabola opens downward, the solution is $(-\infty, 2 - \sqrt{2}] \cup [2 + \sqrt{2}, \infty)$.

60. $2x(1 - x) = 2 \Rightarrow -2x^2 + 2x - 2 = 0 \Rightarrow x = \dfrac{-2 \pm \sqrt{(2)^2 - 4(-2)(-2)}}{2(-2)} = \dfrac{-2 \pm \sqrt{-12}}{-4} \Rightarrow$ no solutions

Since the parabola has no x-intercepts and it opens downward, there are no solutions.

61.   Graph $Y_1 = \pi X \wedge 2 - \sqrt{(3)} X$ and $Y_2 = 3/11$ in $[-4.7, 4.7, 1]$ by $[-3.1, 3.1, 1]$. The solution is $[-0.128, 0.679]$.

   Figure 61a   Figure 61b

62.   Graph $Y_1 = \sqrt{(5)} X \wedge 2 - \pi \wedge 2 X$ and $Y_2 = 10.3$ in $[-10, 10, 1]$ by $[0, 20, 2]$. The solution is $(-\infty, -0.872] \cup [5.285, \infty)$.

Figure 62a

Figure 62b

Applications

63.   (a)   Graph $Y_1 = 0.0000375X^2 - 0.175X + 1000$ and $Y_2 = 850$ in [0, 4000, 1000] by [500, 1200, 100].

See Figures 63a & 63b. The elevation is 850 feet or less from 1131 feet to 3535 feet (approximately).

(b)   The elevation is 850 feet or more before 1131 feet or after 3535 feet (approximately).

[0, 4000, 1000] by [500, 1200, 100]   [0, 4000, 1000] by [500, 1200, 100]

Figure 63a   Figure 63b

64.   (a)   Note that 2 million is 2000 thousand. $163x^2 - 146x + 205 \geq 2000$

(b) $163x^2 - 146x + 205 = 2000 \Rightarrow 163x^2 - 146x - 1795 = 0 \Rightarrow$

$$x = \frac{-(-146) \pm \sqrt{(-146)^2 - 4(163)(-1795)}}{2(163)} = \frac{146 \pm \sqrt{1,191,656}}{326} \Rightarrow x \approx -2.9 \text{ or } x \approx 3.8$$

Since $x \approx -2.9$ has no meaning, there were 2 million or more subscribers after about year 3.8.

This is after about 1989.

65.   (a)   From the formula, $f(1985) = -0.05107(1985)^2 + 194.74(1985) - 184,949 \approx 383$.

From the graph $f(1985) \approx 383$.

(b)   The death rate was 500 or less about 1969 and after.

(c) $-0.05107x^2 + 194.74x - 184,949 = 500 \Rightarrow -0.05107x^2 + 194.74x - 185,449 = 0 \Rightarrow$

$$x = \frac{-194.74 \pm \sqrt{(194.74)^2 - 4(-0.05107)(-185,449)}}{2(-0.05107)} \approx 1969 \text{ or after} .$$

The only valid solution is 1969. The death rate was 250 or less about 1969 or after.

66.   (a)   From the formula, $f(1955) = -0.001918(1955)^2 + 6.93(1955) - 6156 \approx 61.5$. From the graph

$f(1955) \approx 61.5$.

(b)   The death rate was 60 or more about 1958 or earlier. *Answers may vary.*

(c) $-0.001918x^2 + 6.93x - 6156 = 60 \Rightarrow -0.001918x^2 + 6.93x - 6216 = 0 \Rightarrow$

$$x = \frac{-6.93 \pm \sqrt{(6.93)^2 - 4(-0.001918)(-6216)}}{2(-0.001918)} \approx 1656 \text{ or } 1958 .$$

The only valid solution is 1958. The death rate was 60 or more about 1958 or earlier.

67. Let w represent the width of the pen. Then $w+5$ represents the length and the area is given by

$w(w+5) = w^2 + 5w$. We want to find w so that $w^2 + 5w \geq 176$ and $w^2 + 5w \leq 500$.

$w^2 + 5w - 176 = 0 \Rightarrow (w+16)(w-16) = 0 \Rightarrow w = -16$ or $w = 11$, so $w \geq 11$. The values $w \leq -16$ have no

meaning. $w^2 + 5w - 500 = 0 \Rightarrow (w+25)(w-20) = 0 \Rightarrow w = -25$ or $w = 20$, so $w \leq 20$. The values $w \leq -25$

have no meaning. The width must be from 11 feet to 20 feet.

68. We want to find r so that $6\pi r^2 \geq 50$.

$6\pi r^2 = 50 \Rightarrow r^2 = \dfrac{50}{6\pi} \Rightarrow r = \pm\sqrt{\dfrac{50}{6\pi}} \Rightarrow r \approx -1.6$ or $r \approx 1.6$, so $r \geq 1.6$. The values $r \leq -1.6$ have no

meaning. The radius must be 1.6 inches or more.

8.6: Equations in Quadratic Form

Concepts

1. $u^2 - 7u + 6 = 0 \Rightarrow (u-1)(u-6) = 0 \Rightarrow u = 1$ or 6

When $u = 1$, $x^2 = 1 \Rightarrow x = \pm 1$. When $u = 6$, $x^2 = 6 \Rightarrow x = \pm\sqrt{6}$.

2. $2u^2 - 7u + 6 = 0 \Rightarrow (2u-3)(u-2) = 0 \Rightarrow u = \dfrac{3}{2}$ or 2

When $u = \dfrac{3}{2}$, $k^2 = \dfrac{3}{2} \Rightarrow k = \pm\dfrac{\sqrt{3}}{\sqrt{2}} = \pm\dfrac{\sqrt{6}}{2}$. When $u = 2$, $k^2 = 2 \Rightarrow k = \pm\sqrt{2}$.

3. $3u^2 + u - 10 = 0 \Rightarrow (u+2)(3u-5) = 0 \Rightarrow u = -2$ or $\dfrac{5}{3}$

When $u = -2$, $z^3 = -2 \Rightarrow z = -\sqrt[3]{2}$. When $u = \dfrac{5}{3}$, $z^3 = \dfrac{5}{3} \Rightarrow z = \sqrt[3]{\dfrac{5}{3}}$.

4. $2u^2 + 17u + 8 = 0 \Rightarrow (u+8)(2u+1) = 0 \Rightarrow u = -8$ or $-\dfrac{1}{2}$

When $u = -8$, $x^3 = -8 \Rightarrow x = -\sqrt[3]{8} = -2$. When $u = -\dfrac{1}{2}$, $x^3 = -\dfrac{1}{2} \Rightarrow x = -\sqrt[3]{\dfrac{1}{2}}$.

5. $4u^2 + 17u + 15 = 0 \Rightarrow (u+3)(4u+5) = 0 \Rightarrow u = -3$ or $-\dfrac{5}{4}$

When $u = -3$, $n^{-1} = -3 \Rightarrow n = -\dfrac{1}{3}$. When $u = -\dfrac{5}{4}$, $n^{-1} = -\dfrac{5}{4} \Rightarrow n = -\dfrac{4}{5}$.

6. $u^2 + 24 = 10u \Rightarrow u^2 - 10u + 24 = 0 \Rightarrow (u-6)(u-4) = 0 \Rightarrow u = 6$ or 4

When $u = 6$, $m^{-1} = 6 \Rightarrow m = \dfrac{1}{6}$. When $u = 4$, $m^{-1} = 4 \Rightarrow m = \dfrac{1}{4}$.

7. Let $u = x^2$. Then $u^2 = 8u + 9 \Rightarrow u^2 - 8u - 9 = 0 \Rightarrow (u+1)(u-9) = 0 \Rightarrow u = -1$ or 9.

When $u = -1$, $x^2 = -1 \Rightarrow$ no solutions. When $u = 9$, $x^2 = 9 \Rightarrow x = \pm\sqrt{9} = -3$ or 3.

8. Let $u = x^2$. Then $3u^2 = 10u + 8 \Rightarrow 3u^2 - 10u - 8 = 0 \Rightarrow (3u + 2)(u - 4) = 0 \Rightarrow u = -\dfrac{2}{3}$ or 4.

When $u = -\dfrac{2}{3}$, $x^2 = -\dfrac{2}{3} \Rightarrow$ no solutions. When $u = 4$, $x^2 = 4 \Rightarrow x = \pm\sqrt{4} = -2$ or 2.

9. Let $u = x^3$. Then $3u^2 - 5u - 2 = 0 \Rightarrow (3u + 1)(u - 2) = 0 \Rightarrow u = -\dfrac{1}{3}$ or 2.

When $u = -\dfrac{1}{3}$, $x^3 = -\dfrac{1}{3} \Rightarrow x = -\sqrt[3]{\dfrac{1}{3}}$. When $u = 2$, $x^3 = 2 \Rightarrow x = \sqrt[3]{2}$.

10. Let $u = x^3$. Then $6u^2 + 11u + 4 = 0 \Rightarrow (3u + 4)(2u + 1) = 0 \Rightarrow u = -\dfrac{4}{3}$ or $-\dfrac{1}{2}$.

When $u = -\dfrac{4}{3}$, $x^3 = -\dfrac{4}{3} \Rightarrow x = -\sqrt[3]{\dfrac{4}{3}}$. When $u = -\dfrac{1}{2}$, $x^3 = -\dfrac{1}{2} \Rightarrow x = -\sqrt[3]{\dfrac{1}{2}}$.

11. Let $u = z^{-1}$. Then $2u^2 + 11u = 40 \Rightarrow 2u^2 + 11u - 40 = 0 \Rightarrow (u + 8)(2u - 5) = 0 \Rightarrow u = -8$ or $\dfrac{5}{2}$.

When $u = -8$, $z^{-1} = -8 \Rightarrow z = -\dfrac{1}{8}$. When $u = \dfrac{5}{2}$, $z^{-1} = \dfrac{5}{2} \Rightarrow z = \dfrac{2}{5}$.

12. Let $u = z^{-1}$. Then $u^2 - 10u + 25 = 0 \Rightarrow (u - 5)^2 = 0 \Rightarrow u = 5$. When $u = 5$, $z^{-1} = 5 \Rightarrow z = \dfrac{1}{5}$.

13. Let $u = x^{1/3}$. Then $u^2 - 2u + 1 = 0 \Rightarrow (u - 1)^2 = 0 \Rightarrow u = 1$. When $u = 1$, $x^{1/3} = 1 \Rightarrow x = 1^3 = 1$.

14. Let $u = x^{1/3}$. Then $3u^2 + 18u = 48 \Rightarrow 3u^2 + 18u - 48 = 0 \Rightarrow 3(u + 8)(u - 2) = 0 \Rightarrow u = -8$ or 2.

When $u = -8$, $x^{1/3} = -8 \Rightarrow x = (-8)^3 = -512$. When $u = 2$, $x^{1/3} = 2 \Rightarrow x = 2^3 = 8$.

15. Let $u = x^{1/5}$. Then $u^2 - 33u + 32 = 0 \Rightarrow (u - 1)(u - 32) = 0 \Rightarrow u = 1$ or 32.

When $u = 1$, $x^{1/5} = 1 \Rightarrow x = 1^5 = 1$. When $u = 32$, $x^{1/5} = 32 \Rightarrow x = 32^5 = 33{,}554{,}432$.

16. Let $u = x^{1/5}$. Then $u^2 - 80u - 81 = 0 \Rightarrow (u + 1)(u - 81) = 0 \Rightarrow u = -1$ or 81.

When $u = -1$, $x^{1/5} = -1 \Rightarrow x = (-1)^5 = -1$. When $u = 81$, $x^{1/5} = 81 \Rightarrow x = 81^5 = 3{,}486{,}784{,}401$.

17. Let $u = x^{1/2}$. Then $u^2 - 13u + 36 = 0 \Rightarrow (u - 4)(u - 9) = 0 \Rightarrow u = 4$ or 9.

When $u = 4$, $x^{1/2} = 4 \Rightarrow x = 4^2 = 16$. When $u = 9$, $x^{1/2} = 9 \Rightarrow x = 9^2 = 81$.

18. Let $u = x^{1/2}$. Then $u^2 - 17u + 16 = 0 \Rightarrow (u - 1)(u - 16) = 0 \Rightarrow u = 1$ or 16.

When $u = 1$, $x^{1/2} = 1 \Rightarrow x = 1^2 = 1$. When $u = 16$, $x^{1/2} = 16 \Rightarrow x = 16^2 = 256$.

19. Let $u = z^{1/4}$. Then $u^2 - 2u + 1 = 0 \Rightarrow (u - 1)^2 = 0 \Rightarrow u = 1$. When $u = 1$, $z^{1/4} = 1 \Rightarrow x = 1^4 = 1$.

20. Let $u = z^{1/4}$. Then $u^2 - 4u + 4 = 0 \Rightarrow (u - 2)^2 = 0 \Rightarrow u = 2$. When $u = 2$, $z^{1/4} = 2 \Rightarrow x = 2^4 = 16$.

21. Let $u = x + 1$. Then $u^2 - 5u - 14 = 0 \Rightarrow (u + 2)(u - 7) = 0 \Rightarrow u = -2$ or 7.

When $u = -2$, $x + 1 = -2 \Rightarrow x = -3$. When $u = 7$, $x + 1 = 7 \Rightarrow x = 6$.

22. Let $u = x - 5$. Then $2u^2 + 5u + 3 = 0 \Rightarrow (2u + 3)(u + 1) = 0 \Rightarrow u = -\dfrac{3}{2}$ or -1.

When $u = -\dfrac{3}{2}$, $x - 5 = -\dfrac{3}{2} \Rightarrow x = \dfrac{7}{2}$. When $u = -1$, $x - 5 = -1 \Rightarrow x = 4$.

23. Let $u = x^2 - 1$. Then $u^2 - 4 = 0 \Rightarrow (u + 2)(u - 2) = 0 \Rightarrow u = -2$ or 2.

When $u = -2$, $x^2 - 1 = -2 \Rightarrow x^2 = -1 \Rightarrow$ no solutions.

When $u = 2$, $x^2 - 1 = 2 \Rightarrow x^2 = 3 \Rightarrow x = -\sqrt{3}$ or $\sqrt{3}$.

24. Let $u = x^2 - 9$. Then $u^2 - 8u + 16 = 0 \Rightarrow (u - 4)^2 = 0 \Rightarrow u = 4$.

When $u = 4$, $x^2 - 9 = 4 \Rightarrow x^2 = 13 \Rightarrow x = -\sqrt{13}$ or $\sqrt{13}$.

Equations Having Complex Solutions

25. $x^4 - 16 = 0 \Rightarrow (x^2 - 4)(x^2 + 4) = 0 \Rightarrow (x - 2)(x + 2)(x^2 + 4) = 0 \Rightarrow x = 2$ or $x = -2$ or

$x^2 = -4 \Rightarrow x = \pm\sqrt{-4} \Rightarrow x = \pm 2i$

26. $\dfrac{1}{3}x^4 - 27 = 0 \Rightarrow \dfrac{1}{3}(x^4 - 81) = 0 \Rightarrow \dfrac{1}{3}(x^2 - 9)(x^2 + 9) = 0 \Rightarrow \dfrac{1}{3}(x - 3)(x + 3)(x^2 + 9) = 0 \Rightarrow x = 3$ or x $= -3$ or

$x^2 = -9 \Rightarrow x = \pm\sqrt{-9} \Rightarrow x = \pm 3i$

27. $x^3 + x = 0 \Rightarrow x(x^2 + 1) = 0 \Rightarrow x = 0$ or $x^2 = -1 \Rightarrow x = \pm\sqrt{-1} \Rightarrow x = \pm i$

28. $4x^3 + x = 0 \Rightarrow x(4x^2 + 1) = 0 \Rightarrow x = 0$ or $x^2 = -\dfrac{1}{4} \Rightarrow x = \pm\sqrt{-\dfrac{1}{4}} \Rightarrow x = \pm\dfrac{1}{2}i$

29. $x^4 + 2 = x^2 \Rightarrow x^4 - x^2 + 2 = 0 \Rightarrow (x^2 - 2)(x^2 + 1) = 0 \Rightarrow x^2 = 2$ or $x^2 = -1 \Rightarrow x = \pm\sqrt{2}$ or $x = \pm i$

30. $x^4 - 3 = 2x^2 \Rightarrow x^4 - 2x^2 - 3 = 0 \Rightarrow (x^2 - 3)(x^2 + 1) = 0 \Rightarrow x^2 = 3$ or $x^2 = -1 \Rightarrow x = \pm\sqrt{3}$ or $x = \pm i$

31. $\dfrac{1}{x} + \dfrac{1}{x^2} = -\dfrac{1}{2} \Rightarrow 2x^2\left(\dfrac{1}{x} + \dfrac{1}{x^2}\right) = 2x^2\left(-\dfrac{1}{2}\right) \Rightarrow 2x + 2 = -x^2 \Rightarrow x^2 + 2x + 2 = 0 \Rightarrow x^2 + 2x = -2$

$\Rightarrow x^2 + 2x + 1 = -2 + 1 \Rightarrow (x + 1)^2 = -1 \Rightarrow x + 1 = \pm\sqrt{-1} \Rightarrow x = -1 \pm i$

32. $\dfrac{2}{x - 1} - \dfrac{1}{x} = -1 \Rightarrow x(x - 1)\left(\dfrac{2}{x - 1} - \dfrac{1}{x}\right) = x(x - 1)(-1) \Rightarrow 2x - (x - 1) = -x^2 + x \Rightarrow x^2 + 1 = 0$

$\Rightarrow x^2 = -1 \Rightarrow x = \pm i$

33. $\dfrac{2}{x - 2} - \dfrac{1}{x} = -\dfrac{1}{2} \Rightarrow 2x(x - 2)\left(\dfrac{2}{x - 2} - \dfrac{1}{x}\right) = 2x(x - 2)\left(-\dfrac{1}{2}\right) \Rightarrow 4x - 2(x - 2) = -x(x - 2)$

$\Rightarrow 4x - 2x + 4 = -x^2 + 2x \Rightarrow x^2 + 4 = 0 \Rightarrow x^2 = -4 \Rightarrow x = \pm\sqrt{-4} \Rightarrow x = \pm 2i$

34. $\dfrac{1}{x} - \dfrac{1}{x^2} = \dfrac{1}{2} \Rightarrow 2x^2\left(\dfrac{1}{x} - \dfrac{1}{x^2}\right) = 2x^2\left(\dfrac{1}{2}\right) \Rightarrow 2x - 2 = x^2 \Rightarrow x^2 - 2x + 2 = 0 \Rightarrow$

$x^2 - 2x = -2 \Rightarrow x^2 - 2x + 1 = -2 + 1 \Rightarrow (x - 1)^2 = -1 \Rightarrow x - 1 = \pm\sqrt{-1} \Rightarrow x = 1 \pm i$

Checking Basic Concepts for Sections 8.5 & 8.6

1. $x^2 - x - 6 = 0 \Rightarrow (x+2)(x-3) = 0 \Rightarrow x = -2$ or $x = 3$

    Since the parabola opens upward, the solution is $(-\infty, \ -2) \cup (3, \ \infty)$.

2. $3x^2 + 5x + 2 = 0 \Rightarrow (x+1)(3x+2) = 0 \Rightarrow x = -1$ or $x = -\dfrac{2}{3}$

    Since the parabola opens upward, the solution is $\left[-1, \ -\dfrac{2}{3}\right]$.

3. Let $u = x^3$. Then $u^2 + 6u - 16 = 0 \Rightarrow (u+8)(u-2) = 0 \Rightarrow u = -8$ or 2.

    When $u = -8$, $x^3 = -8 \Rightarrow x = \sqrt[3]{-8} = -2$. When $u = 2$, $x^3 = 2 \Rightarrow x = \sqrt[3]{2}$.

4. Let $u = x^{1/3}$. Then $u^2 - 7u - 8 = 0 \Rightarrow (u+1)(u-8) = 0 \Rightarrow u = -1$ or 8.

    When $u = -1$, $x^{1/3} = -1 \Rightarrow x = (-1)^3 = -1$. When $u = 8$, $x^{1/3} = 8 \Rightarrow x = 8^3 = 512$.

5. $x^4 + 2x^2 + 1 = 0 \Rightarrow (x^2 + 1)^2 = 0 \Rightarrow x^2 + 1 = 0 \Rightarrow x^2 = -1 \Rightarrow x = \pm\sqrt{-1} \Rightarrow x = \pm i$

Chapter 8 Review Exercises

Section 8.1

1. Vertex: $(-3, 4)$; Axis of symmetry: $x = -3$; Opens downward; Increasing: $x \le -3$; Decreasing: $x \ge -3$

2. Vertex: $(1, \ 0)$; Axis of symmetry: $x = 1$; Opens upward; Increasing: $x \ge 1$; Decreasing: $x \le 1$

3. (a) See Figure 3.

    (b) The vertex is $(0, -2)$. The axis of symmetry is $x = 0$.

    (c) $f(-1) = (-1)^2 - 2 = 1 - 2 = -1$

4. (a) See Figure 4.

    (b) The vertex is $(2, 1)$. The axis of symmetry is $x = 2$.

    (c) $f(3) = -(3)^2 + 4(3) - 3 = -9 + 12 - 3 = 0$

Figure 3

Figure 4

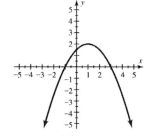
Figure 5

5. (a) See Figure 5.

    (b) The vertex is $(1, 2)$. The axis of symmetry is $x = 1$.

    (c) $f(-2) = -\dfrac{1}{2}(-2)^2 + (-2) + \dfrac{3}{2} = -2 - 2 + \dfrac{3}{2} = -2.5$

6.   (a) See Figure 6.

(b) The vertex is $(-2, -3)$. The axis of symmetry is $x = -2$.

(c) $f(-3) = 2(-3)^2 + 8(-3) + 5 = 18 - 24 + 5 = -1$

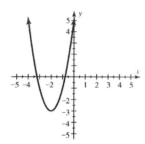

Figure 6

7.   Because $-\dfrac{b}{2a} = -\dfrac{-6}{2(2)} = \dfrac{3}{2}$ and $f\left(\dfrac{3}{2}\right) = 2\left(\dfrac{3}{2}\right)^2 - 6\left(\dfrac{3}{2}\right) + 1 = -\dfrac{7}{2}$, the vertex is $\left(\dfrac{3}{2}, \ -\dfrac{7}{2}\right)$.

The minimum y-value on the graph is $-\dfrac{7}{2}$.

8.   Because $-\dfrac{b}{2a} = -\dfrac{2}{2(-3)} = \dfrac{1}{3}$ and $f\left(\dfrac{1}{3}\right) = -3\left(\dfrac{1}{3}\right)^2 + 2\left(\dfrac{1}{3}\right) - 5 = -\dfrac{14}{3}$, the vertex is $\left(\dfrac{1}{3}, \ -\dfrac{14}{3}\right)$.

The maximum y-value on the graph is $-\dfrac{14}{3}$.

9. $x = -\dfrac{b}{2a} = -\dfrac{(-4)}{2(1)} = 2, \ f(2) = (2)^2 - 4(2) - 2 = -6$; The vertex is $(2, -6)$.

10. $x = -\dfrac{b}{2a} = -\dfrac{(0)}{2(-1)} = 0, \ f(0) = 5 - (0)^2 = 5$; The vertex is $(0, 5)$.

11. $x = -\dfrac{b}{2a} = -\dfrac{(1)}{2(-\frac{1}{4})} = 2, \ f(2) = -\dfrac{1}{4}(2)^2 + (2) + 1 = 2$; The vertex is $(2, 2)$.

12. $x = -\dfrac{b}{2a} = -\dfrac{(2)}{2(1)} = -1, \ f(-1) = 2 + 2(-1) + (-1)^2 = 1$; The vertex is $(-1, 1)$.

Section 8.2

13.   (a) See Figure 13.

(b) This graph is a shift of the graph of $y = x^2$ upward 2 units.

14.   (a) See Figure 14.

(b) This graph is more narrow than the graph of $y = x^2$.

Figure 13   Figure 14   Figure 15

15.   (a) See Figure 15.

(b) This graph is a shift of the graph of $y = x^2$ right 2 units.

16.   (a) See Figure 16.

(b) This graph is a shift of the graph of $y = x^2$ left 1 unit and downward 3 units.

17.   (a) See Figure 17.

(b) This graph is wider than the graph of $y = x^2$ and is shifted left 1 unit and upward 2 units.

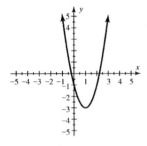

Figure 16   Figure 17   Figure 18

18.   (a) See Figure 18.

(b) This graph is more narrow than the graph of $y = x^2$ and is shifted right 1 unit and downward 3 units.

19. $y = a(x-h)^2 + k$ where (h, k) is the vertex , gives $y = -4(x-2)^2 - 5$.

20.   Opening downward means $a = -1$. $y = a(x-h)^2 + k$, gives $y = -1(x+4)^2 + 6$.

21. $y = x^2 + 4x - 7 \Rightarrow y = (x^2 + 4x + 4) - 7 - 4 \Rightarrow y = (x+2)^2 - 11$. The vertex is $(-2, -11)$.

22. $y = x^2 - 7x + 1 \Rightarrow y = \left(x^2 - 7x + \frac{49}{4}\right) + 1 - \frac{49}{4} \Rightarrow y = \left(x - \frac{7}{2}\right)^2 - \frac{45}{4}$. The vertex is $\left(\frac{7}{2}, -\frac{45}{2}\right)$.

23. $y = 2x^2 - 3x - 8 \Rightarrow y = 2\left(x^2 - \frac{3}{2}x + \frac{9}{16}\right) - 8 - \frac{9}{8} \Rightarrow y = 2\left(x - \frac{3}{4}\right)^2 - \frac{73}{8}$. The vertex is $\left(\frac{3}{4}, -\frac{73}{8}\right)$.

24. $y = 3x^2 + 6x - 2 \Rightarrow y = 3(x^2 + 2x + 1) - 2 - 3 \Rightarrow y = 3(x+1)^2 - 5$. The vertex is $(-1, -5)$.

25. $a(-1)^2 - 1 = 2 \Rightarrow a = 3$

26. $a(-1)^2 - 1 = -\frac{3}{4} \Rightarrow a = \frac{1}{4}$

27. $f(x) = -5(x-3)^2 + 4 \Rightarrow f(x) = -5(x^2 - 6x + 9) + 4$

$\Rightarrow f(x) = -5x^2 + 30x - 45 + 4 \Rightarrow f(x) = -5x^2 + 30x - 41$; the y-intercept is $c = -41$.

28. $f(x) = 3(x+2)^2 - 4 \Rightarrow f(x) = 3(x^2 + 4x + 4) - 4 \Rightarrow f(x) = 3x^2 + 12x + 12 - 4 \Rightarrow f(x) = 3x^2 + 12x + 8$; the y-intercept is $c = 8$.

Section 8.3

29. $-2, 3$

30. -1

31. No real solutions.

32. $-4, 6$

33. $-10, 5$

34. $-0.5, 0.25$

35. (a) Graph $Y_1 = X^2 - 5X - 50$ in $[-10, 20, 5]$ by $[-100, 20, 10]$. See Figures 35a & 35b.

The solutions are the x-intercepts, $x = -5$ and $x = 10$.

(b) Table $Y_1 = X^2 - 5X - 50$ with TblStart $= -10$ and ΔTbl $= 5$. See Figure 35c.

Since $Y_1 = 0$ when $x = -5$ and when $x = 10$, the solutions are $x = -5$ or $x = 10$.

$[-10, 20, 5]$ by $[-100, 20, 10]$ $[-10, 20, 5]$ by $[-100, 20, 10]$

Figure 35a   Figure 35b   Figure 35c

36. (a) Graph $Y_1 = (1/2)X^2 + X - (3/2)$ in $[-5, 5, 1]$ by $[-5, 5, 1]$. See Figures 36a & 36b.

The solutions are the x-intercepts, $x = -3$ or $x = 1$.

(b) Table $Y_1 = (1/2)X^2 + X - (3/2)$ with TblStart $= -4$ and ΔTbl $= 1$. See Figure 36c.

Since $Y_1 = 0$ when $x = -3$ and when $x = 1$, the solutions are $x = -3$ and $x = 1$.

$[-5, 5, 1]$ by $[-5, 5, 1]$ $[-5, 5, 1]$ by $[-5, 5, 1]$

Figure 36a   Figure 36b   Figure 36c

37. (a) Graph $Y_1 = (1/4)X^2 + (1/2)X - 2$ in $[-5, 5, 1]$ by $[-3, 3, 1]$. See Figures 37a & 37b.

The solutions are the x-intercepts, $x = -4$ and $x = 2$.

(b) Table $Y_1 = (1/4)X^2 + (1/2)X - 2$ with TblStart $= -8$ and ΔTbl $= 2$. See Figure 37c.

Since $Y_1 = 0$ when $x = -4$ and when $x = 2$, the solutions are $x = -4$, and $x = 2$.

[-5, 5, 1] by [-3, 3, 1]   [-5, 5, 1] by [-3, 3, 1]

Figure 37a   Figure 37b   Figure 37c

38. (a) Graph $Y_1 = (1/4)X^2 - (1/2)X - (3/4)$ in $[-5, 5, 1]$ by $[-3, 3, 1]$. See Figures 38a & 38b.

The solutions are the x-intercepts, $x = -1$ and $x = 3$.

(b) Table $Y_1 = (1/4)X^2 - (1/2)X - (3/4)$ with TblStart $= -2$ and ΔTbl $= 1$. See Figure 38c.

Since $Y_1 = 0$ when $x = -1$ and when $x = 3$, the solutions are $x = -1$ and $x = 3$.

[-5, 5, 1] by [-3, 3, 1]   [-5, 5, 1] by [-3, 3, 1]

Figure 38a   Figure 38b   Figure 38c

39. $x^2 + x - 20 = 0 \Rightarrow (x+5)(x-4) = 0 \Rightarrow x = -5 \text{ or } x = 4$

40. $x^2 + 11x + 24 = 0 \Rightarrow (x+8)(x+3) = 0 \Rightarrow x = -8 \text{ or } x = -3$

41. $15x^2 - 4x - 4 = 0 \Rightarrow (5x+2)(3x-2) = 0 \Rightarrow x = -\frac{2}{5} \text{ or } x = \frac{2}{3}$

42. $7x^2 - 25x + 12 = 0 \Rightarrow (7x-4)(x-3) = 0 \Rightarrow x = \frac{4}{7} \text{ or } x = 3$

43. $x^2 = 100 \Rightarrow x = \pm\sqrt{100} \Rightarrow x = \pm 10$

44. $3x^2 = \frac{1}{3} \Rightarrow x^2 = \frac{1}{9} \Rightarrow x = \pm\sqrt{\frac{1}{9}} \Rightarrow x = \pm\frac{1}{3}$

45. $4x^2 - 6 = 0 \Rightarrow x^2 = \frac{6}{4} \Rightarrow x = \pm\sqrt{\frac{6}{4}} \Rightarrow x = \pm\frac{\sqrt{6}}{2}$

46. $5x^2 = x^2 - 4 \Rightarrow 4x^2 = -4 \Rightarrow x^2 = -1 \Rightarrow x = \pm\sqrt{-1} \Rightarrow$ No real solutions.

47. $x^2 + 6x = -2 \Rightarrow x^2 + 6x + 9 = -2 + 9 \Rightarrow (x+3)^2 = 7 \Rightarrow x + 3 = \pm\sqrt{7} \Rightarrow x = -3 \pm\sqrt{7}$

48. $x^2 - 4x = 6 \Rightarrow x^2 - 4x + 4 = 6 + 4 \Rightarrow (x-2)^2 = 10 \Rightarrow x - 2 = \pm\sqrt{10} \Rightarrow x = 2 \pm\sqrt{10}$

49. $x^2 - 2x - 5 = 0 \Rightarrow x^2 - 2x + 1 = 5 + 1 \Rightarrow (x-1)^2 = 6 \Rightarrow x - 1 = \pm\sqrt{6} \Rightarrow x = 1 \pm\sqrt{6}$

50. $2x^2 + 6x - 1 = 0 \Rightarrow x^2 + 3x + \frac{9}{4} = \frac{1}{2} + \frac{9}{4} \Rightarrow \left(x + \frac{3}{2}\right)^2 = \frac{11}{4} \Rightarrow x + \frac{3}{2} = \pm\sqrt{\frac{11}{4}} \Rightarrow x = \frac{-3 \pm\sqrt{11}}{2}$

51. $F = \frac{k}{(R+r)^2} \Rightarrow F(R+r)^2 = k \Rightarrow (R+r)^2 = \frac{k}{F} \Rightarrow R + r = \pm\sqrt{\frac{k}{F}} \Rightarrow R = -r \pm\sqrt{\frac{k}{F}}$

52. $2x^2 + 3y^2 = 12 \Rightarrow 3y^2 = 12 - 2x^2 \Rightarrow y^2 = \dfrac{12 - 2x^2}{3} \Rightarrow y = \pm\sqrt{\dfrac{12 - 2x^2}{3}}$

Section 8.4

53. $x = \dfrac{-(-9) \pm \sqrt{(-9)^2 - 4(1)(18)}}{2(1)} = \dfrac{9 \pm \sqrt{9}}{2} = \dfrac{9 \pm 3}{2} \Rightarrow x = 3 \text{ or } x = 6$

54. $x = \dfrac{-(-24) \pm \sqrt{(-24)^2 - 4(1)(143)}}{2(1)} = \dfrac{24 \pm \sqrt{4}}{2} = \dfrac{24 \pm 2}{2} \Rightarrow x = 11 \text{ or } x = 13$

55. $x = \dfrac{-1 \pm \sqrt{(1)^2 - 4(6)(-1)}}{2(6)} = \dfrac{-1 \pm \sqrt{25}}{12} = \dfrac{-1 \pm 5}{12} \Rightarrow x = -\dfrac{1}{2} \text{ or } x = \dfrac{1}{3}$

56. $x = \dfrac{-(-5) \pm \sqrt{(-5)^2 - 4(5)(1)}}{2(5)} = \dfrac{5 \pm \sqrt{5}}{10}$

57. $x = \dfrac{-(-8) \pm \sqrt{(-8)^2 - 4(1)(-5)}}{2(1)} = \dfrac{8 \pm \sqrt{84}}{2} = \dfrac{8 \pm 2\sqrt{21}}{2} = \dfrac{2(4 \pm \sqrt{21})}{2} = 4 \pm \sqrt{21}$

58. $x = \dfrac{-(-6) \pm \sqrt{(-6)^2 - 4(2)(3)}}{2(2)} = \dfrac{6 \pm \sqrt{12}}{4} = \dfrac{6 \pm 2\sqrt{3}}{4} = \dfrac{2(3 \pm \sqrt{3})}{2(2)} = \dfrac{3 \pm \sqrt{3}}{2}$

59. $x^2 - 4 = 0 \Rightarrow (x - 2)(x + 2) = 0 \Rightarrow x = 2 \text{ or } x = -2$

60. $4x^2 - 1 = 0 \Rightarrow (2x - 1)(2x + 1) = 0 \Rightarrow x = \dfrac{1}{2} \text{ or } x = -\dfrac{1}{2}$

61. $2x^2 + 15 = 11x \Rightarrow 2x^2 - 11x + 15 = 0 \Rightarrow (2x - 5)(x - 3) = 0 \Rightarrow x = \dfrac{5}{2} \text{ or } x = 3$

62. $2x^2 + 15 = 13x \Rightarrow 2x^2 - 13x + 15 = 0 \Rightarrow (2x - 3)(x - 5) = 0 \Rightarrow x = \dfrac{3}{2} \text{ or } x = 5$

63. $x(5 - x) = 2x + 1 \Rightarrow 5x - x^2 - 2x - 1 = 0 \Rightarrow -x^2 + 3x - 1 = 0; \; a = -1, b = 3, c = -1$

$x = \dfrac{-b \pm \sqrt{b^2 - 4(ac)}}{2a} \Rightarrow x = \dfrac{-3 \pm \sqrt{3^2 - 4(-1)(-1)}}{2(-1)} \Rightarrow x = \dfrac{-3 \pm \sqrt{5}}{-2} \Rightarrow x = \dfrac{3 \pm \sqrt{5}}{2}$

64. $-2x(x - 1) = x - \dfrac{1}{2} \Rightarrow 2(-2x)(x - 1) = 2\left(x - \dfrac{1}{2}\right) \Rightarrow -4x^2 + 4x = 2x - 1 \Rightarrow -4x^2 + 2x + 1 = 0;$

$a = -4, b = 2, c = 1 \quad x = \dfrac{-b \pm \sqrt{b^2 - 4ac}}{2a} \Rightarrow x = \dfrac{-2 \pm \sqrt{2^2 - 4(-4)(1)}}{2(-4)}$

$\Rightarrow x = \dfrac{-2 \pm \sqrt{20}}{-8} \Rightarrow x = \dfrac{-2 \pm 2\sqrt{5}}{-8} \Rightarrow x = \dfrac{1 \pm \sqrt{5}}{4}$

65.   (a) Since the parabola opens upward, $a > 0$.

(b) The solutions are the *x*-intercepts, $x = -2 \text{ or } x = 3$.

(c) Since there are two unique solutions, the discriminant is positive.

66. (a) Since the parabola opens upward, $a > 0$.

(b) The solution is the *x*-intercept, $x = 2$.

(c) Since there is one solution, the discriminant is zero.

67. (a) Since the parabola opens downward, $a < 0$.

(b) There are no *x*-intercepts. No real solutions.

(c) Since there are no real solutions, the discriminant is negative.

68. (a) Since the parabola opens downward, $a < 0$.

(b) The solutions are the *x*-intercepts, $x = -4$ or $x = 2$.

(c) Since there are two unique solutions, the discriminant is positive.

69. (a) $(-3)^2 - 4(2)(1) = 1$

(b) Since the discriminant is positive, there are two real solutions.

(c) Graph $Y_1 = 2X^2 - 3X + 1$ in [0, 2, 1] by [–1, 1, 1]. See Figure 69. There are two *x*-intercepts.

70. (a) $(2)^2 - 4(7)(-5) = 144$

(b) Since the discriminant is positive, there are two real solutions.

(c) Graph $Y_1 = 7X^2 + 2X - 5$ in [–2, 2, 1] by [–10, 5, 1]. See Figure 70. There are two *x*-intercepts.

[0, 2, 1] by [–1, 1, 1]   [–2, 2, 1] by [–10, 5, 1]

Figure 69   Figure 70

71. (a) $(1)^2 - 4(3)(2) = -23$

(b) Since the discriminant is negative, there are no real solutions.

(c) Graph $Y_1 = 3X^2 + X + 2$ in [–3, 3, 1] by [–5, 10, 1]. See Figure 71. There are no *x*-intercepts.

[–3, 3, 1] by [–5, 10, 1]   [0, 3, 1] by [–5, 10, 1]

Figure 71   Figure 72

72. (a) $(-12.6)^2 - 4(4.41)(9) = 0$

(b) Since the discriminant is zero, there is one real solution.

(c) Graph $4.41X^2 - 12.6X + 9$ in [0, 3, 1] by [–5, 10, 1]. See Figure 72. There is one *x*-intercept.

73. $x = \dfrac{-1 \pm \sqrt{(1)^2 - 4(1)(5)}}{2(1)} = \dfrac{-1 \pm \sqrt{-19}}{2} = -\dfrac{1}{2} \pm i \dfrac{\sqrt{19}}{2}$

74. $2x^2 + 8 = 0 \Rightarrow 2x^2 = -8 \Rightarrow x^2 = -4 \Rightarrow x = \pm\sqrt{-4} \Rightarrow x = \pm 2i$

75. $x = \dfrac{-(-1) \pm \sqrt{(-1)^2 - 4(2)(1)}}{2(2)} = \dfrac{1 \pm \sqrt{-7}}{4} = \dfrac{1}{4} \pm i\dfrac{\sqrt{7}}{4}$

76. $x = \dfrac{-(-2) \pm \sqrt{(-2)^2 - 4(7)(5)}}{2(7)} = \dfrac{2 \pm \sqrt{-136}}{14} = \dfrac{2 \pm 2\sqrt{-34}}{14} = \dfrac{2(1 \pm \sqrt{-34})}{14} = \dfrac{1}{7} \pm i\dfrac{\sqrt{34}}{7}$

Section 8.5

77. (a) The solutions are the *x*-intercepts, $x = -2$ or $x = 6$.

  (b) $-2 < x < 6$

  (c) $x < -2$ or $x > 6$

78. (a) The solutions are the *x*-intercepts, $x = -2$ or $x = 0$.

  (b) $x < -2$ or $x > 0$

  (c) $-2 < x < 0$

79. (a) The solutions are $x = -4$ or $x = 4$.

  (b) $-4 < x < 4$

  (c) $x < -4$ or $x > 4$

80. (a) The solutions are $x = -2$ or $x = 1$.

  (b) $-2 < x < 1$

  (c) $x < -2$ or $x > 1$

81. (a) $x^2 - 2x - 3 = 0 \Rightarrow (x+1)(x-3) = 0 \Rightarrow x = -1$ or $x = 3$

  (b) Since the parabola opens upward, the solution is $-1 < x < 3$.

  (c) Since the parabola opens upward, the solution is $x < -1$ or $x > 3$.

82. (a) $2x^2 - 7x - 15 = 0 \Rightarrow (2x+3)(x-5) = 0 \Rightarrow x = -\dfrac{3}{2}$ or $x = 5$

  (b) Since the parabola opens upward, the solution is $-\dfrac{3}{2} \leq x \leq 5$.

  (c) Since the parabola opens upward, the solution is $x \leq -\dfrac{3}{2}$ or $x \geq 5$.

83. $x^2 + 4x + 3 = 0 \Rightarrow (x+3)(x+1) = 0 \Rightarrow x = -3$ or $x = -1$

  Since the parabola opens upward, the solution is $[-3, \ -1]$.

84. $5x^2 - 16x + 3 = 0 \Rightarrow (5x-1)(x-3) = 0 \Rightarrow x = \dfrac{1}{5}$ or $x = 3$

  Since the parabola opens upward, the solution is $\left(\dfrac{1}{5}, \ 3\right)$.

85. $6x^2 - 13x + 2 = 0 \Rightarrow (6x-1)(x-2) = 0 \Rightarrow x = \dfrac{1}{6}$ or $x = 2$

Since the parabola opens upward, the solution is $\left(-\infty, \dfrac{1}{6}\right) \cup (2, \infty)$.

86. $x^2 = 5 \Rightarrow \Rightarrow x = -\sqrt{5}$ or $x = \sqrt{5}$

Since the parabola opens upward, the solution is $(-\infty, \sqrt{5}] \cup [\sqrt{5}, \infty)$.

87.   The graph of the parabola $y = (x-1)^2$ lies on or above the x-axis for all real numbers x. The interval is

$(-\infty, \infty)$.

88. $x^2 + 3 < 2 \Rightarrow x^2 < -1$, which is not true for any real number x. The graph of the parabola $y = x^2 + 1$ lies

above the x-axis for all real numbers, so there are no solutions.

Section 8.6

89.   Let $u = x^2$. Then $u^2 - 14u + 45 = 0 \Rightarrow (u-5)(u-9) = 0 \Rightarrow u = 5$ or 9.

When $u = 5$, $x^2 = 5 \Rightarrow x = \pm\sqrt{5}$. When $u = 9$, $x^2 = 9 \Rightarrow x = \pm\sqrt{9} = \pm 3$.

90.   Let $u = z^{-1}$. Then $2u^2 + u - 28 = 0 \Rightarrow (u+4)(2u-7) = 0 \Rightarrow u = -4$ or $\dfrac{7}{2}$.

When $u = -4$, $z^{-1} = -4 \Rightarrow z = -\dfrac{1}{4}$. When $u = \dfrac{7}{2}$, $z^{-1} = \dfrac{7}{2} \Rightarrow z = \dfrac{2}{7}$.

91.   Let $u = x^{1/3}$. Then $u^2 - 9u + 8 = 0 \Rightarrow (u-1)(u-8) = 0 \Rightarrow u = 1$ or 8.

When $u = 1$, $x^{1/3} = 1 \Rightarrow x = 1^3 = 1$. When $u = 8$, $x^{1/3} = 8 \Rightarrow x = 8^3 = 512$.

92.   Let $u = x - 1$. Then $u^2 + 2u + 1 = 0 \Rightarrow (u+1)^2 = 0 \Rightarrow u = -1$. When $u = -1$, $x - 1 = -1 \Rightarrow x = 0$.

93. $4x^4 + 4x^2 + 1 = 0 \Rightarrow (2x^2 + 1)^2 = 0 \Rightarrow 2x^2 + 1 = 0 \Rightarrow x^2 = -\dfrac{1}{2} \Rightarrow x = \pm\sqrt{-\dfrac{1}{2}} \Rightarrow x = \pm i \dfrac{\sqrt{1}}{\sqrt{2}}$

$\Rightarrow x = \pm i \dfrac{1}{\sqrt{2}} \Rightarrow x = \pm i \dfrac{\sqrt{2}}{2}$

94. $\dfrac{1}{x-2} - \dfrac{3}{x} = -1 \Rightarrow x(x-2)\left(\dfrac{1}{x-2} - \dfrac{3}{x}\right) = x(x-2)(-1) \Rightarrow x - 3(x-2) = -x^2 + 2x \Rightarrow x^2 - 4x + 6 = 0$

$\Rightarrow x^2 - 4x = -6 \Rightarrow x^2 - 4x + 4 = -6 + 4 \Rightarrow (x-2)^2 = -2 \Rightarrow x - 2 = \pm\sqrt{-2} \Rightarrow x = 2 \pm i\sqrt{2}$

Applications

95.   (a) $f(x) = x(12 - 2x)$

(b)   Note that $f(x) = x(12 - 2x) \Rightarrow f(x) = -2x^2 + 12 + 0$. Then $-\dfrac{b}{2a} = -\dfrac{12}{2(-2)} = 3$.

The maximum area occurs when $x = 3$. The dimensions should be 6 inches by 3 inches.

96.   (a) $-16t^2 + 44t + 4 = 32 \Rightarrow -16t^2 + 44t - 28 = 0 \Rightarrow 4x^2 - 11x + 7 = 0 \Rightarrow (x-1)(4x-7) = 0 \Rightarrow$

$x = 1$ or $x = \dfrac{7}{4}$. The height of the stone is 32 feet at 1 second and 1.75 seconds.

(b) Find the vertex. $-\dfrac{b}{2a} = -\dfrac{44}{2(-16)} = 1.375;\ f(1.375) = -16(1.375)^2 + 44(1.375) + 4 = 34.25$

After 1.375 seconds, the stone is at a height of 34.25 feet.

97. (a) $f(x) = x(90 - 3x)$

(b) Graph $Y_1 = X(90 - 3X)$ in [0, 30, 5] by [0, 800, 100]. See Figure 97a.

(c) Graph $Y_1 = X(90 - 3X)$ and $Y_2 = 600$ in [0, 30, 5] by [0, 800, 100]. See Figures 97b & 97c. 10 or 20 rooms.

(d) Graph $Y_1 = X(90 - 3X)$ in [0, 30, 5] by [0, 800, 100]. See Figure 97d. Rent 15 rooms.

[0, 30, 5] by [0, 800, 100]   [0, 30, 5] by [0, 800, 100]

Figure 97a   Figure 97b

[0, 30, 5] by [0, 800, 100]   [0, 30, 5] by [0, 800, 100]

Figure 97c   Figure 97d

98. (a) $f(1999) = 0.4(1999 - 1997)^2 + 0.8 = 2.4$; In 1999 there were 2.4 complaints per 100,000 passengers.

(b) Graph $Y_1 = 0.4(X - 1997)^2 + 0.8$ in [1997, 1999, 1] by [0.5, 3, 0.5]. See Figure 98. They have increased.

[1997, 1999, 1] by [0.5, 3, 0.5]   [1935, 1995, 10] by [0, 100, 10]   [1950, 1970, 5] by [200, 350, 25]

Figure 98   Figure 101   Figure 102

99. (a) $\dfrac{x^2}{12} = 144 \Rightarrow x^2 = 1728 \Rightarrow x = \sqrt{1728} \approx 41.6$ mph ($-\sqrt{1728}$ mph has no meaning).

(b) $\dfrac{x^2}{12} = 300 \Rightarrow x^2 = 3600 \Rightarrow x = \sqrt{3600} = 60$ mph (–60 mph has no meaning).

100. (a) $x(x + 2) = 143$ or $x^2 + 2x - 143 = 0$

(b) $x^2 + 2x - 143 = 0 \Rightarrow (x + 13)(x - 11) = 0 \Rightarrow x = -13$ or 11. There are two possible number pairs.

Either $x = -13$, and the other number is -11, or $x = 11$, and the other number is 13.

101. (a) Plot the data in [1935, 1995, 10] by [0, 100, 10]. See Figure 101.

(b) Yes, the data is nearly linear.

(c) Since $m = \dfrac{78-25}{1991-1940} = \dfrac{53}{51} \approx 1.04$.

The function could be $f(x) = 1.04(x-1940)+25$. *Answers may vary.*

(d) $f(1995) = 1.04(1995-1940)+25 = 1.04(55)+25 = 82.2$,

$f(2005) = 1.04(2005-1940)+25 = 1.04(65)+25 = 92.6$. *Answers may vary.*

102. (a) The vertex is (1950, 220). In 1950 the per-capita energy consumption was at a low of 220 million Btu.

(b) Graph $Y_1 = (1/4)(X-1950)^2 + 220$ in [1950, 1970, 5] by [200, 350, 25]. See Figure 102. It Increased.

(c) $f(1996) = \dfrac{1}{4}(1996-1950)^2 + 220 = 749$. The function is not a good model for 1996 because the trend

represented by the model did not continue after 1970.

103. $\sqrt{123} \approx 11.1$; the screen is about 11.1 inches by 11.1 inches.

104. $x^2 + (x+70)^2 = 130^2 \Rightarrow x^2 + x^2 + 140x + 4900 = 16,900 \Rightarrow 2x^2 + 140x - 12,000 = 0 \Rightarrow$

$2(x-50)(x+120) = 0 \Rightarrow x = 50$ or $x = -120$. The solution is $x = 50$ feet ($x = -120$ has no meaning).

105. $(30+2x)(50+2x) - 30(50) = 250 \Rightarrow 1500 + 160x + 4x^2 - 1500 = 250 \Rightarrow 4x^2 + 160x - 250 = 0 \Rightarrow$

$x = \dfrac{-160 \pm \sqrt{(160)^2 - 4(4)(-250)}}{2(4)} = \dfrac{-160 \pm \sqrt{29,600}}{8} \Rightarrow x \approx -41.5$ or $x \approx 1.5$

The width of the strip of grass is about 1.5 feet. The value $x \approx -41.5$ has no physical meaning.

106. We must find r so that $750 \le \dfrac{1}{3}\pi r^2 (20) \le 1700$.

$\dfrac{1}{3}\pi r^2 (20) \ge 750 \Rightarrow r^2 \ge \dfrac{2250}{20\pi} \Rightarrow r \ge \sqrt{\dfrac{2250}{20\pi}} \approx 5.98$

$\dfrac{1}{3}\pi r^2 (20) \le 1700 \Rightarrow r^2 \ge \dfrac{5100}{20\pi} \Rightarrow r \ge \sqrt{\dfrac{5100}{20\pi}} \approx 9.01$

The values or r can range from about 6 inches to about 9 inches.

Chapter 8 Test

1. $x = -\dfrac{b}{2a} = -\dfrac{1}{2(-\frac{1}{2})} = \dfrac{1}{1} = 1, f(1) = -\dfrac{1}{2}(1)^2 + (1) + 1 = \dfrac{3}{2}$; Vertex: $\left(1, \dfrac{3}{2}\right)$; Axis of symmetry: $x = 1$.

$f(-2) = -\dfrac{1}{2}(-2)^2 + (-2) + 1 = -\dfrac{1}{2}(4) + (-2) + 1 = -3$

2. Because $-\dfrac{b}{2a} = -\dfrac{3}{2(1)} = -\dfrac{3}{2}$ and $f\left(-\dfrac{3}{2}\right) = \left(-\dfrac{3}{2}\right)^2 + 3\left(-\dfrac{3}{2}\right) - 5 = -\dfrac{29}{4}$, the vertex is $\left(-\dfrac{3}{2}, -\dfrac{29}{4}\right)$.

The minimum y-value on the graph is $-\dfrac{29}{4}$.

3.   Since $f(x) = 0$ when $x = -2$, $a(-2)^2 + 2 = 0 \Rightarrow 4a = -2 \Rightarrow a = -\dfrac{1}{2}$.

4.   See Figure 4.

This graph is wider than the graph of $y = x^2$ and is shifted right 3 units and upward 2 units.

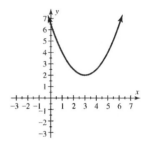

Figure 4

5. $y = x^2 - 6x + 2 \Rightarrow y = (x^2 - 6x + 9) + 2 - 9 \Rightarrow y = (x-3)^2 - 7$. The vertex is $(3, -7)$. The axis of symmetry

is $x = 3$.

6.   The solutions are the x-intercepts, $x = -1$ or $x = 2$. $f(1) = 2$.

7. $3x^2 + 11x - 4 = 0 \Rightarrow (x+4)(3x-1) = 0 \Rightarrow x = -4$ or $x = \dfrac{1}{3}$

8. $2x^2 = 2 - 6x^2 \Rightarrow 8x^2 = 2 \Rightarrow x^2 = \dfrac{1}{4} \Rightarrow x = \pm\sqrt{\dfrac{1}{4}} \Rightarrow x = -\dfrac{1}{2}$ or $x = \dfrac{1}{2}$

9. $x^2 - 8x = 1 \Rightarrow x^2 - 8x + 16 = 1 + 16 \Rightarrow (x-4)^2 = 17 \Rightarrow x - 4 = \pm\sqrt{17} \Rightarrow x = 4 \pm \sqrt{17}$

10. $x = \dfrac{-3 \pm \sqrt{(3)^2 - 4(-2)(1)}}{2(-2)} = \dfrac{-3 \pm \sqrt{17}}{-4} = \dfrac{3 \pm \sqrt{17}}{4}$

11. $9x^2 - 16 = 0 \Rightarrow (3x+4)(3x-4) = 0 \Rightarrow x = \pm\dfrac{4}{3}$

12. $F = \dfrac{Gm^2}{r^2} \Rightarrow Fr^2 = Gm^2 \Rightarrow m^2 = \dfrac{Fr^2}{G} \Rightarrow m = \pm\sqrt{\dfrac{Fr^2}{G}}$

13.   (a) Since the parabola opens downward, $a < 0$.

(b) The solutions are the x-intercepts, $x = -3$ or $x = 1$.

(c) Since there are two real solutions, the discriminant is positive.

14.   (a) $(4)^2 - 4(-3)(-5) = -44$

(b) Since the discriminant is negative, there are no real solutions.

(c) Graph $Y_1 = -3X^2 + 4X - 5$ in $[-5, 5, 1]$ by $[-20, 10, 5]$. See Figure 14. It does not intersect the x-axis.

[–5, 5, 1] by [–20, 10, 5]   [0, 6, 1] by [0, 150, 50]

Figure 14   Figure 24

15.   (a) The solutions are the x-intercepts, $x = -1$ or $x = 1$.

  (b) $-1 < x < 1$

  (c) $x < -1$ or $x > 1$

16.   (a) The solutions are the x-intercepts, $x = -10$ or $x = 20$.

  (b) $x < -10$ or $x > 20$

  (c) $-10 < x < 20$

17.   (a) $8x^2 - 2x - 3 = 0 \Rightarrow (2x+1)(4x-3) = 0 \Rightarrow x = -\dfrac{1}{2}$ or $x = \dfrac{3}{4}$

  (b) Since the parabola opens upward, the solution is $\left[-\dfrac{1}{2}, \dfrac{3}{4} \right]$.

  (c) Since the parabola opens upward, the solution is $\left(-\infty, -\dfrac{1}{2} \right] \cup \left[\dfrac{3}{4}, \infty \right)$.

18. $x^2 + 2x = 0 \Rightarrow x(x+2) = 0 \Rightarrow x = -2$ or $x = 0$. Solutions to $x^2 + 2x \le 0$ lie between and include these two

  values. The solution set is $[-2, 0]$.

19.   Let $u = x^3$. Then $u^2 - 3u + 2 = 0 \Rightarrow (u-1)(u-2) = 0 \Rightarrow u = 1$ or 2.

  When $u = 1$, $x^3 = 1 \Rightarrow x = \sqrt[3]{1} = 1$. When $u = 2$, $x^3 = 2 \Rightarrow x = \sqrt[3]{2}$.

20. $2x^2 + 4x + 3 = 0 \Rightarrow x = \dfrac{-4 \pm \sqrt{(4)^2 - 4(2)(3)}}{2(2)} = \dfrac{-4 \pm \sqrt{-8}}{4} = -1 \pm i\dfrac{\sqrt{2}}{2}$

21.   Graph $Y_1 = \sqrt{2} - \pi X^2$ and $Y_2 = 2.12X - 0.5\pi$ in $[-5, 5, 1]$ by $[-7, 3, 1]$.

Figure 21a   Figure 21b

The solutions are approximately $x = -1.37$ and $x = 0.69$.

22. $\dfrac{x^2}{9} = 250 \Rightarrow x^2 = 2250 \Rightarrow x = \sqrt{2250} \approx 47.4$ mph (the value $x \approx -47.4$ mph has no physical meaning).

23.   (a) $2z + 2x + 20 = 200 \Rightarrow 2x + 2z = 180 \Rightarrow z = 90 - x$, so the formula is $f(x) = (x+20)(90-x)$.

(b) Note that $f(x) = (x+20)(90-x) \Rightarrow f(x) = -x^2 + 70x + 1800$. The area is greatest for the value of x at

the vertex of the parabola, $x = -\dfrac{b}{2a} = -\dfrac{70}{2(-1)} = 35$. The enclosed area is greatest when $x = 35$.

24. (a) Graph $Y_1 = -16X^2 + 88X + 8$ in [0, 6, 1] by [0, 150, 50]. See Figure 24.

(b) $t = \dfrac{-88 \pm \sqrt{(88)^2 - 4(-16)(8)}}{2(-16)} = \dfrac{-88 \pm \sqrt{8256}}{-32} \approx 5.6$ seconds (the value $t \approx -0.089$ has no meaning).

(c) The stone reaches a maximum height of 129 feet after 2.75 seconds. See Figure 24.

Chapter 8 Extended and Discovery Exercises

1. (a) For the first 3 years of life, the likelihood of survival increases with age. After 3 years of life, it

decreases with age.

(b) Plot the data in [0, 10, 1] by [0, 75, 5]. See Figure 1b. A quadratic function could model these data since

the data points form a parabola.

(c) Graph $Y_1 = -3.57X + 71.1$ in [0, 10, 1] by [0, 75, 5]. See Figure 1c.

Graph $Y_1 = -2.07X^2 + 17.1X + 33$ in [0, 10, 1] by [0, 75, 5]. See Figure 1d.

The function f_2 models the data better.

(d) Evaluate f at $x = 6.5$ to find the likelihood of a 5.5-year-old sparrowhawk living 1 more year.

$f_2(6.5) = -2.07(6.5)^2 + 17.1(6.5) + 33 \approx 56.7 \%$

[0, 10, 1] by [0, 75, 5]	[0, 10, 1] by [0, 75, 5]	[0, 10, 1] by [0, 75, 5]
Figure 1b	Figure 1c	Figure 1d

2. (a) Plot the data in [−5, 35, 5] by [0, 100, 10]. See Figure 2.

(b) A quadratic function could model these data since the data points form a parabola.

(c) Using the data point (12, 95) as the vertex, the function has the form $f(x) = a(x-12)^2 + 95$.

By trial and error we find that $a = -0.25$ gives a fairly good fit. The function is given by

$f(x) = -0.25(x-12)^2 + 95$. *Answers may vary.*

(d) The x-coordinate of the vertex, 12°C, represents the the temperature that photosynthesis is most efficient.

[−5, 35, 5] by [0, 100, 10]	[−4, 4, 1] by [0, 6, 1]	[−4, 4, 1] by [0, 6, 1]
Figure 2	Figure 3a	Figure 3b

3. (a) Plot $(1, 5)$ and graph $Y_1 = -0.4X^2 + 4$ in $[-4, 4, 1]$ by $[0, 6, 1]$. See Figure 3a.

    (b) After 10 seconds the plane would have moved 2 kilometers. We will shift the parabola 2 units left.

        Plot $(1, 5)$ and graph $Y_1 = -0.4(X + 2)^2 + 4$ in $[-4, 4, 1]$ by $[0, 6, 1]$. See Figure 3b.

4. We would need to translate the mountain both to the right and downward so that the airplane would appear to move to the left and upward. One example could be $f(x) = -0.4(x - 2)^2 + 4 - 2$.

5. The discriminant is $(-1)^2 - 4(10)(-3) = 121 = 11^2$. The trinomial factors as $(2x + 1)(5x - 3)$.

6. The discriminant is $(-3)^2 - 4(4)(-6) = 105$. The trinomial will not factor.

7. The discriminant is $(2)^2 - 4(3)(-2) = 28$. The trinomial will not factor.

8. The discriminant is $(1)^2 - 4(2)(3) = -23$. The trinomial will not factor.

9. $x^3 - x^2 - 6x = 0 \Rightarrow x(x^2 - x - 6) = 0 \Rightarrow x(x - 3)(x + 2) = 0 \Rightarrow x = 0, 3,$ or -2

    In the interval $(-\infty, -2)$, we test $x = -3$. $f(-3) = (-3)^3 - (-3)^2 - 6(-3) = -18 < 0$

    In the interval $(-2, 0)$, we test $x = -1$. $f(-1) = (-1)^3 - (-1)^2 - 6(-1) = 4 > 0$

    In the interval $(0, 3)$, we test $x = 1$. $f(1) = (1)^3 - (1)^2 - 6(1) = -6 < 0$

    In the interval $(3, \infty)$, we test $x = 4$. $f(4) = (4)^3 - (4)^2 - 6(4) = 24 > 0$

    The solution to the given inequality is $(-2, 0) \cup (3, \infty)$.

10. $x^3 - 3x^2 + 2x = 0 \Rightarrow x(x^2 - 3x + 2) = 0 \Rightarrow x(x - 1)(x - 2) = 0 \Rightarrow x = 0, 1,$ or 2

    In the interval $(-\infty, 0)$, we test $x = -1$. $f(-1) = (-1)^3 - 3(-1)^2 + 2(-1) = -6 < 0$

    In the interval $(0, 1)$, we test $x = 0.5$. $f(0.5) = (0.5)^3 - 3(0.5)^2 + 2(0.5) = 0.375 > 0$

    In the interval $(1, 2)$, we test $x = 1.5$. $f(1.5) = (1.5)^3 - 3(1.5)^2 + 2(1.5) = -0.375 < 0$

    In the interval $(2, \infty)$, we test $x = 3$. $f(3) = (3)^3 - 3(3)^2 + 2(3) = 6 > 0$

    The solution to the given inequality is $(-\infty, 0) \cup (1, 2)$.

11. $x^3 - 7x^2 + 14x - 8 = 0 \Rightarrow (x^3 - 8) - 7x^2 + 14x = 0 \Rightarrow (x - 2)(x^2 + 2x + 4) - 7x(x - 2) = 0 \Rightarrow$

    $(x - 2)((x^2 + 2x + 4) - 7x) = 0 \Rightarrow (x - 2)(x^2 - 5x + 4) = 0 \Rightarrow (x - 2)(x - 1)(x - 4) = 0 \Rightarrow x = 1, 2,$ or 4

    In the interval $(-\infty, 1)$, we test $x = 0$. $f(0) = (0)^3 - 7(0)^2 + 14(0) - 8 = -8 \le 0$

    In the interval $(1, 2)$, we test $x = 1.5$. $f(1.5) = (1.5)^3 - 7(1.5)^2 + 14(1.5) - 8 = 0.625 \ge 0$

    In the interval $(2, 4)$, we test $x = 3$. $f(3) = (3)^3 - 7(3)^2 + 14(3) - 8 = -2 \le 0$

    In the interval $(4, \infty)$, we test $x = 5$. $f(5) = (5)^3 - 7(5)^2 + 14(5) - 8 = 12 \ge 0$

    The solution to the given inequality is $(-\infty, 1] \cup [2, 4]$.

12. $9x - x^3 = 0 \Rightarrow x(9 - x^2) = 0 \Rightarrow x(3 - x)(3 + x) = 0 \Rightarrow x = 0, 3,$ or -3

In the interval $(-\infty,\ -3)$, we test $x=-4$. $f(-4)=9(-4)-(-4)^3=28\geq 0$

In the interval $(-3,\ 0)$, we test $x=-1$. $f(-1)=9(-1)-(-1)^3=-8\leq 0$

In the interval $(0,\ 3)$, we test $x=1$. $f(1)=9(1)-(1)^3=8\geq 0$

In the interval $(3,\ \infty)$, we test $x=4$. $f(4)=9(4)-(4)^3=-28\leq 0$

The solution to the given inequality is $(-\infty,\ -3]\cup[0,\ 3]$.

13. $x^4-5x^2+4=0\Rightarrow(x^2-1)(x^2-4)=0\Rightarrow(x-1)(x+1)(x-2)(x+2)=0\Rightarrow x=-2,\ -1,\ 1,\ \text{or}\ 2$

In the interval $(-\infty,\ -2)$, we test $x=-3$. $f(-3)=(-3)^4-5(-3)^2+4=40>0$

In the interval $(-2,\ -1)$, we test $x=-1.5$. $f(-1.5)=(-1.5)^4-5(-1.5)^2+4=-2.1875<0$

In the interval $(-1,\ 1)$, we test $x=0$. $f(0)=(0)^4-5(0)^2+4=4>0$

In the interval $(1,\ 2)$, we test $x=1.5$. $f(1.5)=(1.5)^4-5(1.5)^2+4=-2.1875<0$

In the interval $(2,\ \infty)$, we test $x=3$. $f(3)=(3)^4-5(3)^2+4=40>0$

The solution to the given inequality is $(-\infty,\ -2)\cup(-1,\ 1)\cup(2,\ \infty)$.

14. $1-x^4=0\Rightarrow(1-x^2)(1+x^2)=0\Rightarrow(1-x)(1+x)(1+x^2)=0\Rightarrow x=-1\ \text{or}\ 1$

In the interval $(-\infty,\ -1)$, we test $x=-2$. $f(-2)=1-(-2)^4=-15<0$

In the interval $(-1,\ 1)$, we test $x=0$. $f(0)=1-(0)^4=1>0$

In the interval $(1,\ \infty)$, we test $x=2$. $f(2)=1-(2)^4=-15<0$

The solution to the given inequality is $(-\infty,\ -1)\cup(1,\ \infty)$.

15. $\dfrac{3-x}{3x}=0\Rightarrow 3-x=0\Rightarrow x=3$. The expression is undefined when $3x=0\Rightarrow x=0$.

In the interval $(-\infty,\ 0)$, we test $x=-1$. $f(-1)=\dfrac{3-(-1)}{3(-1)}=-\dfrac{4}{3}\leq 0$

In the interval $(0,\ 3)$, we test $x=1$. $f(1)=\dfrac{3-(1)}{3(1)}=\dfrac{2}{3}\geq 0$

In the interval $(3,\ \infty)$, we test $x=4$. $f(4)=\dfrac{3-(4)}{3(4)}=-\dfrac{1}{12}\leq 0$

The solution to the given inequality is $(0,\ 3]$.

16. $\dfrac{x-2}{x+2}=0\Rightarrow x-2=0\Rightarrow x=2$. The expression is undefined when $x+2=0\Rightarrow x=-2$.

In the interval $(-\infty,\ -2)$, we test $x=-3$. $f(-3)=\dfrac{(-3)-2}{(-3)+2}=5>0$

In the interval $(-2,\ 2)$, we test $x=0$. $f(0)=\dfrac{(0)-2}{(0)+2}=-1<0$

In the interval $(2, \infty)$, we test $x = 3$. $f(3) = \dfrac{(3)-2}{(3)+2} = \dfrac{1}{5} > 0$

The solution to the given inequality is $(-\infty, -2) \cup (2, \infty)$.

17. $\dfrac{3-2x}{1+x} = 3 \Rightarrow 3-2x = 3+3x \Rightarrow 5x = 0 \Rightarrow x = 0.$

The expression is undefined when $1+x = 0 \Rightarrow x = -1.$

In the interval $(-\infty, -1)$, we test $x = -2$. $f(-2) = \dfrac{3-2(-2)}{1+(-2)} - 3 = -10 < 0$

In the interval $(-1, 0)$, we test $x = -0.5$. $f(-0.5) = \dfrac{3-2(-0.5)}{1+(-0.5)} - 3 = 5 > 0$

In the interval $(0, \infty)$, we test $x = 1$. $f(1) = \dfrac{3-2(1)}{1+(1)} - 3 = -\dfrac{5}{2} < 0$

The solution to the given inequality is $(-\infty, -1) \cup (0, \infty)$.

18. $\dfrac{x+1}{4-2x} = 1 \Rightarrow x+1 = 4-2x \Rightarrow 3x = 3 \Rightarrow x = 1.$

The expression is undefined when $4-2x = 0 \Rightarrow 2x = 4 \Rightarrow x = 2.$

In the interval $(-\infty, 1)$, we test $x = 0$. $f(0) = \dfrac{(0)+1}{4-2(0)} - 1 = -\dfrac{3}{4} \le 0$

In the interval $(1, 2)$, we test $x = 1.5$. $f(1.5) = \dfrac{(1.5)+1}{4-2(1.5)} - 1 = \dfrac{3}{2} \ge 0$

In the interval $(2, \infty)$, we test $x = 3$. $f(3) = \dfrac{(3)+1}{4-2(3)} - 1 = -3 \le 0$

The solution to the given inequality is $[1, 2)$.

19. The expression is undefined when $x^2 - 4 = 0 \Rightarrow (x+2)(x-2) = 0 \Rightarrow x = -2$ or 2.

In the interval $(-\infty, -2)$, we test $x = -3$. $f(-3) = \dfrac{5}{(-3)^2 - 4} = 1 > 0$

In the interval $(-2, 2)$, we test $x = 0$. $f(0) = \dfrac{5}{(0)^2 - 4} = -\dfrac{5}{4} < 0$

In the interval $(2, \infty)$, we test $x = 3$. $f(3) = \dfrac{5}{(3)^2 - 4} = 1 > 0$

The solution to the given inequality is $(-2, 2)$.

20. $\dfrac{x}{x^2 - 1} = 0 \Rightarrow x = 0.$ The expression is undefined when $x^2 - 1 = 0 \Rightarrow (x+1)(x-1) = 0 \Rightarrow x = -1$ or 1.

In the interval $(-\infty, -1)$, we test $x = -2$. $f(-2) = \dfrac{(-2)}{(-2)^2 - 1} = -\dfrac{2}{3} \le 0$

In the interval $(-1, 0)$, we test $x = -0.5$. $f(-0.5) = \dfrac{(-0.5)}{(-0.5)^2 - 1} = \dfrac{2}{3} \geq 0$

In the interval $(0, 1)$, we test $x = 0.5$. $f(0.5) = \dfrac{(0.5)}{(0.5)^2 - 1} = -\dfrac{2}{3} \leq 0$

In the interval $(1, \infty)$, we test $x = 2$. $f(2) = \dfrac{(2)}{(2)^2 - 1} = \dfrac{2}{3} \geq 0$

The solution to the given inequality is $(-1, \ 0] \cup (1, \ \infty)$.

Chapters 1–8 Cumulative Review Exercises

1. $F = \dfrac{5}{(-2)^2 + 1} = \dfrac{5}{4 + 1} = \dfrac{5}{5} = 1$

2.   Natural number: $\sqrt[3]{8} = 2$; whole number: $0, \sqrt[3]{8}$; integer: $0, -5, \sqrt[3]{8}$; rational number: $0.\overline{4}, 0, -5, \sqrt[3]{8}, -\dfrac{4}{3}$;

   irrational number: $\sqrt{7}$

3.   (a) $\left(\dfrac{x^2 y^6}{x^{-3}}\right)^2 = \dfrac{x^4 y^{12}}{x^{-6}} = x^{4-(-6)} y^{12} = x^{10} y^{12}$

   (b) $\dfrac{(xy^{-3})^2}{x(y^{-2})^{-1}} = \dfrac{x^2 y^{-6}}{xy^2} = x^{2-1} y^{-6-2} = x^1 y^{-8} = \dfrac{x}{y^8}$

   (c) $(a^2 b)^2 (ab^3)^{-4} = a^4 b^2 a^{-4} b^{-12} = a^{4-4} b^{2-12} = a^0 b^{-10} = \dfrac{1}{b^{10}}$

4. $9{,}290{,}000 = 9.29 \times 10^6$

5. $f(-2) = \sqrt{2 - (-2)} = \sqrt{4} = 2$; the radicand must be greater than or equal to zero, so $2 - x \geq 0 \Rightarrow x \leq 2$.

6. $(2, 5)$ lies on the graph of f.

7.   See Figure 7.   8.   See Figure 8.

Figure 7

Figure 8

Figure 16

9.   Parallel lines have the same slope, so $m = \dfrac{4-1}{-2-0} = \dfrac{3}{-2} = -\dfrac{3}{2}$.

   $y - (-1) = -\dfrac{3}{2}(x - 4) \Rightarrow y = -\dfrac{3}{2}x + 6 - 1 \Rightarrow y = -\dfrac{3}{2}x + 5$

10. $x = -3$

11. $2x - 3(x+2) = 6 \Rightarrow 2x - 3x - 6 = 6 \Rightarrow -x = 12 \Rightarrow x = -12$

12. $7 - x > 3x \Rightarrow 7 > 4x \Rightarrow \dfrac{7}{4} > x$; $\left(-\infty, \dfrac{7}{4}\right)$

13. $|3x - 2| \le 1 \Rightarrow 3x - 2 \le 1$ and $3x - 2 \ge -1 \Rightarrow 3x \le 3$ and $3x \ge 1 \Rightarrow x \le 1$ and $x \ge \dfrac{1}{3}$; $\left[\dfrac{1}{3}, 1\right]$

14. $-4 \le 1 - x < 2 \Rightarrow -5 \le -x < 1 \Rightarrow 5 \ge x > -1 \Rightarrow -1 < x \le 5; \, (-1, 5]$

15. Multiply the first equation by 5 and add to the second equation.

$$\begin{array}{l} -5x - 20y = -15 \\ \underline{5x + y = -4} \\ -19y = -19 \end{array} \Rightarrow y = 1$$

Substitute $y = 1$ into the first equation: $-x - 4(1) = -3 \Rightarrow -x = -3 + 4 \Rightarrow -x = 1 \Rightarrow x = -1$

The solution is $(-1, 1)$.

16. Note that $3x + y \le 3 \Rightarrow y \le -3x + 3$ and $x - 3y \le 3 \Rightarrow -3y \le -x + 3 \Rightarrow y \ge \dfrac{1}{3}x - 1$. See Figure 16.

17. Add the first two equations.

$$\begin{array}{l} x + y - z = 3 \\ \underline{x - y + z = 1} \\ 2x = 4 \end{array} \Rightarrow x = 2$$

Add the second and third equations.

$$\begin{array}{l} x - y + z = 1 \\ \underline{2x - y - z = 1} \\ 3x - 2y = 2 \end{array} \Rightarrow 3(2) - 2y = 2 \Rightarrow 6 - 2y = 2 \Rightarrow -2y = -4 \Rightarrow y = 2$$

Substitute $x = 2$ and $y = 2$ into the first equation.

$2 + 2 - z = 3 \Rightarrow 4 - z = 3 \Rightarrow -z = -1 \Rightarrow z = 1$

The solution is $(2, 2, 1)$.

18. $(3x - 2)(2x + 7) = 6x^2 + 21x - 4x - 14 = 6x^2 + 17x - 14$

19. $3xy(x^2 + y^2) = 3x^3y + 3xy^3$

20. $(\sqrt{x} + 3)(\sqrt{x} - 3) = (\sqrt{x})^2 - (3)^2 = x - 9$

21. $x^3 - x^2 - 2x = x(x^2 - x - 2) = x(x - 2)(x + 1)$

22. $4x^2 - 25 = (2x - 5)(2x + 5)$

23. $x^2 - 3 = 0 \Rightarrow x^2 = 3 \Rightarrow x = \pm\sqrt{3}$

24. $x^2 + 1 = 2x \Rightarrow x^2 - 2x + 1 = 0 \Rightarrow (x - 1)^2 = 0 \Rightarrow x - 1 = 0 \Rightarrow x = 1$

25. $\dfrac{(x+3)^2}{x+2} \cdot \dfrac{x+2}{2x+6} = \dfrac{(x+3)(x+3)(x+2)}{(x+2)(2)(x+3)} = \dfrac{x+3}{2}$ or $\dfrac{1}{2}(x+3)$

26. $\dfrac{1}{x+2} - \dfrac{1}{x} = \dfrac{1}{x+2} \cdot \dfrac{x}{x} - \dfrac{1}{x} \cdot \dfrac{x+2}{x+2} = \dfrac{x}{x(x+2)} - \dfrac{x+2}{x(x+2)} = \dfrac{x - x - 2}{x(x+2)} = \dfrac{-2}{x(x+2)}$

27. $\sqrt{16x^6} = \sqrt{16} \cdot \sqrt{x^6} = 4x^3$

28. $16^{-3/2} = (16^{1/2})^{-3} = 4^{-3} = \dfrac{1}{64}$

29. $\dfrac{\sqrt[3]{81x}}{\sqrt[3]{3x}} = \sqrt[3]{\dfrac{81x}{3x}} = \sqrt[3]{27} = 3$

30. $\sqrt{8x} + \sqrt{2x} = \sqrt{4 \cdot 2x} + \sqrt{2x} = 2\sqrt{2x} + \sqrt{2x} = 3\sqrt{2x}$

31.   See Figure 31.

        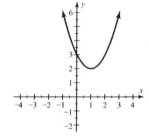

Figure 31   Figure 36

32. $d = \sqrt{(x_2 - x_1)^2 + (y_2 - y_1)^2} = \sqrt{(4 - (-1))^2 + (3 - 2)^2} = \sqrt{(5)^2 + (1)^2} = \sqrt{25 + 1} = \sqrt{26}$

33. $\dfrac{3 - i}{2 + i} = \dfrac{3 - i}{2 + i} \cdot \dfrac{2 - i}{2 - i} = \dfrac{6 - 3i - 2i + i^2}{4 - i^2} = \dfrac{6 - 5i - 1}{4 - (-1)} = \dfrac{5 - 5i}{5} = 1 - i$

34. $3\sqrt{x+1} = 2x \Rightarrow 9(x+1) = 4x^2 \Rightarrow 9x + 9 = 4x^2 \Rightarrow 4x^2 - 9x - 9 = 0 \Rightarrow (x-3)(4x+3) = 0 \Rightarrow x = 3$ ($x = -\dfrac{3}{4}$

       does not check).

35.   Graph $Y_1 = 2X$ and $Y_2 = \sqrt{(2.1 - X)} + (0.1X) \wedge (1/3)$ in $[-4.7, 4.7, 1]$ by $[-3.1, 3.1, 1]$. The solution is

       $x \approx 0.79$.

       Figure 35

36.   See Figure 36.

       (a) $(1, 2)$

       (b) $f(-1) = (-1)^2 - 2(-1) + 3 = 1 + 2 + 3 = 6$

       (c) $x = 1$

       (d) f is increasing when $x \geq 1$

37. $f(x) = 2x^2 - 4x - 1 \Rightarrow f(x) = 2(x^2 - 2x) - 1 \Rightarrow f(x) = 2(x^2 - 2x + 1) - 1 - 2 \Rightarrow f(x) = 2(x-1)^2 - 3$

38.   The graph is shifted 1 unit left and 2 units downward. The graph of $f(x)$ is narrower.

39. $x^2 + 6x = 2 \Rightarrow x^2 + 6x + 9 = 2 + 9 \Rightarrow (x+3)^2 = 11 \Rightarrow x + 3 = \pm\sqrt{11} \Rightarrow x = -3 \pm \sqrt{11}$

40. $2x^2 - 3x = 1 \Rightarrow 2x^2 - 3x - 1 = 0$; $a = 2, b = -3, c = -1$

$$x = \frac{-b \pm \sqrt{b^2 - 4ac}}{2a} = \frac{-(-3) \pm \sqrt{(-3)^2 - 4(2)(-1)}}{2(2)} = \frac{3 \pm \sqrt{17}}{4}$$

41. $x(4 - x) = 3 \Rightarrow 4x - x^2 = 3 \Rightarrow x^2 - 4x + 3 = 0 \Rightarrow (x-3)(x-1) = 0 \Rightarrow x = 3$ or $x = 1$

42. (a) $x = -2$ or $x = 1$

    (b) $-2 \le x \le 1$

43. $x^2 - 3x + 2 > 0 \Rightarrow (x-2)(x-1) > 0 \Rightarrow x < 1$ or $x > 2$

44. $x^4 - 256 = 0 \Rightarrow (x^2 - 16)(x^2 + 16) = 0 \Rightarrow (x-4)(x+4)(x^2 + 16) = 0 \Rightarrow x = 4$ or $x = -4$ or

    $x^2 = -16 \Rightarrow x = \pm\sqrt{-16} \Rightarrow x = \pm 4i$

45. c; $y = ax - b$ is a linear equation and $a > 0$.

46. f; $y = b$ is a horizontal line.

47. g; $y = -ax^2 + c$ is a quadratic equation whose graph is a parabola opening downward (since $a > 0$).

48. e; $y = \dfrac{a}{x}$ is a rational equation, undefined when $x = 0$ and $y = 0$.

49. d; $y = ax^3$ is a cubic equation.

50. a; $y = |ax + b|$ has only nonnegative values.

51. b; $y = a\sqrt{x}$ is a radical function defined only for $x \ge 0$.

52. h; $y = a\sqrt[3]{x}$ is a cube root equation.

53. (a) $G(0) = 300$ gallons ; initially, the tank holds 300 gallons.

    (b) The t-intercept is 6; after 6 minutes the tank is empty.

    (c) (0, 300) and (6, 0) are on the graph so $m = \dfrac{0 - 300}{6 - 0} = \dfrac{-300}{6} = -50$; water is pumped out at 50 gallons per minute.

    (d) Since (0, 300) is on the graph and $m = -50$, $G(t) = -50t + 300$ or $G(t) = 300 - 50t$

54. Let x, y, and z be the amounts invested at 4% ,5%, and 6% interest, respectively. The system needed is

    $$
    \begin{array}{ll}
    x + y + z = 4000 & \qquad x + y + z = 4000 \\
    z = y + 1000 \qquad \Rightarrow & \qquad y - z = -1000 \\
    0.04x + 0.05y + 0.06z = 216 & \qquad 4x + 5y + 6z = 21{,}600
    \end{array}
    $$

    Multiply the first equation by -4 and add to the third equation

    $$
    \begin{array}{r}
    -4x - 4y - 4z = -16{,}000 \\
    \underline{4x + 5y + 6z = 21{,}600} \\
    y + 2z = 5600
    \end{array}
    $$

    Multiply the second equation by 2 and add to this new equation.

$$2y - 2z = -2000$$
$$\underline{y + 2z = 5600}$$
$$3y = 3600 \qquad \Rightarrow y = 1200$$

Substitute $y = 1200$ into the second equation.

$$1200 - z = -1000 \Rightarrow -z = -2200 \Rightarrow z = 2200$$

Substitute $y = 1200$ and $z = 2200$ into the first equation.

$$x + 1200 + 2200 = 4000 \Rightarrow x = 600$$

$600 is invested at 4%, $1200 is invested at 5%, and $2200 is invested at 6%.

55.   Let x represent the length of one of the two equal sides of the garden without the gate. Then the other sides of

the garden have lengths $\dfrac{1}{2}(490 - 2x + 10) = \dfrac{1}{2}(500 - 2x) = 250 - x$. $(250 - x)x = 250x - x^2$; The graph of

$y = -x^2 + 250x$ is a parabola opening downward; its vertex is its maximum point. The x-value of the vertex is

on the axis of symmetry, so $x = -\dfrac{b}{2a} = -\dfrac{250}{2(-1)} = 125$. The dimensions of the garden of largest area are 125

feet by 125 feet.

56.   Let h represent the height of the tree.

$$\dfrac{6}{10} = \dfrac{h}{55} \quad \Rightarrow \quad 10h = 6(55) \Rightarrow 10h = 330 \Rightarrow h = 33 \text{ feet}$$

Critical Thinking Solutions for Chapter 8

Section 8.2

• The productof $(4)(4) = 16$ goes in the remaining square.

Section 8.3

• The product of $(3)(3) = 9$ goes in the remaining square.

• If we write the equation in $x^2 + kx = d$ form, it would become $x^2 + 0x = 7$. To complete the square we would add zero to both sides of the equation. Completing the square will not work in this case. The square root property should be used for this equation.

Section 8.4

• Both expressions equal zero because these values of x are the solutions to $2x^2 - 3x - 1 = 0$.

• Both expressions equal zero because these values of x are the solutions to $2x^2 + x + 3 = 0$.

Section 8.5

• i.   The parabola is above the x-axis for values of x between the intercepts: $(-3, 4)$.

ii.   The parabola is below the x-axis for values of x outside of the intercepts: $(-\infty, -3) \cup (4, \infty)$.

Chapter 9: Exponential and Logarithmic Functions

9.1: Composite and Inverse Functions

Concepts

1. $g(f(7))$

2. $f(g(x))$

3.   No

4.   inputs; outputs

5.   No

6.   one-to-one

7.   adding 10

8.   7

9.   8; 6

10. $x; y$

11.   one-to-one

12.   reflection; $y = x$

Composite Functions

13.   (a) $f(-2) = (-2)^2 = 4$, then $(g \circ f)(-2) = g(f(-2)) = g(4) = 4 + 3 = 7$

  (b) $g(4) = 4 + 3 = 7$, then $(f \circ g)(4) = f(g(4)) = f(7) = 7^2 = 49$

  (c) $(g \circ f)(x) = g(f(x)) = g(x^2) = x^2 + 3$

  (d) $(f \circ g)(x) = f(g(x)) = f(x+3) = (x+3)^2$

14.   (a) $f(-2) = 4(-2)^2 = 16$, then $(g \circ f)(-2) = g(f(-2)) = g(16) = 5(16) = 80$

  (b) $g(4) = 5(4) = 20$, then $(f \circ g)(4) = f(g(4)) = f(20) = 4(20)^2 = 1600$

  (c) $(g \circ f)(x) = g(f(x)) = g(4x^2) = 5(4x^2) = 20x^2$

  (d) $(f \circ g)(x) = f(g(x)) = f(5x) = 4(5x)^2 = 100x^2$

15.   (a) $f(-2) = 2(-2) = -4$, then $(g \circ f)(-2) = g(f(-2)) = g(-4) = (-4)^3 - 1 = -65$

  (b) $g(4) = 4^3 - 1 = 63$, then $(f \circ g)(4) = f(g(4)) = f(63) = 2(63) = 126$

  (c) $(g \circ f)(x) = g(f(x)) = g(2x) = (2x)^3 - 1 = 8x^3 - 1$

  (d) $(f \circ g)(x) = f(g(x)) = f(x^3 - 1) = 2(x^3 - 1) = 2x^3 - 2$

16. (a) $f(-2) = 3(-2) + 1 = -5$, then $(g \circ f)(-2) = g(f(-2)) = g(-5) = (-5)^2 + 4(-5) = 5$

 (b) $g(4) = 4^2 + 4(4) = 32$, then $(f \circ g)(4) = f(g(4)) = f(32) = 3(32) + 1 = 97$

 (c) $(g \circ f)(x) = g(f(x)) = g(3x + 1) = (3x + 1)^2 + 4(3x + 1) = 9x^2 + 18x + 5$

 (d) $(f \circ g)(x) = f(g(x)) = f(x^2 + 4x) = 3(x^2 + 4x) + 1 = 3x^2 + 12x + 1$

17. (a) $f(-2) = \frac{1}{2}(-2) = -1$, then $(g \circ f)(-2) = g(f(-2)) = g(-1) = |(-1) - 2| = 3$

 (b) $g(4) = |4 - 2| = 2$, then $(f \circ g)(4) = f(g(4)) = f(2) = \frac{1}{2}(2) = 1$

 (c) $(g \circ f)(x) = g(f(x)) = g\left(\frac{1}{2}x\right) = \left|\frac{1}{2}x - 2\right|$

 (d) $(f \circ g)(x) = f(g(x)) = f(|x - 2|) = \frac{1}{2}|x - 2|$

18. (a) $f(-2) = 6(-2) = -12$, then $(g \circ f)(-2) = g(f(-2)) = g(-12) = \frac{2}{-12 - 5} = -\frac{2}{17}$

 (b) $g(4) = \frac{2}{4 - 5} = -2$, then $(f \circ g)(4) = f(g(4)) = f(-2) = 6(-2) = -12$

 (c) $(g \circ f)(x) = g(f(x)) = g(6x) = \frac{2}{6x - 5}$

 (d) $(f \circ g)(x) = f(g(x)) = f\left(\frac{2}{x - 5}\right) = 6\left(\frac{2}{x - 5}\right) = \frac{12}{x - 5}$

19. (a) $f(-2) = \frac{1}{-2} = -\frac{1}{2}$, then $(g \circ f)(-2) = g(f(-2)) = g\left(-\frac{1}{2}\right) = 3 - 5\left(-\frac{1}{2}\right) = \frac{11}{2}$

 (b) $g(4) = 3 - 5(4) = -17$, then $(f \circ g)(4) = f(g(4)) = f(-17) = \frac{1}{-17} = -\frac{1}{17}$

 (c) $(g \circ f)(x) = g(f(x)) = g\left(\frac{1}{x}\right) = 3 - 5\left(\frac{1}{x}\right) = 3 - \frac{5}{x}$

 (d) $(f \circ g)(x) = f(g(x)) = f(3 - 5x) = \frac{1}{3 - 5x}$

20. (a) $f(-2) = \sqrt{(-2) + 3} = 1$, then $(g \circ f)(-2) = g(f(-2)) = g(1) = 1^3 - 3 = -2$

 (b) $g(4) = 4^3 - 3 = 61$, then $(f \circ g)(4) = f(g(4)) = f(61) = \sqrt{61 + 3} = 8$

 (c) $(g \circ f)(x) = g(f(x)) = g(\sqrt{x + 3}) = (\sqrt{x + 3})^3 - 3 = (x + 3)^{3/2} - 3$

 (d) $(f \circ g)(x) = f(g(x)) = f(x^3 - 3) = \sqrt{(x^3 - 3) + 3} = \sqrt{x^3}$

21. (a) $f(-2) = 2(-2) = -4$, then $(g \circ f)(-2) = g(f(-2)) = g(-4) = 4(-4)^2 - 2(-4) + 5 = 77$

(b) $g(4) = 4(4)^2 - 2(4) + 5 = 61$, then $(f \circ g)(4) = f(g(4)) = f(61) = 2(61) = 122$

(c) $(g \circ f)(x) = g(f(x)) = g(2x) = 4(2x)^2 - 2(2x) + 5 = 16x^2 - 4x + 5$

(d) $(f \circ g)(x) = f(g(x)) = f(4x^2 - 2x + 5) = 2(4x^2 - 2x + 5) = 8x^2 - 4x + 10$

22.   (a) $f(-2) = 9(-2) - \dfrac{1}{3(-2)} = -\dfrac{107}{6}$, then $(g \circ f)(-2) = g(f(-2)) = g\left(-\dfrac{107}{6}\right) = \dfrac{-\frac{107}{6}}{3} = -\dfrac{107}{18}$

      (b) $g(4) = \dfrac{4}{3}$, then $(f \circ g)(4) = f(g(4)) = f\left(\dfrac{4}{3}\right) = 9\left(\dfrac{4}{3}\right) - \dfrac{1}{3\left(\frac{4}{3}\right)} = \dfrac{47}{4}$

      (c) $(g \circ f)(x) = g(f(x)) = g\left(9x - \dfrac{1}{3x}\right) = \dfrac{9x - \frac{1}{3x}}{3} = 3x - \dfrac{1}{9x}$

      (d) $(f \circ g)(x) = f(g(x)) = f\left(\dfrac{x}{3}\right) = 9\left(\dfrac{x}{3}\right) - \dfrac{1}{3\left(\frac{x}{3}\right)} = 3x - \dfrac{1}{x}$

23.   (a) $(f \circ g)(0) = f(g(0)) = f(-1) = 1$

      (b) $(g \circ f)(-1) = g(f(-1)) = g(1) = 2$

24.   (a) $(f \circ g)(1) = f(g(1)) = f(2) = -2$

      (b) $(g \circ f)(-2) = g(f(-2)) = g(2) = -2$

25.   (a) $(f \circ f)(-1) = f(f(-1)) = f(1) = -1$

      (b) $(g \circ g)(0) = g(g(0)) = g(-1) = 1$

26.   (a) $(g \circ g)(2) = g(g(2)) = g(-2) = 0$

      (b) $(f \circ f)(1) = f(f(1)) = f(-1) = 1$

27.   (a) $\left(f^{-1} \circ g\right)(-2) = f^{-1}(g(-2)) = f^{-1}(0) = 0$

      (b) $\left(g^{-1} \circ f\right)(2) = g^{-1}(f(2)) = g^{-1}(-2) = 2$

28.   (a) $\left(f \circ g^{-1}\right)(1) = f(g^{-1}(1)) = f(-1) = 1$

      (b) $\left(g \circ f^{-1}\right)(-2) = g(f^{-1}(-2)) = g(2) = -2$

29.   (a) $(f \circ g)(0) = f(g(0)) = f(-1) = 2$

      (b) $(g \circ f)(1) = g(f(1)) = g(2) = -3$

      (c) $(f \circ f)(-1) = f(f(-1)) = f(2) = -1$

30.   (a) $(f \circ g)(1) = f(g(1)) = f(3) = 4$

(b) $\left(g \circ f\right)(-2) = g\left(f(-2)\right) = g(-1) = -3$

(c) $\left(g \circ g\right)(-2) = g\left(g(-2)\right) = g(0) = 0$

31. $f(1) = f(-1) = 5$; *Answers may vary.*

32. $f(2) = f(-2) = 0$; *Answers may vary.*

33. $f(1) = f(-1) = 101$; *Answers may vary.*

34. $f(3) = f(-3) = \dfrac{9}{10}$; *Answers may vary.*

35. $f(2) = f(-2) = 4$; *Answers may vary.*

36. $f(1) = f(-1) = 0$; *Answers may vary.*

37.   This graph passes the horizontal line test. The function is one-to-one.

38.   This graph passes the horizontal line test. The function is one-to-one.

39.   This graph does not pass the horizontal line test. The function is not one-to-one.

40.   This graph does not pass the horizontal line test. The function is not one-to-one.

41.   This graph passes the horizontal line test. The function is one-to-one.

42.   This graph does not pass the horizontal line test. The function is not one-to-one.

43.   Divide x by 7. $f(x) = 7x$; $g(x) = \dfrac{x}{7}$

44.   Add 10 to x. $f(x) = x - 10$; $g(x) = x + 10$

45.   Multiply x by 2 and then subtract 5. $f(x) = \dfrac{x+5}{2}$; $g(x) = 2x - 5$

46.   Subtract 8 from x and then divide the result by 6. $f(x) = 6x + 8$; $g(x) = \dfrac{x-8}{6}$

47.   Add 3 to x and then multiply the result by 2. $f(x) = \dfrac{1}{2}x - 3$; $g(x) = 2(x+3)$

48.   Subtract 20 from x and then multiply the result by 10. $f(x) = \dfrac{x}{10} + 20$; $g(x) = 10(x - 20)$

49.   Take the cube root of x and then subtract 5. $f(x) = (x+5)^3$; $g(x) = \sqrt[3]{x} - 5$

50.   Cube the sum of x and 2. $f(x) = \sqrt[3]{x} - 2$; $g(x) = (x+2)^3$

51. $\left(f \circ f^{-1}\right)(x) = f\left(f^{-1}(x)\right) = f\left(\dfrac{x}{4}\right) = 4\left(\dfrac{x}{4}\right) = x$ and $\left(f^{-1} \circ f\right)(x) = f^{-1}\left(f(x)\right) = f^{-1}(4x) = \dfrac{4x}{4} = x$

52. $\left(f \circ f^{-1}\right)(x) = f\left(f^{-1}(x)\right) = f\left(\dfrac{3x}{2}\right) = \dfrac{2\left(\frac{3x}{2}\right)}{3} = \dfrac{3x}{3} = x$ and $\left(f^{-1} \circ f\right)(x) = f^{-1}\left(f(x)\right) = f^{-1}\left(\dfrac{2x}{3}\right) = \dfrac{3\left(\frac{2x}{3}\right)}{2} = \dfrac{2x}{2} = x$

53. $\left(f \circ f^{-1}\right)(x) = f\left(f^{-1}(x)\right) = f\left(\dfrac{x-5}{3}\right) = 3\left(\dfrac{x-5}{3}\right) + 5 = x - 5 + 5 = x$

$$\left(f^{-1}\circ f\right)(x)=f^{-1}\left(f\left(x\right)\right)=f^{-1}\left(3x+5\right)=\frac{\left(3x+5\right)-5}{3}=\frac{3x}{3}=x$$

54. $$\left(f\circ f^{-1}\right)(x)=f\left(f^{-1}\left(x\right)\right)=f\left(x-7\right)=\left(x-7\right)+7=x$$

  $$\left(f^{-1}\circ f\ \right)(x)=f^{-1}\left(f\left(x\right)\right)=f^{-1}\left(x+7\right)=\left(x+7\right)-7=x$$

55. $$\left(f\circ f^{-1}\right)(x)=f\left(f^{-1}\left(x\right)\right)=f\left(\sqrt[3]{x}\right)=\left(\sqrt[3]{x}\right)^{3}=x\text{ and }\left(f^{-1}\circ f\right)(x)=f^{-1}\left(f\left(x\right)\right)=f^{-1}\left(x^{3}\right)=\sqrt[3]{x^{3}}=x$$

56. $$\left(f\circ f^{-1}\right)(x)=f\left(f^{-1}\left(x\right)\right)=f\left(x^{3}+4\right)=\sqrt[3]{\left(x^{3}+4\right)-4}=\sqrt[3]{x^{3}}=x$$

  $$\left(f^{-1}\circ f\right)(x)=f^{-1}\left(f\left(x\right)\right)=f^{-1}\left(\sqrt[3]{x-4}\right)=\left(\sqrt[3]{x-4}\right)^{3}+4=\left(x-4\right)+4=x$$

57. $$\left(f\circ f^{-1}\right)(x)=f\left(f^{-1}\left(x\right)\right)=f\left(\frac{1}{x}\right)=\frac{1}{\frac{1}{x}}=x\text{ and }\left(f^{-1}\circ f\right)(x)=f^{-1}\left(f\left(x\right)\right)=f^{-1}\left(\frac{1}{x}\right)=\frac{1}{\frac{1}{x}}=x$$

58. $$\left(f\circ f^{-1}\right)(x)=f\left(f^{-1}\left(x\right)\right)=f\left(7x-7\right)=\frac{\left(7x-7\right)+7}{7}=\frac{7x}{7}=x$$

  $$\left(f^{-1}\circ f\right)(x)=f^{-1}\left(f\left(x\right)\right)=f^{-1}\left(\frac{x+7}{7}\right)=7\left(\frac{x+7}{7}\right)-7=\left(x+7\right)-7=x$$

59. $f(x)=12x\Rightarrow y=12x,$ interchange x and y and solve for $y.$ $x=12y\Rightarrow y=\dfrac{x}{12}\Rightarrow f^{-1}(x)=\dfrac{x}{12}$

60. $f(x)=\dfrac{3}{4}x\Rightarrow y=\dfrac{3}{4}x,$ interchange x and y and solve for $y.$ $x=\dfrac{3}{4}y\Rightarrow y=\dfrac{4}{3}x\Rightarrow f^{-1}(x)=\dfrac{4}{3}x$

61. $f(x)=x+8\Rightarrow y=x+8,$ interchange x and y and solve for $y.$

  $x=y+8\Rightarrow y=x-8\Rightarrow f^{-1}(x)=x-8$

62. $f(x)=x-3\Rightarrow y=x-3,$ interchange x and y and solve for $y.$

  $x=y-3\Rightarrow y=x+3\Rightarrow f^{-1}(x)=x+3$

63. $f(x)=5x-2\Rightarrow y=5x-2,$ interchange x and y and solve for $y.$

  $x=5y-2\Rightarrow 5y=x+2\Rightarrow y=\dfrac{x+2}{5}\Rightarrow f^{-1}(x)=\dfrac{x+2}{5}$

64. $f(x)=3x+4\Rightarrow y=3x+4,$ interchange x and y and solve for $y.$

  $x=3y+4\Rightarrow 3y=x-4\Rightarrow y=\dfrac{x-4}{3}\Rightarrow f^{-1}(x)=\dfrac{x-4}{3}$

65. $f(x)=-\dfrac{1}{2}x+1\Rightarrow y=-\dfrac{1}{2}x+1,$ interchange x and y and solve for $y.$

  $x=-\dfrac{1}{2}y+1\Rightarrow -\dfrac{1}{2}y=x-1\Rightarrow y=-2\left(x-1\right)\Rightarrow f^{-1}(x)=-2\left(x-1\right)$

66. $f(x) = \frac{3}{4}x - \frac{1}{4} \Rightarrow y = \frac{3}{4}x - \frac{1}{4}$, interchange x and y and solve for y.

$x = \frac{3}{4}y - \frac{1}{4} \Rightarrow \frac{3}{4}y = x + \frac{1}{4} \Rightarrow y = \frac{4}{3}\left(x + \frac{1}{4}\right) \Rightarrow f^{-1}(x) = \frac{4}{3}\left(x + \frac{1}{4}\right)$

67. $f(x) = 8 - x \Rightarrow y = 8 - x$, interchange x and y and solve for y.

$x = 8 - y \Rightarrow y = 8 - x \Rightarrow f^{-1}(x) = 8 - x$

68. $f(x) = 5 - x \Rightarrow y = 5 - x$, interchange x and y and solve for y.

$x = 5 - y \Rightarrow y = 5 - x \Rightarrow f^{-1}(x) = 5 - x$

69. $f(x) = \frac{x+1}{2} \Rightarrow y = \frac{x+1}{2}$, interchange x and y and solve for y.

$x = \frac{y+1}{2} \Rightarrow y + 1 = 2x \Rightarrow y = 2x - 1 \Rightarrow f^{-1}(x) = 2x - 1$

70. $f(x) = \frac{3-x}{5} \Rightarrow y = \frac{3-x}{5}$, interchange x and y and solve for y.

$x = \frac{3-y}{5} \Rightarrow 3 - y = 5x \Rightarrow -y = 5x - 3 \Rightarrow y = 3 - 5x \Rightarrow f^{-1}(x) = 3 - 5x$

71. $f(x) = \sqrt[3]{2x} \Rightarrow y = \sqrt[3]{2x}$, interchange x and y and solve for y.

$x = \sqrt[3]{2y} \Rightarrow 2y = x^3 \Rightarrow y = \frac{x^3}{2} \Rightarrow f^{-1}(x) = \frac{x^3}{2}$

72. $f(x) = \sqrt[3]{x+4} \Rightarrow y = \sqrt[3]{x+4}$, interchange x and y and solve for y.

$x = \sqrt[3]{y+4} \Rightarrow y + 4 = x^3 \Rightarrow y = x^3 - 4 \Rightarrow f^{-1}(x) = x^3 - 4$

73. $f(x) = x^3 - 8 \Rightarrow y = x^3 - 8$, interchange x and y and solve for y.

$x = y^3 - 8 \Rightarrow y^3 = x + 8 \Rightarrow y = \sqrt[3]{x+8} \Rightarrow f^{-1}(x) = \sqrt[3]{x+8}$

74. $f(x) = (x-5)^3 \Rightarrow y = (x-5)^3$, interchange x and y and solve for y.

$x = (y-5)^3 \Rightarrow y - 5 = \sqrt[3]{x} \Rightarrow y = \sqrt[3]{x} + 5 \Rightarrow f^{-1}(x) = \sqrt[3]{x} + 5$

75. See Figure 75. The domain of f = the range of $f^{-1} = \{0, 1, 2, 3, 4\}$.

The range of f = the domain of $f^{-1} = \{0, 5, 10, 15, 20\}$.

x	0	5	10	15	20
$f^{-1}(x)$	0	1	2	3	4

x	1	2	3	4	5
$f^{-1}(x)$	-4	-2	0	2	4

Figure 75   Figure 76

76. See Figure 76. The domain of f = the range of $f^{-1} = \{-4, -2, 0, 2, 4\}$.

The range of f = the domain of $f^{-1} = \{1, 2, 3, 4, 5\}$.

77.   See Figure 77. The domain of f = the range of f^{-1} = $\{-5, 0, 5, 10, 15\}$.

The range of f = the domain of f^{-1} = $\{-4, -2, 0, 2, 4\}$.

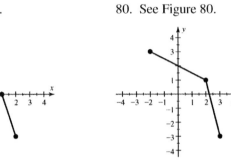

x	4	2	0	-2	-4
$f^{-1}(x)$	-5	0	5	10	15

x	8	6	4	2	0
$f^{-1}(x)$	0	2	4	6	8

Figure 77   Figure 78

78.   See Figure 78. The domain of f = the range of f^{-1} = $\{0, 2, 4, 6, 8\}$.

The range of f = the domain of f^{-1} = $\{0, 2, 4, 6, 8\}$.

79.   See Figure 79.   80. See Figure 80.   81. See Figure 81.

Figure 79   Figure 80   Figure 81

82.   See Figure 82.

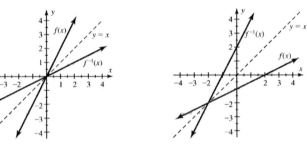

Figure 82   Figure 83   Figure 84

83.   The graph of f^{-1} is a reflection of the graph of f across the line $y = x$. See Figure 83.

84.   The graph of f^{-1} is a reflection of the graph of f across the line $y = x$. See Figure 84.

85.   The graph of f^{-1} is a reflection of the graph of f across the line $y = x$. See Figure 85.

Figure 85   Figure 86

86.   The graph of f^{-1} is a reflection of the graph of f across the line $y = x$. See Figure 86.

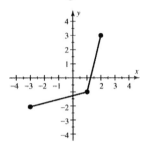

87. (a) $(fg)(2) = (2^2 - 2)(2^2 + 2) = (4 - 2)(4 + 2) = (2)(6) = 12$

(b) $(f - g)(x) = (x^2 - 2) - (x^2 + 2) = x^2 - x^2 - 2 - 2 = -4$

(c) $(f \circ g)(x) = f(g(x)) = f(x^2 + 2) = (x^2 + 2)^2 - 2 = x^4 + 4x^2 + 4 - 2 = x^4 + 4x^2 + 2$

88. (a) $(fg)(2) = (2(2)^2)(2(2) - 1) = 8(4 - 1) = 8(3) = 24$

(b) $(f - g)(x) = 2x^2 - (2x - 1) = 2x^2 - 2x + 1$

(c) $(f \circ g)(x) = f(g(x)) = f(2x - 1) = 2(2x - 1)^2 = 2(4x^2 - 4x + 1) = 8x^2 - 8x + 2$

89. (a) $(fg)(2) = \left(\dfrac{1}{2}\right)\left(\dfrac{2}{2}\right) = \dfrac{2}{4} = \dfrac{1}{2}$

(b) $(f - g)(x) = \dfrac{1}{x} - \dfrac{2}{x} = -\dfrac{1}{x}$

(c) $(f \circ g)(x) = f(g(x)) = f\left(\dfrac{2}{x}\right) = \dfrac{1}{\dfrac{2}{x}} = \dfrac{x}{2}$

90. (a) $(fg)(2) = (2)^3\left(\sqrt[3]{2}\right) = 8\sqrt[3]{2}$

(b) $(f - g)(x) = x^3 - \sqrt[3]{x}$

(c) $(f \circ g)(x) = f(g(x)) = f\left(\sqrt[3]{x}\right) = \left(\sqrt[3]{x}\right)^3 = x$

Applications

91. (a) $(C \circ r)(5) = C(r(5)) = C(2 \cdot 5) = C(10) = 2\pi \cdot 10 = 20\pi$

After 5 seconds, the wave has a circumference of $20\pi \approx 62.8$ feet.

(b) $(C \circ r)(t) = C(r(t)) = C(2t) = 2\pi \cdot 2t = 4\pi t$

92. (a) $(V \circ r)(3) = V(r(3)) = V\left(\sqrt[3]{3}\right) = \dfrac{4}{3}\pi\left(\sqrt[3]{3}\right)^3 = \dfrac{4}{3}\pi \cdot 3 = 4\pi$

After 3 seconds, the balloon has a volume of $4\pi \approx 12.6$ cubic inches.

(b) $(V \circ r)(t) = V(r(t)) = V\left(\sqrt[3]{t}\right) = \dfrac{4}{3}\pi\left(\sqrt[3]{t}\right)^3 = \dfrac{4}{3}\pi t$

93. (a) $P(1980) = 16$; In 1980, 16% of people 25 or older completed 4 or more years of college.

(b) See Figure 93.

(c) $P^{-1}(16) = 1980$

x	8	16	27
$P^{-1}(x)$	1960	1980	2000

x	20	26	29	43
$P^{-1}(x)$	1970	1980	1990	2000

Figure 93   Figure 96

94.   (a) $U(2) = 1.5(2) = 3$; There is a 3% increase in UV radiation when there is a 2% decrease in the thickness

of the ozone layer. $C(3) = 3.5(3) = 10.5$; There is a 10.5% increase in skin cancer cases when the UV

radiation level increases by 3%.

(b) $(C \circ U)(2) = C(U(2)) = C(3) = 10.5$; There is a 10.5% increase in skin cancer cases when there is a 2%

decrease in the thickness of the ozone layer.

(c) $(C \circ U)(x) = C(U(x)) = C(1.5x) = 3.5(1.5x) = 5.25x$; This formula calculates the percent increase in

skin cancer cases when the thickness of the ozone layer decreases by x percent.

95.   (a) $T(1) = 75°$ and $M(75) = 150$

(b) $(M \circ T)(1) = M(T(1)) = M(75) = 150$

One hour after midnight there are 150 mosquitoes per 100 square feet.

(c) $(M \circ T)(h)$ calculates the number of mosquitoes per 100 square feet, h hours after midnight.

(d) For $T(h)$, $m = \dfrac{50-80}{6-0} = \dfrac{-30}{6} = -5$. Since the y-intercept is 80, the equation is $T(h) = -5h + 80$.

For $M(T)$, $m = \dfrac{150-100}{75-50} = \dfrac{50}{25} = 2$. Since the line passes through (50, 100), the equation is

$M(T) = 2T$.

(e) $(M \circ T)(h) = M(T(h)) = M(-5h + 80) = 2(-5h + 80) = -10h + 160$

96.   (a) $P(1970) = 20$; In 1970, 20% of college freshmen had a high school grade average of A or A–.

(b) See Figure 96.

(c) $P^{-1}(43) = 2000$

97.   (a) Yes, this is a one-to-one function because different inputs result in different outputs.

(b) $f(x) = \dfrac{5}{9}x + 32 \Rightarrow y = \dfrac{5}{9}x + 32$, interchange x and y and solve for y.

$x = \dfrac{5}{9}y + 32 \Rightarrow \dfrac{5}{9}y = x - 32 \Rightarrow y = \dfrac{9}{5}(x - 32) \Rightarrow f^{-1}(x) = \dfrac{9}{5}(x - 32)$

This formula converts x degrees Fahrenheit to an equivalent temperature in degrees Celsius.

98.   (a) Yes, this is a one-to-one function because different inputs result in different outputs.

(b) $f(x) = 3x \Rightarrow y = 3x$, interchange x and y and solve for y. $x = 3y \Rightarrow y = \dfrac{x}{3} \Rightarrow f^{-1}(x) = \dfrac{x}{3}$

This formula converts x feet to yards.

99.   Since there are 4 quarts in 1 gallon, the function $f(x) = 4x$ converts x gallons to quarts.

$f(x) = 4x \Rightarrow y = 4x$, interchange x and y and solve for y. $x = 4y \Rightarrow y = \dfrac{x}{4} \Rightarrow f^{-1}(x) = \dfrac{x}{4}$

This formula converts x quarts to gallons.

100. (a) No, this is not a one-to-one function because different inputs result in the same outputs.

(b) No, because the function is not one-to-one.

(c) If a table were constructed, the input 7 would have several different outputs.

(d) Yes, the function could be one-to-one if the wind speed for each month was a unique value.

9.2: Exponential Functions

Concepts

1. $f(x) = Ca^x$

2.   See Figure 2. *Answers may vary.*

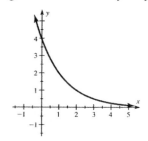

Figure 2

3.   The graph illustrates growth, since $a > 1$.

4. $2^5 = 32; 5^2 = 25$

5. $e \approx 2.718$

6. $e^2 \approx 7.389; \pi^2 \approx 9.870$

7.   factor

8.   The growth factor is 1.5.

Evaluating and Graphing Exponential Functions

9. $f(-2) = 3^{-2} = \dfrac{1}{3^2} = \dfrac{1}{9}$ and $f(2) = 3^2 = 9$

10. $f(-1) = 5^{-1} = \dfrac{1}{5^1} = \dfrac{1}{5}$ and $f(3) = 5^3 = 125$

11. $f(0) = 5(2^0) = 5(1) = 5$ and $f(5) = 5(2^5) = 5(32) = 160$

12. $f(-2) = 3(7^{-2}) = 3\left(\dfrac{1}{7^2}\right) = \dfrac{3}{49}$ and $f(0) = 3(7^0) = 3(1) = 3$

13. $f(-2) = \left(\dfrac{1}{2}\right)^{-2} = 2^2 = 4$ and $f(3) = \left(\dfrac{1}{2}\right)^3 = \dfrac{1}{2^3} = \dfrac{1}{8}$

14. $f(0) = \left(\dfrac{1}{4}\right)^0 = 1$ and $f(2) = \left(\dfrac{1}{4}\right)^2 = \dfrac{1}{4^2} = \dfrac{1}{16}$

15. $f(-1) = 5(3)^{-(-1)} = 5(3)^1 = 15$ and $f(2) = 5(3)^{-2} = 5\left(\dfrac{1}{3^2}\right) = \dfrac{5}{9}$

16. $f(1) = 4\left(\dfrac{3}{7}\right)^1 = \dfrac{12}{7}$ and $f(4) = 4\left(\dfrac{3}{7}\right)^4 = 4\left(\dfrac{3^4}{7^4}\right) = \dfrac{324}{2401}$

17. $f(-3) = 1.8^{-3} \approx 0.17$ and $f(1.5) = 1.8^{1.5} \approx 2.41$

18. $f(5.1) = 0.91^{5.1} \approx 0.62$ and $f(10) = 0.91^{10} \approx 0.39$

19. $f(-1) = 3(0.6)^{-1} = 5$ and $f(2) = 3(0.6)^2 = 1.08$

20. $f(-2.1) = 5(4.5)^{-(-2.1)} = 5(4.5)^{2.1} \approx 117.68$ and $f(5.9) = 5(4.5)^{-5.9} \approx 7.00 \times 10^{-4}$

21. $f(0) = a^0 = 1;\ f(-1) = a^{-1} = \dfrac{1}{a}$

22. $f(0) = (1+r)^{2 \cdot 0} = (1+r)^0 = 1;\ f(-1) = (1+r)^{2(-1)} = (1+r)^{-2} = \dfrac{1}{(1+r)^2}$

23. (a) Exponential decay. For each unit increase in x, $f(x)$ decreases by a factor of $\dfrac{1}{4}$.

    (b) Since $f(x) = 64$ when $x = 0$, $f(x) = 64\left(\dfrac{1}{4}\right)^x$

24. (a) Exponential growth. For each unit increase in x, $f(x)$ increases by a factor of 2.

    (b) Since $f(x) = \dfrac{1}{2}$ when $x = 0$, $f(x) = \dfrac{1}{2}(2)^x$

25. (a) Linear growth. For each unit increase in x, $f(x)$ increases by 3 units.

    (b) Since $f(x) = 8$ when $x = 0$, $f(x) = 3x + 8$

26. (a) Exponential decay. For each unit increase in x, $f(x)$ decreases by a factor of $\dfrac{1}{2}$.

    (b) Since $f(x) = 1$ when $x = 0$, $f(x) = \left(\dfrac{1}{2}\right)^x$

27. (a) Exponential growth. For each unit increase in x, $f(x)$ increases by a factor of 1.25.

    (b) Since $f(x) = 4$ when $x = 0$, $f(x) = 4(1.25)^x$

28. (a) Linear growth. For each unit increase in x, $f(x)$ increases by 4 units.

    (b) Since $f(x) = 2$ when $x = 0$, $f(x) = 4x + 2$

29. Since $y = 1$ when $x = 0$, $1 = Ca^0 \Rightarrow C = 1$. Since $y = 2$ when $x = 1$, $2 = 1(a)^1 \Rightarrow a = 2$.

30. Since $y = 1$ when $x = 0$, $1 = Ca^0 \Rightarrow C = 1$. Since $y = \dfrac{1}{2}$ when $x = 1$, $\dfrac{1}{2} = 1(a)^1 \Rightarrow a = \dfrac{1}{2}$.

31.   Since $y = 4$ when $x = 0$, $4 = Ca^0 \Rightarrow C = 4$. Since $y = 1$ when $x = 1$, $1 = 4(a)^1 \Rightarrow a = \dfrac{1}{4}$.

32.   Since $y = 2$ when $x = 0$, $2 = Ca^0 \Rightarrow C = 2$. Since $y = 3$ when $x = 1$, $3 = 2(a)^1 \Rightarrow a = \dfrac{3}{2}$.

33.   c. This function models exponential growth and passes through the point $(0, 1)$.

34.   b. This function models exponential growth and passes through the point $(2, 1)$.

35.   d. This function models exponential decay and passes through the point $(2, 1)$.

36.   a. This function models exponential decay and passes through the point $(0, 1)$.

37.   See Figure 37. The graph illustrates exponential growth.

38.   See Figure 38. The graph illustrates exponential growth.

Figure 37

Figure 38

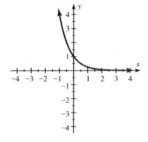
Figure 39

39.   See Figure 39. The graph illustrates exponential decay.

40.   See Figure 40. The graph illustrates exponential decay.

41.   See Figure 41. The graph illustrates exponential decay.

Figure 40

Figure 41

Figure 42

42.   See Figure 42. The graph illustrates exponential decay.

43.   See Figure 43. The graph illustrates exponential growth.

44.   See Figure 44. The graph illustrates exponential growth.

Figure 43

Figure 44

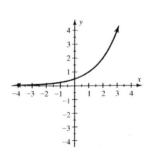
Figure 45

45.   See Figure 45. The graph illustrates exponential growth.

46.   See Figure 46. The graph illustrates exponential growth.

47.   See Figure 47. The graph illustrates exponential decay.

       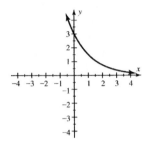

Figure 46   Figure 47   Figure 48

48.   See Figure 48. The graph illustrates exponential decay.

49. $e^2 e^5 = e^{2+5} = e^7$

50. $a^2 \cdot a^{-4} = a^{2+(-4)} = a^{-2} = \dfrac{1}{a^2}$

51. $\dfrac{a^4 a^{-2}}{a^3} = \dfrac{a^{4+(-2)}}{a^3} = \dfrac{a^2}{a^3} = a^{2-3} = a^{-1} = \dfrac{1}{a}$

52. $\dfrac{e^2 e^{-1}}{e} = \dfrac{e^{2+(-1)}}{e} = \dfrac{e}{e} = 1$

53. $e^x e^{y-x} = e^{x+(y-x)} = e^y$

54. $a^{1-x} a^{x-1} = a^{(1-x)+(x-1)} = a^0 = 1$

55. $\dfrac{2^{x+3}}{2^x} = 2^{x+3-x} = 2^3 = 8$

56. $\dfrac{e^{2x}}{e^x} = e^{2x-x} = e^x$

57. $5^{-y} \cdot 5^{3y} = 5^{-y+3y} = 5^{2y} = 25^y$

58. $4^{-x} \cdot 4^{2x} \cdot 4^x = 4^{-x+2x+x} = 4^{2x} = 16^x$

Compound Interest

59. $1500(1+0.09)^{10} = \$3551.05$

60. $1500(1+0.15)^{10} = \$6068.34$

61. $200(1+0.20)^{50} = \$1,820,087.63$

62. $5000(1+0.084)^7 = \$8793.77$

63. $560(1+0.014)^{25} = \$792.75$

64. $750(1+0.10)^{13} = \$2589.20$

65.   Yes. This is equivalent to having two accounts, each containing $1000 initially.

66.   No. At 5%, the interest earned is $500(1+0.05)^{10} - 500 = \$314.45$ and at 10% the interest earned is

$500(1+0.10)^{10} - 500 = \$796.87,$ which is more than twice as much.

67. $A = 300(1+0.0495)^{30} \approx \$1278.2$ billion or about $1.28 trillion

68. $A = 300(1+0.0695)^{30} \approx \$2251.9$ billion or about $2.258 trillion. The national debt is sensitive to interest

rates.

The Natural Exponential Function

69. $f(1.2) = e^{1.2} \approx 3.32$

70. $f(2) = 2e^2 \approx 14.78$

71. $f(-2) = 1 - e^{-2} \approx 0.86$

72. $f(1.5) = 4e^{-1.5} \approx 0.89$

73.   Graph $Y_1 = e\wedge(0.5X)$ in $[-4, 4, 1]$ by $[0, 8, 1]$. See Figure 73. The graph illustrates exponential growth.

74.   Graph $Y_1 = e\wedge(X)+1$ in $[-4, 4, 1]$ by $[0, 8, 1]$. See Figure 74. The graph illustrates exponential growth.

[-4, 4, 1] by [0, 8, 1]   [-4, 4, 1] by [0, 8, 1]

Figure 73   Figure 74

75.   Graph $Y_1 = 1.5e\wedge(-0.32X)$ in $[-4, 4, 1]$ by $[0, 8, 1]$. See Figure 75. The graph illustrates exponential decay.

[-4, 4, 1] by [0, 8, 1]   [-4, 4, 1] by [0, 8, 1]

Figure 75   Figure 76

76.   Graph $Y_1 = 2e\wedge(-X)+1$ in $[-4, 4, 1]$ by $[0, 8, 1]$. See Figure 76. The graph illustrates exponential decay.

Applications

77.   (a) $f(x) = 34e^{0.013x}$

(b) $f(10) = 34e^{0.013(10)} \approx 38.7;$ In 2010, the population of California will be about 38.7 million.

78.   (a) $f(x) = 8e^{0.023x}$

(b) $f(10) = 8e^{0.023(10)} \approx 10.1;$ In 2010, the population of Georgia will be about 10.1 million.

79.   (a) $f(x) = 8e^{0.019x}$

    (b) $f(10) = 8e^{0.019(10)} \approx 9.7$;   In 2010, the population of North Carolina will be about 9.7 million.

80.   (a) $f(x) = 21e^{0.021x}$

    (b) $f(10) = 21e^{0.021(10)} \approx 25.9$;   In 2010, the population of Texas will be about 25.9 million.

81.   (a) $f(x) = 5e^{0.031x}$

    (b)   Graph $Y_1 = 5e \wedge (0.031X)$ in $[0, 10, 1]$ by $[4, 7, 1]$.

       [0, 10, 1] by [4, 7, 1]

    (c)   Since 2010 is 10 years after 2000, evaluate $f(10) = 5e^{0.031(10)} \approx 6.82$ million

82.   (a)   Graph $Y_1 = 10(0.99988) \wedge X$ in $[0, 20{,}000, 5000]$ by $[0, 12, 1]$. See Figure 82. This is an example of

       decay.

    (b)   After 5700 years, $A = 10(0.99988)^{5700} \approx 5$ grams.   This is $\dfrac{1}{2}$ of the original amount.

       [0, 20,000, 5000] by [0, 12, 1]

       Figure 82

83.   (a)   Since $f(t) = 500$ when $t = 0$, $500 = Ca^0 \Rightarrow C = 500$. Since $f(t) = 1000$ when $t = 50$,

$$1000 = 500a^{50/50} \Rightarrow a = \frac{1000}{500} = 2$$

    (b) $f(170) = 500(2)^{170/50} \approx 5278$ thousand bacteria per milliliter or 5.278 million bacteria per milliliter

    (c)   The growth in the number of bacteria is exponential.

84.   (a)   Since $y = 52$ when $x = 0$, $52 = Ca^0 \Rightarrow C = 52$.

       Since y increases by a factor of $\dfrac{67}{52} \approx 1.28$ each year, $a \approx 1.28$. *Answers may vary.*

    (b) $y = 52(1.28)^4 \approx 140$ million

    (c)   This growth can only continue for a short period.

85.   (a) $f(1995) = 0.0272(1.495)^{1995-1980} = 0.0272(1.495)^{15} \approx 11.3$ million.

       In 1995 there were about 11.3 million cellular phone subscribers.

(b) The growth factor is 1.495. This means that each year from 1985 to 2000 the number of subscribers increases by a factor of 1.495 or by 49.5%.

86.   (a) Because $f(0) = 3(0.8)^0 = 3 \cdot 1 = 3$, the initial concentration is 3 ppm.

(b) Since $f(3) = 3(0.8)^3 = 1.536$ and $f(4) = 3(0.8)^4 = 1.2288$, this happens during day 3.

87.   Table $Y_1 = (0.905) \wedge X$ with TblStart = 0 and ΔTbl = 10. See Figure 87.

(a) $f(0) = (0.905)^0 = 1.$

The probability that no vehicle will enter the intersection during a period of zero seconds is 1.

(b) Since $f(30) = (0.905)^{30} = 0.05006$ and $f(31) = (0.905)^{31} = 0.04530$, this occurs after about 30 seconds.

Figure 87

88.   (a) $P(10) = (0.892)^{10} \approx 0.32$

There is a 32% chance that a randomly chosen point in the forest will not have a tree within 10 feet.

$P(20) = (0.892)^{20} \approx 0.10$ and $P(30) = (0.892)^{30} \approx 0.03$. Interpret in the same way as shown above.

(b) As x becomes larger, the probability decreases. In a forest, the trees are generally closely spaced. It is unlikely to find a place in the forest where there is a large area containing no trees.

Checking Basic Concepts for Sections 9.1 & 9.2

1.   (a) $f(1) = 2(1)^2 + 5(1) - 1 = 6$, and so $(g \circ f)(1) = g(f(1)) = g(6) = 6 + 1 = 7$

(b) $(f \circ g)(x) = f(g(x)) = f(x + 1) = 2(x + 1)^2 + 5(x + 1) - 1 = 2x^2 + 9x + 6$

2.   See Figure 2.

(a) No, this is not a one-to-one function because it does not pass the horizontal line test.

(b) No, this function does not have an inverse because it is not one-to-one.

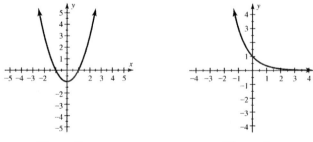

Figure 2   Figure 5

3. $f(x) = 4x - 3 \Rightarrow y = 4x - 3$, interchange x and y and solve for y.

$$x = 4y - 3 \Rightarrow 4y = x + 3 \Rightarrow y = \frac{x+3}{4} \Rightarrow f^{-1}(x) = \frac{x+3}{4}$$

4. $f(-2) = 3\left(2^{-2}\right) = 3 \cdot \dfrac{1}{2^2} = 3 \cdot \dfrac{1}{4} = \dfrac{3}{4}$

5. See Figure 5.

6. Since $y = 2$ when $x = 0$, $2 = Ca^0 \Rightarrow C = 2$. Since $y = 1$ when $x = 1$, $1 = 2(a)^1 \Rightarrow a = \dfrac{1}{2}$.

9.3: Logarithmic Functions

Concepts

1. 10

2. e

3. D: $\{x \mid x > 0\}$; R: all real numbers

4. D: $\{x \mid x > 0\}$; R: all real numbers

5. k

6. k

7. x

8. x

9. log 5

10. $\log_2 5$

11. $\log_a 1 = 0$ because $a^0 = 1$.

12. $\log_a -1$ is undefined because there is no value x such that $a^x = -1$.

Evaluating and Graphing Logarithmic Functions

13. 5

14. 1

15. -4

16. -1

17. $\log 1 = \log 10^0 = 0$

18. $\log \sqrt[3]{100} = \log \sqrt[3]{10^2} = \log 10^{2/3} = \dfrac{2}{3}$

19. $\log \dfrac{1}{100} = \log 10^{-2} = -2$

20. $\log \dfrac{1}{10} = \log 10^{-1} = -1$

21. $\log 10^{4.7} = 4.7$

22. $\log 10^{2x+4} = 2x + 4$

23. $\log_5 5^{6x} = 6x$

24. $\log_3 3^3 = 3$

25. $\log \sqrt{\dfrac{1}{1000}} = \log \sqrt{10^{-3}} = \log 10^{-3/2} = -\dfrac{3}{2}$

26. $\log_2 2^6 = 6$

27. $\log_2 2^8 = 8$

28. $\log_2 2^{-5} = -5$

29. $\log_2 \sqrt{8} = \log_2 \left(2^3\right)^{1/2} = \log_2 2^{3/2} = \dfrac{3}{2}$

30. $\log_2 \sqrt{32} = \log_2 \left(2^5\right)^{1/2} = \log_2 2^{5/2} = \dfrac{5}{2}$

31. $\log_2 \sqrt[3]{\dfrac{1}{4}} = \log_2 \left(2^{-2}\right)^{1/3} = \log_2 2^{-2/3} = -\dfrac{2}{3}$

32. $\log_2 \dfrac{1}{64} = \log_2 2^{-6} = -6$

33. $\log_2 -8$ is undefined.

34. $\log_2 -7$ is undefined.

35. $\log_2 4 = \log_2 2^2 = 2$

36. $\log_2 \dfrac{1}{32} = \log_2 2^{-5} = -5$

37. $\log_2 \dfrac{1}{16} = \log_2 2^{-4} = -4$

38. $\log_3 27 = \log_3 3^3 = 3$

39. $\log_3 \dfrac{1}{9} = \log_3 3^{-2} = -2$

40. $\log_4 16 = \log_4 4^2 = 2$

41. $\ln 1 = \ln e^0 = 0$

42. $\ln e^2 = 2$

43. $\log 0.001 = \log 10^{-3} = -3$

44. $\log 0.001 = \log 10^{-4} = -4$

45. $\log_5 \dfrac{1}{25} = \log_5 5^{-2} = -2$

46. $\log_8 64 = \log_8 8^2 = 2$

47. $10^{\log 2} = 2$

48. $10^{\log 7.5} = 7.5$

49. $10^{\log x^2} = x^2$

50. $10^{\log |x|} = |x|$

51. $5^{\log_5 17} = 17$

52. $9^{\log_9 73} = 73$

53. $4^{\log_4 (2x)^2} = (2x)^2$

54. $b^{\log_b (x-1)} = x - 1$

55. $10^{\log 5} = 5$

56. $\ln e^{3/4} = \dfrac{3}{4}$

57. $\ln e^{-5x} = -5x$

58. $e^{\ln 2x} = 2x$

59. $\log 10^{(2x-7)} = 2x - 7$

60. $\log 10^{(8-4x)} = 8 - 4x$

61. $5^{\log_5 0.6z} = 0.6z$

62. $7^{\log_7 (x-9)} = x - 9$

63. $\log 25 \approx 1.398$

64. $\log 0.501 \approx -0.300$

65. $\log 1.45 \approx 0.161$

66. $\log \dfrac{1}{35} \approx -1.544$

67. $\ln 7 \approx 1.946$

68. $\ln 126 \approx 4.836$

69. $\ln \dfrac{4}{7} \approx -0.560$

70. $\ln 0.67 \approx -0.400$

71. See Figure 71.

72. See Figure 72.

Figure 71   Figure 72

73.   See Figure 73.

74.   See Figure 74.

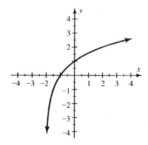

Figure 73   Figure 74

75.   Graph $Y_1 = \ln(\text{abs}(X))$ in [–4, 4, 1] by [–4, 4, 1]. See Figure 75. The graph is a reflection across the *y*-axis

together with the graph of $y = \ln x$. The domain is $\{x \mid x \neq 0\}$.

76.   Graph $Y_1 = \ln(X) - 2$ in [–4, 4, 1] by [–4, 4, 1]. See Figure 76. The graph is shifted 2 units downward.

The domain is $\{x \mid x > 0\}$.

[–4, 4, 1] by [–4, 4, 1]   [–4, 4, 1] by [–4, 4, 1]

    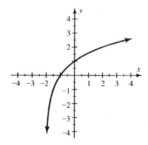

Figure 75   Figure 76

[–4, 4, 1] by [–4, 4, 1]   [–4, 4, 1] by [–4, 4, 1]

Figure 77   Figure 78

77.   Graph $Y_1 = \ln(X + 2)$ in [–4, 4, 1] by [–4, 4, 1]. See Figure 77. The graph is shifted 2 units to the left.

The domain is $\{x \mid x > -2\}$.

78.   Graph $Y_1 = 2\ln(X)$ in [–4, 4, 1] by [–4, 4, 1]. See Figure 78. The graph is stretched vertically.

The domain is $\{x \mid x > 0\}$.

79.   d. The graph of this function passes through the point $(1, 0)$ but does not pass through $(3, 1)$.

80.   b. The graph of this function passes through the point $(1, 0)$ and passes through $(3, 1)$.

81.   a. The graph of this function is shifted 2 units upward.

82.   c. The graph of this function is shifted 1 unit to the left.

83.   See Figure 83. Compared to the graph of $y = \log x$, this graph is shifted 1 unit downward.

84.   See Figure 84. Compared to the graph of $y = \log x$, this graph is shifted 2 units upward.

Figure 83

Figure 84

Figure 85

85.   See Figure 85. Compared to the graph of $y = \log x$, this graph is shifted 1 unit to the left.

86.   See Figure 86. Compared to the graph of $y = \log x$, this graph is shifted 2 units to the left.

87.   See Figure 87. Compared to the graph of $y = \log x$, this graph is shifted 1 unit to the right.

Figure 86

Figure 87

88.   See Figure 88. Compared to the graph of $y = \log x$, this graph is shifted 3 units to the right.

89.   See Figure 89. Compared to the graph of $y = \log x$, this graph increases faster.

Figure 88

Figure 89

Figure 90

90.   See Figure 90. Compared to the graph of $y = \log x$, this graph is reflected across the *x*-axis.

91.   See Figure 91.

x	$\frac{1}{4}$	$\frac{1}{2}$	1	$\sqrt{2}$	64
$\log_2 x$	-2	-1	0	$\frac{1}{2}$	6

Figure 91

x	$\frac{1}{7}$	1	$\sqrt{7}$	7	49
$\log_7 x$	-1	0	$\frac{1}{2}$	1	2

Figure 92

92.   See Figure 92.

Applications

93. $f(10^{-4}) = 160 + 10 \log(10^{-4}) = 160 + 10(-4) = 160 + (-40) = 120$ db.   Yes, this could cause pain.

94.   (a) The runway length increases but it does not double when the weight of the plane doubles.

(b) $L(50) = 1.3 \ln(50) \approx 5.086$; A 50-thousand pound plane needs a runway at least 5086 feet long.

95.   (a) $P(0) = 0.48 \ln(0+1) + 27 = 0.48 \ln(1) + 27 = 0.48(0) + 27 = 27$. The air pressure at the eye of the hurricane is 27 inches of mercury. $P(50) = 0.48 \ln(50+1) + 27 = 0.48 \ln(51) + 27 \approx 28.9$. The air pressure 50 miles from the eye of the hurricane is about 28.9 inches of mercury.

(b) The pressure increases rapidly at first and then more slowly.

(c) The eye of a hurricane is a low pressure area.

96.   (a) $W(10) = 2.76 \log(10+1) + 2.3 \approx 5.17$ meters per second

(b) Wind speeds increase with height rapidly at first and then more slowly.

97.   Most people would want their salaries to increase exponentially since it grows faster over time.

98.   (a) $C(1) = 645 \log(1+1) + 1925 = 645 \log(2) + 1925 \approx 2119$ calories

(b) The caloric intake increases as the amount of land owned increases.

(c) No, the growth levels off and is not linear.

99.   (a) $M = 6 - 2.5 \log \dfrac{10}{1} = 6 - 2.5 \log(10) = 6 - 2.5(1) = 3.5$

(b) $M = 6 - 2.5 \log \dfrac{100}{1} = 6 - 2.5 \log(100) = 6 - 2.5(2) = 1$

(c) The intensity of the star decreases by 2.5.

100.   (a) $f(50) = 0.338(1.035)^{50} \approx 1.89$; In 2000, the population of less industrialized areas was 1.89 billion.

$g(50) = 0.36 + 0.15 \ln(50+1) \approx 0.95$; In 2000, the population in industrialized areas was 0.95 billion.

(b) Graph $Y_1 = 280 \ln(X+1) + 1925$ in [0, 80, 10] by [0, 5, 1]. See Figure 100. The population in less industrialized areas grew faster than the population in industrialized areas.

(c) $\dfrac{f(40)}{f(20)} = \dfrac{0.338(1.035)^{40}}{0.338(1.035)^{20}} \approx \dfrac{1.33823}{0.67255} \approx 1.99$;

$\dfrac{g(40)}{g(20)} = \dfrac{0.36 + 0.15 \ln(40+1)}{0.36 + 0.15 \ln(20+1)} \approx \dfrac{0.91704}{0.81668} \approx 1.12$

[0, 80, 10] by [0, 5, 1]   [1, 10, 1] by [−160, −120, 10]   [0, 250, 50] by [0, 100, 100]

Figure 100   Figure 102   Figure 1

101. (a) $\log \dfrac{x}{1} = 6.0 \Rightarrow \log x = 6.0 \Rightarrow x = 10^6$ and $\log \dfrac{x}{1} = 8.0 \Rightarrow \log x = 8.0 \Rightarrow x = 10^8$

    (b) $10^8 \div 10^6 = 100$ times

102. (a) $D(3) = -121 - 36 \log (3) \approx -138$; At a distance of 3 km, the signal has decreased by 138 decibels.

    (b) Graph $Y_1 = -121 - 36 \log (X)$ in [1, 10, 1] by [−160, −120, 10]. See Figure 102.

    (c) As the distance increases, the signal decreases in strength.

Group Activity Solutions

1.   (a) Since $f(x) = 364$ when $x = 0$, $364 = Ca^0 \Rightarrow C = 364$. Since $f(x) = 467$ when $x = 50$,

$$467 = 364a^{50} \Rightarrow a = \left(\frac{467}{364}\right)^{1/50} \approx 1.005$$

    (b) Graph $Y_1 = 364(1.005)^{\wedge}(X)$ along with the data in [0, 250, 50] by [0, 100, 100]. See Figure 1.

    (c) The level will be 560 ppm in 2086.

9.4: Properties of Logarithms

Concepts

1. 4

2. 4

3. 3

4. $\log m + \log n$

5. $\log m - \log n$

6. $r \log m$

7. No

8. Yes

9. No; $\log(xy) = \log x + \log y$

10. No; $\log\left(\dfrac{x}{y}\right) = \log x - \log y$

11. $\log_a x = \dfrac{\log x}{\log a}$ or $\log_a x = \dfrac{\ln x}{\ln a}$

12. 0; 1

Basic Properties of Logarithms

13. $\ln(3 \cdot 5) = \ln 3 + \ln 5$

14. $\log(7 \cdot 11) = \log 7 + \log 11$

15. $\log_3 xy = \log_3 x + \log_3 y$

16. $\log_5 y^2 = \log_5 (y \cdot y) = \log_5 y + \log_5 y$

17. $\ln 10z = \ln(2 \cdot 5 \cdot z) = \ln 2 + \ln 5 + \ln z$

18. $\log x^2 y = \log(x \cdot x \cdot y) = \log x + \log x + \log y$

19. $\log \dfrac{7}{3} = \log 7 - \log 3$

20. $\ln \dfrac{11}{13} = \ln 11 - \ln 13$

21. $\ln \dfrac{x}{y} = \ln x - \ln y$

22. $\log \dfrac{2x}{z} = \log 2x - \log z$

23. $\log_2 \dfrac{45}{x} = \log_2 45 - \log_2 x$

24. $\log_7 \dfrac{5x}{4z} = \log_7 5x - \log_7 4z$

25. $\log 45 + \log 5 = \log(45 \cdot 5) = \log 225$

26. $\log 30 - \log 10 = \log \dfrac{30}{10} = \log 3$

27. $\ln x + \ln y = \ln xy$

28. $\ln m + \ln n - \ln n = \ln m$

29. $\ln 7x^2 + \ln 2x = \ln(7x^2 \cdot 2x) = \ln 14x^3$

30. $\ln x + \ln y - \ln z = \ln xy - \ln z = \ln \dfrac{xy}{z}$

31. $\ln x + \ln y^2 - \ln y = \ln xy^2 - \ln y = \ln \dfrac{xy^2}{y} = \ln xy$

32. $\ln \sqrt{z} - \ln z^3 + \ln y^3 = \ln z^{1/2} - \ln z^3 + \ln y^3 = \ln \dfrac{z^{1/2}}{z^3} + \ln y^3 = \ln \dfrac{1}{z^{5/2}} + \ln y^3 = \ln \dfrac{y^3}{z^{5/2}}$

33. $\log 20 - \log 4 = \log\left(\dfrac{20}{4}\right) = \log 5$

34. $\log 900 - \log 9 = \log\left(\dfrac{900}{9}\right) = \log 100 = 2$ since $10^2 = 100$

35. $\ln x^4 - \ln x^2 = \ln\left(\dfrac{x^4}{x^2}\right) = \ln x^2$

36. $\ln 9x^2 - \ln 3x = \ln\left(\dfrac{9x^2}{3x}\right) = \ln 3x$

37. $\log_2 12x - \log_2 3x = \log_2\left(\dfrac{12x}{3x}\right) = \log_2 4 = 2$

38. $\log_5 18x^2 - \log_5 2x^2 = \log_5\left(\dfrac{18x^2}{2x^2}\right) = \log_5 9$

39. $\log 3^6 = 6\log 3$

40. $\log x^7 = 7\log x$

41. $\ln 2^x = x\ln 2$

42. $\ln(0.77)^{x+1} = (x+1)\ln 0.77$

43. $\log_2 5^{1/4} = \dfrac{1}{4}\log_2 5$

44. $\log_3 \sqrt{x} = \log_3 x^{1/2} = \dfrac{1}{2}\log_3 x$

45. $\log_4 \sqrt[3]{z} = \log_4 z^{1/3} = \dfrac{1}{3}\log_4 z$

46. $\log_7 3^\pi = \pi \log_7 3$

47. $\log x^{y-1} = (y-1)\log x$

48. $\ln a^{2b} = 2b \ln a$

49. $4\log z - \log z^3 = \log z^4 - \log z^3 = \log\dfrac{z^4}{z^3} = \log z$

50. $2\log_5 y + \log_5 x = \log_5 y^2 + \log_5 x = \log_5 xy^2$

51. $\log x + 2\log x + 2\log y = \log x + \log x^2 + \log y^2 = \log\left(x \cdot x^2 \cdot y^2\right) = \log x^3 y^2$

52. $\log x^2 + 3\log z - 5\log y = \log x^2 + \log z^3 - \log y^5 = \log x^2 z^3 - \log y^5 = \log\dfrac{x^2 z^3}{y^5}$

53. $\log x - 2\log \sqrt{x} = \log x - \log\left(\sqrt{x}\right)^2 = \log x - \log x = 0$

54. $\ln y^2 - 6\ln \sqrt[3]{y} = \ln y^2 - \ln\left(y^{1/3}\right)^6 = \ln y^2 - \ln y^2 = 0$

55. $\ln 2^{x+1} - \ln 2 = \ln \dfrac{2^{x+1}}{2} = \ln 2^x$

56. $\ln 8^{1/2} + \ln 2^{1/2} = \ln\left(2^3\right)^{1/2} + \ln 2^{1/2} = \ln 2^{3/2} + \ln 2^{1/2} = \ln\left(2^{3/2} \cdot 2^{1/2}\right) = \ln 2^2 = \ln 4$

57. $2 \log_3 \sqrt{x} - 3 \log_3 x = \log_3 \left(\sqrt{x}\right)^2 - \log_3 x^3 = \log_3 x - \log_3 x^3 = \log_3 \dfrac{x}{x^3} = \log_3 \dfrac{1}{x^2}$

58. $\ln \sqrt[3]{x} + \ln \sqrt{x} = \ln x^{1/3} + \ln x^{1/2} = \ln\left(x^{1/3} \cdot x^{1/2}\right) = \ln x^{5/6}$

59. $2 \log_a (x+1) - \log_a \left(x^2 - 1\right) = \log_a (x+1)^2 - \log_a \left(x^2 - 1\right) = \log_a \dfrac{(x+1)(x+1)}{(x+1)(x-1)} = \log_a \dfrac{x+1}{x-1}$

60. $\log_b \left(x^2 - 9\right) - \log_b (x-3) = \log_b \dfrac{(x-3)(x+3)}{x-3} = \log_b (x+3)$

61. $\log xy^2 = \log x + \log y^2 = \log x + 2 \log y$

62. $\log \dfrac{x^2}{y^3} = \log x^2 - \log y^3 = 2 \log x - 3 \log y$

63. $\ln \dfrac{x^4 y}{z} = \ln x^4 y - \ln z = \ln x^4 + \ln y - \ln z = 4 \ln x + \ln y - \ln z$

64. $\ln \dfrac{\sqrt{x}}{y} = \ln \dfrac{x^{1/2}}{y} = \ln x^{1/2} - \ln y = \dfrac{1}{2} \ln x - \ln y$

65. $\log_4 \dfrac{\sqrt[3]{z}}{\sqrt{y}} = \log_4 \dfrac{z^{1/3}}{y^{1/2}} = \log_4 z^{1/3} - \log_4 y^{1/2} = \dfrac{1}{3} \log_4 z - \dfrac{1}{2} \log_4 y$

66. $\log_2 \sqrt{\dfrac{x}{y}} = \log_2 \left(\dfrac{x}{y}\right)^{1/2} = \dfrac{1}{2} \log_2 \dfrac{x}{y} = \dfrac{1}{2}\left(\log_2 x - \log_2 y\right) = \dfrac{1}{2} \log_2 x - \dfrac{1}{2} \log_2 y$

67. $\log\left(x^4 y^3\right) = \log x^4 + \log y^3 = 4 \log x + 3 \log y$

68. $\log\left(x^2 y^4 z^3\right) = \log x^2 + \log y^4 + \log z^3 = 2 \log x + 4 \log y + 3 \log z$

69. $\ln \dfrac{1}{y} - \ln \dfrac{1}{x} = \ln y^{-1} - \ln x^{-1} = -1 \ln y - (-1) \ln x = \ln x - \ln y$

70. $\ln \dfrac{1}{xy} = \ln (xy)^{-1} = -1 \ln (xy) = -1(\ln x + \ln y) = -\ln x - \ln y$

71. $\log_4 \sqrt{\dfrac{x^3 y}{z^2}} = \log_4 \left(\dfrac{x^3 y}{z^2}\right)^{1/2} = \dfrac{1}{2} \log_4 \dfrac{x^3 y}{z^2} = \dfrac{1}{2}\left(\log_4 x^3 + \log_4 y - \log_4 z^2\right) = \dfrac{3}{2} \log_4 x + \dfrac{1}{2} \log_4 y - \log_4 z$

72. $\log_3 \left(\dfrac{x^2 \sqrt{z}}{y^3}\right) = \log_3 \left(\dfrac{x^2 z^{1/2}}{y^3}\right) = \log_3 x^2 + \log_3 z^{1/2} - \log_3 y^3 = 2 \log_3 x + \dfrac{1}{2} \log_3 z - 3 \log_3 y$

73.   Graph $Y_1 = \log\left(X^\wedge 3\right)$ and $Y_2 = 3 \log(X)$ in $[-6, 6, 1]$ by $[-4, 4, 1]$. See Figures 73a & 73b.

By the power rule $\log x^3 = 3 \log x$.

[-6, 6, 1] by [-4, 4, 1] [-6, 6, 1] by [-4, 4, 1] [-6, 6, 1] by [-4, 4, 1] [-6, 6, 1] by [-4, 4, 1]

Figure 73a   Figure 73b   Figure 74a   Figure 74b

74.   Graph $Y_1 = \ln(X) + \ln(3)$ and $Y_2 = \ln(3X)$ in [-6, 6, 1] by [-4, 4, 1]. See Figures 74a & 74b.

By the product rule $\ln x + \ln 3 = \ln 3x$.

75.   Graph $Y_1 = \ln(X + 5)$ and $Y_2 = \ln(X) + \ln(5)$ in [-6, 6, 1] by [-4, 4, 1]. See Figure 75a & 75b. Not the

same.

[-6, 6, 1] by [-4, 4, 1] [-6, 6, 1] by [-4, 4, 1] [-6, 6, 1] by [-4, 4, 1] [-6, 6, 1] by [-4, 4, 1]

Figure 75a   Figure 75b   Figure 76a   Figure 76b

76.   Graph $Y_1 = \log(X - 2)$ and $Y_2 = \log(X) - \log(2)$ in [-6, 6, 1] by [-4, 4, 1]. See Figure 76a & 76b. Not the

same.

77. $\log 16 = \log 2^4 = 4 \log 2 = 4(0.3) = 1.2$

78. $\log 125 = \log 5^3 = 3 \log 5 = 3(0.7) = 2.1$

79. $\log 65 = \log(5 \cdot 13) = \log 5 + \log 13 = 0.7 + 1.1 = 1.8$

80. $\log 26 = \log(2 \cdot 13) = \log 2 + \log 13 = 0.3 + 1.1 = 1.4$

81. $\log 130 = \log(2 \cdot 5 \cdot 13) = \log 2 + \log 5 + \log 13 = 0.3 + 0.7 + 1.1 = 2.1$

82. $\log 100 = \log(2^2 \cdot 5^2) = \log 2^2 + \log 5^2 = 2 \log 2 + 2 \log 5 = 2(0.3) + 2(0.7) = 2$

83. $\log \dfrac{5}{2} = \log 5 - \log 2 = 0.7 - 0.3 = 0.4$

84. $\log \dfrac{26}{5} = \log \dfrac{2 \cdot 13}{5} = \log 2 + \log 13 - \log 5 = 0.3 + 1.1 - 0.7 = 0.7$

85. $\log \dfrac{1}{13} = \log 13^{-1} = -\log 13 = -1.1$

86. $\log \dfrac{1}{65} = \log 65^{-1} = -\log 65 = -\left(\log(5 \cdot 13)\right) = -\left(\log 5 + \log 13\right) = -(0.7 + 1.1) = -1.8$

87. $\log_3 5 = \dfrac{\log 5}{\log 3} \approx 1.46$

88. $\log_5 12 = \dfrac{\log 12}{\log 5} \approx 1.54$

89. $\log_2 25 = \dfrac{\log 25}{\log 2} \approx 4.64$

90. $\log_7 8 = \dfrac{\log 8}{\log 7} \approx 1.07$

91. $\log_9 102 = \dfrac{\log 102}{\log 9} \approx 2.10$

92. $\log_6 293 = \dfrac{\log 293}{\log 6} \approx 3.17$

Applications

93. $f(x) = 10\log\left(10^{16} x\right) = 10\left(\log 10^{16} + \log x\right) = 10\left(16 + \log x\right) = 160 + 10\log x$

94. $L = 110.7 - 19.1\log h + 55\log d = 110.7 + \log d^{55} - \log h^{19.1} = 110.7 + \log \dfrac{d^{55}}{h^{19.1}}$

Checking Basic Concepts for Sections 9.3 & 9.4

1.   (a) $\log 10^4 = 4$

(b) $\ln e^x = x$

(c) $\log_2 \dfrac{1}{8} = \log_2 2^{-3} = -3$

(d) $\log_5 \sqrt{5} = \log_5 5^{1/2} = \dfrac{1}{2}$

2.   See Figure 2.

(a) $D:\{x \mid x > 0\}$; R : all real numbers

(b) $f(1) = 0$

(c) Yes, for example $\log \dfrac{1}{10} = -1$.

(d) No, since negative numbers are not in the domain of $f(x) = \log x$.

Figure 2

3. (a) $\log xy = \log x + \log y$

   (b) $\ln \dfrac{x}{yz} = \ln x - \ln yz = \ln x - (\ln y + \ln z) = \ln x - \ln y - \ln z$

   (c) $\ln x^2 = 2 \ln x$

   (d) $\log \dfrac{x^2 y^3}{\sqrt{z}} = \log x^2 y^3 - \log z^{1/2} = \log x^2 + \log y^3 - \log z^{1/2} = 2 \log x + 3 \log y - \dfrac{1}{2} \log z$

4. (a) $\log x + \log y = \log xy$

   (b) $\ln 2x - 3 \ln y = \ln 2x - \ln y^3 = \ln \dfrac{2x}{y^3}$

   (c) $2 \log_2 x + 3 \log_2 y - \log_2 z = \log_2 x^2 + \log_2 y^3 - \log_2 z = \log_2 x^2 y^3 - \log_2 z = \log_2 \dfrac{x^2 y^3}{z}$

9.5: Exponential and Logarithmic Equations

Concepts

1. Add 5 to both sides.

2. Divide both sides by 5.

3. Take the common logarithm of both sides.

4. Exponentiate both sides using base 10.

5. x

6. x

7. $2x$

8. $x + 7$

9. No, $\log \dfrac{5}{4} = \log 5 - \log 4$

10. No, $\log 5 - \log 4 = \log \dfrac{5}{4}$

11. One

12. One

Exponential Equations

13. $10^x = 1000 \Rightarrow 10^x = 10^3 \Rightarrow x = 3$

14. $10^x = 0.01 \Rightarrow 10^x = 10^{-2} \Rightarrow x = -2$

15. $2^x = 64 \Rightarrow 2^x = 2^6 \Rightarrow x = 6$

16. $3^x = 27 \Rightarrow 3^x = 3^3 \Rightarrow x = 3$

17. $2^{x-3} = 8 \Rightarrow 2^{x-3} = 2^3 \Rightarrow x - 3 = 3 \Rightarrow x = 6$

18. $3^{2x} = 81 \Rightarrow 3^{2x} = 3^4 \Rightarrow 2x = 4 \Rightarrow x = 2$

19. $4^x + 3 = 259 \Rightarrow 4^x = 256 \Rightarrow 4^x = 4^4 \Rightarrow x = 4$

20. $3\left(5^{2x}\right) = 300 \Rightarrow 5^{2x} = 100 \Rightarrow \log_5 5^{2x} = \log_5 100 \Rightarrow 2x = \log_5 100 \Rightarrow x = \dfrac{\log 100}{2 \log 5} \approx 1.43$

21. $10^{0.4x} = 124 \Rightarrow \log 10^{0.4x} = \log 124 \Rightarrow 0.4x = \log 124 \Rightarrow x = \dfrac{\log 124}{0.4} \approx 5.23$

22. $0.75^x = 0.25 \Rightarrow \log_{0.75} 0.75^x = \log_{0.75} 0.25 \Rightarrow x = \dfrac{\log 0.25}{\log 0.75} \approx 4.82$

23. $e^{-x} = 1 \Rightarrow e^{-x} = e^0 \Rightarrow -x = 0 \Rightarrow x = 0$

24. $0.5^{-5x} = 5 \Rightarrow \log_{0.5} 0.5^{-5x} = \log_{0.5} 5 \Rightarrow -5x = \log_{0.5} 5 \Rightarrow -5x = \dfrac{\log 5}{\log 0.5} \Rightarrow x = \dfrac{\log 5}{-5 \log 0.5} \Rightarrow 0.46$

25. $e^x = 25 \Rightarrow \ln e^x = \ln 25 \Rightarrow x = \ln 25 \Rightarrow x \approx 3.22$

26. $e^x = 0.4 \Rightarrow \ln e^x = \ln 0.4 \Rightarrow x = \ln 0.4 \Rightarrow x \approx -0.92$

27. $0.4^x = 2 \Rightarrow \ln 0.4^x = \ln 2 \Rightarrow x \ln 0.4 = \ln 2 \Rightarrow x = \dfrac{\ln 2}{\ln 0.4} \Rightarrow x \approx -0.76$

28. $0.7^x = 0.3 \Rightarrow \ln 0.7^x = \ln 0.3 \Rightarrow x \ln 0.7 = \ln 0.3 \Rightarrow x = \dfrac{\ln 0.3}{\ln 0.7} \Rightarrow x \approx 3.38$

29. $e^x - 1 = 6 \Rightarrow e^x = 7 \Rightarrow \ln e^x = \ln 7 \Rightarrow x = \ln 7 \approx 1.95$

30. $2e^{4x} = 15 \Rightarrow e^{4x} = 7.5 \Rightarrow \ln e^{4x} = \ln 7.5 \Rightarrow 4x = \ln 7.5 \Rightarrow x = \dfrac{\ln 7.5}{4} \approx 0.50$

31. $2(10)^{x+2} = 35 \Rightarrow 10^{x+2} = \dfrac{35}{2} \Rightarrow \log 10^{x+2} = \log \dfrac{35}{2} \Rightarrow x + 2 = \log \dfrac{35}{2} \Rightarrow x = \log \dfrac{35}{2} - 2 \approx -0.76$

32. $10^{3x} + 10 = 1500 \Rightarrow 10^{3x} = 1490 \Rightarrow \log 10^{3x} = \log 1490 \Rightarrow 3x = \log 1490 \Rightarrow x = \dfrac{\log 1490}{3} \approx 1.06$

33. $3.1^{2x} - 4 = 16 \Rightarrow 3.1^{2x} = 20 \Rightarrow \log_{3.1} 3.1^{2x} = \log_{3.1} 20 \Rightarrow 2x = \log_{3.1} 20 \Rightarrow x = \dfrac{\log 20}{2 \log 3.1} \approx 1.32$

34. $5.4^{x-1} = 85 \Rightarrow \log_{5.4} 5.4^{x-1} = \log_{5.4} 85 \Rightarrow x - 1 = \log_{5.4} 85 \Rightarrow x = \dfrac{\log 85}{\log 5.4} + 1 \approx 3.63$

35. $e^{3x} = e^{2x-1} \Rightarrow 3x = 2x - 1 \Rightarrow x = -1$

36. $e^{x^2} = e^{3x-2} \Rightarrow x^2 = 3x - 2 \Rightarrow x^2 - 3x + 2 = 0 \Rightarrow (x-1)(x-2) = 0 \Rightarrow x = 1 \text{ or } 2$

37. $5^{4x} = 5^{x^2-5} \Rightarrow 4x = x^2 - 5 \Rightarrow x^2 - 4x - 5 = 0 \Rightarrow (x+1)(x-5) = 0 \Rightarrow x = -1 \text{ or } 5$

38. $2^{4x} = 2^{x+3} \Rightarrow 4x = x + 3 \Rightarrow 3x = 3 \Rightarrow x = 1$

39. $e^{2x} \cdot e^x = 10 \Rightarrow e^{2x+x} = 10 \Rightarrow e^{3x} = 10 \Rightarrow \ln e^{3x} = \ln 10 \Rightarrow 3x = \ln 10 \Rightarrow x = \dfrac{\ln 10}{3} \approx 0.77$

40. $10^{x-2} \cdot 10^x = 1000 \Rightarrow 10^{x-2+x} = 10^3 \Rightarrow 10^{2x-2} = 10^3 \Rightarrow 2x-2 = 3 \Rightarrow 2x = 5 \Rightarrow x = \dfrac{5}{2} = 2.5$

41. $e^x = 2^{x+2} \Rightarrow \ln e^x = \ln 2^{x+2} \Rightarrow x = (x+2)\ln 2 \Rightarrow x = x\ln 2 + 2\ln 2 \Rightarrow x - x\ln 2 = 2\ln 2 \Rightarrow$

     $x(1-\ln 2) = 2\ln 2 \Rightarrow x = \dfrac{2\ln 2}{1-\ln 2} \approx 4.52$

42. $2^{2x} = 3^{x-1} \Rightarrow \log 2^{2x} = \log 3^{x-1} \Rightarrow 2x\log 2 = (x-1)\log 3 \Rightarrow 2x\log 2 = x\log 3 - \log 3 \Rightarrow$

     $x\log 3 - 2x\log 2 = \log 3 \Rightarrow x(\log 3 - 2\log 2) = \log 3 \Rightarrow x = \dfrac{\log 3}{\log 3 - 2\log 2} \approx -3.82$

43. $4^{0.5x} = 5^{x+2} \Rightarrow \log 4^{0.5x} = \log 5^{x+2} \Rightarrow 0.5x\log 4 = (x+2)\log 5 \Rightarrow 0.5x\log 4 = x\log 5 + 2\log 5 \Rightarrow$

     $0.5x\log 4 - x\log 5 = 2\log 5 \Rightarrow x(0.5\log 4 - \log 5) = 2\log 5 \Rightarrow x = \dfrac{2\log 5}{0.5\log 4 - \log 5} \approx -3.51$

44. $3^{2x} = 7^{x+1} \Rightarrow \log 3^{2x} = \log 7^{x+1} \Rightarrow 2x\log 3 = (x+1)\log 7 \Rightarrow 2x\log 3 = x\log 7 + \log 7 \Rightarrow$

     $2x\log 3 - x\log 7 = \log 7 \Rightarrow x(2\log 3 - \log 7) = \log 7 \Rightarrow x = \dfrac{\log 7}{2\log 3 - \log 7} \approx 7.74$

45.   (a) The solution is the x-coordinate of the intersection point, $x = 1$.

     (b) $0.2\left(10^x\right) = 2 \Rightarrow 10^x = 10 \Rightarrow x = 1$

46.   (a) The solution is the x-coordinate of the intersection point, $x = 2$.

     (b) $e^x = 7.4 \Rightarrow \ln e^x = \ln 7.4 \Rightarrow x = \ln 7.4 \approx 2$

47.   (a) The solution is the x-coordinate of the intersection point, $x = -2$.

     (b) $2^{-x} = 4 \Rightarrow 2^{-x} = 2^2 \Rightarrow -x = 2 \Rightarrow x = -2$

48.   (a) The solution is the x-coordinate of the intersection point, $x = 2$.

     (b) $0.1\left(3^x\right) = 0.9 \Rightarrow 3^x = 9 \Rightarrow 3^x = 3^2 \Rightarrow x = 2$

49. $10^x = 0.1 \Rightarrow 10^x = 10^{-1} \Rightarrow x = -1$

     For numerical support, table $Y_1 = 10^\wedge X$ and $Y_2 = 0.1$ with TblStart $= -3$ and ΔTbl $= 1$. See Figure 49.

50. $2\left(10^x\right) = 2000 \Rightarrow 10^x = 1000 \Rightarrow 10^x = 10^3 \Rightarrow x = 3$

     For numerical support, table $Y_1 = 2\left(10^\wedge X\right)$ and $Y_2 = 2000$ with TblStart $= 0$ and ΔTbl $= 1$. See Figure 50.

$[0, 4, 1]$ by $[0, 50, 10]$

Figure 49

Figure 50

Figure 51

Figure 52

51. $4e^x + 5 = 9 \Rightarrow 4e^x = 4 \Rightarrow e^x = 1 \Rightarrow e^x = e^0 \Rightarrow x = 0$

For numerical support, table $Y_1 = 4e^{\wedge}X + 5$ and $Y_2 = 9$ with TblStart $= -3$ and ΔTbl $= 1$. See Figure 51.

52.　$e^x + 6 = 36 \Rightarrow e^x = 30 \Rightarrow \ln e^x = \ln 30 \Rightarrow x = \ln 30 \approx 3.40$

For graphical support, graph $Y_1 = e^{\wedge}(X) + 6$ and $Y_2 = 36$ in $[0, 4, 1]$ by $[0, 50, 10]$. See Figure 52.

53.　$4^x = 1024 \Rightarrow 4^x = 4^5 \Rightarrow x = 5$

For numerical support, table $Y_1 = 4^{\wedge}X$ and $Y_2 = 1024$ with TblStart $= 0$ and ΔTbl $= 1$. See Figure 53.

54.　$3^x = 729 \Rightarrow 3^x = 3^6 \Rightarrow x = 6$

For numerical support, table $Y_1 = 3^{\wedge}X$ and $Y_2 = 729$ with TblStart $= 0$ and ΔTbl $= 1$. See Figure 54.

$[-1, 1, 1]$ by $[0, 3, 1]$　　$[0, 10, 1]$ by $[0, 5, 1]$

Figure 53　　　　　Figure 54　　　　　Figure 55　　　　　Figure 56

55.　$(0.55)^x + 0.55 = 2 \Rightarrow 0.55^x = 1.45 \Rightarrow \log_{0.55} 0.55^x = \log_{0.55} 1.45 \Rightarrow x = \dfrac{\log 1.45}{\log 0.55} \approx -0.62$

For graphical support, graph $Y_1 = 0.55^{\wedge}X + 0.55$ and $Y_2 = 2$ in $[-1, 1, 1]$ by $[0, 3, 1]$. See Figure 55.

56.　$5(0.9)^x = 3 \Rightarrow 0.9^x = 0.6 \Rightarrow \log_{0.9} 0.9^x = \log_{0.9} 0.6 \Rightarrow x = \dfrac{\log 0.6}{\log 0.9} \approx 4.85$

For graphical support, graph $Y_1 = 5(0.9)^{\wedge}X$ and $Y_2 = 3$ in $[0, 10, 1]$ by $[0, 5, 1]$. See Figure 56.

57.　Graph $Y_1 = e^{\wedge}X - X$ and $Y_2 = 2$ in $[-5, 5, 1]$ by $[-5, 5, 1]$. See Figures 57a & 57b.

The solutions are the x-coordinates of the intersection points, $x \approx -1.84$ and $x \approx 1.15$.

$[-5, 5, 1]$ by $[-5, 5, 1]$　　　$[-5, 5, 1]$ by $[-5, 5, 1]$

Figure 57a　　　　　Figure 57b

58.　Graph $Y_1 = X\log(X)$ and $Y_2 = 1$ in $[-5, 5, 1]$ by $[-5, 5, 1]$. See Figure 58.

The solution is the x-coordinate of the intersection point, $x \approx 2.51$.

59.　Graph $Y_1 = \ln(X)$ and $Y_2 = e^{\wedge}(-X)$ in $[-5, 5, 1]$ by $[-5, 5, 1]$. See Figure 59.

The solution is the x-coordinate of the intersection point, $x \approx 1.31$.

60.　Graph $Y_1 = 10^{\wedge}X - 2$ and $Y_2 = \log(X + 2)$ in $[-3, 2, 1]$ by $[-4, 2, 1]$. See Figures 60a & 60b.

The solutions are the x-coordinates of the intersection points, $x \approx -1.99$ and $x \approx 0.38$.

[-5, 5, 1] by [-5, 5, 1]   [-5, 5, 1] by [-5, 5, 1]   [-3, 2, 1] by [-4, 2, 1]   [-3, 2, 1] by [-4, 2, 1]

Figure 58   Figure 59   Figure 60a   Figure 60b

Logarithmic Equations

61. $\log x = 2 \Rightarrow 10^{\log x} = 10^2 \Rightarrow x = 100$

62. $\log x = 0.01 \Rightarrow 10^{\log x} = 10^{0.01} \Rightarrow x = 10^{0.01} \approx 1.02$

63. $\ln x = 5 \Rightarrow e^{\ln x} = e^5 \Rightarrow x = e^5 \approx 148.41$

64. $2 \ln x = 4 \Rightarrow \ln x = 2 \Rightarrow e^{\ln x} = e^2 \Rightarrow x = e^2 \approx 7.39$

65. $\log 2x = 7 \Rightarrow 10^{\log 2x} = 10^7 \Rightarrow 2x = 10,000,000 \Rightarrow x = 5,000,000$

66. $6 \ln 4x = 12 \Rightarrow \ln 4x = 2 \Rightarrow e^{\ln 4x} = e^2 \Rightarrow 4x = e^2 \Rightarrow x = \dfrac{e^2}{4} \approx 1.85$

67. $\log_2 x = 4 \Rightarrow 2^{\log_2 x} = 2^4 \Rightarrow x = 16$

68. $\log_2 x = 32 \Rightarrow 2^{\log_2 x} = 2^{32} \Rightarrow x = 2^{32} = 4,294,967,296$

69. $\log_2 5x = 2.3 \Rightarrow 2^{\log_2 5x} = 2^{2.3} \Rightarrow 5x = 2^{2.3} \Rightarrow x = \dfrac{2^{2.3}}{5} \approx 0.98$

70. $2 \log_3 4x = 10 \Rightarrow \log_3 4x = 5 \Rightarrow 3^{\log_3 4x} = 3^5 \Rightarrow 4x = 243 \Rightarrow x = \dfrac{243}{4} = 60.75$

71. $2 \log x + 5 = 7.8 \Rightarrow 2 \log x = 2.8 \Rightarrow \log x = 1.4 \Rightarrow 10^{\log x} = 10^{1.4} \Rightarrow x = 10^{1.4} \approx 25.12$

72. $\ln (x-1) = 3.3 \Rightarrow e^{\ln (x-1)} = e^{3.3} \Rightarrow x - 1 = e^{3.3} \Rightarrow x = e^{3.3} + 1 \approx 28.11$

73. $5 \ln (2x+1) = 55 \Rightarrow \ln (2x+1) = 11 \Rightarrow e^{\ln (2x+1)} = e^{11} \Rightarrow 2x+1 = e^{11} \Rightarrow x = \dfrac{e^{11} - 1}{2} \approx 29,936.57$

74. $5 - \log (x+3) = 2.6 \Rightarrow \log (x+3) = 2.4 \Rightarrow 10^{\log (x+3)} = 10^{2.4} \Rightarrow x+3 = 10^{2.4} \Rightarrow x = 10^{2.4} - 3 \approx 248.19$

75. $\log x^2 = \log x \Rightarrow x^2 = x \Rightarrow x^2 - x = 0 \Rightarrow x(x-1) = 0 \Rightarrow x = 0 \text{ or } 1$

    The solution $x = 0$ causes an undefined expression in the original equation. The only solution is 1.

76. $\ln x^2 = \ln (3x-2) \Rightarrow x^2 = 3x-2 \Rightarrow x^2 - 3x + 2 = 0 \Rightarrow (x-1)(x-2) = 0 \Rightarrow x = 1 \text{ or } 2$

77. $\ln x + \ln (x+1) = \ln 30 \Rightarrow \ln x(x+1) = \ln 30 \Rightarrow x(x+1) = 30 \Rightarrow x^2 + x - 30 = 0 \Rightarrow$

    $(x+6)(x-5) = 0 \Rightarrow x = -6 \text{ or } 5$

    The solution $x = -6$ causes an undefined expression in the original equation. The only solution is 5.

78. $\log (x-1) + \log (2x+1) = \log 14 \Rightarrow \log (x-1)(2x+1) = \log 14 \Rightarrow (x-1)(2x+1) = 14 \Rightarrow$

$$2x^2 - x - 1 = 14 \Rightarrow 2x^2 - x - 15 = 0 \Rightarrow (2x+5)(x-3) = 0 \Rightarrow x = -\frac{5}{2} \text{ or } 3$$

The solution $x = -\frac{5}{2}$ causes an undefined expression in the original equation. The only solution is 3.

79. $\log_3 3x - \log_3 (x+2) = \log_3 2 \Rightarrow \log_3 \frac{3x}{x+2} = \log_3 2 \Rightarrow \frac{3x}{x+2} = 2 \Rightarrow 3x = 2x + 4 \Rightarrow x = 4$

80. $\log_4 (x^2 - 1) - \log_4 (x-1) = \log_4 6 \Rightarrow \log_4 \frac{x^2-1}{x-1} = \log_4 6 \Rightarrow x + 1 = 6 \Rightarrow x = 5$

81. $\log_2 (x-1) + \log_2 (x+1) = 3 \Rightarrow \log_2 (x^2 - 1) = 3 \Rightarrow 2^{\log_2 (x^2-1)} = 2^3 \Rightarrow x^2 - 1 = 8 \Rightarrow$

$x^2 - 9 = 0 \Rightarrow (x+3)(x-3) = 0 \Rightarrow x = -3 \text{ or } 3$

The solution $x = -3$ causes an undefined expression in the original equation. The only solution is 3.

82. $\log_4 (x^2 + 2x + 1) - \log_4 (x+1) = 2 \Rightarrow \log_4 \frac{(x+1)^2}{x+1} = 2 \Rightarrow \log_4 (x+1) = 2 \Rightarrow 4^{\log_4 (x+1)} = 4^2 \Rightarrow$

$x + 1 = 16 \Rightarrow x = 15$

83. (a) The solution is the x-coordinate of the intersection point, $x = 2$.

    (b) $\ln x = 0.7 \Rightarrow e^{\ln x} = e^{0.7} \Rightarrow x = e^{0.7} \approx 2.01$

84. (a) The solution is the x-coordinate of the intersection point, $x = 3$.

    (b) $\log_2 x = 1.6 \Rightarrow 2^{\log_2 x} = 2^{1.6} \Rightarrow x = 2^{1.6} \approx 3.03$

85. (a) The solution is the x-coordinate of the intersection point, $x = 2$.

    (b) $5 \log 2x = 3 \Rightarrow \log 2x = 0.6 \Rightarrow 10^{\log 2x} = 10^{0.6} \Rightarrow 2x = 10^{0.6} \Rightarrow x = \frac{10^{0.6}}{2} \approx 1.99$

86. (a) The solution is the x-coordinate of the intersection point, $x = 7$.

    (b) $2 \ln x - 3 = 0.9 \Rightarrow 2 \ln x = 3.9 \Rightarrow \ln x = 1.95 \Rightarrow e^{\ln x} = e^{1.95} \Rightarrow x = e^{1.95} \approx 7.03$

87. $\log x = 1.6 \Rightarrow 10^{\log x} = 10^{1.6} \Rightarrow x = 10^{1.6} \approx 39.81$

For graphical support, graph $Y_1 = \log(X)$ and $Y_2 = 1.6$ in $[0, 50, 10]$ by $[-2, 2, 1]$. See Figure 87.

88. $\ln x = 2 \Rightarrow e^{\ln x} = e^2 \Rightarrow x = e^2 \approx 7.39$

For graphical support, graph $Y_1 = \ln(X)$ and $Y_2 = 2$ in $[0, 10, 1]$ by $[-3, 3, 1]$. See Figure 88.

[0, 50, 10] by [−2, 2, 1]   [0, 10, 1] by [−3, 3, 1]   [−1, 2, 1] by [−2, 2, 1]   [0, 50, 10] by [−2, 2, 1]

Figure 87   Figure 88   Figure 89   Figure 90

89. $\ln (x+1) = 1 \Rightarrow e^{\ln (x+1)} = e^1 \Rightarrow x + 1 = e \Rightarrow x = e - 1 \approx 1.72$

For graphical support, graph $Y_1 = \ln (X+1)$ and $Y_2 = 1$ in $[-1, 2, 1]$ by $[-2, 2, 1]$. See Figure 89.

90. $2 \log (2x+3) = 8 \Rightarrow \log (2x+3) = 4 \Rightarrow 10^{\log (2x+3)} = 10^4 \Rightarrow 2x+3 = 10^4 \Rightarrow x = \dfrac{10^4 - 3}{2} \approx 4998.5$

For graphical support, graph $Y_1 = 2 \log (2X+3)$ and $Y_2 = 8$ in $[0, 50, 10]$ by $[-2, 2, 1]$. See Figure 90.

91. $17 - 6 \log_3 x = 5 \Rightarrow 6 \log_3 x = 12 \Rightarrow \log_3 x = 2 \Rightarrow 3^{\log_3 x} = 3^2 \Rightarrow x = 3^2 = 9$

For graphical support, graph $Y_1 = 17 - 6 \left(\ln (X) / \ln (3) \right)$ and $Y_2 = 5$ in $[0, 10, 1]$ by $[-3, 3, 1]$. See Figure 91.

92. $4 \log_2 x + 7 = 12 \Rightarrow 4 \log_2 x = 5 \Rightarrow \log_2 x = 1.25 \Rightarrow 2^{\log_2 x} = 2^{1.25} \Rightarrow x = 2^{1.25} \approx 2.38$

For graphical support, graph $Y_1 = 4 \left(\ln (X) / \ln (2) \right) + 7$ and $Y_2 = 12$ in $[-1, 2, 1]$ by $[-2, 2, 1]$. See Figure 92.

$[0, 10, 1]$ by $[-3, 3, 1]$ $[-1, 2, 1]$ by $[-2, 2, 1]$

Figure 91   Figure 92

Applications

93. $2000(1+0.15)^t = 6000 \Rightarrow 1.15^t = 3 \Rightarrow \log_{1.15} 1.15^t = \log_{1.15} 3 \Rightarrow t = \dfrac{\log 3}{\log 1.15} \approx 7.86 \approx 8$ years

94. $(1+0.06)^t = 2 \Rightarrow 1.06^t = 2 \Rightarrow \log_{1.06} 1.06^t = \log_{1.06} 2 \Rightarrow t = \dfrac{\log 2}{\log 1.06} \approx 11.90 \approx 12$ years

95.   (a) $f(1994) = 2339(1.24)^{(1994-1988)} \approx 8503$; In 1994 there were about 8503 people waiting for liver

transplants.

(b) $2339(1.24)^{(x-1988)} = 20,000 \Rightarrow (1.24)^{(x-1988)} = \dfrac{20,000}{2339} \Rightarrow \log_{1.24} (1.24)^{(x-1988)} = \log_{1.24} \left(\dfrac{20,000}{2339} \right) \Rightarrow$

$x - 1988 = \log_{1.24} \left(\dfrac{20,000}{2339} \right) \Rightarrow x = \log_{1.24} \left(\dfrac{20,000}{2339} \right) + 1988 = \dfrac{\log \left(\frac{20,000}{2339} \right)}{\log 1.24} + 1988 \approx 1998$

96. $10^{-0.42x} = 0.50 \Rightarrow \log 10^{-0.42x} = \log 0.50 \Rightarrow -0.42x = \log 0.50 \Rightarrow x = \dfrac{\log 0.50}{-0.42} \approx 0.72$ year

97. $3 \log x = 3.960 \Rightarrow \log x = 1.320 \Rightarrow 10^{\log x} = 10^{1.320} \Rightarrow x = 10^{1.320} \approx 20.893 = 20,893$ lb

98.   (a) $3 \log 10x = 3(\log 10 + \log x) = 3 \log 10 + 3 \log x = 3(1) + 3 \log x = 3 + 3 \log x$

This means that a plane that is 10 times heavier will need 3000 feet more runway.

(b) The weight can increase by a factor of 10.

99.   (a) $f(1) = 230 \left(10^{-0.055 \cdot 1} \right) \approx 203$; In 1975 there were about 203 thousand bluefin tuna.

(b) About 1979.

(c) $230\left(10^{-0.055x}\right)=115 \Rightarrow 10^{-0.055x}=0.5 \Rightarrow \log 10^{-0.055x}=\log 0.5 \Rightarrow -0.055x=\log 0.5 \Rightarrow$

$x = \dfrac{\log 0.5}{-0.055} \approx 5.47$ or about 1979.

100. (a) $1000 = a + b \log_2 1 \Rightarrow 1000 = a + b(0) \Rightarrow a = 1000$

$1500 = 1000 + b \log_2 2 \Rightarrow 1500 = 1000 + b(1) \Rightarrow b = 500$

(b) See Figure 100.

(c) $y = 1000 + 500 \log_2 12 = 1000 + 500\left(\dfrac{\log 12}{\log 2}\right) \approx 2792$ species

x	1	2	4	8	16
$y = 1000 + 500 \log_2 x$	1000	1500	2000	2500	3000

Figure 100

101. From the data point $(1, 25)$, $25 = a + b \log 1 \Rightarrow 25 = a + b(0) \Rightarrow a = 25$.

Using the data point $(10, 28)$ and the fact that $a = 25$, $28 = 25 + b \log 10 \Rightarrow 28 = 25 + b \Rightarrow b = 3$

102. From the data point $(1, -2)$, $-2 = a + b \log 1 \Rightarrow -2 = a + b(0) \Rightarrow a = -2$.

Using the data point $(100, 6)$ and the fact that $a = -2$, $6 = -2 + b \log 100 \Rightarrow 6 = -2 + 2b \Rightarrow b = 4$

103. (a) Graph $Y_1 = 645 \log (X+1) + 1925$ and $Y_2 = 2200$ in $[0, 4, 1]$ by $[0, 3000, 1000]$. See Figure 103.

A person consuming 2200 calories would typically own about 1.67 acres.

(b) $645 \log (x+1) + 1925 = 2200 \Rightarrow 645 \log (x+1) = 275 \Rightarrow \log (x+1) = \dfrac{275}{645} \Rightarrow$

$10^{\log (x+1)} = 10^{275/645} \Rightarrow x + 1 = 10^{275/645} \Rightarrow x = 10^{275/645} - 1 \approx 1.67$ acres

$[0, 4, 1]$ by $[0, 3000, 1000]$ $[1950, 2030, 10]$ by $[0, 2, 1]$

Figure 103   Figure 104

104. (a) Graph $Y_1 = 0.36 + 0.15 \ln (X - 1949)$ and $Y_2 = 1$ in $[1950, 2030, 10]$ by $[0, 2, 1]$. See Figure 104.

This population may reach one billion in about 2020.

(b) $0.36 + 0.15 \ln (x - 1949) = 1 \Rightarrow 0.15 \ln (x - 1949) = 0.64 \Rightarrow \ln (x - 1949) = \dfrac{64}{15} \Rightarrow$

$e^{\ln (x-1949)} = e^{64/15} \Rightarrow x - 1949 = e^{64/15} \Rightarrow x = e^{64/15} + 1949 \approx 2020$

105. (a) The data is nonlinear. It does not increase at a constant rate.

(b) Each year the amount of fertilizer increases by a factor of 1.06 or 6%.

(c) $5(1.06)^{(x-1950)} = 15 \Rightarrow 1.06^{(x-1950)} = 3 \Rightarrow \log_{1.06} 1.06^{(x-1950)} = \log_{1.06} 3 \Rightarrow$

$x - 1950 = \log_{1.06} 3 \Rightarrow x = \log_{1.06} 3 + 1950 = \dfrac{\log 3}{\log 1.06} + 1950 \approx 1968.85$ or in 1968

106. $364(1.005)^x = 560 \Rightarrow 1.005^x = \dfrac{560}{364} \Rightarrow \log_{1.005} 1.005^x = \log_{1.005}\left(\dfrac{560}{364}\right) \Rightarrow x = \log_{1.005}\left(\dfrac{560}{364}\right) \Rightarrow$

$x = \dfrac{\log\left(\frac{560}{364}\right)}{\log 1.005} \approx 86.37$ or about 2086

107. $160 + 10 \log x = 100 \Rightarrow 10 \log x = -60 \Rightarrow \log x = -6 \Rightarrow 10^{\log x} = 10^{-6} \Rightarrow x = 10^{-6}$ w/cm^2

108.   (a) $160 + 10 \log 10x = 160 + 10(\log 10 + \log x) = 160 + 10(1 + \log x) = 170 + 10 \log x$

(b) Since $1000 = 10^3$, the increase will be $3 \cdot 10 = 30$ decibels.

(c) When the decibel level increases by 20, the intensity will increase by a factor of $10^2 = 100$.

109. $0.48 \ln(x+1) + 27 = 28 \Rightarrow 0.48 \ln(x+1) = 1 \Rightarrow \ln(x+1) = \dfrac{1}{0.48} \Rightarrow e^{\ln(x+1)} = e^{1/0.48} \Rightarrow$

$x + 1 = e^{1/0.48} \Rightarrow x = e^{1/0.48} - 1 \approx 7.03$ or about 7 miles

110.   (a) Since $\dfrac{1000 I_0}{I_0} = 1000$, the Richter scale would show an increase of $\log 1000 = 3$.

(b) Since $8 - 5 = 3$, the intensity increased by a factor of $10^3 = 1000$.

Checking Basic Concepts for Section 9.5

1.   (a) $2(10^x) = 40 \Rightarrow 10^x = 20 \Rightarrow \log 10^x = \log 20 \Rightarrow x = \log 20 \approx 1.30$

(b) $2^{3x} + 3 = 150 \Rightarrow 2^{3x} = 147 \Rightarrow \log_2 2^{3x} = \log_2 147 \Rightarrow 3x = \dfrac{\log 147}{\log 2} \Rightarrow x = \dfrac{\log 147}{3 \log 2} \approx 2.40$

(c) $\ln x = 4.1 \Rightarrow e^{\ln x} = e^{4.1} \Rightarrow x = e^{4.1} \approx 60.34$

(d) $4 \log 2x = 12 \Rightarrow \log 2x = 3 \Rightarrow 10^{\log 2x} = 10^3 \Rightarrow 2x = 1000 \Rightarrow x = 500$

2. $\log(x+4) + \log(x-4) = \log 48 \Rightarrow \log(x^2 - 16) = \log 48 \Rightarrow x^2 - 16 = 48 \Rightarrow$

$x^2 - 64 = 0 \Rightarrow (x+8)(x-8) = 0 \Rightarrow x = -8$ or 8

The solution $x = -8$ causes an undefined expression in the original equation. The only solution is 8.

3. $500(1.03)^x = 900 \Rightarrow 1.03^x = \dfrac{9}{5} \Rightarrow \log_{1.03} 1.03^x = \log_{1.03}\left(\dfrac{9}{5}\right) \Rightarrow x = \dfrac{\log\left(\frac{9}{5}\right)}{\log 1.03} \approx 19.88$ or about 20 years

Chapter 9 Review Exercises

Section 9.1

1.   (a) $f(-2) = 2(-2)^2 - 4(-2) = 16$, then $(g \circ f)(-2) = g(f(-2)) = g(16) = 5(16) + 1 = 81$

(b) $(f \circ g)(x) = f(g(x)) = f(5x+1) = 2(5x+1)^2 - 4(5x+1) = 50x^2 - 2$

2. (a) $f(-2) = \sqrt[3]{-2-6} = -2$, then $(g \circ f)(-2) = g(f(-2)) = g(-2) = 4(-2)^3 = -32$

   (b) $(f \circ g)(x) = f(g(x)) = f(4x^3) = \sqrt[3]{4x^3 - 6}$

3. (a) $(f \circ g)(2) = f(g(2)) = f(3) = 0$

   (b) $(g \circ f)(1) = g(f(1)) = g(2) = 3$

4. (a) $(f \circ g)(-1) = f(g(-1)) = f(2) = 3$

   (b) $(g \circ f)(2) = g(f(2)) = g(3) = -2$

   (c) $(f \circ f)(1) = f(f(1)) = f(0) = -1$

5. $f(1) = f(-1) = 2$

6. $f(0) = f(2) = 1$

7. This graph does not pass the horizontal line test. The function is not one-to-one.

8. This graph passes the horizontal line test. The function is one-to-one.

9. $(f \circ f^{-1})(x) = f(f^{-1}(x)) = f\left(\dfrac{x+9}{2}\right) = 2\left(\dfrac{x+9}{2}\right) - 9 = x + 9 - 9 = x$

   $(f^{-1} \circ f)(x) = f^{-1}(f(x)) = f^{-1}(2x - 9) = \dfrac{(2x-9)+9}{2} = \dfrac{2x}{2} = x$

10. $(f \circ f^{-1})(x) = f(f^{-1}(x)) = f(\sqrt[3]{x-1}) = (\sqrt[3]{x-1})^3 + 1 = x - 1 + 1 = x$

    $(f^{-1} \circ f)(x) = f^{-1}(f(x)) = f^{-1}(x^3 + 1) = \sqrt[3]{(x^3 + 1) - 1} = \sqrt[3]{x^3} = x$

11. $f(x) = 5x \Rightarrow y = 5x$, interchange x and y and solve for y. $x = 5y \Rightarrow y = \dfrac{x}{5} \Rightarrow f^{-1}(x) = \dfrac{x}{5}$

12. $f(x) = x - 11 \Rightarrow y = x - 11$, interchange x and y and solve for y.

    $x = y - 11 \Rightarrow y = x + 11 \Rightarrow f^{-1}(x) = x + 11$

13. $f(x) = 2x + 7 \Rightarrow y = 2x + 7$, interchange x and y and solve for y.

    $x = 2y + 7 \Rightarrow 2y = x - 7 \Rightarrow y = \dfrac{x-7}{2} \Rightarrow f^{-1}(x) = \dfrac{x-7}{2}$

14. $f(x) = \dfrac{4}{x} \Rightarrow y = \dfrac{4}{x}$, interchange x and y and solve for y. $x = \dfrac{4}{y} \Rightarrow xy = 4 \Rightarrow y = \dfrac{4}{x} \Rightarrow f^{-1}(x) = \dfrac{4}{x}$

15. See Figure 15. $D = \{3, 7, 8, 10\}$; $R = \{0, 1, 2, 3\}$

x	10	8	7	3
$f^{-1}(x)$	0	1	2	3

Figure 15

Figure 16

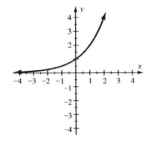

Figure 21

16.   The graph of f^{-1} is a reflection of the graph of f across the line $y = x$. See Figure 16.

Sections 9.2 and 9.3

17. $f(-1) = 6^{-1} = \dfrac{1}{6}$ and $f(2) = 6^2 = 36$

18. $f(0) = 5\left(2^0\right) = 5(1) = 5$ and $f(3) = 5\left(2^{-3}\right) = 5\left(\dfrac{1}{8}\right) = \dfrac{5}{8}$

19. $f(-1) = \left(\dfrac{1}{3}\right)^{-1} = 3$ and $f(4) = \left(\dfrac{1}{3}\right)^4 = \dfrac{1}{3^4} = \dfrac{1}{81}$

20. $f(0) = 3\left(\dfrac{1}{6}\right)^0 = 3(1) = 3$ and $f(1) = 3\left(\dfrac{1}{6}\right)^1 = 3\left(\dfrac{1}{6}\right) = \dfrac{3}{6} = \dfrac{1}{2}$

21.   See Figure 21. The graph illustrates exponential growth.

22.   See Figure 22. The graph illustrates exponential decay.

Figure 22

Figure 23

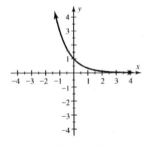

Figure 24

23.   See Figure 23. The graph illustrates logarithmic growth.

24.   See Figure 24. The graph illustrates exponential decay.

25.   (a) Exponential growth. For each unit increase in x, $f(x)$ increases by a factor of 2.

       (b) Since $f(x) = 5$ when $x = 0$, $f(x) = 5(2)^x$

26.   (a) Linear growth. For each unit increase in x, $f(x)$ increases by 5 units.

       (b) Since $f(x) = 5$ when $x = 0$, $f(x) = 5x + 5$

27.   Since $y = \dfrac{1}{2}$ when $x = 0$, $\dfrac{1}{2} = Ca^0 \Rightarrow C = \dfrac{1}{2}$. Since $y = 1$ when $x = 1$, $1 = \dfrac{1}{2}(a)^1 \Rightarrow a = 2$.

28.   Since $y = 2$ when $x = 2$, $2 = k \log_2 2 \Rightarrow 2 = k(1) \Rightarrow k = 2$.

29. $1200(1+0.10)^9 = \$2829.54$

30. $900(1+0.18)^{40} = \$675,340.51$

31. $f(5.3) = 2e^{5.3} - 1 \approx 399.67$

32. $f(2.1) = 0.85^{2.1} \approx 0.71$

33. $f(55) = 2\log 55 \approx 3.48$

34. $f(23) = \ln(2 \cdot 23 + 3) \approx 3.89$

35. $\log 0.001 = \log 10^{-3} = -3$

36. $\log \sqrt{10,000} = \log 100 = 2$

37. $\ln e^{-4} = -4$

38. $\log_4 16 = \log_4 4^2 = 2$

39. $\log 65 \approx 1.813$

40. $\ln 0.85 \approx -0.163$

41. $\ln 120 \approx 4.787$

42. $\log_2 \dfrac{2}{5} \approx -1.322$

43. $10^{\log 7} = 7$

44. $\log_2 2^{5/9} = \dfrac{5}{9}$

45. $\ln e^{6-x} = 6 - x$

46. $e^{2\ln x} = e^{\ln x^2} = x^2$

Section 9.4

47. $\ln xy = \ln x + \ln y$

48. $\log \dfrac{x}{y} = \log x - \log y$

49. $\ln x^2 y^3 = \ln x^2 + \ln y^3 = 2\ln x + 3\ln y$

50. $\log \dfrac{\sqrt{x}}{z^3} = \log \dfrac{x^{1/2}}{z^3} = \log x^{1/2} - \log z^3 = \dfrac{1}{2}\log x - 3\log z$

51. $\log_2 \dfrac{x^2 y}{z} = \log_2 x^2 y - \log_2 z = \log_2 x^2 + \log_2 y - \log_2 z = 2\log_2 x + \log_2 y - \log_2 z$

52. $\log_3 \sqrt[3]{\dfrac{x}{y}} = \log_3 \left(\dfrac{x}{y}\right)^{1/3} = \dfrac{1}{3}\log_3 \left(\dfrac{x}{y}\right) = \dfrac{1}{3}\left(\log_3 x - \log_3 y\right) = \dfrac{1}{3}\log_3 x - \dfrac{1}{3}\log_3 y$

53. $\log 45 + \log 5 - \log 3 = \log(45 \cdot 5) - \log 3 = \log 225 - \log 3 = \log \frac{225}{3} = \log 75$

54. $\log_4 2x + \log_4 5x = \log_4(2x \cdot 5x) = \log_4(10x^2)$

55. $2 \ln x - 3 \ln y = \ln x^2 - \ln y^3 = \ln \frac{x^2}{y^3}$

56. $\log x^4 - \log x^3 + \log y = \log \frac{x^4}{x^3} + \log y = \log x + \log y = \log xy$

57. $\log 6^3 = 3 \log 6$

58. $\ln x^2 = 2 \ln x$

59. $\log_2 5^{2x} = (2x) \log_2 5$

60. $\log_4 (0.6)^{x+1} = (x+1) \log_4 0.6$

Section 9.5

61. $10^x = 100 \Rightarrow 10^x = 10^2 \Rightarrow x = 2$

62. $2^{2x} = 256 \Rightarrow 2^{2x} = 2^8 \Rightarrow 2x = 8 \Rightarrow x = 4$

63. $3e^x + 1 = 28 \Rightarrow 3e^x = 27 \Rightarrow e^x = 9 \Rightarrow \ln e^x = \ln 9 \Rightarrow x = \ln 9 \approx 2.20$

64. $0.85^x = 0.2 \Rightarrow \log_{0.85} 0.85^x = \log_{0.85} 0.2 \Rightarrow x = \log_{0.85} 0.2 = \frac{\log 0.2}{\log 0.85} \approx 9.90$

65. $5 \ln x = 4 \Rightarrow \ln x = 0.8 \Rightarrow e^{\ln x} = e^{0.8} \Rightarrow x = e^{0.8} \approx 2.23$

66. $\ln 2x = 5 \Rightarrow e^{\ln 2x} = e^5 \Rightarrow 2x = e^5 \Rightarrow x = \frac{e^5}{2} \approx 74.21$

67. $2 \log x = 80 \Rightarrow \log x = 40 \Rightarrow 10^{\log x} = 10^{40} \Rightarrow x = 10^{40}$

68. $3 \log x - 5 = 1 \Rightarrow 3 \log x = 6 \Rightarrow \log x = 2 \Rightarrow 10^{\log x} = 10^2 \Rightarrow x = 100$

69. $2^{x+4} = 3^x \Rightarrow \log 2^{x+4} = \log 3^x \Rightarrow (x+4) \log 2 = x \log 3 \Rightarrow x \log 2 + 4 \log 2 = x \log 3 \Rightarrow$

$x \log 3 - x \log 2 = 4 \log 2 \Rightarrow x(\log 3 - \log 2) = 4 \log 2 \Rightarrow x = \frac{4 \log 2}{\log 3 - \log 2} \approx 6.84$

70. $\ln(2x+1) + \ln(x-5) = \ln 13 \Rightarrow \ln(2x+1)(x-5) = \ln 13 \Rightarrow (2x+1)(x-5) = 13 \Rightarrow$

$2x^2 - 9x - 5 = 13 \Rightarrow 2x^2 - 9x - 18 = 0 \Rightarrow (2x+3)(x-6) = 0 \Rightarrow x = -\frac{3}{2}$ or 6

The solution $x = -\frac{3}{2}$ causes an undefined expression in the original equation. The only solution is 6.

71. (a) The solution is the *x*-coordinate of the intersection point, $x = 3$.

  (b) $\frac{1}{2}(2^x) = 4 \Rightarrow 2^x = 8 \Rightarrow 2^x = 2^3 \Rightarrow x = 3$

72.   (a) The solution is the x-coordinate of the intersection point, $x = 4$.

(b) $\log_2 2x = 3 \Rightarrow 2^{\log_2 2x} = 2^3 \Rightarrow 2x = 8 \Rightarrow x = 4$

Applications

73.   (a) $(S \circ r)(8) = S(r(8)) = S(\sqrt{2 \cdot 8}) = S(4) = 4\pi(4)^2 = 64\pi$

After 8 seconds, the balloon has a surface area of $64\pi \approx 201$ square inches.

(b) $(S \circ r)(t) = S(r(t)) = S(\sqrt{2t}) = 4\pi(\sqrt{2t})^2 = 4\pi \cdot 2t = 8\pi t$

74.   (a) Yes, this is a one-to-one function because different inputs result in different outputs.

(b) $f(x) = 0.08x \Rightarrow y = 0.08x$, interchange x and y and solve for y.

$$x = 0.08y \Rightarrow y = \frac{x}{0.08} \Rightarrow f^{-1}(x) = \frac{x}{0.08}$$

This formula calculates the cost of an item whose sales tax is x dollars.

75. $1500(1 + 0.12)^t = 3000 \Rightarrow 1.12^t = 2 \Rightarrow \log_{1.12} 1.12^t = \log_{1.12} 2 \Rightarrow t = \frac{\log 2}{\log 1.12} \approx 6.12 \approx 7$ years

76. $100 = a + b \log 1 \Rightarrow 100 = a + b(0) \Rightarrow a = 100$

$150 = 100 + b \log 10 \Rightarrow 150 = 100 + b(1) \Rightarrow b = 50$

77. $3 = Ca^0 \Rightarrow C = 3$ and $6 = 3a^1 \Rightarrow a = 2$

78. $\log \dfrac{x}{1} = 7 \Rightarrow 10^{\log x} = 10^7 \Rightarrow x = 10^7$

79.   (a) Graph $Y_1 = 2e^\wedge(0.051X)$ in $[0, 10, 2]$ by $[0, 4, 1]$.

$[0, 10, 2]$ by $[0, 4, 1]$

(b) In 2010, $x = 10$ thus $f(10) = 2e^{0.051(10)} \approx 3.3$ million

(c) $2e^{0.051x} = 3 \Rightarrow e^{0.051x} = \dfrac{3}{2} \Rightarrow \ln e^{0.051x} = \ln\left(\dfrac{3}{2}\right)$

$\Rightarrow 0.051x = \ln(1.5) \Rightarrow x = \dfrac{\ln(1.5)}{0.051} \approx 7.95$

That is about 8 years after 2000, which is 2008.

80.   (a) $N(0) = 1000e^{0.0014(0)} = 1000$; There were initially 1000 bacteria.

(b) $1000e^{0.0014x} = 2000 \Rightarrow e^{0.0014x} = 2 \Rightarrow \ln e^{0.0014x} = \ln 2 \Rightarrow 0.0014x = \ln 2 \Rightarrow x = \dfrac{\ln 2}{0.0014} \approx 495.11$ min.

81.   (a) $f(5) = 1.2 \ln 5 + 5 \approx 6.93$ m/sec

(b) $1.2 \ln x + 5 = 8 \Rightarrow 1.2 \ln x = 3 \Rightarrow \ln x = 2.5 \Rightarrow e^{\ln x} = e^{2.5} \Rightarrow x = e^{2.5} \approx 12.18$ meters

Chapter 9 Test

1. $f(1) = 4(1)^3 - 5(1) = -1,$ then $(g \circ f)(1) = g(f(1)) = g(-1) = (-1) + 7 = 6$

  $(f \circ g)(x) = f(g(x)) = f(x + 7) = 4(x + 7)^3 - 5(x + 7)$

2.   (a) $(f \circ g)(-1) = f(g(-1)) = f(-1) = 3$

  (b) $(g \circ f)(1) = g(f(1)) = g(1) = 3$

3.   Two different inputs result in the same output. For example $-5 \neq 5$, but $f(-5) = f(5) = 0$.

4. $f(x) = 5 - 2x \Rightarrow y = 5 - 2x,$ interchange x and y and solve for y.

  $x = 5 - 2y \Rightarrow 2y = 5 - x \Rightarrow y = \dfrac{5 - x}{2} \Rightarrow f^{-1}(x) = \dfrac{5 - x}{2}$

5.   The graph of f^{-1} is a reflection of the graph of f across the line $y = x$. See Figure 5.

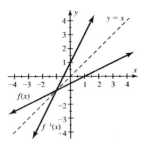

Figure 5

6.   See Figure 6. $D = \{2, 4, 6, 8\}; \ R = \{1, 2, 3, 4\}$

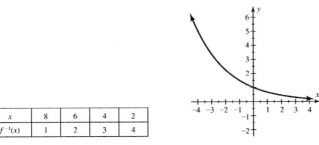

x	8	6	4	2
$f^{-1}(x)$	1	2	3	4

Figure 6

Figure 8

Figure 16

7. $f(2) = 3\left(\dfrac{1}{4}\right)^2 = 3\left(\dfrac{1}{16}\right) = \dfrac{3}{16}$

8.   See Figure 8. This graph represents exponential decay.

9.   (a) Exponential growth. For each unit increase in x, $f(x)$ increases by a factor of 2.

  (b) Since $f(x) = 3$ when $x = 0$, $f(x) = 3(2)^x$

10.   (a) Linear growth. For each unit increase in x, $f(x)$ increases by 1.5 units.

(b) Since $f(x) = -1$ when $x = 0$, $f(x) = 1.5x - 1$

11. $1 = Ca^0 \Rightarrow C = 1$ and $2 = 1a^{-1} \Rightarrow a = \dfrac{1}{2}$

12. $750(1 + 0.07)^5 = \$1051.91$

13. $f(21) = 1.5 \ln(21 - 5) = 1.5 \ln 16 \approx 4.16$

14. $\log \sqrt{10} = \log 10^{1/2} = \dfrac{1}{2}$

15. $\log_2 43 = \dfrac{\log 43}{\log 2} \approx 5.426$

16.   See Figure 16. The graph is shifted 2 units to the right.

17. $\log \dfrac{x^3 y^2}{\sqrt{x}} = \log \dfrac{x^3 y^2}{x^{1/2}} = \log x^3 + \log y^2 - \log x^{1/2} = 3\log x + 2\log y - \dfrac{1}{2}\log z$

18. $4 \ln x - 5 \ln y + \ln z = \ln x^4 - \ln y^5 + \ln z = \ln \dfrac{x^4}{y^5} + \ln z = \ln \dfrac{x^4 z}{y^5}$

19. $\log 7^{2x} = 2x \log 7$

20. $\ln e^{1-3x} = 1 - 3x$

21. $2e^x = 50 \Rightarrow e^x = 25 \Rightarrow \ln e^x = \ln 25 \Rightarrow x = \ln 25 \approx 3.22$

22. $3(10)^x - 7 = 143 \Rightarrow 3(10)^x = 150 \Rightarrow 10^x = 50 \Rightarrow \log 10^x = \log 50 \Rightarrow x = \log 50 \approx 1.70$

23. $5 \log x = 9 \Rightarrow \log x = 1.8 \Rightarrow 10^{\log x} = 10^{1.8} \Rightarrow x = 10^{1.8} \approx 63.10$

24. $3 \ln 5x = 27 \Rightarrow \ln 5x = 9 \Rightarrow e^{\ln 5x} = e^9 \Rightarrow 5x = e^9 \Rightarrow x = \dfrac{e^9}{5} \approx 1620.62$

25. $5 = a + b \log 1 \Rightarrow 5 = a + b(0) \Rightarrow a = 5$ and $8 = 5 + b \log 10 \Rightarrow 8 = 5 + b(1) \Rightarrow b = 3$

26.   (a) $f(0) = 4e^{0.09(0)} = 4e^0 = 4(1) = 4$ million

      (b) $f(5) = 4e^{0.09(5)} \approx 6.27$; After 5 hours there were about 6.27 million bacteria.

      (c) This represents exponential growth.

      (d) $4e^{0.09x} = 6 \Rightarrow e^{0.09x} = 1.5 \Rightarrow \ln e^{0.09x} = \ln 1.5 \Rightarrow 0.09x = \ln 1.5 \Rightarrow x = \dfrac{\ln 1.5}{0.09} \approx 4.51$

      There were 6 million bacteria after about 4.51 hours.

Chapter 9 Extended and Discovery Exercises

1. $a^{5730} = 0.5 \Rightarrow \left(a^{5730}\right)^{1/5730} = 0.5^{1/5730} \Rightarrow a \approx 0.9998790392$

2. $P(10{,}000) = 0.9998790392^{10{,}000} \approx 0.298$ or 29.8%

3. $0.9998790392^x = 0.9 \Rightarrow \log_{0.9998790392} 0.9998790392^x = \log_{0.9998790392} 0.9 \Rightarrow x = \dfrac{\log 0.9}{\log 0.9998790392} \Rightarrow$

    $x \approx 871$ years

4. $0.9998790392^x = 0.01 \Rightarrow \log_{0.9998790392} 0.999879^x = \log_{0.9998790392} 0.01 \Rightarrow x = \dfrac{\log 0.01}{\log 0.9998790392} \Rightarrow$

    $x \approx 38,069$ years   (38,100 rounded to the nearest 100 years)

5. Plot the data and graph $Y_1 = 0.133(0.878(0.73 \wedge X) + 0.122(0.92 \wedge X))$ in [0, 25, 5] by [0, 0.11, 0.01].

    See Figure 5. The fit is quite good.

    [0, 25, 5] by [0, 0.11, 0.01]   [0, 25, 5] by [0, 0.11, 0.01]

    Figure 5   Figure 8

6. $f(0) = 0.133\left(0.878\left(0.73^0\right) + 0.122\left(0.92^0\right)\right) = 0.133(0.878 + 0.122) = 0.133(1) = 0.133$

    The initial concentration is 0.133 mg/mL.

7. The concentration decreases to 0 as the body eliminates the dye from the blood stream.

8. Note that 40% of 0.133 is 0.0532.

    Graph $Y_1 = 0.133(0.878(0.73 \wedge X) + 0.122(0.92 \wedge X))$ and $Y_2 = 0.0532$ in [0, 25, 5] by [0, 0.11, 0.01].

    See Figure 8. This happens after about 3.33 minutes. Solving this problem symbolically would be very difficult.

9. $f\left(10^{-4.7}\right) = -\log 10^{-4.7} = -(-4.7) = 4.7$;   This rain could cause the pH to drop below 5.6.

10. The ion concentration in seawater is $-\log x = 8.2 \Rightarrow \log x = -8.2 \Rightarrow 10^{\log x} = 10^{-8.2} \Rightarrow x = 10^{-8.2}$.

    This is $\dfrac{10^{-4.7}}{10^{-8.2}} \approx 3162$ times greater.

11. $A = 100\left[\dfrac{\left(1 + \frac{0.09}{26}\right)^{260} - 1}{\frac{0.09}{26}}\right] \approx \$42,055.97$

12. A 19-year-old student would have 46 years to deposit money before age 65. *Answers may vary.*

    $x\left[\dfrac{\left(1 + \frac{0.12}{26}\right)^{1196} - 1}{\frac{0.12}{26}}\right] = 1,000,000 \Rightarrow x = 1,000,000\left[\dfrac{\frac{0.12}{26}}{\left(1 + \frac{0.12}{26}\right)^{1196} - 1}\right] = \$18.80$

13. Plot the data in [0, 20, 2] by [0, 700, 100]. See Figure 13.

[0, 20, 2] by [0, 700, 100]   [0, 20, 2] by [0, 700, 100]   [0, 20, 2] by [0, 700, 100]

Figure 13   Figure 15   Figure 16

14.   The yeast grew slowly at first and then, as more yeast was present, the growth rate increased. Finally, as the yeast began to use up the fixed amount of nourishment, the growth rate slowed.

15.   Plot the data and graph $Y_1 = 663/\left(1 + 71.6(0.579)\wedge X\right)$ in [0, 20, 2] by [0, 700, 100]. See Figure 15.

16.   Graph $Y_1 = 663/\left(1 + 71.6(0.579)\wedge X\right)$ and $Y_2 = 400$ in [0, 20, 2] by [0, 700, 100]. See Figure 16.

The amount of yeast was equal to 400 units after about 8.6 hours.

17. $400 = \dfrac{663}{1 + 71.6(0.579)^x} \Rightarrow 400\left(1 + 71.6(0.579)^x\right) = 663 \Rightarrow 400 + 28{,}640(0.579)^x = 663 \Rightarrow$

$28{,}640(0.579)^x = 263 \Rightarrow 0.579^x = \dfrac{263}{28{,}640} \Rightarrow \log_{0.579} 0.579^x = \log_{0.579} \dfrac{263}{28{,}640} \Rightarrow$

$x = \log_{0.579} \dfrac{263}{28{,}640} = \dfrac{\log\left(\frac{263}{28.640}\right)}{\log 0.579} \approx 8.6$ hours

Chapters 1–9 Cumulative Review Exercises

1.   Move the decimal point 4 places to the right: $0.000429 = 4.29 \times 10^{-4}$.

2.   Natural: none; Whole: 0; Integer: $-3, 0$; Rational: $-\dfrac{11}{7}, -3, 0, 5.\overline{18}$; Irrational: $\sqrt{6}, \pi$

3.   By substitution of values, the formula that best fits the data is (iii).

4.   This equation illustrates the commutative property for addition.

5. $\left(\dfrac{1}{d^2}\right)^{-2} = \left(d^2\right)^2 = d^4$

6. $\left(\dfrac{8a^2}{2b^3}\right)^{-3} = \left(\dfrac{4a^2}{b^3}\right)^{-3} = \left(\dfrac{b^3}{4a^2}\right)^3 = \dfrac{\left(b^3\right)^3}{\left(4a^2\right)^3} = \dfrac{b^9}{4^3\left(a^2\right)^3} = \dfrac{b^9}{64a^6}$

7. $\dfrac{\left(2x^{-2}y^3\right)^2}{xy^{-2}} = \dfrac{2^2\left(x^{-2}\right)^2\left(y^3\right)^2}{xy^{-2}} = \dfrac{4x^{-4}y^6}{xy^{-2}} = 4x^{-4-1}y^{6-(-2)} = 4x^{-5}y^8 = \dfrac{4y^8}{x^5}$

8. $\dfrac{x^{-3}y}{4x^2y^{-3}} = \dfrac{1}{4}x^{-3-2}y^{1-(-3)} = \dfrac{1}{4}x^{-5}y^4 = \dfrac{y^4}{4x^5}$

9.   The graph rises 5 units for each 4 units of run. The slope is $\dfrac{5}{4}$. The y-intercept is 1. So $y = \dfrac{5}{4}x + 1$.

10. The function is defined for all values of the variable except -3. The domain is $\{x \mid x \neq -3\}$.

11. The slope is $m = \dfrac{5-1}{2-1} = \dfrac{4}{1} = 4$. Since $f(x) = -3$ when $x = 0$ the y-intercept is -3. Here $y = 4x - 3$.

12. Vertical lines have equations of the form $x = k$. The equation of the vertical line passing through $(4, 7)$ is $x = 4$.

13. $m = \dfrac{-3 - (-1)}{2 - 4} = \dfrac{-2}{-2} = 1$

14. See Figure 14.

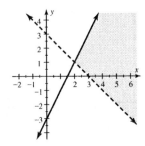

Figure 14   Figure 25

15. Since the line is perpendicular to $y = -\dfrac{1}{7}x - 8$, the slope is $m = 7$. Using the point-slope form gives

$$y = 7(x - 1) + 1 \Rightarrow y = 7x - 7 + 1 \Rightarrow y = 7x - 6$$

16. Since the line is parallel to $y = 3x - 1$, the slope is $m = 3$. The y-intercept is given, so $b = 5$.

    The equation is $y = 3x + 5$.

17. The graphs intersect at the point $(-1, 1)$, so $y_1 = y_2$ when $x = -1$.

18. Here $y < -4$ when $x < 0$.

19. $\dfrac{2}{3}(x - 3) + 8 = -6 \Rightarrow \dfrac{2}{3}(x - 3) = -14 \Rightarrow x - 3 = -21 \Rightarrow x = -18$

20. $\dfrac{1}{3}z + 6 < \dfrac{1}{4}z - (5z - 6) \Rightarrow 4z + 72 < 3z - 12(5z - 6) \Rightarrow 4z + 72 < 3z - 60z + 72 \Rightarrow$

    $4z + 72 < -57z + 72 \Rightarrow 61z < 0 \Rightarrow z < 0$. The interval is $(-\infty, 0)$.

21. $\left(\dfrac{t + 2}{3}\right) - 10 = \dfrac{1}{3}t - (5t + 8) \Rightarrow t + 2 - 30 = t - 3(5t + 8) \Rightarrow 15t = 4 \Rightarrow t = \dfrac{4}{15}$

22. $-10 \leq -\dfrac{3}{5}x - 4 < -1 \Rightarrow -6 \leq -\dfrac{3}{5}x < 3 \Rightarrow 10 \geq x > -5 \Rightarrow -5 < x \leq 10$. The interval is $(-5, 10]$.

23. First divide each side of $-2|t - 4| \geq -12$ by -2 to obtain $|t - 4| \leq 6$.

    The solutions to $|t - 4| \leq 6$ satisfy $c \leq t \leq d$ where c and d are the solutions to $|t - 4| = 6$.

    $|t - 4| = 6$ is equivalent to $t - 4 = -6 \Rightarrow t = -2$ and $t - 4 = 6 \Rightarrow t = 10$. The interval is $[-2, 10]$.

24. $\left|\dfrac{1}{2}x-5\right|=3 \Rightarrow \dfrac{1}{2}x-5=-3 \Rightarrow \dfrac{1}{2}x=2 \Rightarrow x=4$ or $\dfrac{1}{2}x-5=3 \Rightarrow \dfrac{1}{2}x=8 \Rightarrow x=16$

25. See Figure 25.

26. $\det A = -1(4)-3(-2) = -4+6 = 2$

27. Multiply the first equation by 2 and the second equation by 3. Add the equations to eliminate the variable y.

$$
\begin{aligned}
8x-6y &= 2 \\
15x+6y &= 21 \\
\hline
23x &= 23
\end{aligned}
$$

Thus, $x=1$. And so $4(1)-3y=1 \Rightarrow y=1$. The solution is $(1,1)$.

28. Multiplying the first equation by 3 and adding the equations will eliminate both variables.

$$
\begin{aligned}
6x-9y &= -6 \\
-6x+9y &= 5 \\
\hline
0 &= -1
\end{aligned}
$$

Thus, the system has no solutions.

29. Multiply the first equation by 5 and add the first and second equations to eliminate the variable y.

$$
\begin{aligned}
10x-5y+15z &= -10 \\
x+5y-2z &= -8 \\
\hline
11x+13z &= -18
\end{aligned}
$$

Multiply the third equation by 5 and add the second and third equations to eliminate the variable y.

$$
\begin{aligned}
x+5y-2z &= -8 \\
-15x-5y-15z &= 30 \\
\hline
-14x-17z &= 22
\end{aligned}
$$

Multiply the first *new* equation by 14 and the second *new* equation by 11. Add the equations to eliminate x.

$$
\begin{aligned}
154x+182z &= -252 \\
-154x-187z &= 242 \\
\hline
-5z &= -10
\end{aligned}
$$

And so $z=2$. Substitute $z=2$ into the first *new* equation: $11x+13(2)=-18 \Rightarrow x=-4$

Substitute $x=-4$ and $z=2$ into the *original* first equation: $2(-4)-y+3(2)=-2 \Rightarrow y=0$

The solution is $(-4, 0, 2)$.

30.
$$
\begin{bmatrix} 1 & 1 & -1 & | & -1 \\ -1 & -1 & -1 & | & -1 \\ 1 & -2 & 1 & | & 1 \end{bmatrix}
\begin{matrix} \\ R_2+R_1 \rightarrow \\ R_3-R_1 \rightarrow \end{matrix}
\begin{bmatrix} 1 & 1 & -1 & | & -1 \\ 0 & 0 & -2 & | & -2 \\ 0 & -3 & 2 & | & 2 \end{bmatrix}
\begin{matrix} \\ Exchange \\ R_2 \leftrightarrow R_3 \end{matrix}
\begin{bmatrix} 1 & 1 & -1 & | & -1 \\ 0 & -3 & 2 & | & 2 \\ 0 & 0 & -2 & | & -2 \end{bmatrix}
$$

$$
(-1/2)R_3 \rightarrow
\begin{bmatrix} 1 & 1 & -1 & | & -1 \\ 0 & -3 & 2 & | & 2 \\ 0 & 0 & 1 & | & 1 \end{bmatrix}
\begin{matrix} R_1+R_3 \rightarrow \\ R_2-2R_3 \rightarrow \\ \\ \end{matrix}
\begin{bmatrix} 1 & 1 & 0 & | & 0 \\ 0 & -3 & 0 & | & 0 \\ 0 & 0 & 1 & | & 1 \end{bmatrix}
\begin{matrix} R_1+(1/3)R_2 \rightarrow \\ (-1/3)R_2 \rightarrow \\ \\ \end{matrix}
\begin{bmatrix} 1 & 0 & 0 & | & 0 \\ 0 & 1 & 0 & | & 0 \\ 0 & 0 & 1 & | & 1 \end{bmatrix}
$$

The solution is $(0, 0, 1)$.

31. From the graph of the region of feasible solutions (not shown), the vertices are (0, 0), (0, 4), (3, 3), and (4, 0).

The maximum value of R occurs at one of the vertices. For $(0, 0)$, $R = 2(0) + 5(0) = 0$.

For $(0, 4)$, $R = 2(0) + 5(4) = 20$. For $(3, 3)$, $R = 2(3) + 5(3) = 21$. For $(4, 0)$, $R = 2(4) + 5(0) = 8$.

The maximum value is $R = 21$.

32. The triangle has vertices $(-2, -3), (-1, 2)$ and $(2, 1)$. The matrix needed is $A = \begin{bmatrix} -2 & -1 & 2 \\ -3 & 2 & 1 \\ 1 & 1 & 1 \end{bmatrix}$.

    The area is $D = \left| \dfrac{1}{2} \det([A]) \right| = 8 \text{ in}^2$.

33. $2x^3 - 4x^2 + 2x = 2x\left(x^2 - 2x + 1\right) = 2x(x-1)^2$

34. $4a^2 - 25b^2 = (2a)^2 - (5b)^2 = (2a - 5b)(2a + 5b)$

35. $8t^3 - 27 = (2t)^3 - 3^3 = (2t - 3)\left(4t^2 + 6t + 9\right)$

36. $4a^3 - 2a^2 + 10a - 5 = 2a^2(2a - 1) + 5(2a - 1) = \left(2a^2 + 5\right)(2a - 1)$

37. $6x^2 - 7x - 10 = 0 \Rightarrow (6x + 5)(x - 2) = 0 \Rightarrow x = -\dfrac{5}{6}$ or $x = 2$

38. $9x^2 = 4 \Rightarrow 9x^2 - 4 = 0 \Rightarrow (3x + 2)(3x - 2) = 0 \Rightarrow x = -\dfrac{2}{3}$ or $x = \dfrac{2}{3}$

39. $x^4 - 2x^3 = 15x^2 \Rightarrow x^4 - 2x^3 - 15x^2 = 0 \Rightarrow x^2(x + 3)(x - 5) = 0 \Rightarrow x = -3, 0,$ or 5

40. $5x - 10x^2 = 0 \Rightarrow 5x(1 - 2x) = 0 \Rightarrow x = 0$ or $x = \dfrac{1}{2}$

41. $\dfrac{x^2 + 5x + 6}{x^2 - 9} \cdot \dfrac{x - 3}{x + 2} = \dfrac{(x + 2)(x + 3)(x - 3)}{(x - 3)(x + 3)(x + 2)} = 1$

42. $\dfrac{x^2 - 2x - 8}{x^2 + x - 12} \div \dfrac{(x - 4)^2}{x^2 - 16} = \dfrac{x^2 - 2x - 8}{x^2 + x - 12} \cdot \dfrac{x^2 - 16}{(x - 4)^2} = \dfrac{(x + 2)(x - 4)(x - 4)(x + 4)}{(x + 4)(x - 3)(x - 4)(x - 4)} = \dfrac{x + 2}{x - 3}$

43. $\dfrac{2}{x + 2} - \dfrac{1}{x - 2} = \dfrac{-3}{x^2 - 4} \Rightarrow 2(x - 2) - 1(x + 2) = -3 \Rightarrow x - 6 = -3 \Rightarrow x = 3$

44. $\dfrac{3y}{y^2 + y - 2} = \dfrac{1}{y - 1} - 2 \Rightarrow 3y = 1(y + 2) - 2(y + 2)(y - 1) \Rightarrow 3y = y + 2 - 2y^2 - 2y + 4 \Rightarrow$

    $2y^2 + 4y - 6 = 0 \Rightarrow 2(y + 3)(y - 1) = 0 \Rightarrow y = -3$ or $y = 1$. The value $y = 1$ is not valid, thus $y = -3$.

45. $P = \dfrac{J + 2z}{J} \Rightarrow JP = J + 2z \Rightarrow JP - J = 2z \Rightarrow J(P - 1) = 2z \Rightarrow J = \dfrac{2z}{P - 1}$

46. $\dfrac{\dfrac{3}{x^2} + x}{x - \dfrac{3}{x^2}} = \dfrac{\dfrac{3}{x^2} + x}{x - \dfrac{3}{x^2}} \cdot \dfrac{x^2}{x^2} = \dfrac{3 + x^3}{x^3 - 3} = \dfrac{x^3 + 3}{x^3 - 3}$

47. $y = kx \Rightarrow 15 = 3k \Rightarrow k = 5 \Rightarrow y = 5x$, so when $x = 8$, $y = 5(8) = 40$

48.

$$\require{enclose}\begin{array}{r}3x^2 + 6x + 10 \\ x-2\enclose{longdiv}{3x^3 + 0x^2 - 2x - 15}\end{array}$$

$$\underline{3x^2 - 6x^2}$$
$$6x^2 - 2x$$
$$\underline{6x^2 - 12x}$$
$$10x - 15$$
$$\underline{10x - 20}$$
$$5$$

The solution is: $3x^2 + 6x + 10 + \dfrac{5}{x-2}$

49. $\left(\dfrac{x^6}{y^9}\right)^{2/3} = \dfrac{\left(x^6\right)^{2/3}}{\left(y^9\right)^{2/3}} = \dfrac{x^{6 \cdot (2/3)}}{y^{9 \cdot (2/3)}} = \dfrac{x^4}{y^6}$

50. $\sqrt[3]{-x^4} \cdot \sqrt[3]{-x^5} = \sqrt[3]{\left(-x^4\right)\left(-x^5\right)} = \sqrt[3]{x^9} = x^{9/3} = x^3$

51. $\sqrt{5ab} \cdot \sqrt{20ab} = \sqrt{5 \cdot 20 \cdot ab \cdot ab} = \sqrt{100(ab)^2} = \sqrt{(10ab)^2} = 10ab$

52. $2\sqrt{24} - \sqrt{54} = 2\sqrt{4 \cdot 6} - \sqrt{9 \cdot 6} = 2\sqrt{4} \cdot \sqrt{6} - \sqrt{9} \cdot \sqrt{6} = 4\sqrt{6} - 3\sqrt{6} = \sqrt{6}$

53. $\sqrt[3]{a^5 b^4} + 3\sqrt[3]{a^5 b} = \sqrt[3]{(ab)^3 \cdot a^2 b} + 3\sqrt[3]{a^3 \cdot a^2 b} = ab\sqrt[3]{a^2 b} + 3a\sqrt[3]{a^2 b} = (b+3)a\sqrt[3]{a^2 b}$

54. $\left(5 + \sqrt{5}\right)\left(5 - \sqrt{5}\right) = 5^2 - \left(\sqrt{5}\right)^2 = 25 - 5 = 20$

55. $P = \dfrac{2}{5 - \sqrt{3}} = \dfrac{2}{5 - \sqrt{3}} \cdot \dfrac{5 + \sqrt{3}}{5 + \sqrt{3}} = \dfrac{10 + 2\sqrt{3}}{25 - 3} = \dfrac{10 + 2\sqrt{3}}{22} = \dfrac{2\left(5 + \sqrt{3}\right)}{2 \cdot 11} = \dfrac{5 + \sqrt{3}}{11}$

56.   For the function to be defined, $x - 4 > 0 \Rightarrow x > 4$. The interval is $(4, \infty)$.

57. $2(x+1)^2 = 50 \Rightarrow (x+1)^2 = 25 \Rightarrow x+1 = \pm\sqrt{25} \Rightarrow x+1 = \pm 5 \Rightarrow x = -6$ or 4

58. $\sqrt{x+6} = x \Rightarrow x+6 = x^2 \Rightarrow x^2 - x - 6 = 0 \Rightarrow (x+2)(x-3) = 0 \Rightarrow x = -2$ or 3

   The value $x = -2$ does not check. The only solution is 3.

59. $(-2+3i) - (-5-2i) = -2 - (-5) + 3i + 2i = 3 + 5i$

60. $\dfrac{3-i}{1+3i} = \dfrac{3-i}{1+3i} \cdot \dfrac{1-3i}{1-3i} = \dfrac{3 - 9i - i + 3i^2}{1 - 9i^2} = \dfrac{3 - 10i - 3}{1 + 9} = \dfrac{-10i}{10} = -i$

61. $-\dfrac{b}{2a} = -\dfrac{-12}{2(3)} = \dfrac{12}{6} = 2$; $f(2) = 3(2)^2 - 12(2) + 13 = 1$. The vertex is $(2, 1)$.

62. $-\dfrac{b}{2a} = -\dfrac{6}{2(-2)} = \dfrac{6}{4} = \dfrac{3}{2}$; $f\left(\dfrac{3}{2}\right) = -2\left(\dfrac{3}{2}\right)^2 + 6\left(\dfrac{3}{2}\right) - 1 = \dfrac{7}{2}$. The vertex is $\left(\dfrac{3}{2}, \dfrac{7}{2}\right)$. The maximum value is $\dfrac{7}{2}$.

63.   Compared to $y = x^2$, the graph of $f(x)$ is shifted right 3 units and up 2 units.

64. $y = x^2 + 6x - 2 \Rightarrow y = (x^2 + 6x + 9) - 2 - 9 \Rightarrow y = (x+3)^2 - 11$. The vertex is $(-3, -11)$.

65. $x^2 - 13x + 40 = 0 \Rightarrow (x-5)(x-8) = 0 \Rightarrow x = 5$ or $x = 8$

66. $2d^2 - 5 = d \Rightarrow 2d^2 - d - 5 = 0$. Let $a = 2, b = -1$ and $c = -5$ in the quadratic formula.

$$d = \frac{-(-1) \pm \sqrt{(-1)^2 - 4(2)(-5)}}{2(2)} = \frac{1 \pm \sqrt{41}}{4}$$

67. $z^2 - 4z = -2 \Rightarrow z^2 - 4z + 4 = -2 + 4 \Rightarrow (z-2)^2 = 2 \Rightarrow z - 2 = \pm\sqrt{2} \Rightarrow z = 2 \pm \sqrt{2}$

68. $x^4 - 10x^2 + 24 = 0 \Rightarrow (x^2 - 6)(x^2 - 4) = 0 \Rightarrow x^2 - 6 = 0$ or $x^2 - 4 = 0 \Rightarrow x = \pm\sqrt{6}$ or $x = \pm 2$

69. (a) The graph intersects the x-axis at -1 and 3.

   (b) Because the parabola opens downward, $a < 0$.

   (c) Because there are two real solutions, the discriminant is positive.

70. $x^2 + 5x - 14 = 0 \Rightarrow (x+7)(x-2) = 0 \Rightarrow x = -7$ or $x = 2$

   Since the parabola opens upward, the solution is $(-\infty, -7] \cup [2, \infty)$.

71. (a) $g(1) = 2(1) + 1 = 3$, then $(f \circ g)(1) = f(g(1)) = f(3) = (3)^2 - 2 = 7$

   (b) $(g \circ f)(x) = g(f(x)) = g(x^2 - 2) = 2(x^2 - 2) + 1 = 2x^2 - 4 + 1 = 2x^2 - 3$

72. $f(-4) = f(3) = 6$

73. $f(x) = \dfrac{3}{x} \Rightarrow y = \dfrac{3}{x}$, interchange x and y and solve for y. $x = \dfrac{3}{y} \Rightarrow xy = 3 \Rightarrow y = \dfrac{3}{x} \Rightarrow f^{-1}(x) = \dfrac{3}{x}$

74. $A = 800(1 + 0.075)^{15} \approx \$2367.10$

75. $\log_3 81 = \log_3 3^4 = 4$

76. $e^{\ln(2x)} = 2x$

77. $\log \dfrac{\sqrt{x}}{y^2} = \log \dfrac{x^{1/2}}{y^2} = \log x^{1/2} - \log y^2 = \dfrac{1}{2} \log x - 2 \log y$

78. $2 \ln x + \ln 5x = \ln x^2 + \ln 5x = \ln (x^2 \cdot 5x) = \ln (5x^3)$

79. $6 \log x - 2 = 9 \Rightarrow 6 \log x = 11 \Rightarrow \log x = \dfrac{11}{6} \Rightarrow 10^{\log x} = 10^{11/6} \Rightarrow x \approx 68.13$

80. $2^{3x} = 17 \Rightarrow \log_2 2^{3x} = \log_2 17 \Rightarrow 3x = \dfrac{\log 17}{\log 2} \Rightarrow x = \dfrac{\log 17}{3 \log 2} \approx 1.36$

81. $12{,}000(1+r)^5 = 14{,}600 \Rightarrow (1+r)^5 = \dfrac{73}{60} \Rightarrow 1 + r = \sqrt[5]{\dfrac{73}{60}} \Rightarrow r = \sqrt[5]{\dfrac{73}{60}} - 1 \approx 0.04$ or 4%

82. $27.4 \sqrt[3]{W} = 36 \Rightarrow \sqrt[3]{W} = \dfrac{36}{27.4} \Rightarrow W = \left(\dfrac{36}{27.4}\right)^3 \approx 2.27$ pounds

83.   (a) $-\dfrac{b}{2a} = -\dfrac{-975}{2(0.25)} = 1950$

       (b) $f(1950) = 0.25(1950)^2 - 975(1950) + 950,845 = 220$ million Btu

84. $\dfrac{x^2}{12} = 350 \Rightarrow x^2 = 4200 \Rightarrow x = \sqrt{4200} \approx 64.8$ miles per hour

85. $8000(1+r)^{45} = 1,000,000 \Rightarrow (1+r)^{45} = 125 \Rightarrow 1+r = 125^{1/45} \Rightarrow r = 125^{1/45} + 1 \approx 0.113$ or 11.3%

86.   (a) $f(8) = 1.4 \ln 8 + 7 \approx 9.91$ meters per second

       (b) $1.4 \ln x + 7 = 10 \Rightarrow 1.4 \ln x = 3 \Rightarrow \ln x = \dfrac{3}{1.4} \Rightarrow e^{\ln x} = e^{3/1.4} \Rightarrow x \approx 8.52$ meters

Critical Thinking Solutions for Chapter 9

Section 9.2

- Every graph of $y = a^x$ passes through the point $(0, 1)$ because any nonzero base raised to the power 0 equals 1.

- The graph of $y = e^x$ will be between the graphs of $y = 2^x$ and $y = 3^x$ since $2 < e < 3$.

    It is closer to the graph of $y = 3^x$.

Section 9.3

- If the sound level increases by 10 db the intensity increases by a factor of 10.

- $\log_a 1 = 0$ because $a^0 = 1$ for any positive base a.

Section 9.5

- Yes, they are approximately the same since $3 \log x = 3\left(\dfrac{\ln x}{\ln 10}\right) = \dfrac{3}{\ln 10} \cdot \ln x \approx 1.3 \ln x$.

Chapter 10: Conic Sections

10.1: Parabolas and Circles

Concepts

1.   Parabola, ellipse and hyperbola

2.   The first parabola has a vertical axis and the second has a horizontal axis.

3.   No, it does not pass the vertical line test for functions.

4.   See Figure 4.

5.   No, it does not pass the vertical line test for functions.

6. (h, k)

7.   left

8.   right

9.   circle; (h, k)

10. $(0, 0)$; r

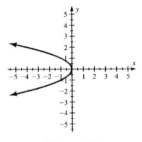

Figure 4	Figure 11	Figure 12

Parabolas

11.   Since $x = (y-0)^2 + 0$, the vertex is $(0, 0)$ and the axis of symmetry is $y = 0$. See Figure 11.

12.   Since $x = -(y-0)^2 + 0$, the vertex is $(0, 0)$ and the axis of symmetry is $y = 0$. See Figure 12.

13.   Since $x = (y-0)^2 + 1$, the vertex is $(1, 0)$ and the axis of symmetry is $y = 0$. See Figure 13.

14.   Since $x = (y-0)^2 - 1$, the vertex is $(-1, 0)$ and the axis of symmetry is $y = 0$. See Figure 14.

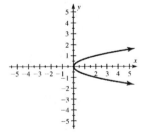

Figure 13	Figure 14	Figure 15

15.   Since $x = 2(y-0)^2 + 0$, the vertex is $(0, 0)$ and the axis of symmetry is $y = 0$. See Figure 15.

16.   Since $x = \frac{1}{4}(y-0)^2 + 0$, the vertex is (0, 0) and the axis of symmetry is $y = 0$. See Figure 16.

17.   Since $x = (y-1)^2 + 2$, the vertex is (2, 1) and the axis of symmetry is $y = 1$. See Figure 17.

Figure 16   Figure 17   Figure 18

18.   Since $x = (y-2)^2 + 1$, the vertex is (1, 2) and the axis of symmetry is $y = 2$. See Figure 18.

19.   Since $y = (x+2)^2 + 1$, the vertex is (–2, 1) and the axis of symmetry is $x = -2$. See Figure 19.

20.   Since $y = (x-4)^2 + 5$, the vertex is (4, 5) and the axis of symmetry is $x = 4$. See Figure 20.

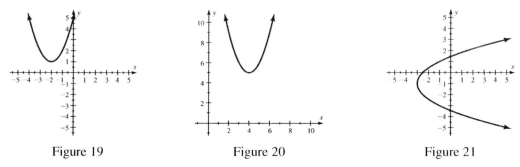

Figure 19   Figure 20   Figure 21

21.   Since $x = \frac{1}{2}(y+1)^2 - 3$, the vertex is (–3, –1) and the axis of symmetry is $y = -1$. See Figure 21.

22.   Since $x = -2(y+3)^2 + 1$, the vertex is (1, –3) and the axis of symmetry is $y = -3$. See Figure 22.

23.   Since $x = -3(y-1)^2 + 0$, the vertex is (0, 1) and the axis of symmetry is $y = 1$. See Figure 23.

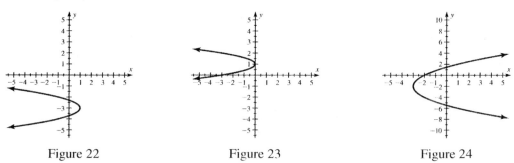

Figure 22   Figure 23   Figure 24

24.   Since $x = \frac{1}{4}(y+2)^2 - 3$, the vertex is (–3, –2) and the axis of symmetry is $y = -2$. See Figure 24.

25.   See Figure 25.

$x = -\dfrac{b}{2a} = -\dfrac{-1}{2(2)} = \dfrac{1}{4}$ and $y = 2\left(\dfrac{1}{4}\right)^2 - \left(\dfrac{1}{4}\right) + 1 = \dfrac{7}{8}$. Vertex: $\left(\dfrac{1}{4}, \dfrac{7}{8}\right)$. Axis of symmetry: $x = \dfrac{1}{4}$.

26. See Figure 26.

$x = -\dfrac{b}{2a} = -\dfrac{2}{2(-1)} = 1$ and $y = -(1)^2 + 2(1) + 2 = 3$. Vertex: $(1, 3)$. Axis of symmetry: $x = 1$.

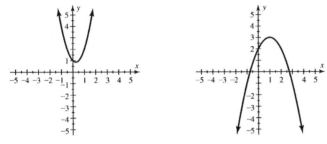

| Figure 25 | Figure 26 | Figure 27 |

27. See Figure 27.

$y = -\dfrac{b}{2a} = -\dfrac{3}{2(-2)} = \dfrac{3}{4}$ and $x = -2\left(\dfrac{3}{4}\right)^2 + 3\left(\dfrac{3}{4}\right) + 2 = \dfrac{25}{8}$. Vertex: $\left(\dfrac{25}{8}, \dfrac{3}{4}\right)$. Axis of symmetry: $y = \dfrac{3}{4}$.

28. See Figure 28.

$y = -\dfrac{b}{2a} = -\dfrac{1}{2\left(\frac{1}{2}\right)} = -1$ and $x = \dfrac{1}{2}(-1)^2 + (-1) - 1 = -\dfrac{3}{2}$. Vertex: $\left(-\dfrac{3}{2}, -1\right)$. Axis of symmetry: $y = -1$.

29. See Figure 29.

$y = -\dfrac{b}{2a} = -\dfrac{1}{2(3)} = -\dfrac{1}{6}$ and $x = 3\left(-\dfrac{1}{6}\right)^2 + \left(-\dfrac{1}{6}\right) = -\dfrac{1}{12}$. Vertex: $\left(-\dfrac{1}{12}, -\dfrac{1}{6}\right)$. Axis of symmetry: $y = -\dfrac{1}{6}$.

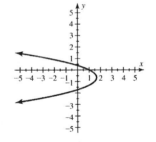

| Figure 28 | Figure 29 | Figure 30 |

30. See Figure 30.

$y = -\dfrac{b}{2a} = -\dfrac{(-2)}{2\left(-\frac{3}{2}\right)} = -\dfrac{2}{3}$ and $x = -\dfrac{3}{2}\left(-\dfrac{2}{3}\right)^2 - 2\left(-\dfrac{2}{3}\right) + 1 = \dfrac{5}{3}$. Vertex: $\left(\dfrac{5}{3}, -\dfrac{2}{3}\right)$. Axis of symmetry:

$y = -\dfrac{2}{3}$.

31. See Figure 31.

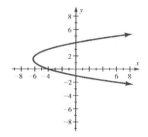

Figure 31   Figure 32

$$y = -\frac{b}{2a} = -\frac{2}{2(1)} = -\frac{2}{2} = -1 \text{ and } x = (-1)^2 + 2(-1) + 1 = 0.$$

Vertex: $(0, -1)$. Axis of symmetry: $y = -1$

32.   See Figure 32.

$$y = -\frac{b}{2a} = -\frac{(-3)}{2(1)} = \frac{3}{2} \text{ and } x = \left(\frac{3}{2}\right)^2 - 3\left(\frac{3}{2}\right) - 4 = -\frac{25}{4}.$$

Vertex: $\left(-\frac{25}{4}, \frac{3}{2}\right)$. Axis of symmetry: $y = \frac{3}{2}$

33.   Since the parabola opens upward and the vertex is (0, 0), the equation has the form $y = a(x-0)^2 + 0$.

Since the parabola passes through (1, 1), $1 = a(1-0)^2 + 0 \Rightarrow a = 1$. The equation is $y = x^2$.

34.   Since the parabola opens to the left and the vertex is (0, 0), the equation has the form $x = a(y-0)^2 + 0$.

Since the parabola passes through (−1, 1), $-1 = a(1-0)^2 + 0 \Rightarrow a = -1$. The equation is $x = -y^2$.

35.   Since the parabola opens to the right and the vertex is (−2, −1), the equation has the form $x = a(y+1)^2 - 2$.

Since the parabola passes through (−1, 0), $-1 = a(0+1)^2 - 2 \Rightarrow a = 1$. The equation is $x = (y+1)^2 - 2$.

36.   Since the parabola opens downward and the vertex is (1, 3), the equation has the form $y = a(x-1)^2 + 3$.

Since the parabola passes through (0, 2), $2 = a(0-1)^2 + 3 \Rightarrow a = -1$. The equation is $y = -(x-1)^2 + 3$.

37.   By plotting the points by hand, we see that the parabola must open upward.

38.   By plotting the points by hand, we see that the parabola must open to the left.

39.   By plotting the points and axis by hand, we see that the parabola must open downward.

40.   By plotting the points and axis by hand, we see that the parabola must open to the right.

41.   Since the parabola opens to the left and the vertex is (0, 0), the possible x-values are $x \geq 0$.

42.   Since the parabola has a horizontal axis, the possible y-values are all real numbers.

43.   Since the parabola opens to the right and the vertex is to the left of the y-axis, the parabola has two y-intercepts.

44.   No, for example it could have vertex (1, 10) and open to the right.

45. $x = 3(0)^2 - (0) + 1 \Rightarrow x = 1$

46. $y^2 - 3y + 2 = 0 \Rightarrow (y-1)(y-2) = 0 \Rightarrow y = 1$ or $y = 2$

Circles

47. $(x-0)^2 + (y-0)^2 = 1^2 \Rightarrow x^2 + y^2 = 1$

48. $(x-2)^2 + (y-3)^2 = 4^2 \Rightarrow (x-2)^2 + (y-3)^2 = 16$

49. $(x-(-1))^2 + (y-5)^2 = 3^2 \Rightarrow (x+1)^2 + (y-5)^2 = 9$

50. $(x-5)^2 + (y-(-3))^2 = 5^2 \Rightarrow (x-5)^2 + (y+3)^2 = 25$

51. $(x-(-4))^2 + (y-(-6))^2 = \left(\sqrt{2}\right)^2 \Rightarrow (x+4)^2 + (y+6)^2 = 2$

52. $(x-0)^2 + (y-4)^2 = \left(\sqrt{6}\right)^2 \Rightarrow x^2 + (y-4)^2 = 6$

53.   Since the center is (0, 0) and the radius is 4, the equation is $x^2 + y^2 = 16$.

54.   Since the center is (1, –1) and the radius is 3, the equation is $(x-1)^2 + (y+1)^2 = 9$.

55.   Since the center is (–3, 2) and the radius is 1, the equation is $(x+3)^2 + (y-2)^2 = 1$.

56.   Since the center is (0, –3) and the radius is 2, the equation is $x^2 + (y+3)^2 = 4$.

57.   The radius is 3 and the center is (0, 0). Solving the equation for *y* results in $y = \pm\sqrt{9 - x^2}$. See Figure 57.

58.   The radius is 1 and the center is (0, 0). Solving the equation for *y* results in $y = \pm\sqrt{1 - x^2}$. See Figure 58.

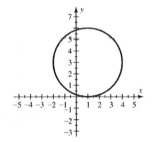

Figure 57   Figure 58   Figure 59

59.   The radius is 3 and the center is (1, 3). Solving the equation for *y* results in $y = 3 \pm \sqrt{9 - (x-1)^2}$.

   See Figure 59.

60.   The radius is 2 and the center is (–2, –1). Solving the equation for *y* results in $y = -1 \pm \sqrt{4 - (x+2)^2}$.

   See Figure 60.

61.   The radius is 5 and the center is (–5, 5). Solving the equation for *y* results in $y = 5 \pm \sqrt{25 - (x+5)^2}$.

   See Figure 61.

Figure 60

Figure 61

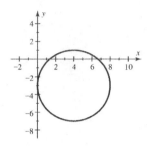

Figure 62

62.   The radius is 4 and the center is (4, –3). Solving the equation for y results in $y = -3 \pm \sqrt{16 - (x-4)^2}$.

See Figure 62.

63. $x^2 + 6x + y^2 - 2y = -1 \Rightarrow x^2 + 6x + 9 + y^2 - 2y + 1 = -1 + 9 + 1 \Rightarrow (x+3)^2 + (y-1)^2 = 9$

The radius is 3 and the center is (–3, 1). Solving the equation for y results in $y = 1 \pm \sqrt{9 - (x+3)^2}$.

See Figure 63.

64. $x^2 + y^2 + 12y + 32 = 0 \Rightarrow x^2 + y^2 + 12y + 36 = -32 + 36 \Rightarrow x^2 + (y+6)^2 = 4$

The radius is 2 and the center is (0, –6). Solving the equation for y results in $y = -6 \pm \sqrt{4 - x^2}$.

See Figure 64.

Figure 63

Figure 64

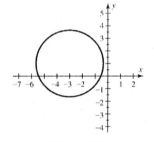

Figure 65

65. $x^2 + 6x + y^2 - 2y + 3 = 0 \Rightarrow x^2 + 6x + 9 + y^2 - 2y + 1 = -3 + 9 + 1 \Rightarrow (x+3)^2 + (y-1)^2 = 7$

The radius is $\sqrt{7}$ and the center is (–3, 1). Solving the equation for y results in $y = 1 \pm \sqrt{7 - (x+3)^2}$.

See Figure 65.

66. $x^2 - 4x + y^2 + 4y = -3 \Rightarrow x^2 - 4x + 4 + y^2 + 4y + 4 = -3 + 4 + 4 \Rightarrow (x-2)^2 + (y+2)^2 = 5$

The radius is $\sqrt{5}$ and the center is (2, –2). Solving the equation for y results in $y = -2 \pm \sqrt{5 - (x-2)^2}$.

See Figure 66.

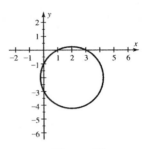

Figure 66

Applications

67. (a) Graph $Y_1 = (32/11025) X^2$ using the DrawInv feature in $[-40, 40, 10]$ by $[-120, 120, 20]$. See Figure 67.

(b) When $y = 105$, $x = \dfrac{32}{11,025}(105)^2 = 32$ feet.

68. (a) Since the parabola opens to the right and the vertex is $(-1, 0)$, the equation has the form

$$x = a(y - 0)^2 - 1.$$

Since the parabola passes through $(0, 2)$, $0 = a(2 - 0)^2 - 1 \Rightarrow a = \dfrac{1}{4}$. So $x = \dfrac{1}{4}(y - 0)^2 - 1$.

(b) The point $(3, 4)$ lies on the tracks. *Answers may vary.*

69. (a) Plot $(-0.1, 0)$ and graph $Y_1 = -2.5 X^2$ using the DrawInv feature in $[-1.5, 1.5, 0.5]$ by $[-1, 1, 0.5]$. See Figure 69.

(b) $d = \sqrt{(-2.5 - (-0.1))^2 + (1 - 0)^2} = \sqrt{(-2.4)^2 + 1^2} = \sqrt{6.76} = 2.6$ A.U. or 241,800,000 miles.

70. (a) As the comet travels farther from the sun, its velocity slows.

(b) When the comet reached the point $(0, 0)$, it is 0.1 A.U. from the sun. This distance is 9,300,000 miles.

Note that $9,300,000$ miles $\approx 1.50 \times 10^{10}$ meters. So $V = \dfrac{1.15 \times 10^{10}}{\sqrt{1.50 \times 10^{10}}} \approx 94,000$ m/sec.

$[-40, 40, 10]$ by $[-120, 120, 20]$ $[-1.5, 1.5, 0.5]$ by $[-1, 1, 0.5]$ $[-50, 50, 10]$ by $[-180, 180, 20]$

Figure 67   Figure 69   Figure 1

Group Activity Solutions

(a) If we let the vertex be located at $(0, 0)$, the equation must have the form $x = a(y - 0)^2 - 0$ or $x = ay^2$.

The parabola must also pass through the points $(44, 150)$ and $(44, -150)$. Use the point $(44, 150)$ to find a.

$$44 = a(150)^2 \Rightarrow 44 = 22,500a \Rightarrow a = \dfrac{44}{22,500} \Rightarrow a = \dfrac{11}{5625}. \text{ The equation is } x = \dfrac{11}{5625} y^2.$$

(b) Graph $Y_1 = (11/5625)X^2$ using the DrawInv feature in [−50, 50, 10] by [−180, 180, 20]. See Figure 1.

10.2: Ellipses and Hyperbolas

Concepts

1.   See Figure 1.

 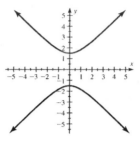

Figure 1   Figure 2

2.   See Figure 2.

3.   horizontal

4.   vertical

5.   2

6.   4

7.   left and right

8.   lower and upper

9.   They are the diagonals extended.

10.   No, these points could not be the endpoints of its major axis if it were centered at the origin.

Ellipses

11.   The ellipse has a vertical major axis with vertices $(0, \pm 5)$ and minor axis endpoints $(\pm 3, 0)$. See Figure 11.

12.   The ellipse has a horizontal major axis with vertices $(\pm 5, 0)$ and minor axis endpoints $(0, \pm 3)$. See Figure 12.

  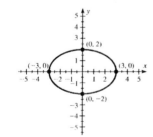

Figure 11   Figure 12   Figure 13

13.   The ellipse has a horizontal major axis with vertices $(\pm 3, 0)$ and minor axis endpoints $(0, \pm 2)$. See Figure 13.

14.   The ellipse has a vertical major axis with vertices $(0, \pm 3)$ and minor axis endpoints $(\pm \sqrt{3}, 0)$. See Figure 14.

15. The ellipse has a vertical major axis with vertices $(0, \pm 2)$ and minor axis endpoints $(\pm 1, 0)$. See Figure 15.

Figure 14   Figure 15   Figure 16

16. The ellipse has a horizontal major axis with vertices $(\pm 3, 0)$ and minor axis endpoints $(0, \pm 1)$. See Figure 16.

17. The ellipse has a horizontal major axis with vertices $\left(\pm\sqrt{7}, 0\right)$ and minor axis endpoints $\left(0, \pm\sqrt{5}\right)$. See Figure 17.

18. The ellipse has a vertical major axis with vertices $\left(0, \pm\sqrt{11}\right)$ and minor axis endpoints $\left(\pm\sqrt{6}, 0\right)$. See Figure 18.

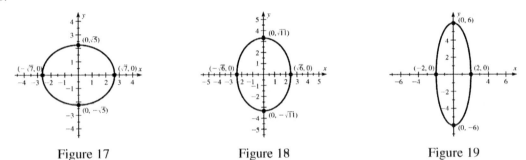

Figure 17   Figure 18   Figure 19

19. $36x^2 + 4y^2 = 144 \Rightarrow \dfrac{36x^2}{144} + \dfrac{4y^2}{144} = 1 \Rightarrow \dfrac{x^2}{4} + \dfrac{y^2}{36} = 1$

   The ellipse has a vertical major axis with vertices $(0, \pm 6)$ and minor axis endpoints $(\pm 2, 0)$. See Figure 19.

20. $25x^2 + 16y^2 = 400 \Rightarrow \dfrac{25x^2}{400} + \dfrac{16y^2}{400} = 1 \Rightarrow \dfrac{x^2}{16} + \dfrac{y^2}{25} = 1$

   The ellipse has a vertical major axis with vertices $(0, \pm 5)$ and minor axis endpoints $(\pm 4, 0)$. See Figure 20.

21. $6y^2 + 7x^2 = 42 \Rightarrow \dfrac{6y^2}{42} + \dfrac{7x^2}{42} = 1 \Rightarrow \dfrac{y^2}{7} + \dfrac{x^2}{6} = 1$

   The ellipse has a vertical major axis with vertices $\left(0, \pm\sqrt{7}\right)$ and minor axis endpoints $\left(\pm\sqrt{6}, 0\right)$. See Figure 21.

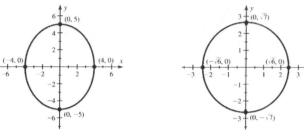

Figure 20   Figure 21   Figure 22

22. $9x^2 + 5y^2 = 45 \Rightarrow \dfrac{9x^2}{45} + \dfrac{5y^2}{45} = 1 \Rightarrow \dfrac{x^2}{5} + \dfrac{y^2}{9} = 1$

The ellipse has a vertical major axis with vertices $(0, \pm 3)$ and minor axis endpoints $\left(\pm\sqrt{5}, 0\right)$. See Figure 22.

23.   Horizontal major axis with vertices $(\pm 3, 0)$ and minor axis endpoints $(0, \pm 2)$ $\Rightarrow \dfrac{x^2}{9} + \dfrac{y^2}{4} = 1$

24.   Vertical major axis with vertices $(0, \pm 3)$ and minor axis endpoints $(\pm 2, 0)$ $\Rightarrow \dfrac{y^2}{9} + \dfrac{x^2}{4} = 1$

25.   Vertical major axis with vertices $(0, \pm 5)$ and minor axis endpoints $(\pm 4, 0)$ $\Rightarrow \dfrac{y^2}{25} + \dfrac{x^2}{16} = 1$

26.   Horizontal major axis with vertices $(\pm 5, 0)$ and minor axis endpoints $(0, \pm 4)$ $\Rightarrow \dfrac{x^2}{25} + \dfrac{y^2}{16} = 1$

Hyperbolas

27.   The hyperbola has a horizontal transverse axis with vertices $(\pm 2, 0)$ and asymptotes $y = \pm\dfrac{3}{2}x.$ See Figure 27.

28.   The hyperbola has a vertical transverse axis with vertices $(0, \pm 2)$ and asymptotes $y = \pm\dfrac{2}{3}x.$ See Figure 28.

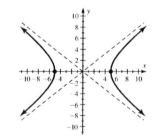

Figure 27   Figure 28   Figure 29

29.   The hyperbola has a horizontal transverse axis with vertices $(\pm 5, 0)$ and asymptotes $y = \pm\dfrac{4}{5}x.$ See Figure 29.

30.   The hyperbola has a vertical transverse axis with vertices $(0, \pm 5)$ and asymptotes $y = \pm\dfrac{5}{4}x.$ See Figure 30.

31. The hyperbola has a horizontal transverse axis with vertices $(\pm 1, 0)$ and asymptotes $y = \pm x$. See Figure 31.

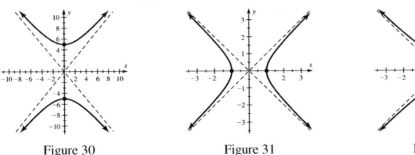

Figure 30   Figure 31   Figure 32

32. The hyperbola has a vertical transverse axis with vertices $(0, \pm 1)$ and asymptotes $y = \pm x$. See Figure 32.

33. The hyperbola has a horizontal transverse axis with vertices $\left(\pm \sqrt{3}, 0\right)$ and asymptotes $y = \pm \dfrac{2}{\sqrt{3}} x$. See

Figure 33.

34. The hyperbola has a vertical transverse axis with vertices $\left(0, \pm \sqrt{5}\right)$ and asymptotes $y = \pm \dfrac{\sqrt{8}}{\sqrt{5}} x$. See Figure

34.

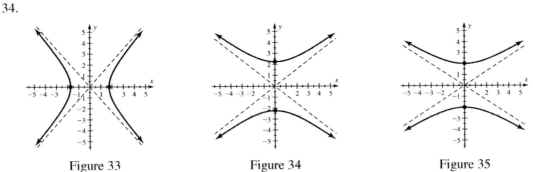

Figure 33   Figure 34   Figure 35

35. $9y^2 - 4x^2 = 36 \Rightarrow \dfrac{9y^2}{36} - \dfrac{4x^2}{36} = 1 \Rightarrow \dfrac{y^2}{4} - \dfrac{x^2}{9} = 1$

The hyperbola has a vertical transverse axis with vertices $(0, \pm 2)$ and asymptotes $y = \pm \dfrac{2}{3} x$. See Figure 35.

36. $36x^2 - 25y^2 = 900 \Rightarrow \dfrac{36x^2}{900} - \dfrac{25y^2}{900} = 1 \Rightarrow \dfrac{x^2}{25} - \dfrac{y^2}{36} = 1$

The hyperbola has a horizontal transverse axis with vertices $(\pm 5, 0)$ and asymptotes $y = \pm \dfrac{6}{5} x$. See Figure

36.

37. $16x^2 - 4y^2 = 64 \Rightarrow \dfrac{16x^2}{64} - \dfrac{4y^2}{64} = 1 \Rightarrow \dfrac{x^2}{4} - \dfrac{y^2}{16} = 1$

The hyperbola has a horizontal transverse axis with vertices $(\pm 2, 0)$ and asymptotes $y = \pm 2x$. See Figure 37.

Figure 36

Figure 37

Figure 38

38. $y^2 - 9x^2 = 9 \Rightarrow \dfrac{y^2}{9} - \dfrac{9x^2}{9} = 1 \Rightarrow \dfrac{y^2}{9} - x^2 = 1$

The hyperbola has a vertical transverse axis with vertices $(0, \pm 3)$ and asymptotes $y = \pm 3x$. See Figure 38.

39.   Horizontal transverse axis with vertices $(\pm 1, 0)$ and asymptotes $y = \pm \dfrac{1}{1} x \;\Rightarrow x^2 - y^2 = 1$

40.   Horizontal transverse axis with vertices $(\pm 2, 0)$ and asymptotes $y = \pm \dfrac{3}{2} x \;\Rightarrow \dfrac{x^2}{4} - \dfrac{y^2}{9} = 1$

41.   Vertical transverse axis with vertices $(0, \pm 2)$ and asymptotes $y = \pm \dfrac{2}{3} x \;\Rightarrow \dfrac{y^2}{4} - \dfrac{x^2}{9} = 1$

42.   Vertical transverse axis with vertices $(0, \pm 4)$ and asymptotes $y = \pm \dfrac{4}{2} x \;\Rightarrow \dfrac{y^2}{16} - \dfrac{x^2}{4} = 1$

Applications

43.   (a) $A = \pi(5)(4) \approx 62.83; \; P = 2\pi \sqrt{\dfrac{5^2 + 4^2}{2}} \approx 28.45$

(b) $A = \pi\left(\sqrt{7}\right)\left(\sqrt{2}\right) \approx 11.75; \; P = 2\pi \sqrt{\dfrac{\left(\sqrt{7}\right)^2 + \left(\sqrt{2}\right)^2}{2}} \approx 13.33$

44. $A = \pi(a)(a) = \pi a^2; \; P = 2\pi \sqrt{\dfrac{a^2 + a^2}{2}} = 2\pi \sqrt{\dfrac{2a^2}{2}} = 2\pi \sqrt{a^2} = 2\pi a.$ The formulas are correct for radius a.

45.   (a) $\dfrac{x^2}{39.44^2} + \dfrac{y^2}{38.20^2} = 1 \Rightarrow \dfrac{y^2}{38.20^2} = 1 - \dfrac{x^2}{39.44^2} \Rightarrow y = \pm \sqrt{38.20^2 \left(1 - \dfrac{x^2}{39.44^2}\right)}$

Graph $Y_1 = \sqrt{\left(38.20^2 \left(1 - \left(X^2 / 39.44^2\right)\right)\right)}$ and $Y_2 = -\sqrt{\left(38.20^2 \left(1 - \left(X^2 / 39.44^2\right)\right)\right)}$ and plot the point

$(9.82, 0)$ in [−60, 60, 10] by [−40, 40, 10]. See Figure 45.

(b) $P = 2\pi \sqrt{\dfrac{39.44^2 + 38.20^2}{2}} \approx 243.9$ A.U. or about 2.27×10^{10} miles

$A = \pi(39.44)(38.20) \approx 4733$ A.U. or about 4.09×10^{19} square miles

[−60, 60, 10] by [−40, 40, 10]   [−21, 21, 5] by [−14, 14, 5]

Figure 45   Figure 46

46.   (a) $\dfrac{x^2}{17.95^2}+\dfrac{y^2}{4.44^2}=1 \Rightarrow \dfrac{y^2}{4.44^2}=1-\dfrac{x^2}{17.95^2} \Rightarrow y=\pm\sqrt{4.44^2\left(1-\dfrac{x^2}{17.95^2}\right)}$

Graph $Y_1=\sqrt{\left(4.44^2\left(1-\left(X^2/17.95^2\right)\right)\right)}$ and $Y_2=-\sqrt{\left(4.44^2\left(1-\left(X^2/17.95^2\right)\right)\right)}$ and plot the point

(17.39, 0) in [−21, 21, 5] by [−14, 14, 5]. See Figure 46.

(b) $P=2\pi\sqrt{\dfrac{17.95^2+4.44^2}{2}}\approx 82.2$ A.U. or about 7.64×10^9 miles

(c) $\dfrac{7.64\times10^9 \text{ miles}}{76 \text{ years}}\cdot\dfrac{1 \text{ year}}{365 \text{ days}}\cdot\dfrac{1 \text{ day}}{24 \text{ hours}}\approx 11,500$ mph

47.   The maximum and minimum heights occur when $y=0$. These values are calculated below.

Earth: $\dfrac{(x-164)^2}{3960^2}+0=1 \Rightarrow (x-164)^2=3960^2 \Rightarrow x-164=\pm3960 \Rightarrow x=4124 \text{ or } x=-3796.$

Explorer VII: $\dfrac{x^2}{4464^2}+0=1 \Rightarrow x^2=4464^2 \Rightarrow x=\pm4464 \Rightarrow x=4464 \text{ or } x=-4464.$

The maximum height is $-3796-(-4464)=668$ miles. The minimum height is $4464-4124=340$ miles.

48.   These values are equal to half of the lengths of the major and minor axes. $r_1=4$ inches and $r_2=10$ inches.

49.   The height is half the length of the minor axis and the width is the full length of the major axis.

$400x^2+10,000y^2=4,000,000 \Rightarrow \dfrac{400x^2}{4,000,000}+\dfrac{10,000y^2}{4,000,000}=1 \Rightarrow \dfrac{x^2}{10,000}+\dfrac{y^2}{400}=1$

The height is $\sqrt{400}=20$ feet and the width is $2\sqrt{10,000}=2(100)=200$ feet.

50.   Its growth becomes nearly linear.

Checking Basic Concepts for Sections 10.1 & 10.2

1.   See Figure 1. Vertex: (1, 2). Axis of symmetry: $y=2$.

2.   The equation is $(x-1)^2+(y+2)^2=4$.

$(x-1)^2+(y+2)^2=4 \Rightarrow (y+2)^2=4-(x-1)^2 \Rightarrow y=-2\pm\sqrt{4-(x-1)^2}$. See Figure 2.

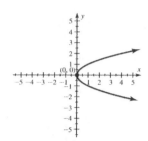

Figure 1   Figure 2   Figure 4a

3. x-intercepts: $\dfrac{x^2}{4}+\dfrac{0^2}{9}=1\Rightarrow\dfrac{x^2}{4}=1\Rightarrow x^2=4\Rightarrow x=\pm2$

y-intercepts: $\dfrac{0^2}{4}+\dfrac{y^2}{9}=1\Rightarrow\dfrac{y^2}{9}=1\Rightarrow y^2=9\Rightarrow y=\pm3$

4.   (a) This parabola has vertex $(0, 0)$ and axis of symmetry $y=0$. See Figure 4a.

(b) This ellipse has a vertical major axis with vertices $(0,\pm5)$ and minor axis endpoints $(\pm4,0)$. See Figure 4b.

(c) This hyperbola has a horizontal transverse axis with vertices $(\pm2,0)$ and asymptotes $y=\pm\dfrac{3}{2}x.$ See Figure 4c.

(d) This circle is centered at $(1,-2)$ and has radius 3. See Figure 4d.

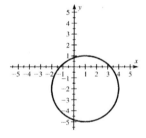

Figure 4b   Figure 4c   Figure 4d

10.3: Nonlinear Systems of Equations and Inequalities

Concepts

1.   Any number.

2.   2

3.   Two, the line intersects the circle twice.

4.   All points inside and including a circle of radius 1 centered at the origin.

5.   No. $5(-2)^2-2(-1)^2=5(4)-2(1)=18\not>18$

6.   No. $(3)^2-2(4)=9-8=1\not\geq4$

7.   See Figure 7. *Answers may vary.*

Figure 7

Figure 8

8. See Figure 8. *Answers may vary.*

Nonlinear Systems of Equations

9. The solutions are the intersection points $(1, 3)$ and $(-1, -3)$. Both solutions check.

10. The solutions are the intersection points $(-2, 2)$ and $(2, -2)$. Both solutions check.

11. The solutions are the intersection points $(0, -1)$ and $(0, 1)$. Both solutions check.

12. The solutions are the intersection points $(-1, 0)$, $(0, 1)$ and $(1, 0)$. All three solutions check.

13. Substitute $y = 2x$ into the second equation.

$$x^2 + (2x)^2 = 45 \Rightarrow x^2 + 4x^2 = 45 \Rightarrow 5x^2 = 45 \Rightarrow x^2 = 9 \Rightarrow x = \pm 3$$

When $x = -3$, $y = 2(-3) = -6$. When $x = 3$, $y = 2(3) = 6$. The solutions are $(-3, -6)$ and $(3, 6)$.

14. Substitute $y = x$ into the second equation. $x^2 = 3 - 2x^2 \Rightarrow 3x^2 = 3 \Rightarrow x^2 = 1 \Rightarrow x = \pm 1$

When $x = -1$, $y = -1$. When $x = 1$, $y = 1$. The solutions are $(-1, -1)$ and $(1, 1)$.

15. From the first equation, $y = 1 - x$. Substitute $y = 1 - x$ into the second equation.

$$x^2 - (1-x)^2 = 3 \Rightarrow x^2 - 1 + 2x - x^2 = 3 \Rightarrow 2x - 1 = 3 \Rightarrow 2x = 4 \Rightarrow x = 2$$

When $x = 2$, $y = 1 - (2) = -1$ The solution is $(2, -1)$.

16. From the first equation, $y = x - 1$. Substitute $y = x - 1$ into the second equation.

$$x - 1 = 2x^2 \Rightarrow 2x^2 - x + 1 = 0. \text{ Note that the discriminant } b^2 - 4ac = (1)^2 - 4(2)(1) = 1 - 8 = -7.$$

Since the discriminant is negative, there are no real solutions.

17. From the first equation, $x^2 = y$. Substitute $x^2 = y$ into the second equation.

$$y + y^2 = 6 \Rightarrow y^2 + y - 6 = 0 \Rightarrow (y+3)(y-2) = 0 \Rightarrow \text{Either } y = -3 \text{ or } y = 2$$

When $y = -3$, $x = \pm\sqrt{-3}$, (not real numbers). When $y = 2$, $x = \pm\sqrt{2}$. The solutions are

$\left(-\sqrt{2}, 2\right)$ and $\left(\sqrt{2}, 2\right)$.

18. Since both expressions are equal to 4, we may set them equal to each other.

$$x^2 - y^2 = x^2 + y^2 \Rightarrow -y^2 = y^2 \Rightarrow 2y^2 = 0 \Rightarrow y^2 = 0 \Rightarrow y = 0$$

In either equation, when $y = 0$, $x^2 = 4 \Rightarrow x = \pm 2$. The solutions are $(2, 0)$ and $(-2, 0)$.

19. Solve the second equation for $x : x = y - 2$. Substitute $x = y - 2$ into the first equation:

$$3(y-2)^2 + 2y^2 = 5 \Rightarrow 3\left(y^2 - 4y + 4\right) + 2y^2 = 5$$

$$\Rightarrow 3y^2 - 12y + 12 + 2y^2 = 5 \Rightarrow 5y^2 - 12y + 7 = 0 \Rightarrow (5y-7)(y-1) = 0$$

$$\Rightarrow y = \frac{7}{5} \text{ or } y = 1 \Rightarrow x = -\frac{3}{5} \text{ or } x = -1. \text{ The solutions are } \left(-\frac{3}{5}, \frac{7}{5}\right) \text{ and } (-1, 1).$$

20.   Multiply the second equation by 2 and add to the first equation.

$$\begin{aligned} x^2 + 2y^2 &= 9 \\ \underline{4x^2 - 2y^2} &= \underline{-4} \\ 5x^2 &= 5 \end{aligned} \qquad \Rightarrow x^2 = 1 \Rightarrow x = \pm 1$$

$$(1)^2 + 2y^2 = 9 \Rightarrow 2y^2 = 8 \Rightarrow y^2 = 4 \Rightarrow y = \pm 2$$

$$(-1)^2 + 2y^2 = 9 \Rightarrow 2y^2 = 8 \Rightarrow y^2 = 4 \Rightarrow y = \pm 2$$

The solutions are $(\pm 1, \pm 2)$

21.   Multiply the second equation by -1 and add to the first equation.

$$\begin{aligned} x^2 + y^2 &= 4 \\ \underline{-x^2 + 9y^2} &= \underline{-9} \\ 10y^2 &= -5 \end{aligned} \qquad y^2 = -\frac{1}{2} \Rightarrow y = \pm\sqrt{-\frac{1}{2}}, \text{ which is not a real number. There are no real solutions.}$$

22.   Multiply the first equation by -4 and add to the second equation.

$$\begin{aligned} -4x^2 - 4y^2 &= -60 \\ \underline{9x^2 + 4y^2} &= \underline{36} \\ 5x^2 &= -24 \end{aligned} \qquad \Rightarrow x^2 = -\frac{24}{5} \Rightarrow x = \pm\sqrt{-\frac{24}{5}}, \text{ which is not a real number. There are no real solutions.}$$

23.   Add the equations.

$$\begin{aligned} x^2 + y^2 &= 10 \\ \underline{2x^2 - y^2} &= \underline{17} \\ 3x^2 &= 27 \end{aligned} \qquad \Rightarrow x^2 = 9 \Rightarrow x = \pm 3$$

$$(3)^2 + y^2 = 10 \Rightarrow y^2 = 1 \Rightarrow y = \pm 1$$

$$(-3)^2 + y^2 = 10 \Rightarrow y^2 = 1 \Rightarrow y = \pm 1$$

The solutions are $(\pm 3, \pm 1)$

24.   Multiply the first equation by 3, multiply the second equation by –2, and add the equations.

$$\begin{aligned} 6x^2 + 9y^2 &= 15 \\ \underline{-6x^2 + 8y^2} &= \underline{2} \\ 17y^2 &= 17 \end{aligned} \qquad \Rightarrow y^2 = 1 \Rightarrow y = \pm 1$$

$$6x^2 + 9(1)^2 = 15 \Rightarrow 6x^2 + 9 = 15 \Rightarrow 6x^2 = 6 \Rightarrow x^2 = 1 \Rightarrow x = \pm 1$$

$6x^2 + 9(-1)^2 = 15 \Rightarrow 6x^2 + 9 = 15 \Rightarrow 6x^2 = 6 \Rightarrow x^2 = 1 \Rightarrow x = \pm 1$

The solutions are $(\pm 1, \pm 1)$

25. Solve the second equation for y. $2x^2 - y = 1 - 3x \Rightarrow y = 2x^2 + 3x - 1$

Graph $Y_1 = X^2 - 3$ and $Y_2 = 2X^2 + 3X - 1$ in $[-5, 5, 1]$ by $[-5, 5, 1]$. See Figures 25a & 25b.

The solutions are the intersection points $(-2, 1)$ and $(-1, -2)$.

$[-5, 5, 1]$ by $[-5, 5, 1]$	$[-5, 5, 1]$ by $[-5, 5, 1]$	$[-9.4, 9.4, 1]$ by $[-6.2, 6.2, 1]$
Figure 25a	Figure 25b	Figure 26

26. Solve both equations for y. $x + y = 2 \Rightarrow y = 2 - x$ and $x - y^2 = 3 \Rightarrow y^2 = x - 3 \Rightarrow y = \pm\sqrt{x-3}$

Graph $Y_1 = 2 - X$, $Y_2 = \sqrt{(X-3)}$ and $Y_3 = -\sqrt{(X-3)}$ in $[-9.4, 9.4, 1]$ by $[-6.2, 6.2, 1]$. See Figure 26.

Since there are no intersection points, there are no real solutions.

27. Solve both equations for y. $y - x = -4 \Rightarrow y = x - 4$ and $x - y^2 = -2 \Rightarrow y^2 = x + 2 \Rightarrow y = \pm\sqrt{x+2}$

Graph $Y_1 = X - 4$, $Y_2 = \sqrt{(X+2)}$ and $Y_3 = -\sqrt{(X+2)}$ in $[-9.4, 9.4, 1]$ by $[-6.2, 6.2, 1]$. See Figures 27a & 27b.

The solutions are the intersection points $(7, \ 3)$ and $(2, \ -2)$.

$[-9.4, 9.4, 1]$ by $[-6.2, 6.2, 1]$	$[-9.4, 9.4, 1]$ by $[-6.2, 6.2, 1]$
Figure 27a	Figure 27b

$[-4.7, 4.7, 1]$ by $[-3.1, 3.1, 1]$	$[-4.7, 4.7, 1]$ by $[-3.1, 3.1, 1]$
Figure 28a	Figure 28b

28. Solve the first equation for y. $xy = 1 \Rightarrow y = \dfrac{1}{x}$

Graph $Y_1 = 1/X$ and $Y_2 = X$ in $[-4.7, 4.7, 1]$ by $[-3.1, 3.1, 1]$. See Figures 28a & 28b.

The solutions are the intersection points $(-1, -1)$ and $(1, 1)$.

29. (a) Substitute $y = -2x$ into the second equation.

$$x^2 + (-2x) = 3 \Rightarrow x^2 - 2x - 3 = 0 \Rightarrow (x+1)(x-3) = 0 \Rightarrow \text{Either } x = -1 \text{ or } x = 3$$

When $x = -1$, $y = -2(-1) = 2$. When $x = 3$, $y = -2(3) = -6$. The solutions are $(-1, 2)$ and $(3, -6)$.

(b) Solve the second equation for y. $x^2 + y = 3 \Rightarrow y = 3 - x^2$

Graph $Y_1 = -2X$ and $Y_2 = 3 - X^2$ in $[-10, 10, 1]$ by $[-10, 10, 1]$. See Figures 29a & 29b.

(c) Table $Y_1 = -2X$ and $Y_2 = 3 - X^2$ with TblStart $= -3$ and ΔTbl $= 1$. See Figure 29c.

$[-10, 10, 1]$ by $[-10, 10, 1]$ $[-10, 10, 1]$ by $[-10, 10, 1]$

Figure 29a   Figure 29b   Figure 29c

30.   (a) From the first equation, $y = 4x$. Substitute $y = 4x$ into the second equation.

$$x^3 - 4x = 0 \Rightarrow x(x^2 - 4) = 0 \Rightarrow x(x+2)(x-2) = 0 \Rightarrow x = 0 \text{ or } x = -2 \text{ or } x = 2$$

When $x = -2$, $y = 4(-2) = -8$. When $x = 0$, $y = 4(0) = 0$. When $x = 2$, $y = 4(2) = 8$.

The solutions are $(-2, -8)$, $(0, 0)$ and $(2, 8)$.

(b) Solve both equations for y. $4x - y = 0 \Rightarrow y = 4x$ and $x^3 - y = 0 \Rightarrow y = x^3$

Graph $Y_1 = 4X$ and $Y_2 = X \wedge 3$ in $[-3, 3, 1]$ by $[-20, 20, 5]$. See Figures 30a, 30b & 30c.

(c) Table $Y_1 = 4X$ and $Y_2 = X \wedge 3$ with TblStart $= -3$ and ΔTbl $= 1$. See Figure 30d.

$[-3, 3, 1]$ by $[-20, 20, 5]$ $[-3, 3, 1]$ by $[-20, 20, 5]$ $[-3, 3, 1]$ by $[-20, 20, 5]$

Figure 30a   Figure 30b   Figure 30c   Figure 30d

31.   (a) From the second equation, $y = x$. Substitute $y = x$ into the first equation.

$$x \cdot x = 1 \Rightarrow x^2 = 1 \Rightarrow x = \pm 1$$

When $x = -1$, $y = -1$. When $x = 1$, $y = 1$. The solutions are $(-1, -1)$ and $(1, 1)$.

(b) Solve both equations for y. $xy = 1 \Rightarrow y = \dfrac{1}{x}$ and $x - y = 0 \Rightarrow y = x$

Graph $Y_1 = 1/X$ and $Y_2 = X$ in $[-4.7, 4.7, 1]$ by $[-3.1, 3.1, 1]$. See Figures 31a & 31b.

(c) Table $Y_1 = 1/X$ and $Y_2 = X$ with TblStart $= -3$ and ΔTbl $= 1$. See Figure 31c.

[–4.7, 4.7, 1] by [–3.1, 3.1, 1]   [–4.7, 4.7, 1] by [–3.1, 3.1, 1]

Figure 31a   Figure 31b   Figure 31c

32.   (a)   From the second equation, $y = x + 2$. Substitute $y = x + 2$ into the first equation.

$$x^2 + (x+2)^2 = 4 \Rightarrow x^2 + x^2 + 4x + 4 = 4 \Rightarrow 2x^2 + 4x = 0 \Rightarrow 2x(x+2) = 0 \Rightarrow x = 0 \text{ or } x = -2$$

When $x = 0$, $y = 0 + 2 = 2$. When $x = -2$, $y = -2 + 2 = 0$. The solutions are $(-2, 0)$ and $(0, 2)$.

(b)   Solve each equation for y. $x^2 + y^2 = 4 \Rightarrow y^2 = 4 - x^2 \Rightarrow y = \pm\sqrt{4 - x^2}$ and $y - x = 2 \Rightarrow y = x + 2$

Graph $Y_1 = -\sqrt{(4 - X^2)}$, $Y_2 = \sqrt{(4 - X^2)}$ and $Y_3 = X + 2$ in [–4.7, 4.7, 1] by [–3.1, 3.1, 1].

See Figures 32a & 32b.

(c)   Table $Y_1 = -\sqrt{(4 - X^2)}$, $Y_2 = \sqrt{(4 - X^2)}$ and $Y_3 = X + 2$ with TblStart $= -4$ and ΔTbl $= 1$. See Figure

32c.

[–4.7, 4.7, 1] by [–3.1, 3.1, 1]   [–4.7, 4.7, 1] by [–3.1, 3.1, 1]

Figure 32a   Figure 32b   Figure 32c

Nonlinear Systems of Inequalities

33.   Sketch the parabola given by $y = x^2$ using a solid line. Try test point $(0, 2)$ to determine shading.

Since $2 \geq 0^2$, we shade the portion of the *xy*-plane containing the point $(0, 2)$. See Figure 33.

34.   Sketch the parabola given by $y = x^2 - 1$ using a solid line. Try test point $(0, -2)$ to determine shading.

Since $-2 \leq 0^2 - 1$, we shade the portion of the *xy*-plane containing the point $(0, -2)$. See Figure 34.

        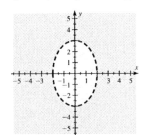

Figure 33   Figure 34   Figure 35

35.   Sketch the ellipse given by $\dfrac{x^2}{4} + \dfrac{y^2}{9} = 1$ using a dashed line. Try test point $(4, 0)$ to determine shading.

Since $\dfrac{4^2}{4} + \dfrac{0^2}{9} = 4 > 1$, we shade the portion of the xy-plane containing the point $(4, 0)$. See Figure 35.

36.   Sketch the circle given by $x^2 + y^2 = 1$ using a solid line. Try test point $(0, 0)$ to determine shading.

       Since $0^2 + 0^2 \le 1$, we shade the portion of the xy-plane containing the point $(0, 0)$. See Figure 36.

37.   Sketch the parabola given by $y = x^2 + 1$ using a dashed line and the line given by $y = 3$ using a dashed line.

       Since the point $(0, 2)$ satisfies both inequalities, we shade the portion of the xy-plane containing the point $(0, 2)$. See Figure 37. One solution is $(0, 2)$. *Answers may vary.*

      Figure 36   Figure 37   Figure 38

38.   Sketch the parabola given by $y = x^2$ using a dashed line and the line given by $y = x + 2$ using a dashed line.

       Since the point $(0, 1)$ satisfies both inequalities, we shade the portion of the xy-plane containing the point $(0, 1)$. See Figure 38. One solution is $(0, 1)$. *Answers may vary.*

39.   Sketch the circle given by $x^2 + y^2 = 1$ using a solid line and the line given by $y = x$ using a dashed line.

       Since the point $\left(\dfrac{1}{2}, -\dfrac{1}{2} \right)$ satisfies both inequalities, we shade the portion of the xy-plane containing the point

       $\left(\dfrac{1}{2}, -\dfrac{1}{2} \right)$. See Figure 39. One solution is $(0.5, -0.5)$. *Answers may vary.*

40.   Sketch the parabola given by $y = x^2 - 2$ using a dashed line and the parabola given by $y = 2 - x^2$ using a solid line.

       Since the point $(0, 0)$ satisfies both inequalities, we shade the portion of the xy-plane containing the point $(0, 0)$. See Figure 40. One solution is $(0, 0)$. *Answers may vary.*

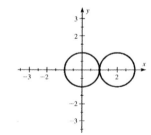

      Figure 39   Figure 40   Figure 41

41.   Sketch the circle given by $x^2 + y^2 = 1$ using a solid line and the circle given by $(x - 2)^2 + y^2 = 1$ using a solid line.

Since the point (1, 0) is the only point that satisfies both inequalities, we mark only the point (1, 0) on the graph. See Figure 41. The only solution is (1, 0).

42. Sketch the parabola given by $y = x^2 - 2$ using a solid line and the circle given by $(x+1)^2 + y^2 = 4$ using a solid line.

    Since the point (–2, 0) satisfies both inequalities, we shade the portion of the xy-plane containing the point (–2, 0). See Figure 42. One solution is (–2, 0). *Answers may vary.*

43. Sketch the hyperbola given by $x^2 - y^2 = 4$ using a solid line and the circle given by $x^2 + y^2 = 9$ using a solid line.

    Since the point (0, 0) satisfies both inequalities, we shade the portion of the xy-plane containing the point (0, 0). See Figure 43. One solution is (0, 0). *Answers may vary.*

Figure 42	Figure 43	Figure 44

44. Sketch the line given by $3x + 2y = 6$ using a dashed line and the circle given by $x^2 + y^2 = 16$ using a solid line.

    Since the point (0, 0) satisfies both inequalities, we shade the portion of the xy-plane containing the point (0, 0). See Figure 44. One solution is (0, 0). *Answers may vary.*

45. a

46. b

47. A parabola with vertex (0, 0) has an equation of the form $y = a(x-0)^2 + 0$ or $y = ax^2$. Since the parabola also passes through the point (1, 1), $1 = a \cdot 1^2 \Rightarrow a = 1$. The equation of the parabola is $y = x^2$.

    Since the line passes through (0, 4) and (4, 0), its slope is $m = \dfrac{0-4}{4-0} = \dfrac{-4}{4} = -1$. The y-intercept is (0, 4).

    The equation of the line is $y = -x + 4$ or $y = 4 - x$. Since the line is dashed and the parabola is solid, the system of inequalities is $y \geq x^2$ and $y < 4 - x$.

48. The equation of a circle of radius 3 centered at the origin is $(x-0)^2 + (y-0)^2 = 3^2$ or $x^2 + y^2 = 9$.

    Since the circle is solid, the inequality is $x^2 + y^2 \leq 9$.

49. See Figure 49.

[−10, 10, 1] by [−10, 10, 1]   [−10, 10, 1] by [−10, 10, 1]

Figure 49   Figure 50

50.   See Figure 50.

Applications

51.   The necessary equations are $\pi r^2 h = 40$ and $2\pi rh = 50$. Start by solving each of these equations for h.

$$\pi r^2 h = 40 \Rightarrow h = \frac{40}{\pi r^2} \text{ and } 2\pi rh = 50 \Rightarrow h = \frac{50}{2\pi r}$$

(a) Graph $Y_1 = 40/\left(\pi X^2\right)$ and $Y_2 = 50/(2\pi X)$ in [0, 5, 1] by [0, 10, 1]. See Figure 51.

The graphs intersect near the point (1.6, 4.97). The dimensions are $r = 1.6$ inches and $h \approx 4.97$ inches.

(b) $\frac{40}{\pi r^2} = \frac{50}{2\pi r} \Rightarrow 80\pi r = 50\pi r^2 \Rightarrow 8r = 5r^2 \Rightarrow 5r^2 - 8r = 0 \Rightarrow r(5r - 8) = 0 \Rightarrow r = 0 \text{ or } r = \frac{8}{5}$

Since $r = 0$ has no physical meaning, $r = \frac{8}{5} = 1.6$. And so $h = \frac{50}{2\pi\left(\frac{8}{5}\right)} = \frac{125}{8\pi} \approx 4.97$.

The dimensions are $r = 1.6$ inches and $h \approx 4.97$ inches.

[0, 5, 1] by [0, 10, 1]   [0, 5, 1] by [0, 10, 1]   [0, 5, 1] by [0, 10, 1]   [0, 20, 4] by [0, 20, 4]

Figure 51   Figure 53a   Figure 53b   Figure 54

52. $\frac{60}{\pi r^2} = \frac{60}{2\pi r} \Rightarrow 120\pi r = 60\pi r^2 \Rightarrow 2r = r^2 \Rightarrow r^2 - 2r = 0 \Rightarrow r(r - 2) = 0 \Rightarrow r = 0 \text{ or } r = 2$

Since $r = 0$ has no physical meaning, $r = 2$. And so $h = \frac{60}{2\pi(2)} = \frac{15}{\pi} \approx 4.77$.

Yes, it is possible to design such a can. The dimensions are $r = 2$ inches and $h \approx 4.77$ inches.

53.   (a) $V = \frac{1}{3}\pi r^2 h \Rightarrow h = \frac{3V}{\pi r^2}$ and $S = \pi r\sqrt{r^2 + h^2} \Rightarrow r^2 + h^2 = \left(\frac{S}{\pi r}\right)^2 \Rightarrow h = \sqrt{\left(\frac{S}{\pi r}\right)^2 - r^2}$

(b) Graph $Y_1 = 102/\left(\pi X^2\right)$ and $Y_2 = \sqrt{\left(\left(52/(\pi X)\right)^2 - X^2\right)}$ in [0, 5, 1] by [0, 10, 1]. See Figures 53a & 53b.

There are two possibilities: $r \approx 2.02$ ft, $h \approx 7.92$ ft or $r \approx 3.76$ ft and $h \approx 2.30$ ft.

54.   (a) $xy = 143$ and $2x + 2y = 48$

(b) Graph $Y_1 = 143/X$ and $Y_2 = 24 - X$ in [0, 20, 4] by [0, 20, 4]. See Figure 54.

The dimensions of the room are $x = 11$ ft and $y = 13$ ft.

Checking Basic Concepts for Section 10.3

1. Symbolically: From the second equation $y = 2x - 3$. Substitute $y = 2x - 3$ into the first equation.

    $x^2 - (2x - 3) = 2x \Rightarrow x^2 - 4x + 3 = 0 \Rightarrow (x-1)(x-3) = 0 \Rightarrow x = 1$ or $x = 3$

    When $x = 1$, $y = 2(1) - 3 = -1$. When $x = 3$, $y = 2(3) - 3 = 3$. The solutions are $(1, -1)$ and $(3, 3)$.

    Graphically: Solve each equation for y. $x^2 - y = 2x \Rightarrow y = x^2 - 2x$ and $2x - y = 3 \Rightarrow y = 2x - 3$

    Graph $Y_1 = X^2 - 2X$ and $Y_2 = 2X - 3$ in [-5, 5, 1] by [-5, 5, 1]. See Figures 1a & 1b.

2. Since graphing these equations would result in a parabola intersected twice by a line, there are two solutions.

3. (a) The point (0, 3) is in the shaded region and is a solution. The point (4, 4) is not in the shaded region and

    is not a solution. *Answers may vary.*

    (b) A parabola with vertex (0, 4) has an equation of the form $y = a(x-0)^2 + 4$ or $y = ax^2 + 4$. Since the

    parabola also passes through the point (2, 0), $0 = a \cdot 2^2 + 4 \Rightarrow 4a = -4 \Rightarrow a = -1$. The equation of the

    parabola is $y = -x^2 + 4$ or $y = 4 - x^2$. Since the line passes through (0, 2) and (2, 0), its slope is

    $m = \dfrac{0-2}{2-0} = \dfrac{-2}{2} = -1$. The y-intercept is (0, 2). The equation of the line is $y = -x + 2$ or $y = 2 - x$.

    Since both the line and the parabola are solid, the system of inequalities is $y \le 4 - x^2$ and $y \ge 2 - x$.

4. Sketch the circle given by $x^2 + y^2 = 4$ using a solid line and the line given by $y = 1$ using a dashed line.

    The point (0, 0) satisfies both inequalities. Shade the portion of the xy-plane containing (0, 0). See Figure 4.

[-5, 5, 1] by [-5, 5, 1]   [-5, 5, 1] by [-5, 5, 1]

                    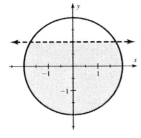

Figure 1a   Figure 1b   Figure 4

Chapter 10 Review Exercises

Section 10.1

1. Since $x = 2(y+0)^2 + 0$, the vertex is (0, 0) and the axis of symmetry is $y = 0$. See Figure 1.

2. Since $x = -(y+1)^2 + 0$, the vertex is (0, -1) and the axis of symmetry is $y = -1$. See Figure 2.

Figure 1   Figure 2   Figure 3

3.   Since $x = -2(y-2)^2 + 0$, the vertex is (0, 2) and the axis of symmetry is $y = 2$. See Figure 3.

4.   Since $x = (y+2)^2 - 1$, the vertex is (–1, –2) and the axis of symmetry is $y = -2$. See Figure 4.

5.   Since $x = -3(y-0)^2 + 1$, the vertex is (1, 0) and the axis of symmetry is $y = 0$. See Figure 5.

      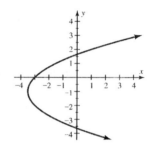

Figure 4   Figure 5   Figure 6

6.   Since $x = \frac{1}{2}(y+1)^2 - \frac{7}{2}$, the vertex is $\left(-\frac{7}{2}, -1\right)$ and the axis of symmetry is $y = -1$. See Figure 6.

7.   Since the vertex is (0, 0), the parabola has an equation of the form $x = a(x-0)^2 + 0$ or $x = ay^2$.

     Since the parabola passes through the point (1, 1), $1 = a(1) \Rightarrow a = 1$. The equation is $x = y^2$.

8.   This is a circle of radius 4 centered at (–2, 2). The equation is $(x+2)^2 + (y-2)^2 = 16$.

9. $(x-0)^2 + (y-0)^2 = 1^2 \Rightarrow x^2 + y^2 = 1$

10. $(x-2)^2 + (y-(-3))^2 = 4^2 \Rightarrow (x-2)^2 + (y+3)^2 = 16$

11. The radius is 5 and the center is (0, 0). Solving the equation for y results in $y = \pm\sqrt{25 - x^2}$. See Figure 11.

12. The radius is 3 and the center is (2, 0). Solving the equation for y results in $y = \pm\sqrt{9 - (x-2)^2}$.

     See Figure 12.

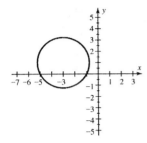

Figure 11	Figure 12	Figure 13

13. The radius is $\sqrt{5}$ and the center is $(-3, 1)$. Solving the equation for y results in $y = 1 \pm \sqrt{5 - (x+3)^2}$.

See Figure 13.

14. $x^2 - 2x + y^2 + 2y = 7 \Rightarrow x^2 - 2x + 1 + y^2 + 2y + 1 = 7 + 1 + 1 \Rightarrow (x-1)^2 + (y+1)^2 = 9$

The radius is 3 and the center is $(1, -1)$. Solving the equation for y results in $y = -1 \pm \sqrt{9 - (x-1)^2}$.

See Figure 14.

Section 10.2

15. The ellipse has a vertical major axis with vertices $(0, \pm 5)$ and minor axis endpoints $(\pm 2, 0)$. See Figure 15.

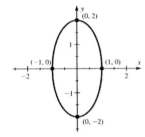

Figure 14	Figure 15	Figure 16

16. The ellipse has a vertical major axis with vertices $(0, \pm 2)$ and minor axis endpoints $(\pm 1, 0)$. See Figure 16.

17. $25x^2 + 20y^2 = 500 \Rightarrow \dfrac{25x^2}{500} + \dfrac{20y^2}{500} = 1 \Rightarrow \dfrac{x^2}{20} + \dfrac{y^2}{25} = 1$

The ellipse has a vertical major axis with vertices $(0, \pm 5)$ and minor axis endpoints $\left(\pm\sqrt{20}, 0 \right)$. See Figure 17.

18. $4x^2 + 9y^2 = 36 \Rightarrow \dfrac{4x^2}{36} + \dfrac{9y^2}{36} = 1 \Rightarrow \dfrac{x^2}{9} + \dfrac{y^2}{4} = 1$

The ellipse has a horizontal major axis with vertices $(\pm 3, 0)$ and minor axis endpoints $(0, \pm 2)$. See Figure 18.

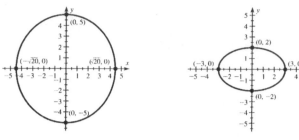

Figure 17   Figure 18

19.   Vertical major axis with vertices $(0, \pm 4)$ and minor axis endpoints $(\pm 2, 0)$ $\Rightarrow \dfrac{y^2}{16} + \dfrac{x^2}{4} = 1$

20.   Horizontal transverse axis with vertices $(\pm 1, 0)$ and asymptotes $y = \pm 2x$ $\Rightarrow x^2 - \dfrac{y^2}{4} = 1$

21.   The hyperbola has a horizontal transverse axis with vertices $(\pm 3, 0)$ and asymptotes $y = \pm \dfrac{2}{3}x$. See Figure 21.

22.   The hyperbola has a vertical transverse axis with vertices $(0, \pm 5)$ and asymptotes $y = \pm \dfrac{5}{4}x$. See Figure 22.

23.   The hyperbola has a vertical transverse axis with vertices $(0, \pm 1)$ and asymptotes $y = \pm x$. See Figure 23.

            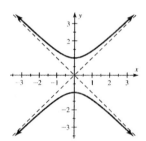

Figure 21   Figure 22   Figure 23

24. $25x^2 - 16y^2 = 400 \Rightarrow \dfrac{25x^2}{400} - \dfrac{16y^2}{400} = 1 \Rightarrow \dfrac{x^2}{16} - \dfrac{y^2}{25} = 1$

The hyperbola has a horizontal transverse axis with vertices $(\pm 4, 0)$ and asymptotes $y = \pm \dfrac{5}{4}x$. See Figure 24.

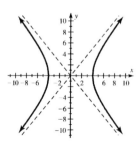

Figure 24

Section 10.3

25.   The solutions are the intersection points (0, 3) and (3, 0). Both solutions check.

26.   The solutions are the intersection points (–1, –2) and (1, 2). Both solutions check.

27.   The solutions are the intersection points (0, 0) and (2, 2). Both solutions check.

28.   The solutions are the intersection points (–2, –1), (–2, 1), (2, –1) and (2, 1). All four solutions check.

29.   Substitute $y = x$ into the second equation.

$$x^2 + (x)^2 = 32 \Rightarrow 2x^2 = 32 \Rightarrow x^2 = 16 \Rightarrow x = \pm 4$$

When $x = -4$, $y = -4$. When $x = 4$, $y = 4$. The solutions are (–4, –4) and (4, 4).

30.   From the first equation, $y = x - 4$. Substitute $y = x - 4$ into the second equation.

$$x^2 + (x-4)^2 = 16 \Rightarrow x^2 + x^2 - 8x + 16 = 16 \Rightarrow 2x^2 - 8x = 0 \Rightarrow 2x(x-4) = 0 \Rightarrow x = 0 \text{ or } x = 4$$

When $x = 0$, $y = (0) - 4 = -4$. When $x = 4$, $y = (4) - 4 = 0$. The solutions are (0, –4) and (4, 0).

31.   Substitute $y = x^2$ into the second equation.

$$2x^2 + (x^2) = 3 \Rightarrow 3x^2 = 3 \Rightarrow x^2 = 1 \Rightarrow x = \pm 1$$

When $x = -1$, $y = (-1)^2 = 1$. When $x = 1$, $y = (1)^2 = 1$. The solutions are (–1, 1) and (1, 1).

32.   Substitute $y = x^2 + 1$ into the second equation.

$$2x^2 - (x^2 + 1) = 3x - 3 \Rightarrow x^2 - 3x + 2 = 0 \Rightarrow (x-1)(x-2) = 0 \Rightarrow x = 1 \text{ or } x = 2$$

When $x = 1$, $y = (1)^2 + 1 = 2$. When $x = 2$, $y = (2)^2 + 1 = 5$. The solutions are (1, 2) and (2, 5).

33.   Solve both equations for y. $2x - y = 4 \Rightarrow y = 2x - 4$ and $x^2 + y = 4 \Rightarrow y = 4 - x^2$

Graph $Y_1 = 2X - 4$ and $Y_2 = 4 - X^2$ in [–8, 8, 1] by [–25, 10, 5]. See Figures 33a & 33b.

The solutions are the intersection points (–4, –12) and (2, 0).

[–8, 8, 1] by [–25, 10, 5]   [–8, 8, 1] by [–25, 10, 5]

Figure 33a   Figure 33b

34.   Solve both equations for y. $x^2 + y = 0 \Rightarrow y = -x^2$ and $x^2 + y^2 = 2 \Rightarrow y = \pm\sqrt{2 - x^2}$

Graph $Y_1 = -X^2$, $Y_2 = \sqrt{(2 - X^2)}$ and $Y_3 = -\sqrt{(2 - X^2)}$ in [–4.7, 4.7, 1] by [–4.1, 2.1, 1].

See Figures 34a and 34b. The solutions are the intersection points (–1, –1) and (1, –1).

[–4.7, 4.7, 1] by [–4.1, 2.1, 1]   [–4.7, 4.7, 1] by [–4.1, 2.1, 1]

Figure 34a   Figure 34b

35. (a) Substitute $y = x$ into the second equation.

$$x^2 + 2(x) = 8 \Rightarrow x^2 + 2x - 8 = 0 \Rightarrow (x+4)(x-2) = 0 \Rightarrow x = -4 \text{ or } x = 2$$

When $x = -4$, $y = -4$. When $x = 2$, $y = 2$. The solutions are $(-4, -4)$ and $(2, 2)$.

(b) Solve the second equation for y. $x^2 + 2y = 8 \Rightarrow y = 4 - \dfrac{x^2}{2}$

Graph $Y_1 = X$ and $Y_2 = 4 - \left(X^2/2\right)$ in [–10, 10, 1] by [–10, 10, 1]. See Figures 35a & 35b.

(c) Table $Y_1 = X$ and $Y_2 = 4 - \left(X^2/2\right)$ with TblStart = –2 and ΔTbl = 1. See Figure 35c.

[–10, 10, 1] by [–10, 10, 1]   [–10, 10, 1] by [–10, 10, 1]

Figure 35a   Figure 35b   Figure 35c

36. (a) Substitute $y = x^3$ into the second equation.

$$x^2 - x^3 = 0 \Rightarrow x^2(1 - x) = 0 \Rightarrow x = 0 \text{ or } x = 1$$

When $x = 0$, $y = 0^3 = 0$. When $x = 1$, $y = 1^3 = 1$. The solutions are $(0, 0)$ and $(1, 1)$.

(b) Solve the second equation for y. $x^2 - y = 0 \Rightarrow y = x^2$

Graph $Y_1 = X \wedge 3$ and $Y_2 = X^2$ in [–1.5, 1.5, 1] by [–1.5, 1.5, 1]. See Figures 36a & 36b.

(c) Table $Y_1 = X \wedge 3$ and $Y_2 = X^2$ with TblStart = –1 and ΔTbl = 0.5. See Figure 36c.

[–1.5, 1.5, 1] by [–1.5, 1.5, 1]   [–1.5, 1.5, 1] by [–1.5, 1.5, 1]

Figure 36a   Figure 36b   Figure 36c

37. Sketch the parabola given by $y = 2x^2$ using a solid line. Try test point $(0, 2)$ to determine shading.

Since $2 \geq 2\left(0^2\right)$, we shade the portion of the xy-plane containing the point $(0, 2)$. See Figure 37.

38. Sketch the line given by $y = 2x - 3$ using a dashed line. Try test point $(3, 0)$ to determine shading.

Since $0 < 2(3) - 3$, we shade the portion of the xy-plane containing the point $(3, 0)$. See Figure 38.

Figure 37

Figure 38

Figure 39

39.   Sketch the parabola given by $y = -x^2$ using a dashed line. Try test point $(0, -1)$ to determine shading.

Since $-1 < -(0)^2$, we shade the portion of the *xy*-plane containing the point $(0, -1)$. See Figure 39.

40.   Sketch the ellipse given by $\dfrac{x^2}{9} + \dfrac{y^2}{16} = 1$ using a solid line. Try test point $(0, 0)$ to determine shading.

Since $0 + 0 \le 1$, we shade the portion of the *xy*-plane containing the point $(0, 0)$. See Figure 40.

41.   Sketch the parabola given by $y = x^2 + 1$ using a solid line and the line given by $y = 2$ using a solid line.

Since the point $(0, 1.5)$ satisfies both inequalities, we shade the portion of the *xy*-plane containing the point $(0, 1.5)$.

See Figure 41.

Figure 40

Figure 41

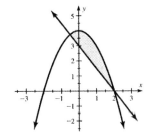

Figure 42

42.   Sketch the parabola given by $y = 4 - x^2$ using a solid line and the line given by $3x + 2y = 6$ using a solid line.

Since the point $(1, 2)$ satisfies both inequalities, we shade the portion of the *xy*-plane containing the point $(1, 2)$.

See Figure 42.

43.   Sketch the parabola given by $y = x^2$ using a dashed line and the parabola given by $y = 4 - x^2$ using a dashed line.

Since the point $(0, 2)$ satisfies both inequalities, we shade the portion of the *xy*-plane containing the point $(0, 2)$.

See Figure 43.

Figure 43   Figure 44

44.   Sketch the ellipse given by $\dfrac{x^2}{4} + \dfrac{y^2}{9} = 1$ using a dashed line and the circle given by $x^2 + y^2 = 16$ using a

dashed line.

Since the point (3, 0) satisfies both inequalities, we shade the portion of the *xy*-plane containing the point (3,

0).

See Figure 44.

45.   A parabola with vertex (0, –2) has an equation of the form $y = a(x - 0)^2 - 2$ or $y = ax^2 - 2$. Since the

parabola also passes through the point (1, –1), $-1 = a \cdot 1^2 - 2 \Rightarrow a = 1$. The equation of the parabola is

$y = x^2 - 2$. Since the line passes through (0, 2) and (2, 0), its slope is $m = \dfrac{0 - 2}{2 - 0} = \dfrac{-2}{2} = -1$.

The *y*-intercept is (0, 2). The equation of the line is $y = -x + 2$ or $y = 2 - x$. Since both the line and the

parabola are solid, the system of inequalities is $y \geq x^2 - 2$ and $y \leq 2 - x$.

46.   A circle of radius 2 centered at (0, 0) has the equation $x^2 + y^2 = 4$. Since the line passes through the points

(0, 0) and (1, 1), its slope is $m = \dfrac{1 - 0}{1 - 0} = \dfrac{1}{1} = 1$. The *y*-intercept is (0, 0). The equation of the line is $y = x$.

Since both the circle and the line are solid, the system of inequalities is $y \geq x$ and $x^2 + y^2 \leq 4$.

Applications

47.   (a) $xy = 1000$ and $2x + 2y = 130$

(b)   Solve each equation for *y*. $xy = 1000 \Rightarrow y = \dfrac{1000}{x}$ and $2x + 2y = 130 \Rightarrow y = 65 - x$

Graph $Y_1 = 1000/X$ and $Y_2 = 65 - X$ in [0, 50, 10] by [0, 50, 10]. See Figure 47.

The table has dimensions $x = 25$ inches and $y = 40$ inches.

(c)   From the second equation, $y = 65 - x$. Substitute $y = 65 - x$ into the first equation.

$x(65 - x) = 1000 \Rightarrow x^2 - 65x + 1000 = 0 \Rightarrow (x - 25)(x - 40) = 0 \Rightarrow x = 25$ or $x = 40$

When $x = 25$, $y = 65 - 25 = 40$. When $x = 40$, $y = 65 - 40 = 25$. These answers are equivalent.

[0, 50, 10] by [0, 50, 10] [0, 16, 4] by [0, 16, 4] [0, 5, 1] by [0, 50, 10]

Figure 47 Figure 48 Figure 49

48. (a) $xy = 60$ and $y - x = 7$

(b) Solve each equation for y. $xy = 60 \Rightarrow y = \dfrac{60}{x}$ and $y - x = 7 \Rightarrow y = x + 7$

Graph $Y_1 = 60/X$ and $Y_2 = X + 7$ in [0, 16, 4] by [0, 16, 4]. See Figure 48.

The numbers are $x = 5$ and $y = 12$.

(c) From the second equation, $y = x + 7$. Substitute $y = x + 7$ into the first equation.

$x(x + 7) = 60 \Rightarrow x^2 + 7x - 60 = 0 \Rightarrow (x + 12)(x - 5) = 0 \Rightarrow x = -12$ or $x = 5$

When $x = -12$, $y = -12 + 7 = -5$. This does not fit the question. When $x = 5$, $y = 5 + 7 = 12$.

49. Solve each equation for h. $V = \pi r^2 h \Rightarrow h = \dfrac{V}{\pi r^2}$ and $A = 2\pi rh \Rightarrow h = \dfrac{A}{2\pi r}$

Graph $Y_1 = 50/\left(\pi X^2\right)$ and $Y_2 = 100/(2\pi X)$ in [0, 5, 1] by [0, 50, 10]. See Figure 49.

The unique answer is $r = 1$ foot and $h \approx 15.92$ feet.

50. Solve each equation for h. $V = \pi r^2 h \Rightarrow h = \dfrac{V}{\pi r^2}$ and $A = 2\pi rh + 2\pi r^2 \Rightarrow h = \dfrac{A - 2\pi r^2}{2\pi r}$

Graph $Y_1 = 35/\left(\pi X^2\right)$ and $Y_2 = \left(80 - 2\pi X^2\right)/(2\pi X)$ in [0, 4, 1] by [−5, 25, 5]. See Figures 50a & 50b.

Two solutions are possible. Either

$r \approx 0.94$ inches and $h \approx 12.60$ inches or $r \approx 3.00$ inches and $h \approx 1.23$ inches. The answer is not unique.

[0, 4, 1] by [−5, 25, 5] [0, 4, 1] by [−5, 25, 5] [−7.5, 7.5, 1] by [−5, 5, 1] [−3, 3, 1] by [−2, 2, 1]

Figure 50a Figure 50b Figure 51 Figure 52

51. (a) $\dfrac{x^2}{5} + \dfrac{y^2}{12} = 1 \Rightarrow \dfrac{y^2}{12} = 1 - \dfrac{x^2}{5} \Rightarrow y^2 = 12\left(1 - \dfrac{x^2}{5}\right) \Rightarrow y = \pm\sqrt{12\left(1 - \dfrac{x^2}{5}\right)}$

Graph $Y_1 = \sqrt{\left(12\left(1 - X^2/5\right)\right)}$ and $Y_2 = -\sqrt{\left(12\left(1 - X^2/5\right)\right)}$ in [−7.5, 7.5, 1] by [−5, 5, 1]. See Figure 51.

(b) $A = \pi\left(\sqrt{12}\right)\left(\sqrt{5}\right) \approx 24.33$ square units and $P = 2\pi\sqrt{\dfrac{5 + 12}{2}} \approx 18.32$ units

52.   (a) $\dfrac{x^2}{1.524^2}+\dfrac{y^2}{1.517^2}=1\Rightarrow\dfrac{y^2}{1.517^2}=1-\dfrac{x^2}{1.524^2}\Rightarrow y=\pm\sqrt{1.517^2\left(1-\dfrac{x^2}{1.524^2}\right)}$

Plot the point (0.15, 0) and Graph $Y_1=\sqrt{\left(1.517^2\left(1-X^2/1.524^2\right)\right)}$ and $Y_2=-\sqrt{\left(1.517^2\left(1-X^2/1.524^2\right)\right)}$

in [–3, 3, 1] by [–2, 2, 1]. See Figure 52.

(b) $P=2\pi\sqrt{\dfrac{1.524^2+1.517^2}{2}}\approx9.55$ A.U. or about 8.9×10^8 miles

$A=\pi(1.524)(1.517)\approx7.26$ square A.U. or about 6.3×10^{16} square miles

Chapter 10 Test

1.   Since $x=(y-4)^2-2$, the vertex is (–2, 4) and the axis of symmetry is $y=4$. See Figure 1.

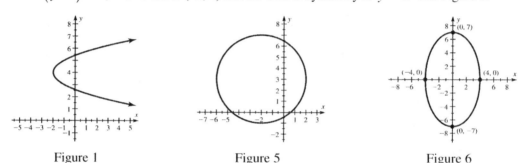

Figure 1   Figure 5   Figure 6

2.   Since the parabola opens to the left and the vertex is (1, 0), the equation has the form $x=a(y-0)^2+1$.

Since the parabola passes through (0, 1), $0=a(1-0)^2+1\Rightarrow a=-1$. The equation is $x=-y^2+1$.

3.   Since the center is (2, –4) and the radius is 2, the equation is $(x-2)^2+(y+4)^2=4$.

4. $\left(x-(-5)\right)^2+(y-2)^2=10^2\Rightarrow(x+5)^2+(y-2)^2=100$

5. $x^2+4x+y^2-6y=3\Rightarrow x^2+4x+4+y^2-6y+9=3+4+9\Rightarrow(x+2)^2+(y-3)^2=16$

The radius is 4 and the center is (–2, 3). Solving the equation for y results in $y=3\pm\sqrt{16-(x+2)^2}$.

See Figure 5.

6.   The ellipse has a vertical major axis with vertices $(0,\pm7)$ and minor axis endpoints $(\pm4,0)$. See Figure 6.

7.   Horizontal major axis with vertices $(\pm10,0)$ and minor axis endpoints $(0,\pm8)$ $\Rightarrow\dfrac{x^2}{100}+\dfrac{y^2}{64}=1$

8. $4x^2-9y^2=36\Rightarrow\dfrac{4x^2}{36}-\dfrac{9y^2}{36}=1\Rightarrow\dfrac{x^2}{9}-\dfrac{y^2}{4}=1$

The hyperbola has a horizontal transverse axis with vertices $(\pm 3, 0)$ and asymptotes $y = \pm \dfrac{2}{3} x.$ See Figure 8.

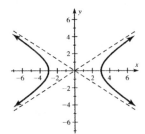

[-10, 10, 1] by [-10, 10, 1]

Figure 11a

[-10, 10, 1] by [-10, 10, 1]

Figure 11b

Figure 8

9.   The solutions are the intersection points $(0, -4)$ and $(4, 0)$. Both solutions check.

10. From the first equation, $y = x - 3$. Substitute $y = x - 3$ into the second equation.

$$x^2 + (x-3)^2 = 17 \Rightarrow x^2 + x^2 - 6x + 9 = 17 \Rightarrow 2(x-4)(x+1) = 0 \Rightarrow x = -1 \text{ or } x = 4$$

When $x = -1$, $y = (-1) - 3 = -4$. When $x = 4$, $y = (4) - 3 = 1$. The solutions are $(-1, -4)$ and $(4, 1)$.

11. Solve both equations for y. $2x^2 - y = 4 \Rightarrow y = 2x^2 - 4$ and $x^2 + y = 8 \Rightarrow y = 8 - x^2$

Graph $Y_1 = 2X^2 - 4$, $Y_2 = 8 - X^2$ in [-10, 10, 1] by [-10, 10, 1]. See Figures 11a & 11b.

The solutions are the intersection points $(-2, 4)$ and $(2, 4)$.

12. Sketch the line given by $3x + y = 6$ using a dashed line and the circle given by $x^2 + y^2 = 25$ using a dashed line.

Since the point $(4, 0)$ satisfies both inequalities, we shade the portion of the *xy*-plane containing the point $(4, 0)$.

See Figure 12.

[-30, 30, 10] by [-20, 20, 10]

Figure 16

Figure 12

13. A parabola with vertex $(0, -4)$ has an equation of the form $y = a(x - 0)^2 - 4$ or $y = ax^2 - 4$. Since the parabola also passes through the point $(2, 0)$, $0 = a \cdot 2^2 - 4 \Rightarrow a = 1$. The equation of the parabola is $y = x^2 - 4$. The other parabola is a reflection of this parabola across the *x*-axis. Its equation is $y = 4 - x^2$.

Since both the parabolas are solid, the system of inequalities is $y \le 4 - x^2$ and $y \ge x^2 - 4$.

14. (a) $xy = 5000$ and $2x + 2y = 300$

(b) $\dfrac{5000}{x} = 150 - x \Rightarrow 5000 = 150x - x^2 \Rightarrow x^2 - 150x + 5000 = 0 \Rightarrow (x - 50)(x - 100) = 0 \Rightarrow$

Either $x = 50$ or $x = 100$. When $x = 50$, $y = 150 - 50 = 100$. When $x = 100$, $y = 150 - 100 = 50$.

Since the width is shorter than the length, $x = 50$ and $y = 100$. The solution is 50 by 100 feet.

15. From the hint, the two equations to graph are $y = \dfrac{1183}{x^2}$ and $y = \dfrac{702 - x^2}{4x}$. Figures not shown. There are two

possible solutions: Either $x \approx 22.08$ and $y \approx 2.43$ or $x \approx 7.29$ and $y \approx 22.24$. The answer is not unique.

16. (a) $\dfrac{x^2}{19.18^2} + \dfrac{y^2}{19.16^2} = 1 \Rightarrow \dfrac{y^2}{19.16^2} = 1 - \dfrac{x^2}{19.18^2} \Rightarrow y = \pm\sqrt{19.16^2\left(1 - \dfrac{x^2}{19.18^2}\right)}$

Plot the point $(0.9, 0)$ and graph $Y_1 = \sqrt{\left(19.16^2\left(1 - X^2/19.18^2\right)\right)}$ and $Y_2 = -\sqrt{\left(19.16^2\left(1 - X^2/19.18^2\right)\right)}$ in $[-$

30, 30, 10] by [–20, 20, 10]. See Figure 16.

(b) The minimum distance occurs when $x = 19.18$ A.U. The distance is $19.18 - 0.9 = 18.28$ A.U.

This is about 1,700,040,000 miles.

Chapter 10 Extended and Discovery Exercises

1. (a) $x^2 = 4y \Rightarrow x^2 = 4(1)y$. Since $p = 1$, the focus is $(0, 1)$. See Figure 1a.

(b) $y^2 = -8x \Rightarrow y^2 = 4(-2)x$. Since $p = -2$, the focus is $(-2, 0)$. See Figure 1b.

(c) $x = 2y^2 \Rightarrow y^2 = \dfrac{1}{2}x \Rightarrow y^2 = 4\left(\dfrac{1}{8}\right)x$. Since $p = \dfrac{1}{8}$, the focus is $\left(\dfrac{1}{8}, 0\right)$. See Figure 1c.

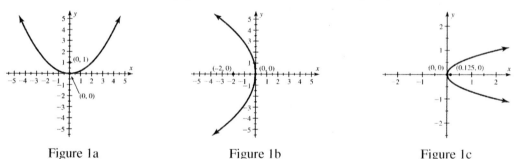

Figure 1a   Figure 1b   Figure 1c

2. (a) Since the vertex of the parabola is $(0, 0)$, the cross section of the dish has an equation of the form

$y = ax^2$.

Since the parabola passes through $(150, 44)$, $44 = a(150)^2 \Rightarrow 44 = 22,500a \Rightarrow a = \dfrac{44}{22,500} = \dfrac{11}{5625}$.

The equation is $y = \dfrac{11}{5625}x^2$.

(b) Writing this equation in the form $x^2 = 4py$ yields $x^2 = 4\left(\dfrac{5625}{44}\right)y$. The focus is located at $\left(0, \dfrac{5625}{44}\right)$.

That is, the focus is $\dfrac{5625}{44} \approx 127.8$ feet from the vertex.

3. (a) This is an ellipse with horizontal major axis, centered at (3, 1). See Figure 3a.

    (b) This is an ellipse with vertical major axis, centered at (–1, –2). See Figure 3b.

    (c) This is a hyperbola centered at (–1, 3). The asymptotes are $y = \pm\dfrac{3}{2}(x+1)+3$. See Figure 3c.

    (d) This is a hyperbola centered at (–1, 4). The asymptotes are $y = \pm 2(x+1)+4$. See Figure 3d.

Figure 3a

Figure 3b

Figure 3c

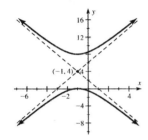

Figure 3d

4. (a) $\dfrac{(x+3)^2}{16}+\dfrac{(y-5)^2}{4}=1$

    (b) $\dfrac{(y+3)^2}{25}+\dfrac{(x-2)^2}{9}=1$

5. (a) $9x^2-18x+4y^2+24y+9=0 \Rightarrow 9\left(x^2-2x+1\right)+4\left(y^2+6y+9\right)=-9+9+36 \Rightarrow$

    $9(x-1)^2+4(y+3)^2=36 \Rightarrow \dfrac{(x-1)^2}{4}+\dfrac{(y+3)^2}{9}=1 \Rightarrow$ Center: $(1,-3)$

    (b) $25x^2+150x-16y^2+32y-191=0 \Rightarrow 25\left(x^2+6x+9\right)-16\left(y^2-2y+1\right)=191+225-16 \Rightarrow$

    $25(x+3)^2-16(y-1)^2=400 \Rightarrow \dfrac{(x+3)^2}{16}-\dfrac{(y-1)^2}{25}=1 \Rightarrow$ Center: $(-3,1)$

Chapters 1-10 Cumulative Review Exercises

1. $K = (4)^2 + (-3)^2 = 16 + 9 = 25$

2. $\dfrac{\left(a^{-2}b\right)^2}{a^{-1}\left(b^3\right)^{-2}} = \dfrac{a^{-4}b^2}{a^{-1}b^{-6}} = a^{-4-(-1)}b^{2-(-6)} = a^{-3}b^8 = \dfrac{b^8}{a^3}$

3. $7.345 \times 10^{-3} = 0.007345$

4. $f(-4) = \dfrac{-4}{-4-4} = \dfrac{-4}{-8} = \dfrac{1}{2}$; the denominator cannot equal zero, so $x - 4 \neq 0 \Rightarrow x \neq 4$.

5. $f(3) = 4$

6. See Figure 6.

7. See Figure 7.

Figure 6   Figure 7

8. A line perpendicular to $y = -\dfrac{2}{3}x + 1$ has slope $m = \dfrac{3}{2}$.

    $y - (-2) = \dfrac{3}{2}(x - 2) \Rightarrow y = \dfrac{3}{2}x - 3 - 2 \Rightarrow y = \dfrac{3}{2}x - 5$

9. $2(1-x) - 4x = x \Rightarrow 2 - 2x - 4x - x = 0 \Rightarrow -7x = -2 \Rightarrow x = \dfrac{2}{7}$

10. $-5 \leq 1 - 2x < 3 \Rightarrow -6 \leq -2x < 2 \Rightarrow 3 \geq x > -1 \Rightarrow -1 < x \leq 3; (-1, 3]$

11. $x^2 - 4 \leq 0$; replace the inequality symbol with an equals sign and solve the resulting equation.

    $x^2 - 4 = 0 \Rightarrow (x-2)(x+2) = 0 \Rightarrow x = 2$ or $x = -2$.

    The graph of $y = x^2 - 4$ is a parabola that lies on or below the x-axis when $x \geq -2$ and $x \leq 2$.

    The solution is $[-2, 2]$.

12. $|1 - x| \geq 2 \Rightarrow 1 - x \geq 2$ or $1 - x \leq -2 \Rightarrow -x \geq 1$ or $-x \leq -3 \Rightarrow x \leq -1$ or $x \geq 3$; The solution is $(-\infty, -1] \cup [3, \infty)$.

13. Add the equations.

    $-2x + y = 1$

    $\underline{5x - y = 2}$

    $3x \quad\;\; = 3 \quad \Rightarrow x = 1.$ Substitute $x = 1$ into the first equation.

$-2(1) + y = 1 \Rightarrow -2 + y = 1 \Rightarrow y = 3.$ The solution is $(1, 3)$.

14.   Note that $x + y \le 4 \Rightarrow y \le -x + 4$ and $x - y \ge 2 \Rightarrow y \le x - 2$. See Figure 14.

Figure 14

15. $(2x - 1)(x + 5) = 2x^2 + 10x - x - 5 = 2x^2 + 9x - 5$

16. $xy(2x - 3y^2 + 1) = 2x^2y - 3xy^3 + xy$

17. $6x^2 - 13x - 5 = (3x + 1)(2x - 5)$

18. $x^3 - 4x = x(x^2 - 4) = x(x - 2)(x + 2)$

19. $x^2 + 3x + 2 = 0 \Rightarrow (x + 2)(x + 1) = 0 \Rightarrow x = -2$ or $x = -1$

20. $x^2 + 1 = -3x \Rightarrow x^2 + 3x + 1 = 0; a = 1, b = 3, c = 1$ $x = \dfrac{-b \pm \sqrt{b^2 - 4ac}}{2a} = \dfrac{-3 \pm \sqrt{3^2 - 4(1)(1)}}{2(1)} = \dfrac{-3 \pm \sqrt{5}}{2}$

21. $\dfrac{x-2}{x+2} \div \dfrac{2x-4}{3x+6} = \dfrac{x-2}{x+2} \cdot \dfrac{3(x+2)}{2(x-2)} = \dfrac{3}{2}$

22. $\dfrac{1}{x+1} + \dfrac{1}{x-1} = \dfrac{1}{x+1} \cdot \dfrac{x-1}{x-1} + \dfrac{1}{x-1} \cdot \dfrac{x+1}{x+1} = \dfrac{x-1}{x^2-1} + \dfrac{x+1}{x^2-1} = \dfrac{x-1+x+1}{x^2-1} = \dfrac{2x}{x^2-1}$

23. $\sqrt{8x^2} = \sqrt{4x^2 \cdot 2} = 2x\sqrt{2}$

24. $8^{2/3} = \left(\sqrt[3]{8}\right)^2 = 2^2 = 4$

25. $\sqrt[3]{2x} \cdot \sqrt[3]{32x^2} = \sqrt[3]{2x \cdot 32x^2} = \sqrt[3]{64x^3} = 4x$

26. $3\sqrt{3x} + \sqrt{12x} = 3\sqrt{3x} + 2\sqrt{3x} = 5\sqrt{3x}$

27.   See Figure 27.

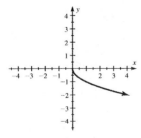

Figure 27

28. $d = \sqrt{(x_2 - x_1)^2 + (y_2 - y_1)^2} = \sqrt{(-2-2)^2 + (0-(-3))^2} = \sqrt{(-4)^2 + (3)^2} = \sqrt{16+9} = \sqrt{25} = 5$

29. $(2+3i)(2-3i) = (2)^2 - (3i)^2 = 4 - 9i^2 = 4 - 9(-1) = 4 + 9 = 13$

30. $\sqrt{x+2} = x \Rightarrow x+2 = x^2 \Rightarrow x^2 - x - 2 = 0 \Rightarrow (x-2)(x+1) = 0 \Rightarrow x = 2$ ($x = -1$ does not check.)

31. $x = -\dfrac{b}{2a} = -\dfrac{(-6)}{2(1)} = \dfrac{-6}{-2} = 3;\ y = (3)^2 - 6(3) + 3 \Rightarrow y = 9 - 18 + 3 \Rightarrow y = -6.$ The vertex is $(3, -6)$.

32. $f(x) = x^2 - 2x + 3 \Rightarrow f(x) = (x^2 - 2x + 1) + 3 - 1 \Rightarrow f(x) = (x-1)^2 + 2$

33. The graph of $f(x)$ is shifted 4 units right.

34. $x(3-x) = 2 \Rightarrow 3x - x^2 - 2 = 0 \Rightarrow x^2 - 3x + 2 = 0 \Rightarrow (x-2)(x-1) = 0 \Rightarrow x = 2$ or $x = 1$

35. $x^3 + x = 0 \Rightarrow x(x^2 + 1) = 0 \Rightarrow x = 0$ or $x^2 = -1 \Rightarrow x = \pm\sqrt{-1} \Rightarrow x = \pm i$

36. (a) $\log 10{,}000 = 4$ because $10^4 = 10{,}000$

   (b) $\log_2 8 = 3$

   (c) $\log_3 3^x = x$

   (d) $e^{\ln 6} = 6$

   (e) $\log 2 + \log 50 = \log(2 \cdot 50) = \log(100) = 2$ because $10^2 = 100$

   (f) $\log_2 24 - \log_2(3) = \log_2\left(\dfrac{24}{3}\right) = \log_2(8) = 3$

37. (a) $(f \circ g)(2) = f(g(2)) = f(2 \cdot 2) = f(4) = 4^2 + 1 = 16 + 1 = 17$

   (b) $(g \circ f)(x) = g(f(x)) = g(x^2 + 1) = 2(x^2 + 1) = 2x^2 + 2$

38. Let $x = 2 - 3y$. Then $x - 2 = -3y \Rightarrow y = \dfrac{x-2}{-3}$ or $f^{-1}(x) = -\dfrac{1}{3}x + \dfrac{2}{3}$

39. $A = 1000(1 + 0.05)^6 = 1000(1.05)^6 \approx \$1340.10$

40. $\log\dfrac{x^2\sqrt{y}}{z^3} = \log\left(x^2\sqrt{y}\right) - \log\left(z^3\right)$

   $= \log\left(x^2\right) + \log\left(y^{1/2}\right) - \log\left(z^3\right)$

   $= 2\log x + \dfrac{1}{2}\log y - 3\log z$

41. $2e^x - 1 = 17 \Rightarrow 2e^x = 18 \Rightarrow e^x = 9 \Rightarrow \ln e^x = \ln 9 \Rightarrow x = \ln 9$

42. $3 + \log 4x = 5 \Rightarrow \log 4x = 2 \Rightarrow 10^{\log 4x} = 10^2 \Rightarrow 4x = 100 \Rightarrow x = 25$

43. (a)

(b)

(c)

(d)

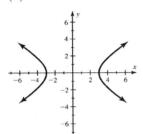

44. Multiply the first equation by −1 and add to the second equation.

$$-x^2 - y^2 = -1$$
$$\underline{x^2 + 9y^2 = 9}$$
$$8y^2 = 8 \quad \Rightarrow y^2 = 1 \Rightarrow y = \pm 1$$

$$x^2 + (\pm 1)^2 = 1 \Rightarrow x^2 + 1 = 1 \Rightarrow x^2 = 0 \Rightarrow x = 0$$

The solutions are $(0, 1)$ and $(0, -1)$.

45. See Figure 45.

Figure 45

Applications

46. (a) $D(0) = 400 - 50(0) = 400$; initially, the driver is 400 miles from home.

(b) $400 - 50x = 0 \Rightarrow 400 = 50x \Rightarrow x = 8$; after 8 hours the driver arrives at home.

(c) -50; the driver is traveling 50 miles per hour toward home.

47. Let x, y, z represent the amounts invested at $5\%, 6\%,$ and $7\%,$ respectively. The system needed is

$$x + y + z = 2000 \qquad\qquad\qquad x + y + z = 2000$$
$$y = x + 500 \qquad\qquad \Rightarrow \qquad -x + y \qquad = 500$$
$$0.05x + 0.06y + 0.07z = 120: \qquad\qquad 5x + 6y = 7z = 12,000$$

Multiply the first equation by −7 and add to the third equation.

$$-7x - 7y - 7z = -14,000$$
$$\underline{5x + 6y + 7z = 12,000}$$
$$-2x - y = -2000$$

Add this new equation to the second equation.

$$-2x - y = -2000$$
$$\underline{-x + y = 500}$$
$$-3x = -1500$$

$$\Rightarrow x = 500 \Rightarrow y = 500 + 500 = 1000$$

Substitute $x = 500$ and $y = 1000$ into the first equation.

$$500 + 1000 + z = 2000 \Rightarrow z = 500,$$

$500 is invested at 5%, $1000 is invested at 6%, and $500 is invested at 7%.

48. Let x represent the length of the garden. Then the area is $x(600 - x) = 600x - x^2$. Find the x-value of the vertex of $y = -x^2 + 600x$.

$$x = -\frac{b}{2a} = -\frac{600}{2(-1)} = \frac{-600}{-2} = 300$$

The dimensions should be 300 feet by 300 feet.

49. $2e^{0.02x} = 4 \Rightarrow e^{0.02x} = 2 \Rightarrow \ln e^{0.02x} = \ln 2 \Rightarrow 0.02x = \ln 2 \Rightarrow x = \dfrac{\ln 2}{0.02} \Rightarrow 50 \ln 2 \approx 34.7$ years

50. $V = \pi r^2 h = 60$ and $S = 2\pi r h = 50$, solve for r

$$\Rightarrow h = \frac{50}{2\pi r}, \text{ substitute into } \pi r^2 h = 60$$

$$\Rightarrow \pi r^2 \left(\frac{50}{2\pi r}\right) = 60 \Rightarrow 25r = 60 \Rightarrow r = \frac{60}{25} = 2.4 \text{ inches}$$

Critical Thinking Solutions for Chapter 10

Section 10.1.

- The circle is undefined since the radius is $\sqrt{-7}$.

Section 10.2

- When the nails are moved farther apart the ellipse becomes more flat (ultimately a straight line).

  When the nails are moved closer together the ellipse becomes more circular.

  When the nails come together, a circle would be formed.

- It is a circle with radius a. We can find the equation of the circle by multiplying both sides of the equation by a^2.

- Minimum distance: about 0.307 A.U. or about 28,551,000 miles

  Maximum distance: about 0.467 A.U. or about 43,431,000 miles

Chapter 11: Sequences and Series

11.1: Sequences

Concepts

1. 1, 2, 3, 4; *Answers may vary.*

2. 1, 3, 5, 7, …; *Answers may vary.*

3. function; natural numbers

4. sequence

5. 6

6. scatterplot

7. $f(2)$

8. a_4

Evaluating and Representing Sequences

9. $f(1) = 1^2 = 1,\ f(2) = 2^2 = 4,\ f(3) = 3^2 = 9,\ f(4) = 4^2 = 16 \Rightarrow 1, 4, 9, 16$

10. $f(1) = 3(1) + 4 = 7,\ f(2) = 3(2) + 4 = 10,\ f(3) = 3(3) + 4 = 13,\ f(4) = 3(4) + 4 = 16 \Rightarrow 7, 10, 13, 16$

11. $f(1) = \dfrac{1}{1+5} = \dfrac{1}{6},\ f(2) = \dfrac{1}{2+5} = \dfrac{1}{7},\ f(3) = \dfrac{1}{3+5} = \dfrac{1}{8},\ f(4) = \dfrac{1}{4+5} = \dfrac{1}{9} \Rightarrow \dfrac{1}{6}, \dfrac{1}{7}, \dfrac{1}{8}, \dfrac{1}{9}$

12. $f(1) = 3^1 = 3,\ f(2) = 3^2 = 9,\ f(3) = 3^3 = 27,\ f(4) = 3^4 = 81 \Rightarrow 3, 9, 27, 81$

13. $f(1) = 5\left(\dfrac{1}{2}\right)^1 = \dfrac{5}{2},\ f(2) = 5\left(\dfrac{1}{2}\right)^2 = \dfrac{5}{4},\ f(3) = 5\left(\dfrac{1}{2}\right)^3 = \dfrac{5}{8},\ f(4) = 5\left(\dfrac{1}{2}\right)^4 = \dfrac{5}{16} \Rightarrow \dfrac{5}{2}, \dfrac{5}{4}, \dfrac{5}{8}, \dfrac{5}{16}$

14. $f(1) = 1^2 + 2(1) = 3,\ f(2) = 2^2 + 2(2) = 8,\ f(3) = 3^2 + 2(3) = 15,\ f(4) = 4^2 + 2(4) = 24 \Rightarrow 3, 8, 15, 24$

15. $f(1) = 9,\ f(2) = 9,\ f(3) = 9,\ f(4) = 9 \Rightarrow 9, 9, 9, 9$

16. $f(1) = (-1)^1 = -1,\ f(2) = (-1)^2 = 1,\ f(3) = (-1)^3 = -1,\ f(4) = (-1)^4 = 1 \Rightarrow -1, 1, -1, 1$

17. $a_1 = 1^3 = 1,\ a_2 = 2^3 = 8,\ a_3 = 3^3 = 27 \Rightarrow 1, 8, 27$

18. $a_1 = 5 - 1 = 4,\ a_2 = 5 - 2 = 3,\ a_3 = 5 - 3 = 2 \Rightarrow 4, 3, 2$

19. $a_1 = \dfrac{4(1)}{3+1} = 1,\ a_2 = \dfrac{4(2)}{3+2} = \dfrac{8}{5},\ a_3 = \dfrac{4(3)}{3+3} = 2 \Rightarrow 1, \dfrac{8}{5}, 2$

20. $a_1 = 3^{-1} = \dfrac{1}{3},\ a_2 = 3^{-2} = \dfrac{1}{9},\ a_3 = 3^{-3} = \dfrac{1}{27} \Rightarrow \dfrac{1}{3}, \dfrac{1}{9}, \dfrac{1}{27}$

21. $a_1 = 2(1)^2 + 1 - 1 = 2,\ a_2 = 2(2)^2 + 2 - 1 = 9,\ a_3 = 2(3)^2 + 3 - 1 = 20 \Rightarrow 2, 9, 20$

22. $a_1 = 1^4 - 1 = 0,\ a_2 = 2^4 - 1 = 15,\ a_3 = 3^4 - 1 = 80 \Rightarrow 0, 15, 80$

23. $a_1 = -2,\ a_2 = -2,\ a_3 = -2 \Rightarrow -2, -2, -2$

24. $a_1 = 1^1 = 1, a_2 = 2^2 = 4, a_3 = 3^3 = 27 \Rightarrow 1, 4, 27$

25. $a_1 = b(1) + c = b + c; a_2 = b(2) + c = 2b + c$

26. $a_1 = \dfrac{1+b}{1-c}; a_2 = \dfrac{2+b}{2+c}$

27. $\dfrac{1}{2}(a_1 + a_4) = \dfrac{1}{2}(10+4) = \dfrac{1}{2}(14) = 7$

28. $\dfrac{1}{2}(a_1 + a_4) = \dfrac{1}{2}(-5+30) = \dfrac{1}{2}(25) = 12.5$

29.   The points shown are (1, 3), (2, 4), (3, 5), (4, 3) and (5, 1). The sequence is 3, 4, 5, 3, 1.

30.   The points shown are (1, 1), (2, 2), (3, 4), (4, 8) and (5, 6). The sequence is 1, 2, 4, 8, 6.

31.   The points shown are (1, 6), (2, 5), (3, 4), (4, 3), (5, 2) and (6, 1). The sequence is 6, 5, 4, 3, 2, 1.

32.   The points shown are (1, 4), (2, 1), (3, 0), (4, 1) and (5, 2). The sequence is 4, 1, 0, 1, 2.

33.   Numerical: See Figure 33a. Graphical: See Figure 33b.

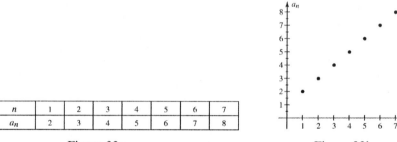

n	1	2	3	4	5	6	7
a_n	2	3	4	5	6	7	8

Figure 33a   Figure 33b

34.   Numerical: See Figure 34a. Graphical: See Figure 34b.

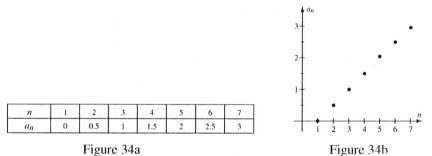

n	1	2	3	4	5	6	7
a_n	0	0.5	1	1.5	2	2.5	3

Figure 34a   Figure 34b

35.   Numerical: See Figure 35a. Graphical: See Figure 35b.

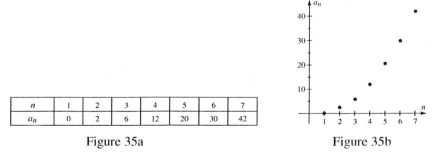

n	1	2	3	4	5	6	7
a_n	0	2	6	12	20	30	42

Figure 35a   Figure 35b

36.   Numerical: See Figure 36a. Graphical: See Figure 36b.

n	1	2	3	4	5	6	7
a_n	0.5	2	4.5	8	12.5	18	24.5

Figure 36a

Figure 36b

37. Numerical: See Figure 37a. Graphical: See Figure 37b.

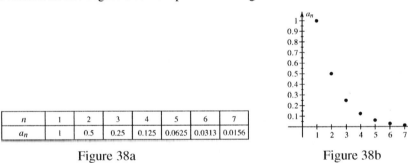

n	1	2	3	4	5	6	7
a_n	2	4	8	16	32	64	128

Figure 37a

Figure 37b

38. Numerical: See Figure 38a. Graphical: See Figure 38b.

n	1	2	3	4	5	6	7
a_n	1	0.5	0.25	0.125	0.0625	0.0313	0.0156

Figure 38a

Figure 38b

Applications

39. Symbolic: $a_n = 30n$ for $n = 1, 2, 3, \ldots, 7$

Graphical: See Figure 39a. Numerical: See Figure 39b.

n	1	2	3	4	5	6	7
a_n	30	60	90	120	150	180	210

Figure 39a

Figure 39b

40. Symbolic: $a_n = 5.8n$ for $n = 1, 2, 3, 4, 5$

Graphical: See Figure 40a. Numerical: See Figure 40b.

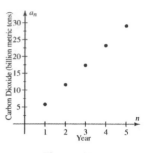

Figure 40a

n	1	2	3	4	5
a_n	5.8	11.6	17.4	23.2	29

Figure 40b

41.   (a) $a_1 = 1^2 = 1, a_2 = 2^2 = 4, a_3 = 3^2 = 9, a_4 = 4^2 = 16 \Rightarrow 1, 4, 9, 16$

(b) $a_1 = 4(1) = 4, a_2 = 4(2) = 8, a_3 = 4(3) = 12, a_4 = 4(4) = 16 \Rightarrow 4, 8, 12, 16$

42.   Symbolic: $a_n = 50,000(1.08)^{n-1}$ for $n = 1, 2, 3, 4, 5$

Numerical: See Figure 42a. Graphical: See Figure 42b.

n	1	2	3	4	5
a_n	50,000	54,000	58,320	62,986	68,024

Figure 42a

Figure 42b

43.   (a)   After 1 year it is worth $25,000(0.80) = \$20,000$. After 2 years it is worth $20,000(0.80) = \$16,000$.

(b) $a_n = 25,000(0.8)^n$

(c)   See Figure 43.

n	1	2	3	4	5	6	7
a_n	20,000	16,000	12,800	10,240	8192	6553.6	5242.9

Figure 43

44.   (a)   The equation $d = cn + b$ is linear. Since the distance increases by 32 feet each second, the slope is 32.

Using the first data point, $16 = 32(1) + b \Rightarrow b = -16$. That is $c = 32$ and $b = -16$.

(b) $d = 32(6) - 16 = 176$ feet

45.   (a) $a_n = 2048(0.5)^{n-1}$ for $n = 1, 2, 3, \ldots, 7$

(b)   See Figure 45b.

(c)   See Figure 45c.

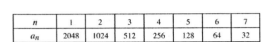

Figure 45b

Figure 45c

46.   (a) See Figure 46a.

(b) $a_n = 50 + 5(n-1)$ or $a_n = 45 + 5n$

(c) $a_{23} = 50 + 5(23-1) = 50 + 5(22) = 50 + 110 = 160$ seats

(d) See Figure 46d.

Figure 46a

Figure 46d

11.2: Arithmetic and Geometric Sequences

Concepts

1.   linear

2.   exponential

3. $a_n = 3n + 1$; the common difference is 3. *Answers may vary.*

4. $a_n = 5(2)^{n-1}$; the common ratio is 2. *Answers may vary.*

5.   add; previous

6.   multiply; common ratio

7.   19; 4

8.   32; –2

9. $a_n = a_1(r)^{n-1}$

10. $a_n = a_1 + (n-1)d$

Arithmetic Sequences

11.   Yes, the common difference is 10.

12.   Yes, the common difference is –3.

13.   Yes, the common difference is –1.

14. Yes, the common difference is $\frac{1}{2}$.

15. No, there is no common difference.

16. No, there is no common difference.

17. Yes, the common difference is 3.

18. Yes, the common difference is 2.

19. Yes, the common difference is –3.

20. No, there is no common difference.

21. No, there is no common difference.

22. Yes, the common difference is 1.5.

23. Yes, the common difference is 1.

24. Yes, the common difference is –1.

25. No, there is no common difference.

26. No, there is no common difference.

27. Yes, the common difference is 2.

28. Yes, the common difference is –0.5.

29. $a_n = 7 + (n-1)(-2) \Rightarrow a_n = 7 - 2n + 2 \Rightarrow a_n = -2n + 9$

30. Note: $d = 9 - 5 = 4$, thus $a_n = 5 + (n-1)(4) \Rightarrow a_n = 5 + 4n - 4 \Rightarrow a_n = 4n + 1$

31. Note: $d = \frac{6 - (-2)}{2} = 4$, thus $a_n = -2 + (n-1)(4) \Rightarrow a_n = -2 + 4n - 4 \Rightarrow a_n = 4n - 6$

32. Note: $d = 10 - 7 = 3$ and $a_1 = 7 - 3 = 4$, thus $a_n = 4 + (n-1)(3) \Rightarrow a_n = 4 + 3n - 3 \Rightarrow a_n = 3n + 1$

33. Note: $d = \frac{8 - 16}{4} = -2$ and $a_1 = 16 - 7(-2) = 30$, thus

$a_n = 30 + (n-1)(-2) \Rightarrow a_n = 30 - 2n + 2 \Rightarrow a_n = -2n + 32$

34. Note: $a_1 = 7 - 2(-5) = 17$, thus $a_n = 17 + (n-1)(-5) \Rightarrow a_n = 17 - 5n + 5 \Rightarrow a_n = -5n + 22$

35. $a_{32} = -3 + (32-1)(2) \Rightarrow -3 + (31)(2) = -3 + 62 = 59$

36. $a_{19} = 2 + (19-1)(-3) \Rightarrow 2 + (18)(-3) = 2 - 54 = -52$

37. Note: $d = 0 - (-3) = 3$, thus $a_9 = -3 + (9-1)(3) \Rightarrow -3 + (8)(3) = -3 + 24 = 21$

38. Note: $a_1 = -3 - 2(4) = -11$, thus $a_{62} = -11 + (62-1)(4) \Rightarrow -11 + (61)(4) = -11 + 244 = 233$

Geometric Sequences

39. Yes, the common ratio is 3.

40. Yes, the common ratio is 4.

41. Yes, the common ratio is 0.8.

42. No, there is no common ratio.

43.   No, there is no common ratio.

44.   Yes, the common ratio is $-\dfrac{3}{4}$.

45.   Yes, the common ratio is 2.

46.   Yes, the common ratio is $-\dfrac{1}{2}$.

47.   No, there is no common ratio.

48.   No, there is no common ratio.

49.   Yes, the common ratio is 4.

50.   Yes, the common ratio is $\dfrac{1}{2}$.

51.   Yes, the common ratio is 2.

52.   No, there is no common ratio.

53.   No, there is no common ratio.

54.   Yes, the common ratio is $\dfrac{1}{2}$.

55. $a_n = 1.5(4)^{n-1}$

56. $a_n = 3\left(\dfrac{1}{4}\right)^{n-1}$

57.   Note: $r = \dfrac{6}{-3} = -2$, thus $a_n = -3(-2)^{n-1}$

58.   Note: $54 = 2 \cdot r^3 \Rightarrow r^3 = 27 \Rightarrow r = 3$, thus $a_n = 2(3)^{n-1}$

59.   Note: $16 = 1 \cdot r^2 \Rightarrow r^2 = 16 \Rightarrow r = 4$ (since $r > 0$), thus $a_n = 1(4)^{n-1}$

60.   Note: $12 = 3 \cdot r^2 \Rightarrow r^2 = 4 \Rightarrow r = -2$ (since $r < 0$) also $a_1 = \dfrac{3}{-2} = -1.5$, thus $a_n = -1.5(-2)^{n-1}$

61. $a_8 = 2(3)^{8-1} = 2(3)^7 = 4374$

62.   Note: $r = \dfrac{2}{4} = \dfrac{1}{2}$, thus $a_9 = 4\left(\dfrac{1}{2}\right)^{9-1} = 4\left(\dfrac{1}{2}\right)^8 = \dfrac{1}{64}$

63.   Note: $r = \dfrac{3}{-1} = -3$, thus $a_6 = -1(-3)^{6-1} = -1(-3)^5 = 243$

64.   Note: $a_1 \cdot (-3)^2 = 5 \Rightarrow a_1 = \dfrac{5}{9}$, thus $a_7 = \dfrac{5}{9}(-3)^{7-1} = \dfrac{5}{9}(-3)^6 = \dfrac{5}{9}(729) = 405$

Applications

65.   (a) 3000, 6000, 9000, 12,000, 15,000; This sequence is arithmetic.

      (b) $a_n = 3000n$

(c) $a_{20} = 3000(20) = 60,000$; When there are 20 people, the ventilation should be 60,000 cubic feet per hour.

(d) See Figure 65. The points are collinear.

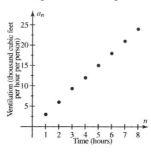

Figure 65   Figure 67

66.   The sequence is arithmetic and the common difference is 2000.

67.   (a) Since 20% of the chlorine dissipates, 80% will remain. The function is $a_n = 3(0.8)^{n-1}$.

       (b) See Figure 67. The points are not collinear. The sequence is geometric.

68.   The sequence is geometric and the common ratio is 1.07.

69.   (a) $a_n = 5(0.85)^{n-1}$

       (b) The sequence is geometric and the common ratio is 0.85.

       (c) $a_8 = 5(0.85)^{8-1} = 5(0.85)^7 \approx 1.6$; On the 8th bounce, the ball reaches a maximum height of about 1.6 feet.

70.   Neither, since there is neither a common difference nor a common ratio.

71.   (a) The number of seats can be modeled by an arithmetic sequence whose common difference is 2.

       (b) Since $a_1 = 40$ and $d = 2$, $a_n = 40 + 2(n-1)$ or $a_n = 2n + 38$

       (c) $a_{20} = 40 + 2(20-1) = 40 + 2(19) = 40 + 38 = 78$ seats

72.   (a) The sequence is geometric and the common ratio is 1.15.

       (b) $a_n = 100,000(1.15)^{n-1}$

       (c) $a_7 = 100,000(1.15)^{7-1} \approx 231,306$; During the 7th year, the home will be worth about $231,306.

       (d) See Figure 72.

Figure 72

Checking Basic Concepts for Sections 11.1 & 11.2

1. $a_1 = \dfrac{1}{1+4} = \dfrac{1}{5}, a_2 = \dfrac{2}{2+4} = \dfrac{1}{3}, a_3 = \dfrac{3}{3+4} = \dfrac{3}{7}, a_4 = \dfrac{4}{4+4} = \dfrac{1}{2} \Rightarrow \dfrac{1}{5}, \dfrac{1}{3}, \dfrac{3}{7}, \dfrac{1}{2}$

2. Graphical: See Figure 2a. Numerical: See Figure 2b.

n	1	2	3	4	5
a_n	2	3	4	5	6

Figure 2a   Figure 2b

3. (a) Arithmetic. Here $d = 1-(-2) = 3$ and $a_1 = -2$, thus $a_n = -2+(n-1)(3) \Rightarrow a_n = 3n-5$

    (b) Geometric. Here $r = \dfrac{-6}{3} = -2$ and $a_1 = 3$, thus $a_n = 3(-2)^{n-1}$

4. $a_n = 5+(n-1)(2) \Rightarrow a_n = 5+2n-2 \Rightarrow a_n = 2n+3$

5. $a_n = 5(2)^{n-1}$

11.3: Series

Concepts

1. series

2. $1+2+3+4 = 10$

3. arithmetic (the common difference is 2)

4. geometric (the common ratio is 3)

5. $n\left(\dfrac{a_1+a_n}{2}\right)$ or $\dfrac{n}{2}\left(2a_1+(n-1)d\right)$

6. $a_1\left(\dfrac{1-r^n}{1-r}\right)$

7. sum

8. $a_1+a_2+a_3+a_4$

9. arithmetic

10. geometric

Sums of Series

11. $6\left(\dfrac{3+13}{2}\right) = 6(8) = 48$

12. $7\left(\dfrac{7.5+(-1.5)}{2}\right) = 7(3) = 21$

13. $40\left(\dfrac{1+40}{2}\right) = 40(20.5) = 820$

14. $50\left(\dfrac{1+99}{2}\right) = 50(50) = 2500$

15. $5\left(\dfrac{-7+5}{2}\right) = 5(-1) = -5$

16. $8\left(\dfrac{89+54}{2}\right) = 8(71.5) = 572$

17.   Here $r = 3$ and $n = 7$ thus $S_7 = 3\left(\dfrac{1-3^7}{1-3}\right) = 3\left(\dfrac{-2186}{-2}\right) = 3(1093) = 3279$

18.   Here $r = -\dfrac{1}{2}$ and $n = 7$ thus $S_7 = 2\left(\dfrac{1-\left(-\frac{1}{2}\right)^7}{1-\left(-\frac{1}{2}\right)}\right) = 2\left(\dfrac{\frac{129}{128}}{\frac{3}{2}}\right) = 2\left(\dfrac{43}{64}\right) = \dfrac{43}{32}$

19.   Here $r = -2$ and $n = 8$ thus $S_8 = 1\left(\dfrac{1-(-2)^8}{1-(-2)}\right) = 1\left(\dfrac{-255}{3}\right) = -85$

20.   Here $r = \dfrac{1}{4}$ and $n = 6$ thus $S_6 = 2\left(\dfrac{1-\left(\frac{1}{4}\right)^6}{1-\left(\frac{1}{4}\right)}\right) = 2\left(\dfrac{\frac{4095}{4096}}{\frac{3}{4}}\right) = 2\left(\dfrac{1365}{1024}\right) = \dfrac{1365}{512}$

21.   Here $r = 3$ and $n = 6$ thus $S_6 = 0.5\left(\dfrac{1-3^6}{1-3}\right) = 0.5\left(\dfrac{-728}{-2}\right) = 0.5(364) = 182$

22.   Here $r = 0.5$ and $n = 5$ thus $S_5 = 0.6\left(\dfrac{1-0.5^5}{1-0.5}\right) = 0.6\left(\dfrac{0.96875}{0.5}\right) = 0.6(1.9375) = 1.1625$

23. $S_{20} = 2000\left(\dfrac{(1+0.08)^{20}-1}{0.08}\right) \approx \$91,523.93$

24. $S_{10} = 500\left(\dfrac{(1+0.15)^{10}-1}{0.15}\right) \approx \$10,151.86$

25. $S_5 = 10,000\left(\dfrac{(1+0.11)^5-1}{0.11}\right) \approx \$65,278.01$

26. $S_{45} = 3000 \left(\dfrac{(1+0.19)^{45} - 1}{0.19} \right) \approx \$39,610,272.68$

Summation Notation

27. $2(1) + 2(2) + 2(3) + 2(4) \Rightarrow 2 + 4 + 6 + 8 = 20$

28. $(1-1) + (2-1) + (3-1) + (4-1) + (5-1) + (6-1) \Rightarrow 0 + 1 + 2 + 3 + 4 + 5 = 15$

29. $4 + 4 + 4 + 4 + 4 + 4 + 4 + 4 = 32$

30. $(5 - 2(2)) + (5 - 2(3)) + (5 - 2(4)) + (5 - 2(5)) + (5 - 2(6)) \Rightarrow 1 + (-1) + (-3) + (-5) + (-7) = -15$

31. $1^2 + 2^2 + 3^2 + 4^2 + 5^2 + 6^2 + 7^2 \Rightarrow 1 + 4 + 9 + 16 + 25 + 36 + 49 = 140$

32. $5(2)^{1-1} + 5(2)^{2-1} + 5(2)^{3-1} + 5(2)^{4-1} \Rightarrow 5 + 10 + 20 + 40 = 75$

33. $(4^2 - 4) + (5^2 - 5) \Rightarrow 12 + 20 = 32$

34. $\log 1 + \log 2 + \log 3 + \log 4 = \log(1 \cdot 2 \cdot 3 \cdot 4) = \log 24$

35. $\displaystyle\sum_{k=1}^{6} k^4$

36. $\displaystyle\sum_{k=1}^{5} \dfrac{1}{5^{k-1}}$

37. $\displaystyle\sum_{k=1}^{5} \dfrac{1}{k^2}$

38. $\displaystyle\sum_{k=1}^{5} \dfrac{1}{10^{k-1}}$

39. $\displaystyle\sum_{k=1}^{n} k = n \left(\dfrac{a_1 + a_n}{2} \right) = n \left(\dfrac{1+n}{2} \right) = \dfrac{n(n+1)}{2}$

40. $\displaystyle\sum_{k=1}^{200} k = \dfrac{200(200+1)}{2} = \dfrac{200(201)}{2} = 20,100$

Applications

41.   (a) $8518 + 9921 + 10,706 + 14,035 + 14,307 + 12,249$

       (b) $8518 + 9921 + 10,706 + 14,035 + 14,307 + 12,249 = 69,736$

42.   (a) $9324 + 9586 + 10,031 + 12,872 + 13,346 + 12,166$

       (b) $9324 + 9586 + 10,031 + 12,872 + 13,346 + 12,166 = 67,325$

       (c) Some escapees were not captured.

43. (a) Each air filter removes 80% or 0.8 of the impurities, so 20% or 0.2 passes through it. If we let 100% or 1 represent the amount of impurities entering the first air filter, the amount removed by n filters equals

$(0.8)(1)+(0.8)(0.2)+(0.8)(0.04)+(0.8)(0.008)+\cdots+(0.8)(0.2)^{n-1}$. In summation notation,

$$\sum_{k=1}^{n} 0.8(0.2)^{k-1}$$

(b) To remove 96% or 0.96 of the impurities requires 2 filters because

$$\sum_{k=1}^{2} 0.8(0.2)^{k-1} = (0.8)(1)+(0.8)(0.2)=0.8+0.16=0.96$$

44. (a) Each air filter removes 70% or 0.7 of the impurities, so 30% or 0.3 passes through it. The amount removed by n filters is $(0.7)(1)+(0.7)(0.3)+(0.7)(0.09)+(0.7)(0.27)+\cdots+(0.7)(0.3)^{n-1}$ or

$$\sum_{k=1}^{n} 0.7(0.3)^{k-1}.$$

(b) To remove 97.3% or 0.973 of the impurities requires 3 filters because

$$\sum_{k=1}^{3} 0.7(0.3)^{k-1} = 0.7(1)+0.7(0.3)+0.7(0.09)=0.973$$

45. (a) Each successive square has half the area of the square before it. $1, \dfrac{1}{2}, \dfrac{1}{4}, \dfrac{1}{8}, \dfrac{1}{16}$

(b) Here $r=\dfrac{1}{2}$ and $n=10$ thus $S_5 = 1\left(\dfrac{1-\left(\frac{1}{2}\right)^{10}}{1-\left(\frac{1}{2}\right)}\right)=\left(\dfrac{\frac{1023}{1024}}{\frac{1}{2}}\right)=\dfrac{1023}{512}$.

46. By the Pythagorean theorem, one side of the first smaller square is $\sqrt{\left(\dfrac{1}{2}\right)^2+\left(\dfrac{1}{2}\right)^2}=\sqrt{\dfrac{2}{4}}=\dfrac{1}{\sqrt{2}}=\dfrac{\sqrt{2}}{2}$.

Hence, the perimeter of the first smaller square is $4 \cdot \dfrac{\sqrt{2}}{2}=2\sqrt{2}$.

The common ratio is $r=\dfrac{2\sqrt{2}}{4}=\dfrac{\sqrt{2}}{2}$. The sum is $4\left(\dfrac{1-(\frac{\sqrt{2}}{2})^{10}}{1-\frac{\sqrt{2}}{2}}\right)\approx 13.23$.

47. The sum is $14+13+12+11+10+9+8+7+6$. This is an arithmetic series with $a_1=14$ and $a_9=6$.

The sum is $S_9 = 9\left(\dfrac{14+6}{2}\right)=9(10)=90$ logs.

48. This is an arithmetic series with $a_1=15$, $n=10$ and $d=1$ (counting from the top down).

The sum is $S_{10}=\dfrac{10}{2}\left(2(15)+(10-1)(1)\right)=5(30+9)=5(39)=195$ logs.

49. This is an arithmetic series with $a_1=35,000$, $n=20$ and $d=2000$

The sum is $S_{20}=\dfrac{20}{2}\left(2(35,000)+(20-1)(2000)\right)=10(70,000+38,000)=10(108,000)=\$1,080,000$.

50.   This is a geometric series with $a_1 = 35,000$, $n = 20$ and $r = 1.10$.

The sum is $S_{20} = 35,000\left(\dfrac{1-1.1^{20}}{1-1.1}\right) \approx \$2,004,624.98$

51.   This is an geometric sequence given by $a_n = 10(0.75)^n$. The distance it falls is $a_4 = 10(0.75)^4 \approx 3.16$ feet.

52.   The ball both rises and falls 75% of the previous height between each bounce. We may obtain the total distance the ball travels by doubling the sum of a geometric series with $a_1 = 10$, $n = 5$ and $r = 0.75$ and subtracting 10 (since the ball did not rise 10 feet at the beginning). The sum is

$$S_5 = 2 \cdot 10\left(\dfrac{1-0.75^5}{1-0.75}\right) - 10 \approx 51.02 \text{ feet.}$$

Group Activity Solutions

(a) Straight-line: 700, 700, 700, 700

Sum-of-digits: $\dfrac{4}{10}(2800), \dfrac{3}{10}(2800), \dfrac{2}{10}(2800), \dfrac{1}{10}(2800) \Rightarrow 1120, 840, 560, 280$

(b) Straight-line: $700+700+700+700$

Sum-of-digits: $1120+840+560+280$

11.4: The Binomial Theorem

Concepts

1.   5

2. $n+1$

3.   Row 4

4.
                1
              1   1
            1   2   1
          1   3   3   1
        1   4   6   4   1

5. $4! = 1 \cdot 2 \cdot 3 \cdot 4 = 24$

6. $1 \cdot 2 \cdot 3 \cdot 4 \cdot 5 \cdot 6 = 6! = 720$

7. $\dfrac{n!}{(n-r)!r!}$

8. $a^2 + 2ab + b^2$

9. $\dfrac{n!}{(n-1)!} = \dfrac{n \cdot (n-1)!}{(n-1)!} = n$

10. $_nC_n = \dfrac{n!}{(n-n)!n!} = \dfrac{n!}{0!n!} = 1$

Using Pascal's Triangle

11. Row 4 of Pascal's triangle is 1, 3, 3, 1. $(x+y)^3 = x^3 + 3x^2 y + 3xy^2 + y^3$

12. Row 5 of Pascal's triangle is 1, 4, 6, 4, 1. $(x+y)^4 = x^4 + 4x^3 y + 6x^2 y^2 + 4xy^3 + y^4$

13. Row 5 of Pascal's triangle is 1, 4, 6, 4, 1. $(2x+1)^4 = (2x)^4 + 4(2x)^3(1) + 6(2x)^2(1)^2 + 4(2x)(1)^3 + (1)^4 \Rightarrow$

$(2x+1)^4 = 16x^4 + 32x^3 + 24x^2 + 8x + 1$

14. Row 5 of Pascal's triangle is 1, 4, 6, 4, 1. $(2x-1)^4 = (2x)^4 - 4(2x)^3(1) + 6(2x)^2(1)^2 - 4(2x)(1)^3 + (1)^4 \Rightarrow$

$(2x-1)^4 = 16x^4 - 32x^3 + 24x^2 - 8x + 1$

15. Row 6 of Pascal's triangle is 1, 5, 10, 10, 5, 1. $(a-b)^5 = a^5 - 5a^4 b + 10a^3 b^2 - 10a^2 b^3 + 5ab^4 - b^5$

16. Row 4 of Pascal's triangle is 1, 3, 3, 1. $(3x+2y)^3 = (3x)^3 + 3(3x)^2(2y) + 3(3x)(2y)^2 + (2y)^3 \Rightarrow$

$(3x+2y)^3 = 27x^3 + 54x^2 y + 36xy^2 + 8y^3$

17. Row 4 of Pascal's triangle is 1, 3, 3, 1. $(x^2+1)^3 = (x^2)^3 + 3(x^2)^2(1) + 3(x^2)(1)^2 + (1)^3 \Rightarrow$

$(x^2+1)^3 = x^6 + 3x^4 + 3x^2 + 1$

18. Row 6 of Pascal's triangle is 1, 5, 10, 10, 5, 1.

$$\left(\frac{1}{2} - x^2\right)^5 = \left(\frac{1}{2}\right)^5 - 5\left(\frac{1}{2}\right)^4(x^2) + 10\left(\frac{1}{2}\right)^3(x^2)^2 - 10\left(\frac{1}{2}\right)^2(x^2)^3 + 5\left(\frac{1}{2}\right)(x^2)^4 - (x^2)^5 \Rightarrow$$

$$\left(\frac{1}{2} - x^2\right)^5 = \frac{1}{32} - \frac{5}{16}x^2 + \frac{5}{4}x^4 - \frac{5}{2}x^6 + \frac{5}{2}x^8 - x^{10}$$

Factorials and Binomial Coefficients

19. $3! = 1 \cdot 2 \cdot 3 = 6$

20. $6! = 1 \cdot 2 \cdot 3 \cdot 4 \cdot 5 \cdot 6 = 720$

21. $\dfrac{4!}{3!} = \dfrac{1 \cdot 2 \cdot 3 \cdot 4}{1 \cdot 2 \cdot 3} = 4$

22. $\dfrac{6!}{3!} = \dfrac{1 \cdot 2 \cdot 3 \cdot 4 \cdot 5 \cdot 6}{1 \cdot 2 \cdot 3} = 4 \cdot 5 \cdot 6 = 120$

23. $\dfrac{2!}{0!} = \dfrac{1 \cdot 2}{1} = 2$

24. $\dfrac{5!}{1!} = \dfrac{1 \cdot 2 \cdot 3 \cdot 4 \cdot 5}{1} = 2 \cdot 3 \cdot 4 \cdot 5 = 120$

25. $\dfrac{5!}{2!3!} = \dfrac{1 \cdot 2 \cdot 3 \cdot 4 \cdot 5}{(1 \cdot 2)(1 \cdot 2 \cdot 3)} = 2 \cdot 5 = 10$

26. $\dfrac{6!}{4!2!} = \dfrac{1 \cdot 2 \cdot 3 \cdot 4 \cdot 5 \cdot 6}{(1 \cdot 2 \cdot 3 \cdot 4)(1 \cdot 2)} = 5 \cdot 3 = 15$

27. $_5C_4 = \dfrac{5!}{4!1!} = \dfrac{1 \cdot 2 \cdot 3 \cdot 4 \cdot 5}{(1 \cdot 2 \cdot 3 \cdot 4)(1)} = 5$

28. $_3C_1 = \dfrac{3!}{1!2!} = \dfrac{1 \cdot 2 \cdot 3}{(1)(1 \cdot 2)} = 3$

29. $_6C_5 = \dfrac{6!}{5!1!} = \dfrac{1 \cdot 2 \cdot 3 \cdot 4 \cdot 5 \cdot 6}{(1 \cdot 2 \cdot 3 \cdot 4 \cdot 5)(1)} = 6$

30. $_2C_2 = \dfrac{2!}{2!0!} = \dfrac{1 \cdot 2}{(1 \cdot 2)(1)} = 1$

31. $_4C_0 = \dfrac{4!}{0!4!} = \dfrac{1 \cdot 2 \cdot 3 \cdot 4}{(1)(1 \cdot 2 \cdot 3 \cdot 4)} = 1$

32. $_4C_3 = \dfrac{4!}{3!1!} = \dfrac{1 \cdot 2 \cdot 3 \cdot 4}{(1 \cdot 2 \cdot 3)(1)} = 4$

33. $_{12}C_7 = 792$

34. $_{13}C_8 = 1287$

35. $_9C_5 = 126$

36. $_{25}C_{14} = 4,457,400$

37. $_{19}C_{11} = 75,582$

38. $_{10}C_6 = 210$

The Binomial Theorem

39. $(m+n)^3 = \left(_3C_0\right)m^3 + \left(_3C_1\right)m^2n + \left(_3C_2\right)mn^2 + \left(_3C_3\right)n^3 \Rightarrow (m+n)^3 = m^3 + 3m^2n + 3mn^2 + n^3$

40. $(m+n)^5 = \left(_5C_0\right)m^5 + \left(_5C_1\right)m^4n + \left(_5C_2\right)m^3n^2 + \left(_5C_3\right)m^2n^3 + \left(_5C_4\right)mn^4 + \left(_5C_5\right)n^5 \Rightarrow$

$(m+n)^5 = m^5 + 5m^4n + 10m^3n^2 + 10m^2n^3 + 5mn^4 + n^5$

41. $(x-y)^4 = \left(_4C_0\right)x^4 - \left(_4C_1\right)x^3y + \left(_4C_2\right)x^2y^2 - \left(_4C_3\right)xy^3 + \left(_4C_4\right)y^4 \Rightarrow$

$(x-y)^4 = x^4 - 4x^3y + 6x^2y^2 - 4xy^3 + y^4$

42. $(1-3x)^4 = \left(_4C_0\right)(1)^4 - \left(_4C_1\right)(1)^3(3x) + \left(_4C_2\right)(1)^2(3x)^2 - \left(_4C_3\right)(1)(3x)^3 + \left(_4C_4\right)(3x)^4 \Rightarrow$

$(1-3x)^4 = 1 - 12x + 54x^2 - 108x^3 + 81x^4$

43. $(2a+1)^3 = \left(_3C_0\right)(2a)^3 + \left(_3C_1\right)(2a)^2(1) + \left(_3C_2\right)(2a)(1)^2 + \left(_3C_3\right)(1)^3 \Rightarrow (2a+1)^3 = 8a^3 + 12a^2 + 6a + 1$

44. $\left(x^2-1\right)^3 = \left(_3C_0\right)\left(x^2\right)^3 - \left(_3C_1\right)\left(x^2\right)^2(1) + \left(_3C_2\right)\left(x^2\right)(1)^2 - \left(_3C_3\right)(1)^3 \Rightarrow \left(x^2-1\right)^3 = x^6 - 3x^4 + 3x^2 - 1$

45. $(x+2)^5 = (_5C_0)x^5 + (_5C_1)x^4(2) + (_5C_2)x^3(2)^2 + (_5C_3)x^2(2)^3 + (_5C_4)x(2)^4 + (_5C_5)(2)^5 \Rightarrow$

$(x+2)^5 = x^5 + 10x^4 + 40x^3 + 80x^2 + 80x + 32$

46. $(a-3)^5 = (_5C_0)a^5 - (_5C_1)a^4(3) + (_5C_2)a^3(3)^2 - (_5C_3)a^2(3)^3 + (_5C_4)a(3)^4 - (_5C_5)(3)^5 \Rightarrow$

$(a-3)^5 = a^5 - 15a^4 + 90a^3 - 270a^2 + 405a - 243$

47. $(3+2m)^4 = (_4C_0)(3)^4 + (_4C_1)(3)^3(2m) + (_4C_2)(3)^2(2m)^2 + (_4C_3)(3)(2m)^3 + (_4C_4)(2m)^4 \Rightarrow$

$(3+2m)^4 = 81 + 216m + 216m^2 + 96m^3 + 16m^4$

48. $(m-3n)^3 = (_3C_0)(m)^3 - (_3C_1)(m)^2(3n) + (_3C_2)(m)(3n)^2 - (_3C_3)(3n)^3 \Rightarrow$

$(m-3n)^3 = 3m^3 - 9m^2n + 27mn^2 - 27n^3$

49. $(2x-y)^3 = (_3C_0)(2x)^3 - (_3C_1)(2x)^2 y + (_3C_2)(2x) y^2 - (_3C_3) y^3 \Rightarrow (2x-y)^3 = 8x^3 - 12x^2 y + 6xy^2 - y^3$

50. $(2a+3b)^4 = (_4C_0)(2a)^4 + (_4C_1)(2a)^3(3b) + (_4C_2)(2a)^2(3b)^2 + (_4C_3)(2a)(3b)^3 + (_4C_4)(3b)^4 \Rightarrow$

$(2a+3b)^4 = 16a^4 + 96a^3b + 216a^2b^2 + 216ab^3 + 81b^4$

51. Here $r = 0$ and $n = 8$. The first term is $(_8C_0)a^{8-0}b^0 = a^8$.

52. Here $r = 1$ and $n = 10$. The second term is the negation of $(_{10}C_1)a^{10-1}b^1 = -10a^9b$.

53. Here $r = 3$ and $n = 7$. The fourth term is $(_7C_3)x^{7-3}y^3 = 35x^4 y^3$.

54. Here $r = 5$ and $n = 9$. The sixth term is $(_9C_5)a^{9-5}b^5 = 126a^4b^5$.

55. Here $r = 0$ and $n = 9$. The first term is $(_9C_0)(2m)^{9-0} n^0 = 512m^9$.

56. Here $r = 7$ and $n = 8$. The first term is the negation of $(_8C_7)(2a)^{8-7} b^7 = -16ab^7$.

Checking Basic Concepts for Sections 11.3 & 11.4

1. (a) Geometric. The common ratio is $\dfrac{1}{2}$.

   (b) Arithmetic. The common difference is 2.

2. $12\left(\dfrac{4+48}{2}\right) = 12(26) = 312$

3. Here $r = -2$ and $n = 10$ thus $S_6 = 1\left(\dfrac{1-(-2)^{10}}{1-(-2)}\right) = 1\left(\dfrac{-1023}{3}\right) = -341$

4. Row 5 of Pascal's triangle is 1, 4, 6, 4, 1. $(x-y)^4 = x^4 - 4x^3 y + 6x^2 y^2 - 4xy^3 + y^4$

5. $(x+2)^3 = (_3C_0)x^3 + (_3C_1)x^2(2) + (_3C_2)x(2)^2 + (_3C_3)(2)^3 \Rightarrow (x^2-1)^3 = x^3 + 6x^2 + 12x + 8$

Chapter 11 Review Exercises

Section 11.1

1. $f(1) = 1^3 = 1,\ f(2) = 2^3 = 8,\ f(3) = 3^3 = 27,\ f(4) = 4^3 = 64 \Rightarrow 1, 8, 27, 64$

2. $f(1) = 5 - 2(1) = 3,\ f(2) = 5 - 2(2) = 1,\ f(3) = 5 - 2(3) = -1,\ f(4) = 5 - 2(4) = -3 \Rightarrow 3, 1, -1, -3$

3. $f(1) = \dfrac{2(1)}{1^2 + 1} = 1,\ f(2) = \dfrac{2(2)}{2^2 + 1} = \dfrac{4}{5},\ f(3) = \dfrac{2(3)}{3^2 + 1} = \dfrac{3}{5},\ f(4) = \dfrac{2(4)}{4^2 + 1} = \dfrac{8}{17} \Rightarrow 1, \dfrac{4}{5}, \dfrac{3}{5}, \dfrac{8}{17}$

4. $f(1) = (-2)^1 = -2,\ f(2) = (-2)^2 = 4,\ f(3) = (-2)^3 = -8,\ f(4) = (-2)^4 = 16 \Rightarrow -2, 4, -8, 16$

5.   The points shown are $(1, -2)$, $(2, 0)$, $(3, 4)$, and $(4, 2)$. The sequence is $-2, 0, 4, 2$.

6.   The points shown are $(1, 5)$, $(2, 3)$, $(3, 2)$, and $(4, 1)$. The sequence is $5, 3, 2, 1$.

7.   Numerical: See Figure 7a. Graphical: See Figure 7b.

n	1	2	3	4	5	6	7
a_n	2	4	6	8	10	12	14

Figure 7a

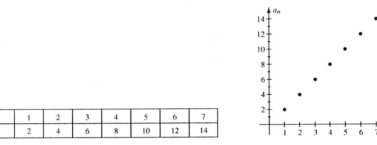

Figure 7b

8.   Numerical: See Figure 8a. Graphical: See Figure 8b.

n	1	2	3	4	5	6	7
a_n	-3	0	5	12	21	32	45

Figure 8a

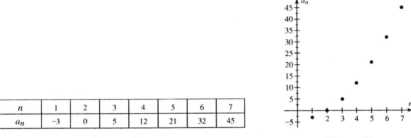

Figure 8b

9.   Numerical: See Figure 9a. Graphical: See Figure 9b.

n	1	2	3	4	5	6	7
a_n	2	1	0.5	0.25	0.125	0.0625	0.0313

Figure 9a

Figure 9b

10.   Numerical: See Figure 10a. Graphical: See Figure 10b.

n	1	2	3	4	5	6	7
a_n	1	1.4142	1.7321	2	2.2361	2.4495	2.6458

Figure 10a

Figure 10b

Section 11.2

11. Yes, the common difference is 5.

12. No, there is no common difference.

13. No, there is no common difference.

14. Yes, the common difference is $-\dfrac{1}{3}$.

15. Yes, the common difference is -3.

16. No, there is no common difference.

17. Yes, the common difference is -1.

18. No, there is no common difference.

19. $a_n = -3 + (n-1)(4) \Rightarrow a_n = -3 + 4n - 4 \Rightarrow a_n = 4n - 7$

20. Note: $d = -3 - 2 = -5$, thus $a_n = 2 + (n-1)(-5) \Rightarrow a_n = 2 - 5n + 5 \Rightarrow a_n = -5n + 7$

21. Yes, the common ratio is 4.

22. No, there is no common ratio.

23. No, there is no common ratio.

24. Yes, the common ratio is 0.7.

25. No, there is no common ratio.

26. Yes, the common ratio is $-\dfrac{1}{3}$.

27. No, there is no common ratio.

28. Yes, the common ratio is 2.

29. $a_n = 5(0.9)^{n-1}$

30. Note: $r = \dfrac{8}{2} = 4$, thus $a_n = 2(4)^{n-1}$

Section 11.3

31. $9\left(\dfrac{4+44}{2}\right) = 9(24) = 216$

32. $5\left(\dfrac{4.5+(-1.5)}{2}\right) = 5(1.5) = 7.5$

33.   Here $r = -4$ and $n = 7$ thus $S_7 = 1\left(\dfrac{1-(-4)^7}{1-(-4)}\right) = \left(\dfrac{16,385}{5}\right) = 3277$

34.   Here $r = \dfrac{1}{2}$ and $n = 9$ thus $S_9 = 1\left(\dfrac{1-\left(\frac{1}{2}\right)^9}{1-\left(\frac{1}{2}\right)}\right) = \left(\dfrac{\frac{511}{512}}{\frac{1}{2}}\right) = \dfrac{511}{256}$

35. $(2(1)+1)+(2(2)+1)+(2(3)+1)+(2(4)+1)+(2(5)+1) \Rightarrow 3+5+7+9+11$

36. $\dfrac{1}{1+1}+\dfrac{1}{2+1}+\dfrac{1}{3+1}+\dfrac{1}{4+1} \Rightarrow \dfrac{1}{2}+\dfrac{1}{3}+\dfrac{1}{4}+\dfrac{1}{5}$

37. $1^3 + 2^3 + 3^3 + 4^3 \Rightarrow 1+8+27+64$

38. $(1-2)+(1-3)+(1-4)+(1-5)+(1-6)+(1-7) \Rightarrow -1+(-2)+(-3)+(-4)+(-5)+(-6)$

39. $\displaystyle\sum_{k=1}^{20} k$

40. $\displaystyle\sum_{k=1}^{20} \dfrac{1}{k}$

41. $\displaystyle\sum_{k=1}^{9} \dfrac{k}{k+1}$

42. $\displaystyle\sum_{k=1}^{7} k^2$

Section 11.4

43.   Row 4 of Pascal's triangle is 1, 3, 3, 1. $(x+4)^3 = x^3 + 3x^2(4) + 3x(4)^2 + (4)^3 \Rightarrow$

       $(x+4)^3 = x^3 + 12x^2 + 48x + 64$

44.   Row 5 of Pascal's triangle is 1, 4, 6, 4, 1. $(2x+1)^4 = (2x)^4 + 4(2x)^3(1) + 6(2x)^2(1)^2 + 4(2x)(1)^3 + (1)^4 \Rightarrow$

       $(2x+1)^4 = 16x^4 + 32x^3 + 24x^2 + 8x + 1$

45.   Row 6 of Pascal's triangle is 1, 5, 10, 10, 5, 1. $(x-y)^5 = x^5 - 5x^4y + 10x^3y^2 - 10x^2y^3 + 5xy^4 - y^5$

46.   Row 7 of Pascal's triangle is 1, 6, 15, 20, 15, 6, 1.

       $(a-1)^6 = a^6 - 6a^5(1) + 15a^4(1)^2 - 20a^3(1)^3 + 15a^2(1)^4 - 6a(1)^5 + (1)^6 \Rightarrow$

       $(a-1)^6 = a^6 - 6a^5 + 15a^4 - 20a^3 + 15a^2 - 6a + 1$

47. $3! = 1 \cdot 2 \cdot 3 = 6$

48. $\dfrac{5!}{3!2!} = \dfrac{1 \cdot 2 \cdot 3 \cdot 4 \cdot 5}{(1 \cdot 2 \cdot 3)(1 \cdot 2)} = 2 \cdot 5 = 10$

49. $_6C_3 = \dfrac{6!}{3!3!} = \dfrac{1 \cdot 2 \cdot 3 \cdot 4 \cdot 5 \cdot 6}{(1 \cdot 2 \cdot 3)(1 \cdot 2 \cdot 3)} = 2 \cdot 5 \cdot 2 = 20$

50. $_4C_3 = \dfrac{4!}{3!1!} = \dfrac{1 \cdot 2 \cdot 3 \cdot 4}{(1 \cdot 2 \cdot 3)(1)} = 4$

51. $(m+2)^4 = (_4C_0)m^4 + (_4C_1)m^3(2) + (_4C_2)m^2(2)^2 + (_4C_3)m(2)^3 + (_4C_4)(2)^4 \Rightarrow$

$(m+2)^4 = m^4 + 8m^3 + 24m^2 + 32m + 16$

52. $(a+b)^5 = (_5C_0)a^5 + (_5C_1)a^4b + (_5C_2)a^3b^2 + (_5C_3)a^2b^3 + (_5C_4)ab^4 + (_5C_5)b^5 \Rightarrow$

$(a+b)^5 = a^5 + 5a^4b + 10a^3b^2 + 10a^2b^3 + 5ab^4 + b^5$

53. $(x-3y)^4 = (_4C_0)x^4 - (_4C_1)x^3(3y) + (_4C_2)x^2(3y)^2 - (_4C_3)x(3y)^3 + (_4C_4)(3y)^4 \Rightarrow$

$(x-3y)^4 = x^4 - 12x^3y + 54x^2y^2 - 108xy^3 + 81y^4$

54. $(3x-2)^3 = (_3C_0)(3x)^3 - (_3C_1)(3x)^2(2) + (_3C_2)(3x)(2)^2 - (_3C_3)(2)^3 \Rightarrow (3x-2)^3 = 27x^3 - 54x^2 + 36x - 8$

Applications

55.   Symbolic: $a_n = 45,000(1.10)^{\wedge}(n-1)$ for $n = 1, 2, 3, \ldots, 7$. This is a geometric sequence.

Numerical: See Figure 55a. Graphical: See Figure 55b.

n	1	2	3	4	5	6	7
a_n	45,000	49,500	54,450	59,895	65,885	72,473	79,720

Figure 55a   Figure 55b

56.   Symbolic: $a_n = 45,000 + 5000(n-1)$ for $n = 1, 2, 3, \ldots, 7$. This is an arithmetic sequence.

Numerical: See Figure 56a. Graphical: See Figure 56b.

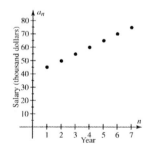

n	1	2	3	4	5	6	7
a_n	45,000	50,000	55,000	60,000	65,000	70,000	75,000

Figure 56a   Figure 56b

57.   Symbolic: $a_n = 49n$ for $n = 1, 2, 3, \ldots, 7$

Graphical: See Figure 57a. Numerical: See Figure 57b.

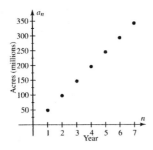

Figure 57a

n	1	2	3	4	5	6	7
a_n	49	98	147	196	245	294	343

Figure 57b

58.   (a) $a_n = 1087(1.025)^{n-1}$

(b)   The sequence is geometric. The common ratio is 1.025.

(c) $a_5 = 1087(1.025)^{5-1} \approx 1200$; The average mortgage payment in 2000 was about $1200.

(d)   See Figure 58.

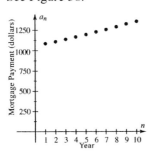

Figure 58

n	1	2	3	4	5	6	7
a_n	0	2	6	12	20	30	42

Figure 3

Chapter 11 Test

1. $f(1) = \dfrac{1^2}{1+1} = \dfrac{1}{2},\ f(2) = \dfrac{2^2}{2+1} = \dfrac{4}{3},\ f(3) = \dfrac{3^2}{3+1} = \dfrac{9}{4},\ f(4) = \dfrac{4^2}{4+1} = \dfrac{16}{5} \Rightarrow \dfrac{1}{2}, \dfrac{4}{3}, \dfrac{9}{4}, \dfrac{16}{5}$

2.   The points shown are $(1, -3), (2, 2), (3, 1), (4, -2)$ and $(5, 3)$. The sequence is $-3, 2, 1, -2, 3$.

3.   See Figure 3.

4.   Row 5 of Pascal's triangle is 1, 4, 6, 4, 1. $(2x-1)^4 = (2x)^4 - 4(2x)^3(1) + 6(2x)^2(1)^2 - 4(2x)(1)^3 + (1)^4 \Rightarrow$

$(2x-1)^4 = 16x^4 - 32x^3 + 24x^2 - 8x + 1$

5.   The sequence is arithmetic. The common difference is -3.

6.   The sequence is geometric. The common ratio is -2.

7. $a_n = 2 + (n-1)(-3) \Rightarrow a_n = 2 - 3n + 3 \Rightarrow a_n = -3n + 5$

8.   Note: $2 \cdot r^2 = 4.5 \Rightarrow r^2 = \dfrac{4.5}{2} \Rightarrow r = 1.5$, thus $a_n = 2(1.5)^{n-1}$

9.   Yes, the common ratio is 2.5.

10.   No, there is no common ratio.

11. $9\left(\dfrac{-1+23}{2}\right) = 9(11) = 99$

12.   Here $r = -\dfrac{2}{3}$ and $n = 7$ thus $S_9 = 1\left(\dfrac{1-\left(-\frac{2}{3}\right)^7}{1-\left(-\frac{2}{3}\right)}\right) = \left(\dfrac{\frac{2315}{2187}}{\frac{5}{3}}\right) = \dfrac{463}{729}$

13. $3(2)+3(3)+3(4)+3(5)+3(6)+3(7) \Rightarrow 6+9+12+15+18+21$

14. $\displaystyle\sum_{k=1}^{60} k^3$

15. $\dfrac{7!}{4!3!} = \dfrac{1\cdot2\cdot3\cdot4\cdot5\cdot6\cdot7}{(1\cdot2\cdot3\cdot4)(1\cdot2\cdot3)} = 5\cdot7 = 35$

16. ${}_5C_3 = \dfrac{5!}{3!2!} = \dfrac{1\cdot2\cdot3\cdot4\cdot5}{(1\cdot2\cdot3)(1\cdot2)} = 2\cdot5 = 10$

17.   This is an arithmetic series with $a_1 = 50$ and $d = 7$. The total number of seats is

$$S_{45} = \dfrac{45}{2}\left(2(50)+(45-1)(7)\right) = 22.5(408) = 9180 \text{ seats.}$$

18.   Symbolic: $a_n = 159,700(1.04)^\wedge(n-1)$ for $n = 1,2,3,\ldots7$. This is a geometric sequence.

Numerical: See Figure 18a. Graphical: See Figure 18b.

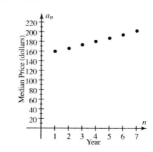

n	1	2	3	4	5	6	7
a_n	159,700	166,088	172,732	179,641	186,826	194,299	202,071

Figure 18a   Figure 18b

19.   (a) $a_n = 2000(2)^{n-1}$

(b)   The sequence is geometric. The common ratio is 2.

(c) $a_6 = 2000(2)^{6-1} \approx 64,000$; After 30 days, there are 64,000 worms.

(d)   See Figure 19.

Figure 19

Chapter 11 Extended and Discovery Exercises

1. Each term of the sequence is obtained by adding the two previous terms. 1, 1, 2, 3, 5, 8, 13, 21, 34, 55, 89, 144

2. (a) Table $u(n) = 2.85u(n-1) - 0.19(u(n-1))^2$ with TblStart = 1 and ΔTbl = 1. See Figure 2a.

   Note: be sure to set nMin = 1 and u(nMin) = {1}.

   (b) Graph $u(n) = 2.85u(n-1) - 0.19(u(n-1))^2$ in [0, 22, 2] by [0, 11, 1]. See Figure 2b.

   Note: be sure to set nMin = 1 and nMax = 20 in the WINDOW settings.

   The moth population increases and then oscillates until it settles to a constant number (about 9.737 thousand).

   $$[0, 22, 2] \text{ by } [0, 11, 1]$$

   Figure 2a   Figure 2b

3. (a) $\pi \approx \left[90 \left(\dfrac{1}{1^4} + \dfrac{1}{2^4} + \dfrac{1}{3^4} + \dfrac{1}{4^4} \right) \right]^{1/4} \approx 3.138997889$

   (b) $\pi \approx 3.141590776$; This is correct to 5 decimal places.

4. (a) $S = \dfrac{2}{1 - \left(-\frac{1}{2} \right)} = \dfrac{2}{\frac{3}{2}} = \dfrac{4}{3}$

   (b) $S = \dfrac{1}{1 - \left(\frac{1}{3} \right)} = \dfrac{1}{\frac{2}{3}} = \dfrac{3}{2}$

   (c) $S = \dfrac{0.1}{1 - (0.1)} = \dfrac{0.1}{0.9} = \dfrac{1}{9} = 0.\overline{1}$

   (d) $S = \dfrac{0.12}{1 - (0.01)} = \dfrac{0.12}{0.99} = \dfrac{4}{33} = 0.\overline{12}$

Chapters 1-11 Cumulative Review Exercises

1. This equation illustrates a distributive property.

2. The domain corresponds to the x-coordinates and the range corresponds to the y-coordinates.

   $D = \{-6, -2, 0, 2\}; R = \{0, 1, 3, 5\}$

3. $\dfrac{x^{-2}y^3}{\left(3xy^{-2} \right)^3} = \dfrac{x^{-2}y^3}{3^3 x^3 \left(y^{-2} \right)^3} = \dfrac{x^{-2}y^3}{27x^3 y^{-6}} = \dfrac{1}{27} x^{-2-3} y^{3-(-6)} = \dfrac{1}{27} x^{-5} y^9 = \dfrac{y^9}{27x^5}$

4. $$\left(\frac{3b}{6a^2}\right)^{-4} = \left(\frac{b}{2a^2}\right)^{-4} = \left(\frac{2a^2}{b}\right)^{4} = \frac{\left(2a^2\right)^4}{b^4} = \frac{2^4\left(a^2\right)^4}{b^4} = \frac{16a^8}{b^4}$$

5. $$\left(\frac{1}{z^2}\right)^{-5} = \left(z^2\right)^5 = z^{10}$$

6. $$\frac{8x^{-3}y^2}{4x^3y^{-1}} = 2x^{-3-3}y^{2-(-1)} = 2x^{-6}y^3 = \frac{2y^3}{x^6}$$

7. The function is defined for all values of the variable except 8. The domain is $\left\{x \mid x \neq 8\right\}$.

8. The slope is $m = \dfrac{1-5}{0-(-2)} = \dfrac{-4}{2} = -2.$ Since $f(x) = 1$ when $x = 0$ the y-intercept is 1. Here $f(x) = -2x + 1$.

9. Horizontal lines have equations of the form $y = k$. The equation of the horizontal line passing through $(2, 3)$

    is $y = 3$.

10. The equation is in the form $f(x) = mx + b$. The slope is -3 and the y-intercept is 5.

11. Since the line is perpendicular to $y = -\dfrac{2}{3}x - 4$, the slope is $m = \dfrac{3}{2}$. Using the point-slope form gives

    $$y = \frac{3}{2}(x-1) + 4 \Rightarrow y = \frac{3}{2}x - \frac{3}{2} + 4 \Rightarrow y = \frac{3}{2}x + \frac{5}{2}$$

12. Since the line is parallel to $y = 2x - 7$, the slope is $m = 2$. Using the point-slope form gives

    $$y = 2(x-5) + 2 \Rightarrow y = 2x - 10 + 2 \Rightarrow y = 2x - 8$$

13. $\dfrac{2}{5}(x-4) = -12 \Rightarrow x - 4 = -30 \Rightarrow x = -26$

14. $\dfrac{2}{5}z + \dfrac{1}{4}z > 2 - (z-1) \Rightarrow 8z + 5z > 40 - 20(z-1) \Rightarrow 13z > 40 - 20z + 20 \Rightarrow$

    $13z > 60 - 20z \Rightarrow 33z > 60 \Rightarrow z > \dfrac{60}{33} \Rightarrow z > \dfrac{20}{11}.$ The interval is $\left(\dfrac{20}{11}, \infty\right)$.

15. First divide each side of $-3|t-5| \leq -18$ by -3 to obtain $|t-5| \geq 6$.

    The solutions to $|t-5| \geq 6$ satisfy $t \leq c$ or $t \geq d$ where c and d are the solutions to $|t-5| = 6$.

    $|t-5| = 6$ is equivalent to $t - 5 = -6 \Rightarrow t = -1$ and $t - 5 = 6 \Rightarrow t = 11$.

    The interval is $(-\infty, -1] \cup [11, \infty)$.

16. $\left|4 + \dfrac{2}{3}x\right| = 6 \Rightarrow 4 + \dfrac{2}{3}x = -6 \Rightarrow \dfrac{2}{3}x = -10 \Rightarrow x = -15$ or $4 + \dfrac{2}{3}x = 6 \Rightarrow \dfrac{2}{3}x = 2 \Rightarrow x = 3$

17. $\dfrac{1}{4}t - (2t+5) + 6 = \dfrac{t+3}{4} \Rightarrow \dfrac{1}{4}t - 2t + 1 = \dfrac{t+3}{4} \Rightarrow t - 8t + 4 = t + 3 \Rightarrow -8t = -1 \Rightarrow t = \dfrac{1}{8}$

18. $-3 \le \dfrac{2}{3}x + 5 < 11 \Rightarrow -8 \le \dfrac{2}{3}x < 6 \Rightarrow -12 \le x < 9.$ The interval is $[-12, 9)$.

19.   By substitution, $(3, -2)$ is a solution to the given system of equations.

20.   See Figure 20.

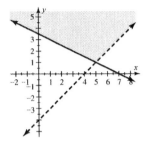

    Figure 20

21.   Multiply the first equation by 2 and add the equations to eliminate the variable x.

$$2x - 4y = 2$$
$$-2x + 7y = 4$$
$$\overline{3y = 6}$$ Thus, $y = 2$. And so $x - 2(2) = 1 \Rightarrow x = 5$. The solution is $(5, 2)$.

22. $\begin{bmatrix} 1 & 1 & 1 & | & 5 \\ -2 & -1 & 1 & | & -10 \\ 1 & 2 & 8 & | & 1 \end{bmatrix} \begin{matrix} \\ R_2 + 2R_1 \to \\ R_3 - R_1 \to \end{matrix} \begin{bmatrix} 1 & 1 & 1 & | & 5 \\ 0 & 1 & 3 & | & 0 \\ 0 & 1 & 7 & | & -4 \end{bmatrix} \begin{matrix} R_1 - R_2 \to \\ \\ R_3 - R_2 \to \end{matrix} \begin{bmatrix} 1 & 0 & -2 & | & 5 \\ 0 & 1 & 3 & | & 0 \\ 0 & 0 & 4 & | & -4 \end{bmatrix}$

$\begin{matrix} \\ \\ (1/4)R_3 \to \end{matrix} \begin{bmatrix} 1 & 0 & -2 & | & 5 \\ 0 & 1 & 3 & | & 0 \\ 0 & 0 & 1 & | & -1 \end{bmatrix} \begin{matrix} R_1 + 2R_3 \to \\ R_2 - 3R_3 \to \\ \end{matrix} \begin{bmatrix} 1 & 0 & 0 & | & 3 \\ 0 & 1 & 0 & | & 3 \\ 0 & 0 & 1 & | & -1 \end{bmatrix}$

    The solution is $(3, 3, -1)$.

23.   From the graph of the region of feasible solutions (not shown), the vertices are (0, 0), (0, 2.5), (2, 2), and (2.5, 0).

    The maximum value of R occurs at one of the vertices. For $(0, 0)$, $R = 3(0) + 8(0) = 0$.

    For $(0, 2.5)$, $R = 3(0) + 8(2.5) = 20$. For $(2, 2)$, $R = 3(2) + 8(2) = 22$. For

    $(2.5, 0)$, $R = 3(2.5) + 8(0) = 7.5$.

    The maximum value is $R = 22$.

24. $\det A = 4(2) - 3(-3) = 8 + 9 = 17$

25. $2x^3 \left(4x^4 - 3x^3 + 5 \right) = 8x^7 - 6x^6 + 10x^3$

26. $(2z - 7)(3z + 4) = 6z^2 + 8z - 21z - 28 = 6z^2 - 13z - 28$

27. $4x^2 - 9y^2 = (2x)^2 - (3y)^2 = (2x - 3y)(2x + 3y)$

28. $2a^3 - a^2 + 8a - 4 = a^2(2a - 1) + 4(2a - 1) = \left(a^2 + 4 \right)(2a - 1)$

29. $4x^2 - x - 3 = 0 \Rightarrow (4x+3)(x-1) = 0 \Rightarrow x = -\dfrac{3}{4}$ or $x = 1$

30. $x^4 - 10x^3 = -24x^2 \Rightarrow x^4 - 10x^3 + 24x^2 = 0 \Rightarrow x^2(x-4)(x-6) = 0 \Rightarrow x = 0, 4,$ or 6

31. $\dfrac{x^2 - 7x + 10}{x^2 - 25} \cdot \dfrac{x+5}{x+1} = \dfrac{(x-2)(x-5)(x+5)}{(x-5)(x+5)(x+1)} = \dfrac{x-2}{x+1}$

32. $\dfrac{x^2 + 7x + 12}{x^2 - 9} \div \dfrac{x^2 - 5x + 6}{(x-3)^2} = \dfrac{x^2 + 7x + 12}{x^2 - 9} \cdot \dfrac{(x-3)^2}{x^2 - 5x + 6} = \dfrac{(x+4)(x+3)(x-3)(x-3)}{(x-3)(x+3)(x-3)(x-2)} = \dfrac{x+4}{x-2}$

33. $\dfrac{2}{x+5} = \dfrac{-3}{x^2 - 25} + \dfrac{1}{x-5} \Rightarrow 2(x-5) = -3 + 1(x+5) \Rightarrow 2x - 10 = x + 2 \Rightarrow x = 12$

34. $\dfrac{2y}{y^2 - 3y + 2} = \dfrac{1}{y-2} + 2 \Rightarrow 2y = 1(y-1) + 2(y-2)(y-1) \Rightarrow 2y = y - 1 + 2y^2 - 6y + 4 \Rightarrow$

    $2y^2 - 7y + 3 = 0 \Rightarrow (2y-1)(y-3) = 0 \Rightarrow y = \dfrac{1}{2}$ or $y = 3$.

35. $R = \dfrac{3C - 2W}{5} \Rightarrow 5R = 3C - 2W \Rightarrow 5R - 3C = -2W \Rightarrow \dfrac{5R - 3C}{-2} = W \Rightarrow W = \dfrac{3C - 5R}{2}$

36. $\dfrac{\dfrac{1}{x^2} + \dfrac{2}{x}}{\dfrac{1}{x^2} - \dfrac{4}{x}} = \dfrac{\dfrac{1}{x^2} + \dfrac{2}{x}}{\dfrac{1}{x^2} - \dfrac{4}{x}} \cdot \dfrac{x^2}{x^2} = \dfrac{1 + 2x}{1 - 4x}$

37. $\sqrt[3]{x^4 y^4} - 2\sqrt[3]{xy} = \sqrt[3]{(xy)^3 \cdot xy} - 2\sqrt[3]{xy} = xy\sqrt[3]{xy} - 2\sqrt[3]{xy} = (xy - 2)\sqrt[3]{xy}$

38. $\left(4 + \sqrt{2}\right)\left(4 - \sqrt{2}\right) = 4^2 - \left(\sqrt{2}\right)^2 = 16 - 2 = 14$

39. $8(x-3)^2 = 200 \Rightarrow (x-3)^2 = 25 \Rightarrow x - 3 = \pm\sqrt{25} \Rightarrow x - 3 = \pm 5 \Rightarrow x = -2$ or 8

40. $3\sqrt{2x+6} = 6x \Rightarrow \sqrt{2x+6} = 2x \Rightarrow 2x + 6 = 4x^2 \Rightarrow 4x^2 - 2x - 6 = 0 \Rightarrow 2(2x-3)(x+1) \Rightarrow$

    $x = \dfrac{3}{2}$ or $x = -1$. The value $x = -1$ does not check. The only solution is $\dfrac{3}{2}$.

41. $(-3 + i)(-4 - 2i) = 12 + 6i - 4i - 2i^2 = 12 + 2i + 2 = 14 + 2i$

42. $\dfrac{2 - 6i}{1 + 2i} = \dfrac{2 - 6i}{1 + 2i} \cdot \dfrac{1 - 2i}{1 - 2i} = \dfrac{2 - 4i - 6i + 12i^2}{1 - 4i^2} = \dfrac{2 - 10i - 12}{1 + 4} = \dfrac{-10 - 10i}{5} = -2 - 2i$

43. $-\dfrac{b}{2a} = -\dfrac{8}{2(3)} = -\dfrac{8}{6} = -\dfrac{4}{3}; \; f\left(-\dfrac{4}{3}\right) = 3\left(-\dfrac{4}{3}\right)^2 + 8\left(-\dfrac{4}{3}\right) + 5 = -\dfrac{1}{3}$. The vertex is $\left(-\dfrac{4}{3}, -\dfrac{1}{3}\right)$.

    The minimum value is $-\dfrac{1}{3}$.

44. $y = 2x^2 + 8x + 17 \Rightarrow y = 2(x^2 + 4x + 4) + 17 - 8 \Rightarrow y = 2(x+2)^2 + 9$. The vertex is $(-2, 9)$.

45. $x^2 - 4x + 13 = 0 \Rightarrow x^2 - 4x + 4 = -13 + 4 \Rightarrow (x-2)^2 = -9 \Rightarrow x - 2 = \pm\sqrt{-9} \Rightarrow x = 2 \pm 3i$

46. $z^2 - 4z = 32 \Rightarrow z^2 - 4z - 32 = 0 \Rightarrow (z+4)(z-8) = 0 \Rightarrow z = -4 \text{ or } z = 8$

47.   (a) The graph intersects the x-axis at -3 and 1.

       (b) Because the parabola opens upward, $a > 0$.

       (c) Because there are two real solutions, the discriminant is positive.

48. $x^2 + 2x + 3 = 0 \Rightarrow x^2 + 2x + 1 = -3 + 1 \Rightarrow (x+1)^2 = -2 \Rightarrow$ no real solutions. This parabola does not cross the

       x-axis and it opens upward. The solution is $(-\infty, \infty)$.

49.   (a) $g(-2) = 3(-2) - 2 = -8$, then $(f \circ g)(-2) = f(g(-2)) = f(-8) = (-8)^2 + 1 = 65$

       (b) $(g \circ f)(x) = g(f(x)) = g(x^2 + 1) = 3(x^2 + 1) - 2 = 3x^2 + 3 - 2 = 3x^2 + 1$

50. $f(x) = \dfrac{3x+1}{2} \Rightarrow y = \dfrac{3x+1}{2}$, interchange x and y and solve for y.

       $x = \dfrac{3y+1}{2} \Rightarrow 2x = 3y + 1 \Rightarrow 3y = 2x - 1 \Rightarrow y = \dfrac{2x-1}{3} \Rightarrow f^{-1}(x) = \dfrac{2x-1}{3}$

51. $\ln\left(x^3 \sqrt{y}\right) = \ln\left(x^3 y^{1/2}\right) = \ln x^3 + \ln y^{1/2} = 3 \ln x + \dfrac{1}{2} \ln y$

52. $2 \log x - \log 4xy = \log x^2 - \log 4xy = \log \dfrac{x^2}{4xy} = \log \dfrac{x}{4y}$

53. $8 \log x + 3 = 17 \Rightarrow 8 \log x = 14 \Rightarrow \log x = \dfrac{7}{4} \Rightarrow 10^{\log x} = 10^{7/4} \Rightarrow x \approx 56.23$

54. $4^{2x} = 5 \Rightarrow \log_4 4^{2x} = \log_4 5 \Rightarrow 2x = \log_4 5 \Rightarrow 2x = \dfrac{\log 5}{\log 4} \Rightarrow x = \dfrac{\log 5}{2 \log 4} \approx 0.58$

55.   See Figure 55. The vertex is $(1, 3)$, and the axis of symmetry is $y = 3$.

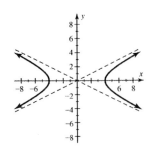

Figure 55   Figure 57   Figure 58

56. $x^2 - 6x + y^2 + 2y = -6 \Rightarrow \left(x^2 - 6x + 9\right) + \left(y^2 + 2y + 1\right) = -6 + 9 + 1 \Rightarrow (x-3)^2 + (y+1)^2 = 4$

       The center is $(3, -1)$, and the radius is 2.

57.   See Figure 57.

58.   See Figure 58.

59.   Vertical transverse axis with vertices $(0, \pm 2)$ and asymptotes $y = \pm \dfrac{2}{4}x \Rightarrow \dfrac{y^2}{4} - \dfrac{x^2}{16} = 1$

60.   Horizontal major axis with vertices $(\pm 4, 0)$ and minor axis endpoints $(0, \pm 2) \Rightarrow \dfrac{x^2}{16} + \dfrac{y^2}{4} = 1$

61.   Substitute $y = x^2 + 1$ in the second equation and solve for x.

$$x^2 + 2(x^2 + 1) = 5 \Rightarrow 3x^2 - 3 = 0 \Rightarrow 3(x^2 - 1) = 0 \Rightarrow 3(x+1)(x-1) = 0 \Rightarrow x = -1 \text{ or } x = 1$$

When $x = -1$, $y = (-1)^2 + 1 = 2$. When $x = 1$, $y = (1)^2 + 1 = 2$. The solutions are $(-1, 2)$ and $(1, 2)$.

62.   See Figure 62.

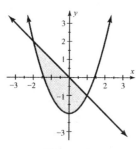

Figure 62   Figure 74

63.   This sequence is arithmetic, the common difference is -2.

64.   This sequence is geometric, the common ratio is 0.2.

65.   This sequence is geometric, the common ratio is 4.

66.   This sequence is arithmetic, the common difference is 6.

67.   Note: $d = 5 - 2 = 3$, thus $a_n = 2 + (n-1)(3) \Rightarrow a_n = 2 + 3n - 3 \Rightarrow a_n = 3n - 1$

68.   Note: $r = \dfrac{12}{4} = 3$, thus $a_n = 4(3)^{n-1}$

69. $9\left(\dfrac{3+35}{2}\right) = 9(19) = 171$

70.   Here $r = -2$ and $n = 11$ thus $S_{11} = 1\left(\dfrac{1 - (-2)^{11}}{1 - (-2)}\right) = 1\left(\dfrac{2049}{3}\right) = 683$

71. $(2x+3)^4 = (_4C_0)(2x)^4 + (_4C_1)(2x)^3(3) + (_4C_2)(2x)^2(3^2) + (_4C_3)(2x)(3^3) + (_4C_4)(3^4) \Rightarrow$

$(2x+3)^4 = 16x^4 + 96x^3 + 216x^2 + 216x + 81$

72. $(2a-5b)^3 = (_3C_0)(2a)^3 - (_3C_1)(2a)^2(5b) + (_3C_2)(2a)(5b)^2 - (_3C_3)(5b)^3 \Rightarrow$

$(2a-5b)^3 = 8a^3 - 60a^2b + 150ab^2 - 125b^3$

Applications

73. $r = \sqrt{\dfrac{14}{\pi}} \approx 2.11$ inches

74.   See Figure 74.

75.   (a) $f(x) = \dfrac{170}{2} + 0.4x \Rightarrow f(x) = 0.4x + 85$

        (b) $0.4(90) + \dfrac{W}{2} = 130 \Rightarrow 36 + \dfrac{W}{2} = 130 \Rightarrow \dfrac{W}{2} = 94 \Rightarrow W = 188$ pounds

76.   Let x and y represent the speed of the airplane and the speed of the wind respectively. Then the system
        needed is $x - y = 360$ and $x + y = 400$. Adding the two equations will eliminate y.

        $x - y = 360$
        $\underline{x + y = 400}$
        $2x = 760$ Thus, $x = 380$. And so $(380) + y = 400 \Rightarrow y = 20$.

        The speed of the airplane is 380 mph and the speed of the wind is 20 mph.

77.   Let x represent the width of the tent floor. Then $2x - 6$ represents the length.

        $x(2x - 6) = 108 \Rightarrow 2x^2 - 6x - 108 = 0 \Rightarrow x^2 - 3x - 54 = 0 \Rightarrow (x+6)(x-9) = 0 \Rightarrow x = -6$ or 9

        Since the value $x = -6$ has no physical meaning, the solution is 9. The dimensions are 9 feet by 12 feet.

78.   Let x represent time required to weed the garden if they worked together. Then $\dfrac{x}{60} + \dfrac{x}{90} = 1$.

        $180 \cdot \left(\dfrac{x}{60} + \dfrac{x}{90} \right) = 1 \cdot 180 \Rightarrow 3x + 2x = 180 \Rightarrow 5x = 180 \Rightarrow x = \dfrac{180}{5} = 36$ minutes

79.   (a) $xy = 96$ and $3x - y = 12$

        (b) Solve the second equation for y and substitute the result in the first equation. $3x - y = 12 \Rightarrow y = 3x - 12$

             $x(3x - 12) = 96 \Rightarrow 3x^2 - 12x - 96 = 0 \Rightarrow x^2 - 4x - 32 = 0 \Rightarrow (x+4)(x-8) = 0 \Rightarrow x = -4$ or $x = 8$. Since

             the numbers must be positive, the solution is $x = 8$. The numbers are 8 and 12.

80.   Find the sum of the series $1 + 3 + 5 + \cdots + 23$. The sum is $12\left(\dfrac{1+23}{2} \right) = 12(12) = 144$ musicians.

Critical Thinking Solutions for Chapter 11

Section 11.1

•   Each year there are r times as many female insects as there were the previous year. The annual growth factor is
    1.04.

Section 11.2

•   No, since we can not determine the sign of r. Note that $r = \pm \sqrt[4]{\dfrac{a_5}{a_1}}$.